USED

Mathematical Methods
in the Physical Sciences

Mathematical Methods in the Physical Sciences

Mary L. Boas

Department of Physics
DePaul University
Chicago, Illinois

John Wiley & Sons, Inc. New York · London · Sydney

Copyright © 1966 by John Wiley & Sons, Inc.

All Rights Reserved
This book or any part thereof
must not be reproduced in any form
without the written permission of the publisher.

ISBN 0 471 08417 4

Library of Congress Catalog Card Number: 66-17646
Printed in the United States of America

20 19 18 17 16 15

To Ralph

Preface

This book is particularly intended for the student with one year of calculus who wants in a short time to develop a basic competence in each of the many areas of mathematics he will need to use in courses in physics, chemistry, and engineering. It may also be used effectively by a more advanced student to review half-forgotten topics and learn new ones, either in independent study or in a class. Although the book was written especially for students of the physical sciences, a student in any field (say, mathematics or mathematics for teaching) may find it useful to survey many topics or to obtain some knowledge of areas he does not have time to study in depth. Since theorems are stated carefully, such a student should not have to unlearn anything in his later work.

The question of proper mathematical training for students in the physical sciences is of concern to both mathematicians and those who use mathematics in applications. Mathematicians are apt to claim that if a student is going to study mathematics at all, he should study it in careful and thorough detail. For the undergraduate physics, chemistry, or engineering student, this means either learning more mathematics than a mathematics major, or learning a few areas of mathematics thoroughly and the others only from snatches in science courses. The second alternative is often advocated; let me say why I think it is unsatisfactory. It is certainly true that motivation is increased by the immediate application of a mathematical technique; however, there are a number of disadvantages. The discussion of the mathematics is apt to be sketchy since that is not the primary concern. The student is faced simultaneously with learning a new mathematical method and applying it to an area of science that is also new to him. Frequently the difficulty in comprehending the new scientific area lies more in the distraction caused by poorly understood mathematics than it does in the new scientific ideas. Finally, the student may meet what is actually the same mathematical principle in two different science courses without recognizing the connection, or even learn apparently contradictory theorems in the two courses! For example, in thermodynamics he learns that the integral of an exact differential around a closed path is always zero. In electricity or hydrodynamics, he runs into $\int_0^{2\pi} d\theta$, which is certainly the integral of an exact differential around a closed path but is not zero! Now it would be fine if every science student could take the separate mathematics courses in differential equations (ordinary and partial), advanced calculus, linear algebra, vector and tensor analysis, complex variable, Fourier series, probability, calculus of variations, special functions, etc. However, most science students have neither the time nor the inclination to study that much mathematics, yet they are constantly hampered in their science courses for lack of the basic techniques of these subjects. It is the intent of this book to give such students enough background in each of the needed areas so that they can cope successfully with junior, senior, and beginning graduate courses in the physical sciences. It is to be hoped, also, that some students will be sufficiently intrigued by one or more of the fields of mathematics to pursue it further.

It is clear that something must be omitted if so many topics are to be compressed into one course. I believe that two things can be left out without serious harm at this stage of a student's work, namely, generality, and detailed proofs. Stating and proving a theorem in its most general form is important to the mathematician and to the advanced student, but it is often unnecessary and may be confusing to the more elementary student. This is not in the least to say that the science student has no use for careful mathematics. The scientist, even more than the mathematician, needs careful statements of the limits of applicability of his mathematical processes, because he cannot so easily supply his own proofs of the accuracy of his work. Consequently I have endeavored to give accurate statements of the needed theorems, although often for special cases or without proof. Interested students can easily find more detail in textbooks in the special fields.

The existing texts on this subject almost invariably assume a degree of mathematical sophistication not yet reached by the student who has just completed one year of calculus. Yet such a student, if given simple and clear explanations, can master these techniques in rapid succession. (He not only *can*, but will *have to* one way or another if he is going to pass his junior and senior physics courses!) Such a student is not ready for detailed applications—these he will get in his science courses—but he does need and want to be given some idea of the use of the methods and some simple applications. This I have tried to do for each new topic. Many existing texts are slanted toward some particular field and contain a good many chapters on advanced topics in that special field. It is the purpose of this text to cover in simple fashion just the basic methods.

In developing this material for my own classes over the last five years, I have found that students with a background of one (or one and a half) years of calculus (or calculus and analytic geometry) can cover twelve or thirteen of the fifteen chapters in a one-year course meeting three times a week. With such students, I usually cover the first six chapters in the first semester, and a selection of the rest of the book the second semester. If differential equations is covered in a separate course, Chapter 7 may serve as a reference chapter. Chapter 9 may also be used satisfactorily as a reference chapter as needed (for gamma functions in connection with Bessel functions in Chapter 12; for the error function in Chapter 15, etc.) With students having more background (either advanced undergraduates or graduate students needing a brush-up course in the more advanced topics), I find it very satisfactory to start with Chapter 8 (or any desired later chapter) and refer back to earlier chapters as needed.

Although the chapters are not independent, a number of rearrangements of the material are possible. With very little difficulty, it is possible to start with Chapter 3 or Chapter 4 or Chapter 5 instead of Chapter 1. Chapter 4 and especially Chapter 5 are good starting places for a class which needs the motivation of many physical applications. Assuming just a little knowledge of partial differentiation and determinants, there is no trouble in starting with Chapter 5. If Chapter 4 precedes Chapter 1, the short section on two-variable power series can be omitted until later. The class should return to Chapters 1 and 2 before going on to Chapters 6 and 7. Chapter 15 is almost independent of the rest of the book and might reasonably be covered much earlier if desired. The following background is used in the other chapters:

For Chapter 8: Differential equations (Ch. 7).

For Chapter 9: Power series (Ch. 1); differentiating integrals (Ch. 4); Lagrange's equations (Ch. 8), used in one example.

For Chapter 10: Matrices (Ch. 3); vectors (Ch. 5); Lagrange's equations (Ch. 8).

For Chapter 11: Power series (Ch. 1); complex numbers (Ch. 2); partial differentiation (Ch. 4); vectors and vector theorems (Ch. 5); transformations (Ch. 10), used in one discussion.

For Chapter 12: Power series (Ch. 1); complex numbers (Ch. 2); partial differentiation (Ch. 4); differential equations (Ch. 7); Lagrange's equations (Ch. 8); gamma function (Ch. 9); background of Chapters 3, 5, 6, 10, used in discussion of eigenvalues and of orthogonal functions.

For Chapter 13: Fourier series (Ch. 6); complex variable (Ch. 11).

For Chapter 14: Legendre polynomials, Bessel functions, orthogonal functions (Ch. 12); Fourier series (Ch. 6); integral transforms (Ch. 13) used at the end of the chapter.

The only way to learn to apply mathematics to the solution of problems is to solve many problems. Consequently a large selection of problems—some applications and some just on the mathematical method itself—are included at the ends of the chapters.

Mary L. Boas

April, 1966

To the Student

As you start each topic in this book, you will no doubt wonder and ask "Just why should I study this subject and what use does it have in applications?" There is a story about a young mathematics instructor who asked an older professor "What do you say when students ask about the practical applications of some mathematical topic?" The experienced professor said "I tell them!" This text will try to follow his advice. However, you must on your part be reasonable in your request. It is not possible in one book or course to cover both the mathematical methods and very many detailed applications of them. You will have to be content with some information as to the areas of application of each topic and some of the simpler applications. In your later courses, you will then use these techniques in more advanced applications.

One point about your study of this material cannot be emphasized too much: To use mathematics effectively in applications, you need not just knowledge, but *skill*. Skill can be obtained only through practice. You can obtain a certain superficial *knowledge* of mathematics by listening to lectures, but you cannot obtain *skill* this way. How many students have I heard say "It looks so easy when you do it," or "I understand it but I can't do the problems!" Such statements show lack of practice and consequent lack of skill. The only way to develop the skill necessary to use this material in your later courses is to practice by solving many problems. You will find both drill problems and harder more challenging ones at the ends of the chapters. You should not feel satisfied with your study of a chapter until you can solve a reasonable fraction of these problems.

M. L. B.

Contents

Mathematical Methods
in the Physical Sciences

1

Infinite Series

1. THE GEOMETRIC SERIES

As a simple example of many of the ideas involved in series, let us consider the geometric series. You may recall that a geometric progression is a sequence of terms obtained by multiplying each term by some fixed number to get the next term. For example, the sequences

(1.1)
$$
\begin{align}
&\text{(a)} \quad 2, 4, 8, 16, 32, \cdots, \\
&\text{(b)} \quad 1, \tfrac{2}{3}, \tfrac{4}{9}, \tfrac{8}{27}, \tfrac{16}{81}, \cdots, \\
&\text{(c)} \quad a, ar, ar^2, ar^3, \cdots.
\end{align}
$$

are geometric progressions. It is easy to think of examples of such progressions. Suppose the number of bacteria in a culture doubles every hour. Then the terms of (1.1a) represent the number by which the bacteria population has been multiplied after 1 hr, 2 hr, etc. Or suppose a bouncing ball rises each time to $\tfrac{2}{3}$ of the height of the previous bounce. Then (1.1b) would represent the heights of the successive bounces in yards if the ball is originally dropped from a height of 1 yd.

In our first example it is clear that the bacteria population would increase without limit as time went on (mathematically, anyway; that is, assuming that nothing like lack of food prevented the assumed doubling each hour). In the second example, however, the height of bounce of the ball decreases with successive bounces, and we might ask for the total distance the ball goes. The ball falls a distance 1 yd, rises a distance $\tfrac{2}{3}$ yd and falls a distance $\frac{2}{3}$ yd, rises a distance $\frac{4}{9}$ yd and falls a distance $\frac{4}{9}$ yd, and so on. Thus it seems reasonable to write the following expression for the total distance the ball goes:

(1.2) $1 + 2 \cdot \frac{2}{3} + 2 \cdot \frac{4}{9} + 2 \cdot \frac{8}{27} + \cdots = 1 + 2(\frac{2}{3} + \frac{4}{9} + \frac{8}{27} + \cdots)$,

where the three dots mean that the terms continue as they have started (each one being $\frac{2}{3}$ the preceding one), and there is never a last term. Let us consider the expression in parentheses in (1.2), namely

(1.3) $\frac{2}{3} + \frac{4}{9} + \frac{8}{27} + \cdots$.

This expression is an example of an infinite series, and we are asked to find its sum. Not all infinite series have sums; you can see that the series formed by adding the terms in (1.1a) does not have a finite sum. However, even when an infinite series does have a finite sum, we cannot find it by adding the terms because no matter how many we add there are always more. Thus we must find another method. (It is actually deeper than this; what we really have to do is to *define* what we mean by the sum of the series.)

Let us first find the sum of n terms in (1.3). The formula (Problem 2) for the sum of n terms of the geometric progression (1.1c) is

(1.4) $$S_n = \frac{a(1 - r^n)}{1 - r}.$$

Using (1.4) in (1.3), we find

(1.5) $S_n = \frac{2}{3} + \frac{4}{9} + \cdots + (\frac{2}{3})^n = \frac{\frac{2}{3}[1 - (\frac{2}{3})^n]}{1 - \frac{2}{3}} = 2[1 - (\frac{2}{3})^n]$.

As n increases, $(\frac{2}{3})^n$ decreases and approaches zero. Then the sum of n terms approaches 2 as n increases, and we say that the sum of the series is 2. (This is really a definition: The sum of an infinite series is the limit of the sum of n terms as $n \to \infty$.) Then from (1.2), the total distance traveled by the ball is $1 + 2 \cdot 2 = 5$. This is an answer to a mathematical problem. A physicist might well object that a bounce the size of an atom is nonsense! However, the infinite number of small terms of the series after a number of bounces, contribute very little to the final answer (see Problem 1). Thus it makes little difference (in our answer for the total distance) whether we insist that the ball rolls after a certain number of bounces or whether we include the entire series, and it is easier to find the sum of the series than to find the sum of, say, twenty terms.

Series such as (1.3) whose terms form a geometric progression are called *geometric series*. We can write a geometric series in the form

(1.6) $a + ar + ar^2 + \cdots + ar^{n-1} + \cdots$.

The sum of the geometric series (if it has one) is by definition

(1.7) $$S = \lim_{n \to \infty} S_n,$$

where S_n is the sum of n terms of the series. By following the method of the example above, you can show (Problem 2) that a geometric series has a sum if and only if $|r| < 1$, and in this case the sum is

(1.8) $$S = \frac{a}{1 - r}.$$

The series is then called *convergent*.

2. DEFINITIONS AND NOTATION

There are many other infinite series besides geometric series. Here are some examples:

(2.1)

$$\text{(a)} \quad 1^2 + 2^2 + 3^2 + 4^2 + \cdots,$$

$$\text{(b)} \quad \frac{1}{2} + \frac{2}{2^2} + \frac{3}{2^3} + \frac{4}{2^4} + \cdots,$$

$$\text{(c)} \quad x - \frac{x^2}{2} + \frac{x^3}{3} - \frac{x^4}{4} + \cdots.$$

In general, an infinite series means an expression of the form

(2.2) $$a_1 + a_2 + a_3 + \cdots + a_n + \cdots,$$

where the a_n's (one for each positive integer n) are numbers or functions given by some formula or rule. The three dots in each case mean that the series never ends. The terms continue according to the law of formation, which is supposed to be evident to you by the time you reach the three dots. If there is apt to be doubt about how the terms are formed, a general or nth term is written like this:

(2.3)

$$\text{(a)} \quad 1^2 + 2^2 + 3^2 + \cdots + n^2 + \cdots,$$

$$\text{(b)} \quad x - x^2 + \frac{x^3}{2} + \cdots + \frac{(-1)^{n-1}x^n}{(n-1)!} + \cdots.$$

(The quantity $n!$, read n factorial, means, for integral n, the product of all integers from 1 to n; for example, $5! = 5 \cdot 4 \cdot 3 \cdot 2 \cdot 1 = 120$. The quantity $0!$ is defined to be 1.) In (2.3a), it is easy to see without the general term that each term is just the square of the number of the term, that is, n^2. However, in (2.3b), if the formula for the general term were missing, you could probably make several reasonable guesses for the next term. To be sure of the law of formation, we must either know a good many more terms or have the formula for the general term. You should verify that the fourth term in (2.3b) is $-x^4/6$.

We can also write series in a shorter abbreviated form using a summation sign Σ followed by the formula for the nth term. For example, (2.3a) would be written

$$1^2 + 2^2 + 3^2 + 4^2 + \cdots = \sum_{n=1}^{\infty} n^2$$

(read "the sum of n^2 from $n = 1$ to ∞"). The series (2.3b) would be written

$$x - x^2 + \frac{x^3}{2} - \frac{x^4}{6} + \cdots = \sum_{n=1}^{\infty} \frac{(-1)^{n-1} x^n}{(n-1)!} .$$

3. APPLICATIONS OF SERIES

In the example of the bouncing ball in Section 1, we saw that it is possible for the sum of an infinite series to be nearly the same as the sum of a fairly small number of terms at the beginning of the series (also see Problem 1). This is the basis for the use of infinite series in applications. Many problems cannot be solved in terms of the so-called elementary functions (powers and roots, trigonometric and inverse trigonometric functions, exponentials and logarithms, and combinations of these). Or, even if they can, the result may be too complicated to work with easily. In such cases, we find an answer in terms of an infinite series, and then use only as many terms as necessary to obtain the accuracy we desire. We shall see many examples of this later in this chapter and also in later chapters. Differential equations are frequently solved by using series. A definite integral, say $\int_0^{0.1} e^{-x^2}\, dx$ for which you cannot find the indefinite integral in terms of elementary functions, can be evaluated by expanding the integrand in a series and integrating term by term. We shall learn how to find series that represent functions; often a complicated function can be approximated by a few terms of its series (see Section 15).

4. CONVERGENT AND DIVERGENT SERIES

We have been talking about series which have a finite sum. We have also seen that there are series which do not have finite sums, for example (2.1a).

If a series has a finite sum, it is called *convergent*. Otherwise it is called *divergent*. It is important to know whether a series is convergent or divergent. Some weird things can happen if you try to apply ordinary algebra to a divergent series. Suppose we try it with the following series.

(4.1) $$S = 1 + 2 + 4 + 8 + 16 + \cdots.$$

Then

$$2S = 2 + 4 + 8 + 16 + \cdots = S - 1,$$
$$S = -1.$$

This is obvious nonsense, and you may laugh at the idea of trying to operate with such a violently divergent series as (4.1). But the same sort of thing can happen in more concealed fashion, and has happened and given wrong answers to people who were not careful enough about the way they used infinite series. At this point you probably would not recognize that the series

(4.2) $$1 + \tfrac{1}{2} + \tfrac{1}{3} + \tfrac{1}{4} + \tfrac{1}{5} + \cdots$$

is divergent, but it is; and the series

(4.3) $$1 - \tfrac{1}{2} + \tfrac{1}{3} - \tfrac{1}{4} + \tfrac{1}{5} - \cdots$$

is convergent as it stands, but can be made to have *any* sum you like by rearranging the order of the terms! (See Section 8.) You can see from these examples how essential it is to know whether a series converges, and also to know how to apply algebra to series correctly. There are even cases in which some divergent series can be used (see Chapter 9), but in this chapter we shall be concerned with convergent series.

Before we consider some tests for convergence, let us repeat the definition of convergence more carefully. Let us call the terms of the series a_n so that the series is

(4.4) $$a_1 + a_2 + a_3 + a_4 + \cdots + a_n + \cdots.$$

Remember that the three dots mean that there is never a last term; the series goes on without end. Now consider the sums S_n that we obtain by adding more and more terms of the series. We define

$$S_1 = a_1,$$
$$S_2 = a_1 + a_2,$$
(4.5) $$S_3 = a_1 + a_2 + a_3,$$
$$\cdots$$
$$S_n = a_1 + a_2 + a_3 + \cdots + a_n.$$

Each S_n is called a *partial sum*; it is the sum of the first n terms of the series. We had an example of this for a geometric progression in (1.4). The letter

n can be any integer; for each n, S_n stops with the nth term. (Since S_n is not an infinite series, there is no question of convergence for it.) As n increases, the partial sums may increase without any limit as in the series (2.1a). They may oscillate as in the series $1 - 2 + 4 - 8 + 16 - \cdots$, or they may have some more complicated behavior. One possibility is that the S_n's may, after a while, not change very much any more; the a_n's may become very small and the S_n's come closer and closer to some value S. We are particularly interested in this case in which the S_n's approach a limiting value, say

$$(4.6) \qquad \lim_{n \to \infty} S_n = S.$$

(It is understood that S is a finite number.) If this happens, we make the following definitions.

(a) If the partial sums S_n of an infinite series tend to a limit S, the series is called *convergent*. We shall use the term *divergent* to mean simply not convergent. (Some texts use the term oscillating for series like $1 - 2 + 3 - 4 + \cdots$, and reserve divergent for cases when $S_n \to \pm \infty$.)

(b) The limiting value S is called the *sum of the series*.

(c) The difference $R_n = S - S_n$ is called the *remainder* (or the remainder after n terms). From (4.6), we see that

$$(4.7) \qquad \lim_{n \to \infty} R_n = \lim_{n \to \infty} (S - S_n) = S - S = 0.$$

5. TESTING SERIES FOR CONVERGENCE; THE PRELIMINARY TEST

We shall consider here a few simple tests for convergence. These tests will illustrate some of the ideas involved in testing series for convergence and will work for a good many, but not all, cases. There are more complicated tests which you can find in other books (also some of them in the problems at the end of this chapter). In some cases it may be quite a difficult mathematical problem to investigate the convergence of a complicated series. However, for our purposes the simple tests we give here will be sufficient.

First we discuss what we shall call the *preliminary test*. In most cases you should apply this to a series before you use other tests.

Preliminary test. If the terms of an infinite series do not tend to zero (that is, if $\lim_{n \to \infty} a_n \neq 0$), the series diverges.

This is *not* a test for convergence; what it does is to weed out some very badly divergent series which you then do not have to spend time testing by other methods. *Note carefully:* The preliminary test can *never* tell you that a series converges. It does *not* say that series converge if $a_n \to 0$ and, in fact, often they do not. A simple example is the harmonic series (4.2); the nth term certainly tends to zero, but we shall soon show that the series $\sum\limits_{n=1}^{\infty} \frac{1}{n}$ is divergent. On the other hand, in the series

$$\tfrac{1}{2} + \tfrac{2}{3} + \tfrac{3}{4} + \tfrac{4}{5} + \cdots$$

the terms are tending to 1, so by the preliminary test, this series diverges and no further testing is needed.

6. TESTS FOR CONVERGENCE OF SERIES OF POSITIVE TERMS; ABSOLUTE CONVERGENCE

We are now going to consider three useful tests for series whose terms are all positive. If some of the terms of a series are negative, we may still want to consider the related series which we get by making all the terms positive; that is, we may consider the series whose terms are the absolute values of the terms of our original series. If this new series converges, we call the original series *absolutely convergent*. It can be proved that if a series converges absolutely, then it converges (Problem 17). This means that if the series of absolute values converges, the series is still convergent when you put back the original minus signs. (The sum is different, of course.) The following three tests may be used, then, either for testing series of positive terms, or for testing any series for absolute convergence.

1. The comparison test. Let

$$m_1 + m_2 + m_3 + m_4 + \cdots$$

be a series of positive terms which you know converges. Then the series you are testing, namely

$$a_1 + a_2 + a_3 + a_4 + \cdots$$

is absolutely convergent if $|a_n| \le m_n$ for all but a finite number of values of n, that is, if the absolute value of each term of the a series is less than (or equal to) the corresponding term of the m series (except perhaps for a finite number of terms).

Example.   Test $\sum\limits_{n=1}^{\infty} \frac{1}{n!} = 1 + \tfrac{1}{2} + \tfrac{1}{6} + \tfrac{1}{24} + \cdots$ for convergence.

As a comparison series, we choose the geometric series

$$\sum\limits_{n=1}^{\infty} \frac{1}{2^n} = \tfrac{1}{2} + \tfrac{1}{4} + \tfrac{1}{8} + \tfrac{1}{16} + \cdots.$$

Notice that we do not care about the first few terms (or, in fact, any finite number of terms) in a series, because they can affect the sum of the series but *not* whether it converges. When we ask whether a series converges or not, we are asking what happens as we add more and more terms for larger and larger n. Does the sum increase indefinitely, or does it approach a limit? What the first five or hundred or million terms are has no effect on whether the sum eventually increases indefinitely or approaches a limit. Consequently we frequently ignore some of the early terms in testing series for convergence.

In our example, the terms of $\sum_{n=1}^{\infty} \frac{1}{n!}$ are smaller than the corresponding terms of $\sum_{n=1}^{\infty} \frac{1}{2^n}$ for all $n > 3$ (Problem 8b). We know that the geometric series converges because its ratio is $\frac{1}{2}$. Therefore $\sum_{n=1}^{\infty} \frac{1}{n!}$ converges also.

The comparison test is really the basic test from which other tests are derived. It is probably the most useful test of all for the experienced mathematician but it is often hard to think of a satisfactory m series until you have had a good deal of experience with series. Consequently you will probably not use it as often as the next two tests.

2. Integral test. We can use this test when the terms of the series are positive and not increasing, that is, when $a_{n+1} \le a_n$. (Again remember that we can ignore any finite number of terms of the series; thus the test can still be used even if the condition $a_{n+1} \le a_n$ does not hold for a finite number of terms.) To apply the test we think of a_n as a function of the variable n, and, forgetting our previous meaning of n, we allow it to take all values, not just integral ones. The test states that the series converges if $\int^{\infty} a_n \, dn$ is finite and diverges if the integral is infinite. (The integral is to be evaluated *only* at the upper limit; no lower limit is needed.)

To understand this test, imagine a graph sketched of a_n as a function of n. For example, in testing the harmonic series $\sum_{n=1}^{\infty} \frac{1}{n}$, we consider the graph of the function $y = 1/n$ (similar to Figs. 6.1 and 6.2) letting n have all values, not just integral ones. Then the values of y on the graph at $n = 1, 2, 3$, etc., are the terms of the series. In Figs. 6.1 and 6.2, the areas of the rectangles are just the terms of the series. Notice that in Fig. 6.1 the top edge of each rectangle is above the curve, so that the area of the rectangles is greater than the corresponding area under the curve. On the other hand, in Fig. 6.2 the rectangles lie below the curve, so their area is less than the corresponding area under the curve. Now the areas of the rectangles are just the terms of the series, and the area under the curve

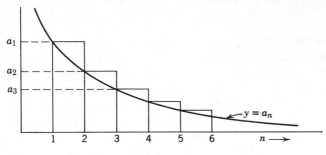

Figure 6.1

is an integral of $y\,dn$ or $a_n\,dn$. The upper limit on the integrals is ∞ and the lower limit could be made to correspond to any term of the series we wanted to start with. For example (see Fig 6.1), $\int_3^\infty a_n\,dn$ is less than the sum of the series from a_3 on, but (see Fig. 6.2) greater than the sum of the series from a_4 on. If the integral is finite, then the sum of the series from a_4 on is finite, that is, the series converges. Note again that the terms at the beginning of a series have nothing to do with convergence. On the other hand, if the integral is infinite, then the sum of the series from a_3 on is infinite and the series diverges. Since the beginning terms are of no interest, there is no need to use a lower limit on the integral, and you should simply evaluate $\int^\infty a_n\,dn$. (Also see Problem 24.)

Example. Test for convergence the harmonic series

(6.1)
$$1 + \tfrac{1}{2} + \tfrac{1}{3} + \tfrac{1}{4} + \cdots.$$

Using the integral test, we evaluate

$$\int^\infty \frac{1}{n}\,dn = \ln n \Big|^\infty = \infty.$$

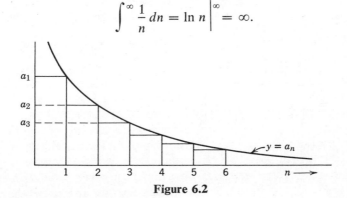

Figure 6.2

(We use the symbol ln to mean a natural logarithm, that is, a logarithm to the base e.) Since the integral is infinite, the series diverges.

3. Ratio test. The integral test depends upon your being able to integrate $a_n \, dn$; this is not always easy! We consider another test which will handle many cases in which we cannot evaluate the integral. Recall that in the geometric series each term could be obtained by multiplying the one before it by the ratio r, that is, $a_{n+1} = ra_n$ or $a_{n+1}/a_n = r$. For other series the ratio a_{n+1}/a_n is not constant but depends on n; let us call the absolute value of this ratio ρ_n. Let us also find the limit (if there is one) of ρ_n as $n \to \infty$ and call this limit ρ. Thus we define ρ_n and ρ by the equations

(6.2)
$$\rho_n = \left| \frac{a_{n+1}}{a_n} \right|,$$

$$\rho = \lim_{n \to \infty} \rho_n.$$

If you recall that a geometric series converges if $|r| < 1$, it may seem plausible that a series with $\rho < 1$ should converge and this is true. This statement can be proved (Problem 18) by comparing the series to be tested with a geometric series. Like a geometric series with $|r| > 1$, a series with $\rho > 1$ also diverges (Problem 18). However, if $\rho = 1$, the ratio test does not tell us anything; some series with $\rho = 1$ converge and some diverge, so we must find another test (say one of the two preceding tests). To summarize the ratio test:

(6.3)   If $\begin{cases} \rho < 1, & \text{the series converges;} \\ \rho = 1, & \text{the test tells nothing;} \\ \rho > 1, & \text{the series diverges.} \end{cases}$

Example 1. Test for convergence the series

$$1 + \frac{1}{2!} + \frac{1}{3!} + \cdots + \frac{1}{n!} + \cdots.$$

Using (6.2), we have

$$\rho_n = \left| \frac{1}{(n+1)!} \div \frac{1}{n!} \right|$$

$$= \frac{n!}{(n+1)!} = \frac{n(n-1) \cdots 3 \cdot 2 \cdot 1}{(n+1)(n)(n-1) \cdots 3 \cdot 2 \cdot 1} = \frac{1}{n+1},$$

$$\rho = \lim_{n \to \infty} \rho_n = \lim_{n \to \infty} \frac{1}{n+1} = 0.$$

Since $\rho < 1$, the series converges.

Example 2. Test for convergence the harmonic series

$$1 + \tfrac{1}{2} + \tfrac{1}{3} + \cdots + \frac{1}{n} + \cdots.$$

We find

$$\rho_n = \left| \frac{1}{n+1} \div \frac{1}{n} \right| = \frac{n}{n+1},$$

$$\rho = \lim_{n \to \infty} \frac{n}{n+1} = \lim_{n \to \infty} \frac{1}{1 + \dfrac{1}{n}} = 1.$$

Here the test tells us nothing and we must use some different test. A word of warning from this example: Notice that $\rho_n = n/(n+1)$ is always less than 1. Careless students often confuse this ratio with ρ and conclude incorrectly that this series converges. (It is actually divergent as we proved by the integral test.) Remember that ρ is *not* the same as the ratio $\rho_n = \left| \dfrac{a_{n+1}}{a_n} \right|$, but is the *limit* of this ratio as $n \to \infty$.

7. ALTERNATING SERIES

So far we have been talking about series of positive terms (including series of absolute values). Now we want to consider one important case of a series whose terms have mixed signs. An *alternating series* is a series whose terms are alternately plus and minus; for example,

$$(7.1) \qquad 1 - \frac{1}{2} + \frac{1}{3} - \frac{1}{4} + \frac{1}{5} - \cdots + \frac{(-1)^{n+1}}{n} + \cdots$$

is an alternating series. We ask two questions about an alternating series. Does it converge? Does it converge absolutely (that is, when we make all signs positive)? Let us consider the second question first. In this example the series of absolute values

$$1 + \tfrac{1}{2} + \tfrac{1}{3} + \tfrac{1}{4} + \cdots + \frac{1}{n} + \cdots$$

is the harmonic series (6.1), which diverges. We say that the series (7.1) is not absolutely convergent. Next we must ask whether (7.1) converges as it stands. If it had turned out to be absolutely convergent, we would not have to ask this question since an absolutely convergent series is also convergent (Problem 17). However, a series which is not absolutely convergent may converge or it may diverge; we must test it further. For alternating series the test is very simple:

Test for alternating series. An alternating series converges if the absolute value of the terms decreases steadily to zero, that is, if $|a_{n+1}| \leq |a_n|$ and $\lim_{n \to \infty} a_n = 0$.

In our example $\dfrac{1}{n+1} < \dfrac{1}{n}$, and $\lim_{n \to \infty} \dfrac{1}{n} = 0$, so (7.1) converges.

8. CONDITIONALLY CONVERGENT SERIES

A series like (7.1) which converges, but does not converge absolutely, is called *conditionally convergent*. You have to use special care in handling conditionally convergent series because the positive terms alone form a divergent series and so do the negative terms alone. If you rearrange the terms, you will probably change the sum of the series and you may even make it diverge! It is possible to rearrange the terms to make the sum any number you wish. Let us do this with the alternating harmonic series $1 - \frac{1}{2} + \frac{1}{3} - \frac{1}{4} + \cdots$. Suppose we want to make the sum equal to 1.5. First we take enough positive terms to add to just over 1.5. The first three positive terms do this:

$$1 + \tfrac{1}{3} + \tfrac{1}{5} = 1\tfrac{8}{15} > 1.5.$$

Then we take enough negative terms to bring the partial sum back under 1.5; the one term $-\frac{1}{2}$ does this. Again we add positive terms until we have a little more than 1.5, and so on. Since the terms of the series are decreasing in absolute value, we are able (as we continue this process) to get partial sums just a little more or a little less than 1.5 but always nearer and nearer to 1.5. But this is what convergence of the series to the sum 1.5 means: that the partial sums should approach 1.5. You should see that we could pick in advance *any* sum that we want, and rearrange the terms of this series to get it. Thus we must not rearrange the terms of a conditionally convergent series since its convergence and its sum depend upon the fact that the terms are added in a particular order.

Here is a physical example of such a series which emphasizes the care needed in applying mathematical approximations in physical problems. Coulomb's law in electricity says that the force between two charges is equal to the product of the charges divided by the square of the distance between them (in electrostatic units; to use other units, say mks, we need only multiply by a numerical constant). Suppose there are unit positive charges at $x = 0$, $\sqrt{2}$, $\sqrt{4}$, $\sqrt{6}$, $\sqrt{8}$, etc., and unit negative charges at $x = 1$, $\sqrt{3}$, $\sqrt{5}$, $\sqrt{7}$, etc. We want to know the total force acting on the unit positive charge at $x = 0$ due to all the other charges. The negative charges attract the charge at $x = 0$ and try to pull it to the right; we call the forces exerted by them positive, since they are in the direction of the positive x-axis. The forces due to the positive charges are in the negative x direction, and we call them negative. For example, the force due to the positive charge at $x = \sqrt{2}$ is $-(1 \cdot 1)/(\sqrt{2})^2 = -\frac{1}{2}$. The total force on the charge at $x = 0$ is, then,

(8.1) $$F = 1 - \tfrac{1}{2} + \tfrac{1}{3} - \tfrac{1}{4} + \tfrac{1}{5} - \tfrac{1}{6} + \cdots .$$

Now we know that this series converges as it stands (Section 7). But we have also seen that its sum (even the fact that it converges) can be changed by rearranging the terms. Physically this means that the force on the charge at the origin depends not only on the size and position of the charges, but also on the *order* in which we place them in their positions! This may very well go strongly against your physical intuition. You feel that a physical problem like this should have a definite answer. Think of it this way. Suppose there are two crews of workmen, one crew placing the positive charges and one placing the negative. If one crew works faster than the other, it is clear that the force at any stage may be far from the F of equation (8.1) because there are many extra charges of one sign. The crews can never place *all* the charges because there are an infinite number of them. At any stage the forces which would arise from the positive charges that are not yet in place, form a divergent series; similarly, the forces due to the unplaced negative charges form a divergent series of the opposite sign. We cannot then stop at some point and say that the rest of the series is negligible as we could in the bouncing ball problem in Section 1. But if we specify the *order* in which the charges are to be placed, then the sum S of the series is determined (S is probably different from F in (8.1) unless the charges are placed alternately). Physically this means that the value of the force as the crews proceed comes closer and closer to S, and we can use the sum of the (properly arranged) *infinite* series as a good approximation to the force.

9. USEFUL FACTS ABOUT SERIES

We state the following facts for reference.

1. The convergence or divergence of a series is not affected by multiplying every term of the series by the same constant. Neither is it affected

by changing a finite number of terms (for example, omitting the first few terms).

2. Two convergent series $\sum\limits_{n=1}^{\infty} a_n$ and $\sum\limits_{n=1}^{\infty} b_n$ may be added (or subtracted) term by term. (Adding "term by term" means that the nth term of the sum is $a_n + b_n$.) The resulting series is convergent, and its sum is obtained by adding (subtracting) the sums of the two given series.

3. The terms of an *absolutely convergent series* may be rearranged in any order without affecting either the convergence or the sum. This is *not true* of conditionally convergent series as we have seen in Section 8.

10. POWER SERIES; INTERVAL OF CONVERGENCE

We have been discussing series whose terms were constants. Even more important and useful are series whose terms are functions of x. There are many such series, but in this chapter we shall consider only series in which the nth term is a constant times x^n. These are called *power series*, because the terms are multiples of powers of x. In later chapters we shall consider Fourier series whose terms involve sines and cosines, and other series (Legendre, Bessel, etc.) in which the terms may be polynomials or other functions.

By definition, a power series is of the form

(10.1) $$\sum_{n=0}^{\infty} a_n x^n = a_0 + a_1 x + a_2 x^2 + a_3 x^3 + \cdots$$

where the coefficients a_n are constants. Here are some examples:

(10.2)

(a) $\quad 1 - \dfrac{x}{2} + \dfrac{x^2}{4} - \dfrac{x^3}{8} + \cdots + \dfrac{(-x)^n}{2^n} + \cdots,$

(b) $\quad x - \dfrac{x^2}{2} + \dfrac{x^3}{3} - \dfrac{x^4}{4} + \cdots + \dfrac{(-1)^{n+1}x^n}{n} + \cdots,$

(c) $\quad x - \dfrac{x^3}{3!} + \dfrac{x^5}{5!} - \dfrac{x^7}{7!} + \cdots + \dfrac{(-1)^{n+1}x^{2n-1}}{(2n-1)!} + \cdots.$

Whether a power series converges or not depends on the value of x we are considering. We often use the ratio test to find the values of x for which a series converges. We illustrate this by testing each of the three series (10.2). Recall that in the ratio test we divide term $n + 1$ by term n and take the absolute value of this ratio to get ρ_n, and then take the limit of ρ_n as $n \to \infty$ to get ρ.

Example. For (10.2a), we have

$$\rho_n = \left| \frac{(-x)^{n+1}}{2^{n+1}} \div \frac{(-x)^n}{2^n} \right| = \left| \frac{x}{2} \right|,$$

$$\rho = \left| \frac{x}{2} \right|.$$

The series converges for $\rho < 1$, that is, for $|x/2| < 1$ or $|x| < 2$, and it diverges for $|x| > 2$ (see Problem 18). Graphically we consider the interval on the x-axis between $x = -2$ and $x = 2$; for any x in this interval the series (10.2a) converges. The endpoints of the interval, $x = 2$ and $x = -2$, must be considered separately. When $x = 2$, (10.2a) is

$$1 - 1 + 1 - 1 + \cdots,$$

which is divergent; when $x = -2$, (10.2a) is $1 + 1 + 1 + 1 + \cdots$, which is divergent. Then the interval of convergence of (10.2a) is stated as $-2 < x < 2$.

Example. For (10.2b) we find

$$\rho_n = \left| \frac{x^{n+1}}{n+1} \div \frac{x^n}{n} \right| = \left| \frac{nx}{n+1} \right|,$$

$$\rho = \lim_{n \to \infty} \left| \frac{nx}{n+1} \right| = |x|.$$

The series converges for $|x| < 1$. Again we must consider the endpoints of the interval of convergence, $x = 1$ and $x = -1$. For $x = 1$, the series (10.2b) is $1 - \frac{1}{2} + \frac{1}{3} - \frac{1}{4} + \cdots$; this is the alternating harmonic series and is convergent. For $x = -1$, (10.2b) is $-1 - \frac{1}{2} - \frac{1}{3} - \frac{1}{4} - \cdots$; this is the harmonic series (times -1) and is divergent. Then we state the interval of convergence of (10.2b) as $-1 < x \leq 1$. Notice carefully how this differs from our result for (10.2a). Series (10.2a) did not converge at either endpoint and we used only $<$ signs in stating its interval of convergence. Series (10.2b) converges at $x = 1$, so we use the sign $\leq$ to include $x = 1$. You must always test a series at its endpoints and include the results in your statement of the interval of convergence. A series may converge at neither, either one, or both of the endpoints.

Example. In (10.2c), the absolute value of the nth term is $\left| \frac{x^{2n-1}}{(2n-1)!} \right|$. To get term $n + 1$ we replace n by $n + 1$; then $2n - 1$ is replaced by $2(n+1) - 1 = 2n + 1$, and the absolute value of term $n + 1$ is

$$\left| \frac{x^{2n+1}}{(2n+1)!} \right|.$$

Thus we get

$$\rho_n = \left| \frac{x^{2n+1}}{(2n+1)!} \div \frac{x^{2n-1}}{(2n-1)!} \right| = \left| \frac{x^2}{(2n+1)(2n)} \right|,$$

$$\rho = \lim_{n \to \infty} \left| \frac{x^2}{(2n+1)(2n)} \right| = 0.$$

Since $\rho < 1$ for all values of x, this series converges for all x.

11. THEOREMS ABOUT POWER SERIES

We have seen that a power series $\sum_{n=0}^{\infty} a_n x^n$ converges in some interval with center at the origin. For each value of x (in the interval of convergence) the series has a finite sum whose value depends, of course, on the value of x. Thus we can write the sum of the series as $S(x) = \sum_{n=0}^{\infty} a_n x^n$. We see then that a power series (within its interval of convergence) defines a function of x, namely $S(x)$. In describing the relation of the series and the function $S(x)$, we may say that the series converges to the function $S(x)$, or that the function $S(x)$ is represented by the series, or that the series is the power series of the function. Here we have thought of obtaining the function from a given series. We shall also (Section 12) be interested in finding a power series that converges to a given function. When we are working with power series and the functions they represent, it is useful to know the following theorems (which we state without proof; see Knopp*). Power series are very useful and convenient because within their interval of convergence they can be handled much like polynomials.

1. A power series may be differentiated or integrated term by term; the resulting series converges to the derivative or integral of the function represented by the original series within the same interval of convergence as the original series (that is, not necessarily at the endpoints of the interval).

2. Two power series may be added, subtracted, or multiplied; the resultant series converges at least in the common interval of convergence. You may divide two series if the denominator series is not zero at $x = 0$, or if it is and the zero is canceled by the numerator [as, for example, in $(\sin x)/x$; see (13.1)]. The resulting series will have *some* interval of convergence (which can be found by the ratio test or more simply by complex variable theory—see Chapter 2, Section 7).

* References in the text will be given by author's last name only; for complete reference, see the list at the end of the book.

3. One series may be substituted in another provided that the values of the substituted series are in the interval of convergence of the other series.

4. The power series of a function is unique, that is, there is just one power series of the form $\sum_{n=0}^{\infty} a_n x^n$ which converges to a given function.

12. EXPANDING FUNCTIONS IN POWER SERIES

Very often in applied work, it is useful to find power series that represent given functions. We illustrate one method of obtaining such series by finding the series for $\sin x$. In this method we *assume* that there *is* such a series (see Section 14 for discussion of this point) and set out to find what the coefficients in the series must be. Thus we write

$$(12.1) \qquad \sin x = a_0 + a_1 x + a_2 x^2 + \cdots + a_n x^n + \cdots$$

and try to find numerical values of the coefficients a_n to make (12.1) an identity (within the interval of convergence of the series). Since the interval of convergence of a power series contains the origin, (12.1) must hold when $x = 0$. If we substitute $x = 0$ into (12.1), we get $0 = a_0$ since $\sin 0 = 0$ and all the terms except a_0 on the right-hand side of the equation contain the factor x. Then to make (12.1) valid at $x = 0$, we must have $a_0 = 0$. Next we differentiate (12.1) term by term to get

$$(12.2) \qquad \cos x = a_1 + 2a_2 x + 3a_3 x^2 + \cdots .$$

(This is justified by Theorem 1 of Section 11.) Again putting $x = 0$, we get $1 = a_1$. We differentiate again, and put $x = 0$ to get

$$(12.3) \qquad \begin{aligned} -\sin x &= 2a_2 + 3 \cdot 2a_3 x + 4 \cdot 3a_4 x^2 + \cdots , \\ 0 &= 2a_2 . \end{aligned}$$

Continuing the process of taking successive derivatives of (12.1) and putting $x = 0$, we get

$$-\cos x = 3 \cdot 2a_3 + 4 \cdot 3 \cdot 2a_4 x + \cdots ,$$
$$-1 = 3! \, a_3, \qquad a_3 = -\frac{1}{3!} \, ;$$

$$(12.4) \qquad \sin x = 4 \cdot 3 \cdot 2a_4 + 5 \cdot 4 \cdot 3 \cdot 2a_5 x + \cdots ,$$
$$0 = a_4 ;$$
$$\cos x = 5 \cdot 4 \cdot 3 \cdot 2a_5 + \cdots ,$$
$$1 = 5! \, a_5, \quad \text{etc.}$$

We substitute these values back into (12.1) and get

(12.5) $$\sin x = x - \frac{x^3}{3!} + \frac{x^5}{5!} - \cdots .$$

You can probably see how to write more terms of this series without further computation.

Series obtained in this way are called *Maclaurin series* or *Taylor series about the origin*. A Taylor series in general means a series of powers of $(x - a)$, where a is some constant. It is found by writing $(x - a)$ instead of x on the right-hand side of (12.1), differentiating just as we have done, but substituting $x = a$ instead of $x = 0$ at each step.

Let us carry out this process in general for a function $f(x)$. We write

(12.6)

$$f(x) = a_0 + a_1(x - a) + a_2(x-a)^2 + a_3(x - a)^3 + a_4(x - a)^4$$
$$+ \cdots + a_n(x - a)^n + \cdots ,$$

$$f'(x) = \quad a_1 \quad + 2a_2(x-a) + 3a_3(x-a)^2 + 4a_4(x - a)^3$$
$$+ \cdots + na_n(x - a)^{n-1} + \cdots ,$$

$$f''(x) = \quad 2a_2 + 3 \cdot 2a_3(x - a) + 4 \cdot 3a_4(x - a)^2$$
$$+ \cdots + n(n - 1)a_n(x - a)^{n-2} + \cdots ,$$

$$f'''(x) = \quad 3! \, a_3 + 4 \cdot 3 \cdot 2a_4(x - a)$$
$$+ \cdots + n(n - 1)(n - 2)a_n(x - a)^{n-3} + \cdots ,$$

$$\cdots$$

$$f^{(n)}(x) = n(n - 1)(n - 2) \cdots 1 \cdot a_n + \text{terms containing powers of } (x - a).$$

[The symbol $f^{(n)}(x)$ means the nth derivative of $f(x)$.] We now put $x = a$ in each equation of (12.6) and obtain

(12.7) $$f(a) = a_0, \quad f'(a) = a_1, \quad f''(a) = 2a_2,$$
$$f'''(a) = 3! \, a_3, \cdots, f^{(n)}(a) = n! \, a_n.$$

[Remember that $f'(a)$ means to differentiate $f(x)$ and then put $x = a$; $f''(a)$ means to find $f''(x)$ and then put $x = a$, etc.]

We can then write the Taylor series for $f(x)$ about $x = a$:

(12.8) $$f(x) = f(a) + (x - a)f'(a) + \frac{1}{2!}(x - a)^2 f''(a) + \cdots$$

$$+ \frac{1}{n!}(x - a)^n f^{(n)}(a) + \cdots .$$

The Maclaurin series for $f(x)$ is the Taylor series about the origin. Putting $a = 0$ in (12.8), we obtain the Maclaurin series for $f(x)$:

$$(12.9) \quad f(x) = f(0) + xf'(0) + \frac{x^2}{2!}f''(0)$$

$$+ \frac{x^3}{3!}f'''(0) + \cdots + \frac{x^n}{n!}f^{(n)}(0) + \cdots.$$

We have written this in general because it is sometimes convenient to have the formulas for the coefficients. In doing problems, however, you should not just substitute into (12.9); you will understand and remember the process of finding the series much better if you do problems as we did the series for $\sin x$, or as shown in the examples of Section 13.

13. TECHNIQUES FOR OBTAINING POWER SERIES EXPANSIONS

There are often simpler ways for finding the power series of a function than the successive differentiation process in Section 12. Theorem 4 in Section 11 tells us that for a given function there is *just one* power series, that is, series of the form $\sum_{n=0}^{\infty} a_n x^n$. Therefore we can obtain it by any correct method and be sure that it is the same Maclaurin series we would get by using the method of Section 12. We shall illustrate a variety of methods for obtaining power series. First of all, it is a great timesaver for you to verify (say by the method of Section 12) and then memorize the following basic series:

convergent for

$$(13.1) \qquad \sin x = x - \frac{x^3}{3!} + \frac{x^5}{5!} - \frac{x^7}{7!} + \cdots, \qquad \text{all } x;$$

$$(13.2) \qquad \cos x = 1 - \frac{x^2}{2!} + \frac{x^4}{4!} - \frac{x^6}{6!} + \cdots, \qquad \text{all } x;$$

$$(13.3) \qquad e^x = 1 + x + \frac{x^2}{2!} + \frac{x^3}{3!} + \frac{x^4}{4!} + \cdots, \qquad \text{all } x;$$

$$(13.4) \quad \ln(1 + x) = x - \frac{x^2}{2} + \frac{x^3}{3} - \frac{x^4}{4} + \cdots, \qquad -1 < x \le 1;$$

$$(13.5) \quad (1 + x)^p = 1 + px + \frac{p(p-1)}{2!}x^2 + \frac{p(p-1)(p-2)}{3!}x^3 + \cdots,$$

$$|x| < 1,$$

(binomial series; p is any real number, positive or negative).

We shall use these series without further derivation when we need them in the following examples. We now outline and give examples of various useful methods of obtaining series expansions.

A. Multiplication of a series by a polynomial or by another series.

Example 1. To find the series for $(x + 1) \sin x$, we multiply $(x + 1)$ times the series (13.1) and collect terms:

$$(x + 1) \sin x = (x + 1)\left(x - \frac{x^3}{3!} + \frac{x^5}{5!} - \cdots \right)$$

$$= x + x^2 - \frac{x^3}{3!} - \frac{x^4}{3!} + \cdots .$$

You can see that this is easier to do than taking the successive derivatives of the product $(x + 1) \sin x$, and Theorem 4 assures us that the results are the same.

Example 2. To find the series for $e^x \cos x$, we multiply (13.2) by (13.3) and collect terms (to save writing, we group together the terms involving each power of x as we multiply):

$$e^x \cos x = \left(1 + x + \frac{x^2}{2!} + \frac{x^3}{3!} + \frac{x^4}{4!} + \cdots \right)\left(1 - \frac{x^2}{2!} + \frac{x^4}{4!} - \cdots \right)$$

$$= 1 + x + \left(\frac{x^2}{2!} - \frac{x^2}{2!} \right) + \left(\frac{x^3}{3!} - \frac{x^3}{2!} \right)$$

$$+ \left(\frac{x^4}{4!} - \frac{x^4}{2! \cdot 2!} + \frac{x^4}{4!} \right) + \cdots$$

$$= 1 + x - \frac{x^3}{3} - \frac{x^4}{6} \cdots .$$

B. Division of two series or of a series by a polynomial.

Example 1. To find the series for $(1/x) \ln (1 + x)$ we divide (13.4) by x:

$$\frac{1}{x} \ln (1 + x) = \frac{1}{x}\left(x - \frac{x^2}{2} + \frac{x^3}{3} - \frac{x^4}{4} + \cdots \right)$$

$$= 1 - \frac{x}{2} + \frac{x^2}{3} - \frac{x^3}{4} + \cdots .$$

Example 2. To find the series for $1/(1 + x)$ we do the long division (see Example 1 in method C below for another way):

$$
\begin{array}{r}
1 - x + x^2 - x^3 \cdots \\
1 + x \overline{)\,1 } \\
\underline{1 + x} \\
-x \\
\underline{-x - x^2} \\
x^2 \\
\underline{x^2 + x^3} \\
-x^3, \quad \text{etc.}
\end{array}
$$

Example 3. To find the series for $\tan x$, we divide the series for $\sin x$ by the series for $\cos x$ by long division:

$$
\begin{array}{r}
x + \dfrac{x^3}{3} + \dfrac{2}{15} x^5 \cdots \\
1 - \dfrac{x^2}{2!} + \dfrac{x^4}{4!} \cdots \overline{)\, x - \dfrac{x^3}{3!} + \dfrac{x^5}{5!} \cdots} \\
\underline{x - \dfrac{x^3}{2!} + \dfrac{x^5}{4!} \cdots} \\
\dfrac{x^3}{3} - \dfrac{x^5}{30} \cdots \\
\underline{\dfrac{x^3}{3} - \dfrac{x^5}{6} \cdots} \\
\dfrac{2x^5}{15} \cdots, \quad \text{etc.}
\end{array}
$$

C. Binomial series. If you recall the binomial theorem, you may see that (13.5) looks just like the beginning of the binomial theorem for the expansion of $(a + b)^n$ if we put $a = 1$, $b = x$, and $n = p$. The difference here is that we allow p to be negative or fractional, and in these cases the expansion is an infinite series. The series converges for $|x| < 1$ as you can verify by the ratio test.

Example 1. We again find the series of Example 2 in method B above, this time by using the binomial series (13.5).

(13.6)

$$
\frac{1}{1 + x} = (1 + x)^{-1} = 1 - x + \frac{(-1)(-2)}{2!} x^2 + \frac{(-1)(-2)(-3)}{3!} x^3 + \cdots
$$

$$
= 1 - x + x^2 - x^3 + \cdots.
$$

D. Substitution of a polynomial or a series for the variable in another series.

Example 1.   Find the series for e^{-x^2}. Since we know the series (13.3) for e^x, we simply replace the x there by $-x^2$ to get

$$e^{-x^2} = 1 - x^2 + \frac{(-x^2)^2}{2!} + \frac{(-x^2)^3}{3!} + \cdots$$

$$= 1 - x^2 + \frac{x^4}{2!} - \frac{x^6}{3!} + \cdots.$$

Example 2.   Find the series for $e^{\tan x}$. Here we must replace the x in (13.3) by the series of Example 3 in method B. Let us agree in advance to keep terms only as far as x^4; we then write only terms which can give rise to powers of x up to 4, and neglect any higher powers:

$$e^{\tan x} = 1 + \left(x + \frac{x^3}{3} + \cdots\right) + \frac{1}{2!}\left(x + \frac{x^3}{3} + \cdots\right)^2$$

$$+ \frac{1}{3!}\left(x + \frac{x^3}{3} + \cdots\right)^3 + \frac{1}{4!}(x + \cdots)^4 + \cdots$$

$$= 1 + x + \frac{x^2}{2!} + \left(\frac{x^3}{3} + \frac{x^3}{3!}\right) + \left(\frac{1}{2!}\frac{2x^4}{3} + \frac{1}{4!}x^4\right) + \cdots$$

$$= 1 + x + \frac{x^2}{2!} + \frac{3x^3}{3!} + \frac{9x^4}{4!} + \cdots.$$

E. Combination of methods.

Example.   Find the series for arc tan x. Since

$$\text{arc tan } x = \int \frac{dx}{1 + x^2},$$

we first write out (as a binomial series) $1/(1 + x^2)$ and then integrate term by term.

$$\frac{1}{1 + x^2} = 1 - x^2 + x^4 - x^6 + \cdots;$$

$$\int \frac{dx}{1 + x^2} = x - \frac{x^3}{3} + \frac{x^5}{5} - \frac{x^7}{7} + \cdots.$$

We must not forget about the constant of integration. But since arc tan $0 = 0$ and all the terms of the series are zero for $x = 0$, the constant term here should be zero, and we have

(13.7) $$\text{arc tan } x = x - \frac{x^3}{3} + \frac{x^5}{5} - \frac{x^7}{7} + \cdots.$$

Compare this simple way of getting the series with the Maclaurin method in Section 12 of finding successive derivatives of arc tan x.

14. QUESTIONS OF CONVERGENCE AND ACCURACY IN COMPUTATION

The thoughtful student might well be disturbed about the mathematical manipulations we have been doing. How do we know whether these processes we have shown really give us series that approximate the functions being expanded? Certainly *some* functions cannot be expanded in a power series; since a power series becomes just a_0 when $x = 0$, it cannot be equal to any function (like $1/x$ or ln x) which is infinite at the origin. So we might ask whether there are other functions (besides those that become infinite at the origin) which cannot be expanded in a power series. All we have done so far is to show methods of finding the power series for a function *if it has one*. Now is there a chance that there might be some functions which do not have series expansions, but for which our formal methods would give us a spurious series? Unfortunately, the answer is "Yes"; fortunately, this is not a very common difficulty in practice. However, you should know of the possibility and what to do about it. You may first think of the fact that, say, the equation

$$\frac{1}{1+x} = 1 - x + x^2 - x^3 + \cdots$$

is not valid for $|x| \geq 1$. This is a fairly easy restriction to determine; from the beginning we recognized that we could use our series expansions only when they converged. But there is another difficulty which can arise. It is possible for a series found by the above methods to converge and still not represent the function being expanded! A simple example of this is $e^{-(1/x^2)}$ for which the formal series is $0 + 0 + 0 + \cdots$ because $e^{-(1/x^2)}$ and all its derivatives are zero at the origin (Problem 49). It is clear that $e^{-(1/x^2)}$ is not zero for $x^2 > 0$, so the series is certainly not correct. You can startle your friends with the following physical interpretation of this. Suppose that at $t = 0$ a car is at rest (zero velocity), and has zero acceleration, zero rate of change of acceleration, etc. (all derivatives of distance with respect to time are zero at $t = 0$). Then according to Newton's second law (force equals mass times acceleration), the instantaneous force acting on the car is also zero (and, in fact, so are all the derivatives of the force). Now we ask "Is it possible for the car to be moving immediately after $t = 0$?" The answer is "Yes"! For example, let its distance from the origin as a function of time be $e^{-(1/t^2)}$.

This strange behavior is really the fault of the function itself and not of our method of finding series. The most satisfactory way of avoiding the difficulty is to recognize (by complex variable theory, Chapter 11) when functions cannot have power series. Since we cannot do this yet, we shall look at another method which is useful also in numerical computation problems. What we always want to know in practical problems is that the sum of several terms of the series is nearly equal to the function. There are various formulas for the *difference* between the function and a partial sum of its series; such a formula is called a *remainder term*, or *the remainder* of the series. You can see that if the remainder after the term in x^n tends to zero as n tends to infinity, then the series converges to the values of the function.

There is a practical use for the remainder term. Suppose we are going to compute numerical values of a function by adding up several terms of its infinite series, and suppose we want accuracy to five decimal places. We need some way of telling how many terms we must take so that the remainder of the series will not affect the fifth decimal place. We state without proof the following simple and useful form of the remainder term for this purpose. (You can find other forms, and derivations of them, in many calculus books.)

Suppose $f(x)$ is expanded in a Maclaurin series $\sum\limits_{n=0}^{\infty} a_n x^n$; by (12.9) the a_n's are

(14.1) $$a_n = \frac{1}{n!} f^{(n)}(0)$$

where $f^{(n)}(0)$ means the nth derivative of $f(x)$ evaluated at $x = 0$. Then for each x, the (absolute value of the) difference between $f(x)$ and the sum of terms of the series through x^n is less than or equal to the value of

(14.2) $$\left| \frac{x^{n+1}}{(n+1)!} \right| \text{ times the largest value of } |f^{(n+1)}| \text{ between 0 and } x.$$

In symbols, if

(14.3) $$R_n(x) = f(x) - (a_0 + a_1 x + \cdots + a_n x^n)$$

and we compute $f(x)$ for $x = b$ using terms of the series through x^n, then the error $R_n(b)$ satisfies the inequality

(14.4) $$|R_n(b)| \leq \left| \frac{b^{n+1}}{(n+1)!} \cdot \max_{0 \leq x \leq b} f^{(n+1)}(x) \right|.$$

We shall use this formula in the next section.

15. SOME USES OF SERIES

In this chapter we are going to consider a few rather straightforward uses of series. In later chapters there will also be many other cases where we need them.

Numerical computation. If you do not have tables handy, or if you want values which are not in your tables, or if you want more accuracy than the tables give, you may find it useful to compute values of the tabulated functions by using their series. Sometimes you may find the answer to a problem as an infinite series whose sum you do not know in terms of tabulated functions; to obtain numerical values, you must then compute them directly from the series. In order to make computation with series worth while, the series you use must be rapidly convergent. If you must add 200 terms to get the accuracy you need, it is clearly preferable to find some other method!

We shall do some numerical problems to illustrate computation by series. You should notice in each case that the given numbers make the series converge rapidly; with different numbers, the methods shown might not be good ones. You have to think to do problems like this and not just compute blindly!

Example 1. Find $1/\sqrt[3]{999}$ to nine decimal places.

We write $999 = 1000 - 1 = 1000(1 - 10^{-3})$ and expand $1/\sqrt[3]{1 - 10^{-3}}$ in a binomial series. Substituting $x = -10^{-3}$, $n = -\frac{1}{3}$ into (13.5), we get

$$\frac{1}{\sqrt[3]{1 - 10^{-3}}} = (1 - 10^{-3})^{-\frac{1}{3}} = 1 + \frac{1}{3} \cdot 10^{-3} + \frac{(-\frac{1}{3})(-\frac{4}{3})}{2!} \cdot 10^{-6} + \cdots$$

$$= 1 + 0.000333333 + 0.000000222 + \cdots .$$

Then

$$\frac{1}{\sqrt[3]{999}} = \frac{1}{\sqrt[3]{1000}\sqrt[3]{1 - 10^{-3}}} = \frac{1}{10}(1.000333555)$$

$$= 0.100033356 \qquad \text{to nine decimal places.}$$

The next term of the series contains the factor 10^{-9} and this is a good indication that we do not need to go any farther to get the desired accuracy. To be really sure, we can compute the remainder term given in (14.4). We have added terms of the series through $x^2 = (10^{-3})^2$; thus in the remainder we find the third derivative of

$$f(x) = (1 - x)^{-\frac{1}{3}},$$

which is

$$f'''(x) = (-\tfrac{1}{3})(-\tfrac{4}{3})(-\tfrac{7}{3})(1 - x)^{-10/3}.$$

The maximum value of $|f'''(x)|$ between $x = 0$ and $x = 10^{-3}$ occurs for $x = 10^{-3}$, but it differs so little from the value at $x = 0$ that we can estimate it there.

$$\max_{0 \le x \le 0.001} |f'''(x)| \text{ is approximately } \tfrac{28}{27} \text{ or about 1.}$$

Then the remainder is approximately $(1/3!)(10^{-3})^3 \cdot 1$ which gives an error in $(1 - 10^{-3})^{-\frac{1}{3}}$ in the tenth decimal place, or an error in our final answer in the eleventh place. We can now confidently state that to nine decimal places

$$\frac{1}{\sqrt[3]{999}} = 0.100033356.$$

Example 2. Find the sum of the alternating harmonic series

$$1 - \tfrac{1}{2} + \tfrac{1}{3} - \tfrac{1}{4} + \cdots.$$

Start with the series (13.4), namely

$$\ln(1 + x) = x - \frac{x^2}{2} + \frac{x^3}{3} - \frac{x^4}{4} + \cdots$$

and put $x = 1$. Then we get

$$\ln 2 = 1 - \tfrac{1}{2} + \tfrac{1}{3} - \tfrac{1}{4} + \cdots.$$

and the sum of the series is $\ln 2$. We can then use a table of natural logarithms to find the sum; or alternatively we can approximate $\ln 2$ by adding terms of the series.

There is a simple way to estimate the remainder when you are making numerical computations with an *alternating* series which meets the alternating series test for convergence (Section 7, $|a_{n+1}| \le |a_n|$, $\lim a_n = 0$). In this case the error is (in absolute value) less than (the absolute value of) the first neglected term. In Example 2, the first four terms of the series give

$$1 - \tfrac{1}{2} + \tfrac{1}{3} - \tfrac{1}{4} = \tfrac{7}{12} = 0.58.$$

By our rule the error in this result is less than $\tfrac{1}{5}$ or 0.2. As a matter of fact the correct sum is $\ln 2 = 0.69$, and the error is 0.11 which, as promised, is less than 0.2.

This estimate for the error may be completely misleading for convergent series that are *not* alternating. For instance,

$$\frac{1}{1^2} + \frac{1}{2^2} + \frac{1}{3^2} + \cdots = 1.6449+,$$

but it takes about 200 terms to get the second decimal place correctly, even though the 200th term is only

$$\frac{1}{200^2} = 0.000025.$$

(Also see Problem 39.)

Example 3.   Find $\sin \frac{1}{10}$ (note that this means $\frac{1}{10}$ *radian*).
Substituting $x = \frac{1}{10}$ into the series (13.1) for $\sin x$, we get

$$\sin \frac{1}{10} = \frac{1}{10} - \frac{1}{3!}\left(\frac{1}{10}\right)^3 + \frac{1}{5!}\left(\frac{1}{10}\right)^5 + \cdots = 0.1 - \frac{0.001}{6} + \frac{0.00001}{120} + \cdots$$

$$= 0.1 - 0.000166667 + 0.000000083 + \cdots$$

$$= 0.099833417.$$

This is again an alternating series with terms of steadily decreasing absolute value, so the remainder is less than the magnitude of the next term, which is $10^{-7}/7!$ or less than 10^{-10}.

Evaluation of definite integrals.   Many integrals which arise in applied problems cannot be evaluated in terms of elementary functions. One useful way of finding the value of a definite integral when the indefinite integral cannot be found is to expand the integrand in a power series and integrate term by term.

Example.   The Fresnel integrals (integrals of $\sin x^2$ and $\cos x^2$) occur in the problem of Fresnel diffraction in optics. We find

$$\int_0^1 \sin x^2 \, dx = \int_0^1 \left(x^2 - \frac{x^6}{3!} + \frac{x^{10}}{5!} - \cdots \right) dx$$

$$= \tfrac{1}{3} - \frac{1}{7 \cdot 3!} + \frac{1}{11 \cdot 5!} - \cdots$$

$$= 0.33333 - 0.02381 + 0.00076 - \cdots = 0.31028 -.$$

By the alternating series method, the error is less than $1/(15 \cdot 7!)$ or about 10^{-5}.

Evaluation of indeterminate forms.   Suppose we want to find

$$\lim_{x \to 0} \frac{1 - e^x}{x}.$$

If we try to substitute $x = 0$, we get $0/0$. Expressions that lead us to such meaningless results when we substitute are called indeterminate forms.

Many times they can be easily evaluated by using series. For example,

$$\lim_{x\to 0}\frac{1-e^x}{x}=\lim_{x\to 0}\frac{1-(1+x+(x^2/2!)+\cdots)}{x}$$

$$=\lim_{x\to 0}\left(-1-\frac{x}{2!}-\cdots\right)=-1.$$

You may recall l'Hospital's rule which says that

$$\lim_{x\to a}\frac{f(x)}{\phi(x)}=\lim_{x\to a}\frac{f'(x)}{\phi'(x)},$$

when $f(a)$ and $\phi(a)$ are both zero, and f'/ϕ' approaches a limit or tends to infinity (that is, does not oscillate) as $x\to a$. Let us use power series to see that this is true in a simple special case. We consider functions $f(x)$ and $\phi(x)$ which are expandable in a power series about the origin (that is, $a=0$) and assume that $\phi'(0)\neq 0$ (also see Problems 44 and 45). Using (12.9), we have

$$\lim_{x\to 0}\frac{f(x)}{\phi(x)}=\lim_{x\to 0}\frac{f(0)+xf'(0)+(x^2/2!)f''(0)+\cdots}{\phi(0)+x\phi'(0)+(x^2/2!)\phi''(0)+\cdots}.$$

If $f(0)=0$ and $\phi(0)=0$, this becomes

$$\lim_{x\to 0}\frac{xf'(0)+(x^2/2!)f''(0)+\cdots}{x\phi'(0)+(x^2/2!)\phi''(0)+\cdots}=\lim_{x\to 0}\frac{f'(0)+(x/2!)f''(0)+\cdots}{\phi'(0)+(x/2!)\phi''(0)+\cdots}$$

$$=\frac{f'(0)}{\phi'(0)}=\lim_{x\to 0}\frac{f'(x)}{\phi'(x)},$$

as l'Hospital's rule says. In any given problem you have to decide whether it is easier to differentiate and use l'Hospital's rule (for example, if you do not know the series for the functions in the numerator and denominator) or to use series (for example, if the derivatives are very complicated).

There are other indeterminate forms besides 0/0, for example, ∞/∞, $0\cdot\infty$, etc. L'Hospital's rule holds for the ∞/∞ form as well as the 0/0 form. Series are most useful for the 0/0 form or others which can easily be put into the 0/0 form. For example, $\lim_{x\to 0}(1/x)\sin x$ is an $\infty\cdot 0$ form, but is easily written as $\lim_{x\to 0}(\sin x)/x$ which is a 0/0 form. Also *note carefully:* Series (of powers of x) are useful mainly in finding limits as $x\to 0$, because for $x=0$ such a series collapses to the constant term; for any other value of x we have an infinite series whose sum we probably do not know (see Problem 48, however).

Series approximations.   When a problem in, say, differential equations or physics is too difficult in its exact form, we often can get an approximate answer by replacing one or more of the functions in the problem by a few terms of its infinite series. We shall illustrate this idea by two examples.

Example 1.   In elementary physics we find that the equation of motion of a simple pendulum is (see Chapter 9, Section 8, or a physics textbook):

$$\frac{d^2\theta}{dt^2} = -\frac{g}{l}\sin\theta.$$

This differential equation cannot be solved for θ in terms of elementary functions (see Chapter 9), and you may recall that what is usually done is to approximate $\sin\theta$ by θ. Recall the infinite series for $\sin\theta$ (13.1); θ is simply the first term of the series for $\sin\theta$. For small values of θ (say $\theta < \frac{1}{2}$ radian or about 30°), this series converges rapidly, and using the first term gives a good approximation. The solutions of the differential equation are then $\theta = A\sin\sqrt{g/l}\,t$ and $\theta = B\cos\sqrt{g/l}\,t$ (A and B constants) as you can verify; we say that the pendulum is executing simple harmonic motion.

Example 2.   Let us consider a radioactive substance containing N_0 atoms at $t = 0$. It is known that the number of atoms remaining at a later time t is given by the formula (see Chapter 7, Section 3):

(15.1) $$N = N_0 e^{-\lambda t}$$

where λ is a constant which is characteristic of the radioactive substance. To find λ for a given substance, a physicist measures in the laboratory the number of decays ΔN during the time interval Δt for a succession of Δt intervals. It is customary to plot each value of $\Delta N/\Delta t$ at the midpoint of the corresponding time interval Δt. If $\lambda\,\Delta t$ is small, this graph is a good approximation to the exact dN/dt graph. A better approximation can be obtained by plotting $\Delta N/\Delta t$ a little to the left of the midpoint. Let us show that the midpoint *does* give a good approximation and also find the more accurate t value. (An approximate value of λ, good enough for calculating the correction, is assumed known from a rough preliminary graph.)

What we should *like* to plot is the graph of dN/dt, that is, the graph of the slope of the curve in Fig. 15.1. What we *measure* is the value of $\Delta N/\Delta t$ for each Δt interval. Consider one such Δt interval in Fig. 15.1, from t_1 to t_2. To get an accurate graph we should plot the measured value of $\Delta N/\Delta t$ at the point between t_1 and t_2 where $\Delta N/\Delta t = dN/dt$. Let us write this condition and find the t which satisfies it. The quantity ΔN is the change in N, that is, $N(t_2) - N(t_1)$; the value of dN/dt we get from (15.1). Then $dN/dt = \Delta N/\Delta t$ becomes

(15.2) $$-\lambda N_0 e^{-\lambda t} = \frac{N_0 e^{-\lambda t_2} - N_0 e^{-\lambda t_1}}{\Delta t}.$$

Multiplying this equation by $(\Delta t/N_0)e^{\lambda(t_1+t_2)/2}$, we get

(15.3) $-\lambda \, \Delta t \, e^{-\lambda[t-(t_1+t_2)/2]} = e^{-\lambda(t_2-t_1)/2} - e^{\lambda(t_2-t_1)/2} = e^{-\lambda \Delta t/2} - e^{\lambda \Delta t/2}$

since $t_2 - t_1 = \Delta t$. Since we assumed $\lambda \, \Delta t$ to be small, we can expand the exponentials on the right-hand side of (15.3) in power series; this gives

(15.4) $-\lambda \, \Delta t \, e^{-\lambda[t-(t_1+t_2)/2]} = -\lambda \, \Delta t - \dfrac{1}{3}\left(\dfrac{\lambda \, \Delta t}{2}\right)^3 \cdots$

or canceling $(-\lambda \, \Delta t)$

(15.5) $e^{-\lambda[t-(t_1+t_2)/2]} = 1 + \tfrac{1}{24}(\lambda \, \Delta t)^2 \cdots .$

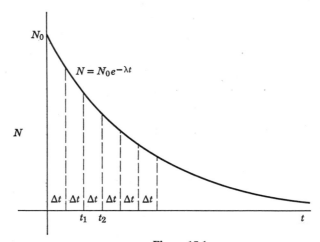

Figure 15.1

Suppose $\lambda \, \Delta t$ is small enough so that we can neglect the term $\tfrac{1}{24}(\lambda \, \Delta t)^2$. Then (15.5) reduces to

$$e^{-\lambda[t-(t_1+t_2)/2]} = 1,$$

$$-\lambda\left(t - \frac{t_1 + t_2}{2}\right) = 0,$$

$$t = \frac{t_1 + t_2}{2}.$$

Thus we have justified the usual practice of plotting $\Delta N/\Delta t$ at the midpoint of the interval Δt.

Next consider a more accurate approximation. From (15.5) we get

$$-\lambda\left(t - \frac{t_1 + t_2}{2}\right) = \ln\left(1 + \frac{1}{24}(\lambda \, \Delta t)^2 \cdots\right).$$

Since $\frac{1}{24}(\lambda\,\Delta t)^2 \ll 1$, we can expand the logarithm by (13.4) to get

$$-\lambda\left(t - \frac{t_1 + t_2}{2}\right) = \frac{1}{24}(\lambda\,\Delta t)^2 \cdots .$$

Then we have

$$t = \frac{t_1 + t_2}{2} - \frac{1}{24\lambda}(\lambda\,\Delta t)^2 \cdots .$$

Thus the measured $\Delta N/\Delta t$ should be plotted a little to the left of the midpoint of Δt, as we claimed.

16. UNIFORM CONVERGENCE

When we say that a series of powers of x (or other functions) converges to a function $f(x)$, we mean that if we substitute any x (within the region of convergence), say $x = a$, the resulting series of constants converges to the sum $f(a)$. Now you know that sometimes series converge rapidly and sometimes very slowly. It can happen that within the region where a series converges to a function, the rapidity of convergence of the series is not "uniform," that is, the series may converge more and more slowly as we approach some value of x. When it does, there may be difficulties in integrating term by term and in some other manipulations. It is therefore worth while to know whether a series is *uniformly convergent*.

We start with a series which is convergent for certain values of x; we consider only these values of x. Let $R_n(x)$ be the remainder; then *for each x*, $R_n(x) \to 0$ as $n \to \infty$ [this is ordinary convergence; see (4.7)]. To define uniform convergence we proceed as follows. For a fixed value of n, choose the largest value which $|R_n(x)|$ takes at all x we are considering; call this

$$U_n = \max |R_n(x)| .$$

Then if $U_n \to 0$ as $n \to \infty$ the original series is called uniformly convergent for the values of x considered.

The usual test for uniform convergence is the Weierstrass M test: If $\sum\limits_{n=0}^{\infty} M_n$ is a convergent series of positive constants, then the series $\sum\limits_{n=0}^{\infty} u_n(x)$ is uniformly convergent if $|u_n(x)| \le M_n$ for all n (except, as usual, for a finite number of values of n) and for all x we are considering. This is easy to prove. For,

$$|R_n(x)| = |u_{n+1}(x) + u_{n+2}(x) + \cdots| \le M_{n+1} + M_{n+2} + \cdots$$

for all x; hence $U_n = \max |R_n(x)| \le M_{n+1} + M_{n+2} + \cdots$. Since the M series converges, the limit of the remainder after term n is zero. Hence $U_n \to 0$, and the series converges uniformly.

The most important properties of uniformly convergent series are given in the following theorems (which we state without proof; see advanced calculus books): The sum of a uniformly convergent series of continuous functions is a continuous function; such a series may be integrated term by term, and the integrated series converges to the integral of the sum function. If, in addition, the terms of the series have continuous derivatives and the series obtained by differentiating term by term is uniformly convergent, then the differentiated series converges to the derivative of the sum function.

REFERENCES

Most textbooks on calculus or advanced calculus, and some books on mathematics in physics and engineering, contain material on infinite series. (For some suggestions, see the list of references at the end of the book; those containing material on Chapter 1 are identified by a [1] after the listing.) For a very detailed discussion, see Knopp.

PROBLEMS

1. In the example of Section 1, find the height of the tenth rebound, and the distance traveled by the ball after it touches the ground the tenth time. Compare this distance with the total distance traveled.

2. Derive the formula (1.4) for the sum S_n of the geometric progression $S_n = a + ar + ar^2 + \cdots + ar^{n-1}$. *Hint:* Start by multiplying S_n by r and subtracting the result from S_n. If necessary you can look up the derivation in an algebra book. Show that the geometric series (1.6) converges if and only if $|r| < 1$; also show that if $|r| < 1$, the sum is given by (1.8).

3. We can write $\frac{1}{3} = 0.3333 \cdots = \frac{3}{10} + \frac{3}{100} + \frac{3}{1000} + \cdots$. Any fraction whose decimal equivalent does not terminate can be written both as a repeating decimal and as an infinite geometric series. Use (1.8) to find the fractions that are equivalent to the following repeating decimals:

   (a) $0.11111 \cdots$ (b) $0.020202 \cdots$

   (c) $0.77777 \cdots$ (d) $0.12454545 \cdots$

   (e) $0.363363363 \cdots$ (f) $0.00757575 \cdots$

4. In a water purification process, one-nth of the impurity is removed in the first stage. In each succeeding stage, the amount of impurity removed is one-nth of that removed in the preceding stage. Show that if $n = 2$, the water can be made as pure as you like, but that if $n = 3$, at least one-half of the impurity will remain no matter how many stages are used.

5. It is useful to write series both in the form $a_1 + a_2 + a_3 + \cdots$ and in the form $\sum_{n=1}^{\infty} a_n$. Write out several terms of the following series (that is, write them in the first form).

(a) $\sum_{n=1}^{\infty} \dfrac{n}{2^n}$

(b) $\sum_{n=1}^{\infty} \dfrac{(-1)^n}{n}$

(c) $\sum_{n=1}^{\infty} \dfrac{n}{n + 5}$

(d) $\sum_{n=1}^{\infty} \dfrac{\sqrt{n}}{n + 1}$

(e) $\sum_{n=1}^{\infty} \dfrac{2n(2n + 1)}{3n + 5}$

(f) $\sum_{n=1}^{\infty} \dfrac{(n!)^2}{(2n)!}$

6. Write the following series in the abbreviated Σ form.

(a) $\frac{1}{3} + \frac{2}{5} + \frac{4}{7} + \frac{8}{9} + \frac{16}{11} + \cdots$

(b) $\dfrac{1}{2 \cdot 3} + \dfrac{1}{3 \cdot 4} + \dfrac{1}{4 \cdot 5} + \dfrac{1}{5 \cdot 6} + \cdots$

(c) $\frac{1}{4} - \frac{1}{9} + \frac{1}{16} - \frac{1}{25} + \cdots$

(d) $\frac{1}{7} + \frac{2}{9} + \frac{3}{11} + \frac{4}{13} + \cdots$

(e) $\frac{1}{4} - \frac{1}{8} + \frac{1}{16} - \frac{1}{32} + \cdots$

(f) $\dfrac{\ln 2}{2} - \dfrac{\ln 3}{3} + \dfrac{\ln 4}{4} - \dfrac{\ln 5}{5} + \cdots$

7. A careful mathematical definition of a convergent infinite series with sum S is this: Given any small positive number (usually called ϵ by mathematicians), it is possible to find an integer N so that $|S - S_n| < \epsilon$ for every $n > N$. In words this means that no matter how tiny an ϵ you think of, all the partial sums S_n of n terms differ less than your ϵ from the final sum S if you add up any number of terms more than N. Select some ϵ's and find the corresponding N's for the following series. (In a, b, c find S first.)

(a) $\sum_{n=1}^{\infty} \dfrac{1}{2^n}$

(b) $\sum_{n=1}^{\infty} \dfrac{1}{5^n}$

(c) $\sum_{n=1}^{\infty} \dfrac{1}{n(n + 1)}$ $\left(\text{Hint: } \dfrac{1}{n(n + 1)} = \dfrac{1}{n} - \dfrac{1}{n + 1} \right)$

(d) $\sum_{n=1}^{\infty} \dfrac{1}{n!}$ $\bigg(\text{Hint: } \dfrac{1}{n!} < \dfrac{1}{2^n}$ when $n > 3$; hence the remainder $S - S_n =$

$\dfrac{1}{(n + 1)!} + \dfrac{1}{(n + 2)!} + \cdots$ is smaller than the remainder of a geometric

series. $\bigg)$

8. (a) Give a proof of the "preliminary test" for convergence of an infinite series. *Hint:* $S_n - S_{n-1} = a_n$.
(b) Show that $n! > 2^n$ for all $n > 3$. *Hint:* Write out a few terms; then consider what you multiply by to go from, say, 5! to 6! and from 2^5 to 2^6.

9. We proved by the integral test that the harmonic series $\sum_{n=1}^{\infty} \frac{1}{n}$ is divergent. Prove it again by comparison with the series

$$1 + \tfrac{1}{2} + (\tfrac{1}{4} + \tfrac{1}{4}) + (\tfrac{1}{8} + \tfrac{1}{8} + \tfrac{1}{8} + \tfrac{1}{8}) + (8 \text{ terms each equal to } \tfrac{1}{16}) + \cdots,$$

which is $1 + \tfrac{1}{2} + \tfrac{1}{2} + \tfrac{1}{2} + \tfrac{1}{2} + \cdots$.

10. Use the integral test to find whether the following series converge or diverge. *Hint* and *warning:* Do *not* use lower limits on your integrals (see problem 24).

(a) $\displaystyle\sum_{n=2}^{\infty} \frac{1}{n \ln n}$ (b) $\displaystyle\sum_{n=1}^{\infty} \frac{n}{n^2 + 4}$

(c) $\displaystyle\sum_{n=3}^{\infty} \frac{1}{n^2 - 4}$ (d) $\displaystyle\sum_{n=1}^{\infty} \frac{e^n}{e^{2n} + 9}$

11. Use the integral test to prove the following so-called *p*-series test. The series

$$\sum_{n=1}^{\infty} \frac{1}{n^p} \text{ is } \begin{cases} \text{convergent if } p > 1, \\ \text{divergent if } p \le 1. \end{cases}$$

Caution: Do $p = 1$ separately.

12. Problem 11 shows that $\sum \frac{1}{n^2}$ converges. Prove the convergence of $\sum \frac{1}{n^2}$ another way, by grouping terms somewhat as in Problem 9.

13. Use the ratio test to find whether the following series converge or diverge:

(a) $\displaystyle\sum_{n=1}^{\infty} \frac{2^n}{n^2}$ (b) $\displaystyle\sum_{n=0}^{\infty} \frac{3^n}{2^{2n}}$ (c) $\displaystyle\sum_{n=0}^{\infty} \frac{n!}{(2n)!}$

(d) $\displaystyle\sum_{n=0}^{\infty} \frac{5^n (n!)^2}{(2n)!}$ (e) $\displaystyle\sum_{n=1}^{\infty} \frac{10^n}{(n!)^2}$ (f) $\displaystyle\sum_{n=1}^{\infty} \frac{n!}{100^n}$

14. Test the following series for convergence or divergence. Decide for yourself which test is easiest to use, but don't forget the preliminary test.

(a) $\displaystyle\sum_{n=1}^{\infty} \frac{n - 1}{(n + 2)(n + 3)}$ (b) $\displaystyle\sum_{n=1}^{\infty} \frac{n^2 - 1}{n^2 + 1}$

(c) $\displaystyle\sum_{n=1}^{\infty} \frac{1}{n^{\ln 3}}$ (d) $\displaystyle\sum_{n=0}^{\infty} \frac{n}{n^3 + 4}$

(e) $\displaystyle\sum_{n=1}^{\infty} \frac{n}{n^3 - 4}$ (f) $\displaystyle\sum_{n=0}^{\infty} \frac{(n!)^2}{(2n)!}$

(g) $\displaystyle\sum_{n=0}^{\infty} \frac{(2n)!}{3^n (n!)^2}$ (h) $\displaystyle\sum_{n=1}^{\infty} \frac{n^5}{5^n}$

(i) $\displaystyle\sum_{n=1}^{\infty} \frac{n^n}{n!}$ (j) $\displaystyle\sum_{n=2}^{\infty} (-1)^n \frac{n}{n - 1}$

(k) $\displaystyle\sum_{n=1}^{\infty} \frac{(-1)^n}{\sqrt{n}}$

(l) $\displaystyle\sum_{n=4}^{\infty} \frac{2n}{n^2 - 9}$

(m) $\displaystyle\sum_{n=1}^{\infty} \frac{(-1)^n}{n^2}$

(n) $\displaystyle\sum_{n=0}^{\infty} (-\tfrac{1}{2})^n$

(o) $\displaystyle\sum_{n=0}^{\infty} (-1)^n 2^n$

(p) $\displaystyle\sum_{n=0}^{\infty} \frac{2 + (-1)^n}{n^2 + 7}$

(q) $\displaystyle\sum_{n=1}^{\infty} \frac{(-1)^n 3^n}{(n!)^2}$

(r) $\displaystyle\sum_{n=1}^{\infty} \frac{(-1)^n n!}{10^n}$

(s) $\displaystyle\sum_{n=1}^{\infty} a_n$ if $a_{n+1} = \dfrac{n}{2n + 3} a_n$

(t) $\dfrac{1}{2^2} - \dfrac{1}{3^2} + \dfrac{1}{2^3} - \dfrac{1}{3^3} + \dfrac{1}{2^4} - \dfrac{1}{3^4} + \cdots$

(u) $\dfrac{1}{2} + \dfrac{1}{2^2} - \dfrac{1}{3} - \dfrac{1}{3^2} + \dfrac{1}{4} + \dfrac{1}{4^2} - \dfrac{1}{5} - \dfrac{1}{5^2} + \cdots$

(v) $\displaystyle\sum_{n=2}^{\infty} \frac{(-1)^n}{n^2 - n}$

(w) $\displaystyle\sum_{n=2}^{\infty} \frac{1}{n^2 - n}$

15. (a) A student said, "In this series there are an infinite number of terms each greater than zero; therefore the series diverges." Show what is wrong with this statement, preferably with some examples. Can you think of a correct statement which the student may have had in mind?
(b) Another student said, "On the contrary, at each step we add less than we did the time before, so the series converges." Comment as in part (a).

16. Show that it is possible to stack a pile of identical books so that the top book is as far as you like to the right of the bottom book. You may use as many books as you need, but for any desired distance it will be *some* finite number. *Hint:* Start at the top of the pile to see how to stack them. Each time place

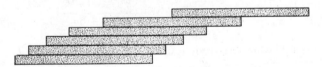

the pile already completed on top of another book so that the pile is just at the point of tipping. (In practice, of course, you can't let them overhang quite this much without having the stack topple.) Find the distance from the right-hand end of each book to the right-hand end of the one beneath it. (To find a general formula for this distance, consider the three forces acting on book n, and write the equation for the torque about its right-hand end.) Show that the sum of these distances is a divergent series. (It is said that some students studying in the library tried this experiment one evening and left the results, to the consternation of the librarian the next morning. It is suggested that you try it instead with one or more decks of cards. Also see "Leaning Tower of *The Physical Reviews*," *American Journal of Physics*, vol. 27, no. 2, p. 121.)

17. Prove that an absolutely convergent series $\sum_{n=1}^{\infty} a_n$ is convergent. *Hint:* Put $b_n = a_n + |a_n|$. Then the b_n are nonnegative; we have $|b_n| \leq 2|a_n|$ and $a_n = b_n - |a_n|$.

18. Prove the ratio test. *Hint:* If $|a_{n+1}/a_n| \to \rho < 1$, take σ so that $\rho < \sigma < 1$. Then $|a_{n+1}/a_n| < \sigma$ if n is large, say $n \geq N$. This means that $|a_{N+1}| < \sigma |a_N|$, $|a_{N+2}| < \sigma |a_{N+1}| < \sigma^2 |a_N|$, etc. Compare with the geometric series

$$\sum_{n=1}^{\infty} \sigma^n |a_N|.$$

Also prove that a series with $\rho > 1$ diverges. *Hint:* Take $\rho > \sigma > 1$, and use the preliminary test.

19. Prove the following test. (a) If $\sum_{n=1}^{\infty} b_n$ is a convergent series of positive terms and $a_n \geq 0$ and a_n/b_n tends to a (finite) limit then $\sum_{n=1}^{\infty} a_n$ converges. (b) If $\sum_{n=1}^{\infty} d_n$ is a divergent series of positive terms and $a_n \geq 0$ and a_n/d_n tends to a limit greater than 0 (or tends to $+\infty$) then $\sum_{n=1}^{\infty} a_n$ diverges. *Hint* (part a): If $a_n/b_n \to L$ and $M > L$, then $a_n < Mb_n$ for large n. Compare $\sum_{n=1}^{\infty} a_n$ with $\sum_{n=1}^{\infty} Mb_n$.

20. Apply the test in Problem 19 to the series

(a) $\displaystyle\sum_{n=9}^{\infty} \frac{(2n+1)(3n-5)}{\sqrt{n^2-73}}$ (b) $\displaystyle\sum_{n=0}^{\infty} \frac{n(n+1)}{(n+2)^2(n+3)^2}$

(c) $\displaystyle\sum_{n=5}^{\infty} \frac{1}{2^n - n^2}$ (d) $\displaystyle\sum_{n=1}^{\infty} \frac{n^2 + 3n + 4}{n^4 + 7n^3 + 6n - 3}$

21. Prove the following test (root test): If $a_n \geq 0$ and $\sqrt[n]{a_n} \to L < 1$, then $\sum_{n=1}^{\infty} a_n$ converges. (*Hint:* Take M between L and 1 and compare $\sum_{n=1}^{\infty} a_n$ with $\sum_{n=1}^{\infty} M^n$.) If $L > 1$, $\sum_{n=1}^{\infty} a_n$ diverges.

22. Apply the root test (Problem 21) to the following series.

(a) $\displaystyle\sum_{n=1}^{\infty} \frac{n^n}{(n+1)^{2n}}$ (b) $\displaystyle\sum_{n=1}^{\infty} n^2 \cdot 2^n$ (c) $\displaystyle\sum_{n=1}^{\infty} \frac{n^{2n}}{(2n)^n}$

23. (a) Show that if $a_n > 0$ and $\sum_{n=1}^{\infty} a_n$ converges, then $\sum_{n=1}^{\infty} \frac{1}{a_n}$ must diverge. Show by an example that the converse is false.

(b) Show that if $a_n \geq 0$ and $\sum_{n=1}^{\infty} a_n$ converges, then $\sum_{n=1}^{\infty} a_n^2$ converges.

24. (a) In testing $\sum 1/n^2$ for convergence, a student evaluates $\int_0^{\infty} n^{-2} \, dn = -n^{-1} \Big|_0^{\infty} = 0 + \infty = \infty$ and concludes (erroneously) that the series diverges. What is wrong? *Hint:* Consider the area under the curve in a diagram such as Fig. 6.1 or 6.2. This example shows the danger of using a lower limit in the integral test.

(b) Use the integral test to show that $\sum_{n=0}^{\infty} e^{-n^2}$ converges. *Hint:* Although you cannot *evaluate* the integral, you can show that it is finite (which is all that is necessary) by comparing it with $\int^{\infty} e^{-n} \, dn$.

25. Invent series $\sum_{n=1}^{\infty} a_n$ and $\sum_{n=1}^{\infty} b_n$ (not of all positive terms) such that $\sum_{n=1}^{\infty} a_n$ converges, $b_n \leq a_n$, but $\sum_{n=1}^{\infty} b_n$ diverges. (The comparison test works only for positive terms!)

26. A student argues that if $a_n = (-1)^n$, we have $a_{n+1}/a_n = -1$ for every n so the test ratio approaches the limit -1 which is less than 1; hence $1 - 1 + 1 - 1 + \cdots$ converges. Explain what is wrong.

27. If $\sum_{n=1}^{\infty} a_n$ is a convergent series of positive terms and $r_n = a_n + a_{n+1} + a_{n+2} + \cdots$ are the remainders, show that $\sum_{n=1}^{\infty} (-1)^n r_n$ converges. If $\sum_{n=1}^{\infty} a_n$ is a divergent series of positive terms and s_n are the partial sums, show that $\sum_{n=1}^{\infty} (-1)^n/s_n$ converges. *Hint:* See Section 7.

28. Prove or disprove that $\sum_{n=1}^{\infty} (a_n + b_n)$ diverges if $\sum_{n=1}^{\infty} a_n$ and $\sum_{n=1}^{\infty} b_n$ diverge.

29. Find the interval of convergence of each of the following power series; be sure to investigate the endpoints of the interval in each case.

(a) $\sum_{n=0}^{\infty} (-1)^n x^n$

(b) $\sum_{n=0}^{\infty} \frac{(2x)^n}{3^n}$

(c) $\sum_{n=1}^{\infty} \frac{(-1)^n x^n}{n(n+1)}$

(d) $\sum_{n=1}^{\infty} \frac{x^{2n}}{2^n n^2}$

(e) $\sum_{n=1}^{\infty} \frac{x^n}{(n!)^2}$

(f) $\sum_{n=1}^{\infty} \frac{(-1)^n x^n}{(2n)!}$

(g) $\sum_{n=1}^{\infty} \frac{(-1)^n n!}{x^n}$

(h) $\sum_{n=1}^{\infty} \frac{(-1)^n x^n}{\sqrt{n}}$

(i) $\sum_{n=1}^{\infty} (-1)^n n^3 x^n$

(j) $\sum_{n=1}^{\infty} \frac{(-1)^n x^{2n}}{(2n)^{3/2}}$

(k) $\sum_{n=2}^{\infty} \frac{(-1)^n x^{n/2}}{n \ln n}$

(l) $\sum_{n=1}^{\infty} \frac{x^{3n}}{n}$

30. Verify the Maclaurin series in (13.1) through (13.5).

31. Find by any convenient method the first few terms of the Maclaurin series for the following functions:

(a) $\dfrac{1 + x}{1 - x}$ 　　　　　　　　　　　(b) $\ln \dfrac{1 + x}{1 - x}$

(c) $\sin x^2$ 　　　　　　　　　　　　　(d) $\cosh x = \dfrac{e^x + e^{-x}}{2}$

(e) $\dfrac{e^x}{1 - x}$ 　　　　　　　　　　　　(f) $e^x \sin x$

(g) $\dfrac{\sin \sqrt{x}}{\sqrt{x}}$ 　$(x > 0)$ 　　(h) $\dfrac{1}{1 + x + x^2}$

(i) $\displaystyle\int_0^x \cos t^2 \, dt$ 　　　　　　　(j) $\displaystyle\int_0^x e^{-t^2} \, dt$

(k) $x^2 \ln (1 - x)$ 　　　　　　　　(l) $\tan^2 x$

(m) $\dfrac{1}{\sqrt{1 - x^2}}$ 　　　　　　　(n) $\arcsin x = \displaystyle\int_0^x \dfrac{dt}{\sqrt{1 - t^2}}$

(o) $\sec x$ 　　　　　　　　　　　(p) $\displaystyle\int_0^u \dfrac{\sin x}{\sqrt{1 - x^2}} \, dx$

32. Find the first few terms of the Maclaurin series of the following functions.

(a) $\ln \cos x$. *Hints:* Method 1: Write $\cos x = 1 + (\cos x - 1) = 1 + u$; use the series you know for $\ln (1 + u)$; replace u by the Maclaurin series for $(\cos x - 1)$. Method 2: Find $\int \tan x \, dx$ by using the series of Example 3 in Section 13B. Remember to check the constant of integration.

(b) $e^{\cos x}$. 　　　　*Hint:* $e^{\cos x} = e \cdot e^{\cos x - 1}$.

33. Find the first few terms of the Taylor series expansions of the given functions about the given points.

(a) $f(x) = \ln x$ 　　　　$a = 1$

(b) $f(x) = \dfrac{1}{x}$ 　　　　$a = 1$

(c) $f(x) = \csc x$ 　　　　$a = \dfrac{\pi}{2}$

(d) $f(x) = \sqrt{x}$ 　　　　$a = 25$

(e) $f(x) = \tan x$ 　　　　$a = \dfrac{\pi}{4}$

34. Calculate the following quantities to three decimal places, using Maclaurin series.

(a) $\sin \frac{1}{2}$ 　　　　　　　　　　　(b) $e^{0.2}$

(c) $\sqrt{26}$

(d) $\int_0^{0.1} e^{-x^2} dx$

(e) arc tan $0.3 = \int_0^{0.3} \dfrac{dx}{1 + x^2}$

(f) $\dfrac{d}{dx} \left(e^{\sin x} \right)_{x=0.1}$

(g) $(1.002)^{25}$

(h) $\dfrac{1}{1.01}$

(i) ln 0.99

35. Calculate the following quantities to three decimal places, using Taylor series. (*Hint:* Use the results of Problem 33.)

(a) ln 1.2

(b) $\dfrac{1}{1.01}$

(c) csc 91°

(d) $\sqrt{26}$ (compare with Problem 34c)

(e) tan 44°

36. If $0 < x < \frac{1}{2}$, show [by using (13.5) and (14.2)] that $\sqrt{1 + x} = 1 + \frac{1}{2}x$ with an error less than 0.032.

37. If $0 < x < 1$, show that $\sin x = x - x^3/6$ with an error less than 0.01. (*Hint:* You can use the remainder after terms in x^4 since the x^4 term has coefficient 0.)

38. From the series for ln $(1-x)$ with $x = \frac{1}{4}$, compute ln $\left(\frac{4}{3}\right) = 0.29$ correct to two decimal places. (Take enough terms to make the remainder less than 0.005.)

39. Find the sum of the series

$$\frac{1}{1 \cdot 2} + \frac{1}{2 \cdot 3} + \frac{1}{3 \cdot 4} + \frac{1}{4 \cdot 5} + \cdots.$$

Hint: $\dfrac{1}{n(n + 1)} = \dfrac{1}{n} - \dfrac{1}{n + 1}.$

Show that the remainder after n terms is $1/(n + 1)$. Hence show that about 200 terms are needed for two decimal place accuracy. Compare the remainder with the value of the 200th term and so show that in computation using series of positive terms the value of the first omitted term may be a completely unreliable estimate of the error.

40. Show that the Maclaurin series for sin x converges to sin x. *Hint:* If $f(x) =$ sin x, $f^{(n+1)}(x) = \pm \sin x$ or $\pm \cos x$, and so $|f^{(n+1)}(x)| \leq 1$ for all x and all n. Let $n \to \infty$ in (14.2).

41. Show as in Problem 40 that the Maclaurin series for e^x converges to e^x.

42. Show that the Maclaurin series for $(1 + x)^p$ converges to $(1 + x)^p$ when $0 < x < 1$.

43. Use Maclaurin series to evaluate the following limits:

(a) $\lim\limits_{x \to 0} \dfrac{1 - \cos x}{x^2}$

(b) $\lim\limits_{x \to 0} \dfrac{\sin x - x}{x^3}$

(c) $\lim\limits_{x \to 0} \dfrac{1 - e^{x^3}}{x^3}$

(d) $\lim\limits_{x \to 0} \dfrac{\sin^2 x}{x}$

(e) $\lim\limits_{x \to 0} \dfrac{\tan x}{x^2}$

(f) $\lim\limits_{x \to 0} \dfrac{\ln (1 + x)}{x}$

44. Evaluate each of the limits in Problem 43 by using l'Hospital's rule.

45. Derive l'Hospital's rule (stated in Section 15) for the case $a \neq 0$ by using a Taylor series in powers of $(x - a)$ instead of a Maclaurin series.

46. Evaluate the following indeterminate forms by using l'Hospital's rule. (Note that Maclaurin series would not be useful here because x does not tend to zero.)

(a) $\lim\limits_{x \to 1} \dfrac{e^{x-1} - 1}{1 - \sin (\pi x/2)}$

(b) $\lim\limits_{x \to \pi} \dfrac{x \sin x}{x - \pi}$

(c) $\lim\limits_{x \to \pi/2} \dfrac{\ln (2 - \sin x)}{\ln (1 + \cos x)}$

(d) $\lim\limits_{x \to 1} \dfrac{\ln (2 - x)}{1 - x}$

47. Although l'Hospital's rule is most frequently stated and used for evaluating indeterminate forms of the type $0/0$, it also holds for the type ∞/∞, that is,

$$\lim_{x \to a} \frac{f(x)}{\phi(x)} = \lim_{x \to a} \frac{f'(x)}{\phi'(x)}$$

if $f(x)$ and $\phi(x)$ both tend to ∞ as x tends to a and the ratio $f'(x)/\phi'(x)$ approaches a limit or tends to infinity (that is, does not oscillate). Use l'Hospital's rule to evaluate the following indeterminate forms. (If necessary rewrite them so that they are ∞/∞ forms.)

(a) $\lim\limits_{x \to \infty} \dfrac{\ln x}{\sqrt{x}}$

(b) $\lim\limits_{x \to 0} x \ln 2x$

(c) $\lim\limits_{x \to \infty} x^n e^{-x}$ (n not necessarily integral)

(d) $\lim\limits_{x \to 1} \dfrac{\ln (1 - x) + x^2}{\ln (1 - x^2) + e^x}$

(e) $\lim\limits_{x \to \pi/2} \dfrac{\ln \cos x}{\ln (1 - \sin x)}$

48. In general, we do not expect power series to be useful in evaluating indeterminate forms except when x tends to zero (see Problem 46). Show, however, that Problem 47c can be done by writing $x^n e^{-x} = x^n/e^x$ and using the series for e^x. *Hint:* Divide numerator and denominator by x^n before you take the limit.

What is special about the e^x series which makes it possible to know what the limit of the infinite series is?

49. Find the values of several derivatives of e^{-1/t^2} at $t = 0$. *Hint:* Calculate a few derivatives (as functions of t); then make the substitution $x = 1/t^2$, and use the result of Problem 47c or 48.

50. The velocity v of electrons from a high energy accelerator is very near the velocity c of light. Given the voltage V of the accelerator, we often want to calculate the ratio v/c. The relativistic formula for this calculation is

$$\frac{v}{c} = \sqrt{1 - \frac{1}{4V^2}}, \qquad V = \text{number of million volts.}$$

Use two terms of the binomial series (13.5) to find v/c if

(a) $V = 100$ million volts,

(b) $V = 500$ million volts,

(c) $V = 25,000$ million volts.

51. The figure shows a heavy weight suspended by a cable and pulled to one side by a force F. We want to know how much force F is required to push the weight aside a given distance (say to place a cornerstone correctly). From elementary physics, $T \cos \theta = W$, and $T \sin \theta = F$.

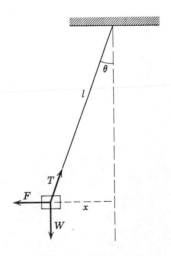

(a) Find F/W using first one term, and then two terms, of the series for $\tan \theta$ in Section 13B, Example 3, for $\theta = \frac{1}{2}$ radian (about 30°); for $\theta = 10°$; for $\theta = 1°$. (*Careful:* θ must be in radians in the series.)

(b) Usually in a problem like this, what we know is not θ, but x and l in the diagram. Show that

$$\tan \theta = \frac{x}{\sqrt{l^2 - x^2}} = \frac{x}{l}\left(1 - \frac{x^2}{l^2}\right)^{-\frac{1}{2}}.$$

Use (13.5) to find F/W for the following cases: $x = 6$ in., $l = 50$ ft; $x = 2$ ft, $l = 50$ ft; $x = 10$ ft, $l = 50$ ft.

52. Given a strong chain and a convenient tree, could you pull your car out of a ditch in the following way? Fasten the chain to the car and to the tree. Pull with a force F at the center of the chain as shown in the figure. From mechanics, we have $F = 2T \sin \theta$, or $T = F/(2 \sin \theta)$, where T is the tension in the chain, that is, the force exerted on the car.

(a) Let the distance from car to tree be 20 ft and let $F = 100$ lb. Find T if x (see diagram) is 1 in.; if $x = 6$ in.; if $x = 1$ ft; if $x = 5$ ft. *Hint:* Write an exact formula for $\sin \theta$ in terms of x and approximate the square root by using (13.5) as in Problem 51.

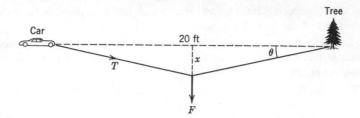

(b) Let $F = 100$ lb, and find T if θ (see diagram) is $1°$; if $\theta = 10°$; if $\theta = 30°$. *Hint: Never* use a series in a denominator for computation, for then you have a messy long division to do after the series computation. Here you should write

$$\frac{1}{\sin \theta} = \frac{1}{\theta - \dfrac{\theta^3}{3!} + \cdots} = \frac{1}{\theta}\left(1 - \frac{\theta^2}{6} + \cdots\right)^{-1}$$

and use (13.5). (Two terms are enough.) *Careful:* θ must be in radians.

53. A tall tower of circular cross section is reinforced by horizontal circular disks (like large coins), one meter apart and of negligible thickness. The radius of

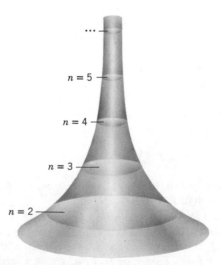

the disk at height n is $1/(n \ln n)$ ($n \geq 2$). Assuming that the tower is of infinite height:

(a) Will the total area of the disks be finite or not?

(b) If the disks are strengthened by wires going around their circumferences like tires, will the total length of wire required be finite or not?

2

Complex Numbers

I. INTRODUCTION

You will probably recall using imaginary and complex numbers in algebra. The general solution of the quadratic equation

$$(1.1) \qquad az^2 + bz + c = 0$$

for the unknown z, is given by the *quadratic formula*

$$(1.2) \qquad z = \frac{-b \pm \sqrt{b^2 - 4ac}}{2a}.$$

If the *discriminant* $d = (b^2 - 4ac)$ is negative, we must take the square root of a negative number in order to find z. Since only positive numbers have real square roots, it is impossible to use (1.2) when $d < 0$ unless we introduce a new kind of number, called an imaginary number. We use the symbol $i = \sqrt{-1}$ with the understanding that $i^2 = -1$. Then

$$\sqrt{-16} = 4i, \qquad \sqrt{-3} = i\sqrt{3}, \qquad i^3 = -i$$

are imaginary numbers, but

$$i^2 = -1, \qquad \sqrt{-2}\,\sqrt{-8} = i\sqrt{2} \cdot i\sqrt{8} = -4, \qquad i^{4n} = 1$$

are real. In (1.2) we also need combinations of real and imaginary numbers.

For example, the solution of

$$z^2 - 2z + 2 = 0$$

is

$$z = \frac{2 \pm \sqrt{4 - 8}}{2} = \frac{2 \pm \sqrt{-4}}{2} = 1 \pm i.$$

We use the term *complex number* to mean any one of the whole set of numbers, real, imaginary, or combinations of the two like $1 \pm i$. Thus $i + 5$, $17i$, 4, $3 + i\sqrt{5}$ are all examples of complex numbers.

Once the new kind of number is admitted into our number system, fascinating possibilities open up. Can we attach any meaning to marks like $\sin i$, $e^{i\pi}$, $\ln(1 + i)$? We shall see later that we can and that, in fact, such expressions may turn up in problems in physics and engineering.

When people first considered taking square roots of negative numbers, they felt very uneasy about the problem. They thought that such numbers could not have any meaning or any connection with reality (hence the term "imaginary"). They certainly would not have believed that the new numbers could be of any practical use. Yet complex numbers are of great importance in a variety of applied fields; for example, the electrical engineer would, to say the least, be severely handicapped without them. The complex notation often simplifies setting up and solving vibration problems in either dynamical or electrical systems, and is useful in solving many differential equations which arise from problems in various branches of physics. (See Chapters 6 and 7.) In addition, there is a highly developed field of mathematics dealing with functions of a complex variable (see Chapter 11) which yields many useful methods for solving problems about fluid flow, elasticity, quantum mechanics, and other applied problems. Almost every field of either pure or applied mathematics makes some use of complex numbers.

2. REAL AND IMAGINARY PARTS OF A COMPLEX NUMBER

A complex number such as $5 + 3i$ is the sum of two terms. The real term (not containing i) is called the *real part* of the complex number. The *coefficient* of i in the other term is called the *imaginary part* of the complex number. In $5 + 3i$, 5 is the real part and 3 is the imaginary part. Notice carefully that the *imaginary part* of a complex number is *not imaginary*! Either the real part or the imaginary part of a complex number may be zero. If the real part is zero, the complex number is called imaginary (or, for emphasis, *pure* imaginary). The zero real part is usually omitted; thus

$0 + 5i$ is written just $5i$. If the imaginary part of the complex number is zero, the number is real. We write $7 + 0i$ as just 7. Complex numbers then include both real numbers and pure imaginary numbers as special cases.

In algebra a complex number is ordinarily written (as we have been doing) as a sum like $5 + 3i$. There is another very useful way of thinking of a complex number. As we have said, every complex number has a real part and an imaginary part (either of which may be zero). These are two *real* numbers, and we could, if we liked, agree to write $5 + 3i$ as $(5, 3)$. Any complex number could be written this way as a pair of real numbers, the real part first and then the imaginary part (which, you must remember, is real). This would not be a very convenient form for computation, but it suggests a very useful geometrical representation of a complex number which we shall now consider.

3. THE COMPLEX PLANE

In analytic geometry we plot the point (5, 3) as shown in Fig. 3.1. As we have seen, the symbol (5,3) could also mean the complex number $5 + 3i$. The point (5, 3) may then be labeled either (5, 3) or $5 + 3i$. Similarly, any

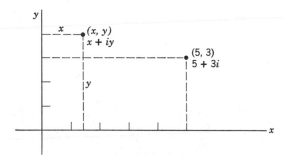

Figure 3.1

complex number $x + iy$ (x and y real) can be represented by a point (x, y) in the (x, y) plane. Also any point (x, y) in the (x, y) plane can be labeled $x + iy$ as well as (x, y). When the (x, y) plane is used in this way to plot complex numbers, it is called the *complex plane*. It is also sometimes called an *Argand diagram*. The x-axis is called the real axis, and the y-axis is called the imaginary axis (note, however, that you plot y and *not iy*).

When a complex number is written in the form $x + iy$, we say that it is in *rectangular form* because x and y are the rectangular coordinates of the point representing the number in the complex plane. In analytic geometry we can locate a point by giving its polar coordinates (r, θ) instead of its rectangular coordinates (x, y). There is a corresponding way to write any complex number. In Fig. 3.2

(3.1)
$$x = r \cos \theta,$$
$$y = r \sin \theta.$$

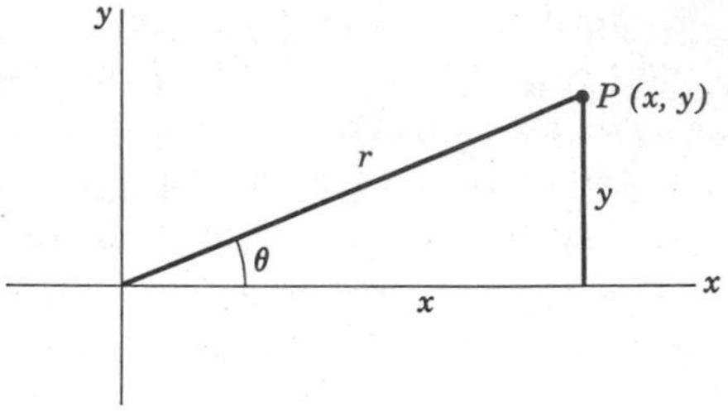

Figure 3.2

Then we have

(3.2)
$$x + iy = r \cos \theta + ir \sin \theta$$
$$= r(\cos \theta + i \sin \theta).$$

This last expression is called the *polar form* of the complex number. As we shall see (Sections 9 to 16), this polar form of a complex number is often simpler to use than the rectangular form.

Example. In Fig. 3.3 the point A could be labeled as $(1, \sqrt{3})$ or as $1 + i\sqrt{3}$. Similarly, using polar coordinates, the point A could be labeled with its (r, θ) values as $(2, \pi/3)$. Notice that r is always taken positive. Using (3.2) we have

$$1 + i\sqrt{3} = 2\left(\cos \frac{\pi}{3} + i \sin \frac{\pi}{3}\right).$$

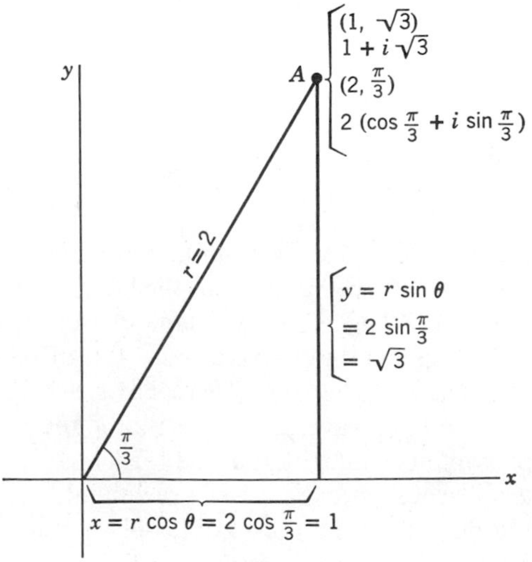

Figure 3.3

This gives a fourth way to label point A in Fig. 3.3. (Sometimes $\cos\theta +$ $i\sin\theta$ is abbreviated as cis θ; we would have in this notation $1 + i\sqrt{3} =$ 2 cis $\pi/3$.)

cis θ

4. TERMINOLOGY AND NOTATION

Both i and j are used to represent $\sqrt{-1}$, j usually in any problem dealing with electricity since i is needed there for current. A physicist should be able to work with ease using either symbol. We shall for consistency use i throughout this book.

We often label a point with a single letter (for example, P in Fig. 3.2 and A in Fig. 3.3) even though it requires two coordinates to locate the point. If you have studied vectors, you will recall that a vector is represented by a single letter, say $\mathbf{v}$, although it has (in two dimensions) two components. It is customary to use a single letter for a complex number even though we realize that it is actually a pair of real numbers. Thus we write

(4.1) $$z = x + iy = r(\cos\theta + i\sin\theta).$$

Here z is a complex number; x is the *real part* of the complex number z, and y is the *imaginary part* of z. The quantity r is called the *modulus* or *absolute value* of z, and θ is called the *angle* of z (or the *phase*, or the *argument*, or the *amplitude* of z). In symbols, these definitions are written

(4.2) $$x = \text{Re } z, \qquad r = \sqrt{x^2 + y^2} = |z| = \text{mod } z.$$
$$y = \text{Im } z,$$

The values of θ should be found from a diagram rather than a formula, although we do sometimes write $\theta = \arctan(y/x)$. An example shows this clearly.

Example. Write $z = -1 - i$ in polar form. Here we have $x = -1$, $y = -1$, $r = \sqrt{2}$ (Fig. 4.1). There are an infinite number of values of θ,

$$\theta = \frac{5\pi}{4} + 2n\pi,$$

where n is any integer, positive or negative. The value $\theta = 5\pi/4$ is sometimes called the *principal angle* of the complex number $z = -1 - i$. Notice carefully, however, that this is not the same as the principal value $\pi/4$ of arc tan 1 as defined in calculus. The angle of a complex number must be in the same quadrant as the point representing the number. Then we

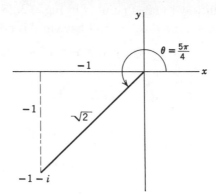

Figure 4.1

have in our example

$$z = -1 - i = \sqrt{2}\left[\cos\left(\frac{5\pi}{4} + 2n\pi\right) + i\sin\left(\frac{5\pi}{4} + 2n\pi\right)\right]$$

$$= \sqrt{2}\left(\cos\frac{5\pi}{4} + i\sin\frac{5\pi}{4}\right).$$

The complex number $x - iy$, obtained by changing the sign of i in $z = x + iy$, is called the *complex conjugate* or simply the *conjugate* of z. We usually write the conjugate of $z = x + iy$ as $\bar{z} = x - iy$. Sometimes we use z^* instead of $\bar{z}$ (in fields such as statistics or quantum mechanics where the bar is used to mean an average value). Notice carefully that the conjugate of $2i - 3$ is $-2i - 3$; that is, it is the i term whose sign is changed.

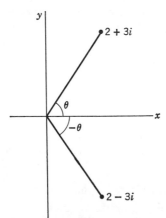

Figure 4.2

Complex numbers come in conjugate pairs; for example, the conjugate of $2 + 3i$ is $2 - 3i$ and the conjugate of $2 - 3i$ is $2 + 3i$. Such a pair of points in the complex plane are mirror images of each other with the x-axis as the mirror (Fig. 4.2). Then in polar form, z and $\bar{z}$ have the same r value, but their θ values are negatives of each other. If $z = r(\cos\theta + i\sin\theta)$, then

$$\bar{z} = r[\cos(-\theta) + i\sin(-\theta)] = r(\cos\theta - i\sin\theta).$$

5. COMPLEX ALGEBRA

Any complex number can be written in the rectangular form $x + iy$. To add, subtract, and multiply complex numbers, remember that they follow the ordinary rules of algebra and that $i^2 = -1$. Thus

$$(1 - i)^2 = 1 - 2i + i^2 = 1 - 2i - 1 = -2i.$$

To divide one complex number by another, first write the quotient as a fraction. Then reduce the fraction to rectangular form by multiplying numerator and denominator by the conjugate of the denominator; this makes the denominator real. For example,

$$\frac{2 + i}{3 - i} = \frac{2 + i}{3 - i} \cdot \frac{3 + i}{3 + i} = \frac{6 + 5i + i^2}{9 - i^2} = \frac{5 + 5i}{10} = \frac{1}{2} + \frac{1}{2}i.$$

It is easy to see that the conjugate of the sum of two complex numbers is the sum of the conjugates of the numbers. If

$$z_1 = x_1 + iy_1 \quad \text{and} \quad z_2 = x_2 + iy_2,$$

then

$$\bar{z}_1 + \bar{z}_2 = x_1 - iy_1 + x_2 - iy_2 = x_1 + x_2 - i(y_1 + y_2).$$

The conjugate of $(z_1 + z_2)$ is

$$\overline{(x_1 + x_2) + i(y_1 + y_2)} = (x_1 + x_2) - i(y_1 + y_2).$$

Similarly, you can show that the conjugate of the difference (or product or quotient) of two complex numbers is equal to the difference (or product or quotient) of the conjugates of the numbers (Problem 3). In other words, you can get the conjugate of an expression containing i's by just changing the signs of all the i terms. We must watch out for hidden i's however. For example, if

$$z = \frac{2 - 3i}{i + 4}, \quad \text{then} \quad \bar{z} = \frac{2 + 3i}{-i + 4}.$$

But if $z = f + ig$, where f and g are themselves complex, then $\bar{z} = \bar{f} - i\bar{g}$ (not $f - ig$).

This theorem makes it easy to find $|z|$. Recall that the definition of $|z|$ is

$$|z| = r = \sqrt{x^2 + y^2} \quad \text{(positive square root!)}.$$

Since $z\bar{z} = (x + iy)(x - iy) = x^2 - i^2y^2 = x^2 + y^2$, we can write

(5.1) $$|z| = \sqrt{x^2 + y^2} = \sqrt{z\bar{z}}.$$

Note that $z\bar{z}$ is always real and not negative since $z\bar{z} = x^2 + y^2$ and x and y are real.

Example.

$$\left| \frac{\sqrt{5} + 3i}{1 - i} \right| = \sqrt{\frac{\sqrt{5} + 3i}{1 - i} \frac{\sqrt{5} - 3i}{1 + i}} = \sqrt{\frac{14}{2}} = \sqrt{7}.$$

This is much easier than reducing the fraction to rectangular form and computing $\sqrt{x^2 + y^2}$. Observe that the absolute value of a quotient of two complex numbers is the quotient of the absolute values (and a similar statement for product).

In working with equations involving complex quantities, we must always remember that a complex number is actually a pair of real numbers. Two complex numbers are equal if and only if their real parts are equal and their imaginary parts are equal. For example, $x + iy = 2 + 3i$ means $x = 2$ and $y = 3$. In other words, any equation involving complex numbers is really two equations involving real numbers.

Example. Find x and y if

$$(5.2) \qquad\qquad (x + iy)^2 = 2i.$$

Since $(x + iy)^2 = x^2 + 2ixy - y^2$, (5.2) is equivalent to the two real equations

$$x^2 - y^2 = 0,$$
$$2xy = 2.$$

(Since x is assumed real, we cannot have $y = -x$ which gives $x^2 = -1$.) Then

$$y = x, \qquad 2x^2 = 2,$$
$$y = x = 1, \qquad \text{or} \quad y = x = -1.$$

Using the graphical representation of the complex number z as the point (x, y) in a plane, we can give geometrical meaning to equations and inequalities involving z.

Example 1. What is the locus of points in the (x, y) plane satisfying the equation $|z| = 3$?
Since

$$|z| = \sqrt{x^2 + y^2},$$

the given equation is

$$\sqrt{x^2 + y^2} = 3 \qquad \text{or} \quad x^2 + y^2 = 9.$$

Then the locus of points satisfying $|z| = 3$ is the circle of radius 3 with center at the origin. Such a locus might describe, for example, the path of an electron or of a satellite. Here are some more examples of locus problems.

Example 2. $|z - 1| = 2$. This is the circle $(x - 1)^2 + y^2 = 4$.

Example 3. (Angle of z) $= \pi/4$. This is the half-line $y = x$ with $x > 0$; this might be the path of a light ray starting at the origin.

Example 4. Re $z > \frac{1}{2}$. This is the half-plane $x > \frac{1}{2}$.

Problems in physics as well as geometry may often be simplified by using one complex equation instead of two real equations. (See Section 16.)

Example. A particle moves in the (x, y) plane so that its position (x, y) as a function of time t is given by

$$z = \frac{i + 2t}{t - i}.$$

Find the magnitudes of its velocity and its acceleration as functions of t. We *could* write z in the $x + iy$ form and so find x and y as functions of t. It is easier to do the problem as follows. We define the complex velocity and complex acceleration by dz/dt and d^2z/dt^2. You can verify that the magnitude v of the velocity is $v = |dz/dt|$ and the magnitude a of the acceleration is $a = |d^2z/dt^2|$ (Problem 10). Then we have

$$\frac{dz}{dt} = \frac{2(t - i) - (i + 2t)}{(t - i)^2} = \frac{-3i}{(t - i)^2},$$

$$v = \left| \frac{dz}{dt} \right| = \sqrt{\frac{-3i}{(t - i)^2} \cdot \frac{+3i}{(t + i)^2}} = \frac{3}{t^2 + 1},$$

$$\frac{d^2z}{dt^2} = \frac{(-3i)(-2)}{(t - i)^3} = \frac{6i}{(t - i)^3},$$

$$a = \left| \frac{d^2z}{dt^2} \right| = \frac{6}{(t^2 + 1)^{3/2}}.$$

6. COMPLEX INFINITE SERIES

In Chapter 1 we considered infinite series whose terms were real. We shall be very much interested in series with complex terms; let us reconsider our definitions and theorems for this case. The partial sums of a series of complex numbers will be complex numbers, say $S_n = X_n + iY_n$, where X_n and Y_n are real. Convergence is defined just as for real series: If S_n approaches a limit $S = X + iY$ as $n \to \infty$, we call the series convergent and call S its sum. This means that $X_n \to X$ and $Y_n \to Y$; in other words, the real and the imaginary parts of the series are each convergent series.

It is useful, just as for real series, to discuss absolute convergence first. It can be proved (Problem 11) that an absolutely convergent series converges. Absolute convergence means here, just as for real series, that the series of absolute values of the terms is a convergent series. Remember that $|z| = r = \sqrt{x^2 + y^2}$ is a positive number. Thus any of the tests given in Chapter 1 for convergence of series of positive terms may be used here to test a complex series for absolute convergence.

Example. Test for convergence

$$1 + \frac{1 + i}{2} + \frac{(1 + i)^2}{4} + \frac{(1 + i)^3}{8} + \cdots + \frac{(1 + i)^n}{2^n} + \cdots.$$

Using the ratio test, we find

$$\rho = \lim_{n \to \infty} \left| \frac{(1 + i)^{n+1}}{2^{n+1}} \div \frac{(1 + i)^n}{2^n} \right| = \lim_{n \to \infty} \left| \frac{1 + i}{2} \right|$$

$$= \left| \frac{1 + i}{2} \right| = \frac{\sqrt{2}}{2} < 1.$$

Since $\rho < 1$, the series is absolutely convergent and therefore convergent.

7. COMPLEX POWER SERIES; CIRCLE OF CONVERGENCE

In Chapter 1 we considered series of powers of x, $\sum a_n x^n$. We are now interested in series of powers of z,

(7.1) $$\sum a_n z^n,$$

where $z = x + iy$, and the a_n are complex numbers. [Notice that (7.1) includes real series as a special case since $z = x$ if $y = 0$.] Here are some examples.

(7.2)
$$(a) \; 1 - z + \frac{z^2}{2} - \frac{z^3}{3} + \frac{z^4}{4} + \cdots,$$

$$(b) \; 1 + iz + \frac{(iz)^2}{2!} + \frac{(iz)^3}{3!} + \cdots = 1 + iz - \frac{z^2}{2!} - \frac{iz^3}{3!} + \cdots.$$

Let us use the ratio test to find for what z these series are absolutely convergent. For (7.2a), we have

$$\rho = \lim_{n \to \infty} \left| \frac{z \cdot n}{n + 1} \right| = |z|.$$

The series converges if $\rho < 1$, that is, if $|z| < 1$, or $\sqrt{x^2 + y^2} < 1$. This is the interior of a circle of radius 1 in the complex plane. This circle is called the *circle of convergence* of the infinite series. It replaces the interval of convergence which we had for real series. In fact (see Fig. 7.1), the interval of convergence for the series $\Sigma\,(-x)^n/n$ is just the interval $(-1, 1)$ on the x-axis contained within the circle of convergence of $\Sigma\,(-z)^n/n$, as it must be since x is the value of z when $y = 0$. For this reason we sometimes speak of the *circle* or *radius* of convergence of a power series even though we are considering only real values of z.

Next consider series (7.2b); here we have

$$\rho = \lim_{n \to \infty} \left| \frac{(iz)^{n+1}}{(n+1)!} \div \frac{(iz)^n}{n!} \right| = \lim_{n \to \infty} \left| \frac{iz}{n+1} \right| = 0.$$

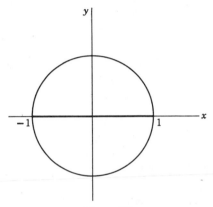

Figure 7.1

This is an example of a series which converges for all values of z.

Just as for real series, if $\rho > 1$, the series diverges (Problem 13). For $\rho = 1$ (that is, on the boundary of the circle of convergence) the series may either converge or diverge. It may be difficult to find out which and we shall not in general need to consider the question.

The four theorems about power series (Chapter 1, Section 11) are true also for complex series (replace *interval* by *circle* of convergence). Also we can now state for Theorem 2 what the circle of convergence is for the quotient of two series. Assume to start with that any common factor z has been canceled. Let r_1 and r_2 be the radii of convergence of the numerator and denominator series. Find the closest point to the origin in the complex plane where the denominator series is zero; call the distance from the origin to this point s. Then the quotient series converges at least inside the smallest of the three circles of radii r_1, r_2, s. (See Chapter 11, Section 2.)

Example. Find the series for $(\sin z)/[z(1 + z^2)]$ and its circle of convergence.

We shall soon see that the series for sin z has the same form as the real series for sin x in Chapter 1. Using this fact we have

$$\frac{\sin z}{z} = \frac{1}{z}\left(z - \frac{z^3}{3!} + \frac{z^5}{5!} - \cdots\right) = 1 - \frac{z^2}{3!} + \frac{z^4}{5!} - \cdots,$$

(7.3)
$$\frac{\sin z}{z(1 + z^2)} = \frac{1 - \dfrac{z^2}{3!} + \dfrac{z^4}{5!}\cdots}{1 + z^2}$$

$$= 1 - \left(1 + \frac{1}{3!}\right)z^2 + \left(1 + \frac{1}{3!} + \frac{1}{5!}\right)z^4 + \cdots$$

$$= 1 - \frac{7z^2}{3!} + \frac{141}{5!}z^4 + \cdots.$$

The numerator series in (7.3) converges for all z (if you like, $r_1 = \infty$). The denominator $1 + z^2$ is not an infinite series, so we do not have to consider r_2. The denominator is zero when $1 + z^2 = 0$, that is, when $z = \pm i$. Thus $s = 1$. We then know that the series for $(\sin z)/[z(1 + z^2)]$ converges inside a circle of radius 1. You can check this by using the ratio test (Problem 15).

8. ELEMENTARY FUNCTIONS OF COMPLEX NUMBERS

The so-called elementary functions are powers and roots, trigonometric and inverse trigonometric functions, logarithmic and exponential functions, and combinations of these. All these you can compute or find in tables, as long as you want them as functions of real numbers. Now we want to find things like i^i, sin $(1 + i)$, or ln i. These are not just curiosities for the amusement of the mathematically inclined, but may turn up to be evaluated in applied problems. To be sure, the values of experimental measurements are not imaginary. But the values of Re z, Im z, $|z|$, angle of z, are real, and these are the quantities which have experimental meaning. Meanwhile, mathematical solutions of problems may involve manipulations of complex numbers before we arrive finally at a real answer to compare with experiment.

Polynomials and rational functions (quotients of polynomials) in z are easily evaluated. Here are some examples.

If $f(z) = z^2 - 2z + 1$, find $f(1 - i)$.

$$f(1 - i) = (1 - i)^2 - 2(1 - i) + 1 = 1 - 2i + i^2 - 2 + 2i + 1 = -1.$$

If $f(z) = (z^2 + 1)/(z - 3)$, find $f(i - 2)$.

$$f(i - 2) = \frac{(i - 2)^2 + 1}{i - 2 - 3} = \frac{-4i + 4}{i - 5} \cdot \frac{-i - 5}{-i - 5} = \frac{8i - 12}{13}.$$

Next we want to investigate the possible meaning of other functions of complex numbers. We should like to define expressions like e^z or $\sin z$ so that they will obey the familiar laws we know for the corresponding real expressions [for example, $\sin 2x = 2 \sin x \cos x$, or $(d/dx)e^x = e^x$]. We must, for consistency, define functions of complex numbers so that any equations involving them reduce to correct real equations when $z = x + iy$ becomes $z = x$, that is, when $y = 0$. These requirements will be met if we define e^z by the power series

(8.1)
$$e^z = 1 + \frac{z}{1!} + \frac{z^2}{2!} + \cdots .$$

This series converges for all values of the complex number z (Problem 14a) and therefore gives us the value of e^z for any z. If we put $z = x$ (x real), we get the familiar series for e^x.

It is easy to show, by multiplying the series (Problem 16), that

(8.2)
$$e^{z_1} \cdot e^{z_2} = e^{z_1 + z_2}.$$

In Chapter 11 we shall consider in detail the meaning of derivatives with respect to a complex z. However, it is worth while for you to know that $(d/dz)z^n = nz^{n-1}$, and that, in fact, the other differentiation and integration formulas which you know from elementary calculus hold also with x replaced by z. You can verify that $(d/dz)e^z = e^z$ when e^z is defined by (8.1) by differentiating (8.1) term by term (Problem 16). It can be shown that (8.1) is the only definition of e^z which preserves these familiar formulas (see Hille, p. 139). We now want to consider the consequences of this definition.

9. EULER'S FORMULA

For real θ, we know from Chapter 1 the power series for $\sin \theta$ and $\cos \theta$:

(9.1)
$$\sin \theta = \theta - \frac{\theta^3}{3!} + \frac{\theta^5}{5!} - \cdots ,$$
$$\cos \theta = 1 - \frac{\theta^2}{2!} + \frac{\theta^4}{4!} - \cdots .$$

From our definition (8.1), we can write the series for e to any power, real or imaginary. We write the series for $e^{i\theta}$, where θ is real:

(9.2)
$$e^{i\theta} = 1 + i\theta + \frac{(i\theta)^2}{2!} + \frac{(i\theta)^3}{3!} + \frac{(i\theta)^4}{4!} + \frac{(i\theta)^5}{5!} + \cdots$$
$$= 1 + i\theta - \frac{\theta^2}{2!} - i\frac{\theta^3}{3!} + \frac{\theta^4}{4!} + i\frac{\theta^5}{5!} \cdots$$
$$= 1 - \frac{\theta^2}{2!} + \frac{\theta^4}{4!} \cdots + i\left(\theta - \frac{\theta^3}{3!} + \frac{\theta^5}{5!} \cdots \right).$$

(The rearrangement of terms is justified because the series is absolutely convergent.) Now compare (9.1) and (9.2); the last line in (9.2) is just $\cos \theta + i \sin \theta$. We then have a very useful equation known as Euler's formula, namely

(9.3) $$e^{i\theta} = \cos \theta + i \sin \theta.$$

Using this formula and (4.1) we can now write any complex number in these ways:

(9.4) $$z = x + iy = r(\cos \theta + i \sin \theta) = re^{i\theta}.$$

Here are some examples of the use of (9.3) and (9.4).

Example 1. Write $z = 1 + i$ in the $re^{i\theta}$ form.
Since $x = 1$ and $y = 1$, we get $r = \sqrt{2}$, $\theta = \pi/4$. Then

$$z = 1 + i = \sqrt{2}\left[\cos \frac{\pi}{4} + i \sin \frac{\pi}{4}\right] = \sqrt{2}\, e^{i\pi/4}.$$

Example 2. Find the values of $e^{i\pi}$, $e^{-i\pi/2}$, $e^{2n\pi i}$.

$$e^{i\pi} = \cos \pi + i \sin \pi = -1 + i \cdot 0 = -1,$$
$$e^{-i\pi/2} = \cos(-\pi/2) + i \sin(-\pi/2) = 0 + i(-1) = -i,$$
$$e^{2n\pi i} = \cos 2n\pi + i \sin 2n\pi = 1 + i(0) = 1.$$

It is often convenient to use Euler's formula when we want to multiply or divide complex numbers. From (8.2) we obtain two familiar looking laws of exponents which are now valid for imaginary exponents:

(9.5)
$$e^{i\theta_1} \cdot e^{i\theta_2} = e^{i(\theta_1+\theta_2)},$$
$$e^{i\theta_1} \div e^{i\theta_2} = e^{i(\theta_1-\theta_2)}.$$

Remembering that *any* complex number can be written in the form $re^{i\theta}$ by (9.4), we get

(9.6)
$$z_1 \cdot z_2 = r_1 e^{i\theta_1} \cdot r_2 e^{i\theta_2} = r_1 r_2 e^{i(\theta_1+\theta_2)},$$
$$z_1 \div z_2 = \frac{r_1}{r_2} e^{i(\theta_1-\theta_2)}.$$

In words, to multiply two complex numbers, we multiply their absolute values and add their angles. To divide two complex numbers, we divide the absolute values and subtract the angles.

Example

$$\frac{(1+i)^2}{1-i} = \frac{(\sqrt{2}\, e^{i\pi/4})^2}{\sqrt{2}\, e^{-i\pi/4}} = \frac{2}{\sqrt{2}}\, e^{3\pi i/4} = -1 + i.$$

10. POWERS AND ROOTS OF COMPLEX NUMBERS

Using the rules (9.6) for multiplication and division of complex numbers, we get DeMoivre's theorem

$$(10.1) \qquad z^n = (re^{i\theta})^n = r^n e^{in\theta}$$

for any integral n. In words, to obtain the nth power of a complex number, we take the nth power of the modulus and multiply the angle by n. The case $r = 1$ is of particular interest. Then (10.1) becomes

$$(10.2) \qquad (e^{i\theta})^n = (\cos\theta + i\sin\theta)^n = \cos n\theta + i\sin n\theta.$$

You can use this equation to find the formulas for $\sin 2\theta$, $\cos 2\theta$, $\sin 3\theta$, etc. (Problem 22).

The nth root of z, $z^{1/n}$, means a complex number whose nth power is z. From (10.1) you can see that this is

$$(10.3) \qquad z^{1/n} = (re^{i\theta})^{1/n} = r^{1/n} e^{i\theta/n} = \sqrt[n]{r}\left(\cos\frac{\theta}{n} + i\sin\frac{\theta}{n}\right).$$

This formula must be used with care (see Example 2 below).

Some examples will show how useful these formulas are.

Example 1. Find $(1 + i)^8$. If $z = 1 + i$, then $r = \sqrt{2}$, $\theta = \pi/4$, so in polar form $1 + i = \sqrt{2}e^{i\pi/4}$. Then we have

$$(1 + i)^8 = (\sqrt{2}\, e^{i\pi/4})^8 = 16e^{2\pi i} = 16(\cos 2\pi + i\sin 2\pi) = 16.$$

Example 2. Find $\sqrt[3]{8i}$. In polar form $8i = 8e^{i\pi/2}$. Then

$$\sqrt[3]{8i} = (8e^{i\pi/2})^{1/3} = 2e^{i\pi/6} = 2\left(\cos\frac{\pi}{6} + i\sin\frac{\pi}{6}\right) = 2\left(\frac{\sqrt{3}}{2} + \frac{1}{2}i\right) = \sqrt{3} + i.$$

But this is not the only answer. The angle θ could also have been taken as $\frac{1}{2}\pi + 2\pi$, or $\frac{1}{2}\pi + 4\pi$, or $\frac{1}{2}\pi + 6\pi$, etc. Let us try each of these θ values. We get

$$\sqrt[3]{8i} = [8e^{i\left(\frac{\pi}{2}+2\pi\right)}]^{1/3} = 2e^{i\left(\frac{\pi}{6}+\frac{2\pi}{3}\right)} = 2e^{5\pi i/6} = -\sqrt{3} + i,$$

$$\sqrt[3]{8i} = [8e^{i\left(\frac{\pi}{2}+4\pi\right)}]^{1/3} = 2e^{i\left(\frac{\pi}{6}+\frac{4\pi}{3}\right)} = 2e^{3\pi i/2} = -2i,$$

$$\sqrt[3]{8i} = [8e^{i\left(\frac{\pi}{2}+6\pi\right)}]^{1/3} = 2e^{i\left(\frac{\pi}{6}+2\pi\right)} = 2e^{\pi i/6} = \sqrt{3} + i.$$

This last answer is the same as our first answer. If we continued to add 2π to our original θ, we would simply repeat the three answers over and over. You should convince yourself that in general any number has three cube

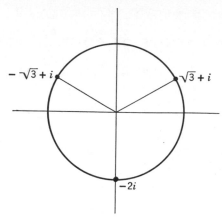

Figure 10.1

roots, ten tenth roots, etc. The solution of the problem of finding $\sqrt[3]{8i}$ can now be written more compactly thus:

$$\sqrt[3]{8i} = \begin{Bmatrix} (8e^{i\pi/2})^{1/3} \\ [8e^{i\left(\frac{\pi}{2}+2\pi\right)}]^{1/3} \\ [8e^{i\left(\frac{\pi}{2}+4\pi\right)}]^{1/3} \end{Bmatrix} = \begin{Bmatrix} 2e^{i\pi/6} \\ 2e^{5\pi i/6} \\ 2e^{3\pi i/2} \end{Bmatrix} = \begin{Bmatrix} \sqrt{3}+i \\ -\sqrt{3}+i \\ -2i \end{Bmatrix}.$$

It is illuminating to plot these three cube roots (Fig. 10.1). Notice that they all lie on a circle of radius 2 and are equally spaced 120° apart. Since the only difference among the n nth roots of a number is in the angle, it will always be true for any set of nth roots that they lie on a circle. Also they will always be equally spaced since the angle increases by $2\pi/n$ from any one root to the next.

11. THE EXPONENTIAL AND TRIGONOMETRIC FUNCTIONS

Although we have already defined e^z by a power series (8.1), it is worth while to write it in another form. By (8.2) we can write

(11.1) $e^z = e^{x+iy} = e^x e^{iy} = e^x(\cos y + i \sin y).$

This is more convenient to use than the infinite series if we want values of e^z for given z. For example,

$$e^{2-i\pi} = e^2 e^{-i\pi} = e^2(\cos \pi - i \sin \pi) = -e^2.$$

We have already seen that there is a close relationship [Euler's formula (9.3)] between complex exponentials and trigonometric functions of real angles. It is useful to write this relation in another form. We write Euler's formula (9.3) as it is, and also write it with θ replaced by $-\theta$. Remember that $\cos(-\theta) = \cos\theta$ and $\sin(-\theta) = -\sin\theta$. Then we have

$$e^{i\theta} = \cos\theta + i\sin\theta,$$

(11.2)

$$e^{-i\theta} = \cos\theta - i\sin\theta.$$

These two equations can be solved for $\sin\theta$ and $\cos\theta$. We get (Problem 26)

$$\sin\theta = \frac{e^{i\theta} - e^{-i\theta}}{2i},$$

(11.3)

$$\cos\theta = \frac{e^{i\theta} + e^{-i\theta}}{2}.$$

These formulas are useful in evaluating integrals since products of exponentials are easier to integrate than products of sines and cosines (Problems 36 and 37).

So far we have discussed only trigonometric functions of real angles. We could define $\sin z$ and $\cos z$ for complex z by their power series as we did for e^z. We could then compare these series with the series for e^{iz} and derive Euler's formula and (11.3) with θ replaced by z. However, it is simpler to use the complex equations corresponding to (11.3) as our definitions for $\sin z$ and $\cos z$. We define

$$\sin z = \frac{e^{iz} - e^{-iz}}{2i},$$

(11.4)

$$\cos z = \frac{e^{iz} + e^{-iz}}{2}.$$

The rest of the trigonometric functions of z are defined in the usual way in terms of these; for example, $\tan z = \sin z/\cos z$.

Example 1.

$$\cos i = \frac{e^{i\cdot i} + e^{-i\cdot i}}{2} = \frac{e^{-1} + e}{2} = \frac{1}{2e} + \frac{e}{2}.$$

Example 2.

$$\sin\left(\frac{\pi}{2} + i\ln 2\right) = \frac{e^{i\left(\frac{\pi}{2} + i\ln 2\right)} - e^{-i\left(\frac{\pi}{2} + i\ln 2\right)}}{2i}$$

$$= \frac{e^{\frac{i\pi}{2} - \ln 2} - e^{-\frac{i\pi}{2} + \ln 2}}{2i} = \frac{\frac{i}{2} + 2i}{2i} = \frac{5}{4}.$$

Notice that even though $\frac{5}{4} > 1$, $\frac{5}{4}$ is still the sine of a (complex) number. We shall see when we discuss inverse trigonometric functions that $\sin z$ can have *any* value we like.

Using the definitions (11.4) of $\sin z$ and $\cos z$, you can show that the trigonometric identities and calculus formulas hold when θ is replaced by z.

Example 1. Prove that $\sin^2 z + \cos^2 z = 1$.

$$\sin^2 z = \left(\frac{e^{iz} - e^{-iz}}{2i} \right)^2 = \frac{e^{2iz} - 2 + e^{-2iz}}{-4} \,,$$

$$\cos^2 z = \left(\frac{e^{iz} + e^{-iz}}{2} \right)^2 = \frac{e^{2iz} + 2 + e^{-2iz}}{4} \,,$$

$$\sin^2 z + \cos^2 z = \tfrac{2}{4} + \tfrac{2}{4} = 1.$$

Example 2. Using the definitions (11.4), verify that $(d/dz) \sin z = \cos z$.

$$\sin z = \frac{e^{iz} - e^{-iz}}{2i} \,,$$

$$\frac{d}{dz} \sin z = \frac{1}{2i} (ie^{iz} + ie^{-iz}) = \frac{e^{iz} + e^{-iz}}{2} = \cos z.$$

12. HYPERBOLIC FUNCTIONS

Let us look at $\sin z$ and $\cos z$ for pure imaginary z, that is, $z = iy$:

(12.1)
$$\sin iy = \frac{e^{-y} - e^{y}}{2i} = i \frac{e^{y} - e^{-y}}{2} \,,$$

$$\cos iy = \frac{e^{-y} + e^{y}}{2} = \frac{e^{y} + e^{-y}}{2} \,.$$

The real functions on the right have special names because these particular combinations of exponentials arise frequently in problems. They are called the hyperbolic sine (abbreviated sinh) and the hyperbolic cosine (abbreviated cosh). Their definitions for all z are

(12.2)
$$\sinh z = \frac{e^{z} - e^{-z}}{2} \,,$$

$$\cosh z = \frac{e^{z} + e^{-z}}{2} \,.$$

The other hyperbolic functions are named and defined in a similar way to parallel the trigonometric functions:

(12.3)
$$\tanh z = \frac{\sinh z}{\cosh z}, \qquad \coth z = \frac{1}{\tanh z},$$
$$\operatorname{sech} z = \frac{1}{\cosh z}, \qquad \operatorname{csch} z = \frac{1}{\sinh z}.$$

We can write (12.1) as

(12.4)
$$\sin iy = i \sinh y,$$
$$\cos iy = \cosh y.$$

Then we see that the hyperbolic functions of y are (except for one i factor) the trigonometric functions of iy. From (12.2) we can show that (12.4) holds with y replaced by z. Because of this relation between hyperbolic and trigonometric functions, the formulas for hyperbolic functions look very much like the corresponding trigonometric identities and calculus formulas. They are not identical, however. You can prove that, for example (see Problem 30),

$$\cosh^2 z - \sinh^2 z = 1 \qquad (\text{compare } \sin^2 z + \cos^2 z = 1),$$
$$\frac{d}{dz} \cosh z = \sinh z \qquad \left(\text{compare } \frac{d}{dz} \cos z = -\sin z \right).$$

13. LOGARITHMS AND COMPLEX POWERS

In elementary mathematics you learned to find logarithms of positive numbers only; in fact, you may have been told that there were no logarithms of negative numbers. This is true if you use only real numbers, but it is not true when we allow complex numbers as answers. We shall now see how to find the logarithm of any complex number (including negative real numbers as a special case). If

(13.1) $$z = e^w,$$

then by definition

(13.2) $$w = \ln z.$$

(We use ln for natural logarithms to avoid the cumbersome $\log_e$ and to avoid confusion with logarithms to the base 10.)

We can write the law of exponents (8.2), using the letters of (13.1), as

(13.3) $$z_1 z_2 = e^{w_1} \cdot e^{w_2} = e^{w_1 + w_2}.$$

Taking logarithms of this equation, that is, using (13.1) and (13.2), we get

(13.4) $$\ln z_1 z_2 = w_1 + w_2 = \ln z_1 + \ln z_2.$$

This is the familiar law for the logarithm of a product, justified now for complex numbers. We can then find the real and imaginary parts of the logarithm of any complex number from the equation

(13.5) $w = \ln z = \ln (re^{i\theta}) = \ln r + \ln e^{i\theta} = \ln r + i\theta,$

where $\ln r$ means the ordinary real logarithm to the base e. Since θ has an infinite number of values (all differing by multiples of 2π), a complex number has infinitely many logarithms, differing from each other by multiples of $2\pi i$.

Example 1.

$$\ln (-1) = \ln 1 + i(\pi + 2n\pi) = i\pi, \; -i\pi, \; 3\pi i, \text{ etc.}$$

Example 2.

$$\ln (1 + i) = \ln \sqrt{2} + i\left(\frac{\pi}{4} + 2n\pi\right) = 0.347 \cdots + i\left(\frac{\pi}{4} + 2n\pi\right).$$

Even a positive real number now has infinitely many logarithms, since its angle can be taken as 0, 2π, -2π, etc. Only one of these logarithms is real, namely the principal value using the angle $\theta = 0$. The principal value of any $\ln z$ is the one using the principal value of θ, that is $0 \le \theta < 2\pi$. (Some books use $-\pi < \theta \le \pi$.)

14. COMPLEX ROOTS AND POWERS

For real positive numbers, the equation $\ln a^b = b \ln a$ is equivalent to $a^b = e^{b \ln a}$. We define complex powers by the same formula with complex a and b. By definition, for complex a and b $(a \ne e)$,

(14.1) $a^b = e^{b \ln a}.$

[The case $a = e$ is excluded because we have already defined powers of e by (8.1).] Since $\ln a$ is multiple valued (because of the infinite number of values of θ), powers a^b are usually multiple valued, and unless you want just the principal value of $\ln z$ or of a^b you must use all values of θ. In the following examples we find all values of each complex power and write the answers in the $x + iy$ form.

Example 1.

$$i^{-2i} = e^{-2i \ln i} = e^{-2i\left[\ln 1 + i\left(\frac{\pi}{2} + 2n\pi\right)\right]}$$

$$= e^{-2i\left[0 + i\left(\frac{\pi}{2} + 2n\pi\right)\right]} = e^{\pi + 4n\pi}.$$

Note the infinite set of values of i^{-2i}, all real!

Example 2.

$$i^{1/2} = e^{\frac{1}{2}\ln i} = e^{\frac{1}{2}\left[\ln 1 + i\left(\frac{\pi}{2} + 2n\pi\right)\right]}$$

$$= e^{i\left(\frac{\pi}{4} + n\pi\right)} = e^{in\pi}e^{i\pi/4}$$

$$= \pm\left(\cos\frac{\pi}{4} + i\sin\frac{\pi}{4}\right) = \pm\frac{1}{\sqrt{2}}(1 + i).$$

We have used the fact that $e^{in\pi} = \cos n\pi + i \sin n\pi$ is $+1$ for even n and -1 for odd n. Note that here we do not get an infinite set of answers but only two as we should for the square roots of a number.

Example 3.

$$(1 + i)^{1-i} = e^{(1-i)\left[\ln\sqrt{2} + i\left(\frac{\pi}{4} + 2n\pi\right)\right]}$$

$$= e^{\ln\sqrt{2} + \frac{\pi}{4} + 2n\pi + i\left(\frac{\pi}{4} + 2n\pi - \ln\sqrt{2}\right)}$$

$$= e^{\ln\sqrt{2}} e^{\frac{\pi}{4} + 2n\pi}$$

$$\times \left[\cos\left(\frac{\pi}{4} + 2n\pi - \ln\sqrt{2}\right) + i\sin\left(\frac{\pi}{4} + 2n\pi - \ln\sqrt{2}\right)\right]$$

$$= \sqrt{2}\, e^{\frac{\pi}{4} + 2n\pi} \left[\cos\left(\frac{\pi}{4} - \ln\sqrt{2}\right) + i\sin\left(\frac{\pi}{4} - \ln\sqrt{2}\right)\right].$$

Sometimes we have to be careful about using the laws of exponents for complex numbers. For example, are $a^b \cdot a^c$ and a^{b+c} the same? This means, are $e^{b\,\ln a} \cdot e^{c\,\ln a}$ and $e^{(b+c)\,\ln a}$ the same? We do not have to take the same value of $\ln a$ in defining a^b and a^c, so $a^b\, a^c$ can have more values than a^{b+c}. It is also not always true that $(ab)^c$ and $a^c b^c$ have the same values or that $(a^b)^c$ and a^{bc} have the same values (Problem 34).

15. INVERSE TRIGONOMETRIC AND HYPERBOLIC FUNCTIONS

We have already defined the trigonometric and hyperbolic functions of a complex number z. For example,

$$(15.1) \qquad\qquad w = \cos z = \frac{e^{iz} + e^{-iz}}{2}$$

defines $w = \cos z$; that is, for each complex number z, (15.1) gives us the complex number w. We now define the inverse cosine or arc cos w by

$$(15.2) \qquad\qquad z = \text{arc cos } w \qquad \text{if} \quad w = \cos z.$$

All the other inverse trigonometric and hyperbolic functions are defined in a similar way.

In dealing with real numbers, you know that sin θ and cos θ are never greater than 1. This is no longer true for sin z and cos z with z complex. To illustrate the method of finding inverse trigonometric (or inverse hyperbolic) functions, we shall find arc cos 2.

Example.   We want z, where

$$z = \text{arc cos } 2 \quad \text{or} \quad \cos z = 2.$$

Then we have

$$\frac{e^{iz} + e^{-iz}}{2} = 2.$$

Multiply this equation by $2e^{iz}$ to get

$$e^{2iz} + 1 = 4e^{iz},$$
$$(e^{iz})^2 - 4e^{iz} + 1 = 0.$$

Solve this last equation (by the quadratic formula) for e^{iz}:

$$e^{iz} = \frac{4 \pm \sqrt{16 - 4}}{2} = 2 \pm \sqrt{3}.$$

Take logarithms of both sides of the equation and solve for z:

$$z = \frac{1}{i} \ln (2 \pm \sqrt{3}) = \text{arc cos } 2.$$

It is instructive now to find cos z and see that it *is* 2.

$$\cos\left[\frac{1}{i} \ln (2 \pm \sqrt{3})\right] = \frac{e^{i \cdot (1/i) \ln (2 \pm \sqrt{3})} + e^{-i \cdot (1/i) \ln (2 \pm \sqrt{3})}}{2}$$

$$= \frac{2 \pm \sqrt{3} + \dfrac{1}{2 \pm \sqrt{3}}}{2}$$

$$= \frac{2 \pm \sqrt{3} + \dfrac{2 \mp \sqrt{3}}{4 - 3}}{2} = \frac{4}{2} = 2.$$

By the same method, you can find all the inverse trigonometric and hyperbolic functions in terms of logarithms. Let us look at one more example.

Example. In integral tables you may find for the indefinite integral

$$\int \frac{dx}{\sqrt{x^2 + a^2}}$$

either

$$\sinh^{-1} \frac{x}{a} \quad \text{or} \quad \ln(x + \sqrt{x^2 + a^2}).$$

How are these related? Put

$$z = \sinh^{-1} \frac{x}{a}$$

or

$$\frac{x}{a} = \sinh z = \frac{e^z - e^{-z}}{2}.$$

We solve for z as in the previous example:

$$e^{2z} - 1 - \frac{2x}{a} e^z = 0,$$

$$a(e^z)^2 - 2xe^z - a = 0,$$

$$e^z = \frac{2x \pm \sqrt{4x^2 + 4a^2}}{2a} = \frac{x \pm \sqrt{x^2 + a^2}}{a}.$$

For real integrals, that is, for real z, $e^z > 0$, so we must use the positive sign. Hence we have

$$z = \ln(x + \sqrt{a^2 + x^2}) - \ln a.$$

The two answers in the integral tables differ only by the constant $\ln a$, which is a constant of integration.

16. SOME APPLICATIONS

Mechanics. We have already seen (end of Section 5) that the path of a particle in the (x, y) plane is given by $z = z(t)$. As another example of this, suppose $z = 1 + 3e^{2it}$. We see that

(16.1) $|z - 1| = |3e^{2it}| = 3.$

Recall that $|z - 1|$ is the distance between the points z and 1; (16.1) says that this distance is 3. Thus the particle traverses a circle of radius 3, with center at $(1, 0)$. The magnitude of its velocity is $|dz/dt| = |6ie^{2it}| = 6$, so it moves around the circle at constant speed. (Also see Problem 38.)

Electricity. In the theory of electric circuits, it is shown that if V is the voltage across a resistance R, and I is the current flowing through the resistor, then

(16.2) $$V = IR \quad \text{(Ohm's law)}.$$

It is also known that the current and voltage across an inductance L are related by

(16.3) $$V = L \frac{dI}{dt}$$

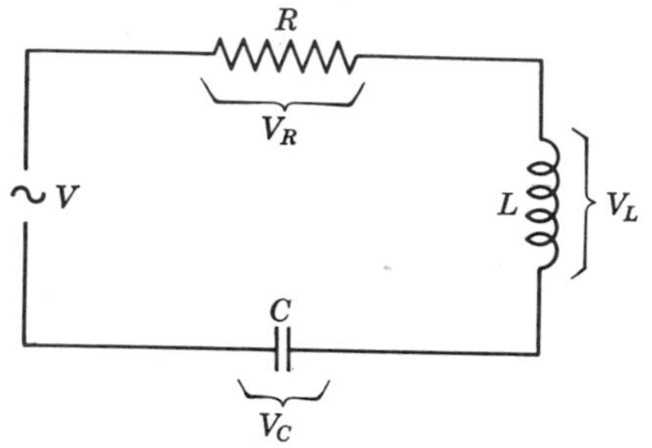

Figure 16.1

and the current and voltage across a capacitor are related by

(16.4) $$\frac{dV}{dt} = \frac{I}{C},$$

where C is the capacitance. Suppose the current I and voltage V in the circuit of Fig. 16.1 vary with time so that I is given by

(16.5) $$I = I_0 \sin \omega t.$$

You can verify that the following voltages across R, L, and C are consistent with (16.2), (16.3), and (16.4):

(16.6) $$V_R = RI_0 \sin \omega t,$$

(16.7) $$V_L = \omega L I_0 \cos \omega t,$$

(16.8) $$V_C = -\frac{1}{\omega C} I_0 \cos \omega t.$$

The total voltage

(16.9) $$V = V_R + V_L + V_C$$

is then a complicated function. A simpler method of discussing a-c circuits uses complex quantities as follows. Instead of (16.5) we write

(16.10) $$I = I_0 e^{i\omega t},$$

where it is understood that the actual physical current is given by the imaginary part of I in (16.10), that is, by (16.5). Note, by comparing (16.5) and (16.10), that the maximum value of I, namely I_0, is given in (16.10) by $|I|$. Now equations (16.6) to (16.9) become

(16.11) $$V_R = RI_0 e^{i\omega t} = RI,$$

(16.12) $$V_L = i\omega L I_0 e^{i\omega t} = i\omega LI,$$

(16.13) $$V_C = \frac{1}{i\omega C} I_0 e^{i\omega t} = \frac{1}{i\omega C} I,$$

(16.14) $$V = V_R + V_L + V_C = \left[R + i\left(\omega L - \frac{1}{\omega C} \right) \right] I.$$

The complex quantity Z defined by

(16.15) $$Z = R + i\left(\omega L - \frac{1}{\omega C} \right)$$

is called the (complex) impedance. Using it we can write (16.14) as

(16.16) $$V = ZI$$

which looks much like Ohm's law. In fact, Z for an a-c circuit corresponds to R for a d-c circuit. The more complicated a-c circuit equations now take the same simple form as the d-c equations except that all quantities are complex. For example, the rules for combining resistances in series and in parallel hold for combining complex impedances. (Problems 40 and 41.)

Optics. In optics we frequently need to combine a number of light waves (which can be represented by sine functions). Often each wave is "out of phase" with the preceding one by a fixed amount; this means that the waves can be written as $\sin t$, $\sin (t + \delta)$, $\sin (t + 2\delta)$, etc. Suppose we want to add all these sine functions together. An easy way to do it is to see that each sine is the imaginary part of a complex number, so what we want is the imaginary part of the series

(16.17) $$e^{it} + e^{i(t+\delta)} + e^{i(t+2\delta)} + \cdots.$$

This is a geometric progression with first term e^{it} and ratio $e^{i\delta}$. If there are n waves to be combined, we want the sum of n terms of this progression, which is

(16.18) $$\frac{e^{it}(1 - e^{in\delta})}{1 - e^{i\delta}}.$$

We can simplify this expression by writing

(16.19) $$1 - e^{i\delta} = e^{i\delta/2}(e^{-i\delta/2} - e^{i\delta/2}) = -e^{i\delta/2} \cdot 2i \sin \frac{\delta}{2}$$

by (11.3). Substituting (16.19) and a similar formula for $(1 - e^{in\delta})$ into (16.18), we get

(16.20)
$$\frac{e^{it}e^{in\delta/2}}{e^{i\delta/2}}\frac{\sin(n\delta/2)}{\sin(\delta/2)} = e^{i\left(t+\frac{n-1}{2}\delta\right)}\frac{\sin(n\delta/2)}{\sin(\delta/2)}.$$

The imaginary part of the series (16.17) which we wanted is then the imaginary part of (16.20), namely

$$\sin\left(t + \frac{n-1}{2}\delta\right)\sin\frac{n\delta}{2}\bigg/\sin\frac{\delta}{2}.$$

REFERENCES

The material of this chapter is discussed in the early chapters of books on complex variable, in some calculus books, and in some books on mathematics in physics and engineering. (Some suggested references are listed at the end of the book and are identified as references for Chapter 2 by a [2] after the listing.)

PROBLEMS

1. Plot the following numbers in the complex plane. For each number give the numerical value of its real part x, its imaginary part y, its modulus or absolute value r, and its principal angle (θ value between 0 and 2π). Label each plotted point in four ways as in Fig. 3.3.

(a) $1 + i$

(b) $1 - i\sqrt{3}$

(c) $-4i$

(d) $-i + 1$

(e) i^4

(f) $\dfrac{1}{1 - i}$

(g) $\dfrac{1}{i - 1}$

(h) $i^2 + 2i + 1$

(i) $-\sqrt{3} - i$

(j) $(i + \sqrt{3})^2$

(k) $2\left(\cos\dfrac{\pi}{6} + i\sin\dfrac{\pi}{6}\right)$

(l) $2\left(\cos\dfrac{\pi}{4} + i\sin\dfrac{\pi}{4}\right)$

(m) $\cos\dfrac{3\pi}{2} + i\sin\dfrac{3\pi}{2}$

(n) $5(\cos 0 + i\sin 0)$

(o) $4\left(\cos\dfrac{4\pi}{3} + i\sin\dfrac{4\pi}{3}\right)$

(p) $\dfrac{3 + i}{2 + i}$

(q) $\left(\dfrac{1 + i}{1 - i}\right)^2$

2. Find and plot the complex conjugate of each number in Problem 1.

3. Prove that the conjugate of the quotient of two complex numbers is the quotient of the conjugates. Also prove the corresponding statements for difference and product.

4. Solve for the real numbers x and y in the following equations.

   (a) $x + iy = 3i - 4$

   (b) $x + iy = 0$

   (c) $x + iy = (2 + 3i)(x - iy)$

   (d) $(2x - 3y - 5) + i(x + 2y + 1) = 0$

   (e) $(x + 2y + 3) + i(3x - y - 1) = 0$

   ●(f) $2ix + 3 = y - i$

5. What is the locus of the points for which

   (a) $|z| = 2$ (b) $\operatorname{Re} z = 0$

   (c) $|z - 1| = 1$ (d) $|z - 1| < 1$

   (e) $z - \bar{z} = 5i$ (f) angle of $z = \dfrac{\pi}{2}$

   (g) $\operatorname{Re}(z^2) = 4$ (h) $\operatorname{Re} z > 2$

   (i) $|z + 3i| = 4$ ● (j) $|z - 1 + i| = 2$

   ● (k) $\operatorname{Im} z < 0$ ● (l) $|z + 1| + |z - 1| = 8$

   (m) $z^2 = \bar{z}^2$ (n) $z^2 = -\bar{z}^2$

6. Show that $|z_1 - z_2|$ is the distance between the points z_1 and z_2 in the complex plane. Use this result to identify the loci of (c), (d), (i), and (j) in Problem 5 without computation.

7. Solve for all possible values of the real numbers x and y in the following equations.

   (a) $(x + iy)^2 = 2i$ (b) $x + iy = (1 - i)^2$

   (c) $(x + iy)^2 = (x - iy)^2$ (d) $\dfrac{x + iy}{x - iy} = -i$

   (e) $(x + iy)^3 = -1$ (f) $\dfrac{x + iy + 2 + 3i}{2x + 2iy - 3} = i + 2$

8. Show that $\operatorname{Re} z = \frac{1}{2}(z + \bar{z})$ and that $\operatorname{Im} z = (1/2i)(z - \bar{z})$. Use these formulas and (5.1) to compute the modulus and the real and imaginary parts of

   (a) $\dfrac{2i - 1}{i - 2}$ (b) $\dfrac{2 + 3i}{1 - i}$

   (c) $(1 + 2i)^3$ (d) $\dfrac{3i}{i - \sqrt{3}}$

   (e) $(2 - 3i)^4$ ●(f) $\dfrac{25}{3 + 4i}$

9. Find each of the following in rectangular $(a + bi)$ form if $z = 2 - 3i$; if $z = x + iy$.

(a) z^{-1}

(b) $\dfrac{1}{z^2}$

(c) $\dfrac{1}{z + 1}$

(d) $\dfrac{1}{z - i}$

(e) $\dfrac{1 + z}{1 - z}$

(f) $z/\bar{z}$

10. (a) Find x and y as functions of t for the example at the end of Section 5, and verify for this case that v and a are correctly given by the method of the example.

(b) Suppose that the path of a particle is the locus of points $z = x(t) + iy(t)$, where $x(t)$ and $y(t)$ are functions of the time t. Show that the magnitude of the velocity is $v = |dz/dt|$, and that the magnitude of the acceleration is $a = |d^2z/dt^2|$.

(c) Find v and a as in (b) if $z = (1 - it)/(2t + i)$.

(d) Find v and a as in (b) if $z = \cos 2t + i \sin 2t$. Can you describe the motion?

11. Prove that an absolutely convergent series of complex numbers converges. This means to prove that $\sum (a_n + ib_n)$ converges (a_n and b_n real) if $\sum \sqrt{a_n^2 + b_n^2}$ converges. *Hint:* Convergence of $\sum (a_n + ib_n)$ means that $\sum a_n$ and $\sum b_n$ *both* converge. Compare $\sum |a_n|$ and $\sum |b_n|$ with $\sum \sqrt{a_n^2 + b_n^2}$, and use Problem 17 of Chapter 1.

12. Test each of the following series for convergence.

(a) $\sum (1 + i)^n$

(b) $\sum \dfrac{1}{(1 + i)^n}$

(c) $\sum \left(\dfrac{1}{n^2} + \dfrac{i}{n} \right)$

(d) $\sum \dfrac{1 + i}{n^2}$

(e) $\sum e^{in\pi/6}$

(f) $\sum \dfrac{i^n}{n}$

(g) $\sum \left(\dfrac{2 + i}{3 - 4i} \right)^{2n}$

(h) $\sum \dfrac{(3 + 2i)^n}{n!}$

13. Prove that a series of complex terms diverges if $\rho > 1$ (ρ = ratio test limit). *Hint:* The nth term of a convergent series tends to zero.

14. Find the circle of convergence for each of the following complex power series.

(a) $e^z = 1 + z + \dfrac{z^2}{2!} + \dfrac{z^3}{3!} + \cdots$　　　[equation (8.1)]

(b) $z - \dfrac{z^2}{2} + \dfrac{z^3}{3} - \dfrac{z^4}{4} + \cdots$

(c) $1 - \dfrac{z^2}{3!} + \dfrac{z^4}{5!} - \cdots$

(d) $\displaystyle\sum_{n=0}^{\infty} z^n$

(e) $\displaystyle\sum_{n=0}^{\infty} \dfrac{(-1)^n z^{2n}}{(2n)!}$

(f) $\displaystyle\sum_{n=1}^{\infty} \dfrac{(iz)^n}{n^2}$

(g) $\displaystyle\sum_{n=0}^{\infty} n(n+1)(z-2i)^n$

(h) $\displaystyle\sum_{n=0}^{\infty} \dfrac{n!\, z^n}{(2n)!}$

(i) $\displaystyle\sum_{n=1}^{\infty} 2^n(z+i-3)^{2n}$

(j) $\displaystyle\sum_{n=0}^{\infty} \dfrac{(-1)^n z^n}{(n!)^2}$

(k) $\displaystyle\sum_{n=1}^{\infty} n^2(3iz)^n$

(l) $\displaystyle\sum_{n=0}^{\infty} \dfrac{z^{2n}}{z^{3n}}$

(m) $\displaystyle\sum_{n=1}^{\infty} \dfrac{z^{2n}}{(2n+1)!}$

15. Check the statement that the series in equation (7.3) converges for $|z| < 1$ by using the ratio test. [The next to the last line in (7.3) is the best form to use.]

16. Show from the power series (8.1) that

(a) $e^{z_1} \cdot e^{z_2} = e^{z_1 + z_2}$,

(b) $\dfrac{d}{dz} e^z = e^z$.

17. Find the power series for $e^x \sin x$ from the series for e^z in the following way. Write the series for e^z; put $z = x + iy$; show that $\operatorname{Im} e^z = e^x \sin y$; take the imaginary terms of the series and replace y by x.

18. Use Euler's formula and DeMoivre's theorem to express the following complex numbers in the rectangular form $x + iy$.

(a) $\dfrac{(i - \sqrt{3})^3}{1 - i}$

(b) $(1 + i\sqrt{3})^6$

(c) $(1 + i)^2 + (1 + i)^4$

(d) $(i - \sqrt{3})(1 + i\sqrt{3})$

(e) $\dfrac{1}{(1+i)^3}$

(f) $\left(\dfrac{1+i}{1-i}\right)^4$

(g) $(1 - i)^8$

(h) $\left(\dfrac{\sqrt{2}}{i-1}\right)^{10}$

19. Show that for any real y, $|e^{iy}| = 1$. Hence show that $|e^z| = e^x$ for any complex z.

20. Express the following complex numbers in the $x + iy$ form by using Euler's formula.

(a) $e^{-i\pi/4}$

(b) $e^{-(i\pi/4)+\ln 3}$

(c) $9e^{3\pi i/2}$

(d) $e^{(1/3)(3+4\pi i)}$

(e) $e^{5\pi i}$

(f) $e^{-2\pi i} - e^{-4\pi i} + e^{-6\pi i}$

(g) $3e^{2(1+i\pi)}$

(h) $2e^{5\pi i/6}$

21. Find *all* values of the indicated roots and plot them.

(a) $\sqrt[6]{-1}$

(b) $\sqrt{i}$

(c) $\sqrt[5]{-1-i}$

(d) $\sqrt{1+i\sqrt{3}}$

(e) $\sqrt[5]{32}$

♦(f) $\sqrt[3]{-8i}$

(g) $\sqrt[4]{-16}$

(h) $\sqrt[3]{2i-2}$

22. Using the fact that a complex equation is really two real equations, find the double angle formulas (for $\sin 2\theta$, $\cos 2\theta$) by using (10.2).

23. Show that the center of mass of three identical particles situated at the points z_1, z_2, z_3 is $(z_1 + z_2 + z_3)/3$.

24. (a) Show that the sum of the three cube roots of 8 is zero.
(b) Show that the sum of the n nth roots of any complex number is zero.
(c) Find the three cube roots of $+1$. These are often called 1, ω, and ω^2. Show that this is reasonable, that is, show that the cube roots of $+1$ are $+1$ and two other numbers, each of which is the square of the other.

25. Define $\sin z$ and $\cos z$ by their power series. Write the power series for e^{iz}. By comparing these series obtain the definition (11.4) of $\sin z$ and $\cos z$.

26. Solve the equations $e^{i\theta} = \cos\theta + i\sin\theta$, $e^{-i\theta} = \cos\theta - i\sin\theta$, for $\cos\theta$ and $\sin\theta$ and so obtain equations (11.3).

27. (a) Show that $\overline{\cos z} = \cos \bar{z}$.

(b) Is $\overline{\sin z} = \sin \bar{z}$?

(c) If $f(z) = 1 + iz$, is $\overline{f(z)} = f(\bar{z})$?

(d) If $f(z)$ is expanded in a power series with *real* coefficients, show that $\overline{f(z)} = f(\bar{z})$.

28. Prove that

$$\cos\theta + \cos 3\theta + \cos 5\theta + \cdots + \cos(2n-1)\theta = \frac{\sin 2n\theta}{2\sin\theta},$$

$$\sin\theta + \sin 3\theta + \sin 5\theta + \cdots + \sin(2n-1)\theta = \frac{\sin^2 n\theta}{\sin\theta}.$$

(*Hint:* use Euler's formula and the geometric progression formula.)

29. In optics, the following expression needs to be evaluated in calculating the intensity of light transmitted through a film after multiple reflections at the surfaces of the film:

$$\left(\sum_{n=0}^{\infty} r^{2n} \cos n\theta \right)^2 + \left(\sum_{n=0}^{\infty} r^{2n} \sin n\theta \right)^2.$$

Show that this is equal to $\left| \sum_{n=0}^{\infty} r^{2n} e^{in\theta} \right|^2$ and so evaluate it assuming $|r| < 1$ (r is the fraction of light reflected each time).

30. Verify each of the following by using the formulas by which we defined these functions of z.

(a) $\sin 2z = 2 \sin z \cos z$

(b) $\cos 3z = 4 \cos^3 z - 3 \cos z$

(c) $\sin z = \sin(x + iy) = \sin x \cosh y + i \cos x \sinh y$

(d) $\cos z = \cos x \cosh y - i \sin x \sinh y$

(e) $\cosh 2z = \cosh^2 z + \sinh^2 z$

(f) $\cosh z = \cosh x \cos y + i \sinh x \sin y$

(g) $\cosh^2 z - \sinh^2 z = 1$

(h) $\tanh iz = i \tan z$

(i) $\dfrac{d}{dz} \cos z = -\sin z$

(j) $\dfrac{d}{dz} \cosh z = \sinh z$

(k) $\arccos z = i \ln(z \pm \sqrt{z^2 - 1})$

(l) $\cosh^{-1} z = \ln(z \pm \sqrt{z^2 - 1})$

(m) $\arctan z = \dfrac{1}{2i} \ln \dfrac{1 + iz}{1 - iz}$

31. Find the real part, the imaginary part, and the absolute value of

(a) $\sin(ix)$
(b) $\cos(x + iy)$
(c) $\sinh(x + iy)$
(d) $\sin(x - iy)$
(e) $\cosh(2 - 3i)$
(f) $\sin(4 + 3i)$
(g) $\cosh(ix)$
(h) $\tan(x + iy)$

32. Show that $e^{nz} = (\cosh z + \sinh z)^n = \cosh nz + \sinh nz$. Use this and a similar equation for e^{-nz} to find formulas for $\cosh 2z$ and $\sinh 2z$ in terms of $\sinh z$ and $\cosh z$.

33. (a) Using the definitions (12.2) and a table of exponentials, sketch graphs of $\sinh x$ and $\cosh x$.

(b) Using (12.2) and (8.1), find the power series for $\sinh z$ and $\cosh z$.

34. Show that $(a^b)^c$ can have more values than a^{bc}. As an example compare

$$[(-i)^{2+i}]^{2-i} \qquad \text{and} \qquad (-i)^{(2+i)(2-i)}.$$

35. Find each of the following in rectangular form $(a + bi)$.

(a) $\sin(1 + i)$ (b) $\cosh(2\pi i)$

(c) $i^{2/3}$ (d) arc $\sin 2$

(e) $\ln(-e)$ (f) $i^{(3+i)}$

(g) arc $\tan 2i$ (h) $\ln i$

(i) $\cosh^{-1}(\frac{1}{2})$ (j) $\cos(i\pi)$

(k) $\ln(i + \sqrt{3})$ (l) $(i - 1)^{(i+1)}$

36. In the following integrals express the sines and cosines in exponential form and then integrate to show that

(a) $\displaystyle\int_{-\pi}^{\pi} \cos 2x \cos 3x \, dx = 0,$ (b) $\displaystyle\int_{-\pi}^{\pi} \cos^2 3x \, dx = \pi,$

(c) $\displaystyle\int_{-\pi}^{\pi} \sin 2x \sin 3x \, dx = 0,$ (d) $\displaystyle\int_{0}^{2\pi} \sin^2 4x \, dx = \pi,$

(e) $\displaystyle\int_{-\pi}^{\pi} \sin 2x \cos 3x \, dx = 0.$

37. Evaluate $\int e^{(a+ib)x} \, dx$ and take real and imaginary parts to show that

$$\int e^{ax} \cos bx \, dx = \frac{e^{ax}(a \cos bx + b \sin bx)}{a^2 + b^2},$$

$$\int e^{ax} \sin bx \, dx = \frac{e^{ax}(a \sin bx - b \cos bx)}{a^2 + b^2}.$$

38. Show that if the line through the origin and the point z is rotated 90° about the origin, it becomes the line through the origin and the point iz. This fact is sometimes expressed by saying that multiplying a complex number by i rotates it through 90°. Use this idea in the following problem. Let $z = ae^{i\omega t}$ be the displacement of a particle from the origin at time t. Show that the particle travels in a circle of radius a at velocity $v = a\omega$ and with acceleration of magnitude v^2/a directed toward the center of the circle.

39. In each of the following problems, z represents the displacement of a particle from the origin. Find (as functions of t) its speed and the magnitude of its acceleration, and describe the motion.

(a) $z = 5e^{i\omega t}$, $\omega = $ const.   *Hint:* See Problem 38.

(b) $z = (1 + i)e^{it}$.

(c) $z = (1 + i)t - (2 + i)(1 - t)$.   *Hint:* Show that the particle moves along a straight line through the points $(1 + i)$ and $(-2 - i)$.

(d) $z = z_1 t + z_2(1 - t)$.   *Hint:* See part (c); the straight line here is through the points z_1 and z_2.

40. In electricity we learn that the resistance of two resistors in series is $R_1 + R_2$ and the resistance of two resistors in parallel is $(R_1^{-1} + R_2^{-1})^{-1}$. Corresponding formulas hold for complex impedances. Find the impedance of Z_1 and Z_2 in series, and in parallel, given that

(a) $Z_1 = 2 + 3i$, $\quad Z_2 = 1 - 5i$,

(b) $Z_1 = 1 - i$, $\quad Z_2 = 3i$,

(c) $Z_1 = 1 + 3i$, $\quad Z_2 = 4 - 3i$.

41. Using Problem 40, find the impedance of the circuit shown (R and L in series, and then C in parallel with them).

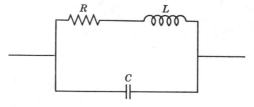

3

Determinants and Matrices

I. INTRODUCTION

Many problems in both pure and applied mathematics lead to the solution of a set of linear equations in several unknowns. For example,

(1.1)
$$x + 2y = 5,$$
$$3x - y = 8$$

is a set of two linear equations in two unknowns. In algebra you learned several methods of solving such sets of linear equations: substitution, elimination by addition or subtraction, and determinants. We shall review the method of solving sets of linear equations by determinats in this chapter. However, there is much more to the subject of determinants and matrices than this.

Consider the following problem: Two unknown weights x and y are to be found in the following way. Hang the weights and also a unit weight (as in Figs. 1.1 and 1.2) from points of a meter stick in such a way that the meter stick balances at its center. Repeat the experiment putting the weights at different positions. Write the lever equations and solve for the unknown weights. In Figs. 1.1 and 1.2 the lever equations are

(1.2)
$$10x + 20y = 50 \cdot 1 \qquad \text{for} \quad \text{Fig. 1.1,}$$
$$15x = 5y + 40 \cdot 1 \qquad \text{for} \quad \text{Fig. 1.2.}$$

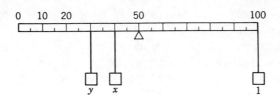

Figure 1.1

When these are simplified, they give equations (1.1) which you can solve in a number of different ways to find the solution $x = 3$, $y = 1$. This seems easy and straightforward, but consider some possible difficulties. Suppose we did the experiment three times or more. Then we would have more equations than unknowns; often such a set of equations does not have a solution. [Here, of course, if we made no mistakes in the experiments, it would turn out that the extra equations were satisfied by the same x and y found from (1.1).] Or suppose we used Fig. 1.1 for the first equation, and for the second equation placed each of the three weights just half as far from the fulcrum as it is in Fig. 1.1. You can easily verify that the two lever equations are then identical, and you cannot solve for x and y without another equation. Finally, suppose we tried to find x and y without using the unit weight by just balancing the two unknown weights. Every experiment would then give the equation

$$x - 3y = 0$$

and again we would be unable to find x and y.

In this simple problem it is not hard to see without any reference to determinants or matrices just when we can solve for x and y. In more complicated problems there may be many equations in many unknowns (not necessarily the same number of equations as unknowns) and it may not be at all obvious whether they can be solved. We should like to have some way of determining whether a given set of linear equations has a solution or not. The facts we shall learn in this chapter about determinants and matrices will enable us to do this.

We have been talking about one application of determinants and matrices, namely, to the analysis and solution of sets of linear equations.

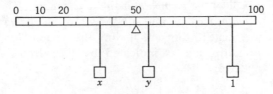

Figure 1.2

Although this is very important and will be the principal topic in this chapter, you should not conclude that this is the only use of the mathematical methods of this chapter. The terminology and techniques which we discuss here are useful in many different problems in physics and engineering. We shall take up some more of these applications in Chapter 10.

2. CRAMER'S RULE

Let us review briefly the method of solving n equations in n unknowns by determinants (when there is a unique solution). For more details and for proofs consult textbooks on college algebra. Consider a set of two linear equations in the two unknowns x and y like (1.1), or in general equations of the form

(2.1)
$$a_1 x + b_1 y = c_1,$$
$$a_2 x + b_2 y = c_2.$$

If we multiply the first equation by b_2, the second by b_1, and then subtract the results and solve for x, we get

(2.2a)
$$x = \frac{c_1 b_2 - c_2 b_1}{a_1 b_2 - a_2 b_1}.$$

Solving for y in a similar way, we get

(2.2b)
$$y = \frac{a_1 c_2 - a_2 c_1}{a_1 b_2 - a_2 b_1}.$$

It is convenient to represent the denominators of x and y by the symbol

(2.3)
$$\begin{vmatrix} a_1 & b_1 \\ a_2 & b_2 \end{vmatrix} = a_1 b_2 - a_2 b_1.$$

The two by two array of numbers with vertical bars on each side is called a *determinant*. More generally any such array consisting of n rows and n columns is called a determinant. The *order* of a determinant is the number of rows (or columns) it contains; thus (2.3) is a *second-order* determinant since it has two rows and two columns. The individual numbers a_1, a_2, b_1, b_2 in (2.3) are called the *elements* of the determinant. The elements a_1 and b_2 form the *main diagonal* and $a_1 b_2 - a_2 b_1$ is the *value of the determinant*. It is convenient to think of finding the value of the two by two determinant by multiplying as indicated by the arrows in (2.4) and attaching the indicated signs.

(2.4)
$$\begin{matrix} + & a_1 & b_1 \\ & & \diagdown\diagup \\ - & a_2 & b_2 \end{matrix}.$$

Using this notation, we can write the solutions (2.2) of (2.1) in the form

$$(2.5) \qquad x = \frac{\begin{vmatrix} c_1 & b_1 \\ c_2 & b_2 \end{vmatrix}}{\begin{vmatrix} a_1 & b_1 \\ a_2 & b_2 \end{vmatrix}}, \qquad y = \frac{\begin{vmatrix} a_1 & c_1 \\ a_2 & c_2 \end{vmatrix}}{\begin{vmatrix} a_1 & b_1 \\ a_2 & b_2 \end{vmatrix}}.$$

It is helpful in remembering (2.5) to say in words how we find the correct determinants in (2.5). First, the equations must be written as in (2.1) with the x terms first, then the y terms, and the constant terms on the right-hand side. Then if we simply write the array of coefficients on the left-hand side of (2.1), these form the denominator determinant (2.3) or (2.5). This determinant (which we shall denote by D) is called the *determinant of the coefficients*. To find the numerator determinant for x, start with D, erase the x coefficients a_1 and a_2, and replace them by the constants c_1 and c_2 from the right-hand sides of the equations. Similarly, we replace the y coefficients in D by the constant terms to find the numerator determinant in y.

Example.   Solve (1.1) by determinants. We find

$$D = \begin{vmatrix} 1 & 2 \\ 3 & -1 \end{vmatrix} = -1 - 6 = -7,$$

$$x = \frac{1}{D} \begin{vmatrix} 5 & 2 \\ 8 & -1 \end{vmatrix} = \frac{-5 - 16}{-7} = \frac{-21}{-7} = 3,$$

$$y = \frac{1}{D} \begin{vmatrix} 1 & 5 \\ 3 & 8 \end{vmatrix} = \frac{8 - 15}{-7} = \frac{-7}{-7} = 1.$$

This method of solution of a set of linear equations is called Cramer's rule. It may be used to solve n equations in n unknowns. The denominator determinant D is then of order n. The numerator determinant for each unknown is the determinant obtained by replacing the column of coefficients of that unknown in D by the constant terms from the right-hand sides of the equations. Then to find the unknowns, we must evaluate each of the determinants and divide. We next review a method of evaluating a determinant of any order.

3. LAPLACE'S DEVELOPMENT

Cramer's rule in Section 2 doesn't tell us anything until we say what we mean by the value of a determinant of order n. We *could* solve n equations in n unknowns by some method other than determinants and then *define* the numerator and denominator determinants so that Cramer's rule would be correct; this is what we did for two equations in two unknowns. Alternatively, we could define the value of a determinant in some other way, and then prove that our definition leads to a correct result by Cramer's rule. This latter method is the usual one. However, we shall simply describe one method of finding the value of a determinant; if you like, this is our definition of its value. It then has to be proved that other methods lead to the same result, and that Cramer's rule gives correct results. We shall assume these facts without proof (see college algebra books for proofs).

First we need some notation and definitions. It is convenient to write an nth order determinant like this:

(3.1)

$$\begin{vmatrix} a_{11} & a_{12} & a_{13} & \cdots & a_{1n} \\ a_{21} & a_{22} & a_{23} & \cdots & a_{2n} \\ a_{31} & & & & \cdot \\ \cdot & & \cdots & & \cdot \\ \cdot & & & & \\ \cdot & & & & \\ a_{n1} & a_{n2} & a_{n3} & \cdots & a_{nn} \end{vmatrix}$$

Notice that a_{23} is the element in the second row and the third column; that is, the first subscript is the number of the row and the second subscript is the number of the column in which the element is. Thus the element a_{ij} is in row i and column j. As an abbreviation for the determinant in (3.1), we sometimes write simply $|a_{ij}|$, that is, the determinant whose elements are a_{ij}. In this form it looks exactly like the absolute value of the element a_{ij} and you have to tell from the context which of these meanings is intended.

If we remove one row and one column from a determinant of order n, we have a determinant of order $n - 1$. Let us remove the row and column containing the element a_{ij} and call the remaining determinant M_{ij}. The determinant M_{ij} is called the *minor* of a_{ij}. For example, in the determinant

(3.2)

$$\begin{vmatrix} 1 & -5 & 2 \\ 7 & 3 & 4 \\ 2 & 1 & 5 \end{vmatrix},$$

the minor of the element $a_{23} = 4$ is

$$M_{23} = \begin{vmatrix} 1 & -5 \\ 2 & 1 \end{vmatrix},$$

obtained by crossing off the row and column containing 4, as shown. The signed minor $(-1)^{i+j}M_{ij}$ is called the *cofactor of* a_{ij}. In (3.2), the element 4 is in the second row ($i = 2$) and third column ($j = 3$), so $i + j = 5$, and the cofactor of 4 is $(-1)^5 M_{23} = -11$. It is very convenient to get the proper sign (plus or minus) for the factor $(-1)^{i+j}$ by thinking of a checkerboard of plus and minus signs like this:

$$
\begin{vmatrix}
+ & - & + & - & & \\
- & + & - & + & & \\
+ & - & + & - & & \text{etc.} \\
- & + & - & + & & \\
& \text{etc.} & & & \ddots & \\
& & & & & + \quad - \\
& & & & & - \quad +
\end{vmatrix}
$$

Then the sign $(-1)^{i+j}$ to be attached to M_{ij} is just the checkerboard sign in the same position as a_{ij}. For the element a_{23}, you can see that the checkerboard sign is minus.

Now we can easily say how to find the *value of a determinant*: *Multiply each element of one row (or one column) by its cofactor and add the results.* It can be shown that we get the same answer whichever row or column we use.

Example. Let us evaluate the determinant in (3.2) using elements of the third column. We get

$$
(3.4) \quad \begin{vmatrix} 1 & -5 & 2 \\ 7 & 3 & 4 \\ 2 & 1 & 5 \end{vmatrix} = 2 \begin{vmatrix} 7 & 3 \\ 2 & 1 \end{vmatrix} - 4 \begin{vmatrix} 1 & -5 \\ 2 & 1 \end{vmatrix} + 5 \begin{vmatrix} 1 & -5 \\ 7 & 3 \end{vmatrix}
$$
$$
= 2 \cdot 1 - 4 \cdot 11 + 5 \cdot 38 = 148.
$$

As a check, using elements of the first row, we get

$$
1 \cdot \begin{vmatrix} 3 & 4 \\ 1 & 5 \end{vmatrix} + 5 \begin{vmatrix} 7 & 4 \\ 2 & 5 \end{vmatrix} + 2 \begin{vmatrix} 7 & 3 \\ 2 & 1 \end{vmatrix} = 11 + 135 + 2 = 148.
$$

The method of evaluating a determinant which we have described here is one form of Laplace's development of a determinant. If the determinant is of fourth order (or higher), using the Laplace development once gives us a set of determinants of order one less than we started with; then we use the Laplace development all over again to evaluate each of these, and so on until we get determinants of second order which we know how to evaluate.

A word of warning to anyone who has learned a special method of evaluating a third-order determinant by recopying columns to the right and multiplying along diagonals: this method *does not work* for fourth order (and higher).

4. SOME USEFUL THEOREMS ABOUT DETERMINANTS

We state these facts without proof; assuming the Laplace development, you can easily supply the proofs using the hints given in Problem 5.

1. If each element of *one* row (or *one* column) of a determinant is multiplied by a number k, the value of the determinant is multiplied by k.
2. The value of a determinant is zero if
   (a) all elements of one row (or column) are zero; or if
   (b) two rows (or two columns) are identical; or if
   (c) two rows (or two columns) are proportional.
3. If two rows (or two columns) of a determinant are interchanged, the value of the determinant changes sign.
4. The value of a determinant is unchanged if
   (a) rows are written as columns and columns as rows; or if
   (b) we add to each element of one row, k times the corresponding element of another row, where k is any number (and a similar statement for columns).

Let us look at a few examples of the use of these theorems.

Example 1. Find the equation of a plane through the three given points $(0, 0, 0)$, $(1, 2, 5)$, and $(2, -1, 0)$.

We shall verify that the answer in determinant form is

$$\begin{vmatrix} x & y & z & 1 \\ 0 & 0 & 0 & 1 \\ 1 & 2 & 5 & 1 \\ 2 & -1 & 0 & 1 \end{vmatrix} = 0.$$

By a Laplace development using elements of the first row, we would find that this is a linear equation in x, y, z; thus it represents a plane. We need now to show that the three given points are in the plane. Suppose $(x, y, z) = (0, 0, 0)$; then the first two rows of the determinant are identical and by Theorem 2b the determinant is zero. Similarly if the point (x, y, z) is either of the other given points, two rows of the determinant are identical and the determinant is zero, so all three points lie in the plane.

Example 2. Evaluate the determinant

$$D = \begin{vmatrix} 0 & a & -b \\ -a & 0 & c \\ b & -c & 0 \end{vmatrix}.$$

If we interchange rows and columns in D, then by Theorems 4a and 1 we have

$$D = \begin{vmatrix} 0 & -a & b \\ a & 0 & -c \\ -b & c & 0 \end{vmatrix} = (-1)^3 \begin{vmatrix} 0 & a & -b \\ -a & 0 & c \\ b & -c & 0 \end{vmatrix},$$

where in the last step we have factored -1 out of each column by Theorem 1. Thus we have $D = -D$, so $D = 0$.

Example 3. Use Theorem 4b to evaluate

$$D = \begin{vmatrix} 4 & 3 & 0 & -1 \\ 9 & 7 & 2 & -3 \\ 4 & 0 & 2 & -1 \\ 3 & -1 & 4 & 5 \end{vmatrix}.$$

The idea here is to get as many zeros as possible in some row or column in order to have fewer terms in the Laplace development. The secret of using this method efficiently is to start by locating an element equal to $+1$ or -1 (or obtain such an element by a preliminary combination of rows or columns). Then by taking appropriate multiples of the row (or column) containing the element 1, we can obtain zeros for all other elements in the column (or row) containing the element 1. Let us do this.

Multiply the last column by 4
and add to the first column:
$$D = \begin{vmatrix} 0 & 3 & 0 & -1 \\ -3 & 7 & 2 & -3 \\ 0 & 0 & 2 & -1 \\ 23 & -1 & 4 & 5 \end{vmatrix}.$$

Multiply the last column by 3
and add to the second column:
$$D = \begin{vmatrix} 0 & 0 & 0 & -1 \\ -3 & -2 & 2 & -3 \\ 0 & -3 & 2 & -1 \\ 23 & 14 & 4 & 5 \end{vmatrix}.$$

Expand by a Laplace development using elements of the first row:

$$D = 1 \cdot \begin{vmatrix} -3 & -2 & 2 \\ 0 & -3 & 2 \\ 23 & 14 & 4 \end{vmatrix} = 2 \cdot \begin{vmatrix} -3 & -2 & 1 \\ 0 & -3 & 1 \\ 23 & 14 & 2 \end{vmatrix}.$$

Multiply the last column by 3 and add to the second column:

$$D = 2 \cdot \begin{vmatrix} -3 & 1 & 1 \\ 0 & 0 & 1 \\ 23 & 20 & 2 \end{vmatrix} = -2 \cdot \begin{vmatrix} -3 & 1 \\ 23 & 20 \end{vmatrix} = -2(-60 - 23) = 166.$$

In using this theorem it is best to change only one row (or column) at a time. Otherwise you may make the mistake discussed in Problem 6. Also you should realize that the whole point of using Theorem 4b is to decrease the amount of arithmetic you have to do; therefore it does not make sense to take fractional multiples of a row or column since this makes the arithmetic complicated.

5. MATRICES

In the set of linear equations (1.1), the important numbers are the coefficients and the constant terms; we could use any letters, say p and q, instead of x and y for the unknowns. The equations (1.1) are then completely described by the following array of numbers:

(5.1)
$$\begin{pmatrix} 1 & 2 & 5 \\ 3 & -1 & 8 \end{pmatrix},$$

if we agree that the first column contains the coefficients of the first unknown in the two equations, the second column contains the coefficients of the second unknown, and the third column contains the constants on the right-hand sides of the equations. Such a rectangular array of numbers is called a *matrix* (plural *matrices*). Notice that matrices are not necessarily square (that is, same number of rows and columns) as determinants must be. Also a matrix does *not* have a *value* as a determinant always does; a matrix is simply a display or table of values. We do sometimes use a single letter, say A, to represent a matrix, but this is then a name of the matrix and not a value. This is much like using P to mean the point (2, 5) in the (x, y) plane; P is a label or name for the point, but P does not have a numerical value.

Let us look at another example. In analytic geometry you studied the "rotation equations"; these equations give the relation between the coordinates (x, y) of a point relative to the (x, y) axes and the coordinates (x', y') of the same point relative to rotated axes (x', y') (see Fig. 5.1). If the rotation angle is θ, the equations are

(5.2)
$$x' = x \cos \theta + y \sin \theta,$$
$$y' = -x \sin \theta + y \cos \theta.$$

All the important information is given by the matrix

(5.3)
$$A = \begin{pmatrix} \cos \theta & \sin \theta \\ -\sin \theta & \cos \theta \end{pmatrix},$$

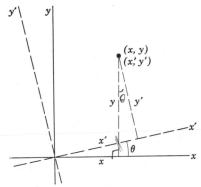

Figure 5.1

called a *rotation matrix*. Equations similar to (5.2) but in three dimensions have important applications to the study of the rotation of a rigid body such as a spinning top; instead of working with equations like (5.2), it is often convenient to work with a matrix like (5.3).

You might be tempted to try to find a value for the matrix A in (5.3) since it is square like a determinant. Sometimes we do want the value of the determinant which has the same elements as a given square matrix; in this case we would write for the matrix in (5.3)

(5.4) $\det A = \begin{vmatrix} \cos \theta & \sin \theta \\ -\sin \theta & \cos \theta \end{vmatrix} = \cos^2 \theta + \sin^2 \theta = 1.$

You should be careful to say that this is the value of the *determinant* of the matrix. Observe that the answer 1 does not contain as much information as the matrix (5.3); the value of the determinant is the same for all

θ, but the matrix tells us both the value of θ and the fact that (x', y'), and (x, y) are connected by a rotation of axes. The difference between a matrix and a determinant is somewhat parallel to the difference between a laboratory data sheet and a single numerical answer computed from it.

We have said that a matrix is a display of a set of quantities. Two matrices are equal, then, if and only if they are identical. The matrix equation

$$\begin{pmatrix} x & r & u \\ y & s & v \end{pmatrix} = \begin{pmatrix} 2 & 1 & -5 \\ 3 & -7i & 1-i \end{pmatrix}$$

is really the set of six equations

$$x = 2, \qquad y = 3, \qquad r = 1, \qquad s = -7i, \qquad u = -5, \qquad v = 1 - i.$$

(Compare the fact that the equation $z = x + iy = 2 - 3i$ in complex numbers is equivalent to the two real equations $x = 2$, $y = -3$.) In complicated problems involving many numbers or variables, it is often possible to save a great deal of writing by using a single matrix equation to replace a whole set of ordinary equations. Any time it is possible to so abbreviate the writing of a mathematical equation (like using a single letter for a complicated parenthesis) it not only saves time but often enables us to think more clearly.

To make it clear whether an array of elements is a determinant or a matrix, we use large parentheses [as in (5.1)] to inclose a matrix, instead of the vertical bars used for determinants. Other notations which are used are square brackets or double bars:

$$(5.5) \qquad \begin{pmatrix} 1 & 2 & 5 \\ 3 & -1 & 8 \end{pmatrix} = \begin{bmatrix} 1 & 2 & 5 \\ 3 & -1 & 8 \end{bmatrix} = \begin{Vmatrix} 1 & 2 & 5 \\ 3 & -1 & 8 \end{Vmatrix}.$$

Just as we did for determinants, we may call the elements of a matrix a_{ij}, where i is the row number and j is the column number of the element a_{ij}. Instead of A, we may use (a_{ij}) as an abbreviation for the matrix, just as we used $|a_{ij}|$ as an abbreviation for a determinant.

6. LINEAR DEPENDENCE AND LINEAR INDEPENDENCE

We want to discuss here some ideas which may help to clarify our work in the next section on solution of simultaneous equations. These same ideas will also prove useful in some of our later work (see Chapter 7).

The two sets of numbers

(6.1)
$$\{\ 4,\ -6, 14\},$$
$$\{10, -15, 35\},$$

are called *proportional* because

(6.2)
$$\frac{4}{10} = \frac{-6}{-15} = \frac{14}{35}.$$

We could also say that the two sets of numbers (6.1) are proportional if there are two numbers k and k' (not both zero) such that

(6.3)
$$4k + 10k' = 0,$$
$$-6k - 15k' = 0,$$
$$14k + 35k' = 0.$$

Equations (6.3) are true, for example, when $k = 5$ and $k' = -2$. In general, the two sets of numbers

(6.4)
$$\{a_1, a_2, a_3, \ldots a_n\},$$
$$\{b_1, b_2, b_3, \ldots b_n\},$$

are called proportional if there are numbers k and k' (not both zero) such that

(6.5)
$$ka_1 + k'b_1 = 0,$$
$$ka_2 + k'b_2 = 0,$$
$$\ldots$$
$$ka_n + k'b_n = 0.$$

Now consider the two linear functions

(6.6)
$$f_1 = 4x - 6y + 14z,$$
$$f_2 = 10x - 15y + 35z,$$

whose coefficients are the sets of numbers in (6.1). When the coefficients of two linear functions are proportional as in (6.6), we call the two functions *linearly dependent*. Using (6.3) and (6.6) we could also write

(6.7)
$$5f_1 - 2f_2 = 0.$$

More generally, for the two linear functions F_1 and F_2 whose coefficients are the sets of numbers (6.4), we could write using (6.5)

(6.8)
$$kF_1 + k'F_2 = 0.$$

The left-hand side of (6.8) is called a *linear combination* of the functions F_1 and F_2. We could then say that two functions are linearly dependent if there is a linear combination of them, $kF_1 + k'F_2$, which is identically zero with k and k' not both zero. By extending this idea, we say that any number of functions are *linearly dependent* if there is a linear combination of them

(6.9) $k_1F_1 + k_2F_2 + k_3F_3 + \cdots + k_nF_n$

which is identically zero with not all the k's equal to zero. For example, the functions

$$F_1 = 2x - y,$$
$$F_2 = x + z,$$
$$F_3 = 2x - 2y - 2z,$$

are linearly dependent since

$$2F_1 - 2F_2 - F_3 = 0.$$

If a set of functions is not linearly dependent, we call them *linearly independent*. For example, $x + y$ and $x - y$ are linearly independent (Problem 13).

   Notice that we have extended our original idea of proportionality of two sets of numbers. We could now return to that idea and generalize it by saying that several sets of constants, say

$$\{a_1, a_2, a_3, \ldots a_n\},$$
(6.10) $\{b_1, b_2, b_3, \ldots b_n\},$
$$\{c_1, c_2, c_3, \ldots c_n\},$$

are linearly dependent if there are numbers k, k', k'' (not all zero) such that

$$ka_1 + k'b_1 + k''c_1 = 0,$$
$$ka_2 + k'b_2 + k''c_2 = 0,$$
(6.11) $ka_3 + k'b_3 + k''c_3 = 0,$
$$\cdots$$
$$ka_n + k'b_n + k''c_n = 0.$$

The given sets of constants (6.10) might be, for example, the rows of a determinant or matrix, or each set of constants might be the components of a vector (see Chapter 5). Notice that the conditions for several linear functions to be linearly dependent are exactly the same as the conditions for the coefficients in the functions to be linearly dependent sets of numbers.

Although we have been particularly interested so far in linear functions, our definition [see (6.9)] of linear dependence of a set of functions holds for any kind of functions. In later work (Chapter 7) we shall be particularly interested in the linear dependence or independence of sets of functions of x. We say that a set of functions $f_1(x), f_2(x), \ldots, f_n(x)$ are linearly dependent if there is a linear combination of them which is identically zero, that is, if there are constants $k_1, k_2, \ldots, k_n$ (not all zero) such that

$$(6.12) \qquad k_1 f_1(x) + k_2 f_2(x) + \cdots + k_n f_n(x) \equiv 0.$$

For example, $\sin^2 x$ and $1 - \cos^2 x$ are linearly dependent since

$$\sin^2 x - (1 - \cos^2 x) = 0.$$

But $\sin x$ and $\cos x$ are linearly independent since there are no numbers k_1 and k_2 such that

$$k_1 \sin x + k_2 \cos x$$

is zero for *all* x (Problem 15).

It is convenient to have some method other than trial and error for finding out whether a set of functions of x is linearly independent. For this purpose we state the following theorem (without proof; see Problem 20, however):

If $f_1(x), f_2(x), \cdots, f_n(x)$ have continuous derivatives of order n, then a necessary and sufficient condition for them to be linearly dependent is that the determinant

$$(6.13) \qquad W = \begin{vmatrix} f_1(x) & f_2(x) & \cdots & f_n(x) \\ f_1'(x) & f_2'(x) & \cdots & f_n'(x) \\ f_1''(x) & f_2''(x) & \cdots & f_n''(x) \\ & & \cdots & \\ f_1^{(n-1)}(x) & f_2^{(n-1)}(x) & \cdots & f_n^{(n-1)}(x) \end{vmatrix}$$

be identically equal to zero. The determinant W is called the Wronskian determinant of the set of functions. As you can see from (6.13), the elements of the first row are just the given functions, the elements of the second row are their derivatives, the elements of the third row are the second derivatives, and so on until we have n rows; thus the elements of the last row are the $(n - 1)$st derivatives of the functions.

Example.   Find out whether the functions $\sin x$, $\cos x$, and $\sin (x - 1)$ are linearly dependent or linearly independent.

The Wronskian determinant is

$$W = \begin{vmatrix} \sin x & \cos x & \sin (x - 1) \\ \cos x & -\sin x & \cos (x - 1) \\ -\sin x & -\cos x & -\sin (x - 1) \end{vmatrix}.$$

Since the last row is just the negative of the first, $W = 0$ by Theorem 2c in Section 4. Thus the three given functions are linearly dependent.

7. RANK OF A MATRIX; SETS OF LINEAR EQUATIONS

The _rank_ of a matrix is the order (number of rows or of columns) of the largest nonzero determinant contained in the matrix. For example, if the matrix is square (n rows and n columns), we find the value of its determinant; if this value is not zero, the rank of the matrix is n; if the value of the determinant of the matrix is zero, we then evaluate the determinants of order $n - 1$ obtained by crossing off any one row and any one column of the matrix; if at least one of these determinants of order $n - 1$ is different from zero, the rank of the matrix is $n - 1$; if they are all zero, we proceed to evaluate determinants of order $n - 2$ obtained by crossing off two rows and two columns, and so on. For a matrix which is not square, say a 3 by 4 matrix as in (7.1),

$$(7.1) \qquad \begin{pmatrix} a_{11} & a_{12} & a_{13} & a_{14} \\ a_{21} & a_{22} & a_{23} & a_{24} \\ a_{31} & a_{32} & a_{33} & a_{34} \end{pmatrix},$$

we first consider the four 3 by 3 determinants we get by crossing off one column at a time. If at least one of these is different from zero, the rank of the matrix is 3. If _all_ the 3 by 3 determinants are zero, we next look at the 2 by 2 determinants obtained by crossing off one row and two columns (there are $3 \cdot 6 = 18$ of these). If at least one of these is different from zero, the rank of the matrix is 2. But if all the 2 by 2 determinants are zero, we look at the 1 by 1 determinants, that is, the elements themselves; unless all elements are zero, the rank is then 1. The rank of the matrix is zero if and only if all elements are zero.

When we are finding the rank of a matrix, it is convenient to know that the rank is not changed by

(a) multiplying or dividing a row (or column) by a constant, or by
(b) adding a multiple of one row to another row (and a similar statement for columns).

If we use these facts to obtain as many zero elements as we can, it is then much easier to find the rank of the matrix. Note carefully that when you do these operations you have a *different matrix*; matrices are equal *only* when they are *identical*. What we have said is that the new matrix has the *same rank* as the original. Thus you should simply tabulate the successive matrices as in the following example; you *must not* connect them by equality signs.

Example.   Find the rank of the matrix

$$\begin{pmatrix} 1 & 2 & 3 & 1 \\ 1 & 4 & 3 & 0 \\ 3 & 8 & 9 & 2 \end{pmatrix}.$$

Subtract twice the first column from the second; then three times the first column from the third; then the first column from the fourth:

$$\begin{pmatrix} 1 & 0 & 0 & 0 \\ 1 & 2 & 0 & -1 \\ 3 & 2 & 0 & -1 \end{pmatrix}.$$

Divide column 2 by 2; then add column 2 to column 4:

$$\begin{pmatrix} 1 & 0 & 0 & 0 \\ 1 & 1 & 0 & 0 \\ 3 & 1 & 0 & 0 \end{pmatrix}.$$

Now we can see that the rank is 2 because all 3 by 3 determinants are zero, and the 2 by 2 determinants are not all zero—for example, $\begin{vmatrix} 1 & 0 \\ 1 & 1 \end{vmatrix} = 1$.

Now let us see how we can use the idea of rank of a matrix to tell when we can solve a given set of linear equations. First we write the equations in the standard form for a Cramer's rule solution (terms involving the same unknowns in the various equations lined up under each other and the constants on the right-hand side). There are two matrices which are of interest here. One is the *matrix M of the coefficients,* which is simply the array of coefficients of the unknowns; it is a matrix of m rows and n columns if we have m equations and n unknowns. Another useful matrix is the *augmented matrix A*; it is a matrix of m rows and $n + 1$ columns [like (5.1)] containing both the coefficients of the unknowns and the column of constants. As examples, we give several sets of equations and their corresponding matrices M and A.

(7.2)
$$2x - 3y = 5,$$
$$-10x + 15y = 8,$$

$$M = \begin{pmatrix} 2 & -3 \\ -10 & 15 \end{pmatrix}, \qquad A = \begin{pmatrix} 2 & -3 & 5 \\ -10 & 15 & 8 \end{pmatrix}.$$

(7.3)
$$2x - 3y = 5,$$
$$-10x + 15y = -25,$$

$$M = \begin{pmatrix} 2 & -3 \\ -10 & 15 \end{pmatrix}, \qquad A = \begin{pmatrix} 2 & -3 & 5 \\ -10 & 15 & -25 \end{pmatrix}.$$

(7.4)
$$2x - 3y = 5,$$
$$2x + y = 1,$$

$$M = \begin{pmatrix} 2 & -3 \\ 2 & 1 \end{pmatrix}, \qquad A = \begin{pmatrix} 2 & -3 & 5 \\ 2 & 1 & 1 \end{pmatrix}.$$

(7.5)
$$x + y = 5,$$
$$x - 3y = 1,$$
$$2x + 2y = 10,$$

$$M = \begin{pmatrix} 1 & 1 \\ 1 & -3 \\ 2 & 2 \end{pmatrix}, \qquad A = \begin{pmatrix} 1 & 1 & 5 \\ 1 & -3 & 1 \\ 2 & 2 & 10 \end{pmatrix}.$$

(7.6)
$$x + y - z = 2,$$
$$x + y + z = 3,$$
$$2x + 2y = 5,$$

$$M = \begin{pmatrix} 1 & 1 & -1 \\ 1 & 1 & 1 \\ 2 & 2 & 0 \end{pmatrix}, \qquad A = \begin{pmatrix} 1 & 1 & -1 & 2 \\ 1 & 1 & 1 & 3 \\ 2 & 2 & 0 & 5 \end{pmatrix}.$$

In (7.2) observe that the functions on the left-hand sides of the equations are linearly dependent (the second is -5 times the first). If we multiply the first equation by -5, we get

$$-10x + 15y = -25.$$

This equation is inconsistent with the second equation in (7.2) so the equations (7.2) have no solution. Let us see what this means about the matrices

M and A. We have observed that the functions on the left-hand sides of the equations are linearly dependent; this means that the two rows in M are proportional. Then det $M = 0$, so the rank of M is 1. To find the rank of A, we consider the values of the three 2 by 2 determinants in A, namely

$$\begin{vmatrix} 2 & -3 \\ -10 & 15 \end{vmatrix}, \quad \begin{vmatrix} 2 & 5 \\ -10 & 8 \end{vmatrix}, \quad \begin{vmatrix} -3 & 5 \\ 15 & 8 \end{vmatrix}.$$

The first of these is just det M which is zero, but the other two determinants are not zero, so the rank of A is 2. Notice the relation between "rank $A >$ rank M" and "equations inconsistent." The 2 by 2 determinants in A which are different from zero (and so make A of rank 2) are the 2 by 2 determinants which contain the numbers 5 and 8 on the right-hand sides of (7.2). It is the fact that 8 *is not* -5 times 5, while $-10x + 15y$ *is* -5 times $2x - 3y$, that makes the equations inconsistent and also makes rank $A >$ rank M. For clarity we have discussed the simple case of two equations in two unknowns but our conclusion is true in general. The inequality "rank $A >$ rank M" always means that the functions on the left-hand sides of the equations are linearly dependent, but the same linear relation does not hold for the constants on the right-hand sides, so the equations are inconsistent.

Now consider the equations (7.3). The left-hand sides are the same as in (7.2), but this time there is the same linear dependence between the constants on the right-hand sides of the equations as between the functions on the left-hand sides, that is, the second equation is just -5 times the first equation. We call such equations dependent. We can assign any value to one of the unknowns and solve for the other. For example, in (7.3) we might solve for x in terms of y to get

$$x = \tfrac{1}{2}(5 + 3y).$$

Then y may have any value and this solution gives the corresponding value of x. Let us see how the ranks of M and A are related. As before, the rank of M is 1. You can easily verify that this time the rank of A is also 1. Thus the ranks of the two matrices are the same and we see that this fact is related to the consistency of the equations. [Recall that in (7.2), rank $A >$ rank M meant inconsistency.] The fact that the rank of M is less than the number of equations has meant in both these examples that the linear functions on the left-hand sides of the equations were related. The rank of M tells us the number of these functions which are linearly independent; if the equations are consistent, the rank of M (which is then the same as the rank of A) is the number of independent equations. Thus the rank of M is the number of unknowns which we can solve for (in terms of the other unknowns), if the equations are consistent, that is, if rank A = rank M.

For equations (7.4), we find rank A = rank M = 2. You can easily verify that the equations are consistent and linearly independent, so that we can solve for two unknowns (2 is the value of rank M and rank A). For equations (7.5), we find rank A = rank M = 2. The fact that the ranks of M and A are equal indicates that the equations are consistent; the fact that their rank is 2 indicates that there are two linearly independent equations, so we can solve for two unknowns. However, we must be careful to choose a linearly independent set of two equations to solve for x and y. This means in (7.5) to choose the first and second equations, or the second and third equations, but *not* the first and third equations which are linearly dependent. In the matrix M, the determinant $\begin{vmatrix} 1 & 1 \\ 2 & 2 \end{vmatrix}$ of the coefficients in the first and third equations is zero; such a zero determinant in M indicates linear dependence of the functions on the left-hand side of the corresponding equations. Thus when the number of given equations is greater than the rank of M (and rank M = rank A so that they are consistent), we must select a set of equations corresponding to a nonzero determinant in M to use in obtaining our solution. In (7.5), the fact that $\begin{vmatrix} 1 & 1 \\ 1 & -3 \end{vmatrix} \neq 0$ shows us that the first two equations are linearly independent and the fact that $\begin{vmatrix} 1 & -3 \\ 2 & 2 \end{vmatrix} \neq 0$ shows us that the second and third equations are linearly independent. We can use either of these pairs of equations to obtain a solution.

In (7.6), we find rank M = rank A = 2. This tells us that the equations are consistent (ranks equal) and that there are two linearly independent equations. Thus we can solve for two of the unknowns x, y, z in terms of a third. However, we still must be careful; it is not possible to solve (7.6) for just *any two* unknowns we like. Suppose we try putting $z = 0$ intending to solve for x and y. Then the resulting three equations $(x + y = 2, x + y = 3, 2x + 2y = 5)$ are inconsistent; this corresponds to the fact that the 2 by 2 determinants in M containing the coefficients of x and y are all equal to zero. Since M is of rank 2 there is at least one 2 by 2 determinant in it which is not zero. To obtain a solution of (7.6), we must locate such a nonzero determinant in M, for example, the determinant $\begin{vmatrix} 1 & -1 \\ 1 & 1 \end{vmatrix}$. We then note that the numbers in this determinant are the coefficients of y and z in the first two equations; thus we solve the first

[handwritten notes in top margin:]
$u + y - z = 2$
$-4 - y + z = -3$
$-2z = -1$
$z = \frac{1}{2}$

two equations for y and z in terms of x to get

$$z = \tfrac{1}{2}, \qquad y = \tfrac{1}{2}(5 - 2x).$$

You should verify that this solution satisfies the third equation and that you get the same results by solving the last two equations for y and z.

By considering some simple examples, we have tried to see what the ranks of the matrices M and A tell us about the solution of a set of linear equations. In general, consider a set of m equations in n unknowns, where we make no assumptions at all about whether there are more equations or fewer equations or the same number of equations as unknowns. Notice, to start with, that any determinant in M is also in A, so the rank of A cannot be less than the rank of M. Then

(7.7)

    (a) If rank $A >$ rank M, the equations are inconsistent and there is *no* solution.

    (b) If rank $A =$ rank $M = n$ (the number of unknowns), there is one solution, given by Cramer's rule; we must, however, solve n equations corresponding to a nonzero determinant in M in case there are more equations than unknowns.

    (c) If rank $A =$ rank $M = r < n$, there are an infinite number of solutions; we select r equations and r unknowns corresponding to a nonzero determinant in M, and solve these equations for these r unknowns in terms of the remaining $n - r$ unknowns.

We should consider separately a very important special case of (7.7). Suppose the constant terms in a set of n linear equations in n unknowns are all zero; the equations are then called *homogeneous*. Since there are no constant terms, the equations are all satisfied if we put every unknown equal to zero, but this is not a very interesting or useful solution; it is usually called the *trivial* solution. We then ask the question: When does such a set of equations have a nontrivial solution? Matrices M and A have the same rank (since A differs from M only by having an extra column of zeros). If this rank equals the number n of unknowns, then by (7.7b) there is one solution given by Cramer's rule. The Cramer's rule solution gives zero for every unknown, since each numerator contains the column of constant terms and these terms are all zero. For a nontrivial solution, we must then have rank $M < n$. Also if rank $M = r < n$, then by (7.7c) we can choose arbitrary values for $n - r$ unknowns, so these at least may be different from zero. Thus a necessary and sufficient condition for n homogeneous equations in n unknowns to have a nontrivial solution is that the determinant of the coefficients equal zero.

Example. For what values of λ do the following equations have nontrivial solutions for x and y?

$$(1 - \lambda)x - 2y = 0,$$
$$x - (1 + \lambda)y = 0.$$

We set the determinant of the coefficients equal to zero and solve for λ. We find

$$\begin{vmatrix} 1 - \lambda & -2 \\ 1 & -(1 + \lambda) \end{vmatrix} = -1 + \lambda^2 + 2 = 0,$$

$$\lambda^2 = -1, \qquad \lambda = \pm i.$$

For these values of λ, we get the following nontrivial solutions of the set of equations:

$$y = \tfrac{1}{2}(1 \pm i)x.$$

(See Problem 22 for further discussion of this kind of problem.)

8. OPERATIONS WITH MATRICES

In order to use matrices in practical problems, we need to know how to combine them, for example, how to add or multiply them, how to multiply a matrix by a number, etc. These are, of course, all questions of definition, but we shall show some applications which might suggest reasonable definitions; or alternatively, given the definitions, we shall see what applications we can make of the matrix operations.

Addition of matrices. In elementary physics we often consider problems like the following. In Fig. 8.1, given weights A, B, and C are connected by an inextensible cord and arranged as shown. Find the total force acting on each weight and determine the motion. We start by drawing a diagram of all the forces and listing in a table the components of all the forces acting on each weight.

	Force on	A	B	C
(8.1)	x-component	F_{xA}	F_{xB}	F_{xC}
	y-component	F_{yA}	F_{yB}	F_{yC}

This table is a matrix, that is, a display of a set of numbers which are the components of three forces. Suppose that originally the surfaces on which A and B rest were frictionless; then the matrix (8.1) contains no friction forces. Let us now change the problem to assume friction, and write

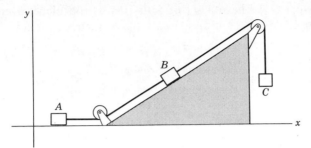

Figure 8.1

another matrix to show the friction forces (which we call F').

Friction force on	A	B	C
(8.2) x-component	F'_{xA}	F'_{xB}	0
y-component	0	F'_{yB}	0

(There are no friction forces on C, and the friction force on A has only an x-component.) The table (8.2) is another matrix. Now we want the components of the total force on each weight; to find these we must add the corresponding F and F' components for each weight. For example, the y-component of the total force on B is $F_{yB} + F'_{yB}$. We can write these components of total force in another table of values, or matrix:

Total force on	A	B	C
(8.3) x-component	$F_{xA} + F'_{xA}$	$F_{xB} + F'_{xB}$	F_{xC}
y-component	F_{yA}	$F_{yB} + F'_{yB}$	F_{yC}

Since we think of adding two forces to get the resultant force, we would like to write

$$(8.4) \quad \begin{pmatrix} F_{xA} & F_{xB} & F_{xC} \\ F_{yA} & F_{yB} & F_{yC} \end{pmatrix} + \begin{pmatrix} F'_{xA} & F'_{xB} & 0 \\ 0 & F'_{yB} & 0 \end{pmatrix}$$
$$= \begin{pmatrix} F_{xA} + F'_{xA} & F_{xB} + F'_{xB} & F_{xC} \\ F_{yA} & F_{yB} + F'_{yB} & F_{yC} \end{pmatrix}.$$

This is, in fact, the way matrices are added; thus matrices are useful in representing things which are added by components. More formally, the sum of two matrices A and B with elements a_{ij} and b_{ij} is a matrix with elements $a_{ij} + b_{ij}$; matrix addition is possible only if A and B have the same number of rows and the same number of columns. You should note carefully that determinants can*not* be added in this way; that is, the determinant of a sum of two square matrices is *not equal* to the sum of the determinants of the matrices.

Next suppose we have a set of four points in a plane given by their coordinates. We could list these in a table or matrix as follows:

(8.5)

Points	P_1	P_2	P_3	P_4
x coordinate	x_1	x_2	x_3	x_4
y coordinate	y_1	y_2	y_3	y_4

or

$$P = \begin{pmatrix} x_1 & x_2 & x_3 & x_4 \\ y_1 & y_2 & y_3 & y_4 \end{pmatrix}.$$

Here P is just an abbreviation for the matrix; it is neither a number nor a point. Let us consider the set of four points whose coordinates are twice the coordinates of the points of our given set. The matrix of the coordinates of the points in the new set is (8.6) below and we might reasonably abbreviate this by $2P$:

(8.6)

$$2P = \begin{pmatrix} 2x_1 & 2x_2 & 2x_3 & 2x_4 \\ 2y_1 & 2y_2 & 2y_3 & 2y_4 \end{pmatrix}.$$

This agrees, in fact, with the definition of multiplication of a matrix by a number; the product of a number k and a matrix with elements a_{ij} is a matrix whose elements are ka_{ij}. For integral k this agrees with our definition of addition of matrices if we think of k times a matrix as the sum of k identical matrices. Again note carefully that we do *not* find k times a determinant this way. To multiply a determinant by k, multiply *one* row (or *one* column) by k; to multiply a matrix by k, multiply *every element* by k.

Example. Given the matrices

$$A = \begin{pmatrix} 1 & 3 & -2 \\ 4 & 7 & 1 \end{pmatrix} \quad \text{and} \quad B = \begin{pmatrix} 2 & -1 & 4 \\ 3 & -7 & -2 \end{pmatrix}$$

find $A + B$, and $2A - B$.

Following the rules we have discussed, we find

$$A + B = \begin{pmatrix} 1+2 & 3-1 & -2+4 \\ 4+3 & 7-7 & 1-2 \end{pmatrix} = \begin{pmatrix} 3 & 2 & 2 \\ 7 & 0 & -1 \end{pmatrix},$$

$$2A - B = \begin{pmatrix} 2 \cdot 1 - 2 & 2 \cdot 3 + 1 & 2(-2) - 4 \\ 2 \cdot 4 - 3 & 2 \cdot 7 + 7 & 2 \cdot 1 + 2 \end{pmatrix}$$

$$= \begin{pmatrix} 0 & 7 & -8 \\ 5 & 21 & 4 \end{pmatrix}.$$

Multiplication of matrices. Let us start by defining the product of two matrices and then see what use we can make of the process. Here is a simple example to show what is meant by the product $AB = C$ of two matrices A and B:

$$(8.7) \qquad AB = \begin{pmatrix} a & b \\ c & d \end{pmatrix} \begin{pmatrix} e & f \\ g & h \end{pmatrix} = \begin{pmatrix} ae + bg & af + bh \\ ce + dg & cf + dh \end{pmatrix} = C.$$

Observe that in the product matrix C, the element in the first row and first column is obtained by multiplying each element of the first row in A times the corresponding element in the first column of B and adding the results. This is referred to as "<u>row times column</u>" multiplication; when we compute $ae + bg$, we say that we have "multiplied the first row of A times the first column of B." Next examine the element $af + bh$ in the first row and second column of C; it is the "first row of A times the second column of B." Similarly, $ce + dg$ in the second row and first column of C is the "second row of A times the first column of B," and $cf + dh$ in the second row and second column of C is the "second row of A times the second column of B." Thus all the elements of C may be obtained by using the following simple rule:

The element in row i and column j of the product matrix AB is equal to row i of A times column j of B.

It is not necessary for matrices to be square in order for us to multiply them. Consider the following example.

Example 1. Find the product of A and B if

$$A = \begin{pmatrix} 4 & 2 \\ -3 & 1 \end{pmatrix} \qquad B = \begin{pmatrix} 1 & 5 & 3 \\ 2 & 7 & -4 \end{pmatrix}.$$

Following the rule we have stated, we get

$$AB = \begin{pmatrix} 4 & 2 \\ -3 & 1 \end{pmatrix} \begin{pmatrix} 1 & 5 & 3 \\ 2 & 7 & -4 \end{pmatrix}$$

$$= \begin{pmatrix} 4 \cdot 1 + 2 \cdot 2 & 4 \cdot 5 + 2 \cdot 7 & 4 \cdot 3 + 2(-4) \\ -3 \cdot 1 + 1 \cdot 2 & -3 \cdot 5 + 1 \cdot 7 & -3 \cdot 3 + 1(-4) \end{pmatrix}$$

$$= \begin{pmatrix} 8 & 34 & 4 \\ -1 & -8 & -13 \end{pmatrix}.$$

Notice that the third column in B caused us no difficulty in following our rule; we simply multiplied each row of A times the third column of B

to obtain the elements in the third column of AB. But suppose we tried to find the product BA. In B a row contains three elements, while in A a column contains only two; thus we are not able to apply our "row times column" method. Whenever this happens, we say that B is *not conformable* with respect to A, and the product BA is not defined (that is, it is meaningless and we do not use it). The product AB (in that order) can be found if and only if the number of elements in a row of A equals the number of elements in a column of B; the matrices A, B in that order are then called *conformable*. (Observe that the number of rows in A and of columns in B have nothing to do with the question of whether we can find AB or not.)

Example 2.   Find AB and BA, given

$$A = \begin{pmatrix} 3 & -1 \\ -4 & 2 \end{pmatrix}, \qquad B = \begin{pmatrix} 5 & 2 \\ -7 & 3 \end{pmatrix}.$$

Note that here the matrices are conformable in both orders, so we can find both AB and BA.

$$AB = \begin{pmatrix} 3 & -1 \\ -4 & 2 \end{pmatrix}\begin{pmatrix} 5 & 2 \\ -7 & 3 \end{pmatrix}$$

$$= \begin{pmatrix} 3\cdot 5 - 1(-7) & 3\cdot 2 - 1\cdot 3 \\ -4\cdot 5 + 2(-7) & -4\cdot 2 + 2\cdot 3 \end{pmatrix} = \begin{pmatrix} 22 & 3 \\ -34 & -2 \end{pmatrix}.$$

$$BA = \begin{pmatrix} 5 & 2 \\ -7 & 3 \end{pmatrix}\begin{pmatrix} 3 & -1 \\ -4 & 2 \end{pmatrix}$$

$$= \begin{pmatrix} 5\cdot 3 + 2(-4) & 5(-1) + 2\cdot 2 \\ -7\cdot 3 + 3(-4) & -7(-1) + 3\cdot 2 \end{pmatrix} = \begin{pmatrix} 7 & -1 \\ -33 & 13 \end{pmatrix}.$$

You may be surprised here to find that AB is *not* the same as BA. In algebra you studied the associative laws for addition and multiplication $[a + (b + c) = (a + b) + c, a \cdot (bc) = (ab) \cdot c]$, the commutative laws $[a + b = b + a, ab = ba]$, and the distributive law $[a(b + c) = ab + ac]$. You may very well have thought these laws were obvious simply because they were so familiar to you for ordinary numbers. But whenever we introduce a new mathematical entity and define operations for it similar to addition and multiplication, it may not be obvious, and it is very important to know, whether or not the operations obey these familiar laws. It can be shown (by using our definitions of matrix addition and multiplication) that all the laws stated above hold for matrix operations *except* the commutative law for multiplication (assuming, of course, that the matrices have the right number of rows and columns so that the indicated operations can be performed). We say that matrix multiplication is not *commutative*, or that, in general, matrices do not *commute* under multiplication. (Of course, two particular matrices may happen to commute.) Thus we can add, subtract, and multiply letters representing matrices just as if they represented ordinary numbers except that we must not rearrange the order of factors in multiplication. Because of this, the distributive law now becomes two laws: $A(B + C) = AB + AC$ and $(B + C)A = BA + CA$.

It can be shown (see, for example, Bôcher, p. 27) that if A and B are square matrices of the same order, then

$$(8.8) \qquad \det(AB) = (\det A) \cdot (\det B).$$

Thus we may, if we like, multiply determinants in the same way we multiply matrices.

Application of matrix multiplication. Consider the rotation equations (5.2); we can write these very simply in matrix notation. The coordinates x, y can be written as a matrix of one row and two columns $(x \quad y)$ called a *row matrix*, or as a matrix of two rows and one column called a column matrix $\begin{pmatrix} x \\ y \end{pmatrix}$. We have already written the rotation matrix A in (5.3). The matrices A and $\begin{pmatrix} x \\ y \end{pmatrix}$ are conformable in that order. Multiplying them, we get

$$(8.9) \qquad \begin{pmatrix} \cos\theta & \sin\theta \\ -\sin\theta & \cos\theta \end{pmatrix} \begin{pmatrix} x \\ y \end{pmatrix} = \begin{pmatrix} x\cos\theta + y\sin\theta \\ -x\sin\theta + y\cos\theta \end{pmatrix}.$$

Recall that two matrices are equal if and only if corresponding elements are equal. Thus the matrix equation

$$(8.10) \qquad \begin{pmatrix} x' \\ y' \end{pmatrix} = \begin{pmatrix} x\cos\theta + y\sin\theta \\ -x\sin\theta + y\cos\theta \end{pmatrix}$$

is equivalent to the rotation equations (5.2). From (8.9) and (8.10) we have

$$(8.11) \qquad \begin{pmatrix} x' \\ y' \end{pmatrix} = \begin{pmatrix} \cos\theta & \sin\theta \\ -\sin\theta & \cos\theta \end{pmatrix} \begin{pmatrix} x \\ y \end{pmatrix}.$$

If we use A to represent the rotation matrix (5.3), and use r to represent the matrix $\begin{pmatrix} x \\ y \end{pmatrix}$ and r' to represent the matrix $\begin{pmatrix} x' \\ y' \end{pmatrix}$, we can write (8.11) in the simple form

$$(8.12) \qquad r' = Ar.$$

This is another example of the fact discussed in Section 5, that matrix notation makes it possible for us to write a set of equations in abbreviated form as a single matrix equation.

Equations (5.2) and the corresponding matrix equation (8.12) correspond to a rotation of axes (x, y) to (x', y') through an angle θ. Consider a further rotation from (x', y') to (x'', y'') through an angle ϕ. The rotation equations are

(8.13)
$$x'' = x' \cos \phi + y' \sin \phi,$$
$$y'' = -x' \sin \phi + y' \cos \phi,$$

or using matrix notation corresponding to (8.12)

(8.14)
$$r'' = Br',$$

where

$$r'' = \begin{pmatrix} x'' \\ y'' \end{pmatrix}, \qquad B = \begin{pmatrix} \cos \phi & \sin \phi \\ -\sin \phi & \cos \phi \end{pmatrix}, \qquad r' = \begin{pmatrix} x' \\ y' \end{pmatrix}.$$

The net result of these two rotations is a rotation through the angle $\theta + \phi$, and we would expect x'', y'' and x, y, to satisfy the equations

(8.15)
$$x'' = x \cos (\theta + \phi) + y \sin (\theta + \phi),$$
$$y'' = -x \sin (\theta + \phi) + y \cos (\theta + \phi).$$

[A direct substitution of (5.2) into (8.13) justifies our expectations! See Problem 29.] Again using matrix notation, we write (8.15) as

(8.16)
$$r'' = Cr,$$

where

$$r'' = \begin{pmatrix} x'' \\ y'' \end{pmatrix}, \qquad C = \begin{pmatrix} \cos (\theta + \phi) & \sin (\theta + \phi) \\ -\sin (\theta + \phi) & \cos (\theta + \phi) \end{pmatrix}, \qquad r = \begin{pmatrix} x \\ y \end{pmatrix}.$$

If we substitute (8.12) into (8.14), we get

(8.17)
$$r'' = B(Ar) = (BA)r.$$

(The last step is correct because matrix multiplication is associative.) Comparing (8.17) and (8.16), we see that we might expect the matrix C to be equal to the matrix product BA; let us check this. We write the matrix equation $BA = C$ with the elements in C expanded by the trigonometric addition formulas:

(8.18)
$$\begin{pmatrix} \cos \phi & \sin \phi \\ -\sin \phi & \cos \phi \end{pmatrix} \begin{pmatrix} \cos \theta & \sin \theta \\ -\sin \theta & \cos \theta \end{pmatrix}$$
$$= \begin{pmatrix} \cos \phi \cos \theta - \sin \phi \sin \theta & \cos \phi \sin \theta + \sin \phi \cos \theta \\ -\sin \phi \cos \theta - \cos \phi \sin \theta & -\sin \phi \sin \theta + \cos \phi \cos \theta \end{pmatrix}.$$

Observe that the elements in C are exactly what they should be according to our "row times column" rule. Thus the way in which we have defined matrix multiplication makes it possible for us to combine the matrix equations (8.12) and (8.14) to get (8.17), treating the letters as if they represented ordinary numbers (except that we must not change the order of the factors). The product matrix BA then correctly represents the rotation matrix for the resultant rotation through an angle $(\theta + \phi)$.

We have discussed this example in detail because it was a simple problem for which we knew the answer (that is, the C matrix) so that we could check our results. However, in a more general problem we might not be dealing with a rotation of axes but simply with a linear change of variables, say

$$x' = ax + by,$$

$$y' = cx + dy,$$

where a, b, c, d are given constants. Similarly, x'' and y'' might be another pair of variables given as linear functions of x' and y', and perhaps we might have even another set of variables x''', y''' given in terms of x'', y''. Then instead of making the algebraic substitutions in the successive sets of equations, we could find the final set of variables in terms of x, y by writing the matrix equations [like (8.12), (8.14), (8.16), (8.17)], and multiplying the matrices as in (8.18). (See Problems 30 to 33.) The same method can be used for any number of variables, say x, y, z in three dimensions; this method is, for example, very useful in working with three-dimensional rotations.

As another example of the use of matrix multiplication, let us write the following set of equations in matrix notation.

$$2x + 3y - z = -3,$$
(8.19)
$$x + y + z = 2,$$
$$-x + y + 2z = 2.$$

Using letters to represent the matrices,

$$M = \begin{pmatrix} 2 & 3 & -1 \\ 1 & 1 & 1 \\ -1 & 1 & 2 \end{pmatrix}, \quad r = \begin{pmatrix} x \\ y \\ z \end{pmatrix}, \quad k = \begin{pmatrix} -3 \\ 2 \\ 2 \end{pmatrix},$$

we can write (8.19) as

(8.20) $Mr = k.$

Now if (8.20) were an ordinary algebraic equation, we would solve it for r to get

$$(8.21) \qquad\qquad r = M^{-1}k.$$

Since M is a matrix, we can do this only if we can give a meaning to M^{-1} which will make (8.21) correct. We shall see how to do this in the next section, and so find a way of solving a consistent set of simultaneous equations using matrix notation. Notice that equations (8.20) could represent a system of any number of equations in any number of unknowns. The matrix M is just the matrix of the coefficients which we used in Section 7. The matrix r is a column matrix of the unknowns, and the matrix k is a column matrix of the constants.

9. SPECIAL MATRICES

There is a good deal of special terminology which is convenient to use when we work with matrices. We shall define a number of these special terms in this section.

A _unit matrix_ is a square matrix (of whatever order is needed in the problem we are doing) which has every element of the main diagonal equal to 1 and all other elements equal to 0. For example,

$$(9.1) \qquad\qquad \begin{pmatrix} 1 & 0 & 0 \\ 0 & 1 & 0 \\ 0 & 0 & 1 \end{pmatrix}$$

is a unit matrix of order three. A unit matrix is called 1 or U or I or E in various books. (See Problem 35.)

The _Kronecker_ δ is defined by

$$(9.2) \qquad\qquad \delta_{ij} = \begin{cases} 1, & \text{if } i = j, \\ 0, & \text{if } i \neq j. \end{cases}$$

For example, $\delta_{11} = 1$, $\delta_{12} = 0$, $\delta_{22} = 1$, $\delta_{31} = 0$, etc. In this notation a unit matrix is one whose elements are δ_{ij} and we can write

$$(9.3) \qquad\qquad U = (\delta_{ij}).$$

The Kronecker δ notation is useful for other purposes. For example, since (for positive integers m and n)

$$(9.4) \qquad \int_{-\pi}^{\pi} \cos nx \cos mx \, dx = \begin{cases} \pi & \text{if } m = n, \\ 0 & \text{if } m \neq n, \end{cases}$$

we can write

(9.5) $$\int_{-\pi}^{\pi} \cos nx \cos mx \, dx = \pi \cdot \delta_{nm}.$$

This is the same as (9.4) because $\delta_{nm} = 0$ if $m \neq n$, and $\delta_{mn} = 1$ if $m = n$.

A _zero_ or _null_ matrix means one with all its elements equal to zero; it is often abbreviated by 0, but we must be careful about this as the following example shows.

Example.   Find AB and BA given

(9.6) $$A = \begin{pmatrix} 1 & 2 \\ 3 & 6 \end{pmatrix}, \qquad B = \begin{pmatrix} 10 & 4 \\ -5 & -2 \end{pmatrix}.$$

Multiplying the matrices in both orders, we find

$$AB = \begin{pmatrix} 1 & 2 \\ 3 & 6 \end{pmatrix}\begin{pmatrix} 10 & 4 \\ -5 & -2 \end{pmatrix}$$

$$= \begin{pmatrix} 10 + 2(-5) & 4 + 2(-2) \\ 3 \cdot 10 + 6(-5) & 12 + 6(-2) \end{pmatrix} = \begin{pmatrix} 0 & 0 \\ 0 & 0 \end{pmatrix},$$

$$BA = \begin{pmatrix} 10 & 4 \\ -5 & -2 \end{pmatrix}\begin{pmatrix} 1 & 2 \\ 3 & 6 \end{pmatrix} = \begin{pmatrix} 22 & 44 \\ -11 & -22 \end{pmatrix}.$$

Again we have an example showing that multiplication of matrices is not commutative. But there is another surprising result here if we call the null matrix 0; we have $AB = 0$, but neither A nor B is zero. Thus you must not conclude from the fact that AB equals the zero matrix that one of the two matrices A or B is the zero matrix. If we write B as a difference of two matrices, say

$$B = \begin{pmatrix} 7 & 6 \\ 2 & 3 \end{pmatrix} - \begin{pmatrix} -3 & 2 \\ 7 & 5 \end{pmatrix} = C - D,$$

then from $AB = 0$ we have

(9.7) $A(C - D) = 0$ or $AC = AD.$

(Or you can get this result directly by finding AC and AD.) Now we have $AC = AD$ with $A \neq 0$, but $C \neq D$. Thus the familiar cancellation law for numbers does not hold for matrices. We shall consider later the general question of division by a matrix.

A square matrix whose determinant is zero is called _singular;_ all non-square matrices are also called _singular._

There are several special matrices which are related to a given matrix A. We outline in (9.8) what these matrices are called, what notations are used for them, and how we get them from A. The notation $|A|$ or det A means the determinant of the matrix A; whenever it is used, A is understood to be square. The cofactor of an element in a square matrix A means exactly the same thing as the cofactor of that element in the determinant of A.

(9.8)

Name of matrix	Notations for it	How to get it from A
Transpose of A, or A transpose.	A' or $\tilde{A}$ or A^{T} or A^t	Interchange rows and columns in A.
Complex conjugate of A.	$\bar{A}$ or A^*	Take the complex conjugate of each element.
Transpose conjugate, or associate, or Hermitian conjugate; also called adjoint in quantum mechanics and differential equations, but note that the term adjoint has another meaning in algebra—see below.	$\bar{A}'$ or $\tilde{A}^*$, etc., or $A^\dagger$ (read A dagger)	Take the complex conjugate of each element and transpose (that is, interchange rows and columns).
Adjoint or adjugate of A (A must be square).	adj A or $\hat{A}$	Replace each element by its cofactor and then transpose.
Reciprocal or inverse of A (A must *not* be singular).	A^{-1}	Divide each element of adj A by det A.

Example. To illustrate these definitions, we shall calculate each of the matrices listed in (9.8) given

$$A = \begin{pmatrix} 1 & 0 & 5i \\ -2i & 2 & 0 \\ 1 & 1+i & 0 \end{pmatrix}.$$

We first find det $A = 5i(-2i + 2 - 2) = 10$. Then following the instructions in column three of (9.8), we find

(handwritten annotation: transpose)
(handwritten annotation: complex conjugate)

$$A' = \begin{pmatrix} 1 & -2i & 1 \\ 0 & 2 & 1+i \\ 5i & 0 & 0 \end{pmatrix}, \qquad \bar{A} = \begin{pmatrix} 1 & 0 & -5i \\ 2i & 2 & 0 \\ 1 & 1-i & 0 \end{pmatrix},$$

$$A^{\dagger} = \begin{pmatrix} 1 & 2i & 1 \\ 0 & 2 & 1-i \\ -5i & 0 & 0 \end{pmatrix},$$

(handwritten annotation: transpose conjugate)

(handwritten annotation: adjoint adjugate)

adj A = transpose of

(handwritten annotation: $\begin{vmatrix} 2 & 0 \\ 1-i & 0 \end{vmatrix}$)

$$\begin{pmatrix} \begin{vmatrix} 2 & 1-i \\ 0 & 0 \end{vmatrix} & \begin{vmatrix} 0 & 1-i \\ 0 & 0 \end{vmatrix} & \begin{vmatrix} -2i & 2 \\ 1 & 1+i \end{vmatrix} \\[6pt] -\begin{vmatrix} 0 & 5i \\ 1+i & 0 \end{vmatrix} & \begin{vmatrix} 1 & 5i \\ 1 & 0 \end{vmatrix} & -\begin{vmatrix} 1 & 0 \\ 1 & 1+i \end{vmatrix} \\[6pt] \begin{vmatrix} 0 & 5i \\ 2 & 0 \end{vmatrix} & -\begin{vmatrix} 1 & 5i \\ -2i & 0 \end{vmatrix} & \begin{vmatrix} 1 & 0 \\ -2i & 2 \end{vmatrix} \end{pmatrix}$$

$$= \begin{pmatrix} 0 & 5i-5 & -10i \\ 0 & -5i & 10 \\ -2i & -1-i & 2 \end{pmatrix},$$

$$A^{-1} = \frac{1}{\det A}\,\text{adj }A = \begin{pmatrix} 0 & \tfrac{1}{2}(i-1) & -i \\ 0 & -\tfrac{1}{2}i & 1 \\ -\tfrac{1}{5}i & -\tfrac{1}{10}(1+i) & \tfrac{1}{5} \end{pmatrix}.$$

You can show (Problem 41) that the reciprocal of A has the properties that its name implies, namely that

(9.9) $AA^{-1} = A^{-1}A = U.$

We can now say when division by a matrix is possible. Dividing by a matrix A means, by definition, multiplying by A^{-1}; therefore we can divide by A only if A has an inverse A^{-1}, that is, if A is square and det $A \neq 0$. You can see now why we could not cancel A in (9.7); from (9.6), det $A = 0$ in (9.7) so A^{-1} is meaningless. This corresponds to the fact that division by zero is not defined for numbers.

Example. Let us now see how to use the idea of the inverse of a matrix to solve the equations (8.19) which we wrote in matrix form (8.20). We first find the inverse of M.

$$\det M = \begin{vmatrix} 2 & 3 & -1 \\ 1 & 1 & 1 \\ -1 & 1 & 2 \end{vmatrix} = \begin{vmatrix} 2 & 3 & -1 \\ 3 & 4 & 0 \\ 3 & 7 & 0 \end{vmatrix} = -1(9) = -9,$$

$$\text{adj } M = \text{transpose of } \begin{pmatrix} 1 & -3 & 2 \\ -7 & 3 & -5 \\ 4 & -3 & -1 \end{pmatrix},$$

(9.10)
$$M^{-1} = -\tfrac{1}{9} \begin{pmatrix} 1 & -7 & 4 \\ -3 & 3 & -3 \\ 2 & -5 & -1 \end{pmatrix}.$$

Now if we multiply both sides of (8.20) by M^{-1}, we get

$$M^{-1}Mr = M^{-1}k.$$

Since $M^{-1}M$ is the unit matrix, and the unit matrix times r is r, we get (8.21)

(9.11)
$$r = M^{-1}k.$$

Notice carefully that we must multiply M^{-1} times k in that order since matrix multiplication is not commutative. From (9.10) and (9.11), we have

$$r = M^{-1}k = -\tfrac{1}{9} \begin{pmatrix} 1 & -7 & 4 \\ -3 & 3 & -3 \\ 2 & -5 & -1 \end{pmatrix} \begin{pmatrix} -3 \\ 2 \\ 2 \end{pmatrix}$$

$$= -\tfrac{1}{9} \begin{pmatrix} -9 \\ 9 \\ -18 \end{pmatrix} = \begin{pmatrix} 1 \\ -1 \\ 2 \end{pmatrix} = \begin{pmatrix} x \\ y \\ z \end{pmatrix}.$$

Thus we find the solution $x = 1$, $y = -1$, $z = 2$.

The amount of numerical calculation involved in solving (8.19) by this method is about the same as for a Cramer's rule solution. However, this example illustrates a much more important point than just another method of solving linear equations. We see here an example of the general fact that matrices make it possible to write complicated problems (here a set of many equations in many unknowns) in a simple way (equation 8.20), and it may be easy to see from the simple form how to solve the problem [equation (8.21) or (9.11)].

There is another set of names for special types of matrices. We list these and their definitions for reference.

(9.12)

A matrix is called	if it satisfies the equation
symmetric	$A = A'$ (matrix = its transpose)
skew-symmetric or antisymmetric	$A = -A'$
real	$A = \bar{A}$
pure imaginary	$A = -\bar{A}$
orthogonal	$AA' = 1$, that is, $A' = A^{-1}$ (inverse = transpose)
Hermitian	$A = \bar{A}' = A^\dagger$ (matrix = its transpose conjugate)
unitary	$AA^\dagger = 1$, that is, $A^\dagger = A^{-1}$ (inverse = transpose conjugate)

(See the problems for examples of the use of these terms.)

REFERENCES

For discussion of determinants and solution of equations by determinants, see college algebra textbooks. For detailed and abstract discussions of matrices, see books on matrices, linear algebra, or modern algebra. For a shorter and simpler discussion, see a general book which has a chapter on matrices. (References at the end of the book containing any of the material of Chapter 3 are identified by a [3] after the listing.)

PROBLEMS

1. Solve the following sets of linear equations by determinants.

(a) $\begin{cases} 2x + y = 4 \\ 7x - 2y = 3 \end{cases}$

(b) $\begin{cases} x - 2y + 13 = 0 \\ y - 4x = 17 \end{cases}$

(c) $\begin{cases} 2x + z = 7 \\ y + 5z = 4 \\ 4x + 6y - 5z = 1 \end{cases}$

(d) $\begin{cases} 14 - x + 5y = 0 \\ 7z + 2x - 15 = 0 \\ x - y + 3z = 9 \end{cases}$

(e) $\begin{cases} x - 2y = 4 \\ 2z + w = 5 \\ w + y = 2 \\ 3x - 5z = 1 \end{cases}$

(f) $\begin{cases} 2s + r = 1 \\ s - p = 6 \\ 3 - q + 2r = 0 \\ r - 2s + 3q = 0 \end{cases}$

2. Evaluate each of the following determinants:

    (i) using the Laplace development;

    (ii) using the theorems of Section 4, especially Theorem 4b, to simplify the determinant before applying the Laplace development.

(a) $\begin{vmatrix} -2 & 3 & 4 \\ 3 & 4 & -2 \\ 5 & 6 & -3 \end{vmatrix}$

(b) $\begin{vmatrix} 7 & 0 & 1 & -3 & 5 \\ 2 & -1 & 0 & 1 & 4 \\ 7 & -3 & 2 & -1 & 4 \\ 8 & 6 & -2 & -7 & 4 \\ 1 & 3 & -5 & 7 & 5 \end{vmatrix}$

(c) $\begin{vmatrix} 5 & 17 & 3 \\ 2 & 4 & -3 \\ 11 & 0 & 2 \end{vmatrix}$

(d) $\begin{vmatrix} 1 & 1 & 1 & 1 \\ 1 & 2 & 3 & 4 \\ 1 & 3 & 6 & 10 \\ 1 & 4 & 10 & 20 \end{vmatrix}$

(e) $\begin{vmatrix} -2 & 4 & 7 & 3 \\ 8 & 2 & -9 & 5 \\ -4 & 6 & 8 & 4 \\ 2 & -9 & 3 & 8 \end{vmatrix}$

3. Write a set of linear equations for each of the following problems and solve them using determinants.

    (a) An object composed of x gm of silver (of specific gravity 10) and y gm of gold (of specific gravity 20) weighs 120 gm in air and 109 gm in water. Find x and y.

    (b) An object composed of x gm of lead (specific gravity 11) and y gm of tin (specific gravity 7) weighs 82 gm in air and 77 gm in oil of specific gravity $\frac{1}{2}$. Find x and y.

    (c) An object composed of x gm of potassium (specific gravity 0.8) and y gm of cesium (specific gravity 2.0) cannot be weighed in air or water because it would react with either. However, it weighs 86 gm in oil of specific gravity 0.6 and 124 gm in oil of specific gravity 0.4. Find x and y.

    (d) The manager of a business is to receive a bonus amounting to 20% of the profits which remain after deducting the business's income tax (but not the manager's bonus) from the gross profits. The income tax is 30% of the profits which remain after deducting the manager's bonus (but, as required by law, not the tax) from the gross profits. The gross profits before deducting either bonus or tax are $47,000. Find the bonus and the tax.

    (e) Determine the unknown weights x, y, and z if a weightless bar of length 11 ft with fulcrum 5 ft from one end balances in all three of the indicated positions.

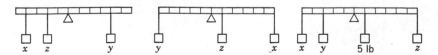

(f) The half-life of a radioactive substance is the time it takes for half of it to decay. Suppose a radioactive sample consists of components A and B of half-lives 2 hr and 3 hr respectively. Assume that the decay products are gases that escape at once. At the end of 12 hr, the sample weighs 56 gm and at the end of 18 hr it weighs 12 gm. Find the amounts of A and B that were originally present.

4. Kirchhoff's laws for electrical networks such as those shown in the diagrams are: (1) At any junction the sum of all the currents flowing toward the junction is equal to the sum of all the currents flowing away. (2) The algebraic sum of all the changes in potential around any closed loop is zero. (To apply this, go around each loop listing as increases in potential: voltages when you go through a battery from $-$ to $+$, and IR values when you go through a

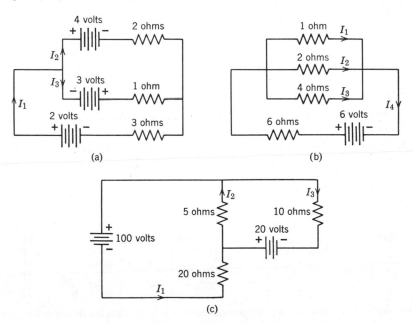

(a)   (b)

(c)

resistance R *against* the current I; decreases in potential correspond to the opposite directions.) *Comment:* You should not waste any time trying to decide which direction currents "really" flow. Just mark an arrow for each I, (as shown, say), and write and solve the Kirchhoff's law equations assuming that the currents "really" flow as you have marked them. Then any currents which "really" flow opposite to the direction you have marked will come out negative.

5. (a) In Section 4, prove Theorems 1, 2a, 3, 4a, simply by using the Laplace development.

(b) Prove Theorem 2b by using Theorem 3, and Theorem 2c by using Theorems 1 and 3.

(c) Show that if each element of one row (or column) of a determinant is the sum of two terms, the determinant can be written as a sum of two determinants; for example,

$$\begin{vmatrix} a_{11} & a_{12}+b_{12} & a_{13} \\ a_{21} & a_{22}+b_{22} & a_{23} \\ a_{31} & a_{32}+b_{32} & a_{33} \end{vmatrix} = \begin{vmatrix} a_{11} & a_{12} & a_{13} \\ a_{21} & a_{22} & a_{23} \\ a_{31} & a_{32} & a_{33} \end{vmatrix} + \begin{vmatrix} a_{11} & b_{12} & a_{13} \\ a_{21} & b_{22} & a_{23} \\ a_{31} & b_{32} & a_{33} \end{vmatrix}.$$

Use this fact to prove Theorem 4b.

6. What is wrong with the following argument? "If we add the first row of a determinant to the second row and the second row to the first row, then the first two rows of the determinant are identical, and the value of the determinant is zero. Therefore all determinants have the value zero."

7. Use the theorems of Section 4 to prove that

$$\begin{vmatrix} 1 & a & bc \\ 1 & b & ac \\ 1 & c & ab \end{vmatrix} = \begin{vmatrix} 1 & a & a^2 \\ 1 & b & b^2 \\ 1 & c & c^2 \end{vmatrix} = (b-a)(c-a)(c-b).$$

Do not prove this by evaluating the determinants.

8. Show that if, in using the Laplace development, you accidentally multiply the elements of one row by the cofactors of another row, you get zero.

9. Evaluate each of the following determinants. *Hint:* You should have to do very little work.

(a)
$$\begin{vmatrix} 1 & 1 & 1 & 1 & 1 & 1 \\ 0 & 1 & 1 & 1 & 1 & 1 \\ 0 & 0 & 1 & 1 & 1 & 1 \\ 0 & 0 & 0 & 1 & 1 & 1 \\ 0 & 0 & 0 & 0 & 1 & 1 \\ 0 & 0 & 0 & 0 & 0 & 1 \end{vmatrix}$$

(b)
$$\begin{vmatrix} 0 & 5 & -3 & -4 & 1 \\ -5 & 0 & 2 & 6 & -2 \\ 3 & -2 & 0 & -3 & 7 \\ 4 & -6 & 3 & 0 & -3 \\ -1 & 2 & -7 & 3 & 0 \end{vmatrix}$$

10. (a) Various methods have been devised to save arithmetic in the numerical evaluation of determinants. Here is one such method (see Pipes, p. 74). First obtain one element which is equal to 1 in the determinant to be evaluated. (Use the theorems of Section 4 if there is not an element equal to 1 in the given determinant.) Then cross off the row and column containing the 1. Subtract from each remaining element the product of the two crossed-off elements in its row and column. Multiply by the checkerboard sign of the 1 in the original determinant. This new determinant of order $n - 1$ has the same value as the original determinant of order n. Use this method to evaluate the determinants in Problem 2.

(b) Prove in the following way that the method outlined in (a) is correct: Start with a determinant of order n whose elements you call a_{ij} except for some one element which you call 1. Divide each column of the determinant by the element in that column which is in the same row as the 1, thus getting a whole row of 1's; put the divided-out factors outside the determinant. By Theorem 4b, subtract the column containing the original 1 from each of the other columns. You now have a row containing all zeros except for the original element 1; thus, by a Laplace development on this row, you get a determinant of order $n - 1$. Multiply back the divided-out factors, and compare your results with the statement in part (a).

11. Solve the rotation equations (5.2) for x and y, and show that your results correspond to a rotation through the angle $-\theta$.

12. (a) Show that

$$\begin{vmatrix} \cos \theta & 1 & 0 \\ 1 & 2 \cos \theta & 1 \\ 0 & 1 & 2 \cos \theta \end{vmatrix} = \cos 3\theta.$$

(b) Show that the n-rowed determinant

$$\begin{vmatrix} \cos \theta & 1 & 0 & 0 & & \cdot & 0 \\ 1 & 2 \cos \theta & 1 & 0 & & \cdot & 0 \\ 0 & 1 & 2 \cos \theta & 1 & & \cdot & 0 \\ 0 & 0 & 1 & 2 \cos \theta & & & 0 \\ & & & & & & \cdot \\ & & \cdots & & & & \cdot \\ & & & & & & \cdot \\ & & & & 2 \cos \theta & 1 & \\ 0 & 0 & 0 & 0 & \cdots & 1 & 2 \cos \theta \end{vmatrix} = \cos n\theta.$$

Hint: Expand using elements of the last row or column. Use mathematical induction and the trigonometric addition formulas.

13. Show that the functions $x + y$ and $x - y$ are linearly independent, or prove the equivalent statement that the two sets of numbers 1, 1 and 1, -1 are linearly independent. *Hint:* Try to find k and k' to satisfy equations of the form (6.5).

14. Think of each row of a determinant as being a set of constants as in (6.10). Show that if these sets of constants are linearly dependent, the value of the determinant is zero. *Hint:* See (6.11) and use Theorems 1 and 4b in Section 4.

15. Show in two ways that $\sin x$ and $\cos x$ are linearly independent.
     (a) Use the definition (6.12). Remember that (6.12) must hold for *all* x if the functions are linearly dependent.
     (b) Use the Wronskian determinant (6.13).

16. For each of the following sets of functions, find the Wronskian determinant and decide whether the set is linearly dependent or linearly independent.

(a) e^x, e^{-x} (b) $e^{ix}, \sin x$

(c) $\sin x, x \sin x$ (d) $5, x, x^2$

(e) $e^x, e^{-x}, \cosh x$ (f) x, e^x, xe^x

(g) $x, e^x, e^x - x$ (h) $\cot x, \cot 2x, \csc 2x$

(i) $\sin^2 x, \sin^2 2x, \sin^4 x$ (j) $\arcsin x, \arccos x, 1$

(k) $\cos x, \cos^3 x, \cos 3x$

17. Find the rank of each of the following matrices.

(a) $\begin{pmatrix} 1 & 1 & 2 \\ 2 & 4 & 6 \\ 3 & 2 & 5 \end{pmatrix}$ (b) $\begin{pmatrix} 2 & -3 & 5 & 3 \\ 4 & -1 & 1 & 1 \\ 3 & -2 & 3 & 4 \end{pmatrix}$ (c) $\begin{pmatrix} 1 & 1 & 4 & 3 \\ 3 & 1 & 10 & 7 \\ 4 & 2 & 14 & 10 \\ 2 & 0 & 6 & 4 \end{pmatrix}$

(d) $\begin{pmatrix} 1 & 0 & 1 & 0 \\ -1 & -2 & -1 & 0 \\ 2 & 2 & 5 & 3 \\ 2 & 4 & 8 & 6 \end{pmatrix}$ (e) $\begin{pmatrix} 2 & 2 & 8 & 6 & 2 \\ -1 & -2 & -1 & 0 & -1 \\ 4 & 6 & 13 & 9 & 4 \\ -4 & -8 & -16 & -12 & -4 \end{pmatrix}$

18. Investigate each of the following sets of equations by finding the ranks of A and M and using Theorem (7.7). Find the solutions, if any, being careful to select equations and unknowns corresponding to a nonzero determinant in M as discussed in the solutions of (7.5) and (7.6).

(a) $\begin{cases} x + y - z = 1 \\ 3x + 2y - 2z = 3 \end{cases}$ (b) $\begin{cases} 2x + y - z = 2 \\ 4x + y - 2z = 3 \end{cases}$

(c) $\begin{cases} 2x + 3y = 1 \\ x + 2y = 2 \\ x + 3y = 5 \end{cases}$ (d) $\begin{cases} -x + y - z = 4 \\ x - y + 2z = 3 \\ 2x - 2y + 4z = 6 \end{cases}$

(e) $\begin{cases} x - y + 2z = 5 \\ 2x + 3y - z = 4 \\ 2x - 2y + 4z = 6 \end{cases}$ (f) $\begin{cases} x - 2y + 3z = 0 \\ x + 4y - 6z = 0 \\ 2x + 2y - 3z = 0 \end{cases}$

(g) $\begin{cases} 2x - y + 3z = 1 \\ 4x - 2y - z = -3 \\ 2x - y - 4z = -4 \\ 10x - 5y - 6z = -10 \end{cases}$ (h) $\begin{cases} 3x + y + 3z + 6w = 0 \\ 4x - 7y - 3z + 5w = 0 \\ x + 3y + 4z - 3w = 0 \\ 3x \quad\quad + 2z + 7w = 0 \end{cases}$

19. For those sets of functions in Problem 16 which you found to be linearly dependent, find a linear relation connecting the functions of the set. *Hint:* Write an equation like (6.12) and differentiate it $n - 1$ times. Solve this set of equations for a set of k values. Remember to consider x a constant in this process. See the discussion of homogeneous equations at the end of Section 7.

20. Prove that if the Wronskian (6.13) is not zero, the functions $f_1, f_2, \ldots, f_n$ are linearly independent. [*Note:* This is equivalent to proving that if the functions are linearly dependent, then $W = 0$. Thus you are proving part of the theorem stated about the Wronskian in (6.13).] *Hints for proof:* See Problem 19. Suppose you tried to solve for the k's in a case when $W \neq 0$; what would happen and what does this say about the functions? See the discussion of homogeneous equations at the end of Section 7 and the definition of linearly independent functions in Section 6.

21. Show that if the matrix

$$W = \begin{pmatrix} a_1 & a_2 & a_3 & \cdots & a_n \\ b_1 & b_2 & b_3 & \cdots & b_n \\ c_1 & c_2 & c_3 & \cdots & c_n \end{pmatrix}$$

has rank 2, its rows are linearly related sets of constants. *Hint:* Write equations (6.11) and consider solving for the k's. Use Theorem (7.7c).

22. For what values of λ does the following set of equations have nontrivial solutions for x, y, z? For each value of λ find the corresponding solutions for x, y, z. (*Comment:* This is an example of what is called an *eigenvalue* or *characteristic value* problem in mathematical physics; the values of λ are the *eigenvalues.* See Chapters 10 and 12.)

$$-(1 + \lambda)x + y + 3z = 0,$$
$$x + (2 - \lambda)y = 0,$$
$$3x + (2 - \lambda)z = 0.$$

23. Find a condition for four points in space to lie in a plane. Your answer should be in the form of a determinant which must be equal to zero. *Hint:* The equation of a plane is of the form $ax + by + cz = d$, where a, b, c, d are constants. The four points (x_1, y_1, z_1), (x_2, y_2, z_2), etc., are all to satisfy this equation. When can you solve for a, b, c, d? See the discussion of homogeneous equations at the end of Section 7.

24. Find a condition for three lines in a plane to intersect in one point. *Hint:* See Problem 23.

25. A college keeps a record in the form of a matrix (that is, a table) of the number of students receiving various grades in various courses each year.

Grade	Course number	1965				1966			
	$\longrightarrow$	1	2	3	4	1	2	3	4
A		1	5	0	3	2	3	1	3
B		4	2	1	2	3	3	2	2
C		10	11	4	7	11	8	5	8
D		7	3	2	5	8	4	1	4
F		1	2	1	0	1	1	2	1

What does the sum of these matrices represent? What does their difference represent? If they happened to be square matrices, would the determinants of the matrices mean anything?

26. Given the matrices

$$A = \begin{pmatrix} 1 & 0 & 2 \\ 3 & -1 & 0 \\ 0 & 5 & 1 \end{pmatrix}, \qquad B = \begin{pmatrix} 1 & 1 & 0 \\ 0 & 2 & 1 \\ 3 & -1 & 0 \end{pmatrix},$$

find $A + B$, AB and BA. Observe that $AB \neq BA$. Show that det $(AB) =$ det $(BA) = (\det A)(\det B)$, but that det $(A + B) \neq \det A + \det B$.

27. Given the matrices

$$A = \begin{pmatrix} 2 & 3 & 1 & -4 \\ 2 & 1 & 0 & 5 \end{pmatrix}, \quad B = \begin{pmatrix} 2 & 4 \\ 1 & -1 \\ 3 & -1 \end{pmatrix}, \quad C = \begin{pmatrix} 2 & 1 & 3 \\ 4 & -1 & -2 \\ -1 & 0 & 1 \end{pmatrix},$$

compute or mark as meaningless all products of two of these matrices $(AB, BA, A^2,$ etc.); of three of them $(ABC, A^2C, A^3,$ etc.).

28. Find AB and BA given

$$A = \begin{pmatrix} 1 & 1 & 1 \\ 0 & 0 & 0 \\ 1 & 1 & 1 \end{pmatrix}, \qquad B = \begin{pmatrix} 1 & 1 & 0 \\ -1 & 0 & 1 \\ 0 & -1 & -1 \end{pmatrix}.$$

29. Verify that (8.15) is the result of substituting (5.2) into (8.13) and using trigonometric addition formulas.

30. Given the equations

$$x' = 2x - 3y, \qquad x'' = x' - 5y',$$
$$y' = x + y, \qquad y'' = 2x' + y',$$

write each of these sets of equations as a matrix equation. Using the abbreviated matrix notation [like (8.12) and (8.14)], solve for r'', that is, $\begin{pmatrix} x'' \\ y'' \end{pmatrix}$, in terms of r. Then, being guided by your matrix solution, find x'' and y'' in terms of x and y using matrix multiplication.

31. Given the equations

$$x' = \tfrac{1}{2}(x + y\sqrt{3}), \qquad x'' = \tfrac{1}{2}(-x' + y'\sqrt{3}),$$
$$y' = \tfrac{1}{2}(-x\sqrt{3} + y), \qquad y'' = -\tfrac{1}{2}(x'\sqrt{3} + y'),$$

write each set as a matrix equation and solve for x'', y'' in terms of x, y by multiplying matrices. These equations represent rotations of axes in two dimensions. By comparing them with (5.2), find the rotation angles and check your results.

32. The equations

$$x' = \frac{1}{\sqrt{2}}(x - z), \qquad\qquad x'' = \frac{1}{\sqrt{2}}(y' - z'),$$

$$y' = \tfrac{1}{2}(x + y\sqrt{2} + z), \qquad\qquad y'' = -\tfrac{1}{2}(x'\sqrt{2} + y' + z'),$$

$$z' = \tfrac{1}{2}(x - y\sqrt{2} + z), \qquad\qquad z'' = \tfrac{1}{2}(-x'\sqrt{2} + y' + z'),$$

represent rotations of axes in three dimensions. Find the matrix of the resultant rotation and describe geometrically the net result of the two rotations.

33. The rectangle in the diagram represents some electrical network (we are not

concerned with the details inside the box!); I_1 and E_1 are the input current and voltage and I_2 and E_2 are the output current and voltage. In certain cases it may be true that I_1 and E_1 are linear combinations of I_2 and E_2; the network is then called a linear four-terminal network. Suppose these equations hold:

$$E_1 = AE_2 + BI_2,$$
$$I_1 = CE_2 + DI_2,$$

where A, B, C, D are constants. Write these equations in matrix form. The square matrix in your equation is called, in electric circuit theory, the transmission matrix T. Consider two identical networks in cascade as

shown, and find I_1, E_1 in terms of I_3, E_3. Show that the overall transmission matrix is T^2. Under certain circumstances the constants A, B, C, D can be written in terms of two other constants a, b as

$$A = D = \cosh a,$$
$$B = b \sinh a,$$
$$C = \frac{1}{b} \sinh a.$$

Using these values of the constants and the formulas for hyperbolic functions from Chapter 2, show that

$$T^2 = \begin{pmatrix} \cosh 2a & b \sinh 2a \\ \frac{1}{b} \sinh 2a & \cosh 2a \end{pmatrix}.$$

(See Pipes, pp. 182 ff.)

34. Show, by multiplying out the matrices, that the equation

$$(x \quad y)\begin{pmatrix} 5 & -7 \\ 7 & 3 \end{pmatrix}\begin{pmatrix} x \\ y \end{pmatrix} = 30$$

represents an ellipse.

35. Prove that the unit matrix U has the property which we associate with the number 1, that is, $UA = A$ for any matrix A which is conformable with U, and $AU = A$ for any matrix A for which the matrices are conformable in this order.

36. The Pauli spin matrices in quantum mechanics are

$$A = \begin{pmatrix} 0 & 1 \\ 1 & 0 \end{pmatrix}, \qquad B = \begin{pmatrix} 0 & -i \\ i & 0 \end{pmatrix}, \qquad C = \begin{pmatrix} 1 & 0 \\ 0 & -1 \end{pmatrix}.$$

Show that $A^2 = B^2 = C^2 = 1$. (Note carefully that this 1 means the unit matrix $\begin{pmatrix} 1 & 0 \\ 0 & 1 \end{pmatrix}$ and *not* the number 1 since a 2 by 2 matrix means a set of *four* numbers, *not* a single number.) Also show that any pair of these matrices anticommute, that is, $AB = -BA$, etc. Show that the commutator of A and B, that is, $AB - BA$, is $2iC$, and similarly for other pairs in cyclic order.

37. Let $C_{ij} = (-1)^{i+j}M_{ij}$ be the cofactor of element a_{ij} in the determinant A. Show that the statement of Laplace's development and the statement of Problem 8 can be combined in the equations

$$\sum_j a_{ij}C_{kj} = \delta_{ik} \cdot \det A,$$

or

$$\sum_i a_{ij}C_{ik} = \delta_{jk} \cdot \det A.$$

38. (a) Show, if possible without computation, that the matrix

$$\begin{pmatrix} 0 & 2 & -3 \\ -2 & 0 & 4 \\ 3 & -4 & 0 \end{pmatrix}$$

is singular, and find its rank. (*Hint:* consider the effect of interchanging rows and columns.)

(b) Show that the determinant of any skew-symmetric matrix of odd order is zero. [See definition of skew-symmetric in (9.12).]

39. Given the matrix

$$A = \begin{pmatrix} 0 & 2i & -1 \\ -i & 2 & 0 \\ 3 & 0 & 0 \end{pmatrix}$$

find the transpose, the adjoint, the reciprocal, the complex conjugate, and the transpose conjugate of A. Verify that $AA^{-1} = A^{-1}A =$ the unit matrix.

40. Given the following set of matrices, find or mark as meaningless these matrices: A', A^{-1}, AB, $\bar{A}$, $A'B'$, $B'A'$, BA', ABC, $AB'C$, $B'AC$, $\hat{A}$, $A^{\dagger}$, $B'C$ $B^{-1}C$, $C^{-1}A$, CB'.

$$A = \begin{pmatrix} 1 & -1 \\ 0 & i \end{pmatrix}, \qquad B = \begin{pmatrix} 2 & 1 & -1 \\ 0 & 3 & 5 \end{pmatrix}, \qquad C = \begin{pmatrix} 0 & 1 \\ -1 & 0 \end{pmatrix}.$$

41. Show that $AA^{-1} = A^{-1}A = U$, where A^{-1} is the inverse of any nonsingular matrix A, and U is the unit matrix of the same number of rows and columns as A. *Hint:* By definition, $A^{-1} = (\text{adj } A)/(\det A)$. Consider the product of the two matrices A and adj A. Recall the Laplace development of a determinant and also Problem 8 or 37.

42. (a) Show that $(AB)' = B'A'$, that is, the transpose of a product of two matrices is equal to the product of the transposes in inverse order.

   (b) Use (a) to show that the matrix AA' is symmetric. [See (9.12).]

43. Given the matrices

$$A = \begin{pmatrix} 1 & -1 & 1 \\ 4 & 0 & -1 \\ 4 & -2 & 0 \end{pmatrix}, \qquad B = \begin{pmatrix} 1 & 0 & 1 \\ 2 & 1 & 1 \\ 2 & 1 & 2 \end{pmatrix}.$$

   (a) Find A^{-1}, B^{-1}, $B^{-1}AB$, and $B^{-1}A^{-1}B$.

   (b) Show that the last two matrices are inverses, that is, that their product is the unit matrix.

   (c) Part (b) is a special case of the general theorem that the inverse of a product of matrices is the product of the inverses in reverse order. Prove this theorem.

44. Compute the product of each of the matrices in Problem 27 with its transpose (in both orders, that is, AA' and $A'A$, etc.) *Hint for check:* All your resulting matrices should be symmetric.

45. Write out the set of simultaneous equations given by the following matrix equation. Solve them (a) by using Cramer's rule; (b) by finding the inverse of the matrix M of the coefficients.

$$\begin{pmatrix} 3 & -2 \\ 1 & 2 \end{pmatrix} \begin{pmatrix} x \\ y \end{pmatrix} = \begin{pmatrix} 5 \\ 8 \end{pmatrix}.$$

46. Solve each of the following sets of equations by the method of finding the inverse of the coefficient matrix. Check your matrix M^{-1} in each case by showing that $MM^{-1} = U$.

(a) $\begin{cases} x - 2y = 5 \\ 3x + y = 15 \end{cases}$ (b) $\begin{cases} 2x + 3y = -1 \\ 5x + 4y = 8 \end{cases}$

(c) $\begin{cases} x + 2z = 8 \\ 2x - y = -5 \\ x + y + z = 4 \end{cases}$ (d) $\begin{cases} x - y + z = 4 \\ 2x + y - z = -1 \\ 3x + 2y + 2z = 5 \end{cases}$

47. Give numerical examples of: a symmetric matrix; a skew-symmetric matrix; a real matrix; a pure imaginary matrix.

48. Show that the matrix of a rotation (5.3) is orthogonal; show that a unit matrix is orthogonal.

49. Show that the definition of a Hermitian matrix $(A = A^\dagger)$ can be written $a_{ij} = \bar{a}_{ji}$ (that is, the diagonal elements are real and the other elements have the property that $a_{12} = \bar{a}_{21}$, etc.). Construct an example of a Hermitian matrix.

50. Show that

$$
\begin{pmatrix}
\tfrac{1}{4}(1 + i\sqrt{3}) & \dfrac{\sqrt{3}}{2\sqrt{2}}(1 + i) \\[2ex]
\dfrac{-\sqrt{3}}{2\sqrt{2}}(1 + i) & \tfrac{1}{4}(\sqrt{3} + i)
\end{pmatrix}
$$

is a unitary matrix.

51. Show that the determinant of an orthogonal matrix is $+1$ or -1. *Hint:* What is the determinant of AA' when A is orthogonal and how do det A and det A' compare? Use (8.8).

4

Partial Differentiation and Multiple Integrals

I. INTRODUCTION AND NOTATION

If $y = f(x)$, then dy/dx can be thought of either as the slope of the curve $y = f(x)$ or as the rate of change of y with respect to x. Rates occur frequently in physics; time rates such as velocity, acceleration, and rate of cooling of a hot body are obvious examples. There are also other rates: rate of change of volume of a gas with applied pressure, rate of decrease of the fuel in your automobile tank with distance traveled, etc. Equations involving rates (differential equations) often need to be solved in applied problems. Derivatives are also used in finding maximum and minimum points of a curve and in finding the power series of a function. All these applications, and more, occur also when we consider a function of several variables.

Let z be a function of two variables x and y; we write $z = f(x, y)$. Just as we think of $y = f(x)$ as a curve in two dimensions, so it is useful to interpret $z = f(x, y)$ geometrically. If x, y, z are rectangular coordinates, then for each x, y the equation gives us a value of z, and so determines a point (x, y, z) in three dimensions. All the points satisfying the equation ordinarily form a surface in three-dimensional space (see Fig. 1.1). (It might happen that an equation would not be satisfied by any real points, for example $x^2 + y^2 + z^2 = -1$, but we shall be interested in equations whose graphs are real surfaces.) Now suppose x is constant; think of a plane $x = $ const. intersecting the surface (see Fig. 1.1). The points satisfying $z = f(x, y)$ *and* $x = $ const. then lie on a curve (the curve of intersection of the surface and the $x = $ const. plane; this is AB in Fig. 1.1). We might

121

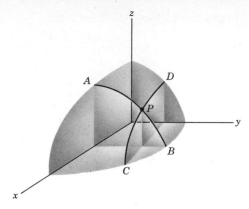

Figure 1.1

want the slope, maximum and minimum points, etc., of this curve. Since z is a function of y (on this curve), we might write dz/dy for the slope. However, to show that z is actually a function of two variables x and y with one of them (x) temporarily a constant, we write $\partial z/\partial y$; we call $\partial z/\partial y$ the partial derivative of z with respect to y. Similarly, we can hold y constant and find $\partial z/\partial x$, the partial derivative of z with respect to x. If these partial derivatives are differentiated further, we write

$$\frac{\partial}{\partial x}\frac{\partial z}{\partial x} = \frac{\partial^2 z}{\partial x^2}, \qquad \frac{\partial}{\partial x}\frac{\partial z}{\partial y} = \frac{\partial^2 z}{\partial x\,\partial y}, \qquad \frac{\partial}{\partial x}\frac{\partial^2 z}{\partial x\,\partial y} = \frac{\partial^3 z}{\partial x^2\,\partial y}, \quad \text{etc.}$$

Other notations are often useful. If $z = f(x, y)$, we may use z_x or f_x or f_1 for $\partial f/\partial x$, and corresponding notations for the higher derivatives.

Example.   Given $z = f(x, y) = x^3 y - e^{xy}$, then

$$\frac{\partial f}{\partial x} = \frac{\partial z}{\partial x} = f_x = z_x = f_1 = 3x^2 y - y e^{xy},$$

$$\frac{\partial f}{\partial y} = \frac{\partial z}{\partial y} = f_y = z_y = f_2 = x^3 - x e^{xy},$$

$$\frac{\partial^2 f}{\partial x\,\partial y} = \frac{\partial^2 z}{\partial x\,\partial y} = f_{yx} = z_{yx} = f_{21} = 3x^2 - e^{xy} - xy e^{xy},$$

$$\frac{\partial^2 f}{\partial x^2} = \frac{\partial^2 z}{\partial x^2} = f_{xx} = z_{xx} = f_{11} = 6xy - y^2 e^{xy},$$

$$\frac{\partial^3 f}{\partial y^3} = \frac{\partial^3 z}{\partial y^3} = f_{yyy} = z_{yyy} = f_{222} = -x^3 e^{xy},$$

$$\frac{\partial^3 f}{\partial x^2\,\partial y} = \frac{\partial^3 z}{\partial x^2\,\partial y} = f_{yxx} = z_{yxx} = f_{211} = 6x - 2y e^{xy} - xy^2 e^{xy}.$$

We can also consider functions of more variables than two, although in this case it is not so easy to give a geometrical interpretation. For example, the temperature T of the air in a room might depend on the point (x, y, z) at which we measured it and on the time t; we would write $T = T(x, y, z, t)$. We could then find, say, $\partial T/\partial y$, meaning the rate at which T is changing with y for fixed x and z at one instant of time t.

When there is doubt as to what the variables are, we may write $(\partial z/\partial x)_y$ meaning $\partial z/\partial x$ when z is expressed as a function of the variables x and y. For example, let $z = x^2 - y^2$. Using polar coordinates r, θ (recall $x = r \cos \theta$, $y = r \sin \theta$, $x^2 + y^2 = r^2$), we can write z in several other ways. For each new expression let us find $\partial z/\partial r$.

$$z = x^2 - y^2,$$

$$z = r^2 \cos^2 \theta - r^2 \sin^2 \theta, \qquad \left(\frac{\partial z}{\partial r}\right)_\theta = 2r(\cos^2 \theta - \sin^2 \theta),$$

$$z = 2x^2 - x^2 - y^2 = 2x^2 - r^2. \qquad \left(\frac{\partial z}{\partial r}\right)_x = -2r,$$

$$z = x^2 + y^2 - 2y^2 = r^2 - 2y^2, \qquad \left(\frac{\partial z}{\partial r}\right)_y = +2r.$$

These three expressions for $\partial z/\partial r$ have different values and are derivatives of three different functions, so we distinguish them as indicated by writing the second independent variable as a subscript. The symbol $(\partial z/\partial r)_x$ is usually read "the partial of z with respect to r, with x held constant." However, the important point to understand is that the notation means that z has been written as a function of the variables r and x only, and then differentiated with respect to r.

A little experimenting will probably convince you that $(\partial/\partial x)(\partial f/\partial y) = (\partial/\partial y)(\partial f/\partial x)$; this is usually (but not always) true in applied problems. It can be proved that if $\partial^2 f/\partial x\, \partial y$ and $\partial^2 f/\partial y\, \partial x$ are both continuous, then they *are* equal. (See Taylor, p. 220.)

2. POWER SERIES IN TWO VARIABLES

In Chapter 1, Section 12, we discussed a method of finding the power series (Taylor series) for a function of one variable (assuming that the function has a power series). To find the Taylor series about $x = a$, we wrote

$$(2.1) \qquad f(x) = a_0 + a_1(x - a) + a_2(x - a)^2$$
$$+ \cdots + a_n(x - a)^n + \cdots$$

and determined the coefficients a_n by differentiating (2.1) repeatedly and then putting $x = a$. Our result was

$$(2.2)\quad f(x) = f(a) + f'(a)(x - a) + \frac{f''(a)}{2!}(x - a)^2 + \cdots$$

$$+ \frac{f^{(n)}(a)}{n!}(x - a)^n + \cdots.$$

By a similar process we can find the coefficients of the power series for a function of two variables $f(x, y)$ (assuming that it can be expanded in a power series). To find the series expansion of $f(x, y)$ about the point (a, b) we write $f(x, y)$ as a series of powers of $(x - a)$ and $(y - b)$ and then differentiate this equation repeatedly as follows.

(2.3)

$$f(x, y) = a_{00} + a_{10}(x - a) + a_{01}(y - b) + a_{20}(x - a)^2 + a_{11}(x - a)(y - b)$$

$$+ a_{02}(y - b)^2 + a_{30}(x - a)^3 + a_{21}(x - a)^2(y - b)$$

$$+ a_{12}(x - a)(y - b)^2 + a_{03}(y - b)^3 + \cdots.$$

$$f_x = a_{10} + 2a_{20}(x - a) + a_{11}(y - b) + \cdots,$$

$$f_y = a_{01} + a_{11}(x - a) + 2a_{02}(y - b) + \cdots,$$

$$f_{xx} = 2a_{20} + \text{terms containing } (x - a) \text{ and/or } (y - b),$$

$$f_{xy} = a_{11} + \text{terms containing } (x - a) \text{ and/or } (y - b).$$

[We have written only a few derivatives to show the idea. You should be able to calculate others in the same way (Problem 7).] Now putting $x = a$, $y = b$ in (2.3), we get

$$(2.4)\qquad \begin{aligned} f(a, b) &= a_{00}, \quad f_x(a, b) = a_{10}, \quad f_y(a, b) = a_{01}, \\ f_{xx}(a, b) &= 2a_{20}, \quad f_{xy}(a, b) = a_{11}, \quad \text{etc.} \end{aligned}$$

[Remember that $f_x(a, b)$ means that we are to find the partial derivative of f with respect to x and then put $x = a$, $y = b$, and similarly for the other derivatives.] Substituting the values for the coefficients into (2.3), we find

$$(2.5)\quad f(x, y) = f(a, b) + f_x(a, b)(x - a) + f_y(a, b)(y - b)$$

$$+ \frac{1}{2!}[f_{xx}(a, b)(x - a)^2 + 2f_{xy}(a, b)(x - a)(y - b)$$

$$+ f_{yy}(a, b)(y - b)^2] + \cdots.$$

This can be written in a simpler form if we put $x - a = h$ and $y - b = k$.

Then the second-order terms (for example) become

(2.6) $\dfrac{1}{2!}[f_{xx}(a, b)h^2 + 2f_{xy}(a, b)hk + f_{yy}(a, b)k^2]$.

We can write this in the form

(2.7) $\dfrac{1}{2!}\left(h\dfrac{\partial}{\partial x} + k\dfrac{\partial}{\partial y}\right)^2 f(a, b)$

if we understand that the parenthesis is to be squared and then a term like $h(\partial/\partial x)k(\partial/\partial y)f(a, b)$ is to mean $hkf_{xy}(a, b)$. It can be shown (Problem 7) that the third-order terms can be written in this notation as

(2.8) $\dfrac{1}{3!}\left(h\dfrac{\partial}{\partial x} + k\dfrac{\partial}{\partial y}\right)^3 f(a, b) = \dfrac{1}{3!}[h^3 f_{xxx}(a, b) + 3h^2 k f_{xxy}(a, b) + \cdots]$

and so on for terms of any order. Thus we can write the series (2.5) in the form

(2.9) $f(x, y) = \displaystyle\sum_{n=0}^{\infty} \dfrac{1}{n!}\left(h\dfrac{\partial}{\partial x} + k\dfrac{\partial}{\partial y}\right)^n f(a, b)$.

The numbers appearing in the nth order terms are the familiar binomial coefficients [in the expansion of $(p + q)^n$] divided by $(n!)$.

Example.   Expand $f(x, y) = \sin x \cos y$ in a two-variable power series. We find the various partial derivatives, and evaluate them at $x = a = 0$, $y = b = 0$:

$$f(0, 0) = 0,$$

$$
\begin{aligned}
f_x &= \cos x \cos y, & f_x(0, 0) &= 1, \\
f_y &= -\sin x \sin y, & f_y(0, 0) &= 0, \\
f_{xx} &= -\sin x \cos y, & f_{xx}(0, 0) &= 0, \\
f_{yy} &= -\sin x \cos y, & f_{yy}(0, 0) &= 0, \\
f_{xy} &= -\cos x \sin y, & f_{xy}(0, 0) &= 0, \\
f_{xxx} &= -\cos x \cos y, & f_{xxx}(0, 0) &= -1, \\
f_{xxy} &= \sin x \sin y, & f_{xxy}(0, 0) &= 0, \\
f_{xyy} &= -\cos x \cos y, & f_{xyy}(0, 0) &= -1, \\
f_{yyy} &= \sin x \sin y, & f_{yyy}(0, 0) &= 0, \text{ etc.}
\end{aligned}
$$

Then

$$\sin x \cos y = 0 + 1 \cdot x + 0 \cdot y + \frac{1}{2!}(0 \cdot x^2 + 0 \cdot 2xy + 0 \cdot y^2)$$

$$+ \frac{1}{3!}(-x^3 - 1 \cdot 3xy^2) + \cdots$$

$$= x - \frac{x^3}{3!} - \tfrac{1}{2}xy^2 + \text{terms of order greater than three.}$$

Just as in the one-variable case discussed in Chapter 1, the power series (about a given point) for a function of two variables is unique, and we may use any convenient method of finding it (see Chapter 1 for methods). We could also get the series of this example by multiplying the two series for $\sin x$ and $\cos y$. This gives

$$\sin x \cos y = \left(x - \frac{x^3}{3!} + \cdots\right)\left(1 - \frac{y^2}{2!} + \cdots\right) = x - \frac{x^3}{3!} - \frac{xy^2}{2!} + \cdots .$$

3. TOTAL DIFFERENTIALS

The graph (Fig. 3.1) of the equation $y = f(x)$ is a curve in the (x, y) plane and

(3.1)
$$y' = \frac{dy}{dx} = \frac{d}{dx}f(x)$$

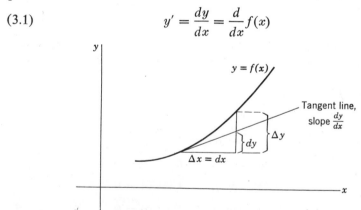

Figure 3.1

is the slope of the tangent to the curve at the point (x, y). In calculus, we use Δx to mean a change in x, and Δy means the corresponding change in y (see Fig. 3.1). By definition

(3.2)
$$\frac{dy}{dx} = \lim_{\Delta x \to 0} \frac{\Delta y}{\Delta x} .$$

We shall now define the differential dx of the independent variable as

(3.3)
$$dx = \Delta x.$$

However, dy is not the same as Δy. From Fig. 3.1 and equation (3.1), we can see that Δy is the change in y along the curve, but $dy = y'dx$ is the change in y along the tangent line. We say that dy is the tangent approximation to Δy.

Example. If $y = f(t)$ represents the distance a particle has gone as a function of t, then dy/dt is the velocity. The actual distance the particle has gone between time t and time $t + dt$ is Δy. The tangent approximation $dy = (dy/dt)\, dt$ is the distance it would have gone if it had continued with the same velocity dy/dt which it had at time t.

You can see from the graph (Fig. 3.1) that dy is a good approximation to Δy if dx is small. We can say this more exactly using (3.2). Saying that dy/dx is the limit of $\Delta y/\Delta x$ as $\Delta x \to 0$ means that the difference $\Delta y/\Delta x - dy/dx \to 0$ as $\Delta x \to 0$. Let us call this difference ϵ; then we can say

(3.4) $$\frac{\Delta y}{\Delta x} = \frac{dy}{dx} + \epsilon, \qquad \text{where } \epsilon \to 0 \quad \text{as} \quad \Delta x \to 0,$$

or since $dx = \Delta x$

(3.5) $$\Delta y = (y' + \epsilon)\, dx, \qquad \text{where } \epsilon \to 0 \quad \text{as} \quad \Delta x \to 0.$$

The differential $dy = y'dx$ is called the principal part of Δy; since ϵ is small for small dx, you can see from (3.5) that dy is then a good approximation to Δy.

In our example, suppose $y = t^2$, $t = 1$, $dt = 0.1$. Then

$$\Delta y = (1.1)^2 - 1^2 = 0.21,$$

$$dy = \frac{dy}{dt}\, dt = 2 \cdot 1 \cdot (0.1) = 0.2,$$

$$\epsilon = \frac{\Delta y}{\Delta t} - \frac{dy}{dt} = 2.1 - 2 = 0.1,$$

$$\Delta y = (y' + \epsilon)dt = (2 + 0.1)(0.1) = dy + \epsilon\, dt = 0.2 + 0.01.$$

Thus dy is a good approximation to Δy.

We want to do something similar to this for a function of two variables, $z = f(x, y)$. We have said that this equation represents a surface and that the derivatives $\partial f/\partial x$, $\partial f/\partial y$, at a point, are the slopes of the two tangent lines to the surface in the x and y directions at that point. The symbols $\Delta x = dx$ and $\Delta y = dy$ represent changes in the independent variables x

and y. The quantity Δz means the corresponding change in z along the surface. We define dz by the equation

(3.6) $$dz = \frac{\partial z}{\partial x}\, dx + \frac{\partial z}{\partial y}\, dy.$$

The differential dz is called the *total differential* of z. Let us consider the geometrical meaning of dz. Recall (Fig. 3.1) that for $y = f(x)$, dy was the change in y along the tangent line; here we shall see that dz is the change in

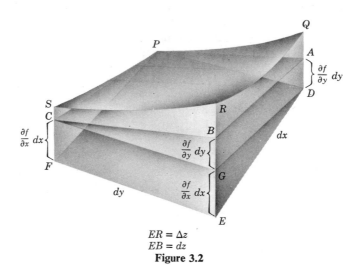

$ER = \Delta z$
$EB = dz$
Figure 3.2

z along the tangent plane. In Fig. 3.2, $PQRS$ is a surface, $PABC$ is the plane tangent to the surface at P, and $PDEF$ is a horizontal plane through P. Thus $PSCF$ is the plane $y = $ const. (through P), PS is the curve of intersection of this plane with the surface, and PC is the tangent line to this curve and so has the slope $\partial f/\partial x$; then (just as in Fig. 3.1), if $PF = dx$, we have $CF = (\partial f/\partial x)dx$. Similarly, $PQAD$ is a plane $x = $ const., intersecting the surface in the curve PQ, whose tangent is PA; with $PD = dy$, we have $DA = (\partial f/\partial y)dy$. From the figure, $GE = CF$, and $BG = AD$, so

$$EB = CF + DA = \frac{\partial f}{\partial x}\, dx + \frac{\partial f}{\partial y}\, dy = dz.$$

Thus, as we said, dz is the change in z along the tangent plane when x changes by dx and y by dy. In the figure, $ER = \Delta z$, the change in z along the surface.

From the geometry, we can reasonably expect dz to be a good approximation to Δz if dx and dy are small. However, we should like to say this more accurately in an equation corresponding to (3.5). We can do this if $\partial f/\partial x$ and $\partial f/\partial y$ are continuous functions. By definition

(3.7) $$\Delta z = f(x + \Delta x, y + \Delta y) - f(x, y).$$

By adding and subtracting a term, we get

(3.8) $$\Delta z = f(x + \Delta x, y) - f(x, y)$$
$$+ f(x + \Delta x, y + \Delta y) - f(x + \Delta x, y).$$

Recall from calculus that the mean value theorem (law of the mean) says that for a differentiable function $f(x)$,

(3.9) $$f(x + \Delta x) - f(x) = (\Delta x)f'(x_1),$$

where x_1 is between x and $x + \Delta x$. Geometrically this says (Fig. 3.3) that there is a tangent line somewhere between x and $x + \Delta x$ which has the

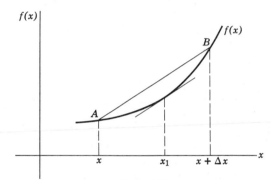

Figure 3.3

same slope as the line AB. In the first two terms of the right side of (3.8), y is constant, and we can use (3.9) if we write $\partial f/\partial x$ for f'. In the last two terms of (3.8), x is constant and we can use an equation like (3.9) with y as the variable; y_1 will mean a value of y between y and $y + \Delta y$. Then (3.8) becomes

(3.10) $$\Delta z = \frac{\partial f(x_1, y)}{\partial x} \Delta x + \frac{\partial f(x + \Delta x, y_1)}{\partial y} \Delta y.$$

If the partial derivatives of f are continuous, then their values in (3.10) at points *near* (x, y) differ from their values *at* (x, y) by quantities which approach zero as Δx and Δy approach zero. Let us call these quantities ϵ_1 and ϵ_2. Then we can write

(3.11) $$\Delta z = \left(\frac{\partial f}{\partial x} + \epsilon_1\right) \Delta x + \left(\frac{\partial f}{\partial y} + \epsilon_2\right) \Delta y = dz + \epsilon_1 \Delta x + \epsilon_2 \Delta y$$

$$(\epsilon_1 \text{ and } \epsilon_2 \to 0 \text{ as } \Delta x \text{ and } \Delta y \to 0),$$

where $\partial f/\partial x$ and $\partial f/\partial y$ in (3.11) are evaluated at (x, y). Equation (3.11) [like (3.5) for the $y = f(x)$ case] tells us algebraically what we suspected from the geometry, that (if $\partial f/\partial x$ and $\partial f/\partial y$ are continuous) dz is a good approximation to Δz for small dx and dy. The differential dz is called the principal part of Δz.

Everything we have said about functions of two variables works just as well for functions of any number of variables. If $u = f(x, y, z, \ldots)$, then by definition

$$(3.12) \qquad du = \frac{\partial f}{\partial x}\, dx + \frac{\partial f}{\partial y}\, dy + \frac{\partial f}{\partial z}\, dz + \cdots$$

and du is a good approximation to Δu if the partial derivatives of f are continuous and dx, dy, dz, etc., are small.

4. APPROXIMATE CALCULATIONS USING DIFFERENTIALS

There is an immediate practical application of differentials, which you can see best from some examples.

Example 1. A sphere of radius 10 cm is heated and expands. Find its increase in volume if the radius increases by 0.1 cm.

The actual change in the volume V is of course ΔV, that is, the difference between the initial and the final volumes. But we get a good approximation by finding dV. The formula for the volume is $V = \frac{4}{3}\pi r^3$. Then we find

$$dV = 4\pi r^2\, dr = 4\pi \cdot 10^2 \cdot (0.1) = 40\pi \text{ cm}^3.$$

(For comparison, $\Delta V = 40.40\pi$ cm^3 to four figure accuracy.)

Example 2. A cylindrical tin can has inside radius 2 in., inside height 4 in. and wall thickness 0.05 in. Find the volume of tin required to make it.

From the volume formula $V = \pi r^2 h$ we get

$$dV = 2\pi rh\, dr + \pi r^2\, dh.$$

Here $dr = 0.05$ in. and $dh = 2 \cdot (0.05)$ in. since the difference between the inside and outside heights includes the thickness of both top and bottom. Then we find

$$dV = 2\pi \cdot 2 \cdot 4 \cdot (0.05) + \pi \cdot 2^2 \cdot (0.1) = \tfrac{4}{5}\pi + \tfrac{2}{5}\pi = \tfrac{6}{5}\pi \text{ in.}^3$$

Example 3. The resistance R of a wire is proportional to its length and inversely proportional to the square of its radius, that is, $R = kl/r^2$. If the relative error in length measurement is 5% and the relative error in radius measurement is 10%, find the relative error in R in the worst possible case.

The relative error in l means the actual error in measuring l divided by the length measured. Since we might measure l either too large or too small, the relative error dl/l might be either $+0.05$ or -0.05 in the worst cases. Similarly $|dr/r|$ might be as large as 0.10. We want the largest value which $|dR/R|$ could have; we can find dR/R by differentiating $\ln R$. From $R = kl/r^2$ we find

$$\ln R = \ln k + \ln l - 2 \ln r.$$

Then

$$\frac{dR}{R} = \frac{dl}{l} - 2\frac{dr}{r}.$$

In the worst case (that is, largest value of $|dR/R|$), dl/l and dr/r might have opposite signs so the two terms would add. Then we would have

$$\text{Largest} \left|\frac{dR}{R}\right| = \left|\frac{dl}{l}\right| + 2\left|\frac{dr}{r}\right| = 0.05 + 2(0.10) = 0.25 \qquad \text{or} \quad 25\%.$$

Example 4. Find without tables an approximate value of $\dfrac{\text{arc tan } 0.99}{5.2}$.

This is not very different from $\dfrac{\text{arc tan } 1}{5}$, which we can easily find:

$$\frac{\text{arc tan } 1}{5} = \frac{\pi}{20} = 9°.$$

We use differentials to find the approximate change in

$$z = \frac{\text{arc tan } x}{y}$$

when we change x from 1 to 0.99 and y from 5 to 5.2. We want the value of dz when $x = 1$, $dx = -0.01$ (note that these are values in radians), $y = 5$, $dy = 0.2$. We find

$$dz = \frac{dx}{(1 + x^2)y} - \frac{\text{arc tan } x}{y^2}\, dy,$$

$$dz = \frac{-0.01}{(1 + 1) \cdot 5} \cdot \left(\frac{180}{\pi}\right)° - \frac{45°}{25}(0.2) = -0.06° - 0.36° = -0.42°,$$

$$\frac{\text{arc tan } 0.99}{5.2} = z + dz = 9° - 0.4° = 8.6°.$$

5. CHAIN RULE OR DIFFERENTIATING A FUNCTION OF A FUNCTION

You already know about the chain rule whether you have called it that or not. Look at this example.

Example 1.   Find dy/dx if $y = \ln \sin 2x$.
You would say

$$\frac{dy}{dx} = \frac{1}{\sin 2x} \cdot \frac{d}{dx}(\sin 2x) = \frac{1}{\sin 2x} \cdot \cos 2x \cdot \frac{d}{dx}(2x) = 2 \cot 2x.$$

We *could* write this problem as

$$y = \ln u, \qquad \text{where} \quad u = \sin v \text{ and } v = 2x.$$

Then we would say

$$\frac{dy}{dx} = \frac{dy}{du}\frac{du}{dv}\frac{dv}{dx}.$$

This is an example of the chain rule. We shall want a similar equation for a function of several variables. Consider another example.

Example 2.   Find dz/dt if $z = 2t^2 \sin t$.
Differentiating the product, we get

$$\frac{dz}{dt} = 4t \sin t + 2t^2 \cos t.$$

We *could* have written this problem as

$$z = xy, \qquad \text{where} \quad x = 2t^2 \quad \text{and} \quad y = \sin t,$$

$$\frac{dz}{dt} = y\frac{dx}{dt} + x\frac{dy}{dt}.$$

But since x is $\partial z/\partial y$ and y is $\partial z/\partial x$, we could also write

(5.1) $$\frac{dz}{dt} = \frac{\partial z}{\partial x}\frac{dx}{dt} + \frac{\partial z}{\partial y}\frac{dy}{dt}.$$

We would like to be sure that (5.1) is a correct formula in general, when we are given any function $z(x, y)$ with continuous partial derivatives and x and y are differentiable functions of t. To see this, recall from our discussion of differentials that we had

(5.2) $$\Delta z = \frac{\partial z}{\partial x}\Delta x + \frac{\partial z}{\partial y}\Delta y + \epsilon_1 \Delta x + \epsilon_2 \Delta y,$$

where ϵ_1 and $\epsilon_2 \to 0$ with Δx and Δy. Divide this equation by Δt and let $\Delta t \to 0$; since Δx and $\Delta y \to 0$, ϵ_1 and $\epsilon_2 \to 0$ also, and we get (5.1).

It is often convenient to use differentials rather than derivatives as in (5.1). We would like to be able to use (3.6), but in (3.6) x and y were independent variables and now they are functions of t. However, it is possible to show (Problem 20) that dz as defined in (3.6) is a good approximation to Δz even though x and y are related. We may then write

(5.3)
$$dz = \frac{\partial z}{\partial x}\, dx + \frac{\partial z}{\partial y}\, dy$$

whether or not x and y are independent variables, and we may think of getting (5.1) by dividing (5.3) by dt. This is very convenient in doing problems. Thus we could do Example 2 in the following way:

$$dz = x\, dy + y\, dx = x \cos t\, dt + y \cdot 4t\, dt = (2t^2 \cos t + 4t \sin t)\, dt,$$

$$\frac{dz}{dt} = 2t^2 \cos t + 4t \sin t.$$

In doing problems, we may then use either differentials or derivatives. Here is another example.

Example 3.   Find dz/dt given $z = x^y$, where $y = \tan^{-1} t$, $x = \sin t$. Using differentials, we find

$$dz = yx^{y-1}\, dx + x^y \ln x\, dy = yx^{y-1} \cos t\, dt + x^y \ln x \cdot \frac{dt}{1+t^2},$$

$$\frac{dz}{dt} = yx^{y-1} \cos t + x^y \ln x \cdot \frac{1}{1+t^2}.$$

You may wonder in a problem like this why we don't just substitute x and y as functions of t into $z = x^y$ to get z as a function of t and then differentiate. Sometimes this may be the best thing to do but not always. For example, the resulting formula may be very complicated and it may save a lot of algebra to use (5.1) or (5.3). This is especially true if we want dz/dt for a numerical value of t. Then there are cases when we *cannot* substitute; for example, if x as a function of t is given by $x + e^x = t$, we cannot solve for x as a function of t in terms of elementary functions. But we *can* find dx/dt, and so we can find dz/dt by (5.1). Finding dx/dt from such an equation is called implicit differentiation; we shall now discuss this process.

6. IMPLICIT DIFFERENTIATION

Example 1.   Given $x + e^x = t$, find dx/dt and d^2x/dt^2.

If we give values to x, find the corresponding t values, and plot x against t, we have a graph whose slope is dx/dt. In other words, x *is* a function of t even though we cannot solve the equation for x in terms of elementary functions of t. To find dx/dt, we realize that x *is* a function of t

and just differentiate each term of the equation with respect to t (this is called implicit differentiation). We get

(6.1)
$$\frac{dx}{dt} + e^x \frac{dx}{dt} = 1.$$

Solving for dx/dt, we get

$$\frac{dx}{dt} = \frac{1}{1 + e^x}.$$

Alternatively, we could use differentials here, and write first $dx + e^x \, dx = dt$; dividing by dt then gives (6.1).

We can also find higher derivatives by implicit differentiation (but do *not* use differentials for this since we have not given any meaning to the derivative or differential of a differential). Let us differentiate each term of (6.1) with respect to t; we get

(6.2)
$$\frac{d^2x}{dt^2} + e^x \frac{d^2x}{dt^2} + e^x \left(\frac{dx}{dt}\right)^2 = 0.$$

Solving for d^2x/dt^2 and substituting the value already found for dx/dt, we get

(6.3)
$$\frac{d^2x}{dt^2} = \frac{-e^x \left(\frac{dx}{dt}\right)^2}{1 + e^x} = \frac{-e^x}{(1 + e^x)^3}.$$

This problem is even easier if we want only the numerical values of the derivatives at a point. For $x = 0$ and $t = 1$, (6.1) gives

$$\frac{dx}{dt} + 1 \cdot \frac{dx}{dt} = 1 \quad \text{or} \quad \frac{dx}{dt} = \frac{1}{2},$$

and (6.2) gives

$$\frac{d^2x}{dt^2} + 1 \cdot \frac{d^2x}{dt^2} + 1 \cdot (\tfrac{1}{2})^2 = 0 \quad \text{or} \quad \frac{d^2x}{dt^2} = -\frac{1}{8}.$$

Implicit differentiation is the best method to use in finding slopes of curves with complicated equations.

Example 2. Find the equation of the tangent line to $x^3 - 3y^3 + xy + 21 = 0$ at the point $(1, 2)$.

We differentiate the given equation implicitly with respect to x to get

$$3x^2 - 9y^2 \frac{dy}{dx} + x \frac{dy}{dx} + y = 0.$$

Substitute $x = 1, y = 2$:

$$3 - 36 \frac{dy}{dx} + \frac{dy}{dx} + 2 = 0, \quad \frac{dy}{dx} = \frac{5}{35} = \frac{1}{7}.$$

Then the equation of the tangent line is

$$\frac{y-2}{x-1} = \frac{1}{7} \quad \text{or} \quad x - 7y + 13 = 0.$$

7. MORE CHAIN RULE

Above we have considered $z = f(x, y)$, where x and y are functions of t. Now suppose $z = f(x, y)$ as before, but x and y are each functions of two variables s and t. Then z is a function of s and t and we want to find $\partial z/\partial s$ and $\partial z/\partial t$. We show by some examples how to do problems like this.

Example 1.　Find $\partial z/\partial s$ and $\partial z/\partial t$ given

$$z = xy, \quad x = \sin(s + t), \quad y = s - t.$$

We take differentials of each of the three equations to get

$$dz = y\,dx + x\,dy, \quad dx = \cos(s+t)(ds+dt), \quad dy = ds - dt.$$

Substituting dx and dy into dz, we get

(7.1)
$$\begin{aligned} dz &= y\cos(s+t)(ds+dt) + x(ds-dt) \\ &= [y\cos(s+t) + x]\,ds + [y\cos(s+t) - x]\,dt. \end{aligned}$$

Now if s is constant, $ds = 0$, z is a function of one variable t, and we can divide (7.1) by dt [see (5.1) and the discussion following it]. For $dz \div dt$ on the left we write $\partial z/\partial t$ because that is the notation which properly describes what we are finding, namely, the rate of change of z with t when s is constant. Thus we have

$$\frac{\partial z}{\partial t} = y\cos(s+t) - x$$

and similarly

$$\frac{\partial z}{\partial s} = y\cos(s+t) + x.$$

Note that in (7.1) the coefficient of ds is $\partial z/\partial s$ and the coefficient of dt is $\partial z/\partial t$ [also compare (5.3)]. If you realize this, you can simply read off $\partial z/\partial s$ and $\partial z/\partial t$ from (7.1).

We can do problems with more variables in the same way.

Example 2.　Find $\partial u/\partial s$, $\partial u/\partial t$, given $u = x^2 + 2xy - y\ln z$ and $x = s + t^2$, $y = s - t^2$, $z = 2t$.

We find

$$du = 2x\,dx + 2x\,dy + 2y\,dx - \frac{y}{z}\,dz - \ln z\,dy$$

$$= (2x + 2y)(ds + 2t\,dt) + (2x - \ln z)(ds - 2t\,dt) - \frac{y}{z}\,(2\,dt)$$

$$= (4x + 2y - \ln z)\,ds + \left(4yt + 2t\ln z - \frac{2y}{z}\right)\,dt.$$

Then

$$\frac{\partial u}{\partial s} = 4x + 2y - \ln z, \qquad \frac{\partial u}{\partial t} = 4yt + 2t\ln z - \frac{2y}{z}.$$

If we want just one derivative, say $\partial u/\partial t$, we can save some work by letting $ds = 0$ to start with. To make it clear that we have done this, we write

$$du_s = (2x + 2y)(2t\,dt) + (2x - \ln z)(-2t\,dt) - \frac{y}{z}\,(2\,dt)$$

$$= \left(4yt + 2t\ln z - \frac{2y}{z}\right)\,dt.$$

The subscript s indicates that s is being held constant. Then dividing by dt, we have $\partial u/\partial t$ as before. We could also use derivatives instead of differentials. By an equation like (5.1), we have

(7.2)
$$\frac{\partial u}{\partial t} = \frac{\partial u}{\partial x}\frac{\partial x}{\partial t} + \frac{\partial u}{\partial y}\frac{\partial y}{\partial t} + \frac{\partial u}{\partial z}\frac{\partial z}{\partial t},$$

where we have written all the t derivatives as partials since u, x, y, and z depend on both s and t. Using (7.2), we get

$$\frac{\partial u}{\partial t} = (2x + 2y)(2t) + (2x - \ln z)(-2t) + \left(-\frac{y}{z}\right)(2)$$

$$= 4yt + 2t\ln z - \frac{2y}{z}.$$

Again in these problems, you may say, why not just substitute? Look at this problem.

Example 3. Find dz/dt given $z = x - y$ and

$$x^2 + y^2 = t^2,$$
$$x\sin t = ye^y.$$

From the z equation, we have

$$dz = dx - dy.$$

We need dx and dy; here we cannot solve for x and y in terms of t. But we *can* find dx and dy in terms of dt from the other two equations and this is all we need. Take differentials of both equations to get

$$2x\,dx + 2y\,dy = 2t\,dt,$$
$$\sin t\,dx + x\cos t\,dt = (ye^y + e^y)\,dy.$$

Rearrange terms:

$$x\,dx + y\,dy = t\,dt,$$
$$\sin t\,dx - (y+1)e^y\,dy = -x\cos t\,dt.$$

Solve for dx and dy (in terms of dt) by determinants:

$$dx = \frac{\begin{vmatrix} t\,dt & y \\ -x\cos t\,dt & -(y+1)e^y \end{vmatrix}}{\begin{vmatrix} x & y \\ \sin t & -(y+1)e^y \end{vmatrix}} = \frac{-t(y+1)e^y + xy\cos t}{-x(y+1)e^y - y\sin t}\,dt$$

and similarly for dy. Substituting dx and dy into the formula for dz and dividing by dt, we get dz/dt.

We can also do problems like this when x and y are given implicitly as functions of two variables s and t.

Example 4.　Find $\partial z/\partial s$ and $\partial z/\partial t$ given $z = x^2 + xy$ and

$$x^2 + y^3 = st + 5,$$
$$x^3 - y^2 = s^2 + t^2.$$

We have $dz = 2x\,dx + x\,dy + y\,dx$. To find dx and dy from the other two equations, we take differentials of each equation:

(7.3)
$$2x\,dx + 3y^2\,dy = s\,dt + t\,ds,$$
$$3x^2\,dx - 2y\,dy = 2s\,ds + 2t\,dt.$$

We can solve these two equations for dx and dy in terms of ds and dt to get

$$dx = \frac{\begin{vmatrix} s\,dt + t\,ds & 3y^2 \\ 2s\,ds + 2t\,dt & -2y \end{vmatrix}}{\begin{vmatrix} 2x & 3y^2 \\ 3x^2 & -2y \end{vmatrix}} = \frac{(-2ys - 6ty^2)\,dt + (-2yt - 6sy^2)\,ds}{-4xy - 9x^2y^2}$$

and a similar expression for dy. We substitute these values of dx and dy into dz and find dz in terms of ds and dt just as in Example 1; we can then write $\partial z/\partial s$ and $\partial z/\partial t$ just as we did there (Problem 43). Notice that if we want only one derivative, say $\partial z/\partial t$, we could save some algebra by putting

$ds = 0$ in (7.3). Also note that we can save some algebra if we want the derivatives only at one point. Suppose we were asked for $\partial z/\partial s$ and $\partial z/\partial t$ at $x = 3$, $y = 1$, $s = 1$, $t = 5$. We substitute these values into (7.3) to get

$$6\,dx + 3\,dy = dt + 5\,ds,$$
$$27\,dx - 2\,dy = 10\,dt + 2\,ds.$$

We solve these equations for dx and dy and substitute into dz just as before, but the algebra is easier with the numerical coefficients (Problem 43).

So far, we have been assuming that the independent variables were "natural" pairs like x and y, or s and t. For example, we wrote $\partial x/\partial s$ above, taking it for granted that the variable held constant was t. In some applications (particularly thermodynamics), it is not at all clear what the other independent variable is and we have to be more explicit. We write $(\partial x/\partial s)_t$; this means that s and t are the two independent variables, that x is thought of as a function of them, and then x is differentiated partially with respect to s. Suppose we try to find from the three equations of Example 4 a rather peculiar looking derivative.

Example 5.   Given

$$z = x^2 + xy,$$
$$x^2 + y^3 = st + 5,$$
$$x^3 - y^2 = s^2 + t^2,$$

find $(\partial s/\partial z)_x$.

First, let us see that the question makes sense. There are five variables in the three equations. If we give values to two of them, we can solve for the other three; that is, there are *two independent* variables, and the other three are functions of these two. If z and x are the independent ones, then s, t, and y are functions of z and x; we should be able to find their partial derivatives, for example $(\partial s/\partial z)_x$ which we wanted. To carry out the necessary work, we take differentials of all three equations:

$$dz = 2x\,dx + x\,dy + y\,dx,$$
$$2x\,dx + 3y^2\,dy = s\,dt + t\,ds,$$
$$3x^2\,dx - 2y\,dy = 2s\,ds + 2t\,dt.$$

Rearranging the equations, we get

$$-x\,dy = (2x + y)\,dx - dz,$$
$$t\,ds + s\,dt - 3y^2\,dy = 2x\,dx,$$
$$2s\,ds + 2t\,dt + 2y\,dy = 3x^2\,dx.$$

From these three equations we could solve for ds, dt, and dy in terms of dx and dz (by determinants or by elimination—the same methods you use to solve any set of linear equations). Then we could find any partial derivative of $s(x, z)$, $t(x, z)$, or $y(x, z)$ with respect to x or z. For example, to find $(\partial y/\partial z)_x$, we get from the first equation

$$dy = \frac{1}{x} dz - \frac{2x + y}{x} dx,$$

$$\left(\frac{\partial y}{\partial z}\right)_x = \frac{1}{x}.$$

Note that we would not need to differentiate all three equations if we wanted only this derivative; you should always look ahead to see how much differentiation is necessary! To find the derivative we wanted we must solve the three equations for ds in terms of dx and dz; we can save ourselves some work [if we want *only* $(\partial s/\partial z)_x$] by putting $dx = 0$ to start with. To make it clear that we have done this we write ds_x and dz_x. Then we get

$$ds_x = \frac{\begin{vmatrix} -dz_x & 0 & -x \\ 0 & s & -3y^2 \\ 0 & 2t & 2y \\ 0 & 0 & -x \\ t & s & -3y^2 \\ 2s & 2t & 2y \end{vmatrix}}{} = \frac{-(2sy + 6ty^2)\, dz_x}{-x(2t^2 - 2s^2)},$$

$$\left(\frac{\partial s}{\partial z}\right)_x = \frac{sy + 3ty^2}{x(t^2 - s^2)}.$$

Example 6. Let x, y be rectangular coordinates and r, θ be polar coordinates in a plane. Then the equations relating them are

$$x = r \cos \theta, \qquad r = \sqrt{x^2 + y^2},$$
$$\text{or}$$
$$y = r \sin \theta, \qquad \theta = \tan^{-1} \frac{y}{x}.$$

Suppose we want to find $\partial \theta/\partial x$. Remembering that if $y = f(x)$, dy/dx and dx/dy are reciprocals, you might be tempted to find $\partial \theta/\partial x$ by taking the reciprocal of $\partial x/\partial \theta$, which is easier to find than $\partial \theta/\partial x$. This is wrong. From $\theta = \tan^{-1}(y/x)$ we get

(7.4)
$$\frac{\partial \theta}{\partial x} = \frac{-y/x^2}{1 + (y^2/x^2)} = -\frac{y}{r^2}.$$

From $x = r \cos \theta$ we get

$$\frac{\partial x}{\partial \theta} = -r \sin \theta = -y.$$

These are not reciprocals. You should think carefully about the reason for this; $\partial\theta/\partial x$ means $(\partial\theta/\partial x)_y$, whereas $\partial x/\partial\theta$ means $(\partial x/\partial\theta)_r$. In one case y is held constant and in the other case r is held constant; this is why the two derivatives are not reciprocals. It *is* true that $(\partial\theta/\partial x)_y$ and $(\partial x/\partial\theta)_y$ are reciprocals. But to find $(\partial x/\partial\theta)_y$ directly, we have to express x as a function of θ and y. We find $x = y\cot\theta$, so we get

$$(7.5) \qquad \left(\frac{\partial x}{\partial\theta}\right)_y = y(-\csc^2\theta) = \frac{-y}{\sin^2\theta} = \frac{-y}{y^2/r^2} = -\frac{r^2}{y},$$

which *is* the reciprocal of $\partial\theta/\partial x$ in (7.4). This is a general rule: $\partial u/\partial v$ and $\partial v/\partial u$ are *not* usually reciprocals; they *are* reciprocals if the other independent variables (besides u or v) are the same in both cases. You can see this clearly from the equations involving differentials. From $\theta = \arctan(y/x)$, we can find

$$(7.6) \qquad d\theta = \frac{x\,dy - y\,dx}{x^2} \Big/ \left(1 + \frac{y^2}{x^2}\right) = \frac{x\,dy - y\,dx}{r^2}.$$

From $x = r\cos\theta$, we get

$$(7.7) \qquad dx = \cos\theta\,dr - r\sin\theta\,d\theta = \frac{x}{r}\,dr - y\,d\theta.$$

From (7.6), if y is constant, $dy = 0$, and we can write

$$(7.8) \qquad d\theta_y = -\frac{y}{r^2}\,dx_y,$$

where the y subscript indicates that y is constant. From (7.8) we then find either

$$\left(\frac{\partial\theta}{\partial x}\right)_y = \frac{d\theta_y}{dx_y} \qquad \text{or} \qquad \left(\frac{\partial x}{\partial\theta}\right)_y = \frac{dx_y}{d\theta_y}$$

and these are reciprocals. From (7.7), however, we can find $(\partial x/\partial\theta)_r$ or $(\partial\theta/\partial x)_r$; these are again reciprocals of each other, but are different from the derivatives found from (7.8).

8. APPLICATION OF PARTIAL DIFFERENTIATION TO MAXIMUM AND MINIMUM PROBLEMS

You will recall that derivatives give slopes as well as rates and that you find maximum and minimum points of $y = f(x)$ by setting $dy/dx = 0$. Often in applied problems we want to find maxima or minima of functions of more than one variable. Think of $z = f(x, y)$ which represents a surface.

If there is a maximum point on it (like the top of a hill), then the curves for $x =$ const. and $y =$ const. which pass through the maximum point also have maxima at the same point. That is, $\partial z/\partial x$ and $\partial z/\partial y$ are zero at the maximum point. Recall that $dy/dx = 0$ was a necessary condition for a maximum point of $y = f(x)$, but not sufficient; the point might have been a minimum or perhaps a point of inflection with a horizontal tangent. Something similar can happen for $z = f(x, y)$. The point where $\partial z/\partial x = 0$ and $\partial z/\partial y = 0$ may be a maximum point, a minimum point, or neither. (An interesting example of neither is a "saddle point"—a curve from front to back on a saddle has a minimum; one from side to side has a maximum.) In finding maxima of $y = f(x)$, it is sometimes possible to tell from the geometry or physics that you have a maximum. If necessary you can find d^2y/dx^2; if it is negative, then you know you have a maximum point. There is a similar (rather complicated) second derivative test for functions of two variables (see Problem 123), but we use it only if we have to; usually we can tell from the problem whether we have a maximum, a minimum, or neither. Let us consider some examples of maximum or minimum problems.

Example. A pup tent (Fig. 8.1) of given volume V, with ends but no floor, is to be made using the least possible material. Find the proportions.

Figure 8.1

Using the letters indicated in the figure, we find the volume V and the area A.

$$V = \tfrac{1}{2} \cdot 2w \cdot l \cdot w \tan \theta = w^2 l \tan \theta,$$

$$A = 2w^2 \tan \theta + \frac{2lw}{\cos \theta}.$$

Since V is given, only two of the three variables w, l, and θ are independent, and we must eliminate one of them from A before we try to minimize A. Solving the V equation for l and substituting into A, we get

$$A = 2w^2 \tan \theta + \frac{2w}{\cos \theta} \frac{V}{w^2 \tan \theta} = 2w^2 \tan \theta + \frac{2V}{w} \csc \theta.$$

We now have A as a function of two independent variables w and θ. To minimize A we find $\partial A/\partial w$ and $\partial A/\partial \theta$ and set them equal to zero.

$$\frac{\partial A}{\partial w} = 4w \tan \theta - \frac{2V \csc \theta}{w^2} = 0,$$

$$\frac{\partial A}{\partial \theta} = 2w^2 \sec^2 \theta - \frac{2V}{w} \csc \theta \cot \theta = 0.$$

Solving each of these equations for w^3 and setting the results equal, we get

$$w^3 = \frac{V \csc \theta}{2 \tan \theta} = \frac{V \csc \theta \cot \theta}{\sec^2 \theta} \quad \text{or} \quad \frac{\cos \theta}{2 \sin^2 \theta} = \frac{\cos \theta \cos^2 \theta}{\sin^2 \theta}.$$

You should convince yourself that neither $\sin \theta = 0$ nor $\cos \theta = 0$ is possible (the tent collapses to zero volume in both cases). Therefore we may assume $\sin \theta \neq 0$ and $\cos \theta \neq 0$ and cancel these factors, getting $\cos^2 \theta = \frac{1}{2}$ or $\theta = 45°$. Then $\tan \theta = 1$, $V = w^2 l$, and from the $\partial A/\partial w$ equation we have $2w = l\sqrt{2}$. Then the height of the tent (at the peak) is $w \tan \theta = w = l/\sqrt{2}$.

9. MAXIMUM AND MINIMUM PROBLEMS WITH CONSTRAINTS; LAGRANGE MULTIPLIERS

Example 1.   A wire is bent to fit the curve $y = 1 - x^2$ (Fig. 9.1). A string is stretched from the origin to a point (x, y) on the curve. Find (x, y) to minimize the length of the string.

We want to minimize the distance $d = \sqrt{x^2 + y^2}$ from the origin to the point (x, y); this is equivalent to minimizing $f = d^2 = x^2 + y^2$. But x and y are not independent; they are related by the equation of the curve. This

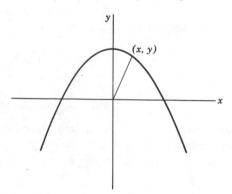

Figure 9.1

extra relation between the variables is what we mean by a *constraint*. Problems involving constraints occur frequently in applications.

There are several ways to do a problem like this. We shall discuss the following methods: (a) elimination, (b) implicit differentiation, (c) Lagrange multipliers.

(a) Elimination. The most obvious method is to eliminate y. Then we want to minimize

$$f = x^2 + (1 - x^2)^2 = x^2 + 1 - 2x^2 + x^4 = x^4 - x^2 + 1.$$

This is just an ordinary calculus problem:

$$\frac{df}{dx} = 4x^3 - 2x = 0, \qquad x = 0, \qquad \text{or} \quad x = \pm\sqrt{\tfrac{1}{2}}.$$

It is not immediately obvious which of these points is a maximum and which is a minimum, so in this simple problem it is worth while to find the second derivative:

$$\frac{d^2f}{dx^2} = 12x^2 - 2 = \begin{cases} -2 & \text{at } x = 0 \qquad\quad \text{(maximum)}, \\ 4 & \text{at } x = \pm\sqrt{\tfrac{1}{2}} \quad \text{(minimum)}. \end{cases}$$

The minimum we wanted then occurs at $x = \pm\sqrt{\tfrac{1}{2}}, y = \tfrac{1}{2}$.

(b) Implicit differentiation. Suppose it had not been possible to solve for y and substitute; we could still do the problem. From $f = x^2 + y^2$, we find

(9.1) $\qquad df = 2x\,dx + 2y\,dy \qquad$ or $\qquad \dfrac{df}{dx} = 2x + 2y\dfrac{dy}{dx}$.

From an equation like $y = 1 - x^2$ relating x and y, we could find dy in terms of dx even if the equation were not solvable for y. Here we get

$$dy = -2x\,dx.$$

Eliminating dy from df, we have

$$df = (2x - 4xy)\,dx \qquad \text{or} \qquad \frac{df}{dx} = 2x - 4xy.$$

To minimize f, we put $df/dx = 0$ (or in the differential notation we put $df = 0$ for arbitrary dx). This gives

$$2x - 4xy = 0.$$

This equation must now be solved simultaneously with the equation of the curve $y = 1 - x^2$. We get $2x - 4x(1 - x^2) = 0$, $x = 0$ or $\pm\sqrt{\tfrac{1}{2}}$ as before.

To test for maxima or minima we need d^2f/dx^2. Differentiating df/dx in (9.1) with respect to x, we get

$$\frac{d^2f}{dx^2} = 2 + 2\left(\frac{dy}{dx}\right)^2 + 2y\,\frac{d^2y}{dx^2}.$$

At $x = 0$, we find $y = 1$, $dy/dx = 0$, $d^2y/dx^2 = -2$, so

$$\frac{d^2f}{dx^2} = 2 - 4 = -2;$$

this is a maximum point. At $x = \pm\sqrt{\tfrac{1}{2}}$, we find

$$y = \tfrac{1}{2}, \qquad \frac{dy}{dx} = \mp\sqrt{2}, \qquad \frac{d^2y}{dx^2} = -2,$$

so

$$\frac{d^2f}{dx^2} = 2 + 4 - 2 = 4;$$

this point is the required minimum. Notice particularly here that you could do every step of (b) even if the equation of the curve could not be solved for y.

We can do problems with several independent variables by methods similar to those we have just used in Example 1. Consider this problem.

Example 2. Find the shortest distance from the origin to the plane $x - 2y - 2z = 3$.

We want to minimize the distance $d = \sqrt{x^2 + y^2 + z^2}$ from the origin to a point (x, y, z) on the plane. This is equivalent to minimizing $f = d^2 = x^2 + y^2 + z^2$ if $x - 2y - 2z = 3$. We can eliminate one variable, say x, from f using the equation of the plane. Then we have

$$f = (3 + 2y + 2z)^2 + y^2 + z^2.$$

Here f is a function of the two independent variables y and z, so to minimize f we put $\partial f/\partial y = 0$, $\partial f/\partial z = 0$.

$$\frac{\partial f}{\partial y} = 2(3 + 2y + 2z) \cdot 2 + 2y = 0,$$

$$\frac{\partial f}{\partial z} = 2(3 + 2y + 2z) \cdot 2 + 2z = 0.$$

Solving these equations for y and z, we get $y = z = -\tfrac{2}{3}$, so from the equation of the plane we get $x = \tfrac{1}{3}$. Then

$$f_{\min} = (\tfrac{1}{3})^2 + (\tfrac{2}{3})^2 + (\tfrac{2}{3})^2 = 1, \quad d_{\min} = 1.$$

It is clear from the geometry that there *is* a minimum distance from the origin to a plane; therefore this is it without a second-derivative test.

Problems with any number of variables *can* be done this way, or by method (b) if the equations are implicit.

(c) **Lagrange multipliers.** However, methods (a) and (b) can involve an enormous amount of algebra. We can shortcut this algebra by a process known as the method of *Lagrange multipliers* or undetermined multipliers. We want to consider a problem like the one in (a) or (b). In general, we want to find the maximum or minimum of a function $f(x, y)$, where x and y are related by an equation $\phi(x, y) = $ const. As in (b) we take differentials of both f and ϕ. Since $\phi = $ const., we get $d\phi = 0$. We *put* $df = 0$ because we want to find maximum or minimum points of f.

(9.2)
$$df = \frac{\partial f}{\partial x} dx + \frac{\partial f}{\partial y} dy = 0,$$

$$d\phi = \frac{\partial \phi}{\partial x} dx + \frac{\partial \phi}{\partial y} dy = 0.$$

In method (b) we solved the $d\phi$ equation for dy in terms of dx and substituted it into df; this often involves messy algebra. Instead, we shall multiply the $d\phi$ equation by λ (this is the undetermined multiplier—we shall find its value later) and add it to the df equation; then we have

(9.3)
$$\left(\frac{\partial f}{\partial x} + \lambda \frac{\partial \phi}{\partial x}\right) dx + \left(\frac{\partial f}{\partial y} + \lambda \frac{\partial \phi}{\partial y}\right) dy = 0.$$

We now pick λ so that

(9.4)
$$\frac{\partial f}{\partial y} + \lambda \frac{\partial \phi}{\partial y} = 0.$$

(That is, we pick $\lambda = -(\partial f/\partial y)/(\partial \phi/\partial y)$, but it isn't necessary to write it in this complicated form! In fact, this is exactly the point of the Lagrange multiplier λ; by using the abbreviation λ for a complicated expression, we avoid some algebra.) Then from (9.3) and (9.4) we have

(9.5)
$$\frac{\partial f}{\partial x} + \lambda \frac{\partial \phi}{\partial x} = 0.$$

Equations (9.4), (9.5), and $\phi(x, y) = $ const. can now be solved for the three unknowns x, y, λ. We don't actually want the value of λ, but often the algebra is simpler if we do find it and use it in finding x and y which we do want. Note that equations (9.4) and (9.5) are exactly the equations we would write if we had a function

(9.6)
$$F(x, y) = f(x, y) + \lambda\phi(x, y)$$

of two independent variables x and y and we wanted to find its maximum and minimum values. Actually, of course, x and y are not independent; they are related by the ϕ equation. However, (9.6) gives us a simple way of stating and remembering how to get equations (9.4) and (9.5). Thus we can state the method of Lagrange multipliers in the following way:

(9.7)   To find the maximum or minimum values of $f(x, y)$ when x and y are related by the equation $\phi(x, y) = $ const., form the function $F(x, y)$ as in (9.6) and set the two partial derivatives of F equal to zero [equations (9.4) and (9.5)]. Then solve these two equations and the equation $\phi(x, y) = $ const. for the three unknowns x, y, and λ.

As a simple illustration of the method we shall do the problem of Example 1 by Lagrange multipliers. Here

$$f(x, y) = x^2 + y^2, \qquad \phi(x, y) = y + x^2 = 1,$$

and we write the equations to minimize

$$F(x, y) = f + \lambda\phi = x^2 + y^2 + \lambda(y + x^2),$$

namely

(9.8)

$$\frac{\partial F}{\partial x} = 2x + \lambda \cdot 2x = 0,$$

$$\frac{\partial F}{\partial y} = 2y + \lambda = 0.$$

We solve these simultaneously with the ϕ equation $y + x^2 = 1$. From the first equation in (9.8), either $x = 0$ or $\lambda = -1$. If $x = 0$, $y = 1$ from the ϕ equation (and $\lambda = -2$). If $\lambda = -1$, the second equation gives $y = \frac{1}{2}$, and then the ϕ equation gives $x^2 = \frac{1}{2}$. These are the same values we had before. The method offers nothing new in testing whether we have found a maximum or a minimum, so we shall not repeat that work; if it is possible to see from the geometry or the physics what we have found, we don't bother to test.

Lagrange multipliers simplify the work enormously in more complicated problems. Consider this problem.

Example 3. Find the volume of the largest rectangular parallelepiped (that is, box), with edges parallel to the axes, inscribed in the ellipsoid

$$\frac{x^2}{a^2} + \frac{y^2}{b^2} + \frac{z^2}{c^2} = 1.$$

Let the point (x, y, z) be the corner in the first octant where the box touches the ellipsoid. Then (x, y, z) satisfies the ellipsoid equation and the volume of the box is $8xyz$ (since there are 8 octants). Our problem is to maximize $f(x, y, z) = 8xyz$, where x, y, z are related by the ellipsoid equation

$$\phi(x, y, z) = \frac{x^2}{a^2} + \frac{y^2}{b^2} + \frac{z^2}{c^2} = 1.$$

By the method of Lagrange multipliers we write

$$F(x, y, z) = f + \lambda\phi = 8xyz + \lambda\left(\frac{x^2}{a^2} + \frac{y^2}{b^2} + \frac{z^2}{c^2}\right)$$

and set the three partial derivatives of F equal to 0:

$$\frac{\partial F}{\partial x} = 8yz + \lambda \cdot \frac{2x}{a^2} = 0,$$

$$\frac{\partial F}{\partial y} = 8xz + \lambda \cdot \frac{2y}{b^2} = 0,$$

$$\frac{\partial F}{\partial z} = 8xy + \lambda \cdot \frac{2z}{c^2} = 0.$$

We solve these three equations and the equation $\phi = 1$ simultaneously for x, y, z, and λ. (Although we don't *have* to find λ, it may be simpler to find it first.) Multiply the first equation by x, the second by y, and the third by z, and add to get

$$3 \cdot 8xyz + 2\lambda\left(\frac{x^2}{a^2} + \frac{y^2}{b^2} + \frac{z^2}{c^2}\right) = 0.$$

Using the equation of the ellipsoid, we can simplify this to

$$24xyz + 2\lambda = 0 \quad \text{or} \quad \lambda = -12xyz.$$

Substituting λ into the $\partial F/\partial x$ equation, we find that

$$8yz - 12xyz \cdot \frac{2x}{a^2} = 0.$$

From the geometry it is clear that the corner of the box should not be where y or z is equal to zero, so we divide by yz and solve for x, getting

$$x^2 = \tfrac{1}{3}a^2.$$

The other two equations could be solved in the same way. However, it is pretty clear from symmetry that the solutions will be $y^2 = \tfrac{1}{3}b^2$ and $z^2 = \tfrac{1}{3}c^2$. Then the maximum volume is

$$8xyz = \frac{8abc}{3\sqrt{3}}.$$

You might contrast this fairly simple algebra with what would be involved in method (a). There you would have to solve the ellipsoid equation for, say, z, substitute this into the volume formula, and then differentiate the square root. Even by method (b) you would have to find $\partial z/\partial x$ or similar expressions from the ellipsoid equation.

We should show that the Lagrange method is justified for problems involving several independent variables. We want to find maximum or minimum values of $f(x, y, z)$ if $\phi(x, y, z) = $ const. (You might note at each step that the proof could easily be extended to more variables.) We take differentials of both the f and the ϕ equations. Since $\phi = $ const., we have $d\phi = 0$. We *put* $df = 0$ because we want maximum and minimum values of f. Thus we write

(9.9)
$$df = \frac{\partial f}{\partial x} dx + \frac{\partial f}{\partial y} dy + \frac{\partial f}{\partial z} dz = 0,$$
$$d\phi = \frac{\partial \phi}{\partial x} dx + \frac{\partial \phi}{\partial y} dy + \frac{\partial \phi}{\partial z} dz = 0.$$

We *could* find dz from the $d\phi$ equation and substitute it into the df equation; this corresponds to method (b) and may involve complicated algebra. Instead, we form the sum $F = f + \lambda \phi$ and find, using (9.9),

(9.10) $dF = df + \lambda \, d\phi$

$$= \left(\frac{\partial f}{\partial x} + \lambda \frac{\partial \phi}{\partial x} \right) dx + \left(\frac{\partial f}{\partial y} + \lambda \frac{\partial \phi}{\partial y} \right) dy + \left(\frac{\partial f}{\partial z} + \lambda \frac{\partial \phi}{\partial z} \right) dz.$$

There are two independent variables in this problem (since x, y, and z are related by $\phi = $ const.). Suppose x and y are the independent ones; then z is determined from the ϕ equation. Similarly, dx and dy may have any values we choose, and dz is determined. Let us select λ so that

(9.11)
$$\frac{\partial f}{\partial z} + \lambda \frac{\partial \phi}{\partial z} = 0.$$

Then from (9.10), for $dy = 0$, we get

(9.12)
$$\frac{\partial f}{\partial x} + \lambda \frac{\partial \phi}{\partial x} = 0$$

and for $dx = 0$ we get

(9.13)
$$\frac{\partial f}{\partial y} + \lambda \frac{\partial \phi}{\partial y} = 0.$$

We can state a rule similar to (9.7) for obtaining equations (9.11), (9.12), and (9.13).

(9.14) To find the maximum and minimum values of $f(x, y, z)$ if $\phi(x, y, z) = $ const., we form the function $F = f + \lambda\phi$ and set the three partial derivatives of F equal to zero. We solve these equations and the equation $\phi = $ const. for x, y, z, and λ. (For a problem with still more variables there are more equations, but no change in method.)

A similar method can be used if there are several ϕ equations. Suppose we want to find the maximum or minimum of $f(x, y, z, w)$ if $\phi_1(x, y, z, w) = $ const. and $\phi_2(x, y, z, w) = $ const. There are two independent variables, say x and y. We write

$$df = \frac{\partial f}{\partial x} dx + \frac{\partial f}{\partial y} dy + \frac{\partial f}{\partial z} dz + \frac{\partial f}{\partial w} dw = 0,$$

(9.15) $$d\phi_1 = \frac{\partial \phi_1}{\partial x} dx + \frac{\partial \phi_1}{\partial y} dy + \frac{\partial \phi_1}{\partial z} dz + \frac{\partial \phi_1}{\partial w} dw = 0,$$

$$d\phi_2 = \frac{\partial \phi_2}{\partial x} dx + \frac{\partial \phi_2}{\partial y} dy + \frac{\partial \phi_2}{\partial z} dz + \frac{\partial \phi_2}{\partial w} dw = 0.$$

Again we *could* use the $d\phi_1$ and $d\phi_2$ equations to eliminate dz and dw from df (method b), but the algebra is forbidding! Instead, by the Lagrange method we form the function $F = f + \lambda_1\phi_1 + \lambda_2\phi_2$ and write, using (9.15),

(9.16)

$$dF = df + \lambda_1 \, d\phi_1 + \lambda_2 \, d\phi_2$$
$$= \left(\frac{\partial f}{\partial x} + \lambda_1 \frac{\partial \phi_1}{\partial x} + \lambda_2 \frac{\partial \phi_2}{\partial x}\right) dx + \left(\frac{\partial f}{\partial y} + \lambda_1 \frac{\partial \phi_1}{\partial y} + \lambda_2 \frac{\partial \phi_2}{\partial y}\right) dy$$
$$+ \left(\frac{\partial f}{\partial z} + \lambda_1 \frac{\partial \phi_1}{\partial z} + \lambda_2 \frac{\partial \phi_2}{\partial z}\right) dz + \left(\frac{\partial f}{\partial w} + \lambda_1 \frac{\partial \phi_1}{\partial w} + \lambda_2 \frac{\partial \phi_2}{\partial w}\right) dw.$$

We determine λ_1 and λ_2 from the two equations

(9.17)
$$\frac{\partial f}{\partial z} + \lambda_1 \frac{\partial \phi_1}{\partial z} + \lambda_2 \frac{\partial \phi_2}{\partial z} = 0,$$
$$\frac{\partial f}{\partial w} + \lambda_1 \frac{\partial \phi_1}{\partial w} + \lambda_2 \frac{\partial \phi_2}{\partial w} = 0.$$

Then for $dy = 0$, we have

(9.18) $$\frac{\partial f}{\partial x} + \lambda_1 \frac{\partial \phi_1}{\partial x} + \lambda_2 \frac{\partial \phi_2}{\partial x} = 0$$

and for $dx = 0$, we have

(9.19)
$$\frac{\partial f}{\partial y} + \lambda_1 \frac{\partial \phi_1}{\partial y} + \lambda_2 \frac{\partial \phi_2}{\partial y} = 0.$$

As before, we can remember the method of finding (9.17), (9.18), and (9.19) by thinking:

(9.20) To find the maximum or minimum of f subject to the conditions $\phi_1 = $ const. and $\phi_2 = $ const., define $F = f + \lambda_1\phi_1 + \lambda_2\phi_2$ and set each of the partial derivatives of F equal to zero. Solve these equations and the ϕ equations for the variables and the λ's.

Example 4. Find the minimum distance from the origin to the intersection of $xy = 12$ with $x + 2z = 0$.

We are to minimize $x^2 + y^2 + z^2$ subject to the two conditions $xy = 12$ and $x + 2z = 0$. By the Lagrange method we find the three partial derivatives of
$$F = x^2 + y^2 + z^2 + \lambda_1(x + 2z) + \lambda_2 xy$$

and set each of them equal to zero. We get

(9.21)
$$2x + \lambda_1 + \lambda_2 y = 0,$$
$$2y + \lambda_2 x = 0,$$
$$2z + 2\lambda_1 = 0.$$

These equations can be solved with $xy = 12$ and $x + 2z = 0$ to get (Problem 80)
$$x = \pm 2\sqrt[4]{\tfrac{36}{5}}, \qquad y = \pm 6\sqrt[4]{\tfrac{5}{36}}, \qquad z = \mp\sqrt[4]{\tfrac{36}{5}}.$$

Then the required minimum distance is (Problem 80)
$$d = \sqrt{x^2 + y^2 + z^2} = \sqrt{12\sqrt{5}}.$$

10. ENDPOINT OR BOUNDARY POINT PROBLEMS

So far we have been assuming that if there is a maximum or minimum point, calculus will find it. Some simple examples (see Figs. 10.1 to 10.4) show that this may not be true. Suppose, in a given problem, x can have values only between 0 and 1; this sort of restriction occurs frequently in applications. For example, if $x = |\cos \theta|$, the *graph* of $f(x) = 2 - x^2$ exists for all real x, but it has no meaning if $x = |\cos \theta|$, except for x between 0 and 1. As another example, suppose x is the length of a rectangle whose perimeter is 2; then $x < 0$ is meaningless in this problem since x

is a length, and $x > 1$ is impossible because the perimeter is 2. Let us ask for the largest and smallest values of each of the functions in Figs. 10.1 to 10.4 for $0 \leq x \leq 1$. In Fig. 10.1, calculus will give us the minimum point, but the maximum of $f(x)$ *for x between* 0 *and* 1 occurs at $x = 1$ and cannot be obtained by calculus, since $f'(x) \neq 0$ there. In Fig. 10.2, both the maximum and the minimum of $f(x)$ are at endpoints, the maximum at $x = 0$ and the minimum at $x = 1$. In Fig. 10.3 a relative maximum at P and a relative minimum at Q are given by calculus, but the absolute minimum between 0 and 1 occurs at $x = 0$, and the absolute maximum at $x = 1$. Here is a practical example of this sort of function. It is said that geographers used to give as the highest point in Florida the top of the highest hill; then it was found that the highest point is on the Alabama border! [See H. A. Thurston, *Amer. Math. Monthly*, vol. 68 (1961), pp. 650–652.] Figure 10.4 illustrates another way in which calculus may fail to give us a desired maximum or minimum point; here the derivative is discontinuous at the maximum point.

These are difficulties we must watch out for whenever there is any restriction on the values any of the variables may take (or any discontinuity in the functions or their derivatives). These restrictions are not

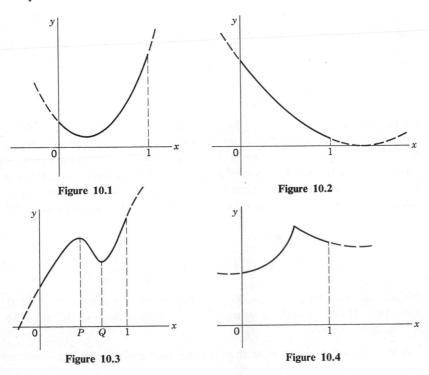

Figure 10.1

Figure 10.2

Figure 10.3

Figure 10.4

usually stated in so many words; you have to see them for yourself. For example, if $x^2 + y^2 = 25$, x and y are both between -5 and $+5$. If $y^2 = x^2 - 1$, then $|x|$ must be greater than or equal to 1. If $x = \csc \theta$, where θ is a first-quadrant angle, then $x \geq 1$. If $y = \sqrt{x}$, y' is discontinuous at the origin.

Example 1. A piece of wire 40 cm long is to be used to form the perimeters of a square and a circle in such a way as to make the total area (of square and circle) a maximum. Call the radius of the circle r; then the circumference of the circle is $2\pi r$. A length $40 - 2\pi r$ is left for the four sides of the square, so one side is $10 - \frac{1}{2}\pi r$. The total area is

$$A = \pi r^2 + (10 - \tfrac{1}{2}\pi r)^2.$$

Then

$$\frac{dA}{dr} = 2\pi r + 2(10 - \tfrac{1}{2}\pi r)(-\tfrac{1}{2}\pi) = 2\pi r\left(1 + \frac{\pi}{4}\right) - 10\pi.$$

If $dA/dr = 0$, we get

$$r\left(1 + \frac{\pi}{4}\right) = 5, \qquad r = \frac{5}{1 + \dfrac{\pi}{4}}.$$

The careless student would stop here claiming that this r gives maximum area. But let us apply the second derivative test to see whether we have a maximum. We find

$$\frac{d^2A}{dr^2} = 2\pi + \frac{\pi^2}{2} > 0$$

for the r found; that is, this r gives a minimum! The problem asks for a maximum. One way to find it would be to sketch A as a function of r and look at the graph to see where A has its largest value. A simpler way is this: A is a continuous function of r with a continuous derivative. If there were an interior maximum (that is, one between $r = 0$ and $2\pi r = 40$), calculus would find it. Therefore the maximum must be at one end or the other.

At $r = 0$, $A = 100$.

At $r = \dfrac{40}{2\pi}$, $A = \pi\left(\dfrac{40}{2\pi}\right)^2 + 0^2 = \dfrac{20^2}{\pi} = \dfrac{400}{\pi}$.

We see that A is larger at $r = 40/(2\pi)$; this value of A is then the desired maximum. It corresponds to using all the wire to make a circle; the side of the square is zero.

A similar difficulty can arise in problems with more variables.

Example 2. The temperature in a rectangular plate bounded by $x = 0$, $y = 0$, $x = 3$, and $y = 5$ is

$$T = xy^2 - x^2y + 100.$$

Find the hottest and coldest points of the plate.

We first set the partial derivatives of T equal to zero to find any interior maxima and minima. We get

$$\frac{\partial T}{\partial x} = y^2 - 2xy = 0,$$

$$\frac{\partial T}{\partial y} = 2xy - x^2 = 0.$$

The only solution of these equations is $x = y = 0$, for which $T = 100$.

We must next ask whether there are points around the boundary of the plate where T has a value larger or smaller than 100. To see that this might happen, think of a graph of T plotted as a function of x and y; this is a surface above the (x, y) plane. The mathematical surface does not have to stop at $x = 3$ and $y = 5$, but it has no meaning for our problem beyond these values. Just as for the curves in Fig. 10, the graph of the temperature may be increasing or decreasing as we cross a boundary; calculus will not then give us a zero derivative even though the temperature at the boundary may be larger (or smaller) than at other points of the plate. Thus we must consider the complete boundary of the plate (*not* just the corners!). The lines $x = 0$, $y = 0$, $x = 3$, and $y = 5$ are the boundaries; we consider each of them in turn. On $x = 0$ and $y = 0$ the temperature is 100. On the line $x = 3$, we have

$$T = 3y^2 - 9y + 100.$$

We can use calculus to see whether T has maxima or minima as a function of y along this line. We have

$$\frac{dT}{dy} = 6y - 9 = 0,$$

$$y = \tfrac{3}{2}, \qquad T = 93\tfrac{1}{4}.$$

Similarly along the line $y = 5$, we find

$$T = 25x - 5x^2 + 100,$$

$$\frac{dT}{dx} = 25 - 10x = 0,$$

$$x = \tfrac{5}{2}, \qquad T = 131\tfrac{1}{4}.$$

Finally, we must find T at the corners.

$$\text{At } (0, 0), (0, 5), \text{ and } (3, 0), \quad T = 100.$$
$$\text{At } (3, 5), \quad T = 130.$$

Putting all our results together, we see that the hottest point is $(\frac{5}{2}, 5)$ with $T = 131\frac{1}{4}$, and the coldest point is $(3, \frac{3}{2})$ with $T = 93\frac{1}{4}$.

Example 3. Find the point (or points) on the surface $x^2 - z^2 = 1$ closest to the origin. We want to minimize $f = x^2 + y^2 + z^2$, where $x^2 - z^2 = 1$. Suppose we eliminate z. Then $f = 2x^2 + y^2 - 1$. We would like to put $\partial f/\partial x = 0$, which implies $x = 0$, but this is not possible; since $z^2 = x^2 - 1$, x cannot be zero. We have to start over and eliminate x. Then

$$f = y^2 + 2z^2 + 1, \qquad \frac{\partial f}{\partial y} = 2y, \qquad \frac{\partial f}{\partial z} = 4z.$$

Setting both partial derivatives equal to zero, we get $y = z = 0$. Then $x = \pm 1$, and the points closest to the origin are $(1, 0, 0)$ and $(-1, 0, 0)$. We can see now why we had trouble: the values of x for a minimum occurred at the endpoints of the allowed region for x (that is, the region $|x| \geq 1$) and could not be found by calculus.

Let us do the same problem by the method of Lagrange multipliers. We write

$$F = x^2 + y^2 + z^2 + \lambda(x^2 - z^2).$$

$$\frac{\partial F}{\partial x} = 2x + 2x\lambda = 0. \qquad\qquad \text{Since } x \text{ can't be } 0, \lambda = -1.$$

$$\frac{\partial F}{\partial y} = 2y = 0, \qquad\qquad\qquad y = 0.$$

$$\frac{\partial F}{\partial z} = 2z - 2\lambda z = 0. \qquad\qquad \text{Since } \lambda = -1, z = 0.$$

Then from $x^2 - z^2 = 1$, we find $x^2 = 1$, $x = \pm 1$ as before.

We see that by using the method of Lagrange multipliers in this problem, we avoided our previous difficulty of having to start over with different variables. However, the Lagrange multiplier method still relies on calculus; consequently, it can work only if the maximum or minimum can be found by calculus using *some* set of variables (y and z, *not* x and y, in Example 3). For example, a problem in which the maximum or minimum occurs at endpoints in all variables cannot be done by *any* method that depends on setting derivatives equal to zero.

Example 4. Find the maximum value of $y - x$ for nonnegative x and y if $x^2 + y^2 = 1$.

Here we must have both x and y between 0 and 1. Then the values $y = 1$ and $x = 0$ give $y - x$ its largest value; these are both endpoint values which cannot be found by calculus.

11. CHANGE OF VARIABLES

One important use of partial differentiation is in making changes of variables (for example, from rectangular to polar coordinates). This may give a simpler expression or a simpler differential equation or one more suited to the physical problem one is doing. For example, if you are working with the vibration of a circular membrane, or the flow of heat in a circular cylinder, polar coordinates are better; for a problem about sound waves in a room, rectangular coordinates are better. Consider this problem.

Example 1. Change the variables to polar coordinates in the partial differential equation

(11.1)
$$x \frac{\partial F}{\partial x} + y \frac{\partial F}{\partial y} = x^2 + y^2$$

and solve the equation.

The transformation equations (relating old and new variables) are

(11.2)
$$x = r \cos \theta,$$
$$y = r \sin \theta,$$

or

(11.3)
$$r = \sqrt{x^2 + y^2},$$
$$\theta = \tan^{-1} \frac{y}{x}.$$

We want F to be a function of r and θ, so we write

(11.4)
$$dF = \frac{\partial F}{\partial r} dr + \frac{\partial F}{\partial \theta} d\theta.$$

Next we must express dr and $d\theta$ in terms of dx and dy in order to write (11.4) in terms of dx and dy. We can then find from (11.4) the expressions for $\partial F/\partial x$ and $\partial F/\partial y$ in terms of $\partial F/\partial r$ and $\partial F/\partial \theta$, and these are what we want to substitute into (11.1). There are two ways to find dr and $d\theta$; we can take differentials of either (11.2) or (11.3). If we take differentials of (11.2), we then have to solve two equations for dr and $d\theta$. Alternatively we solve (11.2) for r and θ to get (11.3) and then take differentials. Here the two methods involve about the same amount of algebra, but in other transformations we choose whichever method seems simpler. From (11.3) we find

(11.5)
$$dr = \tfrac{1}{2}(x^2 + y^2)^{-\frac{1}{2}}(2x\,dx + 2y\,dy) = \frac{x}{r}\,dx + \frac{y}{r}\,dy,$$

$$d\theta = \frac{x\,dy - y\,dx}{x^2}\bigg/\left(1 + \frac{y^2}{x^2}\right) = \frac{x\,dy - y\,dx}{r^2}.$$

Substituting these values into (11.4) and collecting coefficients of dx and dy, we get

(11.6) $$dF = \left(\frac{\partial F}{\partial r}\frac{x}{r} - \frac{\partial F}{\partial \theta}\frac{y}{r^2}\right) dx + \left(\frac{\partial F}{\partial r}\frac{y}{r} + \frac{\partial F}{\partial \theta}\frac{x}{r^2}\right) dy.$$

The coefficient of dx is $\partial F/\partial x$ and the coefficient of dy is $\partial F/\partial y$. We substitute these expressions into (11.1) to get

(11.7) $$x\left(\frac{\partial F}{\partial r}\frac{x}{r} - \frac{\partial F}{\partial \theta}\frac{y}{r^2}\right) + y\left(\frac{\partial F}{\partial r}\frac{y}{r} + \frac{\partial F}{\partial \theta}\frac{x}{r^2}\right) = x^2 + y^2$$

or

$$\frac{x^2 + y^2}{r}\frac{\partial F}{\partial r} + \frac{xy - xy}{r^2}\frac{\partial F}{\partial \theta} = x^2 + y^2.$$

The partial differential equation then simplifies to

(11.8) $$\frac{\partial F}{\partial r} = r.$$

We can easily solve (11.8) to find

(11.9) $$F = \tfrac{1}{2}r^2 + g(\theta),$$

where $g(\theta)$ is any function of θ. The function $g(\theta)$ is like an integration constant; observe that (11.9) *does* satisfy (11.8) when we add to $\tfrac{1}{2}r^2$ not just a constant, but any function of θ.

The algebra becomes more involved but the ideas are the same if we change variables in an expression containing second derivatives.

Example 2.   Find

(11.10) $$\frac{\partial^2 F}{\partial x^2} + \frac{\partial^2 F}{\partial y^2}$$

in terms of s and t if

(11.11) $$x = e^s \cos t, \qquad y = e^s \sin t.$$

We start by finding the first derivatives of F with respect to x and y in terms of the derivatives of F with respect to s and t; this much of the work is just like what we did in Example 1. Thinking of F as a function of s and t, we write

(11.12)
$$dF = \frac{\partial F}{\partial s} \, ds + \frac{\partial F}{\partial t} \, dt.$$

From (11.11) we want ds and dt in terms of dx and dy. We *could* solve (11.11) for s and t, and then take differentials [just as we found dr and $d\theta$ from (11.3)]. Or we could take differentials of (11.11) and solve for ds and dt. Let us use this second method (note that you could do this even if (11.11) were not solvable for s and t). From (11.11), we get

(11.13)
$$dx = e^s \cos t \, ds - e^s \sin t \, dt,$$
$$dy = e^s \sin t \, ds + e^s \cos t \, dt.$$

We can solve (11.13) for ds and dt to get (Problem 95)

(11.14)
$$ds = e^{-s} \cos t \, dx + e^{-s} \sin t \, dy,$$
$$dt = -e^{-s} \sin t \, dx + e^{-s} \cos t \, dy.$$

Substituting (11.14) into (11.12) and collecting coefficients of dx and dy, we get

(11.15)
$$dF = e^{-s}\left(\cos t \frac{\partial F}{\partial s} - \sin t \frac{\partial F}{\partial t}\right) dx + e^{-s}\left(\sin t \frac{\partial F}{\partial s} + \cos t \frac{\partial F}{\partial t}\right) dy.$$

Thus we have

(11.16)
$$\frac{\partial F}{\partial x} = e^{-s}\left(\cos t \frac{\partial F}{\partial s} - \sin t \frac{\partial F}{\partial t}\right),$$
$$\frac{\partial F}{\partial y} = e^{-s}\left(\sin t \frac{\partial F}{\partial s} + \cos t \frac{\partial F}{\partial t}\right).$$

The quantities $\partial F/\partial x$ and $\partial F/\partial y$ in (11.16) are functions of x, y or of s, t. As an abbreviation let us call these functions $G(s, t)$ and $H(s, t)$:

(11.17)
$$\frac{\partial F}{\partial x} = G(s, t),$$
$$\frac{\partial F}{\partial y} = H(s, t).$$

From (11.17), we can write

(11.18)
$$\frac{\partial^2 F}{\partial x^2} = \frac{\partial G}{\partial x},$$
$$\frac{\partial^2 F}{\partial y^2} = \frac{\partial H}{\partial y},$$
$$\frac{\partial^2 F}{\partial x^2} + \frac{\partial^2 F}{\partial y^2} = \frac{\partial G}{\partial x} + \frac{\partial H}{\partial y}.$$

This last expression is then what we were to find in (11.10). Now equations (11.16) are correct for *any* function F; in particular, they are correct if we replace F by G or by H. Let us replace F in the first of equations (11.16) by G, and F in the second equation by H. Then we have

(11.19)
$$\frac{\partial G}{\partial x} = e^{-s}\left(\cos t \frac{\partial G}{\partial s} - \sin t \frac{\partial G}{\partial t}\right),$$
$$\frac{\partial H}{\partial y} = e^{-s}\left(\sin t \frac{\partial H}{\partial s} + \cos t \frac{\partial H}{\partial t}\right).$$

Substituting (11.19) into (11.18) and collecting terms, we get

(11.20)
$$\frac{\partial^2 F}{\partial x^2} + \frac{\partial^2 F}{\partial y^2} = e^{-s}\cos t\left(\frac{\partial G}{\partial s} + \frac{\partial H}{\partial t}\right) + e^{-s}\sin t\left(\frac{\partial H}{\partial s} - \frac{\partial G}{\partial t}\right).$$

The four partial derivatives in (11.20) can now be found by differentiating G and H which are [by (11.17)] the right-hand sides of (11.16). From (11.16), we get

(11.21)
$$\frac{\partial G}{\partial s} = -e^{-s}\left(\cos t \frac{\partial F}{\partial s} - \sin t \frac{\partial F}{\partial t}\right)$$
$$+ e^{-s}\left(\cos t \frac{\partial^2 F}{\partial s^2} - \sin t \frac{\partial^2 F}{\partial s\,\partial t}\right),$$
$$\frac{\partial H}{\partial t} = e^{-s}\left(\cos t \frac{\partial F}{\partial s} + \sin t \frac{\partial^2 F}{\partial t\,\partial s} - \sin t \frac{\partial F}{\partial t} + \cos t \frac{\partial^2 F}{\partial t^2}\right),$$
$$\frac{\partial G}{\partial s} + \frac{\partial H}{\partial t} = e^{-s}\cos t\left(\frac{\partial^2 F}{\partial s^2} + \frac{\partial^2 F}{\partial t^2}\right).$$

Similarly, we can find (Problem 96)

(11.22)
$$\frac{\partial H}{\partial s} - \frac{\partial G}{\partial t} = e^{-s}\sin t\left(\frac{\partial^2 F}{\partial s^2} + \frac{\partial^2 F}{\partial t^2}\right).$$

Then substituting (11.21) and (11.22) into (11.20), we have

(11.23)
$$\frac{\partial^2 F}{\partial x^2} + \frac{\partial^2 F}{\partial y^2} = e^{-2s}\left(\frac{\partial^2 F}{\partial s^2} + \frac{\partial^2 F}{\partial t^2}\right).$$

We next discuss a simple kind of change of variables which is very useful in thermodynamics and mechanics. This process is sometimes known as a *Legendre transformation*. Suppose we are given a function $f(x, y)$; then we can write

(11.24)
$$df = \frac{\partial f}{\partial x}\,dx + \frac{\partial f}{\partial y}\,dy.$$

Let us call $\partial f/\partial x = p$, and $\partial f/\partial y = q$; then we have

(11.25) $$df = p\,dx + q\,dy.$$

If we now subtract from df the quantity $d(qy)$, we have

(11.26) $$df - d(qy) = p\,dx + q\,dy - q\,dy - y\,dq \qquad \text{or}$$
$$d(f - qy) = p\,dx - y\,dq.$$

If we define the function g by

(11.27) $$g = f - qy,$$

then by (11.26)

(11.28) $$dg = p\,dx - y\,dq.$$

Because dx and dq appear in (11.28), it is convenient to think of g as a function of x and q. The partial derivatives of g are then of simple form, namely,

(11.29) $$\frac{\partial g}{\partial x} = p, \qquad \frac{\partial g}{\partial q} = -y.$$

Similarly, we could replace the $p\,dx$ term in df by $-x\,dp$ by considering the function $f - xp$. This sort of change of independent variables is a Legendre transformation. See Problems 102 and 103 for applications.

12. DIFFERENTIATION OF INTEGRALS; LEIBNIZ' RULE

According to the definition of an integral as an antiderivative, if

(12.1) $$f(x) = \frac{dF(x)}{dx},$$

then

(12.2) $$\int_a^x f(t)\,dt = F(t)\Big|_a^x = F(x) - F(a),$$

where a is a constant. If we differentiate (12.2) with respect to x, we have

(12.3) $$\frac{d}{dx}\int_a^x f(t)\,dt = \frac{d}{dx}[F(x) - F(a)] = \frac{dF(x)}{dx} = f(x)$$

by (12.1). Similarly,

$$\int_x^a f(t)\,dt = F(a) - F(x),$$

so

(12.4) $$\frac{d}{dx}\int_x^a f(t)\,dt = -\frac{dF(x)}{dx} = -f(x).$$

Example 1.   Find $\dfrac{d}{dx} \displaystyle\int_{\pi/4}^{x} \sin t \, dt$.

By (12.3), we find immediately that the answer is $\sin x$. We can check this by finding the integral and then differentiating. We get

$$\int_{\pi/4}^{x} \sin t \, dt = -\cos t \, \Big|_{\pi/4}^{x} = -\cos x + \tfrac{1}{2}\sqrt{2}$$

and the derivative of this is $\sin x$ as before.

By replacing x in (12.3) by v, and replacing x in (12.4) by u, we can then write

(12.5) $$\frac{d}{dv} \int_{a}^{v} f(t) \, dt = f(v)$$

and

(12.6) $$\frac{d}{du} \int_{u}^{b} f(t) \, dt = -f(u).$$

Suppose u and v are functions of x and we want dI/dx where

$$I = \int_{u}^{v} f(t) \, dt.$$

When the integral is evaluated, the answer depends on the limits u and v. Finding dI/dx is then a partial differentiation problem; I is a function of u and v, which are functions of x. We can write

(12.7) $$\frac{dI}{dx} = \frac{\partial I}{\partial u}\frac{du}{dx} + \frac{\partial I}{\partial v}\frac{dv}{dx}.$$

But $\partial I/\partial v$ means to differentiate I with respect to v when u is a constant; this is just (12.5), so $\partial I/\partial v = f(v)$. Similarly, $\partial I/\partial u$ means that v is constant and we can use (12.6) to get $\partial I/\partial u = -f(u)$. Then we have

(12.8) $$\frac{d}{dx} \int_{u(x)}^{v(x)} f(t) \, dt = f(v)\frac{dv}{dx} - f(u)\frac{du}{dx}.$$

Example 2.   Find dI/dx if $I = \displaystyle\int_{0}^{\sqrt[3]{x}} t^2 \, dt$.

By (12.8) we get

$$\frac{dI}{dx} = (\sqrt[3]{x})^2 \frac{d}{dx}(\sqrt[3]{x}) = x^{2/3} \cdot \frac{1}{3} x^{-2/3} = \frac{1}{3}.$$

We *could* also integrate first and then differentiate with respect to x:

$$I = \int_{0}^{\sqrt[3]{x}} t^2 \, dt = \frac{t^3}{3}\Big|_{0}^{\sqrt[3]{x}} = \frac{x}{3}, \qquad \frac{dI}{dx} = \frac{1}{3}.$$

This last method seems so simple you may wonder why we need (12.8). Look at another example.

Example 3. Find dI/dx if

$$I = \int_{x^2}^{\tan^{-1} x} \frac{\sin t}{t}\, dt.$$

Here the indefinite integral cannot be evaluated in terms of elementary functions; however, we can find dI/dx by using (12.8). We get

$$\frac{dI}{dx} = \frac{\sin(\tan^{-1} x)}{\tan^{-1} x} \frac{1}{1 + x^2} - \frac{\sin x^2}{x^2} \cdot 2x$$

$$= \frac{x}{\sqrt{1 + x^2}\, \tan^{-1} x} \frac{1}{1 + x^2} - \frac{2}{x} \sin x^2$$

$$= \frac{x}{(1 + x^2)^{3/2}\, \tan^{-1} x} - \frac{2}{x} \sin x^2.$$

Finally, we may want to find dI/dx when $I = \int_a^b f(x, t)\, dt$, where a and b are constants. Under not too restrictive conditions,

(12.9) $$\frac{d}{dx} \int_a^b f(x, t)\, dt = \int_a^b \frac{\partial f(x, t)}{\partial x}\, dt;$$

that is, we can differentiate under the integral sign. [A set of sufficient conditions for this to be correct would be that $\partial f/\partial x$ is continuous and $|\partial f(x, t)/\partial x| \leq g(t)$, where $\int_a^b g(t)\, dt$ converges. For most practical purposes this means that if the right-hand side of (12.9) converges, then (12.9) is correct.] Equation (12.9) is often useful in evaluating definite integrals.

Example 4. Find $\int_0^\infty t^n e^{-at^2}\, dt$ for odd n.

First we evaluate the integral

$$I = \int_0^\infty t e^{-xt^2}\, dt = -\frac{1}{2x} e^{-xt^2} \Big|_0^\infty = \frac{1}{2x}.$$

Putting $x = a$, we have

$$\int_0^\infty t e^{-at^2}\, dt = \frac{1}{2a}.$$

Now we calculate successive derivatives of I with respect to x, and put $x = a$ in each case.

$$\frac{dI}{dx} = \int_0^\infty -t^3 e^{-xt^2}\, dt = -\frac{1}{2x^2}$$

or, for $x = a$,

$$\int_0^\infty t^3 e^{-at^2}\, dt = \frac{1}{2a^2}.$$

Differentiating again, we get

$$\frac{d^2 I}{dx^2} = \int_0^\infty t^5 e^{-xt^2}\, dt = \frac{1}{x^3}$$

or, for $x = a$,

$$\int_0^\infty t^5 e^{-at^2}\, dt = \frac{1}{a^3}.$$

Continuing, we can easily find any integral we like of this form.

Example 5. Evaluate

$$I = \int_0^1 \frac{t^a - 1}{\ln t}\, dt, \qquad a \geq 0.$$

First we differentiate I with respect to a, and evaluate the resulting integral.

$$\frac{dI}{da} = \int_0^1 \frac{t^a \ln t}{\ln t}\, dt = \int_0^1 t^a\, dt = \frac{t^{a+1}}{a+1}\Big|_0^1 = \frac{1}{a+1}.$$

Now we integrate dI/da with respect to a to get I back again (plus an integration constant):

$$I = \int \frac{da}{a+1} = \ln(a+1) + C.$$

This is the value of the integral I which we wanted, except that we need to find C. When $a = 0$, $I = (\ln 1) + C = C$. From the original integral, when $a = 0$, the integrand $(t^a - 1)/\ln t$ is $(t^0 - 1)/\ln t = 0$, so $I = 0$. Thus $C = 0$ and we have

$$I = \ln(a+1).$$

It is convenient to collect formulas (12.8) and (12.9) into one formula known as *Leibniz' rule*:

(12.10) $\quad \dfrac{d}{dx} \displaystyle\int_{u(x)}^{v(x)} f(x, t)\, dt = f(x, v)\dfrac{dv}{dx} - f(x, u)\dfrac{du}{dx} + \displaystyle\int_u^v \dfrac{\partial f}{\partial x}\, dt.$

Example 6. Find dI/dx if

$$I = \int_x^{2x} \frac{e^{xt}}{t}\, dt.$$

By (12.10) we get

$$\frac{dI}{dx} = \frac{e^{x \cdot 2x}}{2x} \cdot 2 - \frac{e^{x \cdot x}}{x} \cdot 1 + \int_x^{2x} \frac{te^{xt}}{t} \, dt$$

$$= \frac{1}{x} (e^{2x^2} - e^{x^2}) + \left[\frac{e^{xt}}{x} \right]_x^{2x}$$

$$= \frac{1}{x} (e^{2x^2} - e^{x^2} + e^{2x^2} - e^{x^2}) = \frac{2}{x} (e^{2x^2} - e^{x^2}).$$

13. APPLICATIONS OF INTEGRATION; SINGLE AND MULTIPLE INTEGRALS

In calculus and elementary physics you have learned a number of uses for integration, such as finding areas, arc lengths, volumes, moments, centroids, etc. Let us do some simple problems to review these ideas briefly. The basic idea which you should recall and use in setting up the integrals in these problems is that an integral is the "limit of a sum." Thus we imagine the physical object (whose volume, moment of inertia, etc., we are trying to find) cut into a large number of small pieces called *elements*. We write an approximate formula for the volume, moment of inertia, etc., of an element and then sum over all elements of the object. The limit of this sum (as the number of elements tends to infinity and the size of each element tends to zero) is what we find by integration and is what we want in the physical problem.

Example 1. Given the curve $y = x^2$ from $x = 0$ to $x = 1$, find
(a) the area under the curve (that is, the area bounded by the curve, the x-axis, and the line $x = 1$; see Fig. 13.1);
(b) the mass of a plane sheet of material cut in the shape of this area if its density (mass per unit area) is xy;
(c) the arc length of the curve;
(d) the centroid of the area;
(e) the centroid of the arc;
(f) the moments of inertia about the x, y, and z-axes of the lamina in (b).

(a) The area is

$$A = \int_{x=0}^{1} y \, dx = \int_0^1 x^2 \, dx = \frac{x^3}{3} \bigg|_0^1 = \tfrac{1}{3}.$$

We could also find the area as a double integral of $dA = dy \, dx$ (see Fig. 13.1). We have then

$$A = \int_{x=0}^{1} \int_{y=0}^{x^2} dy \, dx = \int_0^1 x^2 \, dx$$

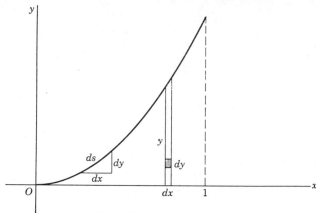

Figure 13.1

as before. Although the double integral is entirely unnecessary in finding the area in this problem, we shall need to use a double integral to find the mass in part (b).

(b) The element of area, as in the double integral method in (a), is $dA = dy \, dx$. Since the density is $\rho = xy$, the element of mass is $dM = xy \, dy \, dx$, and the total mass is

$$M = \int_{x=0}^{1} \int_{y=0}^{x^2} xy \, dy \, dx = \int_{0}^{1} x \, dx \left[\frac{y^2}{2} \right]_{0}^{x^2} = \int_{0}^{1} \frac{x^5}{2} \, dx = \frac{1}{12}.$$

Observe that we could not do this problem as a single integral because the density depends on both x and y.

(c) The element of arc length ds is defined as indicated in Figs. 13.1 and 13.2. Thus we have

$$ds^2 = dx^2 + dy^2,$$

(13.1) $$ds = \sqrt{dx^2 + dy^2}$$
$$= \sqrt{1 + (dy/dx)^2} \, dx = \sqrt{(dx/dy)^2 + 1} \, dy.$$

If $y = f(x)$ has a continuous first derivative dy/dx (except possibly at a finite number of points), we can find the arc length of the curve $y = f(x)$ between a and b by calculating $\int_{a}^{b} ds$. For our example, we have

$$\frac{dy}{dx} = 2x, \qquad ds = \sqrt{1 + 4x^2} \, dx,$$

(13.2)
$$s = \int_{0}^{1} \sqrt{1 + 4x^2} \, dx = \frac{2\sqrt{5} + \ln(2 + \sqrt{5})}{4}$$

(by tables and some simplification).

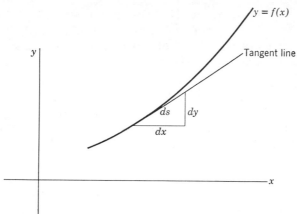

Figure 13.2

(d) Recall from elementary physics that the *center of mass* of a body has coordinates $\bar{x}$, $\bar{y}$, $\bar{z}$ given by the equations

$$(13.3) \qquad \int \bar{x}\, dM = \int x\, dM, \qquad \int \bar{y}\, dM = \int y\, dM, \qquad \int \bar{z}\, dM = \int z\, dM,$$

where dM is an element of mass and the integrals are over the whole body. Although we have written single integrals in (13.3), they may be single, double, or triple integrals depending on the problem and the method of evaluation. Since $\bar{x}$, $\bar{y}$, and $\bar{z}$ are constants, we *can* take them outside the integrals in (13.3) and solve for them. However, you may find it easier to remember the definitions in the form (13.3). For the example we are doing, $\bar{z} = 0$ since the body is a sheet of material in the (x, y) plane. The element of mass is $dM = \rho\, dA = \rho\, dx\, dy$, where ρ is the density (mass per unit area in this problem). For a variable density as in (b), we would substitute the value of ρ into (13.3) and integrate both sides of each equation to find the coordinates of the center of mass. However, let us suppose the density is a constant. Then the first integral in (13.3) is

$$(13.4) \qquad \int \bar{x}\rho\, dA = \int x\rho\, dA \qquad \text{or} \qquad \int \bar{x}\, dA = \int x\, dA.$$

Similarly, a *constant* density ρ can be canceled from all the equations in (13.3). The quantities $\bar{x}$, $\bar{y}$, $\bar{z}$, are then called the coordinates of the *centroid* of the area (or volume or arc); that is, the centroid of a body is the center of mass when we assume constant density. In our example, we have

$$(13.5) \qquad \begin{aligned} \int_{x=0}^{1} \int_{y=0}^{x^2} \bar{x}\, dy\, dx &= \int_{x=0}^{1} \int_{y=0}^{x^2} x\, dy\, dx \qquad \text{or} \qquad \bar{x}A = \left.\frac{x^4}{4}\right|_0^1 = \frac{1}{4}, \\ \int_{x=0}^{1} \int_{y=0}^{x^2} \bar{y}\, dy\, dx &= \int_{x=0}^{1} \int_{y=0}^{x^2} y\, dy\, dx \qquad \text{or} \qquad \bar{y}A = \left.\frac{x^5}{10}\right|_0^1 = \frac{1}{10}. \end{aligned}$$

(Double integrals are not really necessary for any of these but the last.)
Using the value of A from part (a), we find $\bar{x} = \frac{3}{4}$, $\bar{y} = \frac{3}{10}$.

(e) The center of mass $(\bar{x}, \bar{y})$ of a wire bent in the shape of the curve
$y = f(x)$ is given by

(13.6)
$$\int \bar{x}\rho \, ds = \int x\rho \, ds, \qquad \int \bar{y}\rho \, ds = \int y\rho \, ds,$$

where ρ is the density (mass per unit length) and the integrals are *single*
integrals with ds given by (13.1). If ρ is constant, (13.6) defines the co-

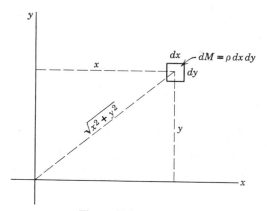

Figure 13.3

ordinates of the centroid. In our example we have

(13.7)
$$\int_0^1 \bar{x}\sqrt{1 + 4x^2} \, dx = \int_0^1 x\sqrt{1 + 4x^2} \, dx,$$
$$\int_0^1 \bar{y}\sqrt{1 + 4x^2} \, dx = \int_0^1 y\sqrt{1 + 4x^2} \, dx = \int_0^1 x^2\sqrt{1 + 4x^2} \, dx.$$

Note carefully here that it is correct to put $y = x^2$ in the last integral of
(13.7), but it would *not* have been correct to do this in the last integral of
(13.5); the reason is that over the *area*, y could take values from zero to
x^2, but *on* the arc, y takes only the value x^2. By calculating the integrals
in (13.7) we can find $\bar{x}$ and $\bar{y}$.

(f) The *moment of inertia I* of a point mass m about an axis is by
definition the product ml^2 of m times the square of the distance l from m
to the axis. For an extended object we must integrate $l^2 \, dM$ over the whole
object, where l is the distance from dM to the axis. In our example with
variable density $\rho = xy$, we have $dM = xy \, dy \, dx$. The distance from dM
to the x-axis is y (Fig. 13.3); similarly, the distance from dM to the

y-axis is x. The distance from dM to the z-axis (the z-axis is perpendicular to the paper in Fig. 13.3) is $\sqrt{x^2 + y^2}$. Then the three moments of inertia about the three coordinate axes are:

$$I_x = \int_{x=0}^{1} \int_{y=0}^{x^2} y^2 xy \, dy \, dx = \int_0^1 \frac{x^9}{4} \, dx = \frac{1}{40},$$

$$I_y = \int_{x=0}^{1} \int_{y=0}^{x^2} x^2 xy \, dy \, dx = \int_0^1 \frac{x^7}{2} \, dx = \frac{1}{16},$$

$$I_z = \int_{x=0}^{1} \int_{y=0}^{x^2} (x^2 + y^2) xy \, dy \, dx = I_x + I_y = \frac{7}{80}.$$

(The fact that $I_x + I_y = I_z$ for a plane lamina in the (x, y) plane is known as the perpendicular axis theorem.) It is customary to write moments of inertia as multiples of the mass; using $M = \frac{1}{12}$ from (b), we write

$$I_x = \frac{12}{40} M = \frac{3}{10} M, \qquad I_y = \frac{12}{16} M = \frac{3}{4} M, \qquad I_z = \frac{7 \cdot 12}{80} M = \frac{21}{20} M.$$

Example 2. Rotate the area of Example 1 about the x-axis to form a volume and surface of revolution, and find
  (a) the volume;
  (b) the moment of inertia about the x-axis of a solid of constant density occupying the given volume;
  (c) the area of the curved surface;
  (d) the centroid of the curved surface.

(a) The easiest way to find a volume of revolution is to take as volume element a thin slab of the solid as shown in Fig. 13.4. The slab has circular cross section of radius y and thickness dx; thus its volume is $\pi y^2 \, dx$. Then the volume is

(13.8) $$V = \int_0^1 \pi y^2 \, dx = \int_0^1 \pi x^4 \, dx = \frac{\pi}{5}.$$

We have really avoided part of the integration here because we knew the formula for the area of a circle. In finding volumes of solids which are not solids of revolution, we may have to use double or triple integrals. Even for a solid of revolution we might need multiple integrals to find the mass if the density is variable.

To illustrate setting up such integrals, let us do the above problem using triple integrals. For this we need the equation of the surface which is (see Problem 130)

(13.9) $$y^2 + z^2 = x^4, \qquad x > 0.$$

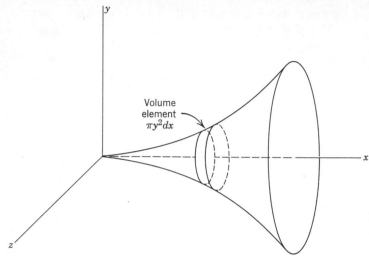

Figure 13.4

To set up a multiple integral for the volume of a solid, we cut the solid into slabs as in Fig. 13.4 (not necessarily circular slabs, although they are in our example) and then as in Fig. 13.5 we cut each slab into strips and each strip into tiny boxes of volume $dx\,dy\,dz$. The volume is

$$V = \int\int\int dx\,dy\,dz;$$

the only problem is to find the limits! To do this, we start by adding up tiny boxes to get a strip; as we have drawn Fig. 13.5, this means to integrate with respect to y from one side of the circle $y^2 + z^2 = x^4$ to the other,

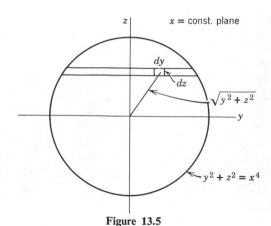

Figure 13.5

that is, from

$$y = -\sqrt{x^4 - z^2} \qquad \text{to} \qquad y = +\sqrt{x^4 - z^2}.$$

Next we add all the strips in a slab. This means that, in Fig. 13.5, we integrate with respect to z from the bottom to the top of the circle $y^2 + z^2 = x^4$; thus the z limits are $z = \pm$ radius of circle $= \pm x^2$. And finally we add all the slabs to obtain the solid. This means to integrate in Fig. 13.4 from $x = 0$ to $x = 1$; this is just what we did in our first simple method. The final integral is then

(13.10)

$$
\begin{aligned}
V &= \int_{x=0}^{1} \int_{z=-x^2}^{x^2} \int_{y=-\sqrt{x^4-z^2}}^{\sqrt{x^4-z^2}} dy \, dz \, dx \\
&= \int_{0}^{1} dx \int_{z=-x^2}^{x^2} dz \cdot 2\sqrt{x^4 - z^2} \\
&= \int_{0}^{1} dx \cdot 2 \cdot \tfrac{1}{2} \left[z\sqrt{x^4 - z^2} + x^4 \arcsin \frac{z}{x^2} \right]_{-x^2}^{x^2} \qquad \text{(see integral tables)} \\
&= \int_{0}^{1} dx \cdot x^4 \left(\frac{\pi}{2} \cdot 2 \right) = \int_{0}^{1} \pi x^4 \, dx
\end{aligned}
$$

as in (13.8).

Although the triple integral is an unnecessarily complicated way of finding a volume of revolution, this simple problem illustrates the general method of setting up an integral for any kind of volume. Once we have the volume as a triple integral, it is easy to write the integrals for the mass with a given variable density, for the coordinates of the centroid, for the moments of inertia, etc. The limits of integration are the same as for the volume; we need only insert the proper expressions (density, etc.) in the integrand to get the mass, centroid, etc.

(b) To find the moment of inertia of the solid about the x-axis, we must integrate $l^2 \, dM$, where l is the distance from dM to the x-axis; from Fig. 13.5, since the x-axis is perpendicular to the paper, $l^2 = y^2 + z^2$. The limits on the integrals are the same as in (13.10). We are assuming constant density, so the factor ρ can be written outside the integrals. Then we have

$$I_x = \rho \int_{x=0}^{1} \int_{z=-x^2}^{x^2} \int_{y=-\sqrt{x^4-z^2}}^{\sqrt{x^4-z^2}} (y^2 + z^2) \, dy \, dz \, dx = \frac{\pi}{18} \rho.$$

Since from (13.8) the mass of the solid is

$$M = \rho V = \frac{\pi}{5} \rho$$

we can write I_x (as is customary) as a multiple of M:

$$I_x = \frac{\pi}{18}\frac{5}{\pi} M = \frac{5}{18} M.$$

(c) We find the area of the surface of revolution by using as element the curved surface of a thin slab as in Fig. 13.4. This is a strip of circumference $2\pi y$ and width ds. To see this clearly and to understand why we use ds here but dx in the volume element in (13.8), think of the slab as a thin section of a cone (Fig. 13.6) between planes perpendicular to the axis of the cone. If you wanted to find the total volume $V = \frac{1}{3}\pi r^2 h$ of the cone, you would use the height h perpendicular to the base, but in finding the total curved surface area $S = \frac{1}{2} \cdot 2\pi r \cdot s$, you would use the *slant* height s. The same ideas hold in finding the volume and surface elements. The approximate volume of the thin slab is the area of a face of the slab times its thickness (dh in Fig. 13.6, dx in Fig. 13.4). But if you think of a narrow strip of paper just covering the curved surface of the thin slab, the width of the strip of paper is ds, and its length is the circumference of the thin slab.

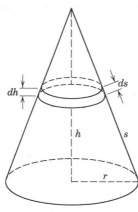

Figure 13.6

The element of surface area (in Fig. 13.4) is then

$$dA = 2\pi y\ ds.$$

The total area is [using ds from (13.2)]

$$A = \int_{x=0}^{1} 2\pi y\ ds = \int_{0}^{1} 2\pi x^2 \sqrt{1 + 4x^2}\ dx.$$

(For more general surfaces, there is a way to calculate areas by double integration; we shall take this up in Chapter 5, Section 14.)

(d) The y- and z-coordinates of the centroid of the surface area are zero by symmetry. For the x-coordinate, we have by (13.4)

$$\int \bar{x}\ dA = \int x\ dA,$$

or, using $dA = 2\pi y\ ds$ and the total area A from (c), we have

$$\bar{x}A = \int_{x=0}^{1} x \cdot 2\pi y\ ds = \int_{0}^{1} x \cdot 2\pi x^2 \sqrt{1 + 4x^2}\ dx.$$

14. CHANGE OF VARIABLES IN INTEGRALS; JACOBIANS

In many applied problems, it is more convenient to use other coordinate systems instead of the rectangular coordinates we have been using. For example, in the plane we often use polar coordinates, and in three dimensions we often use cylindrical coordinates or spherical coordinates. It is important to know how to set up multiple integrals directly in these coordinate systems which occur so frequently in practice. That is, we need to know what the area, volume, and arc length elements are, what the variables r, θ, etc., mean geometrically, and how they are related to the rectangular coordinates. We are going to discuss finding elements of area, etc., geometrically for several important coordinate systems. However, if we are given equations like $x = r \cos \theta$, $y = r \sin \theta$, relating new variables to the rectangular ones, it is useful to know how to find the elements of area, etc., *algebraically*, without having to rely on the geometry. We are going to discuss this and illustrate it by verifying the results which we can get geometrically for the familiar coordinate systems.

In the plane, the polar coordinates r, θ are related to the rectangular coordinates x, y by the equations

(14.1)
$$x = r \cos \theta,$$
$$y = r \sin \theta.$$

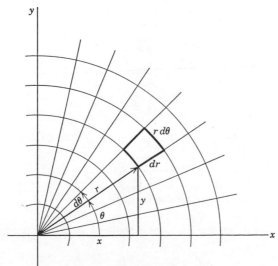

Figure 14.1

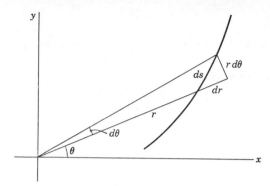

Figure 14.2

Recall that the area element $dy\,dx$ was obtained by drawing a grid of lines $x = \text{const.}$, $y = \text{const.}$, which cut the plane into little rectangles dx by dy; the area of one rectangle was then $dy\,dx$. We can make a similar construction for polar coordinates by drawing lines $\theta = \text{const.}$ and circles $r = \text{const.}$; we then obtain the grid shown in Fig. 14.1. Observe that the sides of the area element are not dr and $d\theta$, but dr and $r\,d\theta$, and its area is then

(14.2) $$dA = dr \cdot r\,d\theta = r\,dr\,d\theta.$$

Similarly, we can see from Fig. 14.2 that the arc length element ds is given by

$$ds^2 = dr^2 + r^2\,d\theta^2,$$

(14.3) $$ds = \sqrt{\left(\frac{dr}{d\theta}\right)^2 + r^2}\;d\theta$$

$$= \sqrt{1 + r^2\left(\frac{d\theta}{dr}\right)^2}\;dr.$$

Example 1. Given a semicircular sheet of material of radius a and constant density ρ, find

(a) the centroid of the semicircular area;

(b) the moment of inertia of the sheet of material about the diameter forming the straight side of the semicircle.

(a) In Fig. 14.3, we see by symmetry that $\bar{y} = 0$. We want to find $\bar{x}$. By (13.4), we have

$$\int \bar{x}r\,dr\,d\theta = \int xr\,dr\,d\theta.$$

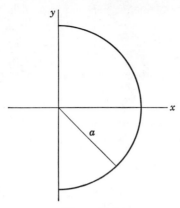

Figure 14.3

Changing the x to polar coordinates and putting in the limits, we get

$$\bar{x}\int_{r=0}^{a}\int_{\theta=-\pi/2}^{\pi/2} r\, dr\, d\theta = \int_{r=0}^{a}\int_{\theta=-\pi/2}^{\pi/2} r\cos\theta\, r\, dr\, d\theta.$$

We calculate the integrals and find $\bar{x}$:

$$\bar{x}\,\frac{a^2}{2}\,\pi = \frac{a^3}{3}\sin\theta \,\Big|_{-\pi/2}^{\pi/2} = \frac{a^3}{3}\cdot 2,$$

$$\bar{x} = \frac{4a}{3\pi}.$$

(b) We want the moment of inertia about the y-axis in Fig. 14.3; by definition this is $\int x^2\, dM$. In polar coordinates, $dM = \rho\, dA = \rho r\, dr\, d\theta$. We are given that the density ρ is constant. Then we have

$$I_y = \rho\int x^2 r\, dr\, d\theta = \rho\int_{r=0}^{a}\int_{\theta=-\pi/2}^{\pi/2} r^2\cos^2\theta\, r\, dr\, d\theta = \rho\,\frac{\pi a^4}{8}.$$

Since the mass of the semicircular object is

$$M = \rho\int r\, dr\, d\theta = \rho\int_{r=0}^{a}\int_{\theta=-\pi/2}^{\pi/2} r\, dr\, d\theta = \rho\,\frac{\pi a^2}{2},$$

we have

$$I_y = \frac{2M}{\pi a^2}\frac{\pi a^4}{8} = \frac{Ma^2}{4}.$$

Jacobians. Although for polar coordinates the diagram (Fig. 14.1) makes it very simple for us to get the area element, it is convenient to know an algebraic way of finding it also. We state without proof (see Brand, *Advanced Calculus*, p. 364) the following theorem which tells us how to do this. If we are given x and y as functions of two new variables

s and t, then the area element $dy\,dx$ is replaced in the s, t system by the area element

(14.4) $\qquad dA = \text{the absolute value of} \begin{vmatrix} \dfrac{\partial x}{\partial s} & \dfrac{\partial x}{\partial t} \\[2mm] \dfrac{\partial y}{\partial s} & \dfrac{\partial y}{\partial t} \end{vmatrix} ds\,dt.$

The determinant in (14.4) is called a *Jacobian*, or specifically the Jacobian of x, y with respect to s, t. It is often abbreviated in one of the following ways:

$\qquad\qquad$ JACOBIAN

(14.5) $\qquad \begin{vmatrix} \dfrac{\partial x}{\partial s} & \dfrac{\partial x}{\partial t} \\[2mm] \dfrac{\partial y}{\partial s} & \dfrac{\partial y}{\partial t} \end{vmatrix} = \dfrac{\partial(x, y)}{\partial(s, t)} = J(s, t).$

Let us find the Jacobian of x, y with respect to the polar coordinates r, θ, and thus verify that (14.4) and our geometric method give the same result (14.2) for the polar coordinate area element. We have

(14.6) $\qquad \dfrac{\partial(x, y)}{\partial(r, \theta)} = \begin{vmatrix} \dfrac{\partial x}{\partial r} & \dfrac{\partial x}{\partial \theta} \\[2mm] \dfrac{\partial y}{\partial r} & \dfrac{\partial y}{\partial \theta} \end{vmatrix} = \begin{vmatrix} \cos\theta & -r\sin\theta \\ \sin\theta & r\cos\theta \end{vmatrix} = r.$

Thus by (14.4) the area element is $r\,dr\,d\theta$ as in (14.2).

Spherical and cylindrical coordinates. The two most important coordinate systems (besides rectangular) in three dimensions are the spherical and the cylindrical coordinate systems. Figures 14.4 and 14.5 and equations (14.7) and (14.8) show the geometrical meaning of the variables, their algebraic relation to x, y, z, and the appearance of the volume elements.

(14.7) Cylindrical
$\qquad\qquad$ coordinates:
$$x = r\cos\theta$$
$$y = r\sin\theta$$
$$z = z$$

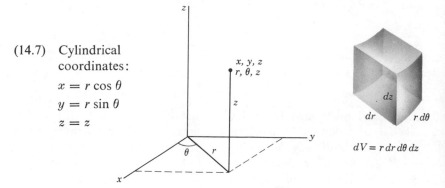

$$dV = r\,dr\,d\theta\,dz$$

Figure 14.4

(14.8)   Spherical coordinates:

$$x = r \sin \theta \cos \phi$$
$$y = r \sin \theta \sin \phi$$
$$z = r \cos \theta$$

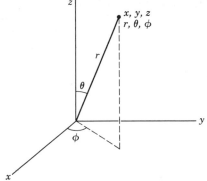
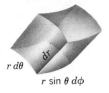

$$dV = r^2 \sin \theta \, dr \, d\theta \, d\phi$$

Figure 14.5

Cylindrical coordinates are just polar coordinates in the (x, y) plane with z for the third variable. Note that the spherical coordinates r and θ in Fig. 14.5 are different from the cylindrical or polar coordinates r and θ in Figs. 14.4 and 14.1. Since we seldom use both systems in the same problem, this should cause no confusion. Watch out, however, for the discrepancy in notation for spherical coordinates in various texts. The notation of Fig. 14.5 is almost universal in applied mathematics, physics, and engineering books, but many pure mathematics books interchange θ and ϕ.

We want to know the volume elements in these two systems. Since cylindrical coordinates are polar coordinates plus z, you can probably guess that $dV = dx \, dy \, dz$ becomes $dV = r \, dr \, d\theta \, dz$. By calculating the Jacobian $\partial(x, y, z)/\partial(r, \theta, z)$ (Problem 142) you can verify this. Let us do the corresponding calculation for spherical coordinates. From (14.8), we have

(14.9)

$$\frac{\partial(x, y, z)}{\partial(r, \theta, \phi)} = \begin{vmatrix} \dfrac{\partial x}{\partial r} & \dfrac{\partial x}{\partial \theta} & \dfrac{\partial x}{\partial \phi} \\[2mm] \dfrac{\partial y}{\partial r} & \dfrac{\partial y}{\partial \theta} & \dfrac{\partial y}{\partial \phi} \\[2mm] \dfrac{\partial z}{\partial r} & \dfrac{\partial z}{\partial \theta} & \dfrac{\partial z}{\partial \phi} \end{vmatrix} = \begin{vmatrix} \sin \theta \cos \phi & r \cos \theta \cos \phi & -r \sin \theta \sin \phi \\[2mm] \sin \theta \sin \phi & r \cos \theta \sin \phi & r \sin \theta \cos \phi \\[2mm] \cos \theta & -r \sin \theta & 0 \end{vmatrix}$$

$$= r^2 \sin \theta [-\sin^2 \phi(-\sin^2 \theta - \cos^2 \theta) - \cos^2 \phi(-\sin^2 \theta - \cos^2 \theta)]$$
$$= r^2 \sin \theta.$$

Thus the spherical coordinate volume element is

$$(14.10) \qquad\qquad dV = r^2 \sin\theta\, dr\, d\theta\, d\phi.$$

It is very useful to be able to find the volume elements for these two systems geometrically as well as by Jacobians. To find the polar coordinate area element, we drew (in Fig. 14.1) a grid of curves $r = $ const., $\theta = $ const. In three dimensions we want to draw a grid of surfaces. In cylindrical coordinates these surfaces are the cylinders $r = $ const., the half-planes $\theta = $ const. (through the z-axis), and the planes $z = $ const. [parallel to the

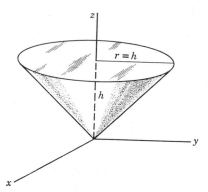

Figure 14.6

(x, y) plane]. One of the elements formed by this grid of surfaces is sketched in Fig. 14.4. From the geometry we see that three edges of the element are dr, $r\, d\theta$, and dz, giving the volume element $dV = r\, dr\, d\theta\, dz$. Similarly for the spherical coordinate case, we draw the spheres $r = $ const., the cones $\theta = $ const., and the half-planes $\phi = $ const. The volume elements formed by this grid (Fig. 14.5) have edges dr, $r\, d\theta$, and $r \sin\theta\, d\phi$; thus we get $dV = r^2 \sin\theta\, dr\, d\theta\, d\phi$ as in (14.10).

Example 2. Find the z-coordinate of the centroid of a uniform solid cone (part of one nappe) of height h equal to the radius of the base r. Also find the moment of inertia of the solid about its axis.

If we take the cone as shown in Fig. 14.6, its equation in cylindrical coordinates is $r = z$, since at any height z, the cross section is a circle of radius equal to the height. To find the mass we must integrate $dM = \rho r\, dr\, d\theta\, dz$, where ρ is the constant density. The limits of integration are

$$\theta: \quad 0 \text{ to } 2\pi,$$

$$r: \quad 0 \text{ to } z,$$

$$z: \quad 0 \text{ to } h.$$

Then we have

(14.11)

$$M = \int \rho \, dV = \rho \int_{z=0}^{h} \int_{r=0}^{z} \int_{\theta=0}^{2\pi} r \, dr \, d\theta \, dz = \rho \cdot 2\pi \int_0^h \frac{z^2}{2} \, dz = \frac{\rho \pi h^3}{3},$$

$$\int \bar{z} \, dV = \int z \, dV = \int_{z=0}^{h} \int_{r=0}^{z} \int_{\theta=0}^{2\pi} zr \, dr \, d\theta \, dz$$

$$= 2\pi \int_0^h \bar{z} \cdot \tfrac{1}{2} z^2 \, dz = \frac{\pi h^4}{4},$$

Why could this z be pulled out and not the other z on dy the [handwritten annotation]

$$\bar{z} \cdot \frac{\pi h^3}{3} = \frac{\pi h^4}{4},$$

$$\bar{z} = \tfrac{3}{4} h.$$

?($r \, \partial$) [handwritten annotation]

For the moment of inertia about the z-axis we have

$$I = \rho \int_{z=0}^{h} \int_{r=0}^{z} \int_{\theta=0}^{2\pi} r^2 r \, dr \, d\theta \, dz = \rho \cdot 2\pi \int_0^h \frac{z^4}{4} \, dz$$

dV [handwritten annotation]

$$= \rho \frac{\pi h^5}{10}.$$

Using the value of M from (14.11), we write I in the usual form as a multiple of M:

$$I = \frac{3M}{\pi h^3} \frac{\pi h^5}{10} = \frac{3}{10} Mh^2.$$

Example 3. Find the moment of inertia of a sphere of radius a about a diameter.

If we use spherical coordinates, the equation of the sphere is $r = a$. Then the mass is

(14.12)

$$M = \rho \int dV = \rho \int_{\phi=0}^{2\pi} \int_{\theta=0}^{\pi} \int_{r=0}^{a} r^2 \sin\theta \, dr \, d\theta \, d\phi$$

$$= \rho \frac{a^3}{3} \cdot 2 \cdot 2\pi = \frac{4}{3} \pi a^3 \rho.$$

(to no one's surprise!). The moment of inertia about the z-axis is

$$I = \int (x^2 + y^2) \, dM = \rho \int_{\phi=0}^{2\pi} \int_{\theta=0}^{\pi} \int_{r=0}^{a} (r^2 \sin^2\theta) r^2 \sin\theta \, dr \, d\theta \, d\phi$$

$$= \rho \cdot \frac{a^5}{5} \cdot \frac{4}{3} \cdot 2\pi = \frac{8\pi a^5 \rho}{15};$$

or, using the value of M, we get

(14.13)

$$I = \tfrac{2}{5} Ma^2.$$

We have used Jacobians [see (14.4)] in transforming multiple integrals in rectangular coordinates to multiple integrals in some other system. However, it is not necessary to start with rectangular coordinates; let us state a more general theorem. Suppose we have a triple integral

$$\int\int\int f(u, v, w)\ du\ dv\ dw$$

in some set of variables u, v, w. Let r, s, t be another set of variables, related to u, v, w by given equations

$$u = u(r, s, t), \qquad v = v(r, s, t), \qquad w = w(r, s, t).$$

Then if

$$(14.14) \qquad J = \begin{vmatrix} \dfrac{\partial u}{\partial r} & \dfrac{\partial u}{\partial s} & \dfrac{\partial u}{\partial t} \\[2ex] \dfrac{\partial v}{\partial r} & \dfrac{\partial v}{\partial s} & \dfrac{\partial v}{\partial t} \\[2ex] \dfrac{\partial w}{\partial r} & \dfrac{\partial w}{\partial s} & \dfrac{\partial w}{\partial t} \end{vmatrix}$$

is the Jacobian of u, v, w with respect to r, s, t, the triple integral in the new variables is

$$\int\int\int f \cdot |J| \cdot dr\ ds\ dt,$$

where, of course, f and J must both be expressed in terms of r, s, t, and the limits must be properly adjusted to correspond to the new variables.

In order to find arc lengths using spherical or cylindrical coordinates, we need the arc length element ds. Recall that for polar coordinates [see (14.3)] we were able to find ds^2 geometrically from Fig. 14.2. Let us also find it algebraically for polar coordinates and then apply the same method to the three-dimensional systems. From (14.1) we have

$$dx = \cos \theta\ dr - r \sin \theta\ d\theta,$$
$$dy = \sin \theta\ dr + r \cos \theta\ d\theta.$$

Squaring and adding these two equations, we get

$$\begin{aligned} ds^2 &= dx^2 + dy^2 \\ &= (\cos^2 \theta + \sin^2 \theta)\ dr^2 + 0 \cdot dr\ d\theta + r^2(\sin^2 \theta + \cos^2 \theta)\ d\theta^2 \\ &= dr^2 + r^2\ d\theta^2 \end{aligned}$$

as in (14.3). Using the same method for cylindrical coordinates (14.7) we find (Problem 147)

$$(14.15) \quad ds^2 = dr^2 + r^2\ d\theta^2 + dz^2 \qquad \text{(cylindrical coordinates)}.$$

and for spherical coordinates we find (Problem 147)

(14.16) $\quad ds^2 = dr^2 + r^2\,d\theta^2 + r^2 \sin^2\theta\,d\phi^2 \qquad$ (spherical coordinates).

Example 4. Express the velocity of a moving particle in spherical coordinates.

If s represents the distance the particle has moved along some path, then ds/dt is the velocity of the particle. Dividing (14.16) by dt^2, we find for the square of the velocity

$$v^2 = \left(\frac{ds}{dt}\right)^2 = \left(\frac{dr}{dt}\right)^2 + r^2\left(\frac{d\theta}{dt}\right)^2 + r^2 \sin^2\theta\left(\frac{d\phi}{dt}\right)^2.$$

We have just seen how to find the arc length element ds in polar coordinates (or other systems) by calculating $\sqrt{dx^2 + dy^2}$. You might be tempted to try to find the area element by computing $dx\,dy$, but you would discover that this does not work (we must use the Jacobian to get volume or area elements). You can see why by looking at Fig. 14.1. The element of area $r\,dr\,d\theta$ at the point (x, y) is not the same as the element of area $dx\,dy$ at that point. Then consider Fig. 14.2; the element of arc ds is the hypotenuse of the triangle with legs dr and $r\,d\theta$, and it is also the hypotenuse of the triangle with legs dx and dy. Thus ds *is* the same element for both x, y and r, θ and this is why we can compute ds in polar coordinates by calculating $\sqrt{dx^2 + dy^2}$. These comments hold for other coordinate systems, too. We can always find ds by computing $\sqrt{dx^2 + dy^2}$ or $\sqrt{dx^2 + dy^2 + dz^2}$, but we cannot compute area or volume elements directly from the rectangular ones—we must use the Jacobian or else geometrical methods.

REFERENCES

The material of this chapter is discussed in most calculus textbooks and also in some books on mathematics in physics and engineering. (See the reference list at the end of the book; Chapter 4 references have a [4] after the listing.)

PROBLEMS

1. If $u = x^2/(x^2 + y^2)$, find $\partial u/\partial x$, $\partial u/\partial y$.

2. If $s = t^u$, find $\partial s/\partial t$, $\partial s/\partial u$.

3. If $z = \ln\sqrt{u^2 + v^2 + w^2}$, find $\partial z/\partial u$, $\partial z/\partial v$, $\partial z/\partial w$.

4. For $w = x^3 - y^3 - 2xy + 6$, find $\partial^2 w/\partial x^2$ and $\partial^2 w/\partial y^2$ at the points where $\partial w/\partial x = \partial w/\partial y = 0$.

5. For $u = e^x \cos y$, (a) verify that $\partial^2 u / \partial x\, \partial y = \partial^2 u / \partial y\, \partial x$;
(b) verify that $\partial^2 u / \partial x^2 + \partial^2 u / \partial y^2 = 0$.

*6. If $z = x^2 + 2y^2$, $x = r \cos \theta$, $y = r \sin \theta$, find the following partial derivatives.

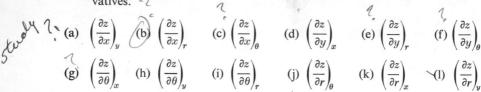

(a) $\left(\dfrac{\partial z}{\partial x} \right)_y$ (b) $\left(\dfrac{\partial z}{\partial x} \right)_r$ (c) $\left(\dfrac{\partial z}{\partial x} \right)_\theta$ (d) $\left(\dfrac{\partial z}{\partial y} \right)_x$ (e) $\left(\dfrac{\partial z}{\partial y} \right)_r$ (f) $\left(\dfrac{\partial z}{\partial y} \right)_\theta$

(g) $\left(\dfrac{\partial z}{\partial \theta} \right)_x$ (h) $\left(\dfrac{\partial z}{\partial \theta} \right)_y$ (i) $\left(\dfrac{\partial z}{\partial \theta} \right)_r$ (j) $\left(\dfrac{\partial z}{\partial r} \right)_\theta$ (k) $\left(\dfrac{\partial z}{\partial r} \right)_x$ (l) $\left(\dfrac{\partial z}{\partial r} \right)_y$

(m) $\dfrac{\partial^2 z}{\partial r\, \partial y}$ (n) $\dfrac{\partial^2 z}{\partial x\, \partial \theta}$ (o) $\dfrac{\partial^2 z}{\partial y\, \partial \theta}$ (p) $\dfrac{\partial^2 z}{\partial r\, \partial x}$ (q) $\dfrac{\partial^2 z}{\partial r\, \partial \theta}$ (r) $\dfrac{\partial^2 z}{\partial x\, \partial y}$.

7. Verify the coefficients of the third-order terms [(2.8) or $n = 3$ in (2.9)] of the power series for $f(x, y)$ by finding the third-order partial derivatives in (2.3) and substituting $x = a$, $y = b$.

8. Find the two-variable power series for the following functions (i) by multiplying two one-variable power series together, and (ii) by (2.5): (a) $e^x \cos y$, (b) $\sin x \sinh y$.

9. Find the two-variable power series for $\sqrt{1 + xy}$ by (a) using the binomial theorem, (b) using (2.5).

10. Consider a function $f(x, y)$ which can be expanded in a two-variable power series, (2.5) or (2.9). Let $x - a = h = \Delta x$, $y - b = k = \Delta y$; then $x = a + \Delta x$, $y = b + \Delta y$ so that $f(x, y)$ becomes $f(a + \Delta x, b + \Delta y)$. The change Δz in $z = f(x, y)$ when x changes from a to $a + \Delta x$ and y changes from b to $b + \Delta y$ is then

$$\Delta z = f(a + \Delta x, b + \Delta y) - f(a, b).$$

Use the series (2.9) to obtain (3.11) and to see explicitly what ϵ_1 and ϵ_2 are and that they approach zero as Δx and $\Delta y \to 0$.

11. A wall in the shape of a semi-ellipse has base $2a = 100$ ft and height $b = 30$ ft. If a increases by 0.1 ft and b decreases by 0.2 ft, find the approximate change in the area of the wall. (The area of an ellipse of semiaxes a and b is πab.)

12. If $u = 3x^2 y - xy^3 + 2$, find du at the point $(1, 2)$.

13. A circular cylindrical tank of radius 25 ft and height 50 ft is to be painted on the top and sides with paint of thickness 0.02 in. About how many gallons of paint (231 in.$^3 = 1$ gal) are required?

14. Find a reasonable approximation (to two decimal places) to

$$\sqrt{(4.98)^2 - (3.03)^2}.$$

15. About how much (in percent) does an error of 1% in a and b affect $a^2 b^3$?

16. Show that the approximate relative error $(df)/f$ of a product $f = gh$ is the sum of the approximate relative errors of the factors.

17. A force of 500 nt is measured with a possible error of 1 nt. Its component in a direction 60° away from its line of action is required, where the angle is subject to an error of 0.5°. What is (approximately) the largest possible error in the component?

18. For a perfect gas we have $pv = RT$, where R is a constant. If T changes from 400° to 402°, and v from 5 m³ to 5.05 m³, find the approximate change in p.

19. In calculating $1325 \div 321$ on a slide rule, you can perhaps read the first number up to an error of 2 and the second up to an error of $\frac{1}{2}$. What accuracy can you expect in the quotient?

20. Prove the statement just after (5.2), that dz given by (3.6) is a good approximation to Δz even though dx and dy are not independent. *Hint:* let x and y be functions of t; then (5.2) is correct, but $\Delta x \neq dx$ and $\Delta y \neq dy$ (because x and y are not independent variables). However, $\Delta x / \Delta t$ is nearly dx/dt for small dt and $dt = \Delta t$ since t is the independent variable. You can then show that

$$\Delta x = \left(\frac{dx}{dt} + \epsilon_x \right) dt = dx + \epsilon_x \, dt,$$

and a similar formula for Δy, and get

$$\Delta z = \frac{\partial z}{\partial x} \, dx + \frac{\partial z}{\partial y} \, dy + (\text{terms containing } \epsilon\text{'s}) \cdot dt$$

$$= dz + \epsilon \, dt,$$

where $\epsilon \to 0$ as $\Delta t \to 0$.

21. Given $z = xe^{-y}$, $x = \cosh t$, $y = \cos t$, find dz/dt.

22. Given $w = \sqrt{u^2 + v^2}$, $u = \cos [\ln \tan (p + \frac{1}{4}\pi)]$, $v = \sin [\ln \tan (p + \frac{1}{4}\pi)]$ find dw/dp.

23. Given $r = e^{-p^2-q^2}$, $p = e^s$, $q = e^{-s}$, find dr/ds.

24. Given $z = (x + y)^5$, $y = \sin 10x$, find dz/dx.

25. Given $c = \sin (a - b)$, $b = ae^{2a}$, find dc/da.

26. If we are given $z = z(x, y)$ and $y = y(x)$, show that the chain rule (5.1) gives

$$\frac{dz}{dx} = \frac{\partial z}{\partial x} + \frac{\partial z}{\partial y} \frac{dy}{dx}.$$

27. If $pv^a = C$ (where a and C are constants), find dv/dp.

28. If $x = yz$ and $y = 2 \sin (y + z)$, find dx/dy and d^2x/dy^2.

29. If $P = r \cos t$ and $r \sin t - 2te^r = 0$, find dP/dt.

30. If $xy^3 - yx^3 = 6$ is the equation of a curve, find the slope and the equation of the tangent line at the point $(1, 2)$.

31. In Problem 30 find d^2y/dx^2 at $(1, 2)$.

32. For the curve $x^{2/3} + y^{2/3} = 4$, find the equations of the tangent lines at $(2\sqrt{2}, -2\sqrt{2})$, at $(8, 0)$, and at $(0, 8)$.

33. If $ye^{xy} = \sin x$ find dy/dx and d^2y/dx^2 at $(0, 0)$.

34. If $x^y = y^x$, find dy/dx at $(2, 4)$.

35. If $z = xe^{-y}$ and $x = \cosh t$, $y = \cos s$, find $\partial z/\partial s$ and $\partial z/\partial t$.

36. If $w = e^{-r^2-s^2}$, $r = uv$, $s = u + 2v$, find $\partial w/\partial u$ and $\partial w/\partial v$.

37. If $u = x^2y^3z$ and $x = \sin(s + t)$, $y = \cos(s + t)$, $z = e^{st}$, find $\partial u/\partial s$ and $\partial u/\partial t$.

38. If $w = (r \cos \theta)^{r \sin \theta}$, find $\partial w/\partial \theta$.

39. If $w = f(x, y)$ and $x = r \cos \theta$, $y = r \sin \theta$, find formulas for $\partial w/\partial r$, $\partial w/\partial \theta$, and $\partial^2 w/\partial r^2$.

40. If $x = r \cos \theta$ and $y = r \sin \theta$, find $(\partial y/\partial \theta)_r$ and $(\partial y/\partial \theta)_x$. Also find $(\partial \theta/\partial y)_x$ in two ways (by eliminating r from the given equations and then differentiating, or by taking differentials in both equations and then eliminating dr). When are $\partial y/\partial \theta$ and $\partial \theta/\partial y$ reciprocals?

41. If $x^2 + y^2 = 2st$ and $2xy = s^2 - t^2$, find $\partial x/\partial s$, $\partial x/\partial t$, $\partial y/\partial s$, $\partial y/\partial t$.

42. If $xs^2 + yt^2 = 1$ and $x^2s + y^2t = xy - 4$, find $\partial x/\partial s$, $\partial x/\partial t$, $\partial y/\partial s$, $\partial y/\partial t$, at $(x, y, s, t) = (1, -3, 2, -1)$. *Hint:* To simplify the work, substitute the numerical values just after you have taken differentials.

43. Finish Example 4 of Section 7, both for the general case and for the given numerical values. Substitute the numerical values into your general formulas to check your answers.

44. If $w = x + y$ with $x^3 + xy + y^3 = s$ and $x^2y + xy^2 = t$, find $\partial w/\partial s$, $\partial w/\partial t$.

45. If $m = pq$ with $a \sin p - p = q$ and $b \cos q + q = p$, find $(\partial p/\partial q)_m$, $(\partial p/\partial q)_a$, $(\partial p/\partial q)_b$, $(\partial b/\partial a)_p$, $(\partial a/\partial q)_m$.

46. If $u = x^2 + y^2 + xyz$ and $x^4 + y^4 + z^4 = 2x^2y^2z^2 + 10$, find $(\partial u/\partial x)_z$ at the point $(x, y, z) = (2, 1, 1)$.

47. Given $x^2u - y^2v = 1$, and $x + y = uv$. Find $(\partial x/\partial u)_v$, $(\partial x/\partial u)_y$.

48. Let $w = x^2 + xy + z^2$.
   (a) If $x^3 + x = 3t$, $y^4 + y = 4t$, $z^5 + z = 5t$, find dw/dt.
   (b) If $y^3 + xy = 1$ and $z^3 - xz = 2$, find dw/dx.
   (c) If $x^3z + z^3y + y^3x = 0$, find $(\partial w/\partial x)_y$.

49. If $p^3 + sq = t$, and $q^3 + tp = s$, find $(\partial p/\partial s)_t$, $(\partial p/\partial s)_q$.

50. If $m = a + b$ and $n = a^2 + b^2$ find $(\partial b/\partial m)_n$ and $(\partial m/\partial b)_a$.

51. If $z = r + s^2$, $x + y = s^3 + r^3$, $xy = s^2 - r^2$, find $(\partial x/\partial z)_s$, $(\partial x/\partial z)_r$, $(\partial x/\partial z)_y$.

52. If $u^2 + v^2 = x^3 - y^3$, $u^2 - v^2 = x^2y^2$, find $(\partial u/\partial x)_y$, $(\partial u/\partial x)_v$, $(\partial x/\partial u)_y$, $(\partial x/\partial u)_v$.

53. Given $x^2 + y^2 + z^2 = 4$ and $w^3 + z^3 = 5xy$, find

$$\left(\frac{\partial z}{\partial x}\right)_y, \quad \left(\frac{\partial z}{\partial x}\right)_w, \quad \left(\frac{\partial z}{\partial y}\right)_x, \quad \left(\frac{\partial z}{\partial y}\right)_w, \quad \left(\frac{\partial w}{\partial x}\right)_z, \quad \left(\frac{\partial x}{\partial w}\right)_z.$$

54. If $w = f(ax + by)$, show that

$$b\frac{\partial w}{\partial x} - a\frac{\partial w}{\partial y} = 0.$$

Hint: let $ax + by = z$.

55. If $u = f(x - ct) + g(x + ct)$, show that   *let* $4-ct=p$

$$\frac{\partial^2 u}{\partial x^2} = \frac{1}{c^2}\frac{\partial^2 u}{\partial t^2}.$$ $4+ct=q$

56. If $z = \cos(xy)$, show that

$$x\frac{\partial z}{\partial x} - y\frac{\partial z}{\partial y} = 0.$$

57. (a) Given $f(x, y, z) = 0$, find a formula for $(\partial z/\partial x)_y$.
(b) Given $f(x, y, z) = 0$ and $g(x, y, z) = 0$, find a formula for dy/dx.

58. Given $u(x, y)$ and $y(x, z)$, show that

$$\left(\frac{\partial u}{\partial x}\right)_z = \left(\frac{\partial u}{\partial x}\right)_y + \left(\frac{\partial u}{\partial y}\right)_x\left(\frac{\partial y}{\partial x}\right)_z.$$

59. Given $s(v, T)$ and $v(p, T)$, we define $c_p = T(\partial s/\partial T)_p$, $c_v = T(\partial s/\partial T)_v$. (The c's are specific heats in thermodynamics.) Show that

$$c_p - c_v = T\left(\frac{\partial s}{\partial v}\right)_T\left(\frac{\partial v}{\partial T}\right)_p.$$

60. A roof gutter is to be made from a long strip of sheet metal, 24 cm wide, by bending up equal amounts at each side through equal angles. Find the angle and the dimensions that will make the carrying capacity of the gutter as large as possible.

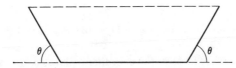

61. An aquarium with rectangular sides and bottom (and no top) is to hold 5 gal. Find its proportions so that it will use the least amount of material.

62. Repeat Problem 61 if the bottom is to be three times as thick as the sides.

63. Find the most economical proportions for a tent as in the figure, with no floor.

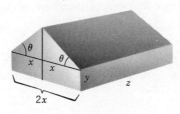

64. Find the shortest distance from the origin to the surface $z = xy + 5$.

65. Given particles of masses m, $2m$, and $3m$ at the points $(0, 1)$, $(1, 0)$, and $(2, 3)$, find the point P about which their total moment of inertia will be least. (Recall that to find the moment of inertia of m about P, you multiply m by the square of its distance from P.)

66. Repeat Problem 65 for masses m_1, m_2, m_3 at (x_1, y_1), (x_2, y_2), (x_3, y_3). Show that the point you find is the center of mass.

67. Find the shortest distance from the origin to $x^2 - y^2 = 1$.

68. What proportions will maximize the area shown in the figure (rectangle with isosceles triangles at its ends) if the perimeter is given?

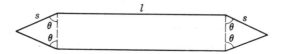

69. What proportions will maximize the volume of a projectile in the form of a circular cylinder with one conical end and one flat end, if the surface area is given?

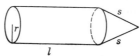

70. Find the largest rectangular parallelepiped (box) that can be shipped by parcel post (length + girth = 100 in.).

71. Find the largest box (with faces parallel to the coordinate axes) that can be inscribed in

$$\frac{x^2}{4} + \frac{y^2}{9} + \frac{z^2}{25} = 1.$$

72. Find the point on $2x + 3y + z - 11 = 0$ for which $4x^2 + y^2 + z^2$ is a minimum.

73. A box has three of its faces in the coordinate planes and one vertex on the plane $2x + 3y + 4z = 6$. Find the maximum volume for the box.

74. Repeat Problem 73 if the plane is $ax + by + cz = d$.

75. A point moves in the (x, y) plane on the line $2x + 3y - 4 = 0$. Where will it be when the sum of the squares of its distances from $(1, 0)$ and $(-1, 0)$ is smallest?

76. Find the largest triangle that can be inscribed in the ellipse $\dfrac{x^2}{a^2} + \dfrac{y^2}{b^2} = 1$

(assume the triangle symmetric about one axis of the ellipse with one side perpendicular to this axis).

77. Find the largest and smallest distances from the origin to the conic whose equation is $5x^2 - 6xy + 5y^2 - 32 = 0$ and hence determine the lengths of the semiaxes of this conic.

78. Find the smallest distance from the origin to the quadric surface whose equation is $x^2 + y^2 - 2zx = 4$. (*Warning:* A careless analysis may give you $d = 2$; this is *not* the *smallest* distance.)

79. Find the largest z for which $2x + 4y = 5$ and $x^2 + z^2 = 2y$.

80. Complete Example 4 in Section 9.

81. If the temperature at the point (x, y, z) is $T = xyz$, find the hottest point (or points) on the surface of the sphere $x^2 + y^2 + z^2 = 12$, and find the temperature there.

82. Find the point on the line through $(1, 0, 0)$ and $(0, 1, 0)$ that is closest to the line $x = y = z$. Also find the point on the line $x = y = z$ that is closest to the line through $(1, 0, 0)$ and $(0, 1, 0)$.

83. Curve fitting by least squares: Find the straight line $y = mx + b$ such that the sum of the squares of the deviations at $x = -1, 0, 1$ from the observed points $(-1, -2)$, $(0, 0)$, $(1, 3)$ is a minimum, that is, $(-2 - y_1)^2 + (0 - y_2)^2 + (3 - y_3)^2$ is a minimum, where $(-1, y_1)$, $(0, y_2)$, $(1, y_3)$ are on the line.

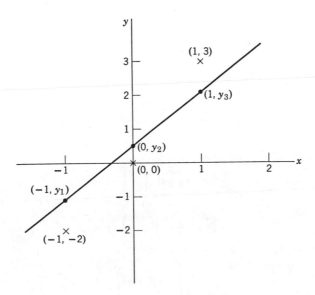

84. Find the shortest distance from the origin to the line of intersection of the planes $2x + y - z = 1$ and $x - y + z = 2$.

85. Find the right triangular prism of given volume and least area if the base is required to be a right triangle.

86. The temperature T of the circular plate $x^2 + y^2 \leq 1$ is given by $T = 2x^2 - 3y^2 - 2x$. Find the hottest and coldest points of the plate.

87. The temperature at a point (x, y, z) in the sphere $x^2 + y^2 + z^2 \leq 1$ is given by $T = y^2 + xz$. Find the largest and smallest values which T takes
(a) on the circle $y = 0$, $x^2 + z^2 = 1$,
(b) on the surface $x^2 + y^2 + z^2 = 1$,
(c) in the whole sphere.

88. The temperature of a rectangular plate bounded by the lines $x = \pm 1$, $y = \pm 1$, is given by $T = 2x^2 - 3y^2 - 2x + 10$. Find the hottest and coldest points of the plate.

89. (a) Find the largest and smallest values of the sum of the acute angles that a line through the origin makes with the three coordinate axes.
(b) Find the largest and smallest values of the sum of the acute angles that a line through the origin makes with the three coordinate planes.

90. The diagram shows a parking lot, 20 by 60 yd. A contractor has to run a power line from A to C; he can put it on poles around ABC at \$12 a yard or go underground part or all the way at \$15 a yard. If he is honest and wants to minimize the cost, to what point D (if any) should he run the underground part? If he is dishonest and wants to maximize the cost, but will run the line straight along AD (because an inspector is watching), where will D be?

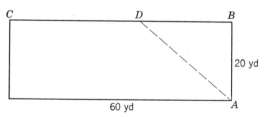

91. If $F(x, y, z) = 0$ show that

$$\left(\frac{\partial x}{\partial y}\right)_z \left(\frac{\partial y}{\partial x}\right)_z = 1$$

and

$$\left(\frac{\partial x}{\partial y}\right)_z \left(\frac{\partial y}{\partial z}\right)_x \left(\frac{\partial z}{\partial x}\right)_y = -1.$$

Hint: See Problem 57.

92. Reduce the equation

$$x^2 \left(\frac{d^2 y}{dx^2}\right) + 2x \left(\frac{dy}{dx}\right) - 5y = 0$$

to a differential equation with constant coefficients in $d^2 y/dz^2$, dy/dz, and y by the change of variable $x = e^z$.

93. If $w = f(x, s, t)$, $s = 2x + y$, $t = 2x - y$, find $(\partial w/\partial x)_y$ in terms of f and its derivatives.

94. If $w = f(x, x^2 + y^2, 2xy)$, find $(\partial w/\partial x)_y$ (compare Problem 93).

95. Solve equations (11.13) to get equations (11.14.)

96. Complete the details in Example 2 of Section 11 to get equations (11.22) and (11.23).

97. Change the independent variable from x to θ by $x = \cos \theta$ and show that the Legendre equation

$$(1 - x^2)\frac{d^2y}{dx^2} - 2x\frac{dy}{dx} + 2y = 0$$

becomes

$$\frac{d^2y}{d\theta^2} + \cot \theta \frac{dy}{d\theta} + 2y = 0.$$

98. Change the independent variable from x to $u = 2\sqrt{x}$ in the Bessel equation

$$x^2\frac{d^2y}{dx^2} + x\frac{dy}{dx} - (1 - x)y = 0$$

and show that the equation becomes

$$u^2\frac{d^2y}{du^2} + u\frac{dy}{du} + (u^2 - 4)y = 0.$$

99. In the partial differential equation

$$\frac{\partial^2 z}{\partial x^2} - 5\frac{\partial^2 z}{\partial x \, \partial y} + 6\frac{\partial^2 z}{\partial y^2} = 0$$

put $s = y + 2x$, $t = y + 3x$ and show that the equation becomes $\partial^2 z / \partial s \, \partial t = 0$.

100. Suppose that $w = f(x, y)$ satisfies

$$\frac{\partial^2 w}{\partial x^2} - \frac{\partial^2 w}{\partial y^2} = 1.$$

Put $x = u + v$, $y = u - v$, and show that w satisfies $\partial^2 w / \partial u \, \partial v = 1$.

101. If w satisfies

$$\frac{\partial^2 w}{\partial x^2} + \frac{\partial^2 w}{\partial y^2} = 0$$

and we put $x = r \cos \theta$, $y = r \sin \theta$, show that w satisfies

$$\frac{1}{r}\frac{\partial}{\partial r}\left(r\frac{\partial w}{\partial r}\right) + \frac{1}{r^2}\frac{\partial^2 w}{\partial \theta^2} = 0.$$

102. Given $du = T\,ds - p\,dv$, find a Legendre transformation giving
   (a) a function $f(T, v)$;
   (b) a function $h(s, p)$;
   (c) a function $g(T, p)$.
   Hint for (c): Perform a Legendre transformation on both terms in du.

103. Given $L(q, \dot{q})$ such that $dL = \dot{p}\,dq + p\,d\dot{q}$, find $H(p, q)$ so that $dH = \dot{q}\,dp - \dot{p}\,dq$.

Comments: L and H are functions used in mechanics called the Lagrangian and the Hamiltonian. The quantities $\dot{q}$ and $\dot{p}$ are actually time derivatives of p and q, but you make no use of the fact in this problem. Treat $\dot{p}$ and $\dot{q}$ as if they were two more variables having nothing to do with p and q. *Hint:* Use a Legendre transformation. On your first try you will probably get $-H$. Look at the text discussion of Legendre transformations and satisfy yourself that $g = qy - f$ would have been just as satisfactory as $g = f - qy$ in (11.27).

104. If $y = \int_0^{\sqrt{x}} \sin t^2 \, dt$, find dy/dx.

105. If $y = \int_0^\pi \sin xt \, dt$, find dy/dx (a) by evaluating the integral and then differentiating, (b) by differentiating first and then evaluating the integral.

106. Find dy/dx explicitly if $y = \int_0^1 \frac{e^{xu} - 1}{u} \, du$.

107. If $s = \int_u^v \frac{1 - e^t}{t} \, dt$, find $\partial s/\partial v$ and $\partial s/\partial u$ and also their limits as u and v tend to zero.

108. (a) If $z = \int_{\sin x}^{\cos x} \frac{\sin t}{t} \, dt$, find $\frac{dz}{dx}$.

(b) Use l'Hospital's rule to evaluate $\lim\limits_{x \to 2} \dfrac{1}{x - 2} \int_2^x \dfrac{\sin t}{t} \, dt$.

109. If $u = \int_x^{y-x} \frac{\sin t}{t} \, dt$, find $\frac{\partial u}{\partial x}$.

110. If $w = \int_{xy}^{2x + 3y} \frac{du}{\ln u}$, find $\frac{\partial w}{\partial x}$.

111. If $\int_u^v e^{-t^2} \, dt = x$ and $u^v = y$, find $\left(\dfrac{\partial u}{\partial x}\right)_y$ and $\left(\dfrac{\partial u}{\partial y}\right)_x$.

112. If $\int_0^x e^{-s^2} \, ds = u$, find $\dfrac{dx}{du}$.

113. Find $\dfrac{d}{dx} \int_{3-x}^{x^2} (x - t) \, dt$ both by evaluating the integral first and by differentiating first.

114. (a) Show that $y = \int_0^x f(x - t) \, dt$ satisfies $\dfrac{dy}{dx} = f(x)$. (*Hint:* it is helpful to make the change of variable $x - t = u$ in the integral.)

(b) Show that $y = \int_0^x (x - u) f(u) \, du$ satisfies $y'' = f(x)$.

(c) Show that $y = \dfrac{1}{(n - 1)!} \int_0^x (x - u)^{n-1} f(u) \, du$ satisfies $y^{(n)} = f(x)$.

115. Find $\dfrac{d}{dx}\displaystyle\int_{x}^{x^2}\dfrac{du}{\ln\,(x+u)}$.

116. Show that $u(x,\,y)=\dfrac{y}{\pi}\displaystyle\int_{-\infty}^{\infty}\dfrac{f(t)\,dt}{(x-t)^2+y^2}$ satisfies $u_{xx}+u_{yy}=0$.

117. Show that $y=\displaystyle\int_{0}^{x}f(u)\,\sin(x-u)\,du$ satisfies $y''+y=f(x)$.

118. Given that $\displaystyle\int_{0}^{\infty}\dfrac{dx}{y^2+x^2}=\dfrac{\pi}{2y}$, differentiate with respect to y and so evaluate

$$\int_{0}^{\infty}\dfrac{dx}{(y^2+x^2)^2}.$$

119. Given that

$$\int_{0}^{\infty}e^{-ax}\,\sin kx\,dx=\dfrac{k}{a^2+k^2},$$

show that

$$\int_{0}^{\infty}xe^{-ax}\,\sin kx\,dx=\dfrac{2ka}{(a^2+k^2)^2}$$

and that

$$\int_{0}^{\infty}xe^{-ax}\,\cos kx\,dx=\dfrac{a^2-k^2}{(a^2+k^2)^2}.$$

120. In kinetic theory we have to evaluate integrals of the form $I=\displaystyle\int_{0}^{\infty}t^n e^{-at^2}\,dt$.
Given that $\displaystyle\int_{0}^{\infty}e^{-at^2}\,dt=\tfrac{1}{2}\sqrt{\pi/a}$, evaluate I for $n=2$ and $n=4$.

121. A function $f(x,\,y,\,z)$ is called homogeneous of degree n if $f(tx,\,ty,\,tz)=t^n f(x,\,y,\,z)$. For example, $z^2\ln\,(x/y)$ is homogeneous of degree 2 since

$$(tz)^2\ln\dfrac{tx}{ty}=t^2\!\left(z^2\ln\dfrac{x}{y}\right).$$

Euler's theorem on homogeneous functions says that if f is homogeneous of degree n, then

$$x\,\dfrac{\partial f}{\partial x}+y\,\dfrac{\partial f}{\partial y}+z\,\dfrac{\partial f}{\partial z}=nf.$$

Prove this theorem. *Hints:* Differentiate $f(tx,\,ty,\,tz)=t^n f(x,\,y,\,z)$ with respect to t, and then let $t=1$. It is convenient to call $\partial f/\partial(tx)=f_1$, etc., that is, the partial derivative of f with respect to its first variable. Or, you can at first call $tx=u$, $ty=v$, $tz=w$. (Both the definition and the theorem can be extended to any number of variables.)

122. Use the Taylor series about $x=a$ to verify the familiar "second derivative test" for a maximum or minimum point. That is, show that if $f'(a)=0$, then $f''(a)>0$ implies a minimum point at $x=a$ and $f''(a)<0$ implies a maximum point at $x=a$. *Hint:* for a minimum point, say, you must show that $f(x)>f(a)$ for all x near enough to a.

123. Using the two-variable Taylor series [say (2.9)] prove the following "second derivative tests" for maximum or minimum points of functions of two variables. If $f_x = f_y = 0$ at (a, b), then

  (a, b) is a minimum point if at (a, b), $\quad f_{xx} > 0, \quad f_{yy} > 0, \quad$ and $f_{xx}f_{yy} > f_{xy}^2$;

  (a, b) is a maximum point if at (a, b), $\quad f_{xx} < 0, \quad f_{yy} < 0, \quad$ and $f_{xx}f_{yy} > f_{xy}^2$;

  (a, b) is neither a maximum nor a minimum point if $\quad f_{xx}f_{yy} < f_{xy}^2$.
(Note that this includes $f_{xx}f_{yy} < 0$, that is, f_{xx} and f_{yy} of opposite sign.)
Hint: Let $f_{xx} = A, f_{xy} = B, f_{yy} = C$; then the second derivative terms in the Taylor series are $Ah^2 + 2Bhk + Ck^2$; this can be written $A(h + Bk/A)^2 + (C - B^2/A)k^2$. Find out when this expression is positive for *all* small h, k [that is, all (x, y) near (a, b)]; also find out when it is negative for all small h, k, and when it has both positive and negative values for small h, k.

124. Use the facts stated in Problem 123 to find the maximum and minimum points of the following functions.

  (a) $x^2 + y^2 + 2x - 4y + 10$ $\qquad$ (b) $x^2 - y^2 + 2x - 4y + 10$

  (c) $4 + x + y - x^2 - xy - \frac{1}{2}y^2$ $\quad$ (d) $x^3 - y^3 - 2xy + 2$

125. Given $z = (y - x^2)(y - 2x^2)$, show that z has neither a maximum nor a minimum at $(0, 0)$, although z has a minimum on every straight line through $(0, 0)$.

126. (a) Find the center of mass and moment of inertia about one end of a rod of length l if the density is constant.

  (b) A thin rod 10 ft long has a density which varies uniformly from 4 to 24 lb/ft. Find the center of mass. $7, 8 \frac{8}{9} \mu$

127. Given a circle of radius a, find by integration

  (a) its area;

  (b) the centroid of one quadrant;

  (c) the moment of inertia of a circular lamina about a diameter;

  (d) its circumference;

  (e) the centroid of a quarter circle arc. $\quad \int ds$

128. (a) Revolve the curve $y = x^{-1}$, from $x = 1$ to $x = \infty$, about the x-axis to create a surface and a volume. Write integrals for the surface area and the volume. Find the volume, and show that the surface area is infinite. *Hint:* The surface area integral is not easy to evaluate, but you can easily show that it is greater than $\displaystyle\int_1^\infty \frac{dx}{x}$ which you can evaluate.

  (b) The following question is a challenge to your ability to fit together your mathematical calculations and physical facts: In (a) you found a finite volume and an infinite area. Suppose you fill the finite volume with a finite amount of paint and then pour off the excess leaving what sticks to the surface. Apparently you have painted an infinite area with a finite amount of paint! What is wrong?

129. Using polar coordinates,

(a) write the equation of the circle sketched;

(b) find its area by integration;

(c) find the centroid of the first quadrant semicircular area;

(d) find the moments of inertia of a circular lamina in this position about each of the three coordinate axes, assuming constant density;

(e) find the length and the centroid of the semicircular arc in the first quadrant;

(f) find the center of mass and the moments of inertia of the circular area if the density is r;

(g) find the area common to the circle sketched and the circle $r \leq a$.

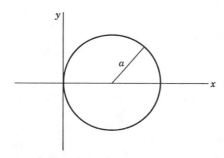

130. Let a curve $y = f(x)$ be revolved about the x-axis, thus forming a surface of revolution. Show that the cross sections of this surface in any plane $x = $ const. [that is, parallel to the (y, z) plane] are circles of radius $f(x)$. Thus write the general equation of a surface of revolution and verify the special case $f(x) = x^2$ in (13.9).

131. For the curve $y = \sqrt{x}$, between $x = 0$ and $x = 2$, find

(a) the area under the curve;

(b) the arc length;

(c) the volume of the solid generated when the area is revolved about the x-axis;

(d) the curved area of this solid;

(e, f, g) the centroids of the arc, the volume, and the surface area;

(h, i, j, k) the moments of inertia about the x-axis of a lamina in the shape of the plane area under the curve; of a wire bent along the arc of the curve; of the solid of revolution; and of a thin shell whose shape is the curved surface of the solid (assuming constant density for all these problems);

(l) the mass of a wire bent in the shape of the arc if its density (mass per unit length) is proportional to $\sqrt{x}$;

(m) the mass of the solid of revolution if the density (mass per unit volume) is $|xy|$;

(n) the moment of inertia about the y-axis of the solid of revolution if the density is $|xy|$.

132. Find the centroid of the volume cut from a sphere of radius a by a cone of vertex half-angle 60°, with vertex at the center of the sphere. Use spherical coordinates.

133. For a sphere of radius a find by integration
    (a) its volume;
    (b) its surface area;
    (c) the centroid of a solid hemisphere;
    (d) the centroid of the curved surface area of the hemisphere;
    (e) the moment of inertia of the whole spherical shell (that is, surface) about a diameter (assuming constant density).

134. Write a triple integral in spherical coordinates for the volume of the part of the cone $z^2 = x^2 + y^2$ that is between the planes $z = 1$ and $z = 2$. Evaluate the integral.

135. Write a triple integral in cylindrical coordinates for the volume inside the cylinder $x^2 + y^2 = 4$ and between $z = 2x^2 + y^2$ and the (x, y) plane. Evaluate the integral.

136. The volume of a sphere of radius r is $V = \frac{4}{3}\pi r^3$. Then $dV = 4\pi r^2\, dr = A\, dr$, where A is the area of the sphere. What is the geometrical meaning of the fact that the derivative of the volume is the area? Could you use this fact to find the volume formula given the area formula?

137. (a) Write a triple integral in cylindrical coordinates for the volume of the solid cut from a sphere of radius 2 by a cylinder of radius 1, one of whose elements is a diameter of the sphere. *Hint:* Take the axis of the cylinder parallel to the z-axis; a cross section of the cylinder then looks like the figure in Problem 129.
    (b) Write triple integrals for the moment of inertia about the z-axis of a uniform solid occupying this volume, and for the center of mass of the solid.
    (c) Evaluate the integrals and find I as a multiple of the mass.
    (d) Prove the "parallel axis theorem": The moment of inertia I of a body about a given axis is $I = I_m + Mr^2$, where M is the mass of the body, I_m is the moment of inertia of the body about an axis through the center of mass and parallel to the given axis, and r is the distance between the two axes.
    (e) Use (d) to find the moment of inertia of the solid in (b) about the axis of the cylinder.

138. (a) Write a triple integral in cylindrical coordinates for the volume of the part of a sphere between two parallel planes which intersect the sphere.
    (b) Evaluate the integral in (a). *Warning hint:* Do the r and θ integrals first.
    (c) Find the centroid of this volume.

139. Use the spherical coordinates θ and ϕ to find the area of a zone of a sphere (that is, the spherical surface area between two parallel planes). *Hint:* The spherical coordinate r is constant, say $r = a$, on the surface of a sphere. From Fig. 14.5, the area element for constant r is $r\, d\theta \cdot r \sin\theta\, d\phi$ or for $r = a$, $dA = a^2 \sin\theta\, d\theta\, d\phi$.

140. Find the center of mass of a hemispherical shell of constant density (mass per unit area) by using double integrals and the area element in Problem 139. (Compare Problem 133d.)

141. Express the integral

$$I = \int_0^1 dx \int_0^{\sqrt{1-x^2}} e^{-x^2-y^2} \, dy$$

as an integral in polar coordinates (r, θ) and so evaluate it.

142. Find the cylindrical coordinate volume element by Jacobians.

143. Find the Jacobians $\partial(x, y)/\partial(u, v)$ of the given transformations from variables x, y to variables u, v, given

(a) $x = \frac{1}{2}(u^2 - v^2)$,
    $y = uv$ (u and v are called parabolic cylinder coordinates);

(b) $x = a \cosh u \cos v$,
    $y = a \sinh u \sin v$ (u and v are called elliptic cylinder coordinates).

144. Prove the following theorems about Jacobians.

$$\frac{\partial(u, v)}{\partial(x, y)} \frac{\partial(x, y)}{\partial(u, v)} = 1.$$

$$\frac{\partial(x, y)}{\partial(u, v)} \frac{\partial(u, v)}{\partial(s, t)} = \frac{\partial(x, y)}{\partial(s, t)}.$$

Hint: Multiply the determinants (as you would matrices) and show that each element in the product determinant can be written as a single partial derivative.

145. In the integral

$$I = \int_0^\infty \int_0^\infty \frac{x^2 + y^2}{1 + (x^2 - y^2)^2} e^{-2xy} \, dx \, dy$$

make the change of variables

$$u = x^2 - y^2$$
$$v = 2xy$$

and evaluate I. *Hint:* Use (14.14) and the accompanying discussion.

146. In the integral

$$I = \int_{x=0}^{\frac{1}{2}} \int_{y=x}^{1-x} \left(\frac{x-y}{x+y}\right)^2 dy \, dx,$$

make the change of variables

$$x = \frac{1}{2}(r - s),$$
$$y = \frac{1}{2}(r + s),$$

and evaluate I. *Hints:* See Problem 145. To find the r and s limits, sketch the area of integration in the (x, y) plane and sketch the r- and s-axes. Then show that to cover the same integration area, you may take the r and s limits to be: s from 0 to r, r from 0 to 1.

147. Verify equations (14.15) and (14.16).

148. Use equation (14.15) to set up an integral for the length of wire required to wind a coil spirally about a cylinder of radius 1 in., and length 1 ft, if there are three turns per inch.

149. A loxodrome or rhumb line is a curve on the earth's surface along which a ship sails without changing its course, that is, such that it crosses the meridians at a constant angle α. Show that then $\tan \alpha = \sin \theta \, d\phi/d\theta$ (θ and ϕ are spherical coordinates). Use (14.16) to set up an integral for the distance traveled by a ship along a rhumb line. Show that although a rhumb line winds infinitely many times around either the north or the south pole, its total length is finite.

150. Compute the gravitational attraction on a unit mass at the origin due to the mass (of constant density) occupying the volume inside the sphere $r = 2a$ and above the plane $z = a$. *Hint:* The magnitude of the gravitational force on the unit mass due to the element of mass dM at (r, θ, ϕ) is $(G/r^2) \, dM$. You want the z-component of this since the other components of the total force are zero by symmetry. Use spherical coordinates.

5

Vector Analysis

1. INTRODUCTION AND NOTATION

Many quantities in physics have both a magnitude and a direction; some examples are the displacement or velocity of an object, the force acting on it, and the electric field or the magnetic field at a point. Such quantities are called *vectors*; they should be contrasted with quantities like mass, time, or temperature which have magnitude only and are called *scalars*. The notation and techniques of vector analysis are extremely useful in stating physical laws and in doing problems in two and three dimensions both in geometry and in physical applications.

It is often useful to represent a vector by an arrow (Fig. 2.1); the direction of the arrow specifies the direction of the vector and the length of the arrow specifies the magnitude of the vector. Alternatively, we may specify the vector by giving its projections (A_x, A_y, for **A** in Fig. 2.1) on the axes of some coordinate system; these projections are called the *components* of the vector (relative to that coordinate system). We shall indicate a vector by a boldface letter (for example, **A**), and a component of a vector by a subscript (for example, A_x is the x-component of **A**). The magnitude of a vector **A** means the length of the vector; we shall write the magnitude of **A** as |**A**| or A. Then by the Pythagorean theorem we can easily show that (Problem 1)

$$(1.1) \quad \begin{aligned} A = |\mathbf{A}| = \sqrt{A_x^2 + A_y^2} & \quad \text{in two dimensions} \quad \text{or} \\ A = |\mathbf{A}| = \sqrt{A_x^2 + A_y^2 + A_z^2} & \quad \text{in three dimensions.} \end{aligned}$$

Example.   The force **F** has an x-component of 4 lb and a y-component of 3 lb. Then we write

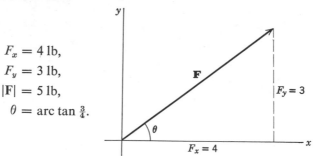

$$F_x = 4 \text{ lb},$$
$$F_y = 3 \text{ lb},$$
$$|\mathbf{F}| = 5 \text{ lb},$$
$$\theta = \text{arc tan } \tfrac{3}{4}.$$

2. VECTOR ADDITION

There are two ways to get the sum of two vectors. One is by the parallelogram law: To find $\mathbf{A} + \mathbf{B}$, place the tail of **B** at the head of **A** and draw the vector from the tail of **A** to the head of **B** as shown in Fig. 2.1. The second way of finding $\mathbf{A} + \mathbf{B}$ is to add components: $\mathbf{A} + \mathbf{B}$ has components $A_x + B_x$ and $A_y + B_y$. You should satisfy yourself from Fig. 2.1 that these two methods of finding $\mathbf{A} + \mathbf{B}$ are equivalent. From Fig. 2.2 and either definition of vector addition, it follows that

$$\mathbf{A} + \mathbf{B} = \mathbf{B} + \mathbf{A} \qquad \text{(commutative law for addition)};$$
$$(\mathbf{A} + \mathbf{B}) + \mathbf{C} = \mathbf{A} + (\mathbf{B} + \mathbf{C}) \qquad \text{(associative law for addition)}.$$

In other words, vectors may be added together by the usual laws of algebra.

It seems reasonable to use the symbol 3**A** for the vector $\mathbf{A} + \mathbf{A} + \mathbf{A}$. By the methods of vector addition above, we can say that the vector $\mathbf{A} + \mathbf{A} + \mathbf{A}$ is a vector three times as long as **A** and in the same direction as **A** and that each component of 3**A** is three times the corresponding component of **A**. As a natural extension of these facts we define the vector $c\mathbf{A}$ (where c is any positive real number) to be a vector c times as long as **A** and in the same direction as **A**; each component of $c\mathbf{A}$ is then c times the corresponding component of **A** (Fig. 2.3).

The negative of a vector is defined as a vector of the same magnitude but in the opposite direction. Then (Fig. 2.4) each component of $-\mathbf{A}$ is the negative of the corresponding component of **A**. We can now define subtraction of vectors by saying that $\mathbf{A} - \mathbf{B}$ means the sum of the vectors **A** and $-\mathbf{B}$. Each component of $\mathbf{A} - \mathbf{B}$ is then obtained by subtracting the corresponding components of **A** and **B**, that is, $(\mathbf{A} - \mathbf{B})_x = A_x - B_x$, etc. Like addition, subtraction of vectors can be done geometrically (by the parallelogram law) or algebraically by subtracting the components (Fig. 2.5).

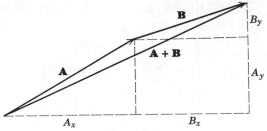

Figure 2.1

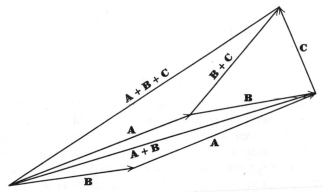

Figure 2.2

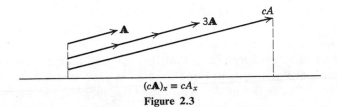

$(c\mathbf{A})_x = cA_x$

Figure 2.3

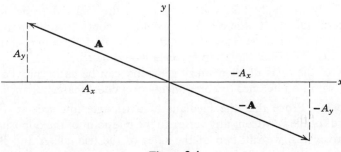

Figure 2.4

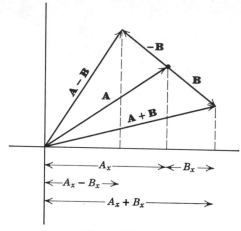

Figure 2.5

Since a vector has two (or three) components in two (or three) dimensions, a vector equation is really a set of two (or three) scalar equations (compare the facts that a complex equation corresponds to two real equations, and a matrix equation may correspond to many ordinary equations). Thus it is a simplification to write physical laws in vector form. However, this is not all. We have seen that there are two ways (geometric and algebraic) of defining vector addition and subtraction. In geometrical and physical applications, there are also always two ways to prove facts about vectors: by geometry (that is, without reference to a specific coordinate system) and by algebra (that is, by use of components, which means that we are using a particular coordinate system). One of the great advantages of vector formulas is that they are true independently of any particular coordinate system. For example, suppose we are discussing the motion of a mass m sliding down an inclined plane. Newton's second law $\mathbf{F} = m\mathbf{a}$ is then a correct equation no matter how we choose our axes. We might, say, take the x-axis horizontal and the y-axis vertical, or alternatively we might take the x-axis along the inclined plane and the y-axis perpendicular to the plane. F_x would, of course, be different in the two cases, but for either case it would be true that $F_x = ma_x$ and $F_y = ma_y$, that is, the *vector* equation $\mathbf{F} = m\mathbf{a}$ would be true.

Many of the facts of elementary geometry can be easily proved using vectors, with no reference to components or a coordinate system.

Example. Prove that the medians of a triangle intersect at a point two-thirds of the way from any vertex to the midpoint of the opposite side.

To prove this, we call two of the sides of the triangle $\mathbf{A}$ and $\mathbf{B}$. The third side of the triangle is then $\mathbf{A} + \mathbf{B}$ by the parallelogram law, with the directions of $\mathbf{A}, \mathbf{B}$, and $\mathbf{A} + \mathbf{B}$ as indicated in Fig. 2.6. If we add the vector $\frac{1}{2}\mathbf{B}$ to the vector $\mathbf{A}$ (head to tail, as in Fig. 2.6b), we have a vector from point O to the midpoint of the opposite side of the triangle, that is, we have the median to side $\mathbf{B}$. Next, take two-thirds of this vector; we now have the vector $\frac{2}{3}(\mathbf{A} + \frac{1}{2}\mathbf{B}) = \frac{2}{3}\mathbf{A} + \frac{1}{3}\mathbf{B}$ extending from O to P in Fig. 2.6b. We want to show that P is the intersection point of the three medians and also the "$\frac{2}{3}$ point" for each. We prove this by showing that P is the "$\frac{2}{3}$ point" on the median to side $\mathbf{A}$; then since $\mathbf{A}$ and $\mathbf{B}$ represent *any* two sides of the triangle, the proof holds for all three medians. The vector from R to Q (Fig. 2.6c) is $\frac{1}{2}\mathbf{A} + \mathbf{B}$; this is the median to $\mathbf{A}$. The "$\frac{2}{3}$ point" on this median is the point P' (Fig. 2.6d); the vector from R to P' is equal to $\frac{1}{3}(\frac{1}{2}\mathbf{A} + \mathbf{B})$. Then the vector from O to P' is $\frac{1}{2}\mathbf{A} + \frac{1}{3}(\frac{1}{2}\mathbf{A} + \mathbf{B}) = \frac{2}{3}\mathbf{A} + \frac{1}{3}\mathbf{B}$. Thus P and P' are the same point and all three medians have their "$\frac{2}{3}$ points" there. Note that we have made no reference to a coordinate system or to components in this proof.

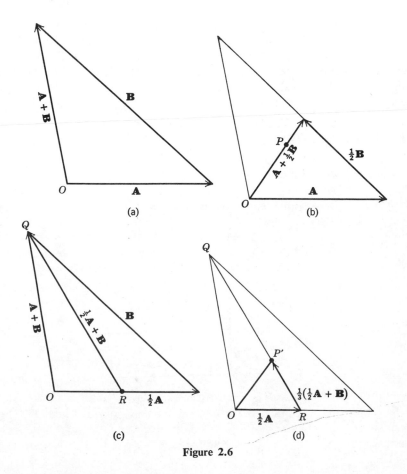

Figure 2.6

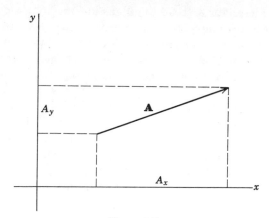

Figure 2.7

We have discussed in some detail the geometric method of adding vectors (parallelogram law or head to tail addition) and its importance in stating and proving geometric and physical facts without the intrusion of a special coordinate system. There are, however, many cases in which algebraic methods (using components relative to a particular coordinate system, Fig. 2.7) are better. We shall now discuss this in more detail.

3. UNIT VECTORS

First we consider a set of rectangular axes as in Fig. 3.1. Let the vector **i** be a vector of unit length in the positive x direction, and let **j** and **k** similarly be vectors of unit length in the positive y and z directions. These

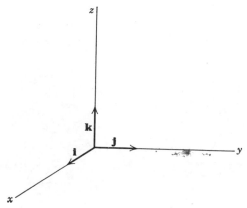

Figure 3.1

three vectors **i**, **j**, and **k** are called *unit* or *base* vectors for this coordinate system. Any vector can be written in terms of its components and the unit vectors in the following way. If A_x and A_y are the (scalar) components of a vector in the (x, y) plane, then $\mathbf{i}A_x$ and $\mathbf{j}A_y$ are its vector components, and their sum is the vector **A** (Fig. 3.2):

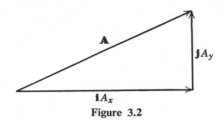

Figure 3.2

$$\mathbf{A} = \mathbf{i}A_x + \mathbf{j}A_y.$$

Similarly, in three dimensions

$$\mathbf{A} = \mathbf{i}A_x + \mathbf{j}A_y + \mathbf{k}A_z.$$

It is easy to add (or subtract) vectors in this form: If **A** and **B** are vectors in two dimensions, then

$$\mathbf{A} + \mathbf{B} = (\mathbf{i}A_x + \mathbf{j}A_y) + (\mathbf{i}B_x + \mathbf{j}B_y) = \mathbf{i}(A_x + B_x) + \mathbf{j}(A_y + B_y).$$

This is just the familiar result of adding components; the unit vectors serve to keep track of the separate components and allow us to write **A** as a single algebraic expression.

4. MULTIPLICATION OF VECTORS

There are two kinds of product of two vectors. One, called the *scalar product* (or *dot product* or *inner product*), gives a result which is a scalar; the other, called the *vector product* (or *cross product* or *outer product*), gives a vector answer.

Scalar product.　By definition, the scalar product of **A** and **B** (written **A · B**) is a scalar equal to the magnitude of **A** times the magnitude of **B** times the cosine of the angle θ between **A** and **B**:

(4.1)　　　　　　　　　$\mathbf{A} \cdot \mathbf{B} = |\mathbf{A}|\,|\mathbf{B}| \cos \theta.$

You should observe from (4.1) that the commutative law (4.2) holds for scalar multiplication:

(4.2)　　　　　　　　　$\mathbf{A} \cdot \mathbf{B} = \mathbf{B} \cdot \mathbf{A}.$

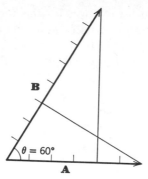

$|\mathbf{B}| = 8$, $|\mathbf{A}| = 6$.

Projection of $\mathbf{B}$ on $\mathbf{A} = 4$;

$\mathbf{A} \cdot \mathbf{B} = 6 \cdot 4 = 24$.

Or, projection of $\mathbf{A}$ on $\mathbf{B} = 3$;

$\mathbf{B} \cdot \mathbf{A} = 3 \cdot 8 = 24$.

Figure 4.1

A useful interpretation of the dot product is shown in Fig. 4.1. Since $|\mathbf{B}| \cos \theta$ is the projection of $\mathbf{B}$ on $\mathbf{A}$, we can write

(4.3) $\qquad \mathbf{A} \cdot \mathbf{B} = |\mathbf{A}|$ times (projection of $\mathbf{B}$ on $\mathbf{A}$)

or alternatively

(4.4) $\qquad \mathbf{A} \cdot \mathbf{B} = |\mathbf{B}|$ times (projection of $\mathbf{A}$ on $\mathbf{B}$).

Also we find from (4.1) that

(4.5) $\qquad \mathbf{A} \cdot \mathbf{A} = |\mathbf{A}|^2 \cos 0° = |\mathbf{A}|^2 = A^2.$

Sometimes $\mathbf{A}^2$ is written instead of $|\mathbf{A}|^2$ or A^2; you should understand that the square of a vector always means the square of its magnitude or its dot product with itself.

From Fig. 4.2 we can see that the projection of $\mathbf{B} + \mathbf{C}$ on $\mathbf{A}$ is equal to the projection of $\mathbf{B}$ on $\mathbf{A}$ plus the projection of $\mathbf{C}$ on $\mathbf{A}$. Then by (4.3)

$$\mathbf{A} \cdot (\mathbf{B} + \mathbf{C}) = |\mathbf{A}| \text{ times (projection of } (\mathbf{B} + \mathbf{C}) \text{ on } \mathbf{A})$$

(4.6) $\qquad\qquad = |\mathbf{A}|$ times (projection of $\mathbf{B}$ on $\mathbf{A}$

$\qquad\qquad\qquad + $ projection of $\mathbf{C}$ on $\mathbf{A}$)

$\qquad\qquad = \mathbf{A} \cdot \mathbf{B} + \mathbf{A} \cdot \mathbf{C}.$

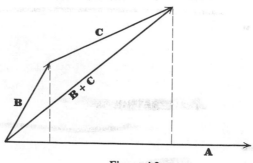

Figure 4.2

This is the distributive law for scalar multiplication. By (4.2) we get also

(4.7) $(\mathbf{B} + \mathbf{C}) \cdot \mathbf{A} = \mathbf{B} \cdot \mathbf{A} + \mathbf{C} \cdot \mathbf{A} = \mathbf{A} \cdot \mathbf{B} + \mathbf{A} \cdot \mathbf{C}.$

It is useful to know $\mathbf{A} \cdot \mathbf{B}$ in component form as well as our definition form (4.1). We write

(4.8) $\mathbf{A} \cdot \mathbf{B} = (\mathbf{i}A_x + \mathbf{j}A_y + \mathbf{k}A_z) \cdot (\mathbf{i}B_x + \mathbf{j}B_y + \mathbf{k}B_z).$

By the distributive law we can multiply this out getting nine terms such as $A_x B_x \mathbf{i} \cdot \mathbf{i}$, $A_x B_y \mathbf{i} \cdot \mathbf{j}$, etc. Using the definition of the scalar product, we get

(4.9)
$$\mathbf{i} \cdot \mathbf{i} = |\mathbf{i}| \cdot |\mathbf{i}| \cos 0° = 1 \cdot 1 \cdot 1 = 1,$$
and similarly $\mathbf{j} \cdot \mathbf{j} = 1, \mathbf{k} \cdot \mathbf{k} = 1,$
$$\mathbf{i} \cdot \mathbf{j} = |\mathbf{i}| \cdot |\mathbf{j}| \cos 90° = 1 \cdot 1 \cdot 0 = 0,$$
and similarly $\mathbf{i} \cdot \mathbf{k} = \mathbf{j} \cdot \mathbf{k} = 0.$

Using (4.9) in (4.8), we get

(4.10) $\mathbf{A} \cdot \mathbf{B} = A_x B_x + A_y B_y + A_z B_z.$

Equation (4.10) is an important formula which should be memorized. There are several immediate uses of this formula and of the dot product.

Angle between two vectors. Given the vectors, we can find the angle between them by using both (4.1) and (4.10) and solving for $\cos \theta$. For example, let us find the angle between the vectors $\mathbf{A} = 3\mathbf{i} + 6\mathbf{j} + 9\mathbf{k}$ and $\mathbf{B} = -2\mathbf{i} + 3\mathbf{j} + \mathbf{k}$.

Using (4.1) and (4.10) we get

$$\mathbf{A} \cdot \mathbf{B} = |\mathbf{A}| \, |\mathbf{B}| \cos \theta = 3 \cdot (-2) + 6 \cdot 3 + 9 \cdot 1 = 21,$$

(4.11) $|\mathbf{A}| = \sqrt{3^2 + 6^2 + 9^2} = 3\sqrt{14}, \qquad |\mathbf{B}| = \sqrt{2^2 + 3^2 + 1^2} = \sqrt{14},$

$$3\sqrt{14}\sqrt{14} \cos \theta = 21, \qquad \cos \theta = \tfrac{1}{2}, \qquad \theta = 60°.$$

Perpendicular and parallel vectors. If two vectors are perpendicular, then $\cos \theta = 0$; thus

(4.12) $A_x B_x + A_y B_y + A_z B_z = 0$

                              if $\mathbf{A}$ and $\mathbf{B}$ are perpendicular vectors.

If two vectors are parallel, their components are proportional; thus

(4.13) $\dfrac{A_x}{B_x} = \dfrac{A_y}{B_y} = \dfrac{A_z}{B_z}$ if $\mathbf{A}$ and $\mathbf{B}$ are parallel vectors.

Work. In elementary physics you learned that work equals force times displacement. If the force and displacement are not parallel, then the component of the force perpendicular to the displacement does no work.

The work in this case is the component of the force parallel to the displacement, multiplied by the displacement; that is, $W = (F \cos \theta) \cdot d = Fd \cos \theta$ (Fig. 4.3). This can now conveniently be written as

(4.14) $W = Fd \cos \theta = \mathbf{F} \cdot \mathbf{d}$.

If the force varies with distance, and perhaps also the direction of motion **d** changes with time, we can write, for an infinitesimal vector displacement $d\mathbf{r}$ (Fig. 4.4)

(4.15) $dW = \mathbf{F} \cdot d\mathbf{r}$.

We shall see later (Section 11) how to integrate dW in (4.15) to find the

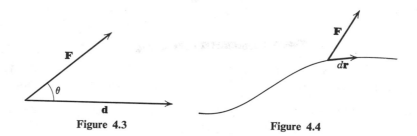

Figure 4.3   Figure 4.4

total work W when a particle is pushed along some path by a variable force.

Vector product. The vector or cross product of **A** and **B** is written $\mathbf{A} \times \mathbf{B}$. By definition, $\mathbf{A} \times \mathbf{B}$ is a vector whose magnitude and direction are given as follows: The magnitude of $\mathbf{A} \times \mathbf{B}$ is

(4.16) $|\mathbf{A} \times \mathbf{B}| = |\mathbf{A}|\,|\mathbf{B}| \sin \theta$,

where θ is the positive angle ($\leq 180°$) between **A** and **B**. The direction of $\mathbf{A} \times \mathbf{B}$ is perpendicular to the plane of **A** and **B** and in the sense of advance of a right-handed screw rotated from **A** to **B** as in Fig. 4.5. It is convenient to find the direction of $\mathbf{C} = \mathbf{A} \times \mathbf{B}$ by the following right-hand rule. Think of grasping the line **C** (or a screwdriver driving a right-handed screw in the direction **C**) with the right hand. The fingers then curl in the direction of rotation of **A** into **B** (arrow in Fig. 4.5) and the thumb points along $\mathbf{C} = \mathbf{A} \times \mathbf{B}$.

Perhaps the most startling result of the vector product definition is that $\mathbf{A} \times \mathbf{B}$ and $\mathbf{B} \times \mathbf{A}$ are not equal; in fact, $\mathbf{A} \times \mathbf{B} = -\mathbf{B} \times \mathbf{A}$. In mathematical language, vector multiplication is not commutative. (Recall that matrix multiplication is also not commutative.)

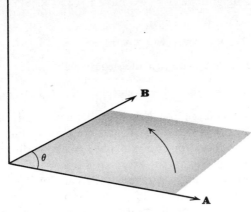

Figure 4.5

Just as for the scalar product, we need to know what the vector products of the unit vectors are. We find from (4.16) that $\mathbf{i} \times \mathbf{i}$ has magnitude $|\mathbf{i}|\,|\mathbf{i}|\sin 0° = 1 \cdot 1 \cdot 0 = 0$, so $\mathbf{i} \times \mathbf{i} = 0$. Evaluating the cross products of the other unit vectors similarly, we have

$$(4.17) \qquad\qquad \mathbf{i} \times \mathbf{i} = \mathbf{j} \times \mathbf{j} = \mathbf{k} \times \mathbf{k} = 0.$$

[In fact, for any vector $\mathbf{A}$, (4.16) gives $\mathbf{A} \times \mathbf{A} = 0$.] Also from (4.16) we get

$$|\mathbf{i} \times \mathbf{j}| = |\mathbf{i}|\,|\mathbf{j}|\sin 90° = 1 \cdot 1 \cdot 1 = 1,$$

and similarly for the absolute value of the cross product of any two different base vectors. From Fig. 4.6, we see that the direction of $\mathbf{i} \times \mathbf{j}$ is

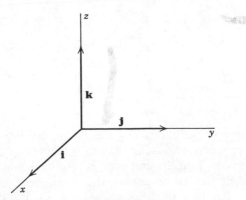

Figure 4.6

k, and since its magnitude is 1, we have $\mathbf{i} \times \mathbf{j} = \mathbf{k}$. Similarly evaluating $\mathbf{j} \times \mathbf{k}$ and $\mathbf{k} \times \mathbf{i}$, we find

(4.18) $\mathbf{i} \times \mathbf{j} = \mathbf{k}, \qquad \mathbf{j} \times \mathbf{k} = \mathbf{i}, \qquad \mathbf{k} \times \mathbf{i} = \mathbf{j}.$

The other three products are just the negatives of these:

(4.19) $\mathbf{j} \times \mathbf{i} = -\mathbf{k}, \qquad \mathbf{k} \times \mathbf{j} = -\mathbf{i}, \qquad \mathbf{i} \times \mathbf{k} = -\mathbf{j}.$

A good way to remember these is to write them cyclically (around a circle as indicated in Fig. 4.7). Reading around the circle counterclockwise, we get the positive products (for example, $\mathbf{i} \times \mathbf{j} = \mathbf{k}$); reading the other way we get the negative products (for example, $\mathbf{i} \times \mathbf{k} = -\mathbf{j}$).

It is well to note here that the results (4.18) and (4.19) depend upon the way we have labeled the axes in Fig. 4.6. We have arranged the (x, y, z)

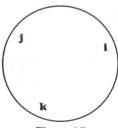

axes so that a rotation of the x-axis into the y-axis (through 90°) corresponds to the rotation of a right-handed screw advancing in the z direction. Such a coordinate system is called a *right-handed system.* If we used a left-handed system (say interchanging x and y), then all the equations in (4.18) and (4.19) would have their signs changed. This would be confusing; consequently, we practically always use right-handed coordinate systems, and we must be careful about this in

Figure 4.7

drawing diagrams. (Some older books use left-handed systems; watch out for this.)

To write $\mathbf{A} \times \mathbf{B}$ in component form we need the distributive law, namely $\mathbf{A} \times (\mathbf{B} + \mathbf{C}) = \mathbf{A} \times \mathbf{B} + \mathbf{A} \times \mathbf{C}$. It is not difficult but very tedious to prove this law (see, for example, Thomas, p. 617), so we shall assume and use it without proof. Then we have

$$\mathbf{A} \times \mathbf{B} = (\mathbf{i}A_x + \mathbf{j}A_y + \mathbf{k}A_z) \times (\mathbf{i}B_x + \mathbf{j}B_y + \mathbf{k}B_z)$$

$$= \mathbf{i}(A_yB_z - A_zB_y) + \mathbf{j}(A_zB_x - A_xB_z) + \mathbf{k}(A_xB_y - A_yB_x)$$

(4.20)

$$= \begin{vmatrix} \mathbf{i} & \mathbf{j} & \mathbf{k} \\ A_x & A_y & A_z \\ B_x & B_y & B_z \end{vmatrix}.$$

The second line in (4.20) is obtained by multiplying out the first line (getting nine products) and using the values from (4.17), (4.18), and (4.19) for the cross products of the unit vectors. The determinant in (4.20) is the most convenient way to remember the component form of the vector product. You should verify (by multiplying out the determinant using the elements of the first row) that the determinant is really identical with what is in the line above it.

Applications of the vector product. Torque.   In doing a seesaw or lever problem (Fig. 4.8), you multiply force times distance; the quantity Fd is called the *torque* or *moment** of F, and the distance d from the fulcrum O to the line of action of F is the *lever arm* of F. The lever arm is by definition the *perpendicular* distance from O to the line of action of F. Then in

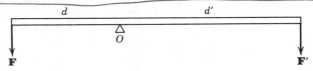

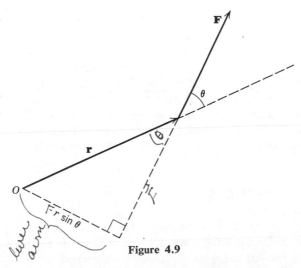

Figure 4.8

Figure 4.9

general (Fig. 4.9) the torque (or moment) of a force about O (really about an axis through O perpendicular to the paper) is defined as the magnitude of the force times its lever arm; in Fig. 4.9 this is $Fr \sin \theta$. Now $\mathbf{r} \times \mathbf{F}$ has magnitude $rF \sin \theta$, so the magnitude of the torque is $|\mathbf{r} \times \mathbf{F}|$. We can also use the direction of $\mathbf{r} \times \mathbf{F}$ in describing the torque, in the following way. If you curve the fingers of your right hand in the direction

---

* If the force F is due to a weight $w = mg$, then the torque about O in Fig. 4.8 is $mg \cdot d = g \cdot (md)$; the moment of inertia (Chapter 4, Section 13f) of m about O is md^2. The quantity md is called the moment (or *first* moment) of m about O, and the quantity md^2 is called the moment of inertia (or *second* moment) of m about O. By extension, we call mgd the moment of mg, or Fd the moment of F. For an object which is not a point mass, the quantities md and md^2 become integrals (Chapter 4, Section 13d and f).

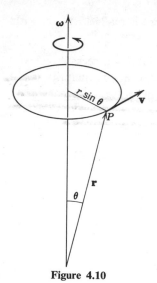

Figure 4.10

of the rotation produced by applying the torque, then your thumb points in a direction parallel to the rotation axis. It is customary to call this the <u>direction of the torque</u>. By comparing Figs. 4.9 and 4.5, we see that this is also the direction of **r** × **F**. With this agreement, then, <u>**r** × **F** is the torque or moment of **F** about an axis through O and perpendicular to the plane of the paper in Fig. 4.9,</u>

Angular velocity. In a similar way, a vector is used to represent the angular velocity of a rotating body. The direction of the vector is along the axis of rotation in the direction of progression of a right-handed screw turned the way the body is rotating. Suppose P in Fig. 4.10 represents a point in a rigid body rotating with angular velocity **ω**. We shall show that the linear velocity **v** of point P is $\mathbf{v} = \boldsymbol{\omega} \times \mathbf{r}$. First of all, **v** is in the right direction: It is perpendicular to the plane of **r** and **ω** and in the right sense. Next we want to show that the magnitude of **v** is the same as $|\boldsymbol{\omega} \times \mathbf{r}| = \omega r \sin \theta$. But $r \sin \theta$ is the radius of the circle in which P is traveling, and **ω** is the angular velocity; thus $(r \sin \theta)\omega$ is $|\mathbf{v}|$, as we claimed.

5. TRIPLE PRODUCTS

There are two products involving three vectors, one called the triple scalar product (because the answer is a scalar) and the other called the triple vector product (because the answer is a vector).

~~The triple scalar product~~ is written $\mathbf{A} \cdot (\mathbf{B} \times \mathbf{C})$. There is a useful geometrical interpretation of the triple scalar product (see Fig. 5.1). Construct a parallelepiped using **A**, **B**, **C** as three intersecting edges. Then $|\mathbf{B} \times \mathbf{C}|$ is the area of the base (Fig. 5.2) because $|\mathbf{B} \times \mathbf{C}| = |\mathbf{B}| \, |\mathbf{C}| \sin \theta$, which is the area of a parallelogram with sides $|\mathbf{B}|$, $|\mathbf{C}|$, and angle θ. The height of the parallelepiped is $|\mathbf{A}| \cos \phi$ (Fig. 5.1). Then the volume of the parallelepiped is

$$|\mathbf{B}| \, |\mathbf{C}| \sin \theta \, |\mathbf{A}| \cos \phi = |\mathbf{B} \times \mathbf{C}| \, |\mathbf{A}| \cos \phi = \mathbf{A} \cdot (\mathbf{B} \times \mathbf{C}).$$

If $\phi > 90°$, this will come out negative, so in general we should say that the volume is $|\mathbf{A} \cdot (\mathbf{B} \times \mathbf{C})|$. Any side may be used as base, so, for example,

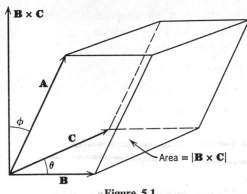

Figure 5.1

$\mathbf{B} \cdot (\mathbf{C} \times \mathbf{A})$ must also be either plus or minus the volume. There are six such triple scalar products, all equal except for sign [or twelve if you count both the type $\mathbf{A} \cdot (\mathbf{B} \times \mathbf{C})$ and the type $(\mathbf{B} \times \mathbf{C}) \cdot \mathbf{A}$].

To write the triple scalar product in component form we first write $\mathbf{B} \times \mathbf{C}$ in determinant form (5.1),

$$(5.1) \qquad \mathbf{B} \times \mathbf{C} = \begin{vmatrix} \mathbf{i} & \mathbf{j} & \mathbf{k} \\ B_x & B_y & B_z \\ C_x & C_y & C_z \end{vmatrix}.$$

Now $\mathbf{A} \cdot (\mathbf{B} \times \mathbf{C}) = A_x(\mathbf{B} \times \mathbf{C})_x + A_y(\mathbf{B} \times \mathbf{C})_y + A_z(\mathbf{B} \times \mathbf{C})_z$, and this is exactly what we get by expanding, by elements of the first row, the determinant in (5.2); this determinant is then equal to $\mathbf{A} \cdot (\mathbf{B} \times \mathbf{C})$.

$$(5.2) \qquad \mathbf{A} \cdot (\mathbf{B} \times \mathbf{C}) = \begin{vmatrix} A_x & A_y & A_z \\ B_x & B_y & B_z \\ C_x & C_y & C_z \end{vmatrix}.$$

Recalling that an interchange of rows changes the sign of a determinant, we can now easily write out the six (or twelve) products mentioned above with their proper signs. You should convince yourself of, and then remember, the following facts: The *order* of the factors is all that counts; the dot and cross may be interchanged. If the order of factors is cyclic (one way around the circle in Fig. 5.3), all such triple scalar products are equal.

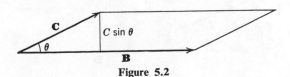

Figure 5.2

If you go the other way, you get another set
all equal to each other and the negatives of
the first set. For example,

(5.3) $(A \times B) \cdot C = A \cdot (B \times C)$

$= C \cdot (A \times B)$

$= -(A \times C) \cdot B$, etc.

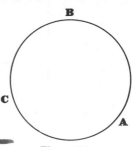

Because it doesn't matter where the dot and
cross are, the triple scalar product is often
written as (ABC), meaning $A \cdot (B \times C)$ or
$(A \times B) \cdot C$.

Figure 5.3

The triple vector product is $A \times (B \times C)$. Before we try to evaluate this,
we can make some observations about it. $B \times C$ is perpendicular to the
plane of B and C. $A \times (B \times C)$ is perpendicular to the plane of A and
$(B \times C)$; we are particularly interested in the fact that $A \times (B \times C)$ is
perpendicular to $(B \times C)$. Now (see Fig. 5.4) *any* vector perpendicular to
$B \times C$ lies in the plane perpendicular to $B \times C$, that is, the plane of B
and C. Thus $A \times (B \times C)$ is *some* vector in the plane of B and C, and can
be written as some combination $aB + bC$, where a and b are scalars which
we want to find. (See Problem 20c.) One way to find a and b is to write out
$A \times (B \times C)$ in component form. We can simplify this work by choosing
our coordinate system intelligently; recall that a vector equation is true
independently of the coordinate system. Given the vectors A, B, C, we

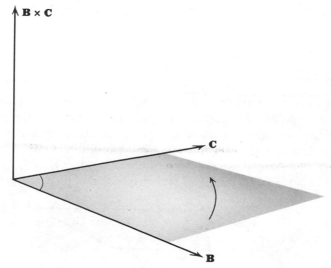

Figure 5.4

take the x-axis along $\mathbf{B}$, and the y-axis in the plane of $\mathbf{B}$ and $\mathbf{C}$; then $\mathbf{B} \times \mathbf{C}$ is in the z direction. The vectors in component form relative to these axes are:

$$\mathbf{B} = B_x\mathbf{i},$$
$$(5.4) \qquad \mathbf{C} = C_x\mathbf{i} + C_y\mathbf{j},$$
$$\mathbf{A} = A_x\mathbf{i} + A_y\mathbf{j} + A_z\mathbf{k}.$$

Using (5.4) we find

$$\mathbf{B} \times \mathbf{C} = B_x\mathbf{i} \times (C_x\mathbf{i} + C_y\mathbf{j}) = B_xC_y(\mathbf{i} \times \mathbf{j}) = B_xC_y\mathbf{k},$$
$$(5.5) \qquad \mathbf{A} \times (\mathbf{B} \times \mathbf{C}) = A_xB_xC_y(\mathbf{i} \times \mathbf{k}) + A_yB_xC_y(\mathbf{j} \times \mathbf{k})$$
$$= A_xB_xC_y(-\mathbf{j}) + A_yB_xC_y(\mathbf{i}).$$

We should like to write $\mathbf{A} \times (\mathbf{B} \times \mathbf{C})$ in (5.5) as a combination of $\mathbf{B}$ and $\mathbf{C}$; we can do this by adding and subtracting $A_xB_xC_x\mathbf{i}$:

$$(5.6) \quad \mathbf{A} \times (\mathbf{B} \times \mathbf{C}) = -A_xB_x(C_x\mathbf{i} + C_y\mathbf{j}) + (A_yC_y + A_xC_x)B_x\mathbf{i}.$$

Each of these expressions is something simple in terms of vectors:

$$(5.7) \qquad \begin{array}{ll} A_xB_x = \mathbf{A} \cdot \mathbf{B}, & A_yC_y + A_xC_x = \mathbf{A} \cdot \mathbf{C}, \\ C_x\mathbf{i} + C_y\mathbf{j} = \mathbf{C}, & B_x\mathbf{i} = \mathbf{B}. \end{array}$$

Using (5.7) in (5.6), we get

$$(5.8) \qquad \mathbf{A} \times (\mathbf{B} \times \mathbf{C}) = (\mathbf{A} \cdot \mathbf{C})\mathbf{B} - (\mathbf{A} \cdot \mathbf{B})\mathbf{C}.$$

This important formula should be learned, but not memorized in terms of letters, because that is confusing when you want some other combination of the same letters. Learn instead the following three facts:

The value of a triple vector product is a linear combination of the two vectors in the parenthesis [$\mathbf{B}$ and $\mathbf{C}$ in (5.8)]; the coefficient of each vector is the dot product of the other two; the middle vector in the triple product [$\mathbf{B}$ in (5.8)] always has the positive sign.

This method also covers triple vector products with the parenthesis first; by the rule just stated in words, the value of $(\mathbf{B} \times \mathbf{C}) \times \mathbf{A}$ is $(\mathbf{A} \cdot \mathbf{B})\mathbf{C} -$ $(\mathbf{A} \cdot \mathbf{C})\mathbf{B}$. This is correct since it is just the negative of what we had above for $\mathbf{A} \times (\mathbf{B} \times \mathbf{C})$.

Example of an application of the triple scalar product. We have shown that the torque of a force $\mathbf{F}$ about an axis may be written as $\mathbf{r} \times \mathbf{F}$ in one special case, namely when $\mathbf{r}$ and $\mathbf{F}$ are in a plane perpendicular to the axis. Now let us consider (Fig. 5.5) the general case of finding the torque produced by a force $\mathbf{F}$ about *any* given line (axis). Let $\mathbf{r}$ be a vector from some (that is, any) point on the given axis to the line of action of $\mathbf{F}$; let

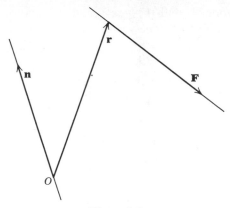

Figure 5.5

O be the tail of **r**. Then we define the torque about the *point O* to be **r** × **F**. Note that this cannot contradict our previous discussion of torque because we were talking about torque about a *line* before, and this definition is of torque about a *point*. However, we shall show how the two notions are connected. Also notice that **r** × **F** is not changed if the *head* of **r** is moved along **F**; for this just adds a multiple of **F** to **r**, and **F** × **F** = 0 (see Problem 40).

We shall now show that the torque of **F** about the given axis through O is **n** · (**r** × **F**), where **n** is a unit vector along the axis. To simplify our calculation, choose the positive z-axis in the direction **n**; then **n** = **k**. Think of a door hinged to rotate about the z-axis as in Fig. 5.6. Let a force **F** be applied to it at the head of the vector **r**. We first find the torque of **F** about the z-axis by elementary methods and definition. Break **F** into its components; the z-component is parallel to the rotation axis and produces no torque about it (pulling straight up or down on a door handle does not tend to open or close the door!). The x and y components can be seen better if we draw them in the (x, y) plane (Fig. 5.7; note that the x- and y-axes are rotated 90° clockwise from their usual position in order to compare this figure more easily with Fig. 5.6). The torque about the z-axis produced by F_x and F_y is $xF_y - yF_x$ by the elementary definition of torque. We want to show that this is the same as **n** · (**r** × **F**) or here **k** · (**r** × **F**). Using the determinant form of the triple scalar product, we find

$$\mathbf{k} \cdot (\mathbf{r} \times \mathbf{F}) = \begin{vmatrix} 0 & 0 & 1 \\ x & y & z \\ F_x & F_y & F_z \end{vmatrix} = xF_y - yF_x.$$

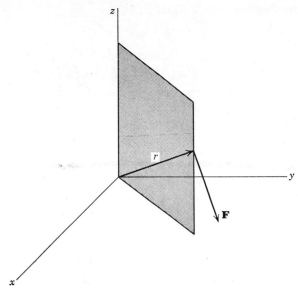

Figure 5.6

This proof can easily be given without reference to a coordinate system. Let the symbols $\parallel$ and $\perp$ stand for parallel and perpendicular to the given rotation axis $\mathbf{n}$. Then any vector ($\mathbf{F}$ or $\mathbf{r}$, say) can be written as the sum of a vector parallel to the axis and a vector perpendicular to the axis (that is, somewhere in the plane perpendicular to $\mathbf{n}$):

$$\mathbf{r} = \mathbf{r}_{\perp} + \mathbf{r}_{\parallel}, \qquad \mathbf{F} = \mathbf{F}_{\perp} + \mathbf{F}_{\parallel}.$$

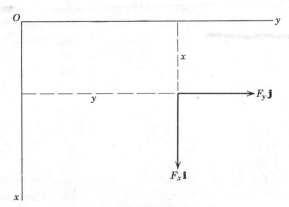

Figure 5.7

Then the torque about O produced by $\mathbf{F}$ is

$$\mathbf{r} \times \mathbf{F} = (\mathbf{r}_{\perp} + \mathbf{r}_{\parallel}) \times (\mathbf{F}_{\perp} + \mathbf{F}_{\parallel})$$
$$= \mathbf{r}_{\perp} \times \mathbf{F}_{\perp} + \mathbf{r}_{\perp} \times \mathbf{F}_{\parallel} + \mathbf{r}_{\parallel} \times \mathbf{F}_{\perp} + \mathbf{r}_{\parallel} \times \mathbf{F}_{\parallel}.$$

The last term is zero (cross product of parallel vectors). Also $\mathbf{r}_{\parallel}$ and $\mathbf{F}_{\parallel}$ are parallel to $\mathbf{n}$; therefore their cross products with anything are in the plane perpendicular to $\mathbf{n}$, and the dot product of $\mathbf{n}$ with these is zero. Hence we have

$$\mathbf{n} \cdot (\mathbf{r} \times \mathbf{F}) = \mathbf{n} \cdot (\mathbf{r}_{\perp} \times \mathbf{F}_{\perp}).$$

Now $\mathbf{r}_{\perp}$ and $\mathbf{F}_{\perp}$ are in a plane perpendicular to $\mathbf{n}$; thus the torque about $\mathbf{n}$ produced by $\mathbf{F}_{\perp}$ is (by Section 4) $\mathbf{r}_{\perp} \times \mathbf{F}_{\perp}$. But since only the component of $\mathbf{F}$ perpendicular to $\mathbf{n}$ produces a torque about $\mathbf{n}$, $\mathbf{r}_{\perp} \times \mathbf{F}_{\perp}$ is the total torque about $\mathbf{n}$ produced by $\mathbf{F}$. The vector torque $\mathbf{r}_{\perp} \times \mathbf{F}_{\perp}$ is in the $\pm\mathbf{n}$ direction since $\mathbf{r}_{\perp}$ and $\mathbf{F}_{\perp}$ are perpendicular to $\mathbf{n}$; the dot product of this vector torque with the unit vector $\mathbf{n}$ gives a scalar torque of the same magnitude; the $\pm$ sign indicates whether the torque is in the $\pm\mathbf{n}$ direction.

The terms *free vector*, *bound vector*, and *sliding vector* are often convenient to use; let us define and illustrate them. We can specify a vector by giving its magnitude and its direction. The vector can then be placed anywhere in space and moved parallel to itself at will. Recall that we do this when we add vectors head to tail. When we want to emphasize the fact that a vector may be moved about in this way, we call it a *free vector*. However, we should realize that the terms *vector* and *free vector* mean exactly the same thing. Sometimes, in physical and geometrical applications we need more information about a vector than just its magnitude and direction. When we calculate the torque $\mathbf{r} \times \mathbf{F}$ of the force $\mathbf{F}$ about the point O, the vector $\mathbf{r}$ must have its tail at O in order for $\mathbf{r} \times \mathbf{F}$ to give the correct torque. We then call $\mathbf{r}$ a *bound vector*; thus a *bound vector* is not just a vector but a vector plus the additional information that its tail must be at a given point. Similarly, in calculating torque, we must have more information about the force $\mathbf{F}$ than just its magnitude and direction; we must know the line of action of $\mathbf{F}$. We then call $\mathbf{F}$ a *sliding vector*. Again this is not just a vector; a *sliding vector* is a vector and a line along which it is to be placed.

6. LINES AND PLANES

A great deal of analytic geometry can be simplified by the use of vector notation. Such things as equations of lines and planes, and distances between points or between lines and planes often occur in physics and it is very useful to be able to find them quickly. We shall talk about three-dimensional space most of the time although the ideas apply also to two dimensions. In analytic geometry a point is a set of three coordinates (x, y, z); we shall think of this point as the ~~head~~ of a vector $\mathbf{r} = \mathbf{i}x + \mathbf{j}y + \mathbf{k}z$ ~~with tail at the origin~~ (that is, $\mathbf{r}$ is a bound vector). Most of the time the *vector* will be in the background of our minds and we shall not draw it; we shall just plot the point (x, y, z) which is the head of the vector.

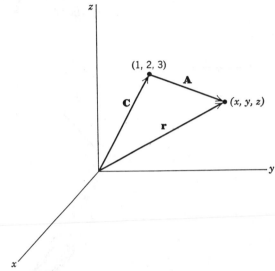

Figure 6.1

In other words, the point (x, y, z) and the vector $\mathbf{r}$ will be synonymous. We shall also use vectors joining two points. In Fig. 6.1 the vector $\mathbf{A}$ from $(1, 2, 3)$ to (x, y, z) is $\mathbf{A} = \mathbf{i}(x - 1) + \mathbf{j}(y - 2) + \mathbf{k}(z - 3)$. Alternatively we could say $\mathbf{A} = \mathbf{r} - \mathbf{C}$; you should verify that this gives the same answer.

In two dimensions, we write the equation of a straight line through (x_0, y_0) with slope m as

(6.1)
$$\frac{y - y_0}{x - x_0} = m.$$

Suppose, instead of the slope, we are given a vector in the direction of the line, say $\mathbf{A} = \mathbf{i}a + \mathbf{j}b$ (Fig. 6.2). Then the line through (x_0, y_0) and in the direction $\mathbf{A}$ is determined and we should be able to write its equation. The directed line segment from (x_0, y_0) to any point (x, y) on the line can be considered a vector $\mathbf{r} - \mathbf{r}_0$ with components $x - x_0$ and $y - y_0$:

(6.2)
$$\mathbf{r} - \mathbf{r}_0 = \mathbf{i}(x - x_0) + \mathbf{j}(y - y_0).$$

This vector is parallel to $\mathbf{A} = \mathbf{i}a + \mathbf{j}b$. Now if two vectors are parallel, their components must be proportional. Thus we can write

(6.3) $$\frac{x - x_0}{a} = \frac{y - y_0}{b} \quad \text{or} \quad \frac{y - y_0}{x - x_0} = \frac{b}{a}.$$

This is the equation of the given straight line. As a check we see that the slope of the line is $m = b/a$, so (6.3) is the same as (6.1).

Another way to write this equation is to say that if $\mathbf{r} - \mathbf{r}_0$ and $\mathbf{A}$ are parallel vectors, one is some scalar multiple of the other, that is,

(6.4) $$\mathbf{r} - \mathbf{r}_0 = \mathbf{A}t,$$

where t is the scalar multiple. We can think of t as a parameter; the

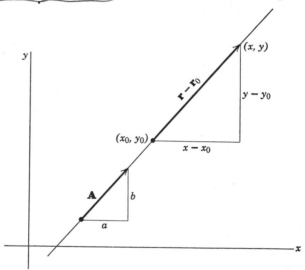

Figure 6.2

component form of (6.4) is a set of parametric equations of the line, namely

(6.5) $$\begin{array}{cc} x - x_0 = at, & x = x_0 + at, \\ y - y_0 = bt, & y = y_0 + bt. \end{array} \quad \text{or}$$

Eliminating t yields our original equation of the line. Still another way to write the equation of the line would be to say that if $\mathbf{r} - \mathbf{r}_0$ and $\mathbf{A}$ are parallel, their cross product is zero:

(6.6) $$(\mathbf{r} - \mathbf{r}_0) \times \mathbf{A} = 0.$$

In three dimensions, the same ideas can be used. We want the equations of a straight line through a given point (x_0, y_0, z_0) and parallel to a given vector $\mathbf{A} = a\mathbf{i} + b\mathbf{j} + c\mathbf{k}$. If (x, y, z) is any point on the line, the vector joining (x_0, y_0, z_0) and (x, y, z) is parallel to $\mathbf{A}$. Then its components $x - x_0$, $y - y_0$, $z - z_0$ are proportional to the components a, b, c of $\mathbf{A}$ and we have

(6.7)
$$\frac{x - x_0}{a} = \frac{y - y_0}{b} = \frac{z - z_0}{c}.$$

These are the equations of a straight line in space. As in the two-dimensional case, these equations could be written

(6.8) $\mathbf{r} - \mathbf{r}_0 = \mathbf{A}t$, or $\begin{aligned} x &= x_0 + at, \\ y &= y_0 + bt, \\ z &= z_0 + ct, \end{aligned}$ or $(\mathbf{r} - \mathbf{r}_0) \times \mathbf{A} = 0$.

If c, for instance, happens to be zero, we would have to write (6.7) in the form

$$\frac{x - x_0}{a} = \frac{y - y_0}{b}, \qquad z = z_0.$$

Going back to two dimensions, suppose we want the equation of a straight line L through the point (x_0, y_0) and perpendicular to a given vector $\mathbf{N} = a\mathbf{i} + b\mathbf{j}$. As above, the vector

$$\mathbf{r} - \mathbf{r}_0 = (x - x_0)\mathbf{i} + (y - y_0)\mathbf{j}$$

lies along the line. This time we want this vector perpendicular to $\mathbf{N}$; recall that two vectors are perpendicular if their dot product is zero. Setting the dot product of $\mathbf{N}$ and $\mathbf{r} - \mathbf{r}_0$ equal to zero gives

(6.9) $a(x - x_0) + b(y - y_0) = 0$ or $\dfrac{y - y_0}{x - x_0} = -\dfrac{a}{b}.$

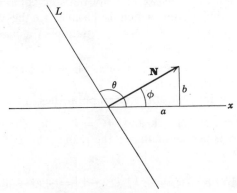

Figure 6.3

This is the desired equation of the straight line L perpendicular to $\mathbf{N}$. As a check, note from Fig. 6.3 that the slope of the line L is

$$\tan \theta = -\cot \phi = -a/b.$$

In three dimensions, we use this method to write the equation of a plane. If (x_0, y_0, z_0) is a given point in the plane and (x, y, z) is any other point in the plane, the vector (Fig. 6.4)

$$\mathbf{r} - \mathbf{r}_0 = (x - x_0)\mathbf{i} + (y - y_0)\mathbf{j} + (z - z_0)\mathbf{k}$$

is in the plane. If $\mathbf{N} = a\mathbf{i} + b\mathbf{j} + c\mathbf{k}$ is normal (perpendicular) to the plane, then $\mathbf{N}$ and $\mathbf{r} - \mathbf{r}_0$ are perpendicular and $\mathbf{N} \cdot (\mathbf{r} - \mathbf{r}_0) = 0$, that is,

(6.10) $$a(x - x_0) + b(y - y_0) + c(z - z_0) = 0.$$

We can also write (6.10) in the form

(6.11) $$ax + by + cz = d,$$

where $d = ax_0 + by_0 + cz_0$. Both (6.10) and (6.11) are forms of the equation of a plane in three dimensions.

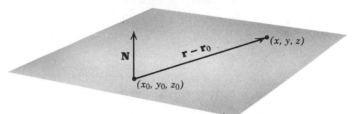

Figure 6.4

If we are given equations like (6.7) or (6.10) or (6.11) we can read backwards to find $\mathbf{A}$ or $\mathbf{N}$. Thus we can say that the equations (6.7) are the equations of a straight line which is parallel to the vector $\mathbf{A} = a\mathbf{i} + b\mathbf{j} + c\mathbf{k}$. Either (6.10) or (6.11) is the equation of a plane perpendicular to the vector $\mathbf{N} = a\mathbf{i} + b\mathbf{j} + c\mathbf{k}$.

Example 1. Find the equation of a plane through the three points $A(-1, 1, 1)$, $B(2, 3, 0)$, $C(0, 1, -2)$.

A vector joining any pair of the given points lies in the plane. Two such vectors are $\overrightarrow{AB} = 3\mathbf{i} + 2\mathbf{j} - \mathbf{k}$ and $\overrightarrow{AC} = \mathbf{i} - 3\mathbf{k}$. The cross product of these two vectors is perpendicular to the plane. This is

$$\mathbf{N} = (\overrightarrow{AB}) \times (\overrightarrow{AC}) = \begin{vmatrix} \mathbf{i} & \mathbf{j} & \mathbf{k} \\ 3 & 2 & -1 \\ 1 & 0 & -3 \end{vmatrix} = -6\mathbf{i} + 8\mathbf{j} - 2\mathbf{k}.$$

Now we write the equation of the plane with normal direction $\mathbf{N}$ through one of the given points, say B, by using (6.10):

$$-6(x - 2) + 8(y - 3) - 2z = 0 \qquad \text{or} \quad 3x - 4y + z + 6 = 0.$$

(Note that we could have divided $\mathbf{N}$ by -2 to save arithmetic.)

Example 2.   Find the equations of a line through $(1, 0, -2)$ and perpendicular to the plane of Example 1.

The vector $3\mathbf{i} - 4\mathbf{j} + \mathbf{k}$ is perpendicular to the plane of Example 1 and so parallel to the desired line. Thus by (6.7) the equations of the line are

$$\frac{(x - 1)}{3} = \frac{y}{-4} = \frac{(z + 2)}{1}.$$

Vectors give us a very convenient way of finding distances between points and lines or planes. Suppose we want to find the distance from a point P to the plane (6.11). (This means the perpendicular distance.) (See Fig. 6.5.) We pick *any* point Q we like in the plane (just by looking at the equation of the plane and thinking of some simple numbers x, y, z

dist from pt. to a plane

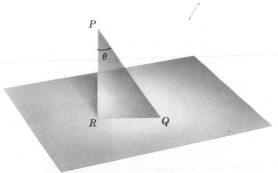

P

θ

R   Q

Figure 6.5

that satisfy it). The distance PR is what we want. Since PR and RQ are perpendicular (because PR is perpendicular to the plane), we have from Fig. 6.5

(6.12) $PR = PQ \cos \theta.$

From the equation of the plane, we can find a vector $\mathbf{N}$ normal to the plane. If we divide $\mathbf{N}$ by its magnitude, we have a unit vector normal to the plane; we denote this unit vector by $\mathbf{n}$. Then $|\overrightarrow{PQ} \cdot \mathbf{n}| = (PQ) \cos \theta$, which is what we need in (6.12) to find PR. (We have put in absolute value signs because $\overrightarrow{PQ} \cdot \mathbf{n}$ might be negative, whereas $(PQ) \cos \theta$, with θ acute as in Fig. 6.5, is positive.)

pt. to plane $\left| \overrightarrow{PQ} \cdot \hat{n} \right|$

Example 3.   Find the distance from the point $P(1, -2, 3)$ to the plane $3x - 2y + z + 1 = 0$.

One point in the plane is $(1, 2, 0)$; call this point Q. Then the vectors $\mathbf{P}$ and $\mathbf{Q}$ from the origin to the points P and Q are

$$\mathbf{P} = \mathbf{i} - 2\mathbf{j} + 3\mathbf{k} \quad \text{and} \quad \mathbf{Q} = \mathbf{i} + 2\mathbf{j}$$

and the vector from P to Q is

$$\overrightarrow{PQ} = \mathbf{Q} - \mathbf{P} = \mathbf{i} + 2\mathbf{j} - (\mathbf{i} - 2\mathbf{j} + 3\mathbf{k}) = 4\mathbf{j} - 3\mathbf{k}.$$

From the equation of the plane we get the normal vector

$$\mathbf{N} = 3\mathbf{i} - 2\mathbf{j} + \mathbf{k}.$$

We get $\mathbf{n}$ by dividing $\mathbf{N}$ by $|\mathbf{N}| = \sqrt{14}$. Then we have

$$|PR| = |\overrightarrow{PQ} \cdot \mathbf{n}| = |(4\mathbf{j} - 3\mathbf{k}) \cdot (3\mathbf{i} - 2\mathbf{j} + \mathbf{k})/\sqrt{14}|$$
$$= |(-8 - 3)/\sqrt{14}| = 11/\sqrt{14}.$$

We can find the distance from a point P to a line in a similar way. In Fig. 6.6 we want the perpendicular distance PR. We select any point

Point to
a line .

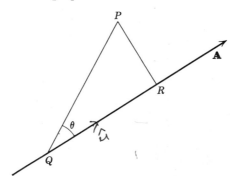

Figure 6.6

on the line (that is, we pick any (x, y, z) satisfying the equations of the line); call this point Q. Then (see Fig. 6.6) $PR = PQ \sin \theta$. Let $\mathbf{A}$ be a vector along the line and $\mathbf{u}$ a unit vector along the line, obtained by dividing $\mathbf{A}$ by its magnitude. Then

$$|\overrightarrow{PQ} \times \mathbf{u}| = |\overrightarrow{PQ}| \sin \theta,$$

so we get

$$\boxed{|PR| = |\overrightarrow{PQ} \times \mathbf{u}|.}$$

Example 4.   Find the distance from $P(1, 2, -1)$ to the line joining $P_1(0, 0, 0)$ and $P_2(-1, 0, 2)$.

Let $\mathbf{A} = \mathbf{P}_2 - \mathbf{P}_1 = -\mathbf{i} + 2\mathbf{k}$; this is a vector along the line. Then a unit vector along the line is $\mathbf{u} = (1/\sqrt{5})(-\mathbf{i} + 2\mathbf{k})$. Let us take Q to be $P_1(0, 0, 0)$. Then $\overrightarrow{PQ} = -\mathbf{i} - 2\mathbf{j} + \mathbf{k}$, so we get for the distance $|PR|$:

$$|PR| = \frac{1}{\sqrt{5}}(-\mathbf{i} - 2\mathbf{j} + \mathbf{k}) \times (-\mathbf{i} + 2\mathbf{k}) = \frac{1}{\sqrt{5}}|-4\mathbf{i} + \mathbf{j} - 2\mathbf{k}| = \sqrt{\frac{21}{5}}.$$

It is also straightforward to find the distance between two skew lines (and if you really want to appreciate vectors, just look up this calculation in an analytic geometry book that doesn't use vectors!). Pick two points

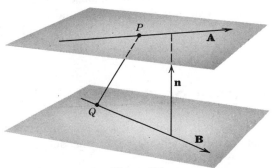

Figure 6.7

P and Q, one on each line (Fig. 6.7). Then $|\overrightarrow{PQ} \cdot \mathbf{n}|$, where $\mathbf{n}$ is a unit vector perpendicular to both lines, is the distance we want. Now if $\mathbf{A}$ and $\mathbf{B}$ are vectors along the two lines, then $\mathbf{A} \times \mathbf{B}$ is perpendicular to both, and $\mathbf{n}$ is just $\mathbf{A} \times \mathbf{B}$ divided by $|\mathbf{A} \times \mathbf{B}|$.

Example 5. Find the distance between the lines $\mathbf{r} = \mathbf{i} - 2\mathbf{j} + (\mathbf{i} - \mathbf{k})t$ and $\mathbf{r} = 2\mathbf{j} - \mathbf{k} + (\mathbf{j} - \mathbf{i})t$.

If we write the first line as $\mathbf{r} = \mathbf{r}_0 + \mathbf{A}t$, then (the head of) $\mathbf{r}_0$ is a simple choice for P, so we have

$$P = (1, -2, 0) \quad \text{or} \quad \mathbf{P} = \mathbf{i} - 2\mathbf{j}, \quad \text{and} \quad \mathbf{A} = \mathbf{i} - \mathbf{k}.$$

Similarly, from the second line we find

$$Q = (0, 2, -1) \quad \text{or} \quad \mathbf{Q} = 2\mathbf{j} - \mathbf{k}, \quad \text{and} \quad \mathbf{B} = \mathbf{j} - \mathbf{i}.$$

Then $\mathbf{A} \times \mathbf{B} = \mathbf{i} + \mathbf{j} + \mathbf{k}$ and $\mathbf{n} = (1/\sqrt{3})(\mathbf{i} + \mathbf{j} + \mathbf{k})$. Also

$$\overrightarrow{PQ} = \mathbf{Q} - \mathbf{P} = (2\mathbf{j} - \mathbf{k}) - (\mathbf{i} - 2\mathbf{j}) = -\mathbf{i} + 4\mathbf{j} - \mathbf{k}.$$

Thus we get for the distance between the lines

$$|\overrightarrow{PQ} \cdot \mathbf{n}| = \left|(-\mathbf{i} + 4\mathbf{j} - \mathbf{k}) \cdot \frac{1}{\sqrt{3}}(\mathbf{i} + \mathbf{j} + \mathbf{k})\right| = \frac{1}{\sqrt{3}}|-1 + 4 - 1| = \frac{2}{\sqrt{3}}.$$

Example 6. Find the direction of the line of intersection of the planes $x - 2y + 3z = 4$ and $2x + y - z = 5$.

The desired direction will be parallel to both planes, hence perpendicular to the two normal vectors to the planes, namely $\mathbf{i} - 2\mathbf{j} + 3\mathbf{k}$ and $2\mathbf{i} + \mathbf{j} - \mathbf{k}$. Then the direction is that of the cross product of these normal vectors, which is easily found to be $-\mathbf{i} + 7\mathbf{j} + 5\mathbf{k}$.

Example 7. Find the cosine of the angle between the planes of Example 6.

The angle between the planes is the same as the angle between the normals to the planes. Thus our problem is to find the angle between the vectors $\mathbf{A} = \mathbf{i} - 2\mathbf{j} + 3\mathbf{k}$ and $\mathbf{B} = 2\mathbf{i} + \mathbf{j} - \mathbf{k}$. Since $\mathbf{A} \cdot \mathbf{B} = |\mathbf{A}|\,|\mathbf{B}| \cos \theta$, we have $-3 = \sqrt{14}\sqrt{6} \cos \theta$, $\cos \theta = -\sqrt{21}/14$.

7. DIFFERENTIATION OF VECTORS

If $\mathbf{A} = \mathbf{i}A_x + \mathbf{j}A_y + \mathbf{k}A_z$, where $\mathbf{i}$, $\mathbf{j}$, $\mathbf{k}$ are fixed unit vectors and A_x, A_y, A_z are functions of t, then we define the derivative $d\mathbf{A}/dt$ by the equation

$$(7.1) \qquad \frac{d\mathbf{A}}{dt} = \mathbf{i}\frac{dA_x}{dt} + \mathbf{j}\frac{dA_y}{dt} + \mathbf{k}\frac{dA_z}{dt}.$$

Thus the derivative of a vector $\mathbf{A}$ means a vector whose components are the derivatives of the components of $\mathbf{A}$.

Example. Let (x, y, z) be the coordinates of a moving particle at time t; then x, y, z are functions of t. The vector displacement of the particle from the origin at time t is

$$(7.2) \qquad \mathbf{r} = \mathbf{i}x + \mathbf{j}y + \mathbf{k}z,$$

where $\mathbf{r}$ is a vector from the origin to the particle at time t. We say that $\mathbf{r}$ is the position vector or vector coordinate of the particle. The components of the velocity of the particle at time t are dx/dt, dy/dt, dz/dt so the velocity vector is

$$(7.3) \qquad \mathbf{v} = \frac{d\mathbf{r}}{dt} = \mathbf{i}\frac{dx}{dt} + \mathbf{j}\frac{dy}{dt} + \mathbf{k}\frac{dz}{dt}.$$

The acceleration vector is

$$(7.4) \qquad \mathbf{a} = \frac{d\mathbf{v}}{dt} = \mathbf{i}\frac{d^2x}{dt^2} + \mathbf{j}\frac{d^2y}{dt^2} + \mathbf{k}\frac{d^2z}{dt^2}.$$

The product of a scalar and a vector and the dot and cross products of vectors are differentiated by the ordinary calculus rules for differentiating a product, with one word of caution: The order of the factors must be kept in a cross product. You can easily prove these facts (7.5) by writing out components (Problem 41) and using (7.1).

$$\frac{d}{dt}(a\mathbf{A}) = \frac{da}{dt}\mathbf{A} + a\frac{d\mathbf{A}}{dt},$$

(7.5)
$$\frac{d}{dt}(\mathbf{A} \cdot \mathbf{B}) = \mathbf{A} \cdot \frac{d\mathbf{B}}{dt} + \frac{d\mathbf{A}}{dt} \cdot \mathbf{B},$$

$$\frac{d}{dt}(\mathbf{A} \times \mathbf{B}) = \mathbf{A} \times \frac{d\mathbf{B}}{dt} + \frac{d\mathbf{A}}{dt} \times \mathbf{B}.$$

The second term in $(d/dt)(\mathbf{A} \cdot \mathbf{B})$ *can* be written $\mathbf{B} \cdot d\mathbf{A}/dt$ if you like since $\mathbf{A} \cdot \mathbf{B} = \mathbf{B} \cdot \mathbf{A}$. But the corresponding term in $(d/dt)(\mathbf{A} \times \mathbf{B})$ must *not* be turned around unless you put a minus sign in front of it since $\mathbf{A} \times \mathbf{B} = -\mathbf{B} \times \mathbf{A}$.

Example. Consider the motion of a particle in a circle at constant speed. We can then write

(7.6)
$$r^2 = \mathbf{r} \cdot \mathbf{r} = \text{const.},$$
$$v^2 = \mathbf{v} \cdot \mathbf{v} = \text{const.}$$

If we differentiate these two equations using (7.5), we get

(7.7)
$$2\mathbf{r} \cdot \frac{d\mathbf{r}}{dt} = 0 \quad \text{or} \quad \mathbf{r} \cdot \mathbf{v} = 0,$$

$$2\mathbf{v} \cdot \frac{d\mathbf{v}}{dt} = 0 \quad \text{or} \quad \mathbf{v} \cdot \mathbf{a} = 0.$$

Also differentiating $\mathbf{r} \cdot \mathbf{v} = 0$, we get

(7.8)
$$\mathbf{r} \cdot \mathbf{a} + \mathbf{v} \cdot \mathbf{v} = 0 \quad \text{or} \quad \mathbf{r} \cdot \mathbf{a} = -v^2.$$

The first of equations (7.7) says that $\mathbf{r}$ is perpendicular to $\mathbf{v}$; the second says that $\mathbf{a}$ is perpendicular to $\mathbf{v}$. Therefore $\mathbf{a}$ and $\mathbf{r}$ are either parallel or antiparallel (since the motion is in a plane) and the angle θ between $\mathbf{a}$ and $\mathbf{r}$ is either $0°$ or $180°$. From (7.8) and the definition of scalar product, we have

(7.9)
$$\mathbf{r} \cdot \mathbf{a} = |\mathbf{r}| \, |\mathbf{a}| \cos \theta = -v^2.$$

Thus we see that $\cos \theta < 0$ or $\theta = 180°$. Then from (7.9) we get

(7.10)
$$|\mathbf{r}| \, |\mathbf{a}| \, (-1) = -v^2 \quad \text{or} \quad a = \frac{v^2}{r}.$$

We have just given a vector proof that for motion in a circle at constant speed the acceleration is toward the center of the circle and of magnitude v^2/r.

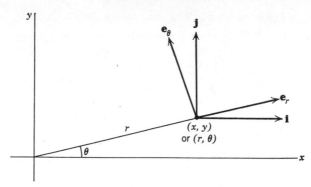

Figure 7.1

So far we have written vectors only in terms of their rectangular components using the unit vectors **i**, **j**, **k**. It is often convenient to use other coordinate systems, for example polar coordinates in two dimensions and spherical or cylindrical coordinates in three dimensions (see Chapter 4, Section 14). We shall consider using vectors in various coordinate systems in detail in Chapter 10, but it will be useful to discuss briefly here the use of plane polar coordinates. In Fig. 7.1, think of starting at the point (x, y) or (r, θ) and moving along the line $\theta = $ const. in the direction of increasing r. We call this the "r direction"; we draw a unit vector (that is, a vector of length 1) in this direction and label it $\mathbf{e}_r$. Similarly, think of moving along the circle $r = $ const. in the direction of increasing θ. We call this the "θ direction"; we draw a unit vector tangent to the circle and label it $\mathbf{e}_\theta$. These two vectors $\mathbf{e}_r$ and $\mathbf{e}_\theta$ are the polar coordinate unit vectors just as **i** and **j** are the rectangular unit vectors. (Other books may use $\mathbf{a}_r$ and $\mathbf{a}_\theta$, $\mathbf{u}_r$ and $\mathbf{u}_\theta$, **n** and **l**, etc.; there is no polar coordinate unit vector notation which is as standard as **i** and **j** for rectangular coordinates.)

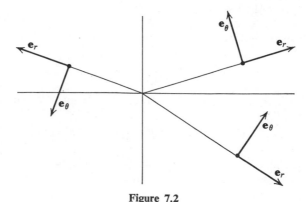

Figure 7.2

We can now write any given vector in terms of its components in the directions $\mathbf{e}_r$ and $\mathbf{e}_\theta$ (by finding its projections in these directions). There is a complication here, however. In rectangular coordinates, the unit vectors $\mathbf{i}$ and $\mathbf{j}$ are constant in magnitude *and direction*. The polar coordinate unit vectors are constant in magnitude, but their directions change from point to point (Fig. 7.2). Thus in calculating the derivative of a vector written in polar coordinates, we must differentiate the unit vectors as well as the components [compare (7.1) where we differentiate the components only]. One straightforward way to do this is to express

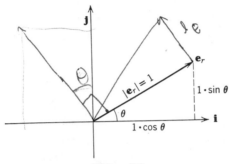

Figure 7.3

the unit vectors $\mathbf{e}_r$ and $\mathbf{e}_\theta$ in terms of $\mathbf{i}$ and $\mathbf{j}$. From Fig. 7.3, we see that the x and y components of $\mathbf{e}_r$ are $\cos\theta$ and $\sin\theta$. Thus we have

(7.11) $$\mathbf{e}_r = \mathbf{i}\cos\theta + \mathbf{j}\sin\theta.$$

Similarly (Problem 41b) we find

(7.12) $$\mathbf{e}_\theta = -\mathbf{i}\sin\theta + \mathbf{j}\cos\theta.$$

Differentiating $\mathbf{e}_r$ and $\mathbf{e}_\theta$ with respect to t, we get

(7.13)
$$\frac{d\mathbf{e}_r}{dt} = -\mathbf{i}\sin\theta\,\frac{d\theta}{dt} + \mathbf{j}\cos\theta\,\frac{d\theta}{dt} = \mathbf{e}_\theta\,\frac{d\theta}{dt},$$
$$\frac{d\mathbf{e}_\theta}{dt} = -\mathbf{i}\cos\theta\,\frac{d\theta}{dt} - \mathbf{j}\sin\theta\,\frac{d\theta}{dt} = -\mathbf{e}_r\,\frac{d\theta}{dt}.$$

We can now use (7.13) in calculating the derivative of any vector which is written in terms of its polar components.

Example.   Given $\mathbf{A} = A_r\mathbf{e}_r + A_\theta\mathbf{e}_\theta$, where A_r and A_θ are functions of t, find $d\mathbf{A}/dt$.

We get

$$\frac{d\mathbf{A}}{dt} = \mathbf{e}_r\,\frac{dA_r}{dt} + A_r\,\frac{d\mathbf{e}_r}{dt} + \mathbf{e}_\theta\,\frac{dA_\theta}{dt} + A_\theta\,\frac{d\mathbf{e}_\theta}{dt}.$$

Using (7.13), we find

$$\frac{d\mathbf{A}}{dt} = \mathbf{e}_r \frac{dA_r}{dt} + \mathbf{e}_\theta A_r \frac{d\theta}{dt} + \mathbf{e}_\theta \frac{dA_\theta}{dt} - \mathbf{e}_r A_\theta \frac{d\theta}{dt}.$$

We can find higher-order derivatives if we like by differentiating again using (7.13) each time to evaluate the derivatives of $\mathbf{e}_r$ and $\mathbf{e}_\theta$.

8. FIELDS

Many physical quantities have different values at different points in space. For example, the temperature in a room is different at different points: high near a register, low near an open window, etc. The electric field around

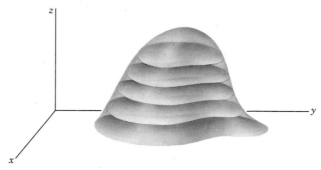

Figure 8.1

a point charge is large near the charge and decreases as we go away from the charge. Similarly the gravitational force acting on a satellite depends on its distance from the earth. The velocity of flow of water in a stream is large in rapids and in narrow channels and small over flat areas and where the stream is wide. In all these examples there is a particular region of space which is of interest for the problem at hand; at every point of this region some physical quantity has a value. The term *field* is used to mean both the region and the value of the physical quantity in the region (for example, electric field, gravitational field). If the physical quantity is a scalar (for example, temperature), we speak of a *scalar field*. If the quantity is a vector (for example, electric field, force, or velocity), we speak of a *vector field*. Note again a point which we discussed in "endpoint problems" in Chapter 4, Section 10: Physical problems are often restricted to certain regions of space, and our mathematics must take account of this.

A simple example of a scalar field is the gravitational potential energy near the earth; its value is $V = mgz$ at every point of height z above some arbitrary reference level [which we take as the (x, y) plane]. Suppose that on a hill (Fig. 8.1) we mark a series of curves each corresponding to some value of z (curves of constant elevation, often called *contour lines* or *level lines*). Any curve or surface on which a potential is constant is called an *equipotential*. Thus these level lines are equipotentials of the gravitational field since along any one curve the value of the gravitational potential energy mgz is constant. The horizontal planes which intersect the hill in these curves are equipotential surfaces (or level surfaces) of the gravitational field.

As another example, let us ask for the equipotential surfaces in the field of an electric point charge q. The potential is $V = 9 \cdot 10^9 q/r$ (in mks units) at a point which is at distance r from the charge. The potential V is constant if r is constant; that is, the equipotentials of this electric field are spheres with centers at the charge. Similarly we could imagine drawing a set of surfaces (probably very irregular) in a room so that at every point of a single surface the temperature would be constant. These surfaces would be like equipotentials; they are called *isothermals* when the constant quantity is the temperature.

9. DIRECTIONAL DERIVATIVE; GRADIENT; NORMAL DERIVATIVE

Suppose that we know the temperature $T(x, y, z)$ at every point of a room, say, or of a metal bar. Starting at a given point we could ask for the rate of change of the temperature with distance (in degrees per centimeter) as we move away from the starting point. The chances are that the temperature increases in some directions and decreases in other directions, and that it increases more rapidly in some directions than others. Thus the rate of change of temperature with distance depends upon the *direction* in which we move; consequently it is called a *directional derivative*. In symbols, we want to find the limiting value of $\Delta T/\Delta s$ where Δs is an element of distance (arc length) in a given direction, and ΔT is the corresponding change in temperature; we write the directional derivative as dT/ds. We could also ask for the direction in which dT/ds has its largest value; this is physically the direction from which heat flows (that is, heat flows from hot to cold, in the opposite direction from the maximum rate of temperature increase).

Before we discuss how to calculate directional derivatives, consider another example. Suppose we are standing at a point on the side of the hill of Fig. 8.1 (not at the top), and ask the question "In what direction does the hill slope downward most steeply from this point?" This is the direction in which you would start to slide if you lost your footing; it is the direction most people would probably call "straight" down. We want to make this vague idea more precise. Suppose we move a small distance Δs on the hill; the vertical distance Δz which we have gone may be positive (uphill) or negative (downhill) or zero (around the hill). Then $\Delta z/\Delta s$ and its limit dz/ds depend upon the *direction* in which we go; dz/ds is a directional derivative. The direction of steepest slope is the direction in which dz/ds has its largest absolute value. Notice that since the gravitational potential energy of a mass m is $V = mgz$, maximizing dz/ds is the same as maximizing dV/ds, where the equipotentials on the hill are $V(x, y) = mgz(x, y) = $ const.

Let us now state and solve the general problem of finding a directional derivative. We are given a scalar field, that is, a function $\phi(x, y, z)$ [or $\phi(x, y)$ in a two-variable problem; the following discussion applies to two-variable problems if we simply drop terms and equations containing z]. We want to find $d\phi/ds$, the rate of change of ϕ with distance, at a given point (x_0, y_0, z_0) and in a given direction. Let $\mathbf{u} = \mathbf{i}a + \mathbf{j}b + \mathbf{k}c$ be a unit vector in the given direction. We write the equations of the straight line through (x_0, y_0, z_0) in the direction $\mathbf{u}$ in the parametric form (6.8), using s for the parameter [instead of t as in (6.8)]:

$$(9.1) \quad \begin{aligned} x &= x_0 + as, \\ y &= y_0 + bs, \\ z &= z_0 + cs. \end{aligned}$$

The parameter s has a geometrical meaning; we shall show that it is just the arc length measured along the line. The distance from (x_0, y_0, z_0) is, using (9.1),

$$(9.2) \quad \sqrt{(x - x_0)^2 + (y - y_0)^2 + (z - z_0)^2} = \sqrt{(as)^2 + (bs)^2 + (cs)^2} = s$$

since $a^2 + b^2 + c^2 = 1$ because $\mathbf{u}$ is a unit vector.

From (9.1) we see that along the line, x, y, and z are each functions of a single variable, namely s [all the other letters in (9.1) are given constants]. If we substitute x, y, z in (9.1) into $\phi(x, y, z)$, then ϕ becomes a function of just the one variable s. That is, *along the straight line* (9.1), ϕ *is a function of one variable*, namely the distance along the line measured from (x_0, y_0, z_0). Since ϕ depends on s alone, we can find $d\phi/ds$:

$$(9.3) \quad \begin{aligned} \frac{d\phi}{ds} &= \frac{\partial \phi}{\partial x}\frac{dx}{ds} + \frac{\partial \phi}{\partial y}\frac{dy}{ds} + \frac{\partial \phi}{\partial z}\frac{dz}{ds} \\ &= \frac{\partial \phi}{\partial x}a + \frac{\partial \phi}{\partial y}b + \frac{\partial \phi}{\partial z}c. \end{aligned}$$

$\hat{u}$ is the direction in which the directional derivative is being taken

This looks like a dot product of $\mathbf{u}$ with something; in fact, with the vector $\mathbf{i}(\partial\phi/\partial x) + \mathbf{j}(\partial\phi/\partial y) + \mathbf{k}(\partial\phi/\partial z)$. This vector is called the *gradient* of ϕ and is written grad ϕ or $\nabla\phi$ (del ϕ). By definition

$$(9.4) \qquad \nabla\phi = \text{grad } \phi = \mathbf{i}\frac{\partial\phi}{\partial x} + \mathbf{j}\frac{\partial\phi}{\partial y} + \mathbf{k}\frac{\partial\phi}{\partial z}.$$

The gradient of a function has useful geometrical and physical meanings

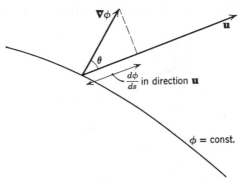

Figure 9.1

which we shall now investigate. Let's write the directional derivative in (9.3) as a dot product:

$$(9.5) \qquad \frac{d\phi}{ds} = \nabla\phi \cdot \mathbf{u}.$$

$\frac{d\phi}{ds}$ is max when $\theta = 0$

Using the definition of a dot product, and the fact that $|\mathbf{u}| = 1$, we have

$$(9.6) \qquad \frac{d\phi}{ds} = |\nabla\phi| \cos\theta,$$

where θ is the angle between $\mathbf{u}$ and the vector $\nabla\phi$. We see first of all that $d\phi/ds$ is the projection of $\nabla\phi$ on the direction $\mathbf{u}$ (Fig. 9.1); hence $|\nabla\phi| \geq d\phi/ds$ so $|\nabla\phi|$ is the largest value the directional derivative can take. *✓ scalar*

Example 1. Find the directional derivative of $\phi = x^2y + xz$ at $(1, 2, -1)$ in the direction $\mathbf{A} = 2\mathbf{i} - 2\mathbf{j} + \mathbf{k}$.

Here $\mathbf{u}$ is a unit vector obtained by dividing $\mathbf{A}$ by $|\mathbf{A}|$. Then we have

$$\mathbf{u} = \tfrac{1}{3}(2\mathbf{i} - 2\mathbf{j} + \mathbf{k}).$$

Using (9.4) we get

$$\nabla\phi = \mathbf{i}\frac{\partial\phi}{\partial x} + \mathbf{j}\frac{\partial\phi}{\partial y} + \mathbf{k}\frac{\partial\phi}{\partial z} = (2xy + z)\mathbf{i} + x^2\mathbf{j} + x\mathbf{k},$$

$$\nabla\phi \text{ at the point } (1, 2, -1) = 3\mathbf{i} + \mathbf{j} + \mathbf{k}.$$

Then from (9.5) we find

$$\frac{d\phi}{ds} \text{ at } (1, 2, -1) = \nabla\phi \cdot \mathbf{u} = 2 - \tfrac{2}{3} + \tfrac{1}{3} = \tfrac{5}{3}.$$

(handwritten: $(3\mathbf{i} + \mathbf{j} + \mathbf{k}) \cdot \frac{1}{3}(2\mathbf{i} - 2\mathbf{j} + \mathbf{k})$)

Next suppose $\mathbf{u}$ is tangent to the surface $\phi = $ const. at the point $P(x_0, y_0, z_0)$ (Fig. 9.2). We want to show that $d\phi/ds$ in the direction $\mathbf{u}$ is then equal to zero. Consider $\Delta\phi/\Delta s$ for paths PA, PB, PC, etc., approaching the tangent $\mathbf{u}$. Since $\phi = $ const. on the surface, and P, A, B, C, etc. are

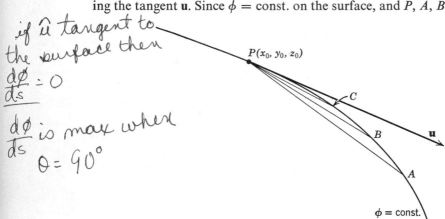

(handwritten: if $\hat{u}$ tangent to the surface then $\frac{d\phi}{ds} = 0$

$\frac{d\phi}{ds}$ is max when $\theta = 90°$)

Figure 9.2

all on the surface, $\Delta\phi = 0$, and $\Delta\phi/\Delta s = 0$ for such paths. But $d\phi/ds$ in the tangent direction is the limit of $\Delta\phi/\Delta s$ as $\Delta s \to 0$ (that is, as PA, PB, etc., approach $\mathbf{u}$), so $d\phi/ds$ in the direction $\mathbf{u}$ is zero also. Then for $\mathbf{u}$ along the tangent to $\phi = $ const., $\nabla\phi \cdot \mathbf{u} = 0$; this means that $\nabla\phi$ is perpendicular to $\mathbf{u}$. Since this is true for any $\mathbf{u}$ tangent to the surface at the point (x_0, y_0, z_0), the vector $\nabla\phi$ is perpendicular to the surface $\phi = $ const. at that point. Since $|\nabla\phi|$ is the value of the directional derivative in the direction normal (that is, perpendicular) to the surface, it is often called the *normal derivative* and written $|\nabla\phi| = d\phi/dn$.

As we said at the beginning of this discussion, the derivation holds also in two dimensions. There $\phi(x, y) = $ const. is a curve, and $\nabla\phi = \mathbf{i}(\partial\phi/\partial x) + \mathbf{j}(\partial\phi/\partial y)$ is a vector perpendicular to the curve at (x_0, y_0).

We now see that the direction of largest rate of change of a given function ϕ with distance is perpendicular to the equipotentials (or level lines) $\phi = $ const. In the temperature problem, the direction of maximum dT/ds is then perpendicular to the isothermals. At any point this is the direction of ∇T and is called the direction of the temperature gradient. In the problem of the hill, the direction of steepest slope at any point is perpendicular to the level lines, that is, along ∇z or ∇V.

Example 2.   Suppose the temperature T at (x, y, z) is given by $T = x^2 - y^2 + xyz + 273$; in which direction is the temperature increasing most rapidly at the point $(-1, 2, 3)$ and what is the rate? Here $\nabla T = (2x + yz)\mathbf{i} + (-2y + xz)\mathbf{j} + xy\mathbf{k} = 4\mathbf{i} - 7\mathbf{j} - 2\mathbf{k}$ at $(-1, 2, 3)$ and the increase in temperature is fastest in the direction of this vector. The rate of increase is $|\nabla T| = \sqrt{16 + 49 + 4} = \sqrt{69}$.

Example 3.   Given the surface $x^3 y^2 z = 12$, find the equations of the tangent plane and normal line at $(1, -2, 3)$.

This is a level surface of the function $w = x^3 y^2 z$, so the normal direction is the direction of

$$\nabla w = 3x^2 y^2 z\mathbf{i} + 2x^3 yz\mathbf{j} + x^3 y^2\mathbf{k} = 36\mathbf{i} - 12\mathbf{j} + 4\mathbf{k} \text{ at } (1, -2, 3).$$

A simpler vector in the same direction is $9\mathbf{i} - 3\mathbf{j} + \mathbf{k}$. Hence the equation of the tangent plane is

$$9(x - 1) - 3(y + 2) + (z - 3) = 0,$$

and the equations of the normal line are

$$\frac{x - 1}{9} = \frac{y + 2}{-3} = \frac{z - 3}{1}.$$

In (9.4) we have written $\nabla\phi$ in terms of its rectangular components. It will be useful to write it in plane polar coordinates also (see Chapter 10, Section 9 for other coordinate systems). What we want are the components of $\nabla\phi$ in the directions $\mathbf{e}_r$ and $\mathbf{e}_\theta$. According to (9.5), the component of $\nabla\phi$ in any direction $\mathbf{u}$ is the directional derivative $d\phi/ds$ in that direction. The element of arc length ds in the r direction is dr, so the directional derivative in the r direction is $d\phi/dr$ (θ constant) which we write as $\partial\phi/\partial r$. In the θ direction, the element of arc length is $r\, d\theta$ (Chapter 4, Section 14), so the directional derivative in the θ direction is $d\phi/(r\, d\theta)$ (r constant) which we write as $(1/r)(\partial\phi/\partial\theta)$. Thus we have

(9.7)
$$\nabla\phi = \mathbf{e}_r \frac{\partial\phi}{\partial r} + \mathbf{e}_\theta \frac{1}{r}\frac{\partial\phi}{\partial\theta}.$$

10. SOME OTHER EXPRESSIONS INVOLVING ∇

If we write $\nabla\phi$ as $[\mathbf{i}(\partial/\partial x) + \mathbf{j}(\partial/\partial y) + \mathbf{k}(\partial/\partial z)]\phi$, we can then call the bracket ∇. By itself ∇ has no meaning (just as d/dx alone has no meaning; we must put some function after it to be differentiated). However, it is useful to use $\mathbf{\nabla}$ much as we use d/dx to indicate a certain operation; in fact, we call $\mathbf{\nabla}$ a *vector operator* and write

(10.1)
$$\mathbf{\nabla} = \mathbf{i}\frac{\partial}{\partial x} + \mathbf{j}\frac{\partial}{\partial y} + \mathbf{k}\frac{\partial}{\partial z}.$$

It is more complicated than d/dx (which is a *scalar operator*) because $\mathbf{\nabla}$ has vector properties too. So far we have considered $\mathbf{\nabla}\phi$ where ϕ is a scalar; we next want to consider whether $\mathbf{\nabla}$ can operate on a vector.

Suppose $\mathbf{V}(x, y, z)$ is a vector function, that is, the three components V_x, V_y, V_z of $\mathbf{V}$ are functions of x, y, z:

$$\mathbf{V}(x, y, z) = \mathbf{i}V_x(x, y, z) + \mathbf{j}V_y(x, y, z) + \mathbf{k}V_z(x, y, z).$$

(The subscripts mean components, *not* partial derivatives.) Physically, $\mathbf{V}$ represents a vector field (for example, the electric field about a point charge). At each point of space there is a vector $\mathbf{V}$, but the magnitude and direction of $\mathbf{V}$ may vary from point to point. We can form two useful combinations of $\mathbf{\nabla}$ and $\mathbf{V}$. We define the *divergence* of $\mathbf{V}$, abbreviated div $\mathbf{V}$ or $\mathbf{\nabla} \cdot \mathbf{V}$, by (10.2):

divergence

(10.2)
$$\mathbf{\nabla} \cdot \mathbf{V} = \text{div } \mathbf{V} \equiv \frac{\partial V_x}{\partial x} + \frac{\partial V_y}{\partial y} + \frac{\partial V_z}{\partial z}.$$

We define the *curl* of $\mathbf{V}$, written $\mathbf{\nabla} \times \mathbf{V}$, by (10.3):

(10.3) $\mathbf{\nabla} \times \mathbf{V} = \text{curl } \mathbf{V}$

curl

$$= \mathbf{i}\left(\frac{\partial V_z}{\partial y} - \frac{\partial V_y}{\partial z}\right) + \mathbf{j}\left(\frac{\partial V_x}{\partial z} - \frac{\partial V_z}{\partial x}\right) + \mathbf{k}\left(\frac{\partial V_y}{\partial x} - \frac{\partial V_x}{\partial y}\right)$$

$$= \begin{vmatrix} \mathbf{i} & \mathbf{j} & \mathbf{k} \\ \dfrac{\partial}{\partial x} & \dfrac{\partial}{\partial y} & \dfrac{\partial}{\partial z} \\ V_x & V_y & V_z \end{vmatrix}.$$

You should study these expressions to see how we are using $\mathbf{\nabla}$ as "almost" a vector. The *definitions* of divergence and curl are the partial derivative expressions, of course. However, the similarity of the formulas (10.2) and (10.3) to those for $\mathbf{A} \cdot \mathbf{B}$ and $\mathbf{A} \times \mathbf{B}$ helps us to remember $\mathbf{\nabla} \cdot \mathbf{V}$ and $\mathbf{\nabla} \times \mathbf{V}$. But you must remember to put the partial derivative "components" of $\mathbf{\nabla}$ *before* the components of $\mathbf{V}$ in each term [for example, in evaluating the determinant in (10.3)]. Note that $\mathbf{\nabla} \cdot \mathbf{V}$ is a scalar and $\mathbf{\nabla} \times \mathbf{V}$ is a vector (compare $\mathbf{A} \cdot \mathbf{B}$ and $\mathbf{A} \times \mathbf{B}$). We shall discuss later the meaning and some of the applications of the divergence and the curl of a vector function.

The quantity $\nabla\phi$ in (9.4) is a vector function; we can then let $\mathbf{V} = \nabla\phi$ in (10.2) and find $\nabla \cdot \nabla\phi = \text{div grad } \phi$. This is a very important expression called the *Laplacian* of ϕ; it is usually written as $\nabla^2\phi$. From (9.4) and (10.2), we have

$$(10.4) \quad \nabla^2\phi = \nabla \cdot \nabla\phi = \text{div grad } \phi = \frac{\partial}{\partial x}\frac{\partial\phi}{\partial x} + \frac{\partial}{\partial y}\frac{\partial\phi}{\partial y} + \frac{\partial}{\partial z}\frac{\partial\phi}{\partial z}$$

$$= \frac{\partial^2\phi}{\partial x^2} + \frac{\partial^2\phi}{\partial y^2} + \frac{\partial^2\phi}{\partial z^2}.$$

The Laplacian is part of several important equations in mathematical physics:

$\nabla^2\phi = 0$ is Laplace's equation,

$\nabla^2\phi = \dfrac{1}{a^2}\dfrac{\partial^2\phi}{\partial t^2}$ is the wave equation,

$\nabla^2\phi = \dfrac{1}{a^2}\dfrac{\partial\phi}{\partial t}$ is the diffusion equation or equation of heat conduction.

These equations arise in numerous problems in heat, hydrodynamics, electricity and magnetism, aerodynamics, elasticity, optics, etc.; we shall discuss solving such equations in Chapter 14.

There are many other more complicated expressions involving ∇ and one or more scalar or vector functions, which arise in various applications of vector analysis. For reference we list a table of such expressions at the end of the chapter. Notice that these are of two kinds: (1) expressions involving two applications of ∇ such as $\nabla \cdot \nabla\phi = \nabla^2\phi$; (2) combinations of ∇ with two functions (vectors or scalars) such as $\nabla \times (\phi\mathbf{V})$. We *can* verify the given values of any of these expressions simply by writing out components. However, it is usually simpler to use the same formulas we would use if ∇ were an ordinary vector, being careful to remember that ∇ is also a differential operator.

Let us illustrate this method by evaluating $\nabla \times (\nabla \times \mathbf{V})$. We use the formula (5.8) for $\mathbf{A} \times (\mathbf{B} \times \mathbf{C})$ being careful to write both ∇'s *before* the vector function $\mathbf{V}$ which they must differentiate. Then we get

$$\nabla \times (\nabla \times \mathbf{V}) = \nabla(\nabla \cdot \mathbf{V}) - (\nabla \cdot \nabla)\mathbf{V}$$

$$= \nabla(\nabla \cdot \mathbf{V}) - \nabla^2\mathbf{V}.$$

This is a vector as it should be; the Laplacian of a vector, $\nabla^2\mathbf{V}$, simply means a vector whose components are $\nabla^2 V_x, \nabla^2 V_y, \nabla^2 V_z$.

As a second example let us find $\nabla \cdot (\phi\mathbf{V})$, where ϕ is a scalar function and $\mathbf{V}$ is a vector function. Here we must differentiate a product, so our result will contain two terms. We could write these as

$$(10.5) \qquad\qquad \nabla \cdot (\phi\mathbf{V}) = \nabla_\phi \cdot (\phi\mathbf{V}) + \nabla_\mathbf{V} \cdot (\phi\mathbf{V}),$$

where the subscripts on $\mathbf{\nabla}$ indicate which function is to be differentiated. Since ϕ is a scalar, it can be moved past the dot. Then

$$\mathbf{\nabla}_\phi \cdot (\phi \mathbf{V}) = (\mathbf{\nabla}_\phi \phi) \cdot \mathbf{V} = \mathbf{V} \cdot (\mathbf{\nabla}\phi),$$

where we have removed the subscript in the last step since $\mathbf{V}$ no longer appears after $\mathbf{\nabla}$. Actually you may see in books $(\mathbf{\nabla}\phi) \cdot \mathbf{V}$ meaning that only the ϕ is to be differentiated, but it is clearer to write it as $\mathbf{V} \cdot (\mathbf{\nabla}\phi)$. [Be careful with $(\mathbf{\nabla}\phi) \times \mathbf{V}$, however; assuming that this means that only ϕ is to be differentiated, the clear way to write it is $-\mathbf{V} \times (\mathbf{\nabla}\phi)$; note the minus sign.] In the second term of (10.5), ϕ is a scalar and is not differentiated; thus it is just like a constant and we can write this term as $\phi(\mathbf{\nabla} \cdot \mathbf{V})$. Collecting our results, we have

(10.6) $\mathbf{\nabla} \cdot (\phi \mathbf{V}) = \mathbf{V} \cdot \mathbf{\nabla}\phi + \phi(\mathbf{\nabla} \cdot \mathbf{V}).$

11. LINE INTEGRALS

In Section 4, we discussed the fact that the work done by a force $\mathbf{F}$ on an object which undergoes an infinitesimal vector displacement $d\mathbf{r}$ can be written as

(11.1) $dW = \mathbf{F} \cdot d\mathbf{r}.$

Suppose the object moves along some path (say A to B in Fig. 11.1), with the force $\mathbf{F}$ acting on it varying as it moves. For example, $\mathbf{F}$ might be the force on a charged particle in an electric field; then $\mathbf{F}$ would vary from point to point, that is, $\mathbf{F}$ would be a function of x, y, z. However, *on a curve,*

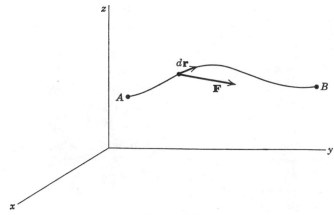

Figure 11.1

x, y, z are related by the equations of the curve. In three dimensions it takes two equations to determine a curve (as an intersection of two surfaces; for example, consider the equations of a straight line in Section 6). Thus along a curve there is only *one* independent variable; we can then write $\mathbf{F}$ and $d\mathbf{r} = \mathbf{i}\,dx + \mathbf{j}\,dy + \mathbf{k}\,dz$ as functions of a single variable. The integral of $dW = \mathbf{F} \cdot d\mathbf{r}$ along the given curve then becomes an ordinary integral of a function of one variable and we can evaluate it to find the total work done by $\mathbf{F}$ in moving an object in Fig. 11.1 from A to B. Such an integral is called a *line integral.* A line integral means an integral along a curve (or line), that is, a single integral as contrasted to a double integral over a surface or area, or a triple integral over a volume. The essential point to understand about a line integral is that there is *one* independent variable, because we are required to remain on a *curve*. In two dimensions, the equation of a curve might be written $y = f(x)$, where x is the independent variable. In three dimensions, the equations of a curve (for example, a straight line) can be written either like (6.7) (where we could take x as the independent variable and find y and z as functions of x), or (6.8) (where t is the independent variable and x, y, z are all functions of t). To evaluate a line integral, then, we must write it as a *single* integral using one independent variable.

Example 1. Given the force $\mathbf{F} = xy\mathbf{i} - y^2\mathbf{j}$, find the work done by $\mathbf{F}$ along the paths indicated in Fig. 11.2 from $(0, 0)$ to $(2, 1)$.

Since $\mathbf{r} = x\mathbf{i} + y\mathbf{j}$ on the (x, y) plane, we have

$$d\mathbf{r} = \mathbf{i}\,dx + \mathbf{j}\,dy,$$

$$\mathbf{F} \cdot d\mathbf{r} = xy\,dx - y^2\,dy.$$

We want to evaluate

$$(11.2) \qquad W = \int (xy\,dx - y^2\,dy).$$

First we must write the integrand in terms of *one* variable. Along path 1 (a straight line), $y = \frac{1}{2}x$, $dy = \frac{1}{2}\,dx$. Substituting these values into (11.2), we obtain an integral in the one variable x. The limits for x (Fig. 11.2) are 0 to 2. Thus we get

$$W_1 = \int_0^2 (x \cdot \tfrac{1}{2}x\,dx - (\tfrac{1}{2}x)^2 \cdot \tfrac{1}{2}\,dx) = \int_0^2 \tfrac{3}{8}x^2\,dx = \frac{x^3}{8}\Big|_0^2 = 1.$$

We could just as well use y as the independent variable and put $x = 2y$, $dx = 2\,dy$, and integrate from 0 to 1. (You should verify that the answer is the same.)

Along path 2 in Fig. 11.2 (a parabola), $y = \frac{1}{4}x^2$, $dy = \frac{1}{2}x\,dx$. Then we get

$$W_2 = \int_0^2 (x \cdot \tfrac{1}{4}x^2\,dx - \tfrac{1}{16}x^4 \cdot \tfrac{1}{2}x\,dx) = \int_0^2 (\tfrac{1}{4}x^3 - \tfrac{1}{32}x^5)\,dx$$

$$= \frac{x^4}{16} - \frac{x^6}{192}\Big|_0^2 = \tfrac{2}{3}.$$

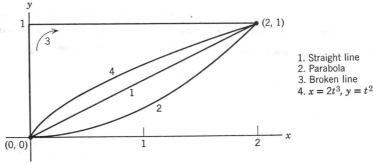

1. Straight line
2. Parabola
3. Broken line
4. $x = 2t^3$, $y = t^2$

Figure 11.2

Along path 3 (the broken line), we have to use a different method. We integrate first from $(0, 0)$ to $(0, 1)$ and then from $(0, 1)$ to $(2, 1)$ and add the results. Along $(0, 0)$ to $(0, 1)$, $x = 0$ and $dx = 0$ so we must use y as the variable. Then we have

$$\int_{y=0}^1 (0 \cdot y \cdot 0 - y^2\,dy) = -\frac{y^3}{3}\Big|_0^1 = -\tfrac{1}{3}.$$

Along $(0, 1)$ to $(2, 1)$, $y = 1$, $dy = 0$, so we use x as the variable. We have

$$\int_{x=0}^2 (x \cdot 1 \cdot dx - 1 \cdot 0) = \frac{x^2}{2}\Big|_0^2 = 2.$$

Then the total $W_3 = -\tfrac{1}{3} + 2 = \tfrac{5}{3}$.

Path 4 illustrates still another technique. Instead of using either x or y as the integration variable, we can use a parameter t. For $x = 2t^3$, $y = t^2$, we have $dx = 6t^2\,dt$, $dy = 2t\,dt$. At the origin, $t = 0$, and at $(2, 1)$, $t = 1$. Substituting these values into (11.2), we get

$$W_4 = \int_0^1 (2t^3 \cdot t^2 \cdot 6t^2\,dt - t^4 \cdot 2t\,dt) = \int_0^1 (12t^7 - 2t^5)\,dt = \tfrac{12}{8} - \tfrac{2}{6} = \tfrac{7}{6}.$$

Example 2. Find the value of

$$I = \int \frac{x\,dy - y\,dx}{x^2 + y^2}$$

along each of the two paths indicated in Fig. 11.3 from $(-1, 0)$ to $(1, 0)$.
[Notice that we *could* have given the integral in the form $\int \mathbf{F} \cdot d\mathbf{r}$ with
$\mathbf{F} = (-i y + x \mathbf{j})/(x^2 + y^2)$; however, there are also many other kinds of
problems in which line integrals may arise.]

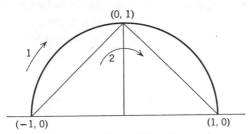

(0, 1)

1

2

(−1, 0)   (1, 0)

Figure 11.3

Along the circle it is simplest to use polar coordinates; then $r = 1$ at
all points of the circle and θ is the only variable. We then have

$$x = \cos\theta, \quad dx = -\sin\theta\, d\theta,$$
$$y = \sin\theta, \quad dy = \cos\theta\, d\theta, \quad x^2 + y^2 = 1,$$
$$\frac{x\, dy - y\, dx}{x^2 + y^2} = \frac{\cos^2\theta - \sin\theta(-\sin\theta)\, d\theta}{1} = d\theta.$$

At $(-1, 0)$, $\theta = \pi$; at $(1, 0)$, $\theta = 0$. Then we get

$$I_1 = \int_{\pi}^{0} d\theta = -\pi.$$

Along path 2, we integrate from $(-1, 0)$ to $(0, 1)$ and from $(0, 1)$ to
$(1, 0)$ and add the results. The first straight line has the equation $y = x + 1$; then $dy = dx$, and the integral is

$$\int_{-1}^{0} \frac{x\, dx - (x + 1)\, dx}{x^2 + (x + 1)^2} = \int_{-1}^{0} \frac{-dx}{2x^2 + 2x + 1} = \int_{-1}^{0} \frac{-2\, dx}{(2x + 1)^2 + 1}$$

$$= -\arctan(2x + 1)\Big|_{-1}^{0} = -\arctan 1 + \arctan(-1)$$

$$= -\frac{\pi}{4} + \left(-\frac{\pi}{4}\right) = -\frac{\pi}{2}.$$

Along the second straight line $y = 1 - x$, $dy = -dx$, and the integral is

$$-\int_{0}^{1} \frac{x\, dx + (1 - x)\, dx}{x^2 + (1 - x)^2} = \int_{0}^{1} \frac{-2\, dx}{(2x - 1)^2 + 1} = -\arctan(2x - 1)\Big|_{0}^{1}$$

$$= -\frac{\pi}{2}.$$

(margin handwriting: Conservative fields: curl F = 0)

Adding the results for the integrals along the two parts of path 2, we get $I_2 = -\pi$.

Conservative fields. Notice that in Example 1 the answers were different for different paths, but in Example 2 they are the same. (See Section 13, however.) We can give a physical meaning to these facts if we interpret the integrals in all cases as the work done by a force on an object which moves along the path of integration. Suppose you want to get a heavy box across a sidewalk and up into a truck. Compare the work done in dragging the box across the sidewalk and then lifting it, with the work done in lifting it and then swinging it across in the air. In the first case work is done against friction in addition to the work required to lift the box; in the second case the only work done is that required to lift the box. Thus we see that the work done in moving an object from one point to another *may* depend on the path the object follows; in fact, it usually will when there is friction. Our example 1 was such a case. A force field for which $W = \int \mathbf{F} \cdot d\mathbf{r}$ depends upon the path as well as the endpoints is called *nonconservative*; physically this means that energy has been dissipated, say by friction. There are however, *conservative fields* for which $\int \mathbf{F} \cdot d\mathbf{r}$ is the same between two given points regardless of what path we calculate it along. For example, the work done in raising a mass m to the top of a mountain of height h is $W = mgh$ whether we lift the mass straight up a cliff or carry it up a slope, as long as no friction is involved. Thus the gravitational field is conservative.

It is useful to be able to recognize conservative and nonconservative fields before we do the integration. We shall see later (Section 13) that ordinarily curl $\mathbf{F} = 0$ [see (10.3) for the definition of curl] is a necessary and sufficient condition for $\int \mathbf{F} \cdot d\mathbf{r}$ to be independent of the path, that is, curl $\mathbf{F} = 0$ for conservative fields and curl $\mathbf{F} \neq 0$ for nonconservative fields. (See Section 13 for a more careful discussion of this.) It is not hard to see why this is usually so. Suppose that for a given $\mathbf{F}$ there is a function $W(x, y, z)$ such that

$$\mathbf{F} = \nabla W = \mathbf{i}\frac{\partial W}{\partial x} + \mathbf{j}\frac{\partial W}{\partial y} + \mathbf{k}\frac{\partial W}{\partial z},$$

(11.3)

$$F_x = \frac{\partial W}{\partial x}, \qquad F_y = \frac{\partial W}{\partial y}, \qquad F_z = \frac{\partial W}{\partial z}.$$

Then using the fact that $\partial^2 W/\partial x\,\partial y = \partial^2 W/\partial y\,\partial x$, etc., we get from (11.3)

(11.4)

$$\frac{\partial F_x}{\partial y} = \frac{\partial^2 W}{\partial y\,\partial x} = \frac{\partial F_y}{\partial x}, \qquad \text{and similarly} \qquad \frac{\partial F_y}{\partial z} = \frac{\partial F_z}{\partial y}, \qquad \frac{\partial F_x}{\partial z} = \frac{\partial F_z}{\partial x}.$$

Using the definition (10.3) of curl **F**, we see that equations (11.4) say that the three components of curl **F** are equal to zero. Thus if $\mathbf{F} = \nabla W$, then curl $\mathbf{F} = 0$. Conversely (as we shall show later), if curl $\mathbf{F} = 0$, then we can find a function $W(x, y, z)$ for which $\mathbf{F} = \nabla W$. Now if $\mathbf{F} = \nabla W$, we can write

(11.5)
$$\mathbf{F} \cdot d\mathbf{r} = \nabla W \cdot d\mathbf{r} = \frac{\partial W}{\partial x}\, dx + \frac{\partial W}{\partial y}\, dy + \frac{\partial W}{\partial z}\, dz = dW,$$
$$\int_A^B \mathbf{F} \cdot d\mathbf{r} = \int_A^B dW = W(B) - W(A),$$

where $W(B)$ and $W(A)$ mean the values of the function W at the endpoints A and B of the path of integration. Since the value of the integral depends only on the endpoints A and B, it is independent of the path along which we integrate from A to B, that is, **F** is conservative.

The differential dW in (11.5) of a function $W(x, y, z)$ is called an *exact differential*. We could then say that curl $\mathbf{F} = 0$ is a necessary and sufficient condition for $\mathbf{F} \cdot d\mathbf{r}$ to be an exact differential (but see Section 13). To make this clear, let us consider some examples in which $\mathbf{F} \cdot d\mathbf{r}$ is, or is not, an exact differential.

Example. Consider the function

(11.6) $W = x^2y - xz^3 - z.$

Then

(11.7) $dW = (2xy - z^3)\, dx + x^2\, dy - (3xz^2 + 1)\, dz.$

Here dW is an exact differential by definition since we got it by differentiating a function W. We can easily verify that if we write $dW = \mathbf{F} \cdot d\mathbf{r}$, then curl $\mathbf{F} = 0$ [that is, equations (11.4) are true]:

(11.8)
$$\frac{\partial}{\partial x}(x^2) = 2x = \frac{\partial}{\partial y}(2xy - z^3),$$
$$\frac{\partial}{\partial x}(-3xz^2 - 1) = -3z^2 = \frac{\partial}{\partial z}(2xy - z^3),$$
$$\frac{\partial}{\partial y}(-3xz^2 - 1) = 0 = \frac{\partial}{\partial z}(x^2).$$

You should observe carefully how to get (11.8) from (11.7); the equations (11.8) say that the partial derivative with respect to x of the coefficient of dy equals the partial derivative with respect to y of the coefficient of dx, etc., in (11.7). These equations (11.8) are called the *reciprocity relations* in thermodynamics; in mechanics they are the components of curl $\mathbf{F} = 0$, as we have said. In both cases they are true because the mixed second partial derivatives of a function are the same in either order, for example $\partial^2 W/\partial x\ \partial y = \partial^2 W/\partial y\ \partial x$.

We obtained dW in (11.7) by taking the differential of (11.6); now suppose we start with a given $dW = \mathbf{F} \cdot d\mathbf{r}$.

Example. Let us consider

$$(11.9) \quad dW = \mathbf{F} \cdot d\mathbf{r} = (2xy - z^3)\ dx + x^2\ dy + (3xz^2 + 1)\ dz.$$

This is almost the same as (11.7); just the sign of the dz term is changed. Then two of the equations corresponding to (11.8) do not hold, so curl $\mathbf{F} \neq 0$, and dW is not an exact differential. We ask whether there is a function W of which (11.9) is the differential; the answer is "No" because if there were, the mixed second partial derivatives of W would be equal, and so curl $\mathbf{F}$ would be zero. Equations like (11.9) often occur in applications. When dW is not exact, then $\mathbf{F}$ is a nonconservative force, and $\int \mathbf{F} \cdot d\mathbf{r}$, which is the work done by $\mathbf{F}$, depends not only on the points A and B but also upon the path along which the object moves. As we have said, this happens when there are friction forces.

On the other hand, we may sometimes be given $\mathbf{F}$ or $dW = \mathbf{F} \cdot d\mathbf{r}$, and find by calculation that curl $\mathbf{F} = 0$. We then know that there *is* a function W and we want to know how to find it (up to an arbitrary additive constant of integration). To do this we can calculate the line integral in (11.5) from some reference point A to the variable point B along any convenient path; since the integral is independent of the path when curl $\mathbf{F} = 0$, this process gives the value of W at the point B. (There is, of course, an additive constant in W whose value depends on our choice of the reference point A.)

Example. Let us integrate (11.7) from the origin to the point x, y, z. As the path of integration, we choose the broken line from $(0, 0, 0)$ to $(x, 0, 0)$ to $(x, y, 0)$ to (x, y, z). From $(0, 0, 0)$ to $(x, 0, 0)$, we have $y = z = 0$, $dy = dz = 0$, so the integral is zero along this part of the path. From $(x, 0, 0)$ to $(x, y, 0)$, we have $x = $ const., $z = 0$, $dx = dz = 0$, so the integral is

$$\int_0^y x^2\ dy = x^2 \int_0^y dy = x^2 y.$$

From $(x, y, 0)$ to (x, y, z) we have $x = $ const., $y = $ const., $dx = dy = 0$, so the integral is

$$-\int_0^z (3xz^2 + 1)\ dz = -xz^3 - z.$$

Adding the three results, we get

$$W = x^2 y - xz^3 - z,$$

which is (11.6).

Potentials. In mechanics, when $\mathbf{F} = \boldsymbol{\nabla} W$, W is the work done by $\mathbf{F}$. For example, if a mass m falls a distance z under gravity, the work done on it is mgz. If, however, we lift the mass a distance z against gravity, the work done *by the force $\mathbf{F}$ of gravity* is $W = -mgz$ since the direction of motion is opposite to $\mathbf{F}$. The increase in potential energy of m in this case is $\phi = +mgz$, that is, $W = -\phi$, or $\mathbf{F} = -\boldsymbol{\nabla}\phi$. The function ϕ is called the potential energy or the *scalar potential* of the force $\mathbf{F}$. (Of course, ϕ can be changed by adding any constant; this corresponds to a choice of the zero level of the potential energy and has no effect on $\mathbf{F}$.) More generally for any vector $\mathbf{V}$, if curl $\mathbf{V} = 0$, there is a function ϕ, called the scalar potential of $\mathbf{V}$, such that $\mathbf{V} = -\boldsymbol{\nabla}\phi$. (This is the customary definition of scalar potential in mechanics and electricity; in hydrodynamics many authors define the *velocity potential* so that $\mathbf{V} = +\boldsymbol{\nabla}\phi$.)

Example. Find the scalar potential for the electric field of a point charge q at the origin.

Recall that the electric field at a point $\mathbf{r} = \mathbf{i}x + \mathbf{j}y + \mathbf{k}z$ means the force on a unit charge at $\mathbf{r}$ due to q and is (in electrostatic units)

$$(11.12) \qquad \mathbf{E} = \frac{q}{r^2}\,\mathbf{e}_r = \frac{q}{r^2}\frac{\mathbf{r}}{r} = \frac{q}{r^3}\,\mathbf{r}.$$

(This is Coulomb's law in electricity.) If we take the zero level of the potential energy at infinity, then the scalar potential ϕ means the negative of the work done by the field on the unit charge as the charge moves from infinity to the point $\mathbf{r}$. This is

$$(11.13) \qquad \phi = -\int_{\infty \text{ to } \mathbf{r}} \mathbf{E}\cdot d\mathbf{r} = q\int_{\mathbf{r}\text{ to }\infty} \frac{\mathbf{r}\cdot d\mathbf{r}}{r^3}.$$

It is simplest to evaluate the line integral using the polar coordinate variable r along a radial line $\theta = \text{const}$. This is justified by showing that curl $\mathbf{E} = 0$, that is, that $\mathbf{E}$ is conservative (Problem 65). Since the differential of $(\mathbf{r}\cdot\mathbf{r})$ can be written as either $d(\mathbf{r}\cdot\mathbf{r}) = 2\mathbf{r}\cdot d\mathbf{r}$ or as $d(\mathbf{r}\cdot\mathbf{r}) = d(r^2) = 2r\,dr$, we have $\mathbf{r}\cdot d\mathbf{r} = r\,dr$ and (11.13) gives

$$(11.14) \qquad \phi = q\int_r^\infty \frac{r\,dr}{r^3} = q\int_r^\infty \frac{dr}{r^2} = -\frac{q}{r}\Big|_r^\infty = \frac{q}{r}.$$

12. THE DIVERGENCE AND THE DIVERGENCE THEOREM

We have defined (in Section 10) the *divergence* of a vector function $V(x, y, z)$ as

(12.1) $$\text{div } \mathbf{V} = \nabla \cdot \mathbf{V} = \frac{\partial V_x}{\partial x} + \frac{\partial V_y}{\partial y} + \frac{\partial V_z}{\partial z}.$$

We now want to investigate the meaning and use of the divergence in physical applications.

Consider a region in which water is flowing. We can imagine drawing at every point a vector $\mathbf{v}$ equal to the velocity of the water at that point. The vector function $\mathbf{v}$ then represents a vector field. The curves tangent to $\mathbf{v}$ are called stream lines. We could in the same way discuss the flow of a gas, of heat, of electricity, or of particles (say from a radioactive source). We are going to show that if $\mathbf{v}$ represents the velocity of flow of any of these things, then div $\mathbf{v}$ is related to the amount of the substance which flows out of a given volume. This could be different from zero either because of a change in density (more air flows out than in as a room is heated) or because there is a source or sink in the volume (alpha particles flow out of but not into a box containing an alpha-radioactive source). Exactly the same mathematics applies to the electric and magnetic fields where $\mathbf{v}$ is replaced by $\mathbf{E}$ or $\mathbf{B}$ and the quantity corresponding to outflow of a material substance is called flux.

For our example of water flow, let $\mathbf{V} = \mathbf{v}\rho$, where ρ is the density of the water. Then the amount of water crossing in time t an area A' which is perpendicular to the direction of flow, is (see Fig. 12.1) the amount of water in a cylinder of cross section A' and length vt. This amount of water is

(12.2) $$(vt)(A')(\rho).$$

The same amount of water crosses area A (see Fig. 12.1) whose normal is inclined at angle θ to $\mathbf{v}$. Since $A' = A \cos \theta$,

(12.3) $$vtA'\rho = vt\rho A \cos \theta.$$

Then if water is flowing in the direction $\mathbf{v}$ making an angle θ with the normal $\mathbf{n}$ to a surface, the amount of water crossing *unit* area of the surface in *unit* time is

(12.4) $$v\rho \cos \theta = V \cos \theta = \mathbf{V} \cdot \mathbf{n}$$

if $\mathbf{n}$ is a unit vector.

Now consider an element of volume $dx\, dy\, dz$ in the region through

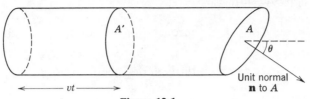

Figure 12.1

which the water is flowing (Fig. 12.2). Water is flowing either in or out of the volume $dx\,dy\,dz$ through each of the six surfaces of the volume element; we shall calculate the net outward flow. In Fig. 12.2, the rate at which water flows into $dx\,dy\,dz$ through surface 1 is [by (12.4)] $\mathbf{V} \cdot \mathbf{i}$ per unit area, or $(\mathbf{V} \cdot \mathbf{i})\,dy\,dz$ through the area $dy\,dz$ of surface 1. Since $\mathbf{V} \cdot \mathbf{i} = V_x$, we find that the rate at which water flows across surface 1 is $V_x\,dy\,dz$. A similar expression gives the rate at which water flows *out* through surface 2, except that V_x must be the x-component of $\mathbf{V}$ at surface 2 instead of at surface 1. We want the difference of the two V_x values at two points, one on surface 1 and one on surface 2, directly opposite each other, that is, for the same y and z. These two values of V_x differ by ΔV_x which can be approximated (as in Chapter 4) by dV_x. For constant y and z, $dV_x = (\partial V_x/\partial x)\,dx$. Then the *net outflow* through these two surfaces is the outflow through surface 2 minus the inflow through surface 1, namely,

$$(12.5) \quad [(V_x \text{ at surface 2}) - (V_x \text{ at surface 1})]\,dy\,dz = \left(\frac{\partial V_x}{\partial x}\,dx\right)\,dy\,dz.$$

We get similar expressions for the net outflow through the other two

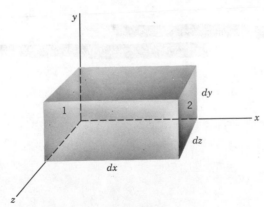

Figure 12.2

pairs of opposite surfaces:

(12.6)

$$\frac{\partial V_y}{\partial y}\, dx\, dy\, dz \qquad \text{through top and bottom,} \qquad \text{and}$$

$$\frac{\partial V_z}{\partial z}\, dx\, dy\, dz \qquad \text{through the other two sides.}$$

Then the total net rate of loss of water from $dx\, dy\, dz$ is

(12.7) $\left(\dfrac{\partial V_x}{\partial x} + \dfrac{\partial V_y}{\partial y} + \dfrac{\partial V_z}{\partial z}\right) dx\, dy\, dz = \text{div } \mathbf{V}\, dx\, dy\, dz$

$$\text{or} \qquad \boldsymbol{\nabla} \cdot \mathbf{V}\, dx\, dy\, dz.$$

If we divide (12.7) by $dx\, dy\, dz$, we have the rate of loss of water per unit volume. This is the physical meaning of a divergence: It is the net rate of outflow *per unit volume* evaluated at a point (let $dx\, dy\, dz$ shrink to a point). This is outflow of actual substance for liquids, gases, or particles; it is called flux for electric and magnetic fields. You should note that this is somewhat like a density. Density is mass *per unit volume*, but it is evaluated *at a point* and may vary from point to point. Similarly, the divergence is evaluated at each point and may vary from point to point.

As we have said, div $\mathbf{V}$ may be different from zero either because of variable density or because of sources and sinks. Let

$\psi = $ *source density* minus *sink density*
  $= $ net mass of fluid being created (or added via something like a minute sprinkler system) per unit time per unit volume;
$\rho = $ density of the fluid $= $ mass per unit volume;
$\partial\rho/\partial t = $ time rate of increase of mass per unit volume.

Then:

Rate of increase of mass in $dx\, dy\, dz$
     $= $ rate of creation minus rate of outward flow,

or in symbols

$$\frac{\partial\rho}{\partial t}\, dx\, dy\, dz = \psi\, dx\, dy\, dz - \boldsymbol{\nabla}\cdot\mathbf{V}\, dx\, dy\, dz.$$

Cancelling $dx\, dy\, dz$, we have

$$\frac{\partial\rho}{\partial t} = \psi - \boldsymbol{\nabla}\cdot\mathbf{V}$$

or

(12.8) $$\boldsymbol{\nabla}\cdot\mathbf{V} = \psi - \frac{\partial\rho}{\partial t}.$$

If there are no sources or sinks, then

(12.9) $$\nabla \cdot \mathbf{V} + \frac{\partial \rho}{\partial t} = 0.$$

Equation (12.9) is often called the *equation of continuity*. If the fluid is incompressible (that is, $\rho = $ const.), then

(12.10) $$\nabla \cdot \mathbf{V} = \psi.$$

In the case of the electric field, the "sources" and "sinks" are electric charges and the equation corresponding to (12.10) is div $\mathbf{D} = \psi$, where ψ is the charge density and $\mathbf{D}$ is the electric displacement. For the magnetic

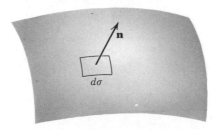

Figure 12.3

field $\mathbf{B}$ you would expect the sources to be magnetic poles; however, there are no free magnetic poles, so div $\mathbf{B} = 0$ always.

We have shown that the mass of fluid crossing a plane area A per unit time is $A\mathbf{V} \cdot \mathbf{n}$, where $\mathbf{n}$ is a unit vector normal to A, $\mathbf{v}$ and ρ are the velocity and density of the fluid, and $\mathbf{V} = \mathbf{v}\rho$. Consider any closed surface, and let $d\sigma$ represent an area element on the surface (Fig. 12.3). For example: for a plane, $d\sigma = dx\,dy$; for a spherical surface,

$$d\sigma = r^2 \sin\theta \, d\theta \, d\phi.$$

Let $\mathbf{n}$ be the unit vector normal to $d\sigma$ and pointing *out* of the surface ($\mathbf{n}$ varies in direction from point to point on the surface). Then the mass of fluid flowing out through $d\sigma$ is $\mathbf{V} \cdot \mathbf{n} \, d\sigma$ by (12.4) and the total outflow from the volume inclosed by the surface is

(12.11) $\text{total outflow} = \iint \mathbf{V} \cdot \mathbf{n} \, d\sigma,$

where the double integral is evaluated over the closed surface. We showed previously that for the volume element $d\tau = dx\,dy\,dz$, the outflow from $d\tau$ is

(12.12) $$\nabla \cdot \mathbf{V} \, d\tau.$$

It is worth noticing here another way [besides (10.2)] of defining the divergence. If we write (12.11) for the surface of a volume element $d\tau$, we have two expressions for the total outflow from $d\tau$, and these must be equal. Thus

(12.13)
$$\nabla \cdot \mathbf{V}\, d\tau = \iint\limits_{\text{surface of } d\tau} \mathbf{V} \cdot \mathbf{n}\, d\sigma.$$

The value of $\nabla \cdot \mathbf{V}$ on the left is, of course, an average value of $\nabla \cdot \mathbf{V}$ in $d\tau$, but if we divide (12.13) by $d\tau$ and let $d\tau$ shrink to a point, we have a definition of $\nabla \cdot \mathbf{V}$ at the point:

(12.14)
$$\nabla \cdot \mathbf{V} = \lim_{d\tau \to 0} \frac{1}{d\tau} \iint\limits_{\text{surface of } d\tau} \mathbf{V} \cdot \mathbf{n}\, d\sigma.$$

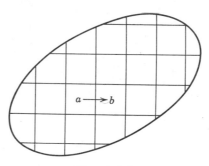

Figure 12.4

If we start with (12.14) as the definition of $\nabla \cdot \mathbf{V}$, then the discussion leading to (12.7) is a proof that $\nabla \cdot \mathbf{V}$ as defined in (12.14) is equal to $\nabla \cdot \mathbf{V}$ as defined in (10.2).

Proof of the divergence theorem (12.17). Consider a large volume τ; imagine it cut up into volume elements $d\tau_i$ (a cross section of this is shown in Fig. 12.4). The outflow from each $d\tau_i$ is $\nabla \cdot \mathbf{V}\, d\tau_i$; let us add together the outflow from all the $d\tau_i$ to get

(12.15)
$$\sum_i \nabla \cdot \mathbf{V}\, d\tau_i.$$

We shall show that (12.15) is the outflow from the large volume τ. Consider the flow between the elements marked a and b in Fig. 12.4 across their common face. An outflow from a to b is an inflow (negative outflow) from b to a, so that in the sum (12.15) such outflows across interior faces cancel. The total sum in (12.15) then equals just the total outflow from the large volume. As the size of the volume elements tends to zero, this sum approaches a triple integral over the volume,

$$(12.16) \qquad\qquad \iiint \nabla \cdot \mathbf{V} \, d\tau.$$

We have shown that both (12.11) and (12.16) are equal to the total out-flow from the large volume; hence they are equal to each other:

$$(12.17) \qquad \underset{\text{volume } \tau}{\iiint \nabla \cdot \mathbf{V} \, d\tau} = \underset{\text{surface inclosing } \tau}{\iint \mathbf{V} \cdot \mathbf{n} \, d\sigma.}$$

This equation (12.17) is the *divergence theorem.* Notice that it converts a volume integral into a surface integral or vice versa; we can then evaluate whichever one is the easier to do.

In (12.17) we have carefully written the volume integral with three integral signs and the surface integral with two integral signs. However, it is rather common to write only one integral sign for either case when the volume or area element is indicated by a single differential ($d\tau$ or $d\sigma$). Thus we might write $\iiint d\tau$ or $\int d\tau$ or $\iiint dx\, dy\, dz$, all meaning the same thing. When the single integral sign is used to indicate a surface or volume integral, you must see from the problem or the words under the integral what is really meant. To indicate a surface integral over a *closed* surface or a line integral around a *closed* curve, the symbol $\oint$ is often used. Thus we might write $\iint d\sigma$ or $\oiint d\sigma$ or $\oint d\sigma$, all meaning a surface integral over a closed surface. A different notation for the integrand $\mathbf{V} \cdot \mathbf{n} \, d\sigma$ is often used. Instead of using a unit vector $\mathbf{n}$ and the scalar magnitude $d\sigma$, we may write the vector $d\boldsymbol{\sigma}$ meaning a vector of magnitude $d\sigma$ in the direction $\mathbf{n}$; thus $d\boldsymbol{\sigma}$ means exactly the same thing as $\mathbf{n}\, d\sigma$, and we may replace $\mathbf{V} \cdot \mathbf{n}\, d\sigma$ by $\mathbf{V} \cdot d\boldsymbol{\sigma}$ in (12.17).

Example of the divergence theorem. Let $\mathbf{V} = \mathbf{i}x + \mathbf{j}y + \mathbf{k}z$ and evaluate $\oint \mathbf{V} \cdot \mathbf{n}\, d\sigma$ over the closed surface of the cylinder shown in Fig. 12.5.

By the divergence theorem this is equal to $\int \nabla \cdot \mathbf{V} \, d\tau$ over the volume of the cylinder. (Note that we are using single integral signs, but it is clear which integral is a volume integral and which a surface integral.) We find from the definition of divergence

$$\nabla \cdot \mathbf{V} = \frac{\partial x}{\partial x} + \frac{\partial y}{\partial y} + \frac{\partial z}{\partial z} = 3.$$

Then by (12.17)

$$\underset{\substack{\text{surface of} \\ \text{cylinder}}}{\oint \mathbf{V} \cdot \mathbf{n}\, d\sigma} = \underset{\substack{\text{volume of} \\ \text{cylinder}}}{\int \nabla \cdot \mathbf{V}\, d\tau} = \int 3\, d\tau = 3\int d\tau = 3 \text{ times volume of cylinder}$$

$$= 3\pi a^2 h.$$

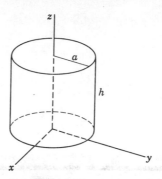

Figure 12.5

It is harder to evaluate $\oint \mathbf{V} \cdot \mathbf{n} \, d\sigma$ directly, but we might do it to show an example of calculating a surface integral and to verify the divergence theorem in a special case. We need the surface normal $\mathbf{n}$. On the top surface (Fig. 12.5) $\mathbf{n} = \mathbf{k}$, and there $\mathbf{V} \cdot \mathbf{n} = \mathbf{V} \cdot \mathbf{k} = z = h$. Then

$$\int_{\text{top surface of cylinder}} \mathbf{V} \cdot \mathbf{n} \, d\sigma = h \int d\sigma = h \cdot \pi a^2.$$

On the bottom surface, $\mathbf{n} = -\mathbf{k}$, $\mathbf{V} \cdot \mathbf{n} = -z = 0$; hence the integral over the bottom surface is zero. On the curved surface we might see by inspection that the vector $\mathbf{i}x + \mathbf{j}y$ is normal to the surface, so for the curved surface we have

$$\mathbf{n} = \frac{\mathbf{i}x + \mathbf{j}y}{\sqrt{x^2 + y^2}} = \frac{\mathbf{i}x + \mathbf{j}y}{a}.$$

If the vector $\mathbf{n}$ is not obvious by inspection, we can easily find it; recall that if the equation of a surface is $\phi(x, y, z) = $ const., then $\nabla \phi$ is perpendicular to the surface. In this problem, the equation of the cylinder is $x^2 + y^2 = a^2$; then $\phi = x^2 + y^2$, $\nabla \phi = 2x\mathbf{i} + 2y\mathbf{j}$, and we get the same unit vector $\mathbf{n}$ as above. Then for the curved surface we find

$$\mathbf{V} \cdot \mathbf{n} = \frac{x^2 + y^2}{a} = \frac{a^2}{a} = a$$

$$\int_{\text{curved surface}} \mathbf{V} \cdot \mathbf{n} \, d\sigma = a \int d\sigma = a \cdot (\text{area of curved surface})$$

$$= a \cdot 2\pi ah.$$

The value of $\oint \mathbf{V} \cdot \mathbf{n} \, d\sigma$ over the whole surface of the cylinder is then $\pi a^2 h + 2\pi a^2 h = 3\pi a^2 h$ as before.

Gauss's law. The divergence theorem is very important in electricity. In order to see how it is used, we need a law in electricity known as

Gauss's law. Let us derive this law from the more familiar Coulomb's law (11.12). Coulomb's law (written this time in rationalized mks units) gives for the electric field at **r** due to a point charge q at the origin

$$(12.18) \qquad \mathbf{E} = \frac{q}{4\pi\epsilon r^2}\, \mathbf{e}_r.$$

(ϵ is the dielectric constant, and $1/4\pi\epsilon = 9 \cdot 10^9$ in a vacuum in mks

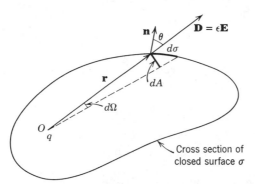

Figure 12.6

units.) The electric displacement **D** is defined by $\mathbf{D} = \epsilon \mathbf{E}$; then

$$(12.19) \qquad \mathbf{D} = \frac{q}{4\pi r^2}\, \mathbf{e}_r.$$

Let σ be a closed surface surrounding the point charge q at the origin; let $d\sigma$ be an element of area of the surface at the point **r**, and let **n** be a unit normal to $d\sigma$ (Figs. 12.3 and 12.6). Also (Fig. 12.6) let dA be the projection of $d\sigma$ onto a sphere of radius r and center at O and let $d\Omega$ be the solid angle subtended by $d\sigma$ (and dA) at O. Then by definition of solid angle

$$(12.20) \qquad d\Omega = \frac{1}{r^2}\, dA.$$

From Fig. 12.6 and equations (12.19) and (12.20), we get

$$(12.21) \quad \mathbf{D} \cdot \mathbf{n}\, d\sigma = D \cos \theta\, d\sigma = D\, dA = \frac{q}{4\pi r^2} \cdot r^2\, d\Omega = \frac{1}{4\pi} q\, d\Omega.$$

We want to find the surface integral of $\mathbf{D} \cdot \mathbf{n}\, d\sigma$ over the closed surface σ; by (12.21) this is

$$(12.22) \quad \oint_{\substack{\text{closed surface } \sigma}} \mathbf{D} \cdot \mathbf{n}\, d\sigma = \frac{q}{4\pi} \int_{\substack{\text{total solid angle}}} d\Omega = \frac{q}{4\pi} \cdot 4\pi = q \qquad (q \text{ inside } \sigma).$$

This is a simple case of Gauss's law when we have only one point charge q; for most purposes we shall want Gauss's law in the forms (12.23) or (12.24) below. Before we derive these, we should note carefully that in (12.22) the charge q is *inside* the closed surface σ. If we repeat the derivation of (12.22) for a point charge q outside the surface (Problem 71), we find that in this case

$$\oint_{\text{closed } \sigma} \mathbf{D} \cdot \mathbf{n} \, d\sigma = 0.$$

Next suppose there are several charges q_i inside the closed surface. For each q_i and the $\mathbf{D}_i$ corresponding to it, we could write an equation like (12.22). But the total electric displacement vector $\mathbf{D}$ at a point due to all the q_i is the vector sum of the vectors $\mathbf{D}_i$. Thus we have

$$\oint_{\text{closed surface } \sigma} \mathbf{D} \cdot \mathbf{n} \, d\sigma = \sum_i \oint_{\text{closed surface } \sigma} \mathbf{D}_i \cdot \mathbf{n} \, d\sigma = \sum q_i.$$

Therefore for any charge distribution inside a closed surface

$$(12.23) \quad \oint_{\text{closed surface}} \mathbf{D} \cdot \mathbf{n} \, d\sigma = \text{total charge inside the closed surface.}$$

If, instead of isolated charges, we have a charge distribution with charge density ρ (which may vary from point to point), then the total charge is $\int \rho \, d\tau$, so

$$(12.24) \quad \oint_{\text{closed surface } \sigma} \mathbf{D} \cdot \mathbf{n} \, d\sigma = \int_{\text{volume bounded by } \sigma} \rho \, d\tau.$$

Since (by Problem 71) charges outside the closed surface σ do not contribute to the integral, (12.23) and (12.24) are correct if $\mathbf{D}$ is the total electric displacement due to all charges inside and outside the surface. The total charge on the right-hand side of these equations is, however, just the charge inside the surface σ. Either (12.23) or (12.24) is called Gauss's law.

We now want to see the use of the divergence theorem in connection with Gauss's law. By the divergence theorem, the surface integral on the left-hand side of (12.23) or (12.24) is equal to

$$\int_{\text{volume bounded by } \sigma} \nabla \cdot \mathbf{D} \, d\tau.$$

Then (12.24) can be written as

$$\int \nabla \cdot \mathbf{D} \, d\tau = \int \rho \, d\tau.$$

Since this is true for *every* volume, we must have $\nabla \cdot \mathbf{D} = \rho$; this is one of the Maxwell equations in electricity. What we have done is to start by assuming Coulomb's law; we have derived Gauss's law from it, and then by use of the divergence theorem, we have derived the Maxwell equation $\nabla \cdot \mathbf{D} = \rho$. From a more sophisticated viewpoint, we might take the Maxwell equation as one of our basic assumptions in electricity. We could then use the divergence theorem to obtain Gauss's law:

$$(12.25) \quad \oint_{\text{closed surface } \sigma} \mathbf{D} \cdot \mathbf{n} \, d\sigma = \int_{\text{volume } \tau \text{ inside } \sigma} \nabla \cdot \mathbf{D} \, d\tau = \int_{\text{volume } \tau} \rho \, d\tau = \text{total charge inclosed by } \sigma.$$

From Gauss's law we could then derive Coulomb's law (Problem 71): more generally we can often use Gauss's law to obtain the electric field produced by a given charge distribution as in the following example.

Example. Find **E** just above a very large conducting plate carrying a surface charge of C coulombs per square meter on each surface.

The electric field inside a conductor is zero when we are considering an electrostatic problem (otherwise current would flow). From the sym-

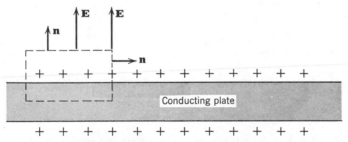

Figure 12.7   Edge view of a metal plate.

metry of the problem (all horizontal directions are equivalent), we can say that **E** (and **D**) must be vertical as shown in Fig. 12.7. We now find $\oint \mathbf{D} \cdot \mathbf{n} \, d\sigma$ over the box whose cross section is shown by the dotted lines. The integral over the bottom surface is zero since $\mathbf{D} = 0$ inside the conductor. The integral over the vertical sides is zero because **D** is perpendicular to **n** there. On the top surface $\mathbf{D} \cdot \mathbf{n} = |\mathbf{D}|$ and $\int \mathbf{D} \cdot \mathbf{n} \, d\sigma = |\mathbf{D}| \cdot (\text{surface area})$. By (12.25) this is equal to the charge inclosed by the box, which is $C \cdot (\text{surface area})$. Thus we have $|\mathbf{D}| \cdot (\text{surface area}) = C \cdot (\text{surface area})$, or $|\mathbf{D}| = C$ and $|\mathbf{E}| = C/\epsilon$.

13. THE CURL AND STOKES' THEOREM

We have already defined curl $\mathbf{V} = \nabla \times \mathbf{V}$ [see (10.3)] and have considered one application of the curl, namely, to determine whether or not a line integral between two points is independent of the path of integration (Section 11). Here is another application of the curl. Suppose a rigid body is rotating with constant angular velocity $\boldsymbol{\omega}$; this means that $|\boldsymbol{\omega}|$ is the magnitude of the angular velocity and $\boldsymbol{\omega}$ is a vector along the axis of rotation (see Fig. 4.10). Then we showed in Section 4 that the velocity $\mathbf{v}$ of a particle in the rigid body is $\mathbf{v} = \boldsymbol{\omega} \times \mathbf{r}$, where $\mathbf{r}$ is a radius vector from a point on the rotation axis to the particle. Let us calculate $\nabla \times \mathbf{v} = \nabla \times (\boldsymbol{\omega} \times \mathbf{r})$; we can evaluate this by the method described in Section 10. We use the formula for the triple vector product $\mathbf{A} \times (\mathbf{B} \times \mathbf{C}) = (\mathbf{A} \cdot \mathbf{C})\mathbf{B} - (\mathbf{A} \cdot \mathbf{B})\mathbf{C}$, being careful to remember that ∇ is not an ordinary vector—it has both vector and differential-operator properties, and so must be written before variables that it differentiates. Then

(13.1) $$\nabla \times (\boldsymbol{\omega} \times \mathbf{r}) = (\nabla \cdot \mathbf{r})\boldsymbol{\omega} - (\boldsymbol{\omega} \cdot \nabla)\mathbf{r}.$$

Since $\boldsymbol{\omega}$ is constant, the first term of (13.1) means

(13.2) $$\boldsymbol{\omega}(\nabla \cdot \mathbf{r}) = \boldsymbol{\omega}\left(\frac{\partial x}{\partial x} + \frac{\partial y}{\partial y} + \frac{\partial z}{\partial z}\right) = 3\boldsymbol{\omega}.$$

In the second term of (13.1) we intentionally wrote $\boldsymbol{\omega} \cdot \nabla$ instead of $\nabla \cdot \boldsymbol{\omega}$ since $\boldsymbol{\omega}$ is constant, and ∇ operates only on $\mathbf{r}$; this term means

$$\left(\omega_x \frac{\partial}{\partial x} + \omega_y \frac{\partial}{\partial y} + \omega_z \frac{\partial}{\partial z}\right)(\mathbf{i}x + \mathbf{j}y + \mathbf{k}z) = \mathbf{i}\omega_x + \mathbf{j}\omega_y + \mathbf{k}\omega_z = \boldsymbol{\omega}$$

since $\partial y/\partial x = \partial z/\partial x = 0$, etc. Then

(13.3) $$\nabla \times \mathbf{v} = \nabla \times (\boldsymbol{\omega} \times \mathbf{r}) = 2\boldsymbol{\omega} \qquad \text{or} \quad \boldsymbol{\omega} = \tfrac{1}{2}(\nabla \times \mathbf{v}).$$

This result gives a clue as to the name curl $\mathbf{v}$ (or rotation $\mathbf{v}$ or rot $\mathbf{v}$ as it is sometimes called). For this simple case curl $\mathbf{v}$ gave the angular velocity of rotation. In a more complicated case such as flow of fluid, the value of curl $\mathbf{v}$ at a point is a measure of the angular velocity of the fluid in the neighborhood of the point. When $\nabla \times \mathbf{v} = 0$ everywhere in some region, the velocity field $\mathbf{v}$ is called *irrotational* in that region. Notice that this is the same mathematical condition as for a force $\mathbf{F}$ to be *conservative*.

Consider a vector field $\mathbf{V}$ (for example, $\mathbf{V} = \mathbf{v}\rho$ for flow of water, or $\mathbf{V} = $ force $\mathbf{F}$). We define the *circulation* as the line integral $\oint \mathbf{V} \cdot d\mathbf{r}$ around a closed plane curve. If $\mathbf{V}$ is a force $\mathbf{F}$, then this integral is equal to the work done by the force. For flow of water, we can get a physical picture of the meaning of the circulation in the following way. Think of placing a tiny paddle-wheel probe (Fig. 13.1c) in any of the flow patterns pictured in Fig. 13.1. If the velocity of the fluid is greater on one side of the wheel than on the other, for example, as in (c), then the wheel will turn. Suppose we calculate the circulation $\oint \mathbf{V} \cdot d\mathbf{r}$ around the axis of the paddle wheel along a closed curve in a plane perpendicular to the axis (plane of the paper in Fig. 13.1). If $\mathbf{V} = v\rho$ is larger on one side of the wheel than the other, then the circulation is different from zero, but if [as in (b)] $\mathbf{V}$

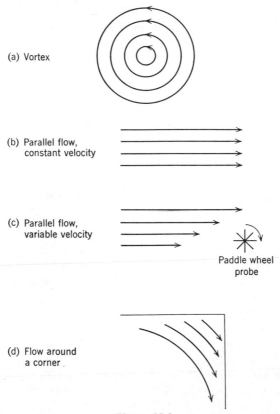

(a) Vortex

(b) Parallel flow,
    constant velocity

(c) Parallel flow,
    variable velocity

Paddle wheel
probe

(d) Flow around
    a corner

Figure 13.1

is the same on both sides, then the circulation is zero. We shall show that the component of curl $\mathbf{V}$ along the axis of the paddle wheel equals

$$(13.4) \qquad \lim_{d\sigma \to 0} \frac{1}{d\sigma} \oint \mathbf{V} \cdot d\mathbf{r}$$

where $d\sigma$ is the area inclosed by the curve along which we calculate the circulation. The paddle wheel then could be thought of as measuring curl $\mathbf{V}$; if it does not rotate, curl $\mathbf{V} = 0$; if it does, then curl $\mathbf{V} \neq 0$. In (a), curl $\mathbf{V} \neq 0$ at the center of the vortex. In (b), curl $\mathbf{V} = 0$. In (c), curl $\mathbf{V} \neq 0$ in spite of the fact that the flow lines are parallel. In (d), it is possible to have curl $\mathbf{V} = 0$ even though the stream lines go around a corner; in fact, for the flow of water around a corner, curl $\mathbf{V} = 0$. What you should realize is that the value of curl $\mathbf{V}$ at a point depends upon the circulation in the neighborhood of the point and not on the overall flow pattern.

We want to show the relation between the circulation $\oint \mathbf{V} \cdot d\mathbf{r}$ and curl $\mathbf{V}$ for a given vector field $\mathbf{V}$. We shall assume that the components of

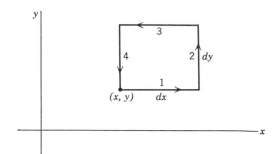

Figure 13.2

$\mathbf{V}$ have continuous partial derivatives; curl $\mathbf{V}$ is then continuous. Given a point and a direction, let us choose coordinate axes with the point in the (x, y) plane and the z-axis parallel to the given direction. The given point is then (x, y) in Fig. 13.2. Let us calculate the circulation $\oint \mathbf{V} \cdot d\mathbf{r}$ around the sides of the area element shown in Fig. 13.2. In the (x, y) plane we have $\mathbf{V} \cdot d\mathbf{r} = V_x \, dx + V_y \, dy$. Along sides 1 and 3 in Fig. 13.2, $dy = 0$, so $\mathbf{V} \cdot d\mathbf{r} = V_x \, dx$; similarly, along sides 2 and 4, $dx = 0$, so $\mathbf{V} \cdot d\mathbf{r} = V_y \, dy$. We consider first $\int \mathbf{V} \cdot d\mathbf{r}$ along sides 2 and 4, following the arrows shown in Fig. 13.2. We get

$$(13.5) \quad \int_{\substack{\text{sides} \\ \text{2 and 4}}} \mathbf{V} \cdot d\mathbf{r} = \int_y^{y+dy} (V_y \text{ on side 2}) \, dy + \int_{y+dy}^{y} (V_y \text{ on side 4}) \, dy$$

$$= \int_y^{y+dy} (V_y \text{ on side 2}) \, dy - \int_y^{y+dy} (V_y \text{ on side 4}) \, dy$$

$$= \int_y^{y+dy} \Delta V_y \, dy,$$

where $\Delta V_y = (V_y \text{ on side 2}) - (V_y \text{ on side 4})$ means the difference between the values of V_y at points on sides 2 and 4 directly opposite each other, that is, for the same y. Since V_y has continuous derivatives, we can approximate ΔV_y by dV_y; for constant y, we have

$$(13.6) \qquad dV_y = \frac{\partial V_y}{\partial x}\, dx.$$

[The derivative $\partial V_y/\partial x$ is evaluated at (x, y). More exactly, (13.6) is $dV_y = (\partial V_y/\partial x + \epsilon)\, dx$, where $\epsilon \to 0$ as $dx \to 0$; it is customary to express this by saying that (13.6) is correct "up to infinitesimals of higher order."] Substituting dV_y in (13.6) for ΔV_y in (13.5), we have

$$(13.7) \qquad \int_{\substack{\text{sides} \\ \text{2 and 4}}} \mathbf{V} \cdot d\mathbf{r} = \int_{y}^{y+dy} \left(\frac{\partial V_y}{\partial x}\, dx \right) dy = \frac{\partial V_y}{\partial x}\, dx\, dy.$$

In the last step of (13.7), we have used the mean value theorem (see Chapter 4, Section 3, Fig. 3.3); this means that $\partial V_y/\partial x$ in the last step is evaluated somewhere between (x, y) and $(x, y + dy)$. Less mathematically we could say that the value of an integral from y to $y + dy$ is practically equal to dy times the value of the integrand.

Following through these same details for sides 1 and 3, we would find (Problem 73)

$$(13.8) \qquad \int_{\substack{\text{sides} \\ \text{1 and 3}}} \mathbf{V} \cdot d\mathbf{r} = - \frac{\partial V_x}{\partial y}\, dx\, dy.$$

The integral around the four sides is then

$$(13.9) \qquad \oint \mathbf{V} \cdot d\mathbf{r} = \left(\frac{\partial V_y}{\partial x} - \frac{\partial V_x}{\partial y} \right) dx\, dy.$$

(Note the symbol $\oint$ indicating a line integral around a *closed* path.) The right-hand side of (13.9) is the z-component of curl $\mathbf{V}$ times $dx\, dy$; since $\mathbf{k}$ is a unit vector in the z direction, we can write

$$\frac{\partial V_y}{\partial x} - \frac{\partial V_x}{\partial y} = (\nabla \times \mathbf{V}) \cdot \mathbf{k},$$

$$(13.10) \qquad \oint_{\text{around } d\sigma} \mathbf{V} \cdot d\mathbf{r} = (\nabla \times \mathbf{V}) \cdot \mathbf{k}\, d\sigma,$$

where $d\sigma = dx\, dy$ is the area element in Fig. 13.2. Recall that we chose our coordinate system to make the z-axis parallel to a given direction. Since the coordinate system may be chosen so that *any* given direction $\mathbf{n}$ is the direction $\mathbf{k}$, we can write (13.10) as

$$(13.11) \qquad \oint_{\text{around } d\sigma} \mathbf{V} \cdot d\mathbf{r} = (\nabla \times \mathbf{V}) \cdot \mathbf{n}\, d\sigma.$$

This equation relates the component of curl $\mathbf{V}$ in the direction $\mathbf{n}$, to the circulation in a plane perpendicular to $\mathbf{n}$.

Equation (13.11) is approximate [because of the approximation in (13.6) and because the partial derivatives in curl $\mathbf{V}$ are not evaluated at (x, y) but at nearby points as in (13.7)]. However, if we divide (13.11) by $d\sigma$ and take the limit as $d\sigma \to 0$, we have an exact equation

$$(13.12) \qquad (\nabla \times \mathbf{V}) \cdot \mathbf{n} = \lim_{d\sigma \to 0} \frac{1}{d\sigma} \oint_{\text{around } d\sigma} \mathbf{V} \cdot d\mathbf{r}.$$

This equation can be used as a definition of curl $\mathbf{V}$; then the discussion above shows that [see equation (13.10)] the components of curl $\mathbf{V}$ are those given in our previous definition (10.3).

In evaluating the line integral we must go around the area element $d\sigma$ in the direction indicated by $\mathbf{n}$ and the right-hand rule; that is, if the thumb of your right hand points in the direction $\mathbf{n}$, your fingers curve in the direction you must go around the boundary of $d\sigma$ in evaluating the line integral. (See Fig. 13.2 with $\mathbf{n} = \mathbf{k}$.)

Proof of Stokes' theorem (13.14). This theorem relates an integral over an open surface to the line integral around the curve bounding the surface (Fig. 13.3). A butterfly net is a good example of what we are talking about; the net is the surface and the sup-porting rim is the curve bounding the sur-face. The surfaces we consider here (and which arise in applications) will be sur-faces which could be obtained by deform-ing a hemisphere (or the butterfly net of Fig. 13.3). In particular, the surfaces we consider must be *two*-sided. You can easily construct a *one*-sided surface by taking a long strip of paper, giving it a half twist, and joining the ends (Fig. 13.4).

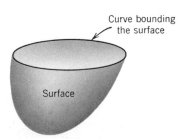

Curve bounding the surface

Surface

Figure 13.3

A belt of this shape is sometimes used for driving machinery. This surface is called a Moebius strip, and you can verify that it has only one side by tracing your finger around it or imagining trying to paint one side. Stokes' theorem does not apply to such surfaces because we cannot define the sense of the normal vector $\mathbf{n}$ to such a surface. Notice that we also rule out surfaces (such as a cylinder with two open ends) which have more than one bounding curve. We require the bounding curve to be simple (that is, it must not cross itself) and closed.

Consider the kind of surface we have described and imagine it divided into area elements $d\sigma$ by a network of curves as in Fig. 13.5. Draw a

Figure 13.4

unit vector **n** perpendicular to each area element; **n**, of course, varies from element to element. Equation (13.11) holds for each element; if we add all such equations together for all the area elements of the whole surface area, we get

$$(13.13) \qquad \sum_{\text{all } d\sigma} \oint \mathbf{V} \cdot d\mathbf{r} = \sum_{\text{all } d\sigma} (\boldsymbol{\nabla} \times \mathbf{V}) \cdot \mathbf{n} \, d\sigma.$$

From Fig. 13.5 we see that all the interior line integrals cancel because along a border between two $d\sigma$'s the two integrals are in opposite directions. Then the left side of (13.13) becomes simply the line integral around the outside curve bounding the surface. The sum on the right approaches a surface integral as $d\sigma \to 0$, namely

$$\int_{\text{surface } \sigma} (\boldsymbol{\nabla} \times \mathbf{V}) \cdot \mathbf{n} \, d\sigma.$$

Thus we have Stokes' theorem:

$$(13.14) \qquad \oint_{\substack{\text{curve} \\ \text{bounding } \sigma}} \mathbf{V} \cdot d\mathbf{r} = \int_{\text{surface } \sigma} (\boldsymbol{\nabla} \times \mathbf{V}) \cdot \mathbf{n} \, d\sigma.$$

You should have it clearly in mind that this is for an open surface bounded by a simple closed curve. Recall the example of a butterfly net. Notice that Stokes' theorem says that the line integral $\oint \mathbf{V} \cdot d\mathbf{r}$ is equal to the

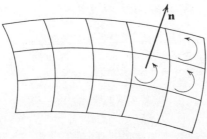

Figure 13.5

surface integral of $(\nabla \times \mathbf{V}) \cdot \mathbf{n}$ over *any* surface of which the curve is a boundary; in other words, you don't change the value of the integral by deforming the butterfly net!

Example 1. Given $\mathbf{V} = 4y\mathbf{i} + x\mathbf{j} + 2z\mathbf{k}$, find $\int (\nabla \times \mathbf{V}) \cdot \mathbf{n}\, d\sigma$ over the hemisphere $x^2 + y^2 + z^2 = a^2$, $z \geq 0$.

Using (10.3), we find that $\nabla \times \mathbf{V} = -3\mathbf{k}$. There are several ways we could do the problem: (a) integrate the expression as it stands; (b) use Stokes' theorem and evaluate $\oint \mathbf{V} \cdot d\mathbf{r}$ around the circle $x^2 + y^2 = a^2$ in the (x, y) plane; (c) use Stokes' theorem to say that the integral is the same over *any* surface bounded by this circle, for example, the plane area inside the circle! Since this plane area is in the (x, y) plane, we have

$$\mathbf{n} = \mathbf{k}, \qquad (\nabla \times \mathbf{V}) \cdot \mathbf{n} = -3\mathbf{k} \cdot \mathbf{k} = -3,$$

so the integral is

$$-3 \int d\sigma = -3 \cdot \pi a^2 = -3\pi a^2.$$

This is the easiest way to do the problem; however, for this simple case it is not too hard by the other methods. We shall leave (b) for you to do and do (a). Since the surface is a sphere with center at the origin, $\mathbf{r}$ is normal to it (but for any surface we could get the normal from the gradient). Then on the surface

$$\mathbf{n} = \frac{\mathbf{r}}{|\mathbf{r}|} = \frac{\mathbf{r}}{a} = \frac{\mathbf{i}x + \mathbf{j}y + \mathbf{k}z}{a},$$

$$(\nabla \times \mathbf{V}) \cdot \mathbf{n} = -3\mathbf{k} \cdot \frac{\mathbf{r}}{a} = -3\frac{z}{a}.$$

We want to evaluate $\int -3(z/a)\, d\sigma$ over the hemisphere. In spherical coordinates (see Chapter 4, Section 14) we have

$$z = r \cos \theta,$$

$$d\sigma = r^2 \sin \theta\, d\theta\, d\phi.$$

For our surface $r = a$. Then the integral is

$$\int_{\phi=0}^{2\pi} \int_{\theta=0}^{\pi/2} -3 \frac{a \cos \theta}{a} a^2 \sin \theta\, d\theta\, d\phi = -3a^2 \int_0^{2\pi} d\phi \int_0^{\pi/2} \sin \theta \cos \theta\, d\theta$$

$$= -3a^2 \cdot 2\pi \cdot \tfrac{1}{2} = -3\pi a^2$$

(as before).

Ampère's law. Stokes' theorem is of interest in the theory of electricity and magnetism. (Compare the use of the divergence theorem in connection

with Gauss's law in Section 12.) Ampère's circuital
law (in mks units) says that

$$\oint_C \mathbf{H} \cdot d\mathbf{r} = I,$$

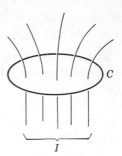

where **H** is the magnetic intensity, C is a closed
curve, and I is the current "linking" C, that is, crossing any surface area bounded by C. The surface area
and the curve C are related just as in Stokes'
theorem (butterfly net and its rim). If we think

Figure 13.6

of a bundle of wires linking a closed curve C
(Fig. 13.6) and then spreading out, we can see that the same current
crosses any surface whose bounding curve is C.

Just as Gauss's law is useful in computing electric fields, so Ampère's
law is useful in computing magnetic fields. Consider, for example, a

long straight wire carrying a current I; the magnetic
field intensity **H** at a distance r from the wire is tangent
to a circle of radius r in a plane perpendicular to the
wire (Fig. 13.7). By symmetry, $|\mathbf{H}|$ is the same at all
points of the circle. We can then find $|\mathbf{H}|$ by Ampère's
law. Taking C to be the circle of radius r, we have

$$\oint_C \mathbf{H} \cdot d\mathbf{r} = \int_0^{2\pi} |\mathbf{H}| \, r \, d\theta = |\mathbf{H}| \, r \cdot 2\pi = I$$

or

Figure 13.7

$$|\mathbf{H}| = \frac{I}{2\pi r}.$$

If, in Fig. 13.6, **J** is the current density (current crossing unit area
perpendicular to **J**), then $\mathbf{J} \cdot \mathbf{n} \, d\sigma$ is the current across a surface element
$d\sigma$ [compare (12.4)] and $\iint_\sigma \mathbf{J} \cdot \mathbf{n} \, d\sigma$, over any surface σ bounded by C,
is the total current I linking C. Then by Ampère's law

$$\oint_C \mathbf{H} \cdot d\mathbf{r} = \iint_\sigma \mathbf{J} \cdot \mathbf{n} \, d\sigma.$$

By Stokes' theorem

$$\oint_\sigma \mathbf{H} \cdot d\mathbf{r} = \iint_\sigma (\nabla \times \mathbf{H}) \cdot \mathbf{n} \, d\sigma,$$

so we have

$$\iint_\sigma (\nabla \times \mathbf{H}) \cdot \mathbf{n} \, d\sigma = \iint_\sigma \mathbf{J} \cdot \mathbf{n} \, d\sigma.$$

Since this is true for any σ, we have $\nabla \times \mathbf{H} = \mathbf{J}$, which is one of the

Maxwell equations. Alternatively, we could start with the Maxwell equation and apply Stokes' theorem to get Ampère's law.

Conservative fields. We next want to state carefully, and use Stokes' theorem to prove, under what conditions a given field **F** is conservative (see Section 11). First, recall that in physical problems we are often interested only in a particular region of space, and our formulas (say for **F**) may very well be correct *only* in that region. For example, the gravitational pull of the earth on an object is proportional to $1/r^2$ for $r \geq$ earth's radius R, but this is not a correct formula for $r < R$ (see Problem 68). The electric field in the region between the plates of a cylindrical capacitor is proportional to $1/r$ (Problem 67), but only *in this region* is this formula correct. We must, then, consider the *kind of region* in which a given field **F** is defined. Consider the shaded regions in Fig. 13.8. We say that a region is *simply-connected* if any simple closed curve in the region can be shrunk to a point without encountering any points not in the region. You can see in Fig. 13.8c that the dotted curve surrounds the "hole" and so cannot be shrunk to a point in the region; this region is then not simply-connected. The "hole" is sometimes only a single point, but this is enough to make the region *not* simply-connected. In three dimensions the region between cylindrical capacitor plates (infinitely long) is not simply-connected since a loop of string around the inner cylinder (see cross section, Fig. 13.8c) cannot be drawn up to a knot.

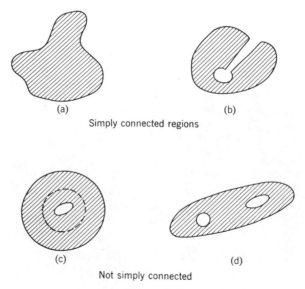

(a)   (b)

Simply connected regions

(c)   (d)

Not simply connected

Figure 13.8

Similarly, the interior of an inner tube is not simply-connected. The region between two concentric spheres *is* simply-connected, however. You should see this by realizing that you could pull up into a knot, a loop of string placed anywhere in this region. We shall now state and prove our theorem.

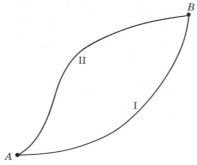

Figure 13.9

If the components of **F** have continuous first partial derivatives in a simply-connected region, then any one of the following five conditions implies all the others.

(a) curl **F** $= 0$ at every point of the region.

(b) $\oint \mathbf{F} \cdot d\mathbf{r} = 0$ around every simple closed curve in the region.

(c) **F** is conservative, that is, $\int_A^B \mathbf{F} \cdot d\mathbf{r}$ is independent of the path of integration from A to B. (The path must, of course, lie entirely in the region.)

(d) $\mathbf{F} \cdot d\mathbf{r}$ is an exact differential.

(e) $\mathbf{F} = \operatorname{grad} W$, W single-valued.

We shall show that each of these conditions implies the one following it. We can use Stokes' theorem to prove (b) assuming (a). First select any simple closed curve and let it be the bounding curve for the surface in Stokes' theorem. Since the region is simply-connected we can think of shrinking the curve to a point in the region; as it shrinks it traces out a surface which we use as the Stokes' theorem surface. Assuming (a), we have curl **F** $= 0$ at every point of the region and so also at every point of the surface. Thus the surface integral in Stokes' theorem is zero and therefore the line integral around the closed curve equals zero. This gives (b).

To show that (b) implies (c), consider any two paths I and II from A to B (Fig. 13.9). From (b) we have

$$\int_{\substack{A \\ \text{path I}}}^{B} \mathbf{F} \cdot d\mathbf{r} + \int_{\substack{B \\ \text{path II}}}^{A} \mathbf{F} \cdot d\mathbf{r} = 0.$$

Since an integral from A to B is the negative of an integral from B to A, we have

$$\int_{A}^{B} \mathbf{F} \cdot d\mathbf{r} - \int_{A}^{B} \mathbf{F} \cdot d\mathbf{r} = 0$$
$$\text{path I} \qquad \text{path II}$$

which is (c).

To show that (c) implies (d), select some reference point O in the region and calculate $\int \mathbf{F} \cdot d\mathbf{r}$ from the reference point to every other point of the region. For each point P we find a single value of the integral no matter what path of integration we choose from O to P. Let this value be the value of the function W at the point P. We then have a single-valued function such that

$$\int_{O \text{ to } P} \mathbf{F} \cdot d\mathbf{r} = W(P).$$

Then we have (since $\mathbf{F}$ is continuous)

$$dW = \mathbf{F} \cdot d\mathbf{r},$$

that is, $\mathbf{F} \cdot d\mathbf{r}$ is the differential of a single-valued function W. Since

$$dW = \frac{\partial W}{\partial x}\, dx + \frac{\partial W}{\partial y}\, dy + \frac{\partial W}{\partial z}\, dz = \nabla W \cdot d\mathbf{r} = \mathbf{F} \cdot d\mathbf{r}$$

for arbitrary $d\mathbf{r}$, we also have (e)

$$\mathbf{F} = \nabla W.$$

Finally (e) implies (a) as we proved in Section 11 (the continuity of the partial derivatives of the components of $\mathbf{F}$ makes the second-order mixed partial derivatives of W equal). Thus we have shown that any one of the five conditions (a) to (e) implies the others under the conditions of the theorem. It is worth observing carefully the requirement that $\mathbf{F}$ must have continuous partial derivatives in a simply-connected region. A simple example makes this clear. Look at Example 2 in Section 11; you can easily compute curl $\mathbf{F}$ and find that it is zero everywhere except at the origin (where it is undefined). You might then be tempted to assume that $\oint \mathbf{F} \cdot d\mathbf{r} = 0$ around any closed path. But we found that $\mathbf{F} \cdot d\mathbf{r} = d\theta$, and the integral of $d\theta$ along a circle with center at the origin is 2π. What is wrong? The trouble is that $\mathbf{F}$ does not have continuous partial derivatives at the origin, and any simply-connected region containing the circle of integration must contain the origin. Then curl $\mathbf{F}$ is not zero *at every point* inside the integration curve. Notice also that $\mathbf{F} \cdot d\mathbf{r} = d\theta$ is an exact differential, but not of a single-valued function; θ increases by 2π every time we go around the origin.

A vector field **V** is called *irrotational* (or *conservative* or *lamellar*) if curl **V** = 0; in this case **V** = grad W, where W (or its negative) is called the *scalar potential*. If div **V** = 0, the vector field is called *solenoidal*; in this case **V** = curl **A**, where **A** is a vector function called the *vector potential*. It is easy to prove (Problem 57d) that if **V** = ∇ × **A**, then div **V** = 0. It is also possible to construct an **A** (actually an infinite number of **A**'s) so that **V** = curl **A** if we know that ∇ · **V** = 0.

Example 2. Given $\mathbf{V} = \mathbf{i}(x^2 - yz) - \mathbf{j}2yz + \mathbf{k}(z^2 - 2zx)$, find **A** such that **V** = ∇ × **A**.
We find

$$\text{div } \mathbf{V} = \frac{\partial}{\partial x}(x^2 - yz) + \frac{\partial}{\partial y}(-2yz) + \frac{\partial}{\partial z}(z^2 - 2zx)$$

$$= 2x - 2z + 2z - 2x = 0.$$

Thus **V** is solenoidal and we proceed to find **A**. We are looking for an **A** such that

$$(13.15) \quad \mathbf{V} = \text{curl } \mathbf{A} = \begin{vmatrix} \mathbf{i} & \mathbf{j} & \mathbf{k} \\ \dfrac{\partial}{\partial x} & \dfrac{\partial}{\partial y} & \dfrac{\partial}{\partial z} \\ A_x & A_y & A_z \end{vmatrix} = \mathbf{l}(x^2 - yz) - \mathbf{j}2yz + \mathbf{k}(z^2 - 2zx).$$

There are many **A**'s satisfying this equation; we shall show first how to find one of them and then a general formula for all. It is possible to find an **A** with one zero component; let us take $A_x = 0$. Then the y- and z-components of curl **A** each involve just one component of **A**. From (13.15), the y- and z-components of curl **A** are

$$(13.16) \qquad -2yz = -\frac{\partial A_z}{\partial x}, \qquad z^2 - 2zx = \frac{\partial A_y}{\partial x}.$$

If we integrate (13.16) partially with respect to x (that is, with y and z constant), we find A_y and A_z except for possible functions of y and z which could be added without changing (13.16):

$$(13.17) \qquad \begin{aligned} A_y &= z^2x - zx^2 + f_1(y, z), \\ A_z &= 2xyz + f_2(y, z). \end{aligned}$$

Substituting (13.17) into the x-component of (13.15), we get

$$(13.18) \quad x^2 - yz = \frac{\partial A_z}{\partial y} - \frac{\partial A_y}{\partial z} = 2xz + \frac{\partial f_2}{\partial y} - 2zx + x^2 - \frac{\partial f_1}{\partial z}.$$

We now select f_1 and f_2 to satisfy (13.18). There is much leeway here and this can easily be done by inspection. We could take $f_2 = 0$, $f_1 = \frac{1}{2}yz^2$, or $f_1 = 0, f_2 = -\frac{1}{2}y^2z$, etc. Using the second choice, we have

(13.19) $$\mathbf{A} = \mathbf{j}(z^2x - zx^2) + \mathbf{k}(2xyz - \frac{1}{2}y^2z).$$

You may wonder why this process works and what div $\mathbf{V} = 0$ has to do with it. We can answer both these questions by following the above process with a general $\mathbf{V}$ rather than a special example. Given that div $\mathbf{V} = 0$, we want an $\mathbf{A}$ such that $\mathbf{V} = \text{curl } \mathbf{A}$. We try to find one with $A_x = 0$. Then the y- and z-components of $\mathbf{V} = \text{curl } \mathbf{A}$ are

(13.20) $$V_y = -\frac{\partial A_z}{\partial x}, \qquad V_z = \frac{\partial A_y}{\partial x}.$$

Then we have

(13.21) $$A_y = \int V_z \, dx + f(y, z), \qquad A_z = -\int V_y \, dx + g(y, z).$$

The x-component of $\mathbf{V} = \text{curl } \mathbf{A}$ is

(13.22) $$V_x = \frac{\partial A_z}{\partial y} - \frac{\partial A_y}{\partial z} = -\int \left(\frac{\partial V_y}{\partial y} + \frac{\partial V_z}{\partial z} \right) dx + h(y, z).$$

Since div $\mathbf{V} = 0$, we can put

(13.23) $$-\left(\frac{\partial V_y}{\partial y} + \frac{\partial V_z}{\partial z} \right) = \frac{\partial V_x}{\partial x}$$

into (13.22), getting

$$V_x = \int \frac{\partial V_x}{\partial x} \, dx + h(y, z).$$

This is correct with proper choice of $h(y, z)$.

When we know one $\mathbf{A}$, for which a given $\mathbf{V}$ is equal to curl $\mathbf{A}$, all others are of the form

(13.24) $$\mathbf{A} + \nabla u,$$

where u is any scalar function. For (see Problem 57b), $\nabla \times \nabla u = 0$, so the addition of ∇u to $\mathbf{A}$ does not affect $\mathbf{V}$. Also we can show that all possible $\mathbf{A}$'s are of the form (13.24). For if $\mathbf{V} = \text{curl } \mathbf{A}_1$ and $\mathbf{V} = \text{curl } \mathbf{A}_2$, then curl $(\mathbf{A}_1 - \mathbf{A}_2) = 0$, so $\mathbf{A}_1 - \mathbf{A}_2$ is the gradient of some scalar function.

A careful statement and proof that div $\mathbf{V} = 0$ is a necessary and sufficient condition for $\mathbf{V} = \text{curl } \mathbf{A}$ requires that $\mathbf{V}$ have continuous partial derivatives at every point of a region which is simply-connected in the sense that every closed surface (rather than closed curve) can be shrunk to a point in the region (for example, the region between two concentric spheres is not simply-connected in this sense).

14. SURFACE INTEGRALS

In the preceding chapter we found surface areas, moments of them, etc., for surfaces of revolution. We now want to consider a way of computing surface integrals in general whether the surface is a surface of revolution or not. Consider a part of a surface as in Fig. 14.1 and its projection in the (x, y) plane. We assume that any line parallel to the z-axis intersects the surface only once. If this is not true, we must work with part of the surface at a time, or project the surface onto a different

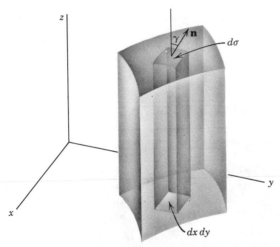

Figure 14.1

plane. For example, if the surface is closed, we could find the areas of the upper and lower parts separately. For a cylinder with elements parallel to the z-axis we could project the front and back parts separately onto the (y, z) plane.

Let $d\sigma$ (Fig. 14.1) be an element of surface area which projects into $dx\,dy$ in the (x, y) plane and let γ be the acute angle between $d\sigma$ (that is, the tangent plane at $d\sigma$) and the (x, y) plane. Then we have

(14.1) $dx\,dy = d\sigma \cos \gamma$ or $d\sigma = \sec \gamma\,dx\,dy.$

The surface area is then

(14.2) $$\iint d\sigma = \iint \sec \gamma\,dx\,dy,$$

where the limits on x and y must be such that we integrate over the projected area in the (x, y) plane. The angle between two planes is the same as the angle between the normals to the planes. If **n** is a unit vector normal to the surface at $d\sigma$, then γ is the angle between **n** and the z-axis, that is, between **n** and **k**, so $\cos \gamma = \mathbf{n} \cdot \mathbf{k}$. If the equation of the surface is $\phi(x, y, z) = \text{const.}$, we can find **n** by finding $\nabla\phi$. Then

(14.3)
$$\mathbf{n} = \frac{\nabla\phi}{|\nabla\phi|}, \quad \cos \gamma = |\mathbf{n} \cdot \mathbf{k}| = \frac{\left|\dfrac{\partial\phi}{\partial z}\right|}{|\nabla\phi|},$$

$$\sec \gamma = \frac{|\nabla\phi|}{\left|\dfrac{\partial\phi}{\partial z}\right|}.$$

Often the equation of a surface is given in the form $z = f(x, y)$. In this case $\phi(x, y, z) = z - f(x, y)$, so $\partial\phi/\partial z = 1$, and (14.3) simplifies to

(14.4)
$$\sec \gamma = \sqrt{(\partial f/\partial x)^2 + (\partial f/\partial y)^2 + 1}.$$

We then substitute (14.4) into (14.2) and integrate to find the area. To find centroids, moments of inertia, etc., we insert the proper factor into (14.2) as we have discussed in Chapter 4, Section 13.

Example. Find the area cut from the upper half of the sphere $x^2 + y^2 + z^2 = 1$ by the cylinder $x^2 + y^2 - y = 0$.

This is the same as the area on the sphere which projects into the circle $x^2 + y^2 - y = 0$ in the (x, y) plane. Thus we want to integrate (14.2) over the area of this circle. Figure 14.2 shows the circle of integration (shaded) and the equatorial circle of the sphere. We compute $\sec \gamma$ from

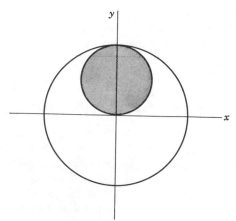

Figure 14.2

the equation of the sphere; we could use (14.4), but it is easier in this problem to use (14.3):

$$\phi = x^2 + y^2 + z^2,$$

$$\sec \gamma = \frac{|\nabla \phi|}{\left|\dfrac{\partial \phi}{\partial z}\right|} = \frac{1}{2z} \sqrt{(2x)^2 + (2y)^2 + (2z)^2} = \frac{1}{z} = \frac{1}{\sqrt{1 - x^2 - y^2}}.$$

We find the limits of integration from the equation of the circle of inter-section of the cylinder with the (x, y) plane (shaded area in Fig. 14.2). Because of symmetry we can integrate over the first-quadrant semicircle and double our result. Then the limits are

$$x \text{ from 0 to } \sqrt{y - y^2},$$
$$y \text{ from 0 to 1.}$$

The desired area is

(14.5)
$$2 \int_{y=0}^{1} \int_{x=0}^{\sqrt{y-y^2}} \frac{dx\, dy}{\sqrt{1 - x^2 - y^2}}.$$

Although this integral could be evaluated as it stands, it is easier to do it in polar coordinates. The equation of the circle of integration is $r = \sin \theta$; thus the limits are

$$r \text{ from 0 to } \sin \theta,$$
$$\theta \text{ from 0 to } \pi/2.$$

Then (14.5) becomes

$$2 \int_0^{\pi/2} \int_0^{\sin\theta} \frac{r\, dr\, d\theta}{\sqrt{1 - r^2}} = 2 \int_0^{\pi/2} -\sqrt{1 - r^2} \, \Big|_0^{\sin\theta} \, d\theta$$

$$= -2 \int_0^{\pi/2} (\sqrt{1 - \sin^2\theta} - 1)\, d\theta = 2 \int_0^{\pi/2} (1 - \cos\theta)\, d\theta$$

$$= 2(\theta - \sin\theta) \, \Big|_0^{\pi/2} = 2\left(\frac{\pi}{2} - 1\right) = \pi - 2.$$

REFERENCES

There are a number of books on vector analysis (for example, Spiegel), and most books on mathematics in physics and engineering discuss the subject. You will find some basic discussion, as well as applications, in physics textbooks on mechanics and electricity. Some suggested references are listed at the end of the book; those containing vector analysis have a [5] after the listing.

TABLE OF VECTOR IDENTITIES INVOLVING ∇

Notice carefully that ϕ and ψ are scalar functions; $\mathbf{U}$ and $\mathbf{V}$ are vector functions.

(a) $\nabla \cdot \nabla \phi = \text{div grad } \phi = \nabla^2 \phi = \text{Laplacian } \phi$

$$= \frac{\partial^2 \phi}{\partial x^2} + \frac{\partial^2 \phi}{\partial y^2} + \frac{\partial^2 \phi}{\partial z^2}$$

(b) $\nabla \times \nabla \phi = \text{curl grad } \phi = 0$

(c) $\nabla(\nabla \cdot \mathbf{V}) = \text{grad div } \mathbf{V}$

$$= \mathbf{i}\left(\frac{\partial^2 V_x}{\partial x^2} + \frac{\partial^2 V_y}{\partial x\, \partial y} + \frac{\partial^2 V_z}{\partial x\, \partial z}\right) + \mathbf{j}\left(\frac{\partial^2 V_x}{\partial x\, \partial y} + \frac{\partial^2 V_y}{\partial y^2} + \frac{\partial^2 V_z}{\partial y\, \partial z}\right)$$

$$+ \mathbf{k}\left(\frac{\partial^2 V_x}{\partial x\, \partial z} + \frac{\partial^2 V_y}{\partial y\, \partial z} + \frac{\partial^2 V_z}{\partial z^2}\right)$$

(d) $\nabla \cdot (\nabla \times \mathbf{V}) = \text{div curl } \mathbf{V} = 0$

(e) $\nabla \times (\nabla \times \mathbf{V}) = \text{curl curl } \mathbf{V} = \nabla(\nabla \cdot \mathbf{V}) - \nabla^2 \mathbf{V}$
$$= \text{grad div } \mathbf{V} - \text{Laplacian } \mathbf{V}$$

(f) $\nabla \cdot (\phi \mathbf{V}) = \phi(\nabla \cdot \mathbf{V}) + \mathbf{V} \cdot (\nabla \phi)$

(g) $\nabla \times (\phi \mathbf{V}) = \phi(\nabla \times \mathbf{V}) - \mathbf{V} \times (\nabla \phi)$

(h) $\nabla \cdot (\mathbf{U} \times \mathbf{V}) = \mathbf{V} \cdot (\nabla \times \mathbf{U}) - \mathbf{U} \cdot (\nabla \times \mathbf{V})$

(i) $\nabla \times (\mathbf{U} \times \mathbf{V}) = (\mathbf{V} \cdot \nabla)\mathbf{U} - (\mathbf{U} \cdot \nabla)\mathbf{V} - \mathbf{V}(\nabla \cdot \mathbf{U}) + \mathbf{U}(\nabla \cdot \mathbf{V})$

(j) $\nabla(\mathbf{U} \cdot \mathbf{V}) = \mathbf{U} \times (\nabla \times \mathbf{V}) + (\mathbf{U} \cdot \nabla)\mathbf{V} + \mathbf{V} \times (\nabla \times \mathbf{U}) + (\mathbf{V} \cdot \nabla)\mathbf{U}$

(k) $\nabla \cdot (\nabla \phi \times \nabla \psi) = 0$

PROBLEMS

1. Draw diagrams and prove (1.1).

2. Given the vectors making the given angles θ with the positive x-axis:

A of magnitude 5, $\theta = 45°$,
B of magnitude 3, $\theta = -30°$,
C of magnitude 7, $\theta = 120°$.

(a) Draw diagrams representing $2\mathbf{A}$, $\mathbf{A} - 2\mathbf{B}$, $\mathbf{C} - \mathbf{B}$, $\frac{2}{5}\mathbf{A} - \frac{1}{7}\mathbf{C}$.
(b) Draw diagrams to show that

$\mathbf{A} + \mathbf{B} = \mathbf{B} + \mathbf{A}$, $\mathbf{A} - (\mathbf{B} - \mathbf{C}) = (\mathbf{A} - \mathbf{B}) + \mathbf{C}$,
$(\mathbf{A} + \mathbf{B}) + \mathbf{C} = (\mathbf{A} + \mathbf{C}) + \mathbf{B}$, $(\mathbf{A} + \mathbf{B})_x = A_x + B_x$,
$(\mathbf{B} - \mathbf{C})_x = B_x - C_x$.

3. Use vectors to prove the following theorems from geometry:

   (a) The diagonals of a parallelogram bisect each other.

   (b) The median to the base of an isosceles triangle is perpendicular to the base.

   (c) The line segment joining the midpoints of two sides of any triangle is parallel to the third side and half its length.

   (d) The diagonals of a rhombus are perpendicular.

4. Let $A = 2i + 3j$ and $B = 4i - 5j$. Show graphically, and find algebraically, the vectors $-A$, $3B$, $A - B$, $B + 2A$, $\frac{1}{2}(A + B)$.

5. If $A + B = 4j - i$ and $A - B = i + 3j$, find A and B algebraically. Show by a diagram how to find A and B geometrically.

6. Let $3i - j + 4k$, $7j - 2k$, $i - 3j + k$ be three vectors with tails at the origin. Then their heads determine three points A, B, C in space which form a triangle. Find vectors representing the sides AB, BC, CA in that order and direction (for example, A to B, not B to A) and show that the sum of these vectors is zero.

7. Find the angle between the vectors $A = -2i + j - 2k$ and $B = 2i - 2j$.

8. If $A = 4i - 3k$ and $B = -2i + 2j - k$, find the scalar projection of A on B, the scalar projection of B on A, and the cosine of the angle between A and B.

9. Find the angles between (a) the space diagonals of a cube; (b) a space diagonal and an edge; (c) a space diagonal and a diagonal of a face.

10. Let $A = 2i - j + 2k$. (a) Find a *unit* vector in the same direction as A. *Hint:* Divide A by $|A|$. (b) Find a vector in the same direction as A but of magnitude 12. (c) Find a vector perpendicular to A. *Hint:* There are *many* such vectors; you are to find any one of them. (d) Find a unit vector perpendicular to A. See hint in (a).

11. Find a unit vector in the same direction as the vector $A = 4i - 2j + 4k$, and another unit vector in the same direction as $B = -4i + 3k$. Show that the vector sum of these unit vectors bisects the angle between A and B. *Hint:* Sketch the rhombus having the two unit vectors as adjacent sides.

12. Find three vectors (none of them parallel to a coordinate axis) which have lengths and directions such that they could be made into a right triangle.

13. Show that $2i - j + 4k$ and $5i + 2j - 2k$ are orthogonal (perpendicular). Find a third vector perpendicular to both.

14. Show that $B|A| + A|B|$ and $A|B| - B|A|$ are orthogonal.

15. Square $(A + B)$; interpret your result geometrically. *Hint:* Your answer is a law which you learned in trigonometry.

16. If $A = 2i - j - k$, $B = 2i - 3j + k$, $C = j + k$, find $(A \cdot B)C$, $A(B \cdot C)$, $(A \times B) \cdot C$, $A \cdot (B \times C)$, $(A \times B) \times C$, $A \times (B \times C)$.

17. If $A = 2i - 3j + k$ and $A \cdot B = 0$, does it follow that $B = 0$? (Either prove that it does or give a specific example to show that it doesn't.) Answer the same question if $A \times B = 0$. And again answer the same question if $A \cdot B = 0$ *and* $A \times B = 0$.

18. What is the value of $(\mathbf{A} \times \mathbf{B})^2 + (\mathbf{A} \cdot \mathbf{B})^2$?

19. There is a one-to-one correspondence between two-dimensional vectors and complex numbers. Show that the real and imaginary parts of the product $z_1 z_2^*$ (the star denotes complex conjugate) are respectively the scalar product and $\pm$ the magnitude of the vector product of the vectors corresponding to z_1 and z_2.

20. (a) Verify that the determinant in (4.20) is equal to the expression in the line above it.

(b) Verify (5.2).

(c) Two vectors **B** and **C** (not parallel) with tails at the same point determine a plane. Show that any vector **V** in this plane can be written as a linear combination of **B** and **C**, that is, $\mathbf{V} = a\mathbf{B} + b\mathbf{C}$, where a and b are constants. *Hints:* Method 1: Let the plane of **B**, **C**, and **V**, be the (x, y) plane; write all three vectors in terms of their components and show that the equations $\mathbf{V} = a\mathbf{B} + b\mathbf{C}$ always have exactly one solution for the constants a and b under the given conditions. See Chapter 3, Sections 6 and 7. Method 2: Take the cross product of **V** with **B** and with **C**.

21. Given $\mathbf{A} = \mathbf{i} + \mathbf{j} - 2\mathbf{k}$, $\mathbf{B} = 2\mathbf{i} - \mathbf{j} + 3\mathbf{k}$, $\mathbf{C} = \mathbf{j} - 5\mathbf{k}$:

(a) Find the work done by a force **B** acting on an object which undergoes a displacement **C**.

(b) Find the total work done by forces **A** and **B** if the object undergoes the displacement **C**. *Hint:* Can you add the two forces first?

(c) Let O be the tail of **B** and let **A** be a force acting at the head of **B**. Find the torque of **A** about O; about a line through O perpendicular to the plane of **A** and **B**; about a line through O parallel to **C**.

(d) Let **A** and **C** be drawn from a common origin and let **C** rotate about **A** with an angular velocity of 2 rad/sec. Find the velocity of the head of **C**.

(e) In (d) draw **B** with its tail at the head of **A**. If the figure is rotating as in (d), find the velocity of the head of **B**. With the same diagram, let **B** be a force; find the torque of **B** about the head of **C**, and about the line **C**.

22. Write out the twelve triple scalar products involving **A**, **B**, and **C** and verify the facts stated just above (5.3).

23. (a) A vector force with components $(1, 2, 3)$ acts at the point $(3, 2, 1)$. Find the vector torque about the origin due to this force and find the torque about each coordinate axis.

(b) The force $\mathbf{F} = 2\mathbf{i} - \mathbf{j} - 5\mathbf{k}$ acts at the point $(-5, 2, 1)$. Find the torque due to **F** about the origin and about the line $2x = -4y = -z$.

24. Prove that the triple scalar product of $(\mathbf{A} \times \mathbf{B})$, $(\mathbf{B} \times \mathbf{C})$, and $(\mathbf{C} \times \mathbf{A})$, is equal to the square of the triple scalar product of **A**, **B**, and **C**. *Hint:* First let $(\mathbf{B} \times \mathbf{C}) = \mathbf{D}$, and evaluate $(\mathbf{A} \times \mathbf{B}) \times \mathbf{D}$.

25. In the figure $\mathbf{u}_1$ is a unit vector in the direction of an incident ray of light, and $\mathbf{u}_3$ and $\mathbf{u}_2$ are unit vectors in the directions of the reflected and refracted rays. If **u** is a unit vector normal to the surface AB, the laws of optics say that $\theta_1 = \theta_3$ and $n_1 \sin \theta_1 = n_2 \sin \theta_2$, where n_1 and n_2 are constants (indices of refraction). Write these laws in vector form (using dot or cross products).

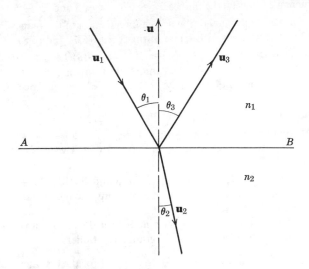

26. (a) Show that (6.6) is equivalent to (6.3). *Hint:* The z-components of all vectors are zero.

   (b) Show that the equations (6.8) are equivalent to (6.7).

27. In this problem, all lines are in the (x, y) plane.

   (a) Write the equation of the straight line through $(2, -3)$ with slope $\frac{3}{4}$, in the parametric form $\mathbf{r} = \mathbf{r}_0 + \mathbf{A}t$.

   (b) Find the slope of the line whose parametric equation is $\mathbf{r} = (\mathbf{i} - \mathbf{j}) + (2\mathbf{i} + 3\mathbf{j})t$.

   (c) Write, in parametric form [as in (a)], the equation of the straight line that joins $(1, -2)$ and $(3, 0)$.

   (d) Write, in parametric form, the equation of the straight line that is perpendicular to $\mathbf{r} = (2\mathbf{i} + 4\mathbf{j}) + (\mathbf{i} - 2\mathbf{j})t$ and goes through $(1, 0)$.

   (e) Write, in parametric form, the equation of the y-axis.

28. Write, in the parametric form (6.8) *and* in the form (6.7), the equations of the straight lines that satisfy each of the following sets of conditions.

   (a) The line joins $(2, 1, 2)$ and $(0, 3, -1)$.

   (b) The line passes through $(1, 2, 3)$ and is parallel to the line $\mathbf{r} = (\mathbf{i} - \mathbf{j} + \mathbf{k}) + (3\mathbf{i} - 2\mathbf{j} + \mathbf{k})t$.

   (c) The line passes through $(0, 1, 0)$ and is perpendicular to the plane $2x - 3y + z = 5$.

   (d) The line passes through $(2, 0, -1)$ and is perpendicular to both of the lines $(x - 1)/2 = (y + 3)/1 = (z - 4)/(-3)$ and $\mathbf{r} = (2\mathbf{i} - \mathbf{j}) + (\mathbf{i} - 3\mathbf{k})t$.

29. Find a unit vector perpendicular to a plane containing the two vectors $\mathbf{i} + 3\mathbf{j} - \mathbf{k}$ and $2\mathbf{i} + \mathbf{j} + \mathbf{k}$.

30. The three points $(0, 1, 1)$, $(2, 1, 3)$, and $(4, 2, 1)$ determine a plane. Find a vector perpendicular to the plane, and find the equation of the plane.

31. Find the angle between the planes $2x + y - 2z = 3$ and $3x - 6y - 2z = 4$.

32. Find a unit vector parallel to the line of intersection of the planes in Problem 31. Write the equations of the line in the forms (6.7) and (6.8).

33. Determine whether the lines $(x - 1)/2 = (y + 3)/1 = (z - 4)/(-3)$ and $(x + 3)/4 = (y + 4)/1 = (8 - z)/4$ intersect. Two suggestions: (1) Can you find the intersection point, if any? (2) Consider the distance between the lines.

34. Find the angle between the lines in Problem 33.

35. Given the planes $2x - y + 3z = 4$, $x + 2y - z = 5$, $-x + 7y + 3z = 27$:
(a) Are any two of them orthogonal? (b) Do any two of them meet at an angle of $60°$?

36. (a) Given the point $(2, 1)$ in the (x, y) plane and the line $3x + 2y = 4$, find the distance from the point to the line by using the method of the text (not the analytic geometry formula).

(b) Solve part (a) by writing a formula for the distance from $(2, 1)$ to (x, y) and minimizing the distance (use Lagrange multipliers).

(c) Derive the formula $D = \left| \dfrac{ax_0 + by_0 - c}{\sqrt{a^2 + b^2}} \right|$ for the distance from (x_0, y_0)

to $ax + by = c$ by the methods suggested in parts (a) and (b).

37. (a) Find the distance from the point $(7, -1, 1)$ to the plane $2x + y + 2z = 9$.

(b) Find the distance from the point $(2, 1, 3)$ to the plane $3x - y + z = 1$.

(c) Derive the formula $D = \dfrac{|ax_0 + by_0 + cz_0 - d|}{\sqrt{a^2 + b^2 + c^2}}$ for the distance from

(x_0, y_0, z_0) to $ax + by + cz = d$.

38. (a) Find the distance from the point $(2, 1, -3)$ to the line $\mathbf{r} = (\mathbf{i} + 2\mathbf{j}) + (2\mathbf{i} - \mathbf{j} - \mathbf{k})t$.

(b) Find the distance from the origin to the line of intersection of the planes $2x - y + 3z = 1$ and $x + y + z = 2$.

39. (a) Find the distance between the lines

$$\mathbf{r} = (2\mathbf{i} + 3\mathbf{j} - \mathbf{k}) + (\mathbf{i} + \mathbf{j} + \mathbf{k})t$$

and

$$\mathbf{r} = (\mathbf{i} + \mathbf{j} + \mathbf{k}) + (\mathbf{i} + 3\mathbf{j} + \mathbf{k})t.$$

(b) Find the distance between the line that joins $(0, 0, 0)$ to $(1, 2, -1)$, and the line that joins $(1, 1, 1)$ to $(2, 3, 4)$.

40. In Fig. 5.5, let $\mathbf{r}'$ be another vector from O to the line of F. Show that $\mathbf{r}' \times \mathbf{F} = \mathbf{r} \times \mathbf{F}$. *Hint:* $\mathbf{r} - \mathbf{r}'$ is a vector along the line of F and so is a scalar multiple of F. (The scalar has physical units of distance divided by force, but this fact is irrelevant for the vector proof.) Show also that moving the tail of $\mathbf{r}$ along $\mathbf{n}$ does not change $\mathbf{n} \cdot \mathbf{r} \times \mathbf{F}$. *Hint:* The triple scalar product is not changed by interchanging the dot and the cross.

41. (a) Verify equations (7.5) by writing out the components.

(b) Sketch a figure and verify equation (7.12).

42. A force $\mathbf{F} = 2\mathbf{i} - 3\mathbf{j} + \mathbf{k}$ acts at the point (1, 5, 2). Find the torque due to $\mathbf{F}$

(a) about the origin;

(b) about the y-axis;

(c) about the line $x/2 = y/1 = z/(-2)$.

43. Let the position vector (tail at the origin) of a moving particle be $\mathbf{r} = \mathbf{r}(t) = t^2\mathbf{i} - 2t\mathbf{j} + (t^2 + 2t)\mathbf{k}$, where t represents time.

(a) Show that the particle goes through the point (4, −4, 8). At what time does it do this?

(b) Find the velocity vector and the speed of the particle at time t; at the time when it passes through the point (4, −4, 8).

(c) Find the equations of the line tangent to the curve described by the particle and the plane normal to this curve, at the point (4, −4, 8).

44. (a) Let $\mathbf{r} = \mathbf{r}(t)$ be a vector whose *length* is always 1 (it may vary in direction). Prove that either $\mathbf{r}$ is a constant vector or $d\mathbf{r}/dt$ is perpendicular to $\mathbf{r}$. (*Hint:* Differentiate $\mathbf{r} \cdot \mathbf{r}$.)

(b) In polar coordinates, the position vector of a particle is $\mathbf{r} = r\mathbf{e}_r$. Using (7.13), find the velocity and acceleration of the particle.

45. A particle is traveling along the line $(x - 2)/2 = (y - 1)/(-3) = z - 1$. Write the equation of its path in the form $\mathbf{r} = \mathbf{r}_0 + \mathbf{A}t$. Find the distance of closest approach of the particle to the origin (that is, the distance from the origin to the line). If t represents time, show that the time of closest approach is $t = -(\mathbf{r}_0 \cdot \mathbf{A})/|\mathbf{A}|^2$. Use this value to check your answer for distance of closest approach.

46. Find the gradient of $w = x^2y^3z$ at (1, 2, −1).

47. Starting from the point (1, 1), in what direction does the function $\phi = x^2 - y^2 + 2xy$ *decrease* most rapidly?

48. (a) Find the derivative of $xy^2 + yz$ at (1, 1, 2) in the direction of the vector $2\mathbf{i} - \mathbf{j} + 2\mathbf{k}$.

(b) Find the derivative of $ze^x \cos y$ at $(1, 0, \pi/3)$ in the direction of the vector $\mathbf{i} + 2\mathbf{j}$.

49. (a) Find ∇r, where $r = \sqrt{x^2 + y^2}$, using (9.7) and also using (9.4). Show that your results are the same by using (7.11) and (7.12).

(b) Similarly, find ∇x in two ways.

50. Find the direction of the line normal to the surface $x^2y + y^2z + z^2x + 1 = 0$ at the point (1, 2, −1). Write the equations of the tangent plane and normal line at this point.

51. Given $\phi = x^2 - yz$ and the point $P(3, 4, 1)$, find

(a) $\nabla\phi$ at P;

(b) a unit vector normal to the surface $\phi = 5$ at P;

(c) a vector in the direction of most rapid increase of ϕ at P;

(d) the magnitude of the vector in (c);

(e) the derivative of ϕ at P in a direction parallel to the line

$$\mathbf{r} = \mathbf{i} - \mathbf{j} + 2\mathbf{k} + (6\mathbf{i} - \mathbf{j} - 4\mathbf{k})t.$$

52. Suppose that the temperature in the (x, y) plane is given by $T = xy - x$. Sketch a few isothermal curves, corresponding, for instance, to $T = 0, 1, 2$. Find the direction in which the temperature changes most rapidly with distance from the point $(1, 1)$, and the maximum rate of change. Find the directional derivative of T at $(1, 1)$ in the direction of the vector $3\mathbf{i} - 4\mathbf{j}$.

53. Find a vector normal to the surface $x^2 + y^2 - z = 0$ at the point $(3, 4, 25)$. Find the equations of the tangent plane and normal line to the surface at that point.

54. Show by the Lagrange multiplier method that the maximum value of $d\phi/ds$ is $|\nabla\phi|$. That is, maximize $d\phi/ds$ given by (9.3) subject to the condition $a^2 + b^2 + c^2 = 1$. You should get two values $(\pm)$ for the Lagrange multiplier λ, and two values (maximum and minimum) for $d\phi/ds$. Which is the maximum and which is the minimum?

55. Compute the divergence and the curl of each of the following vector fields.

  (a) $\mathbf{r} = x\mathbf{i} + y\mathbf{j} + z\mathbf{k}$ (b) $\mathbf{V} = y\mathbf{i} + z\mathbf{j} + x\mathbf{k}$
  (c) $\mathbf{V} = x^2\mathbf{i} + y^2\mathbf{j} + z^2\mathbf{k}$ (d) $\mathbf{V} = x^2y\mathbf{i} + y^2x\mathbf{j} + xyz\mathbf{k}$

56. Calculate the Laplacian ∇^2 of each of the following scalar fields.

  (a) $r = \sqrt{x^2 + y^2}$ (b) $\ln r$ (c) $\dfrac{1}{r}$

  (d) $R = \sqrt{x^2 + y^2 + z^2}$ (e) $\dfrac{1}{R}$

57. Verify formulas (b), (c), (d), (g), (h), (i), (j), (k) of the table of vector identities at the end of the chapter. *Hint* for (j): Start by expanding the two triple vector products on the right.

58. Which, if either, of the two force fields

$$\mathbf{F}_1 = -y\mathbf{i} + x\mathbf{j} + z\mathbf{k}, \qquad \mathbf{F}_2 = y\mathbf{i} + x\mathbf{j} + z\mathbf{k}$$

is conservative? Calculate for each field the work done in moving a particle around the circle $x = \cos t$, $y = \sin t$ in the (x, y) plane.

59. For the force field $\mathbf{F} = -y\mathbf{i} + x\mathbf{j} + z\mathbf{k}$ calculate the work done in moving a particle from $(1, 0, 0)$ to $(-1, 0, \pi)$
  (a) along the helix $x = \cos t$, $y = \sin t$, $z = t$;
  (b) along the straight line joining the points.
Do you expect your answers to be the same? Why or why not?

60. Evaluate the line integral $\int (x^2 - y^2)\, dx - 2xy\, dy$ along each of the following paths from $(0, 0)$ to $(1, 2)$.
  (a) $y = 2x^2$.
  (b) $x = t^2$, $y = 2t$.
  (c) $y = 0$ from $x = 0$ to $x = 2$; then along the straight line joining $(2, 0)$ to $(1, 2)$.

61. Evaluate the line integral $\oint (x + 2y)\, dx - 2x\, dy$ along each of the following closed paths, taken counterclockwise:

(a) the circle $x^2 + y^2 = 1$; (b) the square with corners at $(1, 1)$, $(-1, 1)$, $(-1, -1)$, $(1, -1)$; (c) the square with corners at $(0, 1)$, $(-1, 0)$, $(0, -1)$, $(1, 0)$.

62. For the force field $\mathbf{F} = (y + z)\mathbf{i} - (x + z)\mathbf{j} + (x + y)\mathbf{k}$ find the work done in moving a particle around each of the following closed curves:

(a) the circle $x^2 + y^2 = 1$ in the (x, y) plane, taken counterclockwise;

(b) the circle $x^2 + z^2 = 1$ in the (x, z) plane, taken counterclockwise;

(c) the curve starting from the origin and going successively along the x-axis to $(1, 0, 0)$, parallel to the z-axis to $(1, 0, 1)$, parallel to the (y, z) plane to $(1, 1, 1)$, and back to the origin along $x = y = z$;

(d) from the origin to $(0, 0, 2\pi)$ on the curve $x = 1 - \cos t$, $y = \sin t$, $z = t$, and back to the origin along the z-axis.

63. Evaluate the line integral $\int_C y^2\, dx + 2x\, dy + dz$, where C connects $(0, 0, 0)$ with $(1, 1, 1)$,

(a) along straight lines from $(0, 0, 0)$ to $(1, 0, 0)$ to $(1, 0, 1)$ to $(1, 1, 1)$;

(b) on the circle $x^2 + y^2 - 2y = 0$ to $(1, 1, 0)$ and then on a vertical line to $(1, 1, 1)$.

64. Given $\mathbf{V} = x^2\mathbf{i} + y^2\mathbf{j} + z^2\mathbf{k}$, integrate $\mathbf{V} \cdot \mathbf{n}\, d\sigma$ over the whole surface of the cube of side 1 with four of its vertices at $(0, 0, 0)$, $(0, 0, 1)$, $(0, 1, 0)$, $(1, 0, 0)$. Evaluate the same integral by means of the divergence theorem.

65. Show that the electric field $\mathbf{E}$ of a point charge [equation (11.12)] is conservative. Write ϕ in (11.14) in rectangular coordinates, and find $\mathbf{E} = -\nabla\phi$ using both rectangular coordinates and polar coordinates, (9.4) and (9.7). Verify that your results are equivalent to (11.12).

66. Verify that each of the following force fields is conservative. Then find, for each, a scalar potential ϕ such that $\mathbf{F} = -\nabla\phi$.

(a) $\mathbf{F} = \mathbf{i} - z\mathbf{j} - y\mathbf{k}$.

(b) $\mathbf{F} = (3x^2yz - 3y)\mathbf{i} + (x^3z - 3x)\mathbf{j} + (x^3y + 2z)\mathbf{k}$.

(c) $\mathbf{F} = -k\mathbf{r}$, $\mathbf{r} = i x + j y + k z$, $k = \text{const.}$

(d) $\mathbf{F} = y \sin 2x\, \mathbf{i} + \sin^2 x\, \mathbf{j}$.

67. A cylindrical capacitor consists of two long concentric metal cylinders. If there is a charge of k coulombs per meter on one cylinder and $-k$ coulombs per meter on the other, find the electric field $\mathbf{E}$ between the cylinders. *Hint:* Use Gauss's law and the method indicated in Fig. 12.7. What is $\mathbf{E}$ inside the inner cylinder? Outside the outer cylinder? (Again use Gauss's law.) Find, either by inspection or by direct integration, the potential ϕ such that $\mathbf{E} = -\nabla\phi$ for each of the three regions above. In each case $\mathbf{E}$ is not affected by adding an arbitrary constant to ϕ. Adjust the additive constant to make ϕ a continuous function for all space.

68. (a) For motion near the surface of the earth, we usually assume that the gravitational force on a mass m is

$$\mathbf{F} = -mg\mathbf{k},$$

but for motion involving an appreciable variation in distance r from the center of the earth, we must use

$$\mathbf{F} = -\frac{C}{r^2}\,\mathbf{e}_r = -\frac{C}{r^2}\frac{\mathbf{r}}{|\mathbf{r}|} = -\frac{C}{r^3}\,\mathbf{r},$$

where C is a constant. Show that both these $\mathbf{F}$'s are conservative, and find the potential for each.

(b) Consider a uniform distribution of total mass m' over a spherical shell of radius r'. The potential energy ϕ of a mass m in the gravitational field of the spherical shell is

$$\phi = \begin{cases} \text{const.} & \text{if } m \text{ is inside the spherical shell,} \\ -\dfrac{Cm'}{r} & \text{if } m \text{ is outside the spherical shell, where } r \text{ is the distance} \\ & \text{from the center of the sphere to } m, \text{ and } C \text{ is a constant.} \end{cases}$$

Find the potential and the force on a mass m inside and outside a *solid* sphere of radius R. If the sphere is the earth, evaluate the constants in terms of the acceleration of gravity g, to get

$$\mathbf{F} = -\frac{mgR^2}{r^2}\,\mathbf{e}_r \quad \text{and} \quad \phi = -\frac{mgR^2}{r}, \quad m \text{ outside the earth};$$

$$\mathbf{F} = -\frac{mgr}{R}\,\mathbf{e}_r \quad \text{and} \quad \phi = \frac{mg}{2R}(r^2 - 3R^2), \quad m \text{ inside the earth.}$$

Hint: To find the constants, recall that the magnitude of the force on m at the surface of the earth is mg.

69. Suppose the density ρ of a fluid varies from point to point as well as with time, that is, $\rho = \rho(x, y, z, t)$. Show that $d\rho/dt = \partial\rho/\partial t + \mathbf{v} \cdot \nabla\rho$. Combine this equation with (12.9) to get

$$\rho\nabla \cdot \mathbf{v} + \frac{d\rho}{dt} = 0.$$

(Physically, $d\rho/dt$ is the rate of change of density with time as we follow the fluid along a streamline; $\partial\rho/\partial t$ is the corresponding rate at a fixed point.) For a steady state (that is, time-independent), $\partial\rho/\partial t = 0$, but $d\rho/dt$ is not necessarily zero. Write your equation for this case and show that it agrees with (12.9).

70. If $\mathbf{F} = x\mathbf{i} + y\mathbf{j}$, calculate $\iint \mathbf{F} \cdot \mathbf{n}\, d\sigma$ over the part of the surface $z = 4 - x^2 - y^2$ that is above the (x, y) plane, by applying the divergence theorem to the volume bounded by the surface and the piece that it cuts out of the (x, y) plane. *Hint:* What is $\mathbf{F} \cdot \mathbf{n}$ on the (x, y) plane?

71. (a) Draw a figure similar to Fig. 12.6 but with q outside the surface. A vector (like $\mathbf{r}$ in the figure) from q to the surface now intersects it twice, and for each solid angle $d\Omega$ there are two $d\sigma$'s, one where $\mathbf{r}$ enters and one where it leaves the surface. Show that $\mathbf{D} \cdot \mathbf{n}\, d\sigma$ is given by (12.21) for the $d\sigma$ where $\mathbf{r}$ leaves the surface and the negative of (12.21) for the $d\sigma$ where $\mathbf{r}$

enters the surface. Hence show that the total $\oint \mathbf{D} \cdot \mathbf{n}\, d\sigma$ over the closed surface is zero.

(b) Obtain Coulomb's law from Gauss's law by considering a spherical surface σ with center at q.

72. Each of the following integrals is very easy to evaluate if you use the proper transformation. Evaluate each by the simplest method you can find; in each case state which theorem you are using.

(a) $\iiint (\nabla \cdot \mathbf{F})\, d\tau$ over the region $x^2 + y^2 + z^2 \le 25$, where

$$\mathbf{F} = (x^2 + y^2 + z^2)(x\mathbf{i} + y\mathbf{j} + z\mathbf{k}).$$

(b) $\oint (2y\, dx - 3x\, dy)$ around the square bounded by $x = 3$, $x = 5$, $y = 1$ and $y = 3$.

(c) $\displaystyle\iint_{\text{surface } \sigma} \operatorname{curl}(x^2\mathbf{i} + z^2\mathbf{j} - y^2\mathbf{k}) \cdot \mathbf{n}\, d\sigma$, where σ is the part of the surface $z = 4 - x^2 - y^2$ above the (x, y) plane.

(d) $\iint \operatorname{curl}(y\mathbf{i} + 2\mathbf{j}) \cdot \mathbf{n}\, d\sigma$, where σ is the surface in the first octant

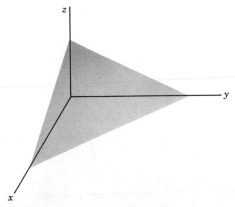

made up of part of the plane $2x + 3y + 4z = 12$, and triangles in the (x, z) and (y, z) planes, as indicated in the figure.

(e) $\iint \mathbf{r} \cdot \mathbf{n}\, d\sigma$ over the surface in part (d), where $\mathbf{r} = i x + j y + k z$.

(f) $\iint \mathbf{V} \cdot \mathbf{n}\, d\sigma$ over the closed surface of the tin can bounded by $x^2 + y^2 = 9$, $z = 0$, $z = 5$, if

$$\mathbf{V} = 2xy\mathbf{i} - y^2\mathbf{j} + (z + xy)\mathbf{k}.$$

(g) $\iint (\operatorname{curl} \mathbf{V}) \cdot \mathbf{n}\, d\sigma$ over any surface whose bounding curve is in the (x, y) plane, where

$$\mathbf{V} = (x - x^2 z)\mathbf{i} + (yz^3 - y^2)\mathbf{j} + (x^2 y - xz)\mathbf{k}.$$

(h) $\displaystyle\int_C (x \sin x - y)\, dx + (x - y^2)\, dy$, where C is the triangle in the (x, y) plane with vertices $(0, 0)$, $(1, 1)$, and $(2, 0)$.

(i) $\oint\!\!\!\oint$ curl $(2ixy - xzk) \cdot \mathbf{n}\, d\sigma$ over the *closed* surface of the ellipsoid

$$\frac{x^2}{4} + \frac{y^2}{9} + \frac{z^2}{16} = 1.$$

Warning: Stokes' theorem applies only to an open surface. *Hints:* Could you cut the given surface into two halves? Also see (d) in the table of vector identities.

73. (a) Write out the details leading to (13.8) following the method used to get (13.7).

    (b) Do case (b) of Example 1, Section 13.

74. Given the vector $\mathbf{A} = (x^2 - y^2)\mathbf{i} + 2xy\mathbf{j}$.

    (a) Find $\nabla \times \mathbf{A}$.

    (b) Evaluate $\iint (\nabla \times \mathbf{A}) \cdot d\sigma$ over a rectangle in the (x, y) plane bounded by the lines $x = 0$, $x = a$, $y = 0$, $y = b$.

    (c) Evaluate $\oint \mathbf{A} \cdot d\mathbf{r}$ around the boundary of the rectangle and thus verify Stokes' theorem for this case.

75. Let C be a simple closed curve in a plane, let A be the plane area inside C, and let $\mathbf{V}$ be a given vector field whose components V_x and V_y have continuous partial derivatives. Use Stokes' theorem to prove that

$$\oint_C V_x\, dx + V_y\, dy = \iint_A \left(\frac{\partial V_y}{\partial x} - \frac{\partial V_x}{\partial y}\right) dx\, dy.$$

This equation is called "Green's theorem in the plane." It is often written with no reference to vectors as

$$\oint_C (P\, dx + Q\, dy) = \iint_A \left(\frac{\partial Q}{\partial x} - \frac{\partial P}{\partial y}\right) dx\, dy.$$

Show that it can also be written in a form which resembles the divergence theorem (stepped down one dimension), namely

$$\iint_A \nabla \cdot \mathbf{V}\, d\sigma = \oint \mathbf{V} \cdot \mathbf{n}\, ds,$$

where $\mathbf{n}$ is the outward normal to the curve C, and s is arc length along C. Derive it from the divergence theorem by considering a vertical cylinder of height 1 whose cross section is the area A.

76. (a) For a simple closed curve C in the plane show (by Green's theorem, Problem 75) that the area inclosed is

$$A = \tfrac{1}{2} \oint_C (x\, dy - y\, dx).$$

    (b) Use part (a) to find the area inside the ellipse $x = a \cos \theta$, $y = b \sin \theta$, $0 \le \theta \le 2\pi$.

77. The following equations are variously known as Green's first and second identities or formulas or theorems. Derive them, as indicated, from the divergence theorem.

(1) $$\int_{\substack{\text{volume } \tau \\ \text{inside } \sigma}} (\phi \nabla^2 \psi + \nabla\phi \cdot \nabla\psi) \, d\tau = \oint_{\text{closed surface } \sigma} (\phi \nabla\psi) \cdot \mathbf{n} \, d\sigma.$$

To prove this, let $\mathbf{V} = \phi \nabla\psi$ in the divergence theorem.

(2) $$\int_{\substack{\text{volume } \tau \\ \text{inside } \sigma}} (\phi \nabla^2 \psi - \psi \nabla^2 \phi) \, d\tau = \oint_{\text{closed surface } \sigma} (\phi \nabla\psi - \psi \nabla\phi) \cdot \mathbf{n} \, d\sigma$$

To prove this, copy Theorem 1 above as is and then with ϕ and ψ interchanged; then subtract the two equations.

78. Derive the following vector integral theorems.

(a) $$\int_{\text{volume } \tau} \nabla\phi \, d\tau = \oint_{\text{surface inclosing } \tau} \phi \mathbf{n} \, d\sigma.$$

Hint: In the divergence theorem (12.17), substitute $\mathbf{V} = \phi\mathbf{C}$, where $\mathbf{C}$ is an arbitrary constant vector, to obtain $\mathbf{C} \cdot \int \nabla\phi \, d\tau = \mathbf{C} \cdot \oint \phi\mathbf{n} \, d\sigma$. Since $\mathbf{C}$ is arbitrary, let $\mathbf{C} = \mathbf{i}$ to show that the x-components of the two integrals are equal; similarly, let $\mathbf{C} = \mathbf{j}$ and $\mathbf{C} = \mathbf{k}$ to show that the y-components are equal and the z-components are equal.

(b) $$\int_{\text{volume } \tau} \nabla \times \mathbf{V} \, d\tau = \oint_{\text{surface inclosing } \tau} \mathbf{n} \times \mathbf{V} \, d\sigma.$$

Hint: Replace $\mathbf{V}$ in the divergence theorem by $\mathbf{V} \times \mathbf{C}$, where $\mathbf{C}$ is an arbitrary constant vector. Follow the last part of the hint in (a).

(c) $$\oint_{\text{curve bounding } \sigma} \phi \, d\mathbf{r} = \int_{\text{surface } \sigma} (\mathbf{n} \times \nabla\phi) \, d\sigma.$$

(d) $$\oint_{\text{curve bounding } \sigma} d\mathbf{r} \times \mathbf{V} = \int_{\text{surface } \sigma} (\mathbf{n} \times \nabla) \times \mathbf{V} \, d\sigma.$$

Hints for (c) *and* (d): Use the substitutions suggested in (a) and (b) but in Stokes' theorem (13.14) instead of the divergence theorem.

79. Use Stokes' theorem to evaluate $\oint_C y \, dx + z \, dy + x \, dz$, where C is the curve of intersection of $x + y = 2$ and $x^2 + y^2 + z^2 = 2(x + y)$.

80. Find vector fields $\mathbf{A}$ such that $\mathbf{V} = \text{curl } \mathbf{A}$ for each given $\mathbf{V}$.

(a) $\mathbf{V} = (x^2 - yz + y)\mathbf{i} + (x - 2yz)\mathbf{j} + (z^2 - 2zx + x + y)\mathbf{k}$
(b) $\mathbf{V} = \mathbf{i}(x^2 - 2xz) + \mathbf{j}(y^2 - 2xy) + \mathbf{k}(z^2 - 2yz + xy)$
(c) $\mathbf{V} = \mathbf{i}(ze^{zy} + x \sin zx) + \mathbf{j}x \cos xz - \mathbf{k}z \sin zx$
(d) $\mathbf{V} = -\mathbf{k}$
(e) $\mathbf{V} = (y + z)\mathbf{i} + (x - z)\mathbf{j} + (x^2 + y^2)\mathbf{k}$

81. In the example in Section 14, find the area of the cylinder inside the sphere.

82. Find the area of the part of the cylinder $y^2 + z^2 = 4$ in the first octant, cut out by the planes $x = 0$ and $y = x$.

83. Find the area of the cylinder $z = x + y^2$ that lies below the second-quadrant area bounded by the x-axis, $x = -1$, and $y^2 = -x$.

84. Find the area of the part of the cone $x^2 + y^2 = z^2$ that is over the circle $(x - 1)^2 + y^2 = 1$.

85. Find the area cut from a spherical surface of radius a by a square hole of side $a\sqrt{2}$, whose axis is along a diameter of the sphere. *Hint for evaluating the integral:* Change to polar coordinates and evaluate the r integral. Then use the following result:

$$\int_0^{\pi/4} \sqrt{2 - \sec^2 \theta}\, d\theta = \frac{\pi}{2}(\sqrt{2} - 1).$$

6

Fourier Series

I. INTRODUCTION

Problems involving vibrations or oscillations occur frequently in physics and engineering. You can think of examples you have already met: a vibrating tuning fork, a pendulum, a weight attached to a spring, water waves, sound waves, alternating electric currents, etc. In addition, there are many more examples which you will meet as you continue to study physics. Some of them—for example heat conduction, electric and magnetic fields, light—do not appear in elementary work to have anything oscillatory about them, but will turn out in your more advanced work to involve the sines and cosines which are used in describing simple harmonic motion and wave motion.

In Chapter 1 we discussed the use of power series to approximate complicated functions. In many problems, series called Fourier series, whose terms are sines and cosines, are more useful than power series. In this chapter we shall see how to find and use Fourier series.

2. SIMPLE HARMONIC MOTION AND WAVE MOTION; PERIODIC FUNCTIONS

We shall need much of the notation and terminology used in discussing simple harmonic motion and wave motion. Let us discuss these two topics briefly.

Let particle P (Fig. 2.1) move at constant speed around a circle of radius A. At the same time, let particle Q move up and down along the straight line segment RS in such a way that the y-coordinates of P and Q are always equal. If ω is the angular velocity of P in radians per second, and (Fig. 2.1) $\theta = 0$ when $t = 0$, then at a later time t

$$(2.1) \qquad \theta = \omega t.$$

The y-coordinate of Q (which is equal to the y-coordinate of P) is

$$(2.2) \qquad y = A \sin \theta = A \sin \omega t.$$

The back and forth motion of Q is called *simple harmonic motion*. By definition, an object is executing simple harmonic motion if its displacement from equilibrium can be written as $A \sin \omega t$ [or $A \cos \omega t$ or

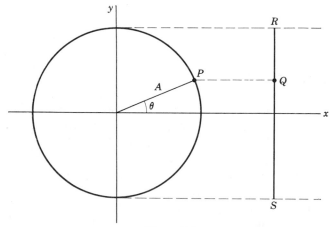

Figure 2.1

$A \sin (\omega t + \phi)$, but these two functions differ from $A \sin \omega t$ only in choice of origin; such functions are called *sinusoidal functions*]. You can think of many physical examples of this sort of simple vibration: a pendulum, a tuning fork, a weight bobbing up and down at the end of a spring.

The x- and y-coordinates of particle P in Fig. 2.1 are

$$(2.3) \qquad x = A \cos \omega t, \qquad y = A \sin \omega t.$$

If we think of P as the point $z = x + iy$ in the complex plane, we could replace (2.3) by a single equation to describe the motion of P:

$$(2.4) \qquad z = x + iy = A(\cos \omega t + i \sin \omega t)$$
$$= A e^{i\omega t}.$$

It is often worth while to use this complex notation even to describe the motion of Q; we then understand that the actual position of Q is equal to the imaginary part of z (or with different starting conditions the real part of z). For example, the velocity of Q is the imaginary part of

(2.5) $$\frac{dz}{dt} = \frac{d}{dt}(Ae^{i\omega t}) = Ai\omega e^{i\omega t} = Ai\omega(\cos \omega t + i \sin \omega t).$$

[The imaginary part of (2.5) is $A\omega \cos \omega t$, which is dy/dt from (2.2).]

It is useful to draw a graph of x or y in (2.2) and (2.3) as a function of t. Figure 2.2 represents any of the functions $\sin \omega t$, $\cos \omega t$, $\sin (\omega t + \phi)$ if we choose the origin correctly. The number A is called the *amplitude of the vibration* or the *amplitude of the function*. Physically it is the maximum displacement of Q from its equilibrium position. The *period of the*

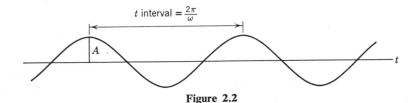

Figure 2.2

simple harmonic motion or the *period of the function* is the time for one complete oscillation, that is, $2\pi/\omega$ (see Fig. 2.2).

We could write the velocity of Q from (2.5) as

(2.6) $$\frac{dy}{dt} = A\omega \cos \omega t = B \cos \omega t.$$

Here B is the maximum value of the velocity and is called the *velocity amplitude*. Note that the velocity has the same period as the displacement. If the mass of the particle Q is m, its kinetic energy is

(2.7) $$\text{Kinetic energy} = \tfrac{1}{2}m\left(\frac{dy}{dt}\right)^2 = \tfrac{1}{2}mB^2 \cos^2 \omega t.$$

We are considering an idealized harmonic oscillator which does not lose energy. Then the total energy (kinetic plus potential) must be equal to the largest value of the kinetic energy, that is, $\tfrac{1}{2}mB^2$. Thus we have

(2.8) $$\text{Total energy} = \tfrac{1}{2}mB^2.$$

Notice that the energy is proportional to the square of the (velocity) amplitude; we shall be interested in this result later when we discuss sound.

Waves are another important example of an oscillatory phenomenon. The mathematical ideas of wave motion are useful in many fields; for example, we talk about water waves, sound waves, and radio waves. Let us consider, as a simple example, water waves in which the shape of the water surface is (unrealistically!) a sine curve. Then if we take a photograph (at the instant $t = 0$) of the water surface, the equation of this picture could be written (relative to appropriate axes)

(2.9)
$$y = A \sin \frac{2\pi x}{\lambda},$$

where x represents horizontal distance and λ is the distance between wave crests. Usually λ is called the *wavelength* but mathematically it is the same

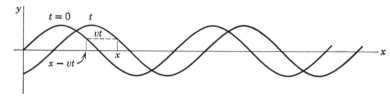

Figure 2.3

as the period of this function of x. Now suppose we take another photograph when the waves have moved forward a distance vt (v is the velocity of the waves and t is the time between photographs). Figure 2.3 shows the two photographs superimposed. Observe that the value of y at the point x on the graph labeled t, is just the same as the value of y at the point $x - vt$ on the graph labeled $t = 0$. If (2.9) is the equation representing the waves at $t = 0$, then

(2.10)
$$y = A \sin \frac{2\pi}{\lambda} (x - vt)$$

represents the waves at time t. We can interpret (2.10) in another way. Suppose you stand at one point in the water [fixed x in (2.10)] and observe the up and down motion of the water, that is, y in (2.10) as a function of t (for fixed x). This is a simple harmonic motion of amplitude A and period λ/v. You are doing something analogous to this when you stand still and listen to a sound (sound waves pass your ear and you observe their frequency) or when you listen to the radio (radio waves pass the receiver and it reacts to their frequency).

We see that y in (2.10) is a periodic function either of x (t fixed) or of t (x fixed); both interpretations are useful. It makes no difference in the basic mathematics, however, what letter we use for the independent variable. To simplify our notation we shall ordinarily use x as the variable, but if the physical problem calls for it, you can replace x by t.

Sines and cosines are periodic functions; once you have drawn $\sin x$ from $x = 0$ to $x = 2\pi$, the rest of the graph from $x = -\infty$ to $x = +\infty$ is just a repetition over and over of the 0 to 2π graph. The number 2π is the period of $\sin x$. A periodic function need not be a simple sine or cosine, but may be any sort of complicated graph that repeats itself (Fig. 2.4). The interval of repetition is the period. For example, if we are describing the vibration of a seconds pendulum, the period is 2 sec (time for one complete back-and-forth oscillation). The reciprocal of the period is the *frequency*, the number of oscillations per second; for the seconds pendulum, the frequency is $\frac{1}{2}$ sec^{-1}. When the radio announcer says, "operating on a frequency of 780 kilohertz," he means that 780,000 radio waves

Figure 2.4

reach you per second, or that the period of one wave is (1/780,000) sec. *By definition, the function $f(x)$ is periodic if $f(x + p) = f(x)$ for every x; the number p is the period.* The period of $\sin x$ is 2π since $\sin(x + 2\pi) = \sin x$; similarly, the period of $\sin 2\pi x$ is 1 since

$$\sin 2\pi(x + 1) = \sin(2\pi x + 2\pi) = \sin 2\pi x,$$

and the period of $\sin(\pi x/l)$ is $2l$ since $\sin(\pi/l)(x + 2l) = \sin(\pi x/l)$. In general, the period of $\sin 2\pi x/T$ is T.

$$\frac{t}{2} = \omega = 2\pi f$$
$$f = \frac{1}{2l}$$
$$T = 2l$$

3. APPLICATIONS OF FOURIER SERIES

We have said that the vibration of a tuning fork is an example of simple harmonic motion. When we hear the musical note produced, we say that a sound wave has passed through the air from the tuning fork to our ears. As the tuning fork vibrates it pushes against the air molecules, creating alternately regions of high and low pressure (Fig. 3.1). If we measure the pressure as a function of x and t from the tuning fork to us, we find that the pressure is of the form of (2.10); if we measure the pressure where we are as a function of t as the wave passes, we find that the pressure is a periodic function of t. The sound wave is a pure sine wave of a definite frequency (in the language of music, a pure tone). Now suppose that several pure tones are heard simultaneously. In the resultant sound wave, the pressure will not be a single sine function but a sum of several sine functions. If you strike a piano key you do not get a sound wave of just one frequency. Instead, you get a fundamental accompanied by a number of overtones (harmonics) of frequencies 2, 3, 4, etc., times the frequency of the fundamental. Higher frequencies mean shorter periods. If sin ωt and cos ωt correspond to the fundamental frequency, then sin $n\omega t$ and cos $n\omega t$ correspond to the higher harmonics. The combination of the fundamental and the harmonics is a complicated periodic function with the period of the fundamental (Problem 3). Given the complicated function, we could ask how to write it as a sum of terms

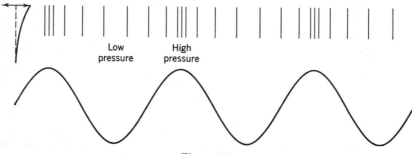

Figure 3.1

corresponding to the various harmonics. In general it might require all the harmonics, that is, an infinite series of terms. This is called a Fourier series. Expanding a function in a Fourier series then amounts to breaking it down into its various harmonics. In fact, this process is sometimes called harmonic analysis.

There are applications to other fields besides sound. Radio waves, visible light, and x-rays are all examples of a kind of wave motion in which the "waves" correspond to varying strengths of electric and magnetic fields. Exactly the same mathematical equations apply as for water waves and sound waves. We could then ask what light frequencies (these correspond to the color) are in a given light beam and in what proportions. To find the answer, we would expand the given function describing the wave in a Fourier series.

You have probably seen a sine curve used to represent an alternating current (a-c) or voltage in electricity. This is a periodic function, but so are the functions shown in Fig. 3.2. Any of these and many others might represent signals (voltages or currents) which are to be applied to an electric circuit. Then we could ask what a-c frequencies (harmonics) make up a given signal and in what proportions. When an electric signal is passed through a network (say a radio), some of the harmonics may be

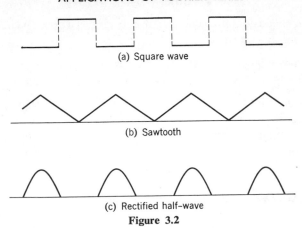

(a) Square wave

(b) Sawtooth

(c) Rectified half-wave

Figure 3.2

lost. If most of the important ones get through for all the signals we are interested in, we say that the radio possesses "high fidelity." To find out which harmonics are the important ones in a given signal, we expand it in a Fourier series. The terms of the series with large coefficients then represent the important harmonics (frequencies).

Since sines and cosines are themselves periodic, it seems rather natural to use series of them, rather than power series, to represent periodic functions. There is another important reason. The coefficients of a power series are obtained, you will recall (Chapter 1, Section 12), by finding successive derivatives of the function being expanded; consequently, only continuous functions with derivatives of all orders can be expanded in power series. Many periodic functions in practice are not continuous or not differentiable (Fig. 3.2). Fortunately, Fourier series (unlike power series) can represent discontinuous functions or functions whose graphs have corners. On the other hand, Fourier series do not usually converge as rapidly as power series and are often not uniformly convergent (Chapter 1, Section 16). Consequently, much more care is needed in manipulating them (differentiating term by term, multiplying series, etc.) to be sure that we do not get a divergent series.

Our problem, then, is to expand a given periodic function in a series of sines and cosines. To simplify our formulas at first, we shall start with functions of period 2π and call our basic functions $\sin nx$ and $\cos nx$ instead of $\sin n\omega t$ and $\cos n\omega t$. Later we shall see how we can change the formulas to fit a different period. The functions $\sin x$ and $\cos x$ have period 2π; so do $\sin nx$ and $\cos nx$ for any integral n since $\sin n(x + 2\pi) = \sin (nx + 2n\pi) = \sin nx$. (It is true that $\sin nx$ and $\cos nx$ also have shorter periods, namely $2\pi/n$, but the fact that they repeat every 2π is what we are interested in here, for this makes them reasonable functions to use in an expansion of a function of period 2π.) Then, given a function $f(x)$ of period 2π, we write

(3.1) $f(x) = \tfrac{1}{2}a_0 + a_1 \cos x + a_2 \cos 2x + a_3 \cos 3x + \cdots$
$+ b_1 \sin x + b_2 \sin 2x + b_3 \sin 3x + \ldots,$

and derive formulas for the coefficients a_n and b_n. (The reason for writing $\tfrac{1}{2}a_0$ as the constant term will be clear later—it makes the formulas for the coefficients simpler to remember—but you must not forget the $\tfrac{1}{2}$ in the series!) Before we find a_n and b_n we need to do some preliminary work.

4. AVERAGE VALUE OF A FUNCTION

The concept of the average value of a function is often useful. You know how to find the average of a set of numbers: you add them and divide by the number of numbers. This process suggests that we ought to get an approximation to the average value of a function $f(x)$ on the interval (a, b) by averaging a number of values of $f(x)$ (Fig. 4.1):

(4.1)   Average of $f(x)$ on (a, b) is approximately equal to

$$\frac{f(x_1) + f(x_2) + \cdots + f(x_n)}{n}.$$

This should become a better approximation as n increases. Let the points $x_1, x_2, \ldots$ be Δx apart. Multiply the numerator and the denominator of the approximate average by Δx. Then (4.1) becomes:

(4.2)   Average of $f(x)$ on (a, b) is approximately equal to

$$\frac{[f(x_1) + \cdots + f(x_n)]\,\Delta x}{n\,\Delta x}.$$

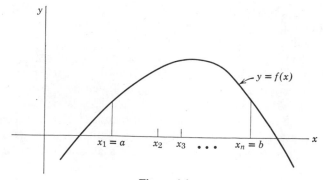

Figure 4.1

Now $n \, \Delta x = b - a$, the length of the interval over which we are averaging, no matter what n and Δx are. If we let $n \to \infty$ and $\Delta x \to 0$, the numerator approaches $\int_a^b f(x) \, dx$, and we have

(4.3)   Average of $f(x)$ on $(a, b) = \dfrac{\displaystyle\int_a^b f(x) \, dx}{b - a}$.

In applications, it often happens that the average value of a given function is zero. For example, the average of $\sin x$ over any number of periods is zero. The average value of the velocity of a simple harmonic

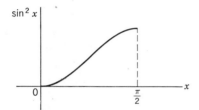

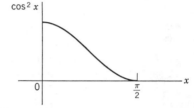

Figure 4.2

oscillator over any number of vibrations is zero. In such cases the average of the square of the function may be of interest. For example, if the alternating electric current flowing through a wire is described by a sine function, the square root of the average of the sine squared is known as the root-mean-square or effective value of the current, and is what you would measure with an a-c ammeter. In the example of the simple harmonic oscillator, the average kinetic energy (average of $\frac{1}{2}mv^2$) is $\frac{1}{2}m$ times the average of v^2.

Now you can, of course, find the average value of $\sin^2 x$ over a period (say $-\pi$ to π) by looking up the integral in (4.3) in tables and evaluating it. There is an easier way which is well worth knowing. By considering the graphs of $\cos^2 x$ and $\sin^2 x$ (Fig. 4.2), you can probably convince yourself that the area under them is the same for any quarter-period. (Also see Problem 5.) Then

(4.4) $\displaystyle\int_{-\pi}^{\pi} \sin^2 x \, dx = \int_{-\pi}^{\pi} \cos^2 x \, dx.$

Similarly (for integral $n \neq 0$),

(4.5) $\displaystyle\int_{-\pi}^{\pi} \sin^2 nx \, dx = \int_{-\pi}^{\pi} \cos^2 nx \, dx.$

But since $\sin^2 nx + \cos^2 nx = 1$,

(4.6) $$\int_{-\pi}^{\pi} (\sin^2 nx + \cos^2 nx)\, dx = \int_{-\pi}^{\pi} dx = 2\pi.$$

Using (4.5), we get

(4.7) $$\int_{-\pi}^{\pi} \sin^2 nx\, dx = \int_{-\pi}^{\pi} \cos^2 nx\, dx = \pi.$$

Then using (4.3) we see that:

(4.8) The average value (over a period) of $\sin^2 nx$
= the average value (over a period) of $\cos^2 nx$

$$= \frac{1}{2\pi} \int_{-\pi}^{\pi} \sin^2 nx\, dx = \frac{1}{2\pi} \int_{-\pi}^{\pi} \cos^2 nx\, dx = \frac{\pi}{2\pi} = \frac{1}{2}.$$

We can say all this more simply in words. By (4.5), the average value of $\sin^2 nx$ equals the average value of $\cos^2 nx$. The average value of $\sin^2 nx + \cos^2 nx = 1$ is 1. Therefore the average value of $\sin^2 nx$ or of $\cos^2 nx$ is $\frac{1}{2}$. (In each case the average value is taken over one or more periods.)

5. FOURIER COEFFICIENTS

In finding formulas for a_n and b_n in (3.1) we need the following integrals:

(5.1) The average value of sin mx cos nx (over a period)

$$= \frac{1}{2\pi} \int_{-\pi}^{\pi} \sin mx \cos nx\, dx = 0.$$

The average value of sin mx sin nx (over a period)

$$= \frac{1}{2\pi} \int_{-\pi}^{\pi} \sin mx \sin nx\, dx = \begin{cases} 0 & m \neq n, \\ \frac{1}{2} & m = n \neq 0, \\ 0 & m = n = 0. \end{cases}$$

The average value of cos mx cos nx (over a period)

$$= \frac{1}{2\pi} \int_{-\pi}^{\pi} \cos mx \cos nx\, dx = \begin{cases} 0 & m \neq n, \\ \frac{1}{2} & m = n \neq 0, \\ 1 & m = n = 0. \end{cases}$$

We have already shown that the average values of $\sin^2 nx$ and $\cos^2 nx$ are $\frac{1}{2}$. The last integral in (5.1) is the average value of 1 which is 1. To show that the other average values in (5.1) are zero, we could use the trigonometry formulas for products like $\sin \theta \cos \phi$ and then integrate. An easier way is to use the formulas for the sines and cosines in terms of complex exponentials. [See (7.1).] We shall show this method for one integral.

$$(5.2) \qquad \int_{-\pi}^{\pi} \sin mx \cos nx \, dx = \int_{-\pi}^{\pi} \frac{e^{imx} - e^{-imx}}{2i} \cdot \frac{e^{inx} + e^{-inx}}{2} \, dx.$$

We can see the result without actually multiplying these out. All terms in the product are of the form e^{ikx}, where k is an integer $\neq 0$ (except for the cross-product terms when $n = m$, and these cancel). We can show that the integral of each such term is zero:

$$(5.3) \qquad \int_{-\pi}^{\pi} e^{ikx} \, dx = \frac{e^{ikx}}{ik} \Big|_{-\pi}^{\pi} = \frac{e^{ik\pi} - e^{-ik\pi}}{ik} = 0 \qquad \textit{U.B,}$$

because $e^{ik\pi} = e^{-ik\pi} = \cos k\pi$ (since $\sin k\pi = 0$). The other integrals in (5.1) may be evaluated similarly (Problem 6).

We now show how to find a_n and b_n in (3.1). To find a_0, we find the average value on $(-\pi, \pi)$ of each term of (3.1).

$$(5.4) \qquad \frac{1}{2\pi} \int_{-\pi}^{\pi} f(x) \, dx = \frac{a_0}{2} \frac{1}{2\pi} \int_{-\pi}^{\pi} dx + a_1 \frac{1}{2\pi} \int_{-\pi}^{\pi} \cos x \, dx$$

$$+ a_2 \frac{1}{2\pi} \int_{-\pi}^{\pi} \cos 2x \, dx + \cdots + b_1 \frac{1}{2\pi} \int_{-\pi}^{\pi} \sin x \, dx + \dots .$$

By (5.1), all the integrals on the right-hand side of (5.4) are zero except the first, because they are integrals of $\sin mx \cos nx$ or of $\cos mx \cos nx$ with $n = 0$ and $m \neq 0$ (that is, $m \neq n$). Then we have

$$(5.5) \qquad \frac{1}{2\pi} \int_{-\pi}^{\pi} f(x) \, dx = \frac{a_0}{2} \frac{1}{2\pi} \int_{-\pi}^{\pi} dx = \frac{a_0}{2} .$$

$$(5.6) \qquad a_0 = \frac{1}{\pi} \int_{-\pi}^{\pi} f(x) \, dx.$$

Given $f(x)$ to be expanded in a Fourier series, we can now evaluate a_0 by calculating the integral in (5.6).

To find a_1, multiply both sides of (3.1) by $\cos x$ and again find the average value of each term:

$$(5.7) \qquad \frac{1}{2\pi} \int_{-\pi}^{\pi} f(x) \cos x \, dx = \frac{a_0}{2} \frac{1}{2\pi} \int_{-\pi}^{\pi} \cos x \, dx + a_1 \frac{1}{2\pi} \int_{-\pi}^{\pi} \cos^2 x \, dx$$

$$+ a_2 \frac{1}{2\pi} \int_{-\pi}^{\pi} \cos 2x \cos x \, dx + \cdots$$

$$+ b_1 \frac{1}{2\pi} \int_{-\pi}^{\pi} \sin x \cos x \, dx + \dots .$$

This time, by (5.1), all terms on the right are zero except

$$\frac{1}{2\pi}\int_{-\pi}^{\pi}\cos^2 x\,dx = \tfrac{1}{2}.$$

Solving for a_1, we have

$$a_1 = \frac{1}{\pi}\int_{-\pi}^{\pi} f(x)\cos x\,dx.$$

The method should be clear by now, so we shall next find a general formula for a_n. Multiply both sides of (3.1) by $\cos nx$ and find the average value of each term:

$$(5.8)\quad \frac{1}{2\pi}\int_{-\pi}^{\pi} f(x)\cos nx\,dx$$

$$= \frac{a_0}{2}\frac{1}{2\pi}\int_{-\pi}^{\pi}\cos nx\,dx + a_1\frac{1}{2\pi}\int_{-\pi}^{\pi}\cos x\cos nx\,dx$$

$$+ a_2\frac{1}{2\pi}\int_{-\pi}^{\pi}\cos 2x\cos nx\,dx + \cdots$$

$$+ b_1\frac{1}{2\pi}\int_{-\pi}^{\pi}\sin x\cos nx\,dx + \ldots.$$

By (5.1), all terms on the right are zero except the one

$$\frac{1}{2\pi}\int_{-\pi}^{\pi}\cos^2 nx\,dx = \tfrac{1}{2}.$$

Solving for a_n, we have

$$(5.9)\qquad a_n = \frac{1}{\pi}\int_{-\pi}^{\pi} f(x)\cos nx\,dx.$$

Notice that this includes the $n = 0$ formula, but only because we called the constant term $\tfrac{1}{2}a_0$.

To obtain a formula for b_n, we multiply both sides of (3.1) by $\sin nx$ and take average values just as we did in deriving (5.9). We find (Problem 14)

$$(5.10)\qquad b_n = \frac{1}{\pi}\int_{-\pi}^{\pi} f(x)\sin nx\,dx.$$

The formulas (5.9) and (5.10) will be used repeatedly in problems and should be memorized.

Example. Expand in a Fourier series the function $f(x)$ sketched in Fig. 5.1. This function might represent, for example, a periodic voltage pulse. The terms of our Fourier series would then correspond to the different a-c frequencies which are combined in this "square wave" voltage, and the magnitude of the Fourier coefficients would indicate the relative importance of the various frequencies.

Note that $f(x)$ is a function of period 2π. Often in problems you will be given $f(x)$ for only one period; you should always sketch several periods so that you see clearly the periodic function you are expanding. For example, in this problem, instead of a sketch, you might have been given

(5.11)
$$f(x) = \begin{cases} 0, & -\pi < x < 0, \\ 1, & 0 < x < \pi. \end{cases}$$

It is then understood that $f(x)$ is to be continued periodically with period 2π outside the interval $(-\pi, \pi)$.

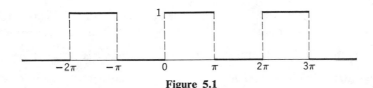

Figure 5.1

We use equations (5.9) and (5.10) to find a_n and b_n:

$$a_n = \frac{1}{\pi} \int_{-\pi}^{\pi} f(x) \cos nx \, dx = \frac{1}{\pi}\left[\int_{-\pi}^{0} 0 \cdot \cos nx \, dx + \int_{0}^{\pi} 1 \cdot \cos nx \, dx \right]$$

$$= \frac{1}{\pi} \int_{0}^{\pi} \cos nx \, dx = \begin{cases} \dfrac{1}{\pi} \cdot \dfrac{1}{n} \sin nx \Big|_{0}^{\pi} = 0 & \text{for } n \neq 0, \\[2mm] \dfrac{1}{\pi} \cdot \pi = 1 & \text{for } n = 0. \end{cases}$$

Thus $a_0 = 1$, and all other $a_n = 0$.

$$b_n = \frac{1}{\pi} \int_{-\pi}^{\pi} f(x) \sin nx \, dx = \frac{1}{\pi}\left[\int_{-\pi}^{0} 0 \cdot \sin nx \, dx + \int_{0}^{\pi} 1 \cdot \sin nx \, dx \right]$$

$$= \frac{1}{\pi} \int_{0}^{\pi} \sin nx \, dx = \frac{1}{\pi}\left[\frac{-\cos nx}{n} \right]_{0}^{\pi} = -\frac{1}{n\pi}[(-1)^n - 1]$$

$$= \begin{cases} 0 & \text{for even } n, \\[2mm] \dfrac{2}{n\pi} & \text{for odd } n. \end{cases}$$

Putting these values for the coefficients into (3.1), we have

(5.12) $$f(x) = \tfrac{1}{2} + \frac{2}{\pi}\left(\frac{\sin x}{1} + \frac{\sin 3x}{3} + \frac{\sin 5x}{5} + \cdots \right).$$

6. DIRICHLET CONDITIONS

Now we have a series, but there are still some questions that we ought to get answered. Does it converge, and if so, does it converge to the values of $f(x)$? You will find, if you try, that for most values of x the series in (5.12) does not respond to any of the tests for convergence that we discussed in Chapter 1. What is the sum of the series at $x = 0$ where $f(x)$ jumps from 0 to 1? You can see from the series (5.12) that the sum at $x = 0$ is $\frac{1}{2}$, but what does this have to do with $f(x)$?

These questions would not be easy for us to answer for ourselves, but they are answered for us for most practical purposes by the *theorem of Dirichlet*:

If $f(x)$ is periodic of period 2π, and if between $-\pi$ and π it is single-valued, has a finite number of maximum and minimum values, and a finite number of discontinuities, and if $\int_{-\pi}^{\pi} |f(x)|\, dx$ is finite, then the Fourier series [with coefficients given by (5.9) and (5.10)] converges to $f(x)$ at all the points where $f(x)$ is continuous; at jumps the Fourier series converges to the midpoint of the jump. (This includes jumps that occur at $\pm\pi$ for the periodic function.)

To see what all this means, we shall consider some special functions. We have already discussed what a periodic function means. A function $f(x)$ is single-valued if there is just one value of $f(x)$ for each x. For example, if $x^2 + y^2 = 1$, y is not a single-valued function of x, unless we select just $y = +\sqrt{1 - x^2}$ or just $y = -\sqrt{1 - x^2}$. An example of a function with an infinite number of maxima and minima is $\sin(1/x)$, which oscillates infinitely many times as $x \to 0$. If we imagine a function constructed from $\sin(1/x)$ by making $f(x) = 1$ for every x for which $\sin(1/x) > 0$, and $f(x) = -1$ for every x for which $\sin(1/x) < 0$, this function would have an infinite number of discontinuities. You can see that most functions you are apt to meet in applied work will not behave like these, but will satisfy the Dirichlet conditions.

Finally, if $y = 1/x$, we find

$$\int_{-\pi}^{\pi} \left|\frac{1}{x}\right|\, dx = 2\int_{0}^{\pi} \frac{1}{x}\, dx = 2\ln x \Big|_{0}^{\pi} = \infty$$

so the function $1/x$ is ruled out by the Dirichlet conditions. On the other hand, if $f(x) = 1/\sqrt{|x|}$, then

$$\int_{-\pi}^{\pi} \frac{1}{\sqrt{|x|}}\, dx = 2\int_{0}^{\pi} \frac{dx}{\sqrt{x}} = 4\sqrt{x} \Big|_{0}^{\pi} = 4\sqrt{\pi},$$

so the periodic function which is $1/\sqrt{|x|}$ between $-\pi$ and π can be expanded in a Fourier series. In most problems it is not necessary to find the value of $\int_{-\pi}^{\pi} |f(x)|\, dx$; let us see why. If $f(x)$ is bounded (that is, all its values lie between $\pm M$ for some positive constant M), then

$$\int_{-\pi}^{\pi} |f(x)|\, dx \le \int_{-\pi}^{\pi} M\, dx = M \cdot 2\pi$$

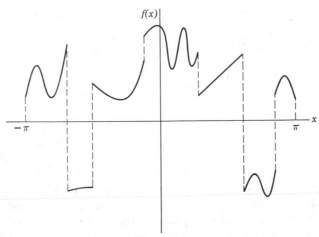

Figure 6.1

and so is finite. Thus you can simply verify that the function you are considering is bounded (if it is) instead of evaluating the integral. Figure 6.1 is an example of a function which satisfies the Dirichlet conditions on $(-\pi, \pi)$.

We see, then, that rather than testing Fourier series for convergence as we did power series, we instead check the function we want expanded; if it satisfies the Dirichlet conditions we are then sure that the Fourier series, when we get it, will converge to the function we expanded except at jumps where it converges to the midpoint of the jump no matter how we may have defined the function at the jump. (See, however, discussions of the Gibbs phenomenon in books on Fourier series.)

We ought to say here that the converse of Dirichlet's theorem is not true—if a function fails to satisfy the Dirichlet conditions, it still *may* be expandable in a Fourier series. The periodic function which is $\sin(1/x)$ on $(-\pi, \pi)$ is an example of such a function. However, such functions are rarely met with in practice.

We can now verify that the series we obtained in the example actually represents the function $f(x)$ we started with at all points in between the points $n\pi$. (We have already noted that *at* $n\pi$ the series gives the value $\frac{1}{2}$, which is half-way between 0 and 1 as Dirichlet's theorem says.) Between $-\pi$ and π the given $f(x)$ is single-valued (one value for each x), bounded (between $+1$ and 0), has a finite number of maximum and minimum values (one of each), and a finite number of discontinuities (at $-\pi$, 0, and π), and therefore satisfies the Dirichlet conditions. Dirichlet's theorem then assures us that the series (5.12) actually converges to the function $f(x)$ in Fig. 5.1 at all points except $x = n\pi$.

7. COMPLEX FORM OF FOURIER SERIES

Recall that real sines and cosines can be expressed in terms of complex exponentials by the formulas [Chapter 2, (11.3)]

$$\sin nx = \frac{e^{inx} - e^{-inx}}{2i},$$

(7.1)

$$\cos nx = \frac{e^{inx} + e^{-inx}}{2}.$$

If we substitute equations (7.1) into a Fourier series like (5.12), we get a series of terms of the forms e^{inx} and e^{-inx}. This is the complex form of a Fourier series. We can also find the complex form directly; this is often easier than finding the sine-cosine form. We can then, if we like, work back the other way and [using Euler's formula, Chapter 2, (9.3)] get the sine-cosine form from the exponential form.

We want to see how to find the coefficients in the complex form directly. We assume a series

$$(7.2) \qquad f(x) = c_0 + c_1 e^{ix} + c_{-1} e^{-ix} + c_2 e^{2ix} + c_{-2} e^{-2ix} + \cdots$$

$$= \sum_{n=-\infty}^{n=+\infty} c_n e^{inx}$$

and try to find the c_n's. From (5.3) we know that the average value of e^{ikx} on $(-\pi, \pi)$ is zero when k is an integer not equal to zero. To find c_0, we find the average values of the terms in (7.2):

$$(7.3) \qquad \frac{1}{2\pi}\int_{-\pi}^{\pi} f(x)\,dx = c_0 \cdot \frac{1}{2\pi}\int_{-\pi}^{\pi} dx + \text{average values of terms of the form } e^{ikx} \text{ with } k \text{ an integer} \neq 0$$

$$= c_0 + 0,$$

$$(7.4) \qquad c_0 = \frac{1}{2\pi}\int_{-\pi}^{\pi} f(x)\,dx.$$

To find c_n, we multiply (7.2) by e^{-inx} and again find the average value of each term. [Note the minus sign in the exponent. In finding a_n, the coefficient of $\cos nx$ in equation (3.1), we multiplied by $\cos nx$; but here in finding the coefficient c_n of e^{inx}, we multiply by the complex conjugate e^{-inx}.]

$$(7.5) \quad \frac{1}{2\pi}\int_{-\pi}^{\pi} f(x)e^{-inx}\,dx = c_0 \frac{1}{2\pi}\int_{-\pi}^{\pi} e^{-inx}\,dx + c_1 \frac{1}{2\pi}\int_{-\pi}^{\pi} e^{-inx}e^{ix}\,dx$$

$$+ c_{-1}\frac{1}{2\pi}\int_{-\pi}^{\pi} e^{-inx}e^{-ix}\,dx + \cdots .$$

The terms on the right are the average values of exponentials e^{ikx}, where the k values are integers. Therefore all these terms are zero except the one where $k = 0$; this is the term containing c_n. We then have

$$\frac{1}{2\pi}\int_{-\pi}^{\pi} f(x)e^{-inx}\,dx = c_n \cdot \frac{1}{2\pi}\int_{-\pi}^{\pi} e^{-inx}e^{inx}\,dx = c_n \cdot \frac{1}{2\pi}\int_{-\pi}^{\pi} dx = c_n,$$

(7.6)

$$c_n = \frac{1}{2\pi}\int_{-\pi}^{\pi} f(x)e^{-inx}\,dx.$$

Note that this formula contains the one for c_0 (no $\frac{1}{2}$ to worry about here!). Also, since (7.6) is valid for negative as well as positive n, you have only one formula to memorize here! You can easily show that for *real* $f(x)$, $c_{-n} = \overline{c_n}$ (Problem 12).

Example. Let us expand the same $f(x)$ we did before, namely (5.11). We have from (7.6)

$$c_n = \frac{1}{2\pi}\int_{-\pi}^{0} e^{-inx}\cdot 0 \cdot dx + \frac{1}{2\pi}\int_{0}^{\pi} e^{-inx}\cdot 1 \cdot dx$$

$$(7.7) \quad = \frac{1}{2\pi}\frac{e^{-inx}}{-in}\Big|_0^{\pi} = \frac{1}{-2\pi in}(e^{-in\pi} - 1) = \begin{cases} \dfrac{1}{\pi in}, & n \text{ odd}, \\ 0, & n \text{ even} \neq 0, \end{cases}$$

$$c_0 = \frac{1}{2\pi}\int_0^{\pi} dx = \tfrac{1}{2}.$$

Then

$$(7.8) \quad f(x) = \sum_{-\infty}^{\infty} c_n e^{inx}$$

$$= \tfrac{1}{2} + \frac{1}{i\pi}\left(\frac{e^{ix}}{1} + \frac{e^{3ix}}{3} + \frac{e^{5ix}}{5} + \cdots\right)$$

$$+ \frac{1}{i\pi}\left(\frac{e^{-ix}}{-1} + \frac{e^{-3ix}}{-3} + \frac{e^{-5ix}}{-5} + \cdots\right).$$

It is interesting to verify that this is the same as the sine-cosine series we had before. We *could* use Euler's formula for each exponential, but it is easier to collect terms like this:

$$(7.9) \qquad f(x) = \tfrac{1}{2} + \frac{2}{\pi}\left(\frac{e^{ix} - e^{-ix}}{2i} + \tfrac{1}{3}\frac{e^{3ix} - e^{-3ix}}{2i} + \cdots \right)$$

$$= \tfrac{1}{2} + \frac{2}{\pi}(\sin x + \tfrac{1}{3}\sin 3x + \cdots)$$

which is the same as (5.12).

8. OTHER INTERVALS

The functions $\sin nx$ and $\cos nx$ and e^{inx} have period 2π. We have been considering $(-\pi, \pi)$ as the basic interval of length 2π. Given $f(x)$ on $(-\pi, \pi)$, we have first sketched it for this interval, and then repeated our sketch for the intervals $(\pi, 3\pi)$, $(3\pi, 5\pi)$, $(-3\pi, -\pi)$, etc. There are (infinitely) many other intervals of length 2π, any one of which could serve as the basic interval. If we are given $f(x)$ on *any* interval of length 2π, we can sketch $f(x)$ for that given basic interval and then repeat it periodically with period 2π. We then want to expand the periodic function so obtained, in a Fourier series. Recall that in evaluating the Fourier coefficients, we used average values *over a period*. The formulas for the coefficients are then unchanged (except for the limits of integration) if we use other basic intervals of length 2π. In practice, the intervals $(-\pi, \pi)$ and $(0, 2\pi)$ are the ones most frequently used. For $f(x)$ defined on $(0, 2\pi)$ and then repeated periodically, (5.9), (5.10), and (7.6) would read

$$a_n = \frac{1}{\pi}\int_0^{2\pi} f(x)\cos nx\, dx, \qquad b_n = \frac{1}{\pi}\int_0^{2\pi} f(x)\sin nx\, dx,$$

$$(8.1)$$

$$c_n = \frac{1}{2\pi}\int_0^{2\pi} f(x)e^{-inx}\, dx,$$

and (3.1) and (7.2) are unchanged.

Notice how important it is to sketch a graph to see clearly what function you are talking about. For example, given $f(x) = x^2$ on $(-\pi, \pi)$, the extended function of period 2π is shown in Fig. 8.1. But given $f(x) = x^2$ on $(0, 2\pi)$, the extended periodic function is different (see Fig. 8.2). On the other hand, given $f(x)$ as in our example (5.11), or given $f(x) = 1$ on $(0, \pi)$, $f(x) = 0$ on $(\pi, 2\pi)$, you can easily verify by sketching that the graphs of the extended functions are identical. In this case you would get

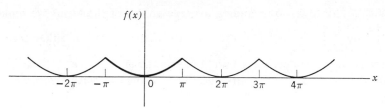

Figure 8.1

the same answer from either formulas (5.9), (5.10), and (7.6) or formulas (8.1).

Physics problems do not always come to us with intervals of length 2π. Fortunately, it is easy now to change to other intervals. Consider intervals of length $2l$, say $(-l, l)$ or $(0, 2l)$. The function $\sin (n\pi x/l)$ has period $2l$, since

$$\sin \frac{n\pi}{l} (x + 2l) = \sin \left(\frac{n\pi x}{l} + 2n\pi\right) = \sin \frac{n\pi x}{l}.$$

Similarly, $\cos (n\pi x/l)$ and $e^{in\pi x/l}$ have period $2l$. Equations (3.1) and (7.2) are now replaced by

$$f(x) = \frac{a_0}{2} + a_1 \cos \frac{\pi x}{l} + a_2 \cos \frac{2\pi x}{l} + \cdots$$

(8.2)
$$+ b_1 \sin \frac{\pi x}{l} + b_2 \sin \frac{2\pi x}{l} + \cdots$$

$$= \frac{a_0}{2} + \sum_{1}^{\infty} \left(a_n \cos \frac{n\pi x}{l} + b_n \sin \frac{n\pi x}{l}\right),$$

$$f(x) = \sum_{-\infty}^{\infty} c_n e^{in\pi x/l}.$$

We have already found the average values *over a period* of all the functions we need to use to find a_n, b_n, and c_n here. The period is now of

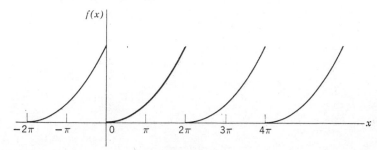

Figure 8.2

length $2l$ ($-l$ to l), so in finding average values of the terms we replace $\dfrac{1}{2\pi}\displaystyle\int_{-\pi}^{\pi}$ by $\dfrac{1}{2l}\displaystyle\int_{-l}^{l}$. Recall that the average of the square of either the sine or the cosine over a period is $\frac{1}{2}$ and the average of $e^{in\pi x/l} \cdot e^{-in\pi x/l} = 1$ is 1. Then the formulas (5.9), (5.10), and (7.6) for the coefficients become

(8.3)
$$a_n = \frac{1}{l}\int_{-l}^{l} f(x)\cos\frac{n\pi x}{l}\,dx,$$
$$b_n = \frac{1}{l}\int_{-l}^{l} f(x)\sin\frac{n\pi x}{l}\,dx,$$
$$c_n = \frac{1}{2l}\int_{-l}^{l} f(x)e^{-in\pi x/l}\,dx.$$

For the basic interval $(0, 2l)$ we need only change the integration limits to 0 to $2l$. The Dirichlet theorem just needs π replaced by l in order to apply here.

Example. Given $f(x) = \begin{cases} 0, & 0 < x < l, \\ 1, & l < x < 2l, \end{cases}$

Expand $f(x)$ in an exponential Fourier series of period $2l$. [The function is given by the same formulas as (5.11) but on a different interval.]

First we sketch a graph of $f(x)$ repeated with period $2l$ (Fig. 8.3). By equations (8.3), we find

(8.4)
$$c_n = \frac{1}{2l}\int_{0}^{l} 0 \cdot dx + \frac{1}{2l}\int_{l}^{2l} 1 \cdot e^{-in\pi x/l}\,dx$$
$$= \frac{1}{2l}\frac{e^{-in\pi x/l}}{-in\pi/l}\Big|_{l}^{2l} = \frac{1}{-2in\pi}(e^{-2in\pi} - e^{-in\pi})$$
$$= \frac{1}{-2in\pi}(1 - e^{in\pi}) = \begin{cases} 0, & \text{even } n \neq 0, \\ -\dfrac{1}{in\pi}, & \text{odd } n, \end{cases}$$
$$c_0 = \frac{1}{2l}\int_{l}^{2l} dx = \tfrac{1}{2}.$$

Then

(8.5)　$f(x) = \tfrac{1}{2} - \dfrac{1}{i\pi}(e^{i\pi x/l} - e^{-i\pi x/l} + \tfrac{1}{3}e^{3i\pi x/l} - \tfrac{1}{3}e^{-3i\pi x/l} + \cdots)$
$$= \tfrac{1}{2} - \frac{2}{\pi}\left(\sin\frac{\pi x}{l} + \tfrac{1}{3}\sin\frac{3\pi x}{l} + \cdots\right).$$

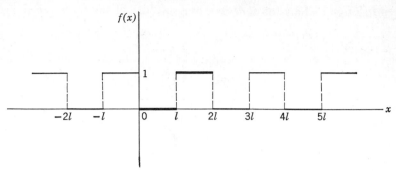

Figure 8.3

9. EVEN AND ODD FUNCTIONS

An *even* function is one like $\cos x$ or x^2 (Fig. 9.1) whose graph for negative x is just a reflection in the y-axis of its graph for positive x. In formulas, the value of $f(x)$ is the same for a given x and its negative; that is,

$$(9.1) \qquad f(x) \qquad \text{is even if} \qquad f(-x) = f(x).$$

An odd function is one like x or $\sin x$ (Fig. 9.2) for which the values of $f(x)$ and $f(-x)$ are negatives of each other. By definition

$$(9.2) \qquad f(x) \qquad \text{is odd if} \qquad f(-x) = -f(x).$$

Notice that even powers of x are even, and odd powers of x are odd; in fact, this is the reason for the names. You should verify (Problem 24a) the following rules for the product of two functions: An even function times an even function, or an odd function times an odd function, gives an even function; an odd function times an even function gives an odd function. Some functions are even, some are odd, and some (for example, e^x) are neither. However, any function can be written as the sum of an

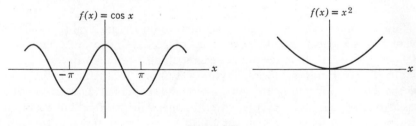

Figure 9.1

even function and an odd function, like this:

$$f(x) = \tfrac{1}{2}[f(x) + f(-x)] + \tfrac{1}{2}[f(x) - f(-x)];$$

the first part is even and the second part is odd. For example,

$$e^x = \tfrac{1}{2}(e^x + e^{-x}) + \tfrac{1}{2}(e^x - e^{-x}) = \cosh x + \sinh x;$$

$\cosh x$ is even and $\sinh x$ is odd.

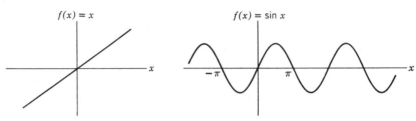

Figure 9.2

Integrals of even functions or of odd functions, over symmetric intervals like $(-\pi, \pi)$ or $(-l, l)$, can be simplified. Look at the graph of $\sin x$ and think about $\int_{-\pi}^{\pi} \sin x \, dx$. The negative area from $-\pi$ to 0 cancels the positive area from 0 to π, so the integral is zero. This integral is still zero for any interval $(-l, l)$ that is symmetric about the origin, as you can see from the graph. The same is true for *any* odd $f(x)$; the areas to the left and to the right cancel. Next look at the cosine graph and the integral $\int_{-\pi/2}^{\pi/2} \cos x \, dx$. You see that the area from $-\pi/2$ to 0 is the same as the area from 0 to $\pi/2$. We could then just as well find the integral from 0 to $\pi/2$ and multiply it by 2. In general, if $f(x)$ is even, the integral of $f(x)$ from $-l$ to l is twice the integral from 0 to l. Then we have

$$(9.3) \qquad \int_{-l}^{l} f(x)\, dx = \begin{cases} 0 & \text{if } f(x) \text{ is odd,} \\ 2\displaystyle\int_{0}^{l} f(x)\, dx & \text{if } f(x) \text{ is even.} \end{cases}$$

Suppose now that we are given a function on the interval $(0, l)$. If we want to represent it by a Fourier series of period $2l$, we must have $f(x)$ defined on $(-l, 0)$ too. There are several things we could do. We *could* define it to be zero (or, indeed, anything else) on $(-l, 0)$ and go ahead as we have done previously to find either an exponential or a sine-cosine series of period $2l$. However, it often happens in practice that we need (for physical reasons—see Chapter 14) to have an even function (or, in a

Even
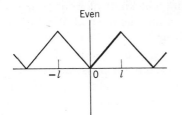

Odd
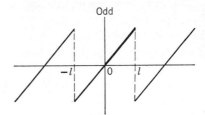

Figure 9.3

different problem, an odd function). When we are free to choose our own graph on $(-l, 0)$, we can choose either an even or an odd function on $(-l, l)$. Then, of course, $f(x)$ is continued further with period $2l$. Some examples are shown in Figs. 9.3 and 9.4; in each case the graph is given from 0 to l, and has been extended on $(-l, 0)$ to be even or odd.

For even or odd functions, the coefficient formulas for a_n and b_n simplify. First suppose $f(x)$ is odd. Since $\sin (n\pi x/l)$ is odd, $f(x) \sin (n\pi x/l)$ is even and $f(x) \cos (n\pi x/l)$ is odd. Then a_n is the integral, over a symmetric interval $(-l, l)$, of an odd function, namely $f(x) \cos (n\pi x/l)$; a_n is therefore zero. But b_n is the integral of an even function over a symmetric interval and is therefore twice the 0 to l integral. We have:

(9.4)   N.B.'   If $f(x)$ is odd, $\begin{cases} b_n = \dfrac{2}{l} \displaystyle\int_0^l f(x) \sin \dfrac{n\pi x}{l}\, dx, \\ a_n = 0. \end{cases}$

We say that we have expanded $f(x)$ in a sine series ($a_n = 0$ so there are no cosine terms). Similarly, if $f(x)$ is even, all the b_n's are zero, and the a_n's are integrals of even functions. We have:

(9.5)   If $f(x)$ is even, $\begin{cases} a_n = \dfrac{2}{l} \displaystyle\int_0^l f(x) \cos \dfrac{n\pi x}{l}\, dx, \\ b_n = 0. \end{cases}$

We say that $f(x)$ is expanded in a cosine series.

Even
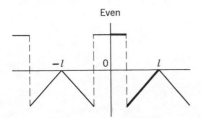

Odd
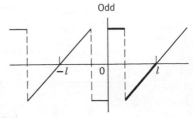

Figure 9.4

You have now learned to find several different kinds of Fourier series that represent a given function $f(x)$ on, let us say, the interval $(0, 1)$. How do you know which to use in a given problem? You have to decide this from the physical problem when you are using Fourier series. There are two things to check: (1) the basic period involved in the physical problem; the functions in your series should have this period; and (2) the physical problem may require either an even function or an odd function for its solution; in these cases you must find the appropriate series. Now consider $f(x)$ defined on $(0, 1)$. We could find for it a sine-cosine or an exponential series of period 1 (that is, $l = \frac{1}{2}$):

$$f(x) = \sum_{-\infty}^{\infty} c_n e^{2in\pi x} \quad \text{where} \quad c_n = \int_0^1 f(x) e^{-2in\pi x}\, dx.$$

(The choice between sine-cosine and exponential series is just one of convenience in evaluating the coefficients—the series are really identical.) But we could also find two other Fourier series representing the same $f(x)$ on $(0, 1)$. These series would have period 2 (that is, $l = 1$). One would be a cosine series

$$f(x) = \sum_{n=0}^{\infty} a_n \cos n\pi x, \qquad a_n = 2\int_0^1 f(x) \cos n\pi x\, dx, \qquad b_n = 0,$$

and represent an even function; the other would be a sine series and represent an odd function. In the problems, you may just be told to expand a function in a cosine series, say. You must then see for yourself what the period is when you have sketched an even function, and so choose the proper l in $\cos(n\pi x/l)$ and in the formula for a_n.

Example. Represent $f(x) = \begin{cases} 1, & 0 < x < \frac{1}{2} \\ 0, & \frac{1}{2} < x < 1 \end{cases}$

in (a) a Fourier sine series, (b) a Fourier cosine series, (c) a Fourier series (the last ordinarily means a sine-cosine or exponential series whose period is the interval over which the function is given; in this case the period is 1).

(a) Sketch the given function between 0 and 1. Extend it to the interval

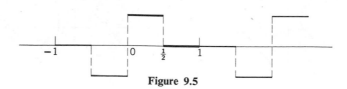

Figure 9.5

$(-1, 0)$ making it odd. The period is now 2, that is, $l = 1$. Continue the function with period 2 (Fig. 9.5). Since we now have an odd function, $a_n = 0$ and

$$b_n = \frac{2}{1} \int_0^1 f(x) \sin n\pi x \, dx = 2 \int_0^{1/2} \sin n\pi x \, dx$$

$$= -\frac{2}{n\pi} \cos n\pi x \Big|_0^{1/2} = -\frac{2}{n\pi} \left(\cos \frac{n\pi}{2} - 1 \right),$$

$$b_1 = \frac{2}{\pi}, \qquad b_2 = \frac{4}{2\pi}, \qquad b_3 = \frac{2}{3\pi}, \qquad b_4 = 0, \quad \text{etc.}$$

Thus we obtain the *Fourier sine series* for $f(x)$:

$$f(x) = \frac{2}{\pi} \left(\sin \pi x + \frac{2 \sin 2\pi x}{2} + \frac{\sin 3\pi x}{3} + \frac{\sin 5\pi x}{5} + \frac{2 \sin 6\pi x}{6} + \cdots \right).$$

(b) Sketch an even function of period 2 (Fig. 9.6).

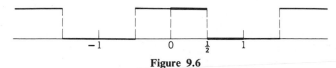

Figure 9.6

Here $l = 1$, $b_n = 0$, and

$$a_0 = 2 \int_0^1 f(x) \, dx = 2 \int_0^{1/2} dx = 1,$$

$$a_n = 2 \int_0^1 f(x) \cos n\pi x \, dx = \frac{2}{n\pi} \sin n\pi x \Big|_0^{1/2} = \frac{2}{n\pi} \sin \frac{n\pi}{2}.$$

Then the *Fourier cosine series* for $f(x)$ is

$$f(x) = \frac{1}{2} + \frac{2}{\pi} \left(\frac{\cos \pi x}{1} - \frac{\cos 3\pi x}{3} + \frac{\cos 5\pi x}{5} \cdots \right).$$

(c) Sketch the given function on $(0, 1)$ and continue it with period 1 (Fig. 9.7). Here $2l = 1$, and we find c_n as we did in the example of Section 8. As in that example, the exponential series here can then be put in

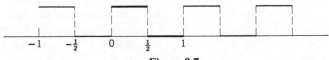

Figure 9.7

sine-cosine form. Alternatively we can find both a_n and b_n directly.

$$c_n = \int_0^1 f(x)e^{-2in\pi x}\,dx = \int_0^{1/2} e^{-2in\pi x}\,dx$$

$$= \frac{1 - e^{-in\pi}}{2in\pi} = \frac{1 - (-1)^n}{2in\pi} = \begin{cases} \dfrac{1}{in\pi}, & n \text{ odd,} \\[2mm] 0, & n \text{ even} \neq 0. \end{cases}$$

$$c_0 = \int_0^{1/2} dx = \tfrac{1}{2}.$$

$$f(x) = \frac{1}{2} + \frac{1}{i\pi}\left(e^{2i\pi x} - e^{-2i\pi x} + \frac{1}{3}e^{6\pi i x} - \frac{1}{3}e^{-6\pi i x} + \cdots\right)$$

$$= \frac{1}{2} + \frac{2}{\pi}\left(\sin 2\pi x + \frac{\sin 6\pi x}{3} + \cdots\right).$$

Alternatively,

$$a_0 = 2\int_0^1 f(x)\,dx = 2\int_0^{1/2} dx = 1.$$

$$a_n = 2\int_0^{1/2} \cos 2n\pi x\,dx = 0.$$

$$b_n = 2\int_0^{1/2} \sin 2n\pi x\,dx = \frac{1}{n\pi}(1 - \cos n\pi)$$

$$= \frac{1}{n\pi}[1 - (-1)^n].$$

$$b_1 = \frac{2}{\pi}, \qquad b_2 = 0, \qquad b_3 = \frac{2}{3\pi}, \qquad b_4 = 0, \quad \text{etc.}$$

There is one other very useful point to notice about even and odd functions. If you are given a function on $(-l, l)$ to expand in a sine-cosine series (of period $2l$) and happen to notice that it is an even function, you should realize that the b_n's are all going to be zero and you do not have to work them out. Also the a_n's can be written as twice an integral from 0 to l just as in (9.5). Similarly, if the given function is odd, you can use (9.4). Recognizing this may save you a good deal of algebra.

10. AN APPLICATION TO SOUND

We have said that when a sound wave passes through the air and we hear it, the air pressure where we are varies with time. Suppose the excess pressure above (and below) atmospheric pressure in a sound wave is given by the graph in Fig. 10.1. (We shall not be concerned here with the units of p; however, reasonable units in Fig. 10.1 would be p in 10^{-6} atmospheres.)

Let us ask what frequencies we hear when we listen to this sound. To find out, we expand $p(t)$ in a Fourier series. The period of $p(t)$ is $\frac{1}{262}$; that is, the sound wave repeats itself 262 times per second. We have called the period $2l$ in our formulas, so here $l = \frac{1}{524}$. The functions we have called $\sin (n\pi x/l)$ here become $\sin 524n\pi t$. We can save some work by observing that $p(t)$ is an odd function; there are then only sine terms in

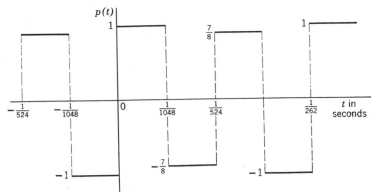

Figure 10.1

its Fourier series and we need compute only b_n. Using (9.4), we have

$$(10.1) \quad b_n = 2(524)\int_0^{\frac{1}{524}} p(t) \sin 524n\pi t \, dt$$

$$= 1048 \int_0^{\frac{1}{1048}} \sin 524n\pi t \, dt - \tfrac{7}{8}(1048)\int_{\frac{1}{1048}}^{\frac{1}{524}} \sin 524n\pi t \, dt$$

$$= 1048 \left(-\frac{\cos \dfrac{n\pi}{2} - 1}{524n\pi} + \frac{7}{8} \frac{\cos n\pi - \cos \dfrac{n\pi}{2}}{524n\pi} \right)$$

$$= \frac{2}{n\pi}\left(-\frac{15}{8}\cos \frac{n\pi}{2} + 1 + \frac{7}{8}\cos n\pi \right).$$

From this we can compute the values of b_n for the first few values of n:

(10.2)

$$b_1 = \frac{2}{\pi}\left(1 - \frac{7}{8}\right) = \frac{2}{\pi}\left(\frac{1}{8}\right) = \frac{1}{\pi}\cdot\frac{1}{4} \qquad b_5 = \frac{1}{5\pi}\cdot\frac{1}{4}$$

$$b_2 = \frac{2}{2\pi}\left(\frac{15}{8} + 1 + \frac{7}{8}\right) = \frac{1}{2\pi}\left(\frac{15}{2}\right) \qquad b_6 = \frac{1}{6\pi}\left(\frac{15}{2}\right)$$

$$b_3 = \frac{2}{3\pi}\left(1 - \frac{7}{8}\right) = \frac{1}{3\pi}\cdot\frac{1}{4} \qquad b_7 = \frac{1}{7\pi}\cdot\frac{1}{4}$$

$$b_4 = \frac{2}{4\pi}\left(-\frac{15}{8} + 1 + \frac{7}{8}\right) = 0 \qquad b_8 = 0, \quad \text{etc.}$$

Then we have

(10.3)

$$p(t) = \frac{1}{4\pi}\left(\frac{\sin 524\pi t}{1} + \frac{30\sin(524\cdot 2\pi t)}{2} + \frac{\sin(524\cdot 3\pi t)}{3}\right.$$

$$\left. + \frac{\sin(524\cdot 5\pi t)}{5} + \frac{30\sin(524\cdot 6\pi t)}{6} + \frac{\sin(524\cdot 7\pi t)}{7} + \cdots\right).$$

We can see just by looking at the coefficients that the most important term is the second one. The first term corresponds to the fundamental with frequency 262 vibrations per second (this is approximately middle C on a piano). But it is much weaker in this case than the first overtone (second harmonic) corresponding to the second term; this tone has frequency 524 vibrations per second (approximately high C). The sixth harmonic (corresponding to $n = 6$) and also the harmonics for $n = 10$, 14, 18, 22, and 26 are all more prominent (that is, have larger coefficients) than the fundamental. We can be even more specific about the relative importance of the various frequencies. Recall that in discussing a simple harmonic oscillator, we showed that its average energy was proportional to the square of its velocity amplitude. It can be proved that the intensity of a sound wave (average energy striking unit area of your ear per second) is proportional to the average of the square of the excess pressure. Thus for a sinusoidal pressure variation $A \sin 2\pi ft$, the intensity is proportional to A^2. In the Fourier series for $p(t)$, the intensities of the various harmonics are then proportional to the squares of the corresponding Fourier coefficients. (The intensity corresponds roughly to the loudness of the tone—not exactly because the ear is not uniformly sensitive to all frequencies.) The relative intensities of the harmonics in our example are then:

n	= 1	2	3	4	5	6	7	8	9	10	
Relative intensity	= 1	225	$\frac{1}{9}$	0	$\frac{1}{25}$	25	$\frac{1}{49}$	0	$\frac{1}{81}$	9	etc.

From this we see even more clearly that we would hear principally the second harmonic with frequency 524 (high C).

11. PARSEVAL'S THEOREM

We shall now find a relation between the average of the square (or absolute square) of $f(x)$ and the coefficients in the Fourier series for $f(x)$. The result is known as *Parseval's theorem* or the *completeness relation*. You should understand that the point of the theorem is *not* to get the average of the square of a given $f(x)$ by using its Fourier series. [Given $f(x)$, it is easy to get its average square just by doing the integration!] The point of the theorem is to show the *relation* between the average of the square of $f(x)$ and the Fourier coefficients. We can derive a form of Parseval's theorem from any of the various Fourier expansions we have made; let us use (3.1).

$$(11.1) \qquad f(x) = \tfrac{1}{2}a_0 + \sum_1^\infty a_n \cos nx + \sum_1^\infty b_n \sin nx.$$

We square $f(x)$ and then average the square over $(-\pi, \pi)$:

$$(11.2) \qquad \text{The average of } [f(x)]^2 \quad \text{is} \quad \frac{1}{2\pi}\int_{-\pi}^{\pi} [f(x)]^2 \, dx.$$

When we square $f(x)$, we get many terms. To avoid writing out a large number of them, consider instead what types of terms there are in $[f(x)]^2$ and what the averages of the different kinds of terms are. First, there are the squares of the individual terms in $f(x)$. Using the fact that the average of the square of a sine or cosine over a period is $\tfrac{1}{2}$, we have:

$$
\begin{aligned}
&\text{The average of } (\tfrac{1}{2}a_0)^2 \quad \text{is} \quad \tfrac{1}{4}a_0^2.\\
(11.3) \quad &\text{The average of } (a_n \cos nx)^2 \quad \text{is} \quad a_n^2 \cdot \tfrac{1}{2}.\\
&\text{The average of } (b_n \sin nx)^2 \quad \text{is} \quad b_n^2 \cdot \tfrac{1}{2}.
\end{aligned}
$$

Then there are cross-product terms of the forms $2 \cdot \tfrac{1}{2}a_0 a_n \cos nx$, $2 \cdot \tfrac{1}{2}a_0 b_n \sin nx$, and $2a_n b_m \cos nx \sin mx$ with $m \neq n$ (we write n in the cosine factor and m in the sine factor since every sine term must be multiplied times every cosine term). By (5.1), the average values of terms of all these types are zero. Then we have

$$(11.4) \quad \text{The average of } [f(x)]^2 \text{ (over a period)} = \tfrac{1}{4}a_0^2 + \tfrac{1}{2}\sum_1^\infty a_n^2 + \tfrac{1}{2}\sum_1^\infty b_n^2.$$

This is one form of Parseval's theorem. You can easily verify (Problem 32) that the theorem is unchanged if $f(x)$ has period $2l$ instead of 2π and its square is averaged over any period of length $2l$. You can also verify (Problem 32) that if $f(x)$ is written as a complex exponential Fourier series, and if in addition we include the possibility that $f(x)$ itself may be complex, then we find:

$$(11.5) \qquad \text{The average of } |f(x)|^2 \text{ (over a period)} = \sum_{-\infty}^\infty |c_n|^2.$$

Parseval's theorem is sometimes called the completeness relation. In the problem of representing a given sound wave as a sum of harmonics, suppose we had left one of the harmonics out of the series. It seems plausible physically, and it can be proved mathematically, that with one or more harmonics left out, we would not be able to represent sound waves containing the omitted harmonics. We say that the set of functions $\sin nx$, $\cos nx$ is a *complete set* of functions on any interval of length 2π; that is, any function (satisfying Dirichlet conditions) can be expanded in a Fourier series whose terms are constants times $\sin nx$ and $\cos nx$. If we left out some values of n, we would have an incomplete set of basic functions and could not use it to expand some given functions. For example, suppose that you made a mistake in finding the period (that is, the value of l) of your given function and tried to use the set of functions $\sin 2nx$, $\cos 2nx$ in expanding a given function of period 2π. You would get a wrong answer because you used an incomplete set of functions (with the $\sin x$, $\sin 3x$, etc., terms missing). If your Fourier series is wrong because the set of basic functions you use is incomplete, then the results you get from Parseval's theorem (11.4) or (11.5) will be wrong too. Conversely, if (11.4) and (11.5) are correct for all $f(x)$, then the basic set of functions used is a complete set. This is why Parseval's theorem is often called the completeness relation.

Let us look at some examples of the physical meaning and the use of Parseval's theorem.

Example 1. In Section 10 we said that the intensity (energy per square centimeter per second) of a sound wave is proportional to the average value of the square of the excess pressure. If for simplicity we write (10.3) with letters instead of numerical values, we have

$$(11.6) \qquad\qquad p(t) = \sum_{1}^{\infty} b_n \sin 2\pi n f t.$$

For this case, Parseval's theorem (11.4) says that:

$$(11.7) \quad \text{The average of } [p(t)]^2 = \sum_{1}^{\infty} b_n^2 \cdot \tfrac{1}{2} = \sum_{1}^{\infty} \text{the average of } b_n^2 \sin^2 2n\pi f t.$$

Now the intensity or energy (per square centimeter per second) of the sound wave is proportional to the average of $[p(t)]^2$, and the energy associated with the nth harmonic is proportional to the average of $b_n^2 \sin^2 2n\pi f t$. Thus Parseval's theorem says that the total energy of the sound wave is equal to the sum of the energies associated with the various harmonics.

Example 2. Let us use Parseval's theorem to find the sum of an infinite series. From Problem 16 we get:

The function $f(x)$ of period 2 which is equal to x on $(-1, 1)$

$$= -\frac{i}{\pi}\left(e^{i\pi x} - e^{-i\pi x} - \frac{1}{2}e^{2\pi ix} + \frac{1}{2}e^{-2\pi ix} + \frac{1}{3}e^{3\pi ix} - \frac{1}{3}e^{-3\pi ix} + \cdots\right).$$

Let us find the average of $[f(x)]^2$ on $(-1, 1)$.

$$\text{The average of } [f(x)]^2 = \frac{1}{2}\int_{-1}^{1} x^2\,dx = \frac{1}{2}\left[\frac{x^3}{3}\right]_{-1}^{1} = \frac{1}{3}.$$

By Parseval's theorem (11.5), this is equal to $\sum_{-\infty}^{\infty} |c_n|^2$, so we have

$$\frac{1}{3} = \sum_{-\infty}^{\infty} |c_n|^2 = \frac{1}{\pi^2}\left(1 + 1 + \frac{1}{4} + \frac{1}{4} + \frac{1}{9} + \frac{1}{9} + \cdots\right) = \frac{2}{\pi^2}\sum_{1}^{\infty}\frac{1}{n^2}.$$

Then we get the sum of the series

$$1 + \frac{1}{4} + \frac{1}{9} + \cdots = \sum_{1}^{\infty}\frac{1}{n^2} = \frac{\pi^2}{2}\cdot\frac{1}{3} = \frac{\pi^2}{6}.$$

REFERENCES

See books on Fourier series by Churchill, Jackson, Rogosinski, and Tolstov. Some advanced calculus books and some books on mathematics in physics and engineering contain discussions of Fourier series. References suggested for Chapter 6 are identified in the list at the end of the book by a [6] after the listing.

PROBLEMS

1. (a) Find the amplitude, period, frequency, and velocity amplitude for the motion of a particle whose distance from the origin is $s = 4\sin(3t + 2)$.

(b) Given $z = 5e^{it/2}$, show that a particle whose coordinate is $x = \text{Re } z$ is undergoing simple harmonic motion, and find the amplitude, period, frequency, and velocity amplitude of the motion. Repeat the problem for a particle whose coordinate is $y = \text{Im } z$.

(c) The charge q on a capacitor in a simple a-c circuit varies with time according to the equation $q = 3\sin(2\pi t + \pi/4)$. Find the amplitude, period, and frequency of this oscillation. By definition, the current flowing in the circuit at time t is $I = dq/dt$. Show that I is also a sinusoidal function of t, and find its amplitude, period, and frequency.

(d) A simple pendulum is a small mass m suspended, as shown, by a (weightless) string. Show that for small oscillations (small θ), both θ and x are sinusoidal functions of time, that is, the motion is simple harmonic.

Hint: Write the differential equation $F = ma$ for the particle m. Use the approximation $\sin \theta = \theta$ for small θ, and show that $\theta = A \sin \omega t$ is a solution of your equation. What are A and ω?

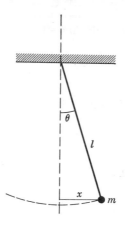

(e) The displacements x [see part (d)] of two simple pendulums are $4 \sin (\pi t/3)$ and $3 \sin (\pi t/4)$. They start together at $x = 0$. How long will it be before they are together again at $x = 0$? *Hint:* Find the period of each and sketch graphs of the two motions on the same axes.

(f) Show that equation (2.10) for a wave can be written in all these forms:

$$y = A \sin \frac{2\pi}{\lambda} (x - vt) = A \sin 2\pi \left(\frac{x}{\lambda} - \frac{t}{T} \right)$$

$$= A \sin \omega \left(\frac{x}{v} - t \right) = A \sin \left(\frac{2\pi x}{\lambda} - 2\pi f t \right)$$

$$= A \sin \frac{2\pi}{T} \left(\frac{x}{v} - t \right).$$

Here λ is the wavelength, f is the frequency, v is the wave velocity, T is the period, and $\omega = 2\pi f$ is called the *angular frequency*. *Hint:* Show that $v = \lambda f$.

(g) Find the velocity, amplitude, period, and frequency of each of the following waves: $2 \sin 5\pi(x - 10t)$, $4 \cos 8(2x + 3t)$, $\sin \pi(\frac{2}{3}x - 4t)$.

(h) Sketch $y = 2 \sin \frac{2}{3}\pi(x - 3t)$ for $t = 0$, for $t = 1$; for $x = 0$, for $x = 1$.

(i) Write the equation for a sinusoidal wave of wavelength 4, amplitude 20, and velocity 6. Sketch graphs of y as a function of t for $x = 0, 1, 2, 3$, and of y as a function of x for $t = 0, \frac{1}{6}, \frac{1}{3}, \frac{1}{2}$. If this wave represents the shape of a long rope which is being shaken back and forth at one end, find the velocity dy/dt of particles of the rope as a function of x and t. (Note that this velocity has nothing to do with the wave velocity v, which is the rate at which crests of the wave move forward.)

(j) Write an equation for a sinusoidal radio wave of amplitude 10 and frequency 600 kilocycles per second. *Hint:* The velocity of a radio wave is the velocity of light, $c = 3 \cdot 10^8$ m/sec.

2. In parts (a) and (b) draw a graph over a whole period of each of the following combinations of a fundamental musical tone and some of its overtones:

(a) $\sin t - \frac{1}{9} \sin 3t$.

(b) $\sin \pi t + \sin 2\pi t + \frac{1}{3} \sin 3\pi t$.

(c) Draw a graph of $\sin 2x + \sin 2(x + \frac{1}{3})$. *Hint:* Use a trigonometry formula to write this as a single harmonic. What are the period and amplitude?

(d) The voltage in a telegraph line is, under certain circumstances, given by

$$ f(x, t) = A \sin\left(t - \frac{x}{v}\right) + A \sin\left(t - 2\tau + \frac{x}{v}\right), $$

where v is the velocity and τ is the time for a wave to travel the length of the line. This represents the combination of a wave starting at one end and the reflection of the wave from the other end. What are the wavelengths and frequencies of the waves? Sketch the graphs of $f(x, t)$ when $A = 2$, $v = 3$, $\tau = 1$, both as a function of t for $x = 2$ (over the time interval for which t is between 1 and 2) and as a function of x (between 0 and 3) when $t = \frac{3}{2}$.

(e) A periodic amplitude modulated (AM) radio signal has the form

$$ y = (A + B \sin 2\pi ft) \sin 2\pi f_c\left(t - \frac{x}{v}\right). $$

The factor $\sin 2\pi f_c\left(t - \frac{x}{v}\right)$ is called the carrier wave; it has a very high frequency (called radio frequency; f_c is of the order of 10^6 cycles per second). The amplitude of the carrier wave is $(A + B \sin 2\pi ft)$. This amplitude varies with time—hence the term "amplitude modulation"—with the much smaller frequency of the sound being transmitted (called audio frequency; f is of the order of 10^2 cycles per second). In order to see the general appearance of such a wave, use the following simple but unrealistic data to sketch a graph of y as a function of t for $x = 0$ over one period of the *amplitude* function: $A = 3$, $B = 1$, $f = 1$, $f_c = 20$. Using trigonometric formulas, show that y can be written as a sum of three waves of frequencies f_c, $f_c + f$, and $f_c - f$; the first of these is the carrier wave and the other two are called side bands.

3. Using the definition (end of Section 2) of a periodic function, show that a sum of terms corresponding to a fundamental musical tone and its overtones has the period of the fundamental.

4. Show that if $f(x)$ has period p, the average value of f is the same over any interval of length p. *Hint:* Write $\int_a^{a+p} f(x)\,dx$ as the sum of two integrals (a to p, and p to $a + p$) and make the change of variable $x = t + p$ in the second integral.

5. (a) Prove that $\int_0^{\pi/2} \sin^2 x \, dx = \int_0^{\pi/2} \cos^2 x \, dx$ by making the change of variable $x = \frac{1}{2}\pi - t$ in one of the integrals.

   (b) Use the same method to prove that the averages of $\sin^2(n\pi x/l)$ and $\cos^2(n\pi x/l)$ are the same over a period.

6. Show that in (5.1) the average values (over a period) of $\sin mx \sin nx$ and of $\cos mx \cos nx$ ($m \neq n$) are zero, by using the complex exponential forms for the sines and cosines as in (5.2).

7. Find the average values of:

   (a) $\sin x$ on $(0, \pi)$,

   (b) $1 - e^{-x}$ on $(0, 1)$,

   (c) $\cos^2 \dfrac{x}{2}$ on $\left(0, \dfrac{\pi}{2}\right)$,

   (d) $\sin x + 2 \sin 2x + 3 \sin 3x$
       on $(0, 2\pi)$,

   (e) $\sin 2x$ on $\left(\dfrac{\pi}{6}, \dfrac{7\pi}{6}\right)$.

8. The displacement (from equilibrium) of a particle executing simple harmonic motion may be either $y = A \sin \omega t$ or $y = A \sin(\omega t + \phi)$ depending on our choice of time origin. Show that the average of the kinetic energy of a particle of mass m (over a period of the motion) is the same for the two formulas (as it must be since both describe the same physical motion). Find the average value of the kinetic energy for the $\sin(\omega t + \phi)$ case in two ways:

   (a) by selecting the integration limits (as you may by Problem 4) so that a change of variable reduces the integral to the $\sin \omega t$ case;

   (b) by expanding $\sin(\omega t + \phi)$ by the trigonometric addition formulas and using (5.1) to write the average values.

9. In each of the following problems you are given a function on the interval $-\pi < x < \pi$. Sketch several periods of the corresponding periodic function of period 2π. Expand the periodic function in a sine-cosine Fourier series.

   (a) $f(x) = 1$ on the interval $0 < x < \pi$, $f(x) = -1$ on the interval $-\pi < x < 0$.

   In this case the sketch is

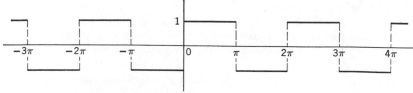

   Your answer for the series is

   $$f(x) = \frac{4}{\pi}\left(\frac{\sin x}{1} + \frac{\sin 3x}{3} + \frac{\sin 5x}{5} + \cdots\right).$$

   (b) $f(x) = x$ on the interval $-\pi < x < \pi$.

   Answer: $f(x) = 2(\sin x - \frac{1}{2}\sin 2x + \frac{1}{3}\sin 3x - \frac{1}{4}\sin 4x + \cdots)$.

(c) $f(x) = |x|$ on the interval $-\pi < x < \pi$.

Answer: $f(x) = \dfrac{\pi}{2} - \dfrac{4}{\pi}\left(\cos x + \dfrac{1}{3^2}\cos 3x + \dfrac{1}{5^2}\cos 5x + \cdots\right).$

(d) $f(x) = 0$ on the interval $-\pi < x \leq 0$; $f(x) = x$ on the interval $0 \leq x < \pi$.

Answer: $f(x) = \dfrac{\pi}{4} - \dfrac{2}{\pi}\left(\cos x + \dfrac{\cos 3x}{3^2} + \dfrac{\cos 5x}{5^2} + \cdots\right)$

$$+ \left(\sin x - \dfrac{\sin 2x}{2} + \dfrac{\sin 3x}{3} - \cdots\right).$$

(e) $f(x) = x^2$ on the interval $-\pi < x < \pi$.

Answer: $f(x) = \dfrac{\pi^2}{3} - 4\left(\cos x - \dfrac{\cos 2x}{2^2} + \dfrac{\cos 3x}{3^2} - \dfrac{\cos 4x}{4^2} + \cdots\right).$

(f) $f(x) = \cosh x$ on the interval $-\pi < x < \pi$.
Answer:

$$f(x) = \dfrac{2\sinh \pi}{\pi}\left(\dfrac{1}{2} - \dfrac{1}{2}\cos x + \dfrac{1}{5}\cos 2x - \dfrac{1}{10}\cos 3x + \dfrac{1}{17}\cos 4x - \cdots\right).$$

10. Expand the same functions as in Problem 9 in Fourier series of complex exponentials e^{inx} on the interval $(-\pi, \pi)$ and verify in each case (by using Euler's formula) that the answer is equivalent to the one given in Problem 9.

11. Sketch a graph of the sum of three terms of each of the series in Problem 9 and compare this approximation with the graph of $f(x)$. *Hint:* Sketch each term separately (on the same axes) and add the terms graphically.

12. (a) Show that if a real $f(x)$ is expanded in a complex exponential Fourier series $\sum\limits_{-\infty}^{\infty} c_n e^{inx}$, then $c_{-n} = \overline{c_n}$, where $\overline{c_n}$ means the complex conjugate of c_n.

(b) If $f(x) = \tfrac{1}{2}a_0 + \sum\limits_{1}^{\infty} a_n \cos nx + \sum\limits_{1}^{\infty} b_n \sin nx = \sum\limits_{-\infty}^{\infty} c_n e^{inx}$,

use Euler's formula to find a_n and b_n in terms of c_n and c_{-n}, and to find c_n and c_{-n} in terms of a_n and b_n.

13. (a) If $f(x) = x$ on the interval $0 < x < 2\pi$, extend $f(x)$ to form a periodic function of period 2π. Sketch the graph. Expand the periodic function in a Fourier series of sines and cosines of period 2π. Note that although the *formula* is the same as in Problem 9b, this is not the same $f(x)$ or the same series.

Answer: $f(x) = \pi - 2\sum\limits_{1}^{\infty} \dfrac{\sin nx}{n}.$

(b) Expand $f(x)$ as in (a) in a complex exponential Fourier series of period 2π. Verify (using Euler's formula) that your series is the same as in (a).

14. Write out the details of the derivation of the formulas (5.10) and (8.3).

15. Let $f(x)$ be defined by the *formulas* in Problem 9a, but for the intervals

$0 < x < l$ and $-l < x < 0$. Sketch the corresponding function of period $2l$ and expand it in a sine-cosine Fourier series of period $2l$.

Answer: $f(x) = \dfrac{4}{\pi}\left(\sin\dfrac{\pi x}{l} + \dfrac{1}{3}\sin\dfrac{3\pi x}{l} + \dfrac{1}{5}\sin\dfrac{5\pi x}{l} + \cdots\right).$

16. Let $f(x) = x$ on the interval $-1 < x < 1$. Sketch the corresponding function of period 2 and expand it in a complex exponential Fourier series of period 2.

Answer: $f(x) = -\dfrac{i}{\pi}(\cdots - \tfrac{1}{3}e^{-3\pi i x} + \tfrac{1}{2}e^{-2\pi i x} - e^{-i\pi x} + e^{i\pi x} - \tfrac{1}{2}e^{2\pi i x}$

$+ \tfrac{1}{3}e^{3\pi i x} - \cdots).$

17. Let $f(x) = x$ on $0 < x < 2$. Sketch the corresponding function of period 2 and expand it in a sine-cosine Fourier series.

Answer: $f(x) = 1 - \dfrac{2}{\pi}\sum_{1}^{\infty}\dfrac{\sin n\pi x}{n}.$

18. Let $f(x)$ be defined by the formulas in Problem 9d but on the intervals $-\tfrac{1}{2} < x < 0$ and $0 < x < \tfrac{1}{2}$. Sketch the corresponding function of period 1 and expand it in a sine-cosine Fourier series.

Answer: $f(x) = \dfrac{1}{8} - \dfrac{1}{\pi^2}\left(\cos 2\pi x + \dfrac{\cos 6\pi x}{3^2} + \dfrac{\cos 10\pi x}{5^2} + \cdots\right)$

$+ \dfrac{1}{2\pi}\left(\sin 2\pi x - \dfrac{\sin 4\pi x}{2} + \dfrac{\sin 6\pi x}{3} - \cdots\right).$

19. The symbol $[x]$ means the greatest integer less than or equal to x (for example, $[3] = 3$, $[2.1] = 2$, $[-4.5] = -5$). Expand $x - [x] - \tfrac{1}{2}$ in an exponential Fourier series of period 1. *Hint:* Sketch the function.

Answer: $\dfrac{i}{2\pi}\left(\cdots - \dfrac{e^{-4\pi i x}}{2} - \dfrac{e^{-2\pi i x}}{1} + \dfrac{e^{2\pi i x}}{1} + \dfrac{e^{4\pi i x}}{2} + \cdots\right).$

20. Given $f(x) = 1$ for $0 < x < \pi$, sketch the even function f_c of period 2π and the odd function f_s of period 2π, each of which equals $f(x)$ on the interval $0 < x < \pi$. Expand f_c in a cosine series and f_s in a sine series.

21. Given $f(x) = x$ for $0 < x < 1$, sketch the even function f_c of period 2 and the odd function f_s of period 2, each of which equals $f(x)$ on $0 < x < 1$. Expand f_c in a cosine series and f_s in a sine series.

Answer: $f_c(x) = \dfrac{1}{2} - \dfrac{4}{\pi^2}\left(\cos \pi x + \dfrac{1}{3^2}\cos 3\pi x + \cdots\right),$

$f_s(x) = \dfrac{2}{\pi}\left(\sin \pi x - \dfrac{1}{2}\sin 2\pi x + \dfrac{1}{3}\sin 3\pi x - \cdots\right).$

22. Given $f(x) = 0$, $0 < x < 1$; $f(x) = 1$, $1 < x < 2$. Sketch the even function f_c of period 4, the odd function f_s of period 4, and the function f_p of period 2, each of which equals $f(x)$ on $(0, 2)$. Expand f_c in a cosine series, f_s in a sine series, and f_p in a sine-cosine series and in a complex exponential series.

23. Give algebraic proofs of (9.3). *Hint:* Write $\int_{-l}^{l} = \int_{-l}^{0} + \int_{0}^{l}$, make the change of variable $x = -t$ in $\int_{-l}^{0}$, and use the definition of even or odd function.

24. Give algebraic proofs that for even and odd functions:

   (a) even times even = even; odd times odd = even; even times odd = odd;

   (b) the derivative of an even function is odd; the derivative of an odd function is even.

25. The following functions are neither even nor odd. Write each of them as the sum of an even function and an odd function.

   (a) e^{inx} (b) xe^x

   (c) $\ln|1 - x|$ (d) $(1 + x)(\sin x + \cos x)$

   (e) $x^5 - x^4 + x^3 - 1$ (f) $1 + e^x$

26. Using what you know about even and odd functions, prove the first part of (5.1).

27. We have said that Fourier series can represent discontinuous functions although power series cannot. It might occur to you to wonder why we could not substitute the power series for $\sin nx$ and $\cos nx$ (which converge for all x) into a Fourier series and collect terms to obtain a power series for a discontinuous function. As an example of what happens if we try this, consider the series in Problem 9a. Show that the coefficients of x, if collected, form a divergent series; similarly, the coefficients of x^3 form a divergent series, and so on.

28. If a violin string is plucked (pulled aside and let go), it is possible to find a formula $f(x, t)$ for the displacement at time t of any point x of the vibrating string from its equilibrium position. It turns out that in solving this problem we need to expand the function $f(x, 0)$, whose graph is the initial shape of the string, in a Fourier sine series. Find this series if a string of length l is pulled aside a small distance h at its center, as shown.

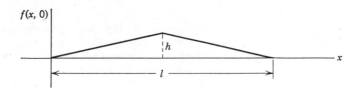

29. Here are several practical examples of electrical signals (voltages or currents). In each case we want to know the harmonic content of the signal, that is, what frequencies it contains and in what proportions. To find this, expand each function in an appropriate Fourier series. Assume in each case that the part of the graph shown is repeated sixty times per second.

(a) Output of a simple d-c generator; the shape of the curve is the absolute value of a sine function. Let the maximum voltage be 100 v.

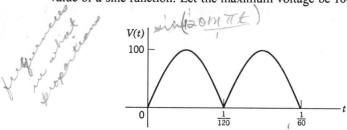

(b) Rectified half-wave; the curve is a sine function for half the cycle and zero for the other half. Let the maximum current be 5 amp.

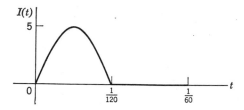

(c) Sawtooth; the graph consists of two straight lines whose equations you must write! The maximum voltage of 100 v occurs at the middle of the cycle.

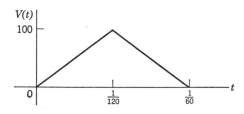

30. The diagram shows a "relaxation" oscillator. The charge q on the capacitor builds up until the neon tube fires and discharges the capacitor (we assume instantaneously). Then the cycle repeats itself over and over.

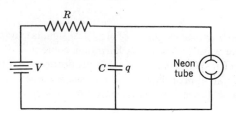

(a) The charge q on the capacitor satisfies the differential equation

$$R\frac{dq}{dt} + \frac{q}{C} = V,$$

where R is the resistance, C is the capacitance, and V is the constant d-c voltage, as shown in the diagram. Show that if $q = 0$ when $t = 0$, then at any later time t (during one cycle, that is, before the neon tube fires)

$$q = CV(1 - e^{-t/RC}).$$

(b) Suppose the neon tube fires at $t = \frac{1}{2}RC$. Sketch q as a function of t for several cycles.

(c) Expand the periodic q in part (b) in an appropriate Fourier series.

31. The graph sketched represents the excess pressure $p(t)$ in a sound wave. Find the important harmonics and their relative intensities.

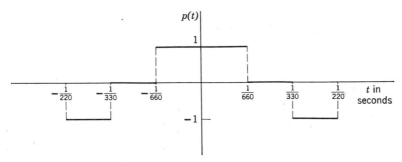

32. (a) Prove (11.4) for a function of period $2l$ expanded in a sine-cosine series.

(b) Prove that if $f(x) = \sum_{-\infty}^{\infty} c_n e^{inx}$, then the average value of $[f(x)]^2$ is $\sum_{-\infty}^{\infty} c_n c_{-n}$. Show by Problem 12a that for real $f(x)$ this becomes (11.5).

(c) If $f(x)$ is complex, we usually want the average of the square of the absolute value of $f(x)$. Recall that $|f(x)|^2 = f(x) \cdot \overline{f(x)}$, where $\overline{f(x)}$ means the complex conjugate of $f(x)$. Show that if a complex $f(x) = \sum_{-\infty}^{\infty} c_n e^{in\pi x/l}$, then (11.5) holds.

33. When a current I flows through a resistance R, the heat energy dissipated per second is the average value of RI^2. Let a periodic (not sinusoidal) current $I(t)$ be expanded in a Fourier series $I(t) = \sum_{-\infty}^{\infty} c_n e^{120in\pi t}$. Give a physical meaning to Parseval's theorem for this problem.

34. (a) Use the results of Problem 9a and Parseval's theorem to find the sum of the series $1 + \frac{1}{3^2} + \frac{1}{5^2} + \cdots$.

(b) Similarly use Problem 9e to find the sum of the series $\sum_{n=1}^{\infty} \frac{1}{n^4}$.

35. A general form of Parseval's theorem says that if two functions are expanded in Fourier series

$$f(x) = \tfrac{1}{2}a_0 + \sum_1^\infty a_n \cos nx + \sum_1^\infty b_n \sin nx,$$

$$g(x) = \tfrac{1}{2}a_0' + \sum_1^\infty a_n' \cos nx + \sum_1^\infty b_n' \sin nx,$$

then the average value of $f(x)g(x)$ is $\tfrac{1}{4}a_0 a_0' + \tfrac{1}{2}\sum_1^\infty a_n a_n' + \tfrac{1}{2}\sum_1^\infty b_n b_a'$. Prove this.

7

Ordinary Differential Equations

I. INTRODUCTION

A great many applied problems involve rates, that is, derivatives. An equation containing derivatives is called a *differential equation*. If it contains partial derivatives, it is called a *partial differential equation*; otherwise it is called an *ordinary differential equation*. In this chapter we shall consider some methods of solving many of the ordinary differential equations which occur frequently in applications. Let us look at a few examples.

Newton's second law in vector form is $\mathbf{F} = m\mathbf{a}$. If we write the acceleration as dv/dt, where $\mathbf{v}$ is the velocity, or as $d^2\mathbf{r}/dt^2$, where $\mathbf{r}$ is the displacement, we have a differential equation (or a set of differential equations, one for each component). Thus any mechanics problem in which we want to describe the motion of a body (automobile, electron, or satellite) under the action of a given force, involves the solution of a differential equation or a set of differential equations.

The rate at which heat escapes through a window or from a hot water pipe is proportional to the area and to the rate of change of temperature with distance in the direction of flow of heat. Thus we have

$$(1.1) \qquad \frac{dH}{dt} = kA\,\frac{dT}{dx}$$

(k is called the thermal conductivity and depends on the material through which the heat is flowing). Here we have two different derivatives in the differential equation. In such a problem we might know either dT/dx or dH/dt and solve the differential equation to find either T as a function of x, or H as a function of t. (See Problems 7 and 8.)

Consider a simple series circuit (Fig. 1.1) containing a resistance R, a capacitance C, an inductance L, and a source of emf E. If the current flowing around the circuit at time t is $I(t)$ and the charge on the capacitor is $q(t)$, then $I = dq/dt$. The voltage across R is RI, the voltage across C is q/C, and the voltage across L is $L(dI/dt)$. Then at any time we must have

$$(1.2) \qquad L\frac{dI}{dt} + RI + \frac{q}{C} = E.$$

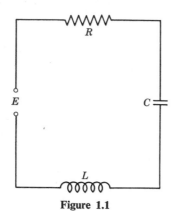

Figure 1.1

If we differentiate this equation with respect to t and substitute $dq/dt = I$, we have

$$(1.3) \qquad L\frac{d^2I}{dt^2} + R\frac{dI}{dt} + \frac{I}{C} = \frac{dE}{dt}$$

as the differential equation satisfied by the current I in a simple series circuit with given L, R, and C, and a given $E(t)$.

There are many more examples of physical problems leading to differential equations; we shall consider some of them later in the text and problems. You might find it interesting at this point to browse through the problems to see the wide range of topics giving rise to differential equations.

order   The *order* of a differential equation is the order of the highest derivative in the equation. Thus the equations

$$y' + xy^2 = 1,$$
$$xy' + y = e^x,$$
$$(1.4) \qquad \frac{dv}{dt} = -g,$$
$$L\frac{dI}{dt} + RI = E,$$

are first-order equations, while (1.3) and

$$m\frac{d^2r}{dt^2} = -kr$$

are second-order equations. A linear differential equation (with x as independent and y as dependent variable) is one of the form

$$a_0y + a_1y' + a_2y'' + a_3y''' + \cdots = b,$$

where the a's and b are either constants or functions of x. The first equation in (1.4) is not linear because of the y^2 term; all the other equations we have mentioned so far are linear. Some other examples of nonlinear equations are

$$y' = \cot y \qquad \text{(not linear because of the term } \cot y\text{)};$$
$$yy' = 1 \qquad \text{(not linear because of the product } yy'\text{)};$$
$$y'^2 = xy \qquad \text{(not linear because of the term } y'^2\text{)}.$$

The term *degree* means the degree of the highest order derivative (if the differential equation is written as a polynomial in y and its derivatives). Note that first degree is not the same as linear; the first equation in (1.4) is of the first degree but is not linear. A large percentage of the differential equations which occur in applied problems are linear and of the first or second order; we shall be particularly interested in these.

degree

A *solution* of a differential equation (in the variables x and y) is a relation between x and y which, if substituted into the differential equation, gives an identity.

Example 1. The relation

(1.5) $$y = \sin x + C$$

is a solution of the differential equation

(1.6) $$y' = \cos x$$

because if we substitute (1.5) into (1.6) we get the identity $\cos x = \cos x$.

Example 2. The equation $y'' = y$ has solutions $y = e^x$ or $y = e^{-x}$ or $y = Ae^x + Be^{-x}$ as you can verify by substitution.

If we integrate $y' = f(x)$, the expression for y, namely

$$y = \int f(x)\, dx + C$$

contains one arbitrary constant of integration. If we integrate $y'' = g(x)$ twice to get y, y contains two independent integration constants. We might expect that in general a differential equation of the nth order would have a solution containing n independent arbitrary constants. This is usually true. Note that in the above examples the solution of the first-order equation $y' = \cos x$ contained one arbitrary constant C, and there was a solution of the second-order equation $y'' = y$ containing two arbitrary constants A and B. Any *linear* differential equation of order n has a solution containing n independent arbitrary constants, from which *all* solutions of the differential equation can be obtained by letting the constants have particular values. This solution is called the *general* solution of the linear differential equation. By analogy, a solution of a nonlinear equation containing the right number of constants is often called a "general solution"; in this case, however, there may be solutions which cannot be obtained from the "general solution" by any choice of the arbitrary constants. (See Problems 2 and 3.)

In applications, we usually want a *particular* solution, that is, one which satisfies the differential equation and some other requirements as well. Here are some examples of this.

Example 3.   Find the distance which an object falls under gravity in t seconds if it starts from rest.

Let x be the distance the object has fallen in time t. The acceleration of the object is g, the acceleration of gravity. Then we have

(1.7) $$\frac{d^2x}{dt^2} = g.$$

Integrating, we get

(1.8) $$\frac{dx}{dt} = gt + \text{const.} = gt + v_0,$$

(1.9) $$x = \tfrac{1}{2}gt^2 + v_0 t + x_0,$$

where v_0 and x_0 are the values of v and x at $t = 0$. Now (1.9) is the *general solution* of (1.7) (because it is a solution of a second-order linear differential equation and contains two independent arbitrary constants). We want the *particular* solution for which $v_0 = 0$ (since the object starts from rest), and $x_0 = 0$ (since the distance the object has fallen is zero at $t = 0$). Then the desired particular solution is

$$x = \tfrac{1}{2}gt^2.$$

Example 4.   Find the solution of $y'' = y$ which passes through the origin and through the point $(\ln 2, \tfrac{3}{4})$.

The general solution of the differential equation is

$$y = Ae^x + Be^{-x}$$

(see Example 2). If the given points satisfy the equation of the curve, we must have

$$0 = A + B \qquad \text{or} \qquad A = -B,$$
$$\tfrac{3}{4} = Ae^{\ln 2} + Be^{-\ln 2} = A \cdot 2 + B \cdot \tfrac{1}{2} = 2A - \tfrac{1}{2}A = \tfrac{3}{2}A.$$

Thus we get

$$A = -B = \tfrac{1}{2},$$

and the desired particular solution is

$$y = \tfrac{1}{2}(e^x - e^{-x}) = \sinh x.$$

The given conditions which are to be satisfied by the particular solution are called *boundary conditions,* or when they are conditions at $t = 0$ they may be called *initial conditions.* Usually (but not always for nonlinear differential equations—see Problems 2 and 3) the desired particular solution can be found from the general solution by determining the values of the constants as we did in Example 4.

2. SEPARABLE EQUATIONS

Every time you evaluate an integral

$$(2.1) \qquad y = \int f(x)\, dx,$$

you are solving a differential equation, namely

$$(2.2) \qquad y' = \frac{dy}{dx} = f(x).$$

This is a simple example of an equation which can be written with only y terms on one side of the equation and only x terms on the other:

$$(2.3) \qquad dy = f(x)\, dx.$$

Whenever we can separate the variables in a differential equation this way, we call the equation *separable,* and we get the solution by just integrating each side of the equation.

Example 1. The rate at which a radioactive substance decays is proportional to the remaining number of atoms. If there are N_0 atoms at $t = 0$, find the number at time t.

The differential equation for this problem is

$$(2.4) \qquad \frac{dN}{dt} = -\lambda N.$$

(The proportionality constant λ is called the decay constant.) This is a separable equation; we write it as

$$\frac{dN}{N} = -\lambda\, dt.$$

Integrating both sides, we get

$$\ln N = -\lambda t + \text{const.}$$

Since we are given $N = N_0$ at $t = 0$, we see that the constant is $\ln N_0$. Solving for N, we have

$$(2.5) \qquad N = N_0 e^{-\lambda t}.$$

(For further discussion of radioactive decay problems, see Section 3 Example 2, and Problem 4.)

Example 2.   Solve the differential equation

$$(2.6) \qquad\qquad xy' = y + 1.$$

We divide both sides of (2.6) by $x(y + 1)$ to get

$$(2.7) \qquad\qquad \frac{y'}{y+1} = \frac{1}{x} \quad \text{or} \quad \frac{dy}{y+1} = \frac{dx}{x}.$$

Integrating each side of (2.7), we have

$$(2.8) \qquad \ln(y + 1) = \ln x + \text{const.} = \ln x + \ln a = \ln(ax).$$

(We have called the constant of integration $\ln a$ for simplicity.) Then (2.8) gives the solution of (2.6), namely

$$(2.9) \qquad\qquad y + 1 = ax.$$

This general solution represents a *family* of curves in the (x, y) plane, one curve for each value of the constant a. Or we may call the general solution (2.9) a *family of solutions* of the differential equation (2.6). Finding a particular solution means selecting one particular curve from the family.

In Fig. 2.1, the straight lines through $(0, -1)$ are the family of curves given by the solutions (2.9) of the differential equation (2.6). They might represent, for example, the lines of electric force due to an electric charge at $(0, -1)$. The circles in Fig. 2.1 are then curves of constant electrostatic potential (equipotentials—see Chapter 5, Sections 8 and 9). Note that the lines of force intersect the equipotential curves at right angles; each family of curves is called a set of *orthogonal trajectories* of the other family. It is often of interest to find the orthogonal trajectories of a given family of curves. Let us do this for the family (2.9). (In this case we know in advance that our answer will be the set of circles in Fig. 2.1.)

First we find the slope of a line of the family (2.9), namely,

$$(2.10) \qquad\qquad y' = a.$$

For each a this gives the slope of *one* line. We want a formula (as a function of x and y) which gives the slope, at any point of the plane, of the line through that point. To obtain this, we eliminate a between (2.9) and (2.10) to get

$$(2.11) \qquad\qquad y' = \frac{y+1}{x}.$$

[Or, given (2.6) rather than (2.9), we could simply solve for y'.] Now recall from analytic geometry (see also Problem 15) that the slopes of two perpendicular lines are negative reciprocals. Then at each point we want

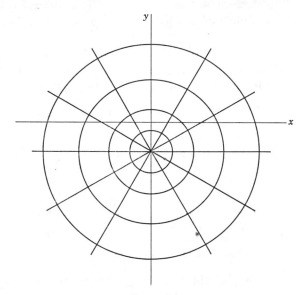

Figure 2.1

the slope of the orthogonal trajectory curve to be the negative reciprocal of the slope of the line given by (2.11). Thus

(2.12)
$$y' = -\frac{x}{y+1}$$

gives the slope of the orthogonal trajectories, and we solve the differential equation (2.12) to obtain the equations of the orthogonal trajectory curves. Equation (2.12) is separable; we obtain

$$(y+1)\,dy = -x\,dx,$$

$$\tfrac{1}{2}y^2 + y = -\tfrac{1}{2}x^2 + C,$$

$$x^2 + y^2 + 2y = 2C,$$

$$x^2 + (y+1)^2 = 2C + 1.$$

This is, as we expected, the equation of a family of circles with centers at the point $(0, -1)$.

3. LINEAR FIRST-ORDER EQUATIONS

A first-order equation contains y' but no higher derivatives. A *linear* first-order equation means one which can be written in the form

$$(3.1) \qquad\qquad y' + Py = Q,$$

where P and Q are functions of x. To see how to solve (3.1), let us first consider the simpler equation when $Q = 0$. The equation

$$(3.2) \qquad\qquad y' + Py = 0 \qquad \text{or} \qquad \frac{dy}{dx} = -Py$$

is separable. As in Section 2, we obtain the solution as follows:

$$\frac{dy}{y} = -P \, dx,$$

$$\ln y = -\int P \, dx + c,$$

$$(3.3) \qquad\qquad y = e^{-\int P \, dx + c} = Ae^{-\int P \, dx},$$

where $A = e^c$. To simplify the notation for future use, let us write

$$(3.4) \qquad\qquad I = \int P \, dx.$$

Then

$$(3.5) \qquad\qquad \frac{dI}{dx} = P$$

and we can write (3.3) as $y = Ae^{-I}$ or

$$(3.6) \qquad\qquad ye^{I} = A.$$

Differentiating (3.6) with respect to x and using (3.5), we get

$$(3.7) \quad \frac{d}{dx}(ye^{I}) = y'e^{I} + ye^{I}\frac{dI}{dx} = y'e^{I} + ye^{I}P = e^{I}(y' + Py).$$

Returning now to (3.1), let us multiply it by e^{I}.

$$(3.8) \qquad\qquad (y' + Py)e^{I} = Qe^{I}.$$

Then we see by (3.7) that we can write (3.8) as

$$(3.9) \qquad\qquad \frac{d}{dx}(ye^{I}) = Qe^{I}.$$

Since Q and e^I are functions of x only, we can now integrate both sides of (3.9) with respect to x to get

(3.10)
$$ye^I = \int Qe^I \, dx + c, \quad \text{or}$$
$$y = e^{-I}\int Qe^I \, dx + ce^{-I},$$

which is the general solution of (3.1). It is worth while to memorize (3.4) and (3.10) since first-order linear equations occur frequently.

Example 1. Solve $x^2 y' - 2xy = 1/x$.
In the form of (3.1), this is

$$y' - \frac{2}{x}y = \frac{1}{x^3}.$$

From (3.4) and (3.10), we get

$$I = \int \left(-\frac{2}{x}\right) dx = -2 \ln x,$$

$$e^I = e^{-2\ln x} = \frac{1}{x^2},$$

$$ye^I = y \cdot \frac{1}{x^2} = \int \frac{1}{x^2} \cdot \frac{1}{x^3} \, dx = \int x^{-5} \, dx = \frac{x^{-4}}{-4} + c,$$

$$y = -\frac{1}{4x^2} + cx^2.$$

Example 2. Radium decays to radon which decays to polonium. If at $t = 0$, a sample is pure radium, how much radon does it contain at time t?

Let $N_0 = $ number of radium atoms at $t = 0$;
$\quad N_1 = $ number of radium atoms at time t;
$\quad N_2 = $ number of radon atoms at time t;
$\quad \lambda_1$ and $\lambda_2 = $ decay constants for Ra and Rn.

As in Section 2, we have for radium

$$\frac{dN_1}{dt} = -\lambda_1 N_1, \quad N_1 = N_0 e^{-\lambda_1 t}.$$

The rate at which radon is being created is the rate at which radium is decaying, namely $\lambda_1 N_1$ or $\lambda_1 N_0 e^{-\lambda_1 t}$. But the radon is also decaying at the rate $\lambda_2 N_2$. Hence we have

$$\frac{dN_2}{dt} = \lambda_1 N_1 - \lambda_2 N_2$$

or

$$\frac{dN_2}{dt} + \underset{P}{\lambda_2 N_2} = \underset{Q}{\lambda_1 N_1} = \lambda_1 N_0 e^{-\lambda_1 t}.$$

This equation is of the form (3.1), and we solve it as follows.

$$I = \int \lambda_2 \, dt = \lambda_2 t,$$

(3.11) $$N_2 e^{\lambda_2 t} = \int \lambda_1 N_0 e^{-\lambda_1 t} e^{\lambda_2 t} \, dt + c$$

$$= \lambda_1 N_0 \int e^{(\lambda_2 - \lambda_1)t} \, dt + c = \frac{\lambda_1 N_0}{\lambda_2 - \lambda_1} e^{(\lambda_2 - \lambda_1)t} + c,$$

if $\lambda_1 \neq \lambda_2$. (For the case $\lambda_1 = \lambda_2$, see Problem 19a.) Since $N_2 = 0$ at $t = 0$ (we assumed pure Ra at $t = 0$), we must have

$$0 = \frac{\lambda_1 N_0}{\lambda_2 - \lambda_1} + c \qquad \text{or} \qquad c = -\frac{\lambda_1 N_0}{\lambda_2 - \lambda_1}.$$

Substituting this value of c into (3.11) and solving for N_2, we get

$$N_2 = \frac{\lambda_1 N_0}{\lambda_2 - \lambda_1} (e^{-\lambda_1 t} - e^{-\lambda_2 t}).$$

4. OTHER METHODS FOR EQUATIONS OF THE FIRST ORDER AND FIRST DEGREE

Separable equations and linear equations are the two types of first-order, first-degree equations you are most apt to meet in elementary applications. However, we shall also mention briefly a few other methods of solving special first-order, first-degree equations. You will find more details in the problems and in most differential equations books.

The Bernoulli equation. The differential equation

(4.1) $$y' + Py = Qy^n,$$

where P and Q are functions of x, is known as the Bernoulli equation. It is not linear but is easily reduced to a linear equation. We make the change of variable

(4.2) $$z = y^{1-n}.$$

Then

(4.3) $$z' = (1 - n)y^{-n}y'.$$

Next multiply (4.1) by $(1 - n)y^{-n}$ and make the substitutions (4.2) and (4.3) to get

$$(1 - n)y^{-n}y' + (1 - n)Py^{1-n} = (1 - n)Q,$$
$$z' + (1 - n)Pz \quad = (1 - n)Q.$$

This is now a first-order linear equation which we can solve as we did the linear equations above. See Section 7 and also Chapter 8, Section 3, for examples of physical problems in which we need to solve Bernoulli equations.

Exact equations; integrating factors. Recall from Chapter 5 that the expression $P(x, y) dx + Q(x, y) dy$ is an *exact differential* [that is, the differential of a function $F(x, y)$] if

(4.4) $$\frac{\partial P}{\partial y} = \frac{\partial Q}{\partial x}.$$

If (4.4) holds, then there is a function $F(x, y)$ such that

(4.5) $$P = \frac{\partial F}{\partial x}, \quad Q = \frac{\partial F}{\partial y}, \quad P\,dx + Q\,dy = dF.$$

In Chapter 5 we considered ways of finding F when (4.4) holds. The differential equation

(4.6) $$P\,dx + Q\,dy = 0 \quad \text{or} \quad y' = -\frac{P}{Q}$$

is called *exact* if (4.4) holds. In this case

$$P\,dx + Q\,dy = dF = 0,$$

and the solution of (4.6) is then

(4.7) $$F(x, y) = \text{const.}$$

We find F as in Chapter 5, Section 11.
    An equation which is not exact may often be made exact by multiplying it by an appropriate factor. For example, the equation

(4.8) $$x\,dy - y\,dx = 0$$

is not exact [by (4.4)]. But the equation

(4.9) $$\frac{x\,dy - y\,dx}{x^2} = \frac{1}{x}\,dy - \frac{y}{x^2}\,dx = 0$$

obtained by dividing (4.8) by x^2 *is* exact [use (4.4)], and its solution is

(4.10) $$\frac{y}{x} = \text{const.}$$

We multiplied (4.8) by $1/x^2$ to make the equation exact; the factor $1/x^2$ is called an *integrating factor*. To see another example of an integrating factor, look back at Section 3. The expression e^I is an integrating factor for equations (3.1) and (3.2); as you can see in (3.8) and (3.9), multiplying (3.1) by e^I makes it an exact equation (3.9).

The method of finding integrating factors and solving the resulting exact equation is useful mainly in simple cases when we can see the result by inspection. It is not usually worth while to spend much time searching for an integrating factor.

Homogeneous equations. An equation of the form

(4.11) $$P(x, y)\, dx + Q(x, y)\, dy = 0,$$

where P and Q are homogeneous functions (see Chapter 4, Problem 121) is called *homogeneous*. (The term homogeneous is also used in another sense; see Section 5.) Equation (4.11) can be written in the form $y' = f(y/x)$; the change of variables $v = y/x$ or

(4.12) $$y = vx$$

reduces (4.11) to a separable equation in the variables v and x. (You might verify these statements for, say, Problems 21h and 25b.)

Change of variables. We have solved both Bernoulli equations and homogeneous equations by making changes of variables. Other equations may yield to this method also. If a differential equation contains some combination of the variables x, y (especially if this combination appears more than once), we try replacing this combination by a new variable. See Problems 1g and 1h for examples.

5. SECOND-ORDER LINEAR EQUATIONS WITH CONSTANT COEFFICIENTS AND ZERO RIGHT-HAND SIDE

Because of their importance in applications, we are going to consider carefully the solution of differential equations of the form

(5.1) $$a_2 \frac{d^2 y}{dx^2} + a_1 \frac{dy}{dx} + a_0 y = 0,$$

where a_2, a_1, a_0 are constants; also we shall consider (Section 6) the corresponding equation when the right-hand side of (5.1) is a function of x. Equations of the form (5.1) are called *homogeneous* because every term contains y or a derivative of y. Equations of the form (6.1) are called *inhomogeneous* because they contain a term which does not depend on y. (Note, however, that this use of the term homogeneous is completely unrelated to its use in Section 4.) Although we shall concentrate on second-order equations, which are the ones that occur most frequently in applications, most of our discussion can be extended immediately to linear equations of higher order with constant coefficients (see Problems 30 and 31). Let us consider an equation of the form (5.1).

Example. Solve the equation

(5.2) $y'' + 5y' + 4y = 0.$

It is convenient to let D stand for d/dx; then

(5.3) $Dy = \dfrac{dy}{dx} = y', \qquad D^2y = \dfrac{d}{dx}\left(\dfrac{dy}{dx}\right) = \dfrac{d^2y}{dx^2} = y''.$

Expressions involving D, such as $D + 1$ or $D^2 + 5D + 4$, are called *differential operators*. (See Problem 26.) In this notation (5.2) becomes

(5.4) $D^2y + 5Dy + 4y = 0 \qquad$ or $\qquad (D^2 + 5D + 4)y = 0.$

The *algebraic* expression $D^2 + 5D + 4$ can be factored as $(D + 1)(D + 4)$ or $(D + 4)(D + 1)$. You should satisfy yourself that

(5.5) $(D + 1)(D + 4)y = (D + 4)(D + 1)y = (D^2 + 5D + 4)y$

when $D = d/dx$, and, in fact, that a similar statement is true for $(D - a)(D - b)$ where a and b are any *constants*. (This is not necessarily true if a and b are functions of x; see Problem 26.) Then we can write (5.2) or (5.4) as

(5.6) $(D + 1)(D + 4)y = 0 \qquad$ or $\qquad (D + 4)(D + 1)y = 0.$

To solve (5.4) [or (5.6) which is the same equation rewritten], we shall first solve the simpler equations

(5.7) $(D + 4)y = 0 \qquad$ and $\qquad (D + 1)y = 0.$

These are separable equations (Section 2) with solutions

(5.8) $y = c_1 e^{-4x}, \qquad y = c_2 e^{-x}.$

Now if $(D + 4)y = 0$, then

$$(D + 1)(D + 4)y = (D + 1) \cdot 0 = 0,$$

so any solution of $(D + 4)y = 0$ is a solution of the differential equation (5.6) or (5.4). Similarly, any solution of $(D + 1)y = 0$ is a solution of (5.6) or (5.4). Since the two solutions (5.8) are linearly independent (Chapter 3, Section 6 and Problem 27), a linear combination of them contains two arbitrary constants and so is the general solution. Thus

$$(5.9) \qquad y = c_1 e^{-4x} + c_2 e^{-x}$$

is the general solution of (5.4).

Now we must investigate whether we can solve all second-order linear equations with constant coefficients (and zero right-hand side) by this method. We first wrote the differential equation using D for d/dx, and then factored the D expression to get (5.5). In this last step, we treated D as if it were an algebraic letter instead of d/dx; this is justified by checking the result (5.5) when $D = d/dx$. Recall from algebra that saying that the algebraic expression $D^2 + 5D + 4$ has the factors $(D + 4)$ and $(D + 1)$ is equivalent to saying that the quadratic equation

$$(5.10) \qquad D^2 + 5D + 4 = 0 \qquad \textit{characteristic equation}$$

has roots -4 and -1. The equation (5.10) is called the *auxiliary* (or characteristic) equation for the given differential equation (5.2). From equations (5.6) to (5.9), we see that to solve a linear second-order equation with constant coefficients, we should first solve the auxiliary equation; if the roots of the auxiliary equation are a and b $(a \neq b)$, the general solution of the equation is

$$(5.11) \qquad y = c_1 e^{ax} + c_2 e^{bx}. \qquad \textit{for real and unequal}$$

(If $a = b$, we get only one solution this way; we shall consider this case shortly.) Recall from algebra that the roots of a quadratic equation (with real coefficients; see Problem 29) can be real and unequal, real and equal, or a complex conjugate pair. The equation (5.2) which we have solved is an example in which the roots are real and unequal. Let us consider the other two cases.

Equal roots of the auxiliary equation. If the two roots of the auxiliary equation are equal, then the differential equation can be written

$$(5.12) \qquad (D - a)(D - a)y = 0,$$

where a is the value of the two equal roots. From our previous discussion (5.5) to (5.11), we know that one solution of (5.12) is $y = c_1 e^{ax}$. But our previous second solution $y = c_2 e^{bx}$ in (5.11) is not a second solution here since $b = a$. To find the second solution for this case, we let

$$(5.13) \qquad u = (D - a)y.$$

Then (5.12) becomes

$$(D - a)u = 0,$$

from which we get

(5.14) $u = Ae^{ax}.$

We substitute (5.14) into (5.13) to get

$$(D - a)y = Ae^{ax} \quad \text{or} \quad y' - ay = Ae^{ax}.$$

This is a first-order linear equation which we solve as in Section 3:

$$ye^{-ax} = \int e^{-ax} Ae^{ax}\, dx = \int A\, dx = Ax + B,$$

solution if real

(5.15) $y = (Ax + B)e^{ax}.$ *and equal roots*

This is the general solution of (5.1) for the case of equal roots of the
auxiliary equation. The solution e^{ax} we already knew; what is new here is
the fact that xe^{ax} is a second (linearly independent; see Problem 27c)
solution of the differential equation when a is a double root of the auxiliary equation. Equations (5.11) and (5.15) then give the general solution
of (5.1) for both unequal and equal roots of the auxiliary equation.

Complex conjugate roots of the auxiliary equation. Suppose the roots
of the auxiliary equation are $\alpha \pm i\beta$. These are unequal roots, so by (5.11)
the general solution of the differential equation is

(5.16) $y = Ae^{(\alpha+i\beta)x} + Be^{(\alpha-i\beta)x} = e^{\alpha x}(Ae^{i\beta x} + Be^{-i\beta x}).$

There are two other very useful forms of (5.16). If we substitute
$e^{\pm i\beta x} = \cos \beta x \pm i \sin \beta x$ [see Chapter 2, equation (9.3)] into (5.16),
then the parenthesis becomes a linear combination of $\sin \beta x$ and $\cos \beta x$
and we can write (5.16) as

(5.17) $y = e^{\alpha x}(c_1 \sin \beta x + c_2 \cos \beta x),$

where c_1 and c_2 are new arbitrary constants. We can also write (5.17) in
the form

(5.18) $y = ce^{\alpha x} \sin (\beta x + \gamma),$

where c and γ are now the arbitrary constants. An easy way to see that
this is correct is to expand $\sin (\beta x + \gamma)$ by the trigonometric addition
formula; this gives a linear combination of $\sin \beta x$ and $\cos \beta x$ as in (5.17).
Although it is not hard to express any one of the sets of arbitrary constants
[A, B in (5.16); c_1, c_2 in (5.17); and c, γ in (5.18)] in terms of either of the
other sets, there is seldom any need to do this. In solving actual problems
we simply write whichever one of the three forms seems best for the problem at hand and then determine the arbitrary constants in that form from
the given data.

Example 1. Solve the differential equation

(5.19) $$y'' + 6y' + 9y = 0.$$

We can write the equation as

(5.20) $(D^2 - 6D + 9)y = 0$ or $(D - 3)(D - 3)y = 0.$

Since the roots of the auxiliary equation are equal, we know that the solution is of the form (5.15) and we simply write the result

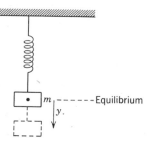

Figure 5.1

(5.21) $$y = (Ax + B)e^{3x}.$$

Example 2. A mass m oscillates at the end of a spring (Fig. 5.1). Find the position of the mass as a function of time.

Let y be the vertical displacement of the mass from its equilibrium position (the point at which it would hang at rest). Recall that the force on m due to the stretched or compressed spring is then $-ky$, where k is the spring constant, and the minus sign indicates that the force and displacement are in opposite directions. Then Newton's second law (mass times acceleration = force) gives

(5.22) $$m \frac{d^2y}{dt^2} = -ky$$

or putting $\omega^2 = k/m$, we have

$$\frac{d^2y}{dt^2} = -\omega^2 y.$$

We can write this differential equation as

(5.23) $D^2 y + \omega^2 y = 0$ or $(D^2 + \omega^2)y = 0$

where $D = d/dt$. The roots of the auxiliary equation are $D = \pm i\omega$; the solution may be written in any of the three forms, (5.16), (5.17), or (5.18):

$$y = Ae^{i\omega t} + Be^{-i\omega t}$$

(5.24) $= c_1 \sin \omega t + c_2 \cos \omega t$ *general solution*

$= c \sin(\omega t + \gamma).$

An object whose displacement from equilibrium satisfies (5.22) or (5.24) is said to be executing simple harmonic motion.

Equations (5.24) are general solutions of (5.22), each containing two arbitrary constants. Let us find a particular solution corresponding to the following initial conditions: The mass is held at rest at a distance

10 cm below equilibrium and then suddenly let go. If we agree to call y positive when m is above the equilibrium position, then at $t = 0$, we have $y = -10$, and $dy/dt = 0$. Using the second solution in (5.24), we get

$$\frac{dy}{dt} = c_1\omega \cos \omega t - c_2\omega \sin \omega t,$$

so the initial conditions give

$$-10 = c_1 \cdot 0 + c_2 \cdot 1,$$
$$0 = c_1\omega \cdot 1 - c_2\omega \cdot 0.$$

Thus we find

$$c_1 = 0, \qquad c_2 = -10,$$

and the particular solution we wanted is

(5.25) $y = -10 \cos \omega t.$

You can verify that either of the other solutions in (5.24) gives the same particular solution (5.25) for the same initial conditions (Problem 32).

The problem we have just done is pretty unrealistic from the practical viewpoint. Equations (5.24) and (5.25) imply that the mass m, once started, will simply oscillate up and down forever! This is certainly not true; what *will* happen is that the oscillations will gradually die down. The reason for the discrepancy between the physical facts and our mathematical answer is that we have neglected "friction" forces. A fairly reasonable assumption for this problem and many other similar ones is that there is a retarding force proportional to the velocity; let us call this force $-l(dy/dt)$ ($l > 0$). Then (5.22), revised to include this force, becomes

(5.26) $m\dfrac{d^2y}{dt^2} = -ky - l\dfrac{dy}{dt} \qquad (l > 0)$

or with the abbreviations

$$\omega^2 = \frac{k}{m}, \qquad 2b = \frac{l}{m} \qquad (b > 0)$$

it is

(5.27) $\dfrac{d^2y}{dt^2} + 2b\dfrac{dy}{dt} + \omega^2 y = 0.$

To solve (5.27), we find the roots of the auxiliary equation

(5.28) $D^2 + 2bD + \omega^2 = 0,$

which are

(5.29) $D = \dfrac{-2b \pm \sqrt{4b^2 - 4\omega^2}}{2} = -b \pm \sqrt{b^2 - \omega^2}.$

There are three possible types of answer here depending on the relative size of b^2 and ω^2, and there are three special names given to the corresponding types of motion. We say that the motion is

overdamped if $b^2 > \omega^2$,

critically damped if $b^2 = \omega^2$,

underdamped or oscillatory if $b^2 < \omega^2$.

Let us discuss the corresponding general solutions of the differential equation for the three cases.

Overdamped motion. Since $\sqrt{b^2 - \omega^2}$ is real and less than b, both roots of the auxiliary equation are negative, and the general solution is a linear combination of two negative exponentials:

$$(5.30) \qquad y = Ae^{-\lambda t} + Be^{-\mu t}, \qquad \text{where} \qquad \begin{aligned} \lambda &= b + \sqrt{b^2 - \omega^2}, \\ \mu &= b - \sqrt{b^2 - \omega^2}. \end{aligned}$$

Critically damped motion. Since $b = \omega$, the auxiliary equation has equal roots and the general solution is

$$(5.31) \qquad\qquad\qquad y = (A + Bt)e^{-bt}.$$

In both overdamped and critically damped motion, the mass m is subject to such a large retarding force that it slows down and returns to equilibrium rather than oscillating repeatedly.

Underdamped or oscillatory motion. In this case $b^2 < \omega^2$ so $\sqrt{b^2 - \omega^2}$ is imaginary. Let $\beta = \sqrt{\omega^2 - b^2}$; then $\sqrt{b^2 - \omega^2} = i\beta$ and the roots (5.29) of the auxiliary equation are $-b \pm i\beta$. The general solution in the form (5.18) is then

$$(5.32) \qquad\qquad\qquad y = ce^{-bt} \sin(\beta t + \gamma).$$

This result is more in accord with what we know actually happens to the mass m in Fig. 5.1; because of the factor e^{-bt}, the oscillations in this case decrease in amplitude as time goes on. Also note that the frequency of the damped vibrations, namely $\beta = \sqrt{\omega^2 - b^2}$, is less than the frequency ω of the undamped vibrations.

Although we have stated a rather special physical problem, the mathematics we have just discussed applies to a great variety of problems. First, there are many kinds of mechanical vibrations besides a mass attached to a spring. Think of a tuning fork, a pendulum, the needle on the scale of a measuring device, and as more involved examples, the vibrations of complicated structures such as bridges or airplanes, and the vibrations of atoms in a crystal lattice. In such problems, we need to solve differential equations similar to the ones we have discussed. Differential equations of the same form arise in electricity. Consider equations (1.2) and (1.3) for $E = 0$. Remembering that $I = dq/dt$, we can write (1.2) as

$$(5.33) \qquad L\frac{d^2q}{dt^2} + R\frac{dq}{dt} + \frac{1}{C}q = 0$$

and (1.3) as

$$(5.34) \qquad L\frac{d^2I}{dt^2} + R\frac{dI}{dt} + \frac{1}{C}I = 0.$$

Both these equations are of the form (5.27) which we have solved. Thus there is an analogy between a series circuit and the motion of a mass m described by (5.26); L corresponds to m, R to the "friction" constant l, and $1/C$ to the spring constant k.

6. SECOND-ORDER LINEAR EQUATIONS WITH CONSTANT COEFFICIENTS AND RIGHT-HAND SIDE NOT ZERO

So far we have considered second-order linear equations with constant coefficients and zero right-hand side (5.1). Such equations describe *free vibrations* or oscillations of mechanical or electrical systems. But often such systems are not free but are subject to an applied force or emf. The vibrations are then called *forced vibrations* and the differential equation describing the system is of the form

$$(6.1) \qquad a_2\frac{d^2y}{dx^2} + a_1\frac{dy}{dx} + a_0y = f(x), \qquad \text{or}$$

$$\frac{d^2y}{dx^2} + \frac{a_1}{a_2}\frac{dy}{dx} + \frac{a_0}{a_2}y = F(x).$$

The function $f(x)$ is often called the forcing function; it represents the applied force or emf. We want to find the general solution of equations of the form (6.1). As an example consider

$$(6.2) \qquad (D^2 + 5D + 4)y = \cos 2x.$$

We already know (from Section 5) the general solution of the corresponding equation (5.2) with the right-hand side equal to zero. This solution (5.9) is called the *complementary function*; it is not a solution of (6.2) but is related to it as we shall see. We shall denote the complementary function by y_c. Thus for equation (6.2) the complementary function is

$$(6.3) \qquad y_c = Ae^{-x} + Be^{-4x}.$$

Now suppose we know just any solution of (6.2); we call this solution a *particular solution* and denote it by y_p. You can easily verify that

$$(6.4) \qquad\qquad y_p = \tfrac{1}{10} \sin 2x$$

is a particular solution of (6.2), and we shall soon consider ways of finding such solutions. Then we have

$$(6.5) \qquad\qquad (D^2 + 5D + 4)y_p = \cos 2x$$

and from Section 5

$$(6.6) \qquad\qquad (D^2 + 5D + 4)y_c = 0.$$

Adding (6.5) and (6.6), we find

$$(D^2 + 5D + 4)(y_p + y_c) = \cos 2x + 0 = \cos 2x.$$

Thus

$$(6.7) \qquad\qquad y = y_c + y_p = Ae^{-x} + Be^{-4x} + \tfrac{1}{10} \sin 2x$$

is a solution of (6.2). In fact, it is the general solution of (6.2) since it contains two independent arbitrary constants (Problem 41). Thus we see that the solution of an equation of the form (6.1) breaks into two parts: to find the complementary function (as done in Section 5) and to find a particular solution. We shall now discuss some ways of finding particular solutions.

Inspection.   If there *is* a very simple particular solution, we may be able to guess and verify it. As a simple example, consider

$$(6.8) \qquad\qquad y'' - 2y' + 3y = 5.$$

It is easy to see that $y_p = \tfrac{5}{3}$ is a particular solution of this equation since if y is constant, y'' and y' are zero. As a less trivial example consider

$$(6.9) \qquad\qquad y'' - 6y' + 9y = 8e^x.$$

We might suspect that a multiple of e^x is a solution of this equation, and it is easy to verify that $y = 2e^x$ is a solution. On the other hand, if we tried the same method for the equation

$$(6.10) \qquad\qquad y'' + y' - 2y = e^x,$$

we would fail to find a particular solution since e^x satisfies

$$y'' + y' - 2y = 0.$$

The method of inspection is very good in simple cases where it gives us an answer quickly, but usually we need other methods.

Successive integration of two first-order equations. This is a straightforward method which can always be used to solve equations of the form (6.1). In practice, however, it often involves more work than various special methods; we shall find it particularly useful in deriving the special methods. As an example of this method, let us solve (6.10); we can write this differential equation as

$$(6.11) \qquad\qquad (D-1)(D+2)y = e^x.$$

Let

$$(6.12) \qquad\qquad u = (D+2)y.$$

Then the differential equation (6.11) becomes

$$(6.13) \qquad\qquad (D-1)u = e^x \qquad \text{or} \qquad u' - u = e^x.$$

This is a first-order linear differential equation which we solve as follows:

$$I = \int -dx = -x,$$

$$(6.14) \qquad\qquad ue^{-x} = \int e^{-x}e^x \, dx = x + c_1,$$

$$u = xe^x + c_1 e^x.$$

Then the differential equation for y becomes

$$(6.15) \quad (D+2)y = xe^x + c_1 e^x \qquad \text{or} \qquad y' + 2y = xe^x + c_1 e^x.$$

This is again a linear first-order equation which we solve as follows:

$$I = \int 2 \, dx = 2x,$$

$$(6.16) \quad ye^{2x} = \int e^{2x}(xe^x + c_1 e^x) \, dx = \tfrac{1}{3}xe^{3x} - \tfrac{1}{9}e^{3x} + \tfrac{1}{3}c_1 e^{3x} + c_2$$

$$= \tfrac{1}{3}xe^{3x} + c_1' e^{3x} + c_2,$$

$$y = \tfrac{1}{3}xe^x + c_1' e^x + c_2 e^{-2x}.$$

Notice that here we have obtained the general solution all in one process rather than getting the complementary function plus a particular solution in two separate processes. Notice also, however, that we could have obtained just the particular solution $\tfrac{1}{3}xe^x$ by this method by omitting the arbitrary constant at each integration (these led to the complementary function) and, if we liked, we could also drop terms which were the same as terms in the complementary function ($-\tfrac{1}{9}e^x$ in our example). Since it is relatively easy to write down the complementary function, it saves time to omit the terms contained in it when we use this method to find a particular solution.

Exponential right-hand side. Let us consider how to find a particular solution when the right-hand side of (6.1) is $F(x) = ke^{cx}$ where k and c are given constants. Observe that c may be complex; we shall be especially interested in this case later. Let a and b be the roots of the auxiliary equation of (6.1); then we can write (6.1) as

$$(6.17) \qquad (D - a)(D - b)y = F(x) = ke^{cx}.$$

Let us first suppose that c is not equal to either a or b. Solving (6.17) by successive integration of two first-order equations as in the last paragraph is straightforward (Problem 42) and gives the result that the particular solution in this case is simply a multiple of e^{cx}. It is not necessary to remember the formula for the constant factor or to go through this process each time. Now that we know the form of the particular solution, we simply assume a solution of this form and solve for the constant. As an example, let us solve

$$(6.18) \qquad (D - 1)(D + 5)y = 7e^{2x}.$$

We observe that $c = 2$ is not equal to either of the roots of the auxiliary equation. To find a particular solution we substitute

$$y_p = Ce^{2x}$$

into (6.18) and get

$$y_p'' + 4y_p' - 5y_p = C(4e^{2x} + 8e^{2x} - 5e^{2x}) = 7e^{2x}.$$

Thus we must have $C = 1$, and the general solution of (6.18) is

$$y = Ae^x + Be^{-5x} + e^{2x}.$$

We have already seen in solving (6.11) that if c is equal to either a or b ($a \neq b$), the particular solution is of the form Cxe^{cx}. By the same method used for (6.11), you can easily discover that if $a = b = c$, the particular solution is of the form Cx^2e^{cx} (Problem 42c). In practice, then, we find a particular solution of (6.17) by assuming a solution of the form:

$$\begin{cases} Ce^{cx} & \text{if } c \text{ is not equal to either } a \text{ or } b; \\ Cxe^{cx} & \text{if } c \text{ equals } a \text{ or } b, a \neq b; \\ Cx^2e^{cx} & \text{if } c = a = b. \end{cases}$$

Now that we know this, we would solve (6.11) as follows. Substitute

$$y_p = Cxe^x, \qquad y_p' = C(xe^x + e^x), \qquad y_p'' = C(xe^x + 2e^x)$$

into (6.11) and get

$$y_p'' + y_p' - 2y_p = C(xe^x + 2e^x + xe^x + e^x - 2xe^x) = e^x.$$

Thus we find $C = \tfrac{1}{3}$ as in (6.16) (but with much less work).

Use of complex exponentials. In applied problems, the function $F(x)$ on the right-hand side of (6.1) is very often a sine or a cosine representing alternating emf or a periodic force. We *could* find y_p for such a problem either by the method of integrating two successive first-order equations or by replacing the sine or cosine by its complex exponential form and using the method of the last paragraph. There is a still more efficient variation of the latter method which we shall show by an example. Solve

$$(6.19) \qquad\qquad y'' + y' - 2y = 4\sin 2x.$$

Instead of tackling this problem directly, we are first going to solve the equation

$$(6.20) \qquad\qquad Y'' + Y' - 2Y = 4e^{2ix}.$$

Since $e^{2ix} = \cos 2x + i\sin 2x$ is complex, the solution Y may be complex also. Then if $Y = Y_R + iY_I$, (6.20) is equivalent to two equations

$$(6.21) \qquad \begin{aligned} Y_R'' + Y_R' - 2Y_R &= \operatorname{Re} 4e^{2ix} = 4\cos 2x, \\ Y_I'' + Y_I' - 2Y_I &= \operatorname{Im} 4e^{2ix} = 4\sin 2x. \end{aligned}$$

Since the second equation in (6.21) is the same as (6.19), we see that the solution of (6.19) is the imaginary part of Y. Thus to find y_p for (6.19), we find Y_p for (6.20) and take its imaginary part. We observe that $2i$ is not equal to either of the roots of the auxiliary equation in (6.20). Following the method of the last paragraph, we assume a solution of the form

$$(6.22) \qquad\qquad Y_p = Ce^{2ix}$$

and substitute it into (6.20) to get

$$(-4 + 2i - 2)Ce^{2ix} = 4e^{2ix},$$

$$C = \frac{4}{2i-6} = \frac{4(-2i-6)}{40} = -\frac{1}{5}(i+3),$$

$$Y_p = -\tfrac{1}{5}(i+3)e^{2ix}.$$

Taking the imaginary part of Y_p, we find y_p for (6.19):

$$(6.23) \qquad\qquad y_p = -\tfrac{1}{5}\cos 2x - \tfrac{3}{5}\sin 2x.$$

Method of undetermined coefficients. The method we have just discussed of assuming an exponential solution and determining the constant factor C is an example (and in practice the most important case) of the *method of undetermined coefficients*. We have seen that to find y_p in (6.1) when $F(x) = ke^{cx}$, we assume $y_p = Ce^{cx}$ when c is not a root of the auxiliary equation; we assume $y_p = Cxe^{cx}$ when c is a simple root and $y_p = Cx^2e^{cx}$ when c is a double root of the auxiliary equation. Note again that sines and cosines are included in "exponential right-hand side" by the use of complex exponentials.

It is straightforward but tedious (Problems 44 and 47) to show that if the right-hand side is an exponential e^{cx} times a polynomial of degree n, and c is not a root of the auxiliary equation, the proper form to assume for y_p is the exponential times a polynomial of degree n with *undetermined coefficients* to be found to satisfy the equation. As before, if c is a root of the auxiliary equation, the solution to assume is the form just described multiplied by x (if c is a simple root) or by x^2 (if c is a double root). We illustrate this for a problem in which $c = 0$ so that the right-hand side is just a polynomial. (For more detail on the general case, see Problems 44 to 47.)

Example. Solve

$$(6.24) \qquad\qquad y'' + y' - 2y = x^2 - x.$$

We assume a particular solution of the form

$$(6.25) \qquad\qquad y_p = Ax^2 + Bx + C$$

and find the undetermined coefficients A, B, C so that (6.25) satisfies (6.24). We get

$$(6.26) \qquad \begin{aligned} y'_p &= 2Ax + B, \\ y''_p &= 2A, \end{aligned}$$

$$y''_p + y'_p - 2y_p = 2A + 2Ax + B - 2Ax^2 - 2Bx - 2C.$$

To make this identically equal to $x^2 - x$, we must have

$$\begin{array}{ll} -2A = 1, & A = -\tfrac{1}{2} \\ 2A - 2B = -1, & B = 0, \\ 2A + B - 2C = 0, & C = -\tfrac{1}{2}. \end{array}$$

Thus a particular solution of (6.24) is

$$(6.27) \qquad\qquad y_p = -\tfrac{1}{2}(x^2 + 1).$$

Several terms on the right-hand side; principle of superposition. So far we have brushed over a question which may have occurred to you: What do we do if there are several terms on the right-hand side of the equation involving different exponentials? As an artificial problem to illustrate the ideas, consider the equation

$$(6.28) \quad y'' + y' - 2y = (D - 1)(D + 2)y = [e^x] + [4 \sin 2x] + [x^2 - x].$$

We have already solved differential equations with the same left-hand sides as (6.28) and with right-hand sides equal in turn to each of the three expressions in brackets in (6.28) [see (6.11) to (6.16), (6.19) to (6.23), and (6.24) to (6.27)]. Thus we know that

$(D - 1)(D + 2)y = e^x$ has the particular solution
$$y_{p1} = \tfrac{1}{3}xe^x;$$

$(D - 1)(D + 2)y = 4\sin 2x$ has the particular solution
$$y_{p2} = -\tfrac{1}{5}\cos 2x - \tfrac{3}{5}\sin 2x;$$

$(D - 1)(D + 2)y = x^2 - x$ has the particular solution
$$y_{p3} = -\tfrac{1}{2}(x^2 + 1).$$

Adding these three equations, we see that

$$(6.29) \quad y_p = y_{p1} + y_{p2} + y_{p3} = \tfrac{1}{3}xe^x - \tfrac{1}{5}\cos 2x - \tfrac{3}{5}\sin 2x - \tfrac{1}{2}(x^2 + 1)$$

is a particular solution of (6.28). This is the easiest way of handling a complicated right-hand side: Solve a separate equation for each different exponential and add the solutions. The fact that this is correct for a linear equation is often called the *principle of superposition*. As we can see from (6.28) and (6.29), this amounts to a fancy name for the fact that the derivative (of any order) of a sum of terms is equal to the sum of the derivatives of the individual terms. Notice that the principle holds only for *linear* equations; for example, if the equation contained y'^2, the principle would not hold since $(y_1' + y_2')^2$ is not equal to $y_1'^2 + y_2'^2$. In fact, an operator (such as the D operators we have been using) which satisfies the principle of superposition is called a *linear operator*. By definition, an operator O is a linear operator if

$$(6.30) \qquad \begin{aligned} O(f_1 + f_2) &= O(f_1) + O(f_2) \qquad \text{and} \\ O(cf) &= cO(f), \qquad c = \text{const.} \end{aligned}$$

For example, differentiation and integration are linear operations, but taking the square root is not, since $\sqrt{f_1 + f_2}$ is not equal to $\sqrt{f_1} + \sqrt{f_2}$. Linear operators are of particular importance because they obey the principle of superposition (6.30). We shall make use of this principle shortly in our discussion of the use of Fourier series in finding particular solutions.

Forced vibrations. Let us return now to the physical problem we were considering at the end of Section 5. There we set up and solved the differential equation which describes the free (this means zero right-hand side, that is, no forcing function) vibrations of a damped oscillator. We commented that the same mathematics applies to a variety of mechanics problems and also to a simple *RLC* series electric circuit. As we know from experiment and as we can see from (5.30), (5.31), and (5.32), the free vibrations we considered in Section 5 die out as time passes. Such oscillations are referred to as *transients*. We next want to consider the vibrations obtained when a periodic force (or emf in the electric case) is applied. This means mathematically that we want to solve (5.27) with a function of t on the right-hand side. The solution will contain the appropriate one of (5.30), (5.31), (5.32); this is the complementary function and it is also the transient since it tends to zero as t tends to infinity. The solution will also contain a particular solution which does not tend to zero as t tends to infinity; this is the *steady-state solution* which we want to find. Let us solve

(6.31) $$\frac{d^2y}{dt^2} + 2b\frac{dy}{dt} + \omega^2 y = F \sin \omega' t \qquad (F = \text{const.}).$$

By the method of complex exponentials, we solve first

(6.32) $$\frac{d^2Y}{dt^2} + 2b\frac{dY}{dt} + \omega^2 Y = Fe^{i\omega' t}.$$

Substitute

(6.33) $$Y_p = Ce^{i\omega' t}$$

into (6.32) to get

(6.34)
$$(-\omega'^2 + 2bi\omega' + \omega^2)Ce^{i\omega' t} = Fe^{i\omega' t},$$

$$C = \frac{F}{(\omega^2 - \omega'^2) + 2bi\omega'} = \frac{[(\omega^2 - \omega'^2) - 2bi\omega']F}{(\omega^2 - \omega'^2)^2 + 4b^2\omega'^2}.$$

It is convenient to write the complex number C in the $re^{i\theta}$ form. We have

(6.35)
$$|C| = \frac{F}{\sqrt{(\omega^2 - \omega'^2)^2 + 4b^2\omega'^2}},$$

angle of $C = -\phi$, where ϕ is given by Fig. 6.1.

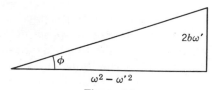

$$\omega^2 - \omega'^2$$

Figure 6.1

Thus

(6.36)
$$C = \frac{F}{\sqrt{(\omega^2 - \omega'^2)^2 + 4b^2\omega'^2}} e^{-i\phi}$$

and from (6.33)

(6.37)
$$Y_p = \frac{F}{\sqrt{(\omega^2 - \omega'^2)^2 + 4b^2\omega'^2}} e^{i(\omega't - \phi)}.$$

To find y_p we take the imaginary part of Y_p:

(6.38)
$$y_p = \frac{F}{\sqrt{(\omega^2 - \omega'^2)^2 + 4b^2\omega'^2}} \sin(\omega't - \phi).$$

This is the steady-state solution, so-called because as t increases, the rest of the solution [given by (5.30), (5.31), or (5.32)] becomes negligible. For example, when you turn on an electric light, the current is given by (5.32) plus (6.38). The transient (5.32) tends to zero rapidly and the steady-state solution (6.38) becomes essentially the whole solution.

We note, by comparing (6.38) and the forcing function in (6.31), that the applied force (or emf) and the solution y (which represents displacement, current, etc.) are *out of phase*; that is, their maximum values do not occur at the same time because of the phase angle ϕ. We also see from (6.38) that for a given forcing frequency ω', the largest amplitude of y (also of dy/dt, Problem 50) occurs if the natural (undamped) frequency ω is equal to ω'. This situation is often called *resonance*. In the *RLC* series circuit problem, y represents the charge q on the capacitor if the forcing function is the emf, and y represents the current $I = dq/dt$ if the forcing function is the time derivative of the emf. For such a circuit, given the frequency ω' of the applied emf, the current (or charge) will have the largest amplitude when the natural (undamped) frequency ω is equal to ω'. This is almost always called the resonance condition for the electrical case. However, there is another question we could ask here which is of particular interest in mechanics. Given the natural (undamped) frequency ω of the system, what frequency of the forcing function will produce the largest amplitude of y? In (6.38), we want to maximize the coefficient of the sine; we can instead minimize the square of the denominator of the coefficient; that is, we want to find the value of ω' which minimizes $(\omega^2 - \omega'^2)^2 + 4b^2\omega'^2$ for given ω. Setting the derivative of this function equal to zero and solving for ω', we get

$$2(\omega^2 - \omega'^2)(-2\omega') + 8b^2\omega' = 0,$$

(6.39)
$$\omega'^2 = \omega^2 - 2b^2.$$

Note that this value of ω' is not equal to either the natural undamped frequency ω or the natural damped frequency β where $\beta^2 = \omega^2 - b^2$ [see (5.32)]. However, if we define *resonance* as the situation in which we get the maximum amplitude for y for a given value of ω, then the resonance condition here is (6.39). (The maximum amplitude for the velocity—or current in the electrical case—is still obtained for $\omega' = \omega$; Problem 50.) The resonance condition (6.39) is of particular importance in mechanics where we are apt to be interested in the displacement y of a given system under the action of various forces. For example, consider a bridge; we would want to avoid periodic forces with an ω' given by (6.39) since such forces would produce large vibrations. In this case resonance is undesirable. It may in other cases be desirable; for example, when you tune your radio to the frequency of a given station, you are given ω' and you adjust the circuit in your radio to make its natural frequency ω equal to the given ω'.

Use of Fourier series in finding particular solutions. In simple problems, the forcing function in either the electrical or mechanical case is just a sine or cosine and the problem can be solved as we have just done. In more complicated (and realistic) cases, however, the forcing function may very well be some more complicated function; it is often a periodic function, however, and we shall assume this. Suppose, for example, that the periodic emf applied to a circuit is given by one of the graphs in Fig. 3.2 of Chapter 6. We learned in Chapter 6 how to expand such a function in a Fourier series. Let us suppose that this has been done, using for definiteness the complex exponential form of the Fourier series. Then we can write (6.1) as

$$(6.40) \qquad a_2 \frac{d^2y}{dx^2} + a_1 \frac{dy}{dx} + a_0 y = f(x) = \sum_{n=-\infty}^{\infty} c_n e^{inx}.$$

We know how to solve the equation

$$(6.41) \qquad a_2 \frac{d^2y}{dx^2} + a_1 \frac{dy}{dx} + a_0 y = c_n e^{inx}$$

with the right-hand side equal to any one term of the series. If we now add the solutions of all the equations (6.41) for all n, we have a solution of (6.40) (see *principle of superposition* above).

Example. Solve

$$(6.42) \qquad \frac{d^2y}{dt^2} + 2\frac{dy}{dt} + 10y = f(t),$$

where $f(t)$ is a function of period 2π and

$$f(t) = \begin{cases} 1, & 0 \le t < \pi, \\ 0, & \pi \le t < 2\pi. \end{cases}$$

The auxiliary equation is

$$D^2 + 2D + 10 = 0;$$

its roots are

$$D = -1 \pm 3i,$$

so the complementary function is

$$y_c = e^{-t}(A \cos 3t + B \sin 3t).$$

To find a particular solution, we first expand $f(t)$ in a Fourier series; from Chapter 6, equation (7.8), we have

(6.43) $f(t) = \tfrac{1}{2} + \dfrac{1}{i\pi} \, [e^{it} - e^{-it} + \tfrac{1}{3}(e^{3it} - e^{-3it}) + \cdots].$

We next write and solve a whole set of differential equations like (6.42) but each having just one term of the series (6.43) on the right-hand side. For the first term (namely $\tfrac{1}{2}$) we see by inspection that a particular solution of

$$\frac{d^2y}{dt^2} + 2\frac{dy}{dt} + 10y = \tfrac{1}{2}$$

is $y = \tfrac{1}{20}$. All the other terms of (6.43) are of the form $(1/ik\pi)e^{ikt}$, where k is a positive or negative odd integer. To solve

(6.44) $\dfrac{d^2y}{dt^2} + 2\dfrac{dy}{dt} + 10y = \dfrac{1}{ik\pi}\, e^{ikt},$

we substitute

(6.45) $$y = Ce^{ikt}$$

into (6.44) and get

$$(-k^2 + 2ik + 10)Ce^{ikt} = \frac{1}{ik\pi}\, e^{ikt}.$$

Then we have

(6.46) $C = \dfrac{1}{ik\pi}\dfrac{1}{(10 - k^2) + 2ik} = \dfrac{1}{ik\pi}\dfrac{(10 - k^2) - 2ik}{\sqrt{(10 - k^2)^2 + 4k^2}}\, .$

By letting $k = \pm1, \pm3, \ldots,$ and substituting the values of C thus obtained into (6.45), we obtain the solutions of (6.44) for the various k values corresponding to the terms of the series (6.43). The sum of all the solutions corresponding to all the terms is the desired particular solution of (6.42). Thus

(6.47)

$$
y_p = \frac{1}{20} + \frac{1}{i\pi} \frac{9 - 2i}{\sqrt{85}} e^{it} - \frac{1}{i\pi} \frac{9 + 2i}{\sqrt{85}} e^{-it}
$$

$$
+ \frac{1}{3i\pi} \frac{1 - 6i}{\sqrt{37}} e^{3it} - \frac{1}{3i\pi} \frac{1 + 6i}{\sqrt{37}} e^{-3it} + \cdots
$$

$$
= \frac{1}{20} + \frac{2}{\pi} \frac{9}{\sqrt{85}} \left(\frac{e^{it} - e^{-it}}{2i} \right) - \frac{4}{\pi\sqrt{85}} \left(\frac{e^{it} + e^{-it}}{2} \right)
$$

$$
+ \frac{2}{3\pi} \frac{1}{\sqrt{37}} \left(\frac{e^{3it} - e^{-3it}}{2i} \right) - \frac{12}{3\pi} \frac{1}{\sqrt{37}} \left(\frac{e^{3it} + e^{-3it}}{2} \right) + \cdots
$$

$$
= \frac{1}{20} + \frac{2}{\pi\sqrt{85}} (9 \sin t - 2 \cos t) + \frac{2}{3\pi\sqrt{37}} (\sin 3t - 6 \cos 3t) + \cdots
$$

is a particular solution of (6.42).

7. OTHER SECOND-ORDER EQUATIONS

Although the second-order linear equations with constant coefficients are the ones used most frequently in applications, there are a few other kinds of second-order equations which are also important. We shall discuss four of these here, namely (a) equations with y missing; (b) equations with x missing; (c) equations of the form $y'' + f(y) = 0$; (d) equations of the form $a_2 x^2 (d^2y/dx^2) + a_1 x (dy/dx) + a_0 y = 0$ (often called Euler or Cauchy equations).

To solve either (a) or (b), we make the substitution

(7.1) $$ p = y'. $$

We then have for case (a)

(7.2) $p' = y''$.   Case (a): dependent variable y missing.

After these substitutions, an equation of the type (a) is of the first order with p as the dependent variable and x as the independent variable. First, we solve it for p as a function of x; then we put back $p = y'$ and solve the resulting first-order equation for y.

For case (b), we write $y' = p$ and

$$(7.3) \quad y'' = \frac{dp}{dx} = \frac{dp}{dy}\frac{dy}{dx} = p\frac{dp}{dy}.$$

Case (b): independent variable x missing.

What we are doing here is to change the independent variable from x to y. Observe that there is *one* independent variable in an ordinary differential equation. We were originally thinking of x as the independent variable with y and $p = dy/dx$ as functions of x. Now we think of y as the independent variable with p a function of y; (7.3) is just the chain rule (Chapter 4, Section 5) for differentiating a function $p(y)$ with respect to x if y is a function of x. With the substitutions (7.1) and (7.3), a differential equation with x missing becomes a first-order equation with p as the dependent variable and y as the independent variable.

Example. In Section 5, we discussed the motion of a mass m subject to a restoring force $-ky$ and a damping force $l(dy/dt)$. Let us now consider a similar problem but with the damping force proportional to the square of the velocity. The differential equation of motion is then [compare (5.26)]

$$(7.4) \qquad m\frac{d^2y}{dt^2} \pm l\left(\frac{dy}{dt}\right)^2 + ky = 0 \qquad (l > 0),$$

where the plus or minus sign must be chosen correctly at each stage of the motion so that the retarding force opposes the motion. Let us solve the following special case of this problem. Discuss the motion of a particle which is released from rest at $t = 0$ at the point $y = 1$, and obeys the equation of motion

$$(7.5) \qquad 4\frac{d^2y}{dt^2} \pm 2\left(\frac{dy}{dt}\right)^2 + y = 0.$$

This is an example of case (b) (for "x missing" read "t missing," that is, the independent variable missing). Using (7.3) (with x replaced by t), we have

$$(7.6) \qquad \begin{aligned} \frac{dy}{dt} &= p, \\[2mm] \frac{d^2y}{dt^2} &= p\frac{dp}{dy}, \end{aligned}$$

so (7.5) becomes

$$(7.7) \qquad 4p\frac{dp}{dy} \pm 2p^2 + y = 0 \qquad \text{or} \qquad \frac{dp}{dy} \pm \tfrac{1}{2}p = -\tfrac{1}{4}yp^{-1}.$$

This is a Bernoulli equation [compare (4.1) with y replaced by p, and P and Q functions of y]. We have $n = -1$, and the substitution (4.2) is

$$(7.8) \qquad z = p^2.$$

Then

$$\frac{dz}{dy} = 2p \frac{dp}{dy}$$

and (7.7) becomes

$$(7.9) \qquad \frac{dz}{dy} \pm z = -\tfrac{1}{2}y.$$

This is a first-order linear equation; solving it (see Section 3), we get

$$(7.10) \qquad ze^{\pm y} = -\tfrac{1}{2} \int ye^{\pm y}\, dy = -\tfrac{1}{2}e^{\pm y}(\pm y - 1) + c,$$

$$z = -\tfrac{1}{2}(\pm y - 1) + ce^{\mp y}.$$

Since initially $dy/dt = 0$ and $y > 0$, we see from (7.5) that the initial acceleration is in the negative direction; since the particle starts from rest, its velocity for small t is also in the negative direction. Then the damping force must be in the positive direction so we must use the lower sign in (7.10) for the first part of the motion. Thus we have

$$(7.11) \qquad z = \tfrac{1}{2}(y + 1) + ce^{y} \qquad \text{(for small } t\text{).}$$

We determine c from the initial conditions $dy/dt = 0$, $y = 1$, at $t = 0$; we have $z = p^2 = (dy/dt)^2 = 0$ when $y = 1$; therefore from (7.11) we get

$$0 = 1 + ce, \qquad c = -e^{-1}.$$

Then we have

$$(7.12) \qquad z = \left(\frac{dy}{dt}\right)^2 = \tfrac{1}{2}(y + 1) - e^{y-1} \qquad \text{(for small } t\text{).}$$

This is a valid solution as long as $dy/dt < 0$ (this is what small t means). Thus the particle initially moves in the negative direction for a while. To continue the problem we would need to find whether it stops and if so where. This means solving a transcendental equation which has to be done by some approximation method. It turns out that when it stops, y is negative; at this point the force $-y$ is in the positive direction and the particle, after stopping, moves in the positive direction. The solution for $(dy/dt)^2$ is then given by (7.10) with the upper sign. After another interval of time, the particle again reverses its motion and we again use the solution (7.11) (with a different c), and so on, the total motion appearing something like a damped vibration. We shall not continue the details further here since we have already accomplished our purpose of illustrating case (b) and the solution of a Bernoulli equation.

Case (c) appears to be very special and is obviously included by (b); however, it is very important to know the easy way to solve it because it so frequently arises in applications. The trick is simply to multiply the equation by y'; we then have

$$y'y'' + f(y)y' = 0 \qquad \text{or} \quad y' \, dy' + f(y) \, dy = 0$$

which can be integrated to give

(7.13) $$\tfrac{1}{2}y'^2 + \int f(y) \, dy = \text{const.}$$

This equation is separable and so can be solved (except for possible difficulty in evaluating the integrals). We say that the problem is reduced to *quadratures* (indicated integrations); this means that we can write the answer in terms of integrals which may or may not be easy to evaluate!

Example. Consider a particle of mass m moving along the x-axis under the action of a force $F(x)$. Then the equation of motion is

(7.14) $$m \frac{d^2 x}{dt^2} = F(x).$$

If we multiply this equation by $v = dx/dt$ and integrate with respect to t, we get

$$mv \frac{dv}{dt} = F(x) \frac{dx}{dt} \qquad \text{or} \quad mv \, dv = F(x) \, dx,$$

(7.15) $$\tfrac{1}{2}mv^2 = \int F(x) \, dx + \text{const.}$$

Recall (Chapter 5, Section 11) that the potential energy of a particle is the negative of the work done by the force. Thus

(7.16) $$\tfrac{1}{2}mv^2 - \int F(x) \, dx$$

is the kinetic energy plus the potential energy; equation (7.15) expresses the law of conservation of energy for this problem. This energy equation is often of more interest than the equation of motion (x as a function of t) and so it is worth while to be able to find it directly, as we have done, without solving the differential equation for x. Equation (7.15) is known as a *first integral* of the differential equation since we have integrated a second-order equation *once* to get it.

(d) An equation of the form

(7.17) $$a_2 x^2 \frac{d^2 y}{dx^2} + a_1 x \frac{dy}{dx} + a_0 y = f(x)$$

(called an Euler or Cauchy equation) can be reduced to a linear equation with constant coefficients by changing the independent variable from x to z where

(7.18) $$x = e^z.$$

For then we have (see Problem 57 and also Chapter 4, Section 11)

(7.19) $$x\frac{dy}{dx} = \frac{dy}{dz} \quad \text{and} \quad x^2\frac{d^2y}{dx^2} = \frac{d^2y}{dz^2} - \frac{dy}{dz}.$$

Substituting (7.18) and (7.19) into (7.17) gives

(7.20) $$a_2\left(\frac{d^2y}{dz^2} - \frac{dy}{dz}\right) + a_1\frac{dy}{dz} + a_0y = f(e^z)$$

which is a linear equation with constant coefficients and so can be solved by the methods of Sections 5 and 6. (See also Problem 58.)

REFERENCES

There are many textbooks on differential equations; a few suggestions are Agnew, Fagg, Lambe and Tranter, Kaplan, and Tenenbaum and Pollard, but there are many others. Also some calculus texts and many books on mathematics in physics and engineering contain material on differential equations. In the reference list at the end of the book, references for Chapter 7 have a [7] after the listing.

PROBLEMS

1. Find the "general solution" (that is, a solution containing an arbitrary constant) of each of the following differential equations, by separation of variables. Then find a particular solution of each equation satisfying the given boundary conditions.

(a) $xy' = y$, $\qquad\qquad\qquad\qquad\qquad$ $y = 3$ when $x = 2$.

(b) $x\sqrt{1 - y^2}\,dx + y\sqrt{1 - x^2}\,dy = 0$, $\quad$ $y = \frac{1}{2}$ when $x = \frac{1}{2}$.

(c) $y' \sin x = y \ln y$, $\qquad\qquad\qquad\quad$ $y = e$ when $x = \dfrac{\pi}{3}$.

(d) $(1 + y^2)\,dx + xy\,dy = 0$, $\qquad\quad$ $y = 0$ when $x = 5$.

(e) $xy' - xy = y$, $\qquad\qquad\qquad\quad$ $y = 1$ when $x = 1$.

(f) $y' = \dfrac{2xy^2 + x}{x^2y - y}$, $\qquad\qquad\qquad$ $y = 0$ when $x = \sqrt{2}$.

(g) $y' = \cos(x + y)$, $y = 1$ when $x = -1$.
(*Hint:* Let $u = x + y$; then $u' = 1 + y'$.)

(h) $y' = \dfrac{y}{x} - \tan\dfrac{y}{x}$, $y = \dfrac{\pi}{2}$ when $x = 1$. (*Hint:* Let $u = y/x$.)

2. (a) By separation of variables, solve the differential equation $dy/dx = \sqrt{1 - y^2}$ to obtain a solution containing one arbitrary constant. Although this solution may be referred to as the "general solution," show that $y = 1$ is a solution of the differential equation not obtainable from the "general solution" by any choice of the arbitrary constant. The solution $y = 1$ is called a *singular solution*; $y = -1$ is another singular solution. Sketch a number of graphs of the "general solution" for different values of the arbitrary constant and observe that $y = 1$ is tangent to all of them. This is characteristic of a singular solution—its graph is tangent at each point to one of the graphs of the "general solution." Note that the given differential equation is not linear; for linear equations, all solutions are contained in the general solution, but nonlinear equations may have singular solutions which cannot be obtained from the "general solution" by specializing the arbitrary constant (or constants). Thus a nonlinear first-order equation in x and y may have two (or more) solutions passing through a given point in the (x, y) plane, whereas a linear first-order equation always has just one such solution. Show that *any* continuous curve made up of pieces of $y = 1$, $y = -1$, and the sine curves of the "general solution," gives a solution of the above differential equation. Sketch such a solution curve on your graphs.

(b) Find singular solutions of Problem 1b by inspection and show that they cannot be obtained from the "general solution" by specializing the arbitrary constant.

3. (a) Find the "general solution" of the equation $y' = \sqrt{y}$ by separation of variables. Find a particular solution satisfying $y = 0$ when $x = 0$. Show that the singular solution $y = 0$ cannot be obtained from the general solution. Sketch graphs of the "general solution" for several values of the arbitrary constant, and observe that each of them is tangent to the singular solution. Thus there are two solutions passing through any point on the x-axis; in particular, there are two solutions satisfying $x = y = 0$. Consider the following physical problems leading to this differential equation.

(b) The velocity of a particle on the x-axis, $x \geq 0$, is always numerically equal to the square root of its displacement x. If $v = 0$ when $x = 0$, find x as a function of t. Show that the given conditions are satisfied if the particle remains at the origin for any arbitrary length of time t_0, and then moves away; find x for $t > t_0$ for this case.

(c) Let the rate of growth dN/dt of a colony of bacteria be proportional to the square root of the number present at any time. If there are no bacteria present at $t = 0$, how many are there at a later time? Observe here that the "general solution" gives an unreasonable answer.

4. Consider a light beam traveling downward into the ocean. As the beam progresses, it is partially absorbed and its intensity decreases. The rate at

which the intensity is decreasing with depth at any point is proportional to the intensity at that depth. The proportionality constant μ is called the *linear absorption coefficient*. Show that if the intensity at the surface is I_0, the intensity at a distance s below the surface is $I = I_0 e^{-\mu s}$. The linear absorption coefficient for water is of the order of 10^{-2} ft^{-1} (the exact value depending on the wavelength of the light and the impurities in the water). For this value of μ, find the intensity as a fraction of the surface intensity at a depth of 1 ft, 50 ft, 500 ft, 1 mile. When the intensity of a light beam has been reduced to half its surface intensity ($I = \frac{1}{2}I_0$), the distance the light has penetrated into the absorbing substance is called the *half-value thickness* of the substance. Find the half-value thickness in terms of μ. Find the half-value thickness for water for the value of μ given above.

Note that the differential equation and its solution in this problem are mathematically the same as those in Example 1 of Section 2, although the physical problem and the terminology are different. In discussing radioactive decay, we call λ the *decay constant*, and we define the *half-life T* of a radio-active substance as the time when $N = \frac{1}{2}N_0$ (compare half-value thickness). Find the relation between λ and T.

5. Consider the following special cases of the simple series circuit [Fig. 1.1 and equation (1.2)].

   (a) *RC* circuit (that is, $L = 0$) with $E = 0$; find q as a function of t if q_0 is the charge on the capacitor at $t = 0$.

   (b) *RL* circuit (that is, no capacitor; this means $1/C = 0$) with $E = 0$; find $I(t)$ given $I = I_0$ at $t = 0$.

   Again note that these are the same differential equations as in Problem 4 and Example 1 of Section 2. The terminology is again different; we define the time constant τ for a circuit as the time required for the charge (or current) to fall to $1/e$ times its initial value. Find the time constant for the circuits (a) and (b). If the same equation, say $y = y_0 e^{-at}$, represented either radioactive decay or light absorption or an *RC* or *RL* circuit, what would be the relations among the half-life, the half-value thickness, and the time constant?

6. (a) Suppose the rate at which bacteria in a culture grow is proportional to the number present at any time. Write and solve the differential equation for the number N of bacteria as a function of time t if there are N_0 bacteria when $t = 0$. Again note that (except for a change of sign) this is the same differential equation and solution as in the preceding problems.

   (b) Solve the equation for the rate of growth of bacteria if the rate of increase is proportional to the number present but the population is being reduced at a constant rate by the removal of bacteria for experimental purposes.

7. (a) Heat is escaping at a constant rate [dH/dt in (1.1) is constant] through the walls of a long cylindrical pipe. Find the temperature T at a distance r from the axis of the cylinder if the inside wall has radius $r = 1$ and temperature $T = 100$ and the outside wall has $r = 2$ and $T = 0$.

   (b) Do the same problem as (a) for a spherical cavity containing a constant source of heat [use the same radii and temperatures as in (a)].

8. Show that the thickness of the ice on a lake increases with the square root of the time in cold weather, making the following simplifying assumptions. Let the water temperature be a constant $10°C$, the air temperature a constant $-10°C$, and assume that at any given time the ice forms a slab of uniform thickness x. The rate of formation of ice is proportional to the rate at which heat is transferred from the water to the air. Let $t = 0$ when $x = 0$.

9. An object of mass m falls from rest under gravity subject to an air resistance proportional to its velocity. Taking the y-axis as positive down, show that the differential equation of motion is $m(dv/dt) = mg - kv$, where k is a positive constant. Find v as a function of t, and find the limiting value of v as t tends to infinity; this limit is called the *terminal velocity*. Can you find the terminal velocity directly from the differential equation without solving it? *Hint:* What is dv/dt after v has reached an essentially constant value?

Consider the following specific examples of this problem.

(a) A person drops from an airplane with a parachute. Find a reasonable value of k.

(b) In the Millikan oil drop experiment to measure the charge of an electron, tiny electrically charged drops of oil fall through air under gravity or rise under the combination of gravity and an electric field. Measurements can be made only after they have reached terminal velocity. Find a formula for the time required for a drop starting at rest to reach 99% of its terminal velocity.

10. According to Newton's law of cooling, the rate at which the temperature of an object changes is proportional to the difference between its temperature and that of its surroundings. A cup of coffee at $200°$ in a room of temperature $70°$ is stirred continually and reaches $100°$ after 10 min. At what time was it at $120°$?

11. A solution containing 90% by volume of alcohol (in water) runs at 1 gal per min into a 100-gal tank of pure water where it is continually mixed. The mixture is withdrawn at the rate of 1 gal per min. When will it start coming out 50% alcohol?

12. A substance evaporates at a rate proportional to the exposed surface. If a spherical mothball of radius $\frac{1}{2}$ cm has radius 0.4 cm after 6 months, how long will it take (a) for the radius to be $\frac{1}{4}$ cm? (b) For the volume of the mothball to be half of what it was originally?

13. If P dollars are left in the bank at interest I percent per year compounded continuously, find the amount A at time t. *Hint:* Find dA, the interest on A dollars for time dt.

14. The mass m of an electron at velocity v near the velocity c of light increases according to the formula $m = \dfrac{m_0}{\sqrt{1 - v^2/c^2}}$, where m_0 is a constant (the rest mass). If an electron is subject to a constant force F, Newton's second law describing its motion is

$$\frac{d}{dt}\left(\frac{m_0 v}{\sqrt{1 - v^2/c^2}}\right) = F.$$

Find the velocity as a function of time and show that the limiting velocity as t tends to infinity is c. Find the distance traveled by the electron in time t if it starts from rest.

15. (a) Recall that if ϕ is a potential, then the force $\mathbf{F} = -\nabla\phi$ at any point is a vector normal to the surface $\phi = $ const. which passes through that point. The *lines of force* are curves tangent to $\mathbf{F}$ at each point, that is, they are curves which intersect the equipotential surfaces $\phi = $ const. at right angles. In the usual iron-filing picture of a magnetic field, the lines of force are the curves outlined by the iron filings. These curves are called *orthogonal trajectories* of the equipotential surfaces $\phi = $ const. To find the orthogonal trajectories of a set of curves $\phi = $ const. in a plane, we have to find (as a function of x and y) the slope of the vector $\mathbf{F} = -\nabla\phi$ at each point (x, y), and then solve the differential equation $dy/dx = $ slope. Show that if the equations of the curves $\phi = $ const. are written solved for y, then the slope of the orthogonal trajectory curve is

$$\left(\frac{dy}{dx}\right)_{\text{orthog. traj.}} = \frac{-1}{\left(\dfrac{dy}{dx}\right)_{\phi\text{ curve}}}.$$

(b) Find the orthogonal trajectories of each of the following families of curves. In each case sketch several of the given curves and several of their orthogonal trajectories. Be careful to eliminate the constant from dy/dx for the original curves; this constant takes different values for different curves of the original family and you want an expression for dy/dx which is valid for all curves of the family crossed by the orthogonal trajectory you are trying to find.

$x^2 + y^2 = $ const.

$y = kx^2$.

$y = kx^n$.   (Assume that n is a given number; the different curves of the family have different values of k.)

$xy = k$.

$(y - 1)^2 = x^2 + k$.

16. Find the general solution of each of the following differential equations.

(a) $y' + y = e^x$

(b) $x^2y' + 3xy = 1$

(c) $dy + (2xy - xe^{-x^2})\, dx = 0$

(d) $2xy' + y = 2x^{5/2}$

(e) $dy/dx + y \tan x = \cos x$

(f) $y' \cos x + y = \cos^2 x$

(g) $y'\sqrt{x^2 + 1} + xy = x$

(h) $(1 + e^x)y' + e^xy = 1$

(i) $(x \ln x)y' + y = \ln x$

(j) $dx + (x - e^y)\, dy = 0$

(k) $\dfrac{dy}{dx} = \dfrac{3y}{3y^{2/3} - x}$

Hint for (j) *and* (k): Solve for x in terms of y.

17. Water with a small salt content (5 lb in 1000 gal) is flowing into a very salty lake at the rate of $4 \cdot 10^5$ gal per hr. The salty water is flowing out at the rate of 10^5 gal per hr. If at some time (say $t = 0$) the volume of the lake is 10^9 gal, and its salt content is 10^7 lb, find the salt content at time t. Assume that the salt is mixed uniformly with the water in the lake at all times.

18. (a) Find the general solution of (1.2) for an RL circuit ($1/C = 0$) with $E = E_0 \cos \omega t$ ($\omega = $ const.).

    (b) Find the general solution of (1.3) for an RC circuit ($L = 0$), with $E = E_0 \cos \omega t$.

    (c) Do parts (a) and (b) with $E = E_0 e^{i\omega t}$. Obtain the solutions of parts (a) and (b) by taking real parts of your solutions in (c).

19. (a) If $\lambda_1 = \lambda_2 = \lambda$ in (3.11), then $\int e^{(\lambda_2 - \lambda_1)t}\, dt = \int dt$. Find N_2 for this case.

    (b) Extend the radioactive decay problem (Example 2, Section 3) one more stage, that is let λ_3 be the decay constant of polonium and find how much polonium there is at time t.

    (c) Generalize part (b) to any number of stages.

20. (a) Find the orthogonal trajectories of the family of curves $x = y + 1 + ce^y$. (See Problem 15.)

    (b) Find the orthogonal trajectories of the family of curves $y = -e^{x^2} \operatorname{erf} x + Ce^{x^2}$. *Hint:* See Chapter 9, equation 9.1 for definition of erf x, and Chapter 4, Section 12, for differentiation of an integral. Solve for x in terms of y.

21. Solve the following differential equations.

    (a) $y' + y = xy^{2/3}$

    (b) $y' + \dfrac{1}{x}y = 2x^{3/2}y^{1/2}$

    (c) $3xy^2 y' + 3y^3 = 1$

    (d) $(2xe^{3y} + e^x)\, dx + (3x^2 e^{3y} - y^2)\, dy = 0$

    (e) $(x - y)\, dy + (y + x + 1)\, dx = 0$

    (f) $(\cos x \cos y + \sin^2 x)\, dx - (\sin x \sin y + \cos^2 y)\, dy = 0$

    (g) $x^2\, dy + (y^2 - xy)\, dx = 0$

    (h) $y\, dy = (-x + \sqrt{x^2 + y^2})\, dx$

    (i) $xy\, dx + (y^2 - x^2)\, dy = 0$

    (j) $(y^2 - xy)\, dx + (x^2 + xy)\, dy = 0$

22. A raindrop falls through a cloud, increasing in size as it picks up moisture. Assume that the rate of increase of its volume with respect to distance fallen is proportional to the cross-sectional area of the drop at any time (that is, the mass increase $dm = \rho\, dV$ is proportional to the volume $\pi r^2\, dy$ swept out by the drop as it falls a distance dy). Show that the radius r of the drop is proportional to the distance y the drop has fallen if $r = 0$ when $y = 0$. Recall that when m is not constant, Newton's second law is properly stated as $(d/dt)(mv) = F$. Use this equation to find the distance y which the drop falls in time t under the force of gravity, if $y = \dot{y} = 0$ at $t = 0$. Show that the acceleration of the drop is $g/7$ where g is the acceleration of gravity. (See Section 7.)

23. If an incompressible fluid flows in a corner bounded by walls meeting at the origin at an angle of 60°, the streamlines of the flow satisfy the equation

$$2xy\, dx + (x^2 - y^2)\, dy = 0.$$

Find the streamlines.

24. Find the shape of a mirror which has the property that rays from a point O on the axis are reflected into a parallel beam. *Hint:* Take the point O at the origin. Show from the figure that $\tan 2\theta = y/x$. Use the formula for $\tan 2\theta$ to express this in terms of $\tan \theta = dy/dx$ and solve the resulting differential equation. (See Section 7.)

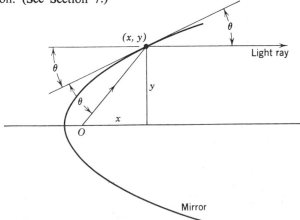

25. (a) Find the family of orthogonal trajectories (see Problem 15) of the circles $(x - h)^2 + y^2 = h^2$.

   (b) Find the family of curves satisfying the differential equation

$$(x + y)\, dy + (x - y)\, dx = 0$$

and also find their orthogonal trajectories.

26. Let D stand for d/dx, that is, $Dy = dy/dx$; then

$$D^2y = D(Dy) = \frac{d}{dx}\left(\frac{dy}{dx}\right) = \frac{d^2y}{dx^2}, \qquad D^3y = \frac{d^3y}{dx^3}, \quad \text{etc.}$$

D (or an expression involving D) is called a differential operator. Two operators are equal if they give the same results when they operate on y. For example,

$$D(D + x) y = \frac{d}{dx}\left(\frac{dy}{dx} + xy\right) = \frac{d^2y}{dx^2} + x\frac{dy}{dx} + y = (D^2 + xD + 1)y$$

so we say that

$$D(D + x) = D^2 + xD + 1.$$

In a similar way show that:

(a) $(D - a)(D - b) = (D - b)(D - a) = D^2 - (b + a)D + ab$ for any constant a and b.

(b) $Dx = xD + 1$.   (Note that D and x do not commute, that is, $Dx \neq xD$.)

(c) $(D - x)(D + x) = D^2 - x^2 + 1$,   but $(D + x)(D - x) = D^2 - x^2 - 1$.

(d) $D^3 + 1 = (D + 1)(D^2 - D + 1)$.

27. Recall from Chapter 3, Section 6, that a set of functions is linearly independent if their Wronskian is different from zero. Calculate the Wronskian of each of the following sets of functions to show that in each case the set of functions is linearly independent.

(a) e^{-x}, e^{-4x}.

(b) e^{ax}, e^{bx}, any a and b, real or complex, if $a \neq b$.

(c) e^{ax}, xe^{ax}.

(d) $e^{ax}, xe^{ax}, x^2e^{ax}$.

28. Solve the following differential equations

(a) $y'' + y' - 2y = 0$

(b) $y'' - 4y' + 4y = 0$

(c) $y'' + 9y = 0$

(d) $y'' + 2y' + 2y = 0$

(e) $(D^2 - 2D + 1)y = 0$

(f) $(D^2 + 16)y = 0$

(g) $(D^2 - 5D + 6)y = 0$

(h) $D(D + 5)y = 0$

29. (a) Solve the algebraic equation

$$D^2 + (1 + 2i)D + i - 1 = 0$$

(note the complex coefficients) and observe that the roots are complex but not complex conjugates. Show that the method of solution of (5.6) (case of unequal roots) is correct here, and so find the general solution of

$$y'' + (1 + 2i)y' + (i - 1)y = 0.$$

(b) Similarly, solve $y'' + (1 - i)y' - iy = 0$. *Hint:* See Chapter 2, Section 10, for a method of finding the square root of a complex number.

30. By the method used in solving (5.4) to get (5.9), show that the solution of

the third-order equation

$$(D - a)(D - b)(D - c)y = 0$$

is

$$y = c_1 e^{ax} + c_2 e^{bx} + c_3 e^{cx}$$

if a, b, c are all different, and find the solutions if two or three of the roots of the auxiliary equation are equal. Generalize the result to higher-order equations.

31. Use the results of Problem 30 to find the general solutions of the following equations.

(a) $(D - 1)(D + 3)(D + 5)y = 0$.

(b) $(D^2 + 1)(D^2 - 1)y = 0$.   Hint: $D^2 + 1 = (D + i)(D - i)$.

(c) $y'' + y = 0$.

(d) $y''' - 3y'' - 9y' - 5y = 0$.

(e) $(D^3 + D^2 - 6D)y = 0$.

(f) $D^2(D - 1)^2(D + 2)^3 y = 0$.

32. In Example 2 of Section 5, we used the second solution in (5.24) and obtained (5.25) as the particular solution satisfying the given initial conditions. Show that the first and third solutions in (5.24) also give the particular solution (5.25) for the given initial conditions.

33. A particle moves along the x-axis subject to a force toward the origin proportional to x (say $-kx$). Show that the particle executes simple harmonic motion (Section 5, Example 2). Find the kinetic energy $\frac{1}{2}mv^2$ and the potential energy $\frac{1}{2}kx^2$ as functions of t and show that the total energy is constant. Find the time averages of the potential energy and the kinetic energy and show that these averages are each equal to one-half the total energy (see average values, Chapter 6, Section 4).

34. A simple pendulum consists of a point mass m suspended by a weightless cord of length l. Find the equation of motion of the pendulum, that is, the differential equation for θ as a function of t. Show that (for small θ) this is approximately a simple harmonic motion equation, and find θ if $\theta = \theta_0$, $\dot{\theta} = 0$ when $t = 0$.

35. The gravitational force on a particle of mass m inside the earth at a distance r from the center ($r <$ the radius of the earth R) is $F = -mgr/R$ (Chapter 5, Problem 68b). Show that a particle placed in an evacuated tube through the center of the earth would execute simple harmonic motion. Find the period of this motion.

36. Find (in terms of L and C) the frequency of electrical oscillations in a series circuit (Fig. 1.1) if $R = 0$ and $E = 0$, but $I \neq 0$. (When you tune a radio, you are adjusting C and/or L to make this frequency equal to that of the radio station.)

37. A block of wood is floating in water; it is depressed slightly and then released to oscillate up and down. Assume that the top and bottom of the block are parallel planes which remain horizontal during the oscillations and that the sides of the block are vertical. Show that the period of the motion (neglecting friction) is $2\pi\sqrt{h/g}$, where h is the vertical height of the part of the block under water when it is floating at rest. *Hint:* Recall that the buoyant force is equal to the weight of displaced water.

38. Solve the RLC circuit equation ((5.33) or (5.34)) with $E = 0$ as we did (5.27), and write the conditions and solutions for overdamped, critically damped, and underdamped electrical oscillations in terms of the quantities R, L, and C.

39. Determine A and B in (5.30) and (5.31), and c and γ in (5.32) if $y = 1$ and $\dot{y} = 0$ at $t = 0$. Sketch graphs of the solutions for the three types of damped motion. Show that although $y \to 0$ as $t \to \infty$ in all cases, it does so most rapidly in the critically damped case. (This is why critical damping is used in measuring devices in which a needle or other mechanism settles down to an equilibrium position after being disturbed.)

40. The natural period of an undamped system is 3 sec, but with a damping force proportional to the velocity the period becomes 5 sec. Find the differential equation of motion of the system and its solution.

41. Verify that (6.4) is a particular solution of (6.2). Verify that

$$y_p = \tfrac{1}{10} \sin 2x - e^{-x}$$

is also a particular solution of (6.2). Observe that we obtain the same general solution (6.7) whichever particular solution we use [since $(A - 1)$ is just as good an arbitrary constant as A]. Show in general that the difference between two particular solutions of $(a_2 D^2 + a_1 D + a_0)y = f(x)$ is always a solution of the homogeneous equation $(a_2 D^2 + a_1 D + a_0)y = 0$, and thus show that the general solution is the same for all choices of a particular solution.

42. Solve (6.17) by the method used in solving (6.11), for the following three cases:

(a) c not equal to either a or b;

(b) $a \neq b$, $c = a$;

(c) $a = b = c$.

43. Find the general solution of the following differential equations (complementary function + particular solution). Find the particular solution by inspection or by the method of undetermined coefficients, using complex exponentials when necessary.

(a) $y'' + y' - 5y = e^{2x}$

(b) $y'' - y' - 2y = 3e^{2x}$

(c) $y'' + 2y' + y = 2e^{-x}$

(d) $(D + 1)(D - 3)y = e^{-3x}$

(e) $(D^2 + 1)y = 2e^x$

(f) $y'' - 4y = 10$

(g) $y'' - 2y' + y = 2\cos x$

(h) $y'' + 16y = 8\cos 4x$

(i) $(D^2 + 1)y = 2\sin x$

(j) $(D - 1)^2 y = e^{2x}$

(k) $y'' - y' - y = 3e^{-x}\cos x$ (*Hint:* First solve $y'' - y' - y = 3e^{(i-1)x}$.)

(l) $y'' - 6y' + 9y = xe^{3x}$

(m) $y'' - y' + 2y = 4xe^{2x}$

(n) $(D - 3)(D + 1)y = x^2 e^{-x}$

(o) $(D^2 + 1)y = x\sin x$

44. Consider the differential equation $(D - a)(D - b)y = P_n(x)$, where $P_n(x)$ is a polynomial of degree n. Show that a particular solution of this equation is

     a polynomial $Q_n(x)$ of degree n if a and b are both different from zero;

$xQ_n(x)$ if $a \neq 0$,   but $b = 0$;

$x^2 Q_n(x)$ if $a = b = 0$.

Hint: To show that $Q_n(x) = \Sigma a_n x^n$ is a solution of the differential equation for a given $P_n = \Sigma b_n x^n$, you have only to show that the coefficients a_n can be found so that $(D - a)(D - b)Q_n(x) \equiv P_n(x)$. Equate coefficients of x^n, x^{n-1}, etc., to see that this is always possible if $a \neq b$. For $b = 0$, the differential equation becomes $(D - a)Dy = P_n$; what is Dy if $y = xQ_n$? Similarly, consider $D^2 y$ if $y = x^2 Q_n$.

45. (a) Show that

$(D - a)e^{cx} = (c - a)e^{cx}$;

$(D^2 + 5D - 3)e^{cx} = (c^2 + 5c - 3)e^{cx}$;

$L(D)e^{cx} = L(c)e^{cx}$, where $L(D)$ is any polynomial in D;

$(D - c)xe^{cx} = e^{cx}$;

$(D - c)^2 x^2 e^{cx} = 2e^{cx}$.

(b) Define the expression $y = [1/L(D)]u(x)$ to mean a solution of the differential equation $L(D)y = u$. Using part (a), show that

$$\frac{1}{D - a} e^{cx} = \frac{e^{cx}}{c - a}, \qquad c \neq a;$$

$$\frac{1}{D^2 + 5D - 3} e^{cx} = \frac{e^{cx}}{c^2 + 5c - 3};$$

$$\frac{1}{L(D)} e^{cx} = \frac{e^{cx}}{L(c)}, \qquad L(c) \neq 0;$$

$$\frac{1}{D - c} e^{cx} = xe^{cx};$$

$$\frac{1}{(D - c)^2} e^{cx} = \frac{1}{2} x^2 e^{cx}.$$

(c) The expressions $1/L(D)$ in (b) are called inverse operators. They can be used to find particular solutions of differential equations. As an example consider Problem 43a. We write

$$(D^2 + D - 5)y = e^{2x},$$

$$y = \frac{1}{D^2 + D - 5} e^{2x} = \frac{e^{2x}}{2^2 + 2 - 5} = e^{2x}.$$

Using inverse operators, find the particular solutions of Problems 43b to 43k. Be careful to use parts 4 or 5 of (b) if c is a root of the auxiliary equation. For example,

$$\frac{1}{(D - a)(D - c)} e^{cx} = \frac{1}{D - c} \frac{1}{D - a} e^{cx} = \frac{1}{D - c} \frac{e^{cx}}{c - a} = \frac{xe^{cx}}{c - a}.$$

46. (a) Show that
$$D(e^{ax}y) = e^{ax}(D + a)y,$$
$$D^2(e^{ax}y) = e^{ax}(D + a)^2y,$$

etc., or for any positive integral n
$$D^n(e^{ax}y) = e^{ax}(D + a)^ny.$$

Thus show that if $L(D)$ is any polynomial in the operator D, then
$$L(D)(e^{ax}y) = e^{ax}L(D + a)y.$$

This is called the *exponential shift*.
   (b) Use (a) to show that
$$(D - 1)^3(e^xy) = e^x D^3 y,$$
$$(D^2 + D - 6)(e^{-3x}y) = e^{-3x}(D^2 - 5D)y.$$

(c) Replace D by $D - a$, to obtain

$$e^{ax}P(D)y = P(D - a)e^{ax}y.$$

This is called the *inverse exponential shift*.

(d) Using (c), we can change a differential equation whose right-hand side is an exponential times a polynomial, to one whose right-hand side is just a polynomial. For example, consider $(D^2 - D - 6)y = 10xe^{3x}$; multiplying both sides by e^{-3x} and using (c), we get

$$e^{-3x}(D^2 - D - 6)y = [(D + 3)^2 - (D + 3) - 6]ye^{-3x}$$
$$= (D^2 + 5D)ye^{-3x} = 10x.$$

Show that a solution of $(D^2 + 5D)u = 10x$ is $u = x^2 - \frac{2}{5}x$; then we have $ye^{-3x} = x^2 - \frac{2}{5}x$ or $y = e^{3x}(x^2 - \frac{2}{5}x)$. Use this method to solve Problems 43(l) to 43(o).

47. Using Problems 44 and 46d, show that a particular solution of

$$(D - a)(D - b)y = P(x)e^{cx},$$

where $P(x)$ is a polynomial, is

(a) $y_p = Q(x)e^{cx}$, a, b, c all different,

(b) $y_p = xQ(x)e^{cx}$, $a \neq b, c = a$,

(c) $y_p = x^2Q(x)e^{cx}$, $a = b = c$,

where $Q(x)$ is a polynomial of the same degree as $P(x)$, with undetermined coefficients.

48. (a) Solve $y'' - 2y' = e^{2x}$ and $y'' - 2y' = -2$; hence by the principle of superposition find the solution of $y'' - 2y' = e^{2x} - 2$. Similarly, solve each of the following differential equations.

(b) $y'' - 5y' + 6y = 2e^x + 6x - 5$.

(c) $(D^2 - 1)y = \sinh x$.

49. Find the solutions of (1.2) (put $I = dq/dt$) and (1.3), if $E = E_0 \sin \omega't$ ($\omega' = \text{const.}$).

50. In (6.38), show that for a given forcing frequency ω', the displacement y and the velocity dy/dt have their largest amplitude when $\omega = \omega'$.

For a given ω, we have shown in Section 6 that the maximum amplitude of y does not correspond to $\omega' = \omega$. Show, however, that the maximum amplitude of dy/dt for a given ω does correspond to $\omega' = \omega$.

State the corresponding results for an electric circuit in terms of L, R, C.

51. Solve the following differential equations by use of Fourier series.

(a) $y'' + 2y' + 2y = |x|$, $-\pi < x < \pi$.

(b) $y'' + 9y = \begin{cases} x, & 0 < x < 1, \\ 0, & -1 < x < 0. \end{cases}$

(You are to assume in each case that the right-hand side is a periodic function whose values are stated for one period.)

52. Consider an equation for damped forced vibrations (mechanical or electrical) in which the right-hand side is a sum of several forces or emfs of different frequencies. For example, in (6.32) let the right-hand side be

$$F_1 e^{i\omega_1' t} + F_2 e^{i\omega_2' t} + F_3 e^{i\omega_3' t}.$$

Write the solution by the principle of superposition. Suppose, for given ω_1', ω_2', ω_3', that we adjust the system so that $\omega = \omega_1'$; show that the principal term in the solution is then the first one. Thus the system acts as a "filter" to select vibrations of one frequency from a given set (for example, a radio tuned to one station selects principally the vibrations of the frequency of that station).

53. Solve the following differential equations.

(a) $y'' + yy' = 0$.

(b) $y'' + 2xy' = 0$.   *Hint:* The solution is $y = c_1 \operatorname{erf} x + c_2$; see Chapter 9, Section 9 for definition of erf x.

54. Solve $y'' + \omega^2 y = 0$ by the method of Section 7 and compare with the solution as a linear equation with constant coefficients.

55. The force of gravitational attraction on a mass m a distance r from the center of the earth ($r >$ radius R of the earth) is mgR^2/r^2. Write the differential equation of motion of a mass m projected radially outward from the surface of the earth, with initial velocity v_0. Integrate this equation once to find v (Section 7c). Find the maximum value of r for a given v_0, that is, the value of r when $v = 0$. Find the *escape velocity*, that is the smallest value of v_0 for which r can tend to infinity.

56. Show that (7.15) is a separable equation. [You may find it helpful to write $\int F(x)\, dx = f(x)$.] Thus solve (7.14) in terms of quadratures (that is, indicated integrations).

57. Verify (7.19) and (7.20). *Hint:* $dy/dz = (dy/dx)(dx/dz)$; write the first equation of (7.19) as $x D_x = D_z$, and find D_z^2.

58. Solve the following equations using the method of Section 7d.

(a) $x^2 y'' + 3xy' - 3y = 0$

(b) $x^2 y'' + xy' + y = x$

(c) $x^2 y'' - xy' + 6y = 1$

(d) $3x^2 y'' + 4xy' - 2y = 6x^2$

8

Calculus of Variations

I. INTRODUCTION

What is the shortest distance between two points? You probably laugh at such a simple question because you know the answer so well. Can you prove it? We shall see how to prove it shortly. Meanwhile we ask the same question about a sphere, for example, the earth. What is the shortest distance between two points on the surface of the earth, measured along the surface? Again you probably know that the answer is the distance measured along a great circle. But suppose you were asked the same question about some other surface, say an ellipsoid or a cylinder or a cone. The curve along a surface which marks the shortest distance between two neighboring points is called a *geodesic* of the surface. Finding geodesics is one of the problems which we can solve using the calculus of variations.

There are many others. To understand what the basic problem is, think about finding maximum and minimum values of $f(x)$ in ordinary calculus. You find $f'(x)$ and set it equal to zero. The values of x you find may correspond to maximum points $\frown$, minimum points $\smile$, or points of inflection with a horizontal tangent $\rightthreetimes$. Suppose that in solving a given physical problem you want the minimum values of a function $f(x)$. The equation $f'(x) = 0$ is a necessary (but not a sufficient) condition for an interior minimum point. To find the desired minimum, you would find all the values of x such that $f'(x) = 0$, and then rely on the physics or on further mathematical tests to sort out the minimum points. We use the general term *stationary point* to mean simply that $f'(x) = 0$ there; that is, stationary points include maximum points, minimum points, and points of inflection with horizontal tangent. In the calculus of variations, we often state problems by saying that a certain quantity is to be minimized. However, what we actually always do is something similar to putting $f'(x) = 0$, above; that is, we make the quantity stationary. The question of whether we have a maximum, a minimum, or neither, is answered by the physics or the geometry in the problems we shall do.

Now what is the quantity which we want to make stationary? It is an integral

$$(1.1) \qquad I = \int_{x_1}^{x_2} F(x, y, y') \, dx \qquad \left(\text{where } y' = \frac{dy}{dx} \right),$$

and our problem is this: Given the points (x_1, y_1) and (x_2, y_2) and the form of the function F of x, y, and y', find the curve $y = y(x)$ (passing through the given points) which makes the integral I have the smallest possible value (or stationary value). Before we try to do this, let us look at several examples. We mentioned geodesics; suppose we want to find the equation $y = y(x)$ of a curve joining two points (x_1, y_1) and (x_2, y_2) in the plane so that the distance between the points measured along the curve (arc length) is a minimum. To find any arc length, we find $\int ds = \int \sqrt{dx^2 + dy^2}$ along the curve. But $\sqrt{dx^2 + dy^2} = \sqrt{1 + y'^2} \, dx$, so we want to minimize

$$(1.2) \qquad I = \int_{x_1}^{x_2} \sqrt{1 + y'^2} \, dx;$$

this is equation (1.1) with $F(x, y, y') = \sqrt{1 + y'^2}$.

As a second example, consider the famous brachistochrone problem (from the Greek: *brachistos* = shortest, *chronos* = time, as in chronometer). The problem is this: In what shape should you bend a wire joining two given points so that a bead will slide down from one point to the other (without friction) in the shortest time? Here we must minimize $\int dt$. If ds is an element of arc length, then the velocity of the particle is $v = ds/dt$. Then we have

$$dt = \frac{1}{v} \, ds = \frac{1}{v} \sqrt{1 + y'^2} \, dx.$$

We shall see later that (using the law of conservation of energy) we can find v as a function of x and y. Then the integral which we want to minimize, namely

$$\int dt = \int \frac{1}{v} \sqrt{1 + y'^2} \, dx,$$

is of the form (1.1).

Another example is the soap film problem. Suppose a soap film is suspended between two circular wire hoops as shown in Fig. 1.1; what is the shape of the surface? It is clear from symmetry that it is a surface of revolution, and it is known that the soap film will adjust itself so that the

surface area is a minimum. The surface area can be written as an integral and again our problem is to minimize an integral.

There are many other examples from physics. A chain suspended between two points hangs so that its center of gravity is as low as possible; the z-coordinate of the center of gravity is given by an integral.

Figure 1.1

Fermat's principle in optics says that light traveling between two given points follows the path requiring the least time (this is a simple, but inaccurate, statement; we *should* say that $t = \int dt$ is stationary—there are examples where it is a maximum! See Problem 1). Various other basic principles in physics are stated in the form that certain integrals have stationary values.

2. THE EULER EQUATION

Before we do the general problem, let us first do the problem of a geodesic on a plane; we shall show that a straight line gives the shortest distance between two points. (The reason for doing this is to clarify the theory; you will not do problems this way.) Our problem is to find $y = y(x)$ which will make

$$I = \int_{x_1}^{x_2} \sqrt{1 + y'^2} \, dx$$

as small as possible. The $y(x)$ which does this is called an *extremal*. We want some way to represent algebraically all the curves passing through the given endpoints, but differing from the (as yet unknown) extremal by small amounts. (We assume that all the curves have continuous second derivatives so that we can carry out needed differentiations later.) These curves are called varied curves; there are infinitely many of them as close as we like to the extremal. We construct a function representing these varied curves in the following way (Fig. 2.1). Let $\eta(x)$ represent a function of x which is zero at x_1 and x_2, and has a continuous second derivative in the interval x_1 to x_2, but is otherwise completely arbitrary. We define the function $Y(x)$ by the equation

(2.1) $$Y(x) = y(x) + \epsilon\eta(x),$$

where $y(x)$ is the desired extremal and ϵ is a parameter. Because of the arbitrariness of $\eta(x)$, $Y(x)$ represents any (single-valued) curve (with continuous second derivative) you want to draw through (x_1, y_1) and (x_2, y_2). Out of all these curves $Y(x)$ we want to pick the one curve that makes

(2.2)
$$I = \int_{x_1}^{x_2} \sqrt{1 + Y'^2} \, dx$$

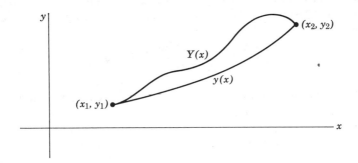

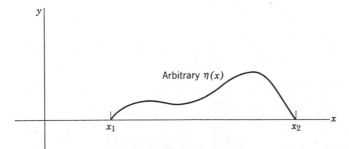

Figure 2.1

a minimum. Now I is a function of the parameter ϵ; when $\epsilon = 0$, $Y = y(x)$, the desired extremal. Our problem then is to make $I(\epsilon)$ take its minimum value when $\epsilon = 0$. In other words, we want

(2.3)
$$\frac{dI}{d\epsilon} = 0 \quad \text{when} \quad \epsilon = 0.$$

Differentiating (2.2) under the integral sign with respect to the parameter ϵ, we get

(2.4)
$$\frac{dI}{d\epsilon} = \int_{x_1}^{x_2} \frac{1}{2} \frac{1}{\sqrt{1 + Y'^2}} 2Y' \left(\frac{dY'}{d\epsilon} \right) dx.$$

Differentiating (2.1) with respect to x, we get

(2.5) $$Y'(x) = y'(x) + \epsilon \eta'(x).$$

Then from (2.5) we have

(2.6) $$\frac{dY'}{d\epsilon} = \eta'(x).$$

We see from (2.1) that putting $\epsilon = 0$ means putting $Y(x) = y(x)$. Then substituting (2.6) into (2.4) and putting $dI/d\epsilon$ equal to zero when $\epsilon = 0$, we get

(2.7) $$\left(\frac{dI}{d\epsilon}\right)_{\epsilon=0} = \int_{x_1}^{x_2} \frac{y'(x)\eta'(x)}{\sqrt{1 + y'^2}}\, dx = 0.$$

We can integrate this by parts (since we assumed that η and y have continuous second derivatives). Let

$$u = y'/\sqrt{1 + y'^2}, \qquad dv = \eta'(x)\, dx.$$

Then

$$du = \frac{d}{dx}\left(\frac{y'}{\sqrt{1 + y'^2}}\right) dx, \qquad v = \eta(x),$$

and

$$\left(\frac{dI}{d\epsilon}\right)_{\epsilon=0} = \frac{y'}{\sqrt{1 + y'^2}}\, \eta(x)\, \Big|_{x_1}^{x_2} - \int_{x_1}^{x_2} \eta(x)\, \frac{d}{dx}\left(\frac{y'}{\sqrt{1 + y'^2}}\right) dx.$$

The first term is zero because $\eta(x) = 0$ at the endpoints. In the second term, recall that $\eta(x)$ is an arbitrary function. This means that

(2.8) $$\frac{d}{dx}\left(\frac{y'}{\sqrt{1 + y'^2}}\right) = 0,$$

for otherwise we could select some function $\eta(x)$ so that the integral would not be zero. Notice carefully here that we are *not* saying that when an integral is zero, the integrand is also zero; this is not true $\left(\text{as, for example, } \int_0^{2\pi} \sin x\, dx = 0 \text{ shows}\right)$. What we *are* saying is that the only way $\int_{x_1}^{x_2} f(x)\eta(x)\, dx$ can *always* be zero for *every* $\eta(x)$ is for $f(x)$ to be zero. You can prove this by contradiction in the following way. If $f(x)$ is not zero, then, since $\eta(x)$ is arbitrary, choose η to be positive where f is positive and negative where f is negative. Then $f\eta$ is positive, so its integral is not zero, in contradiction to the statement that $\int f\eta\, dx = 0$ for every η.

Integrating (2.8) with respect to x, we get

$$\frac{y'}{\sqrt{1 + y'^2}} = \text{const.}$$

or $y' = \text{const.}$ Thus the slope of $y(x)$ is constant, so $y(x)$ is a straight line as we expected.

Now we *could* go through this process with every calculus of variations problem. It is much simpler to do the general problem once for all and find a differential equation which we can use to solve later problems. The problem is to find the y which will make stationary the integral

$$(2.9) \qquad\qquad I = \int_{x_1}^{x_2} F(x, y, y')\, dx,$$

where F is a given function. The $y(x)$ which makes I stationary is called an extremal whether I is a maximum or minimum or neither. The method is the one we have just used with the straight line. We consider a set of varied curves

$$Y(x) = y(x) + \epsilon \eta(x)$$

just as before. Then we have

$$(2.10) \qquad\qquad I(\epsilon) = \int_{x_1}^{x_2} F(x, Y, Y')\, dx,$$

and we want $(d/d\epsilon)I(\epsilon) = 0$ when $\epsilon = 0$. Remembering that Y and Y' are functions of ϵ, and differentiating under the integral sign with respect to ϵ, we get

$$(2.11) \qquad\qquad \frac{dI}{d\epsilon} = \int_{x_1}^{x_2} \left(\frac{\partial F}{\partial Y} \frac{dY}{d\epsilon} + \frac{\partial F}{\partial Y'} \frac{dY'}{d\epsilon} \right) dx.$$

Substituting (2.1) and (2.5) into (2.11), we have

$$(2.12) \qquad\qquad \frac{dI}{d\epsilon} = \int_{x_1}^{x_2} \left[\frac{\partial F}{\partial Y} \eta(x) + \frac{\partial F}{\partial Y'} \eta'(x) \right] dx.$$

We want $dI/d\epsilon = 0$ at $\epsilon = 0$; recall that $\epsilon = 0$ means $Y = y$. Then (2.12) gives

$$(2.13) \qquad\qquad \left(\frac{dI}{d\epsilon} \right)_{\epsilon=0} = \int_{x_1}^{x_2} \left[\frac{\partial F}{\partial y} \eta(x) + \frac{\partial F}{\partial y'} \eta'(x) \right] dx = 0.$$

If y'' is continuous, we can integrate the second term by parts just as in the straight line problem:

$$(2.14) \qquad \int_{x_1}^{x_2} \frac{\partial F}{\partial y'} \eta'(x)\, dx = \frac{\partial F}{\partial y'} \eta(x) \Big|_{x_1}^{x_2} - \int_{x_1}^{x_2} \frac{d}{dx}\left(\frac{\partial F}{\partial y'} \right) \eta(x)\, dx.$$

The integrated term is zero as before because $\eta(x)$ is zero at x_1 and x_2. Then we have

(2.15) $$\left(\frac{dI}{d\epsilon}\right)_{\epsilon=0} = \int_{x_1}^{x_2}\left[\frac{\partial F}{\partial y} - \frac{d}{dx}\frac{\partial F}{\partial y'}\right]\eta(x)\,dx = 0.$$

As before, since $\eta(x)$ is arbitrary, we must have

(2.16) $$\frac{d}{dx}\frac{\partial F}{\partial y'} - \frac{\partial F}{\partial y} = 0.$$

x is the independent variable.

This is the Euler (or Euler-Lagrange) equation.

Any problem in the calculus of variations, then, is solved by setting up the integral which is to be stationary, writing what the function F is, substituting it into the Euler equation, and solving the resulting differential equation. We shall illustrate this process with several problems.

3. GEODESICS

Example 1. Let's find the geodesics in a plane again, this time using the Euler equation as you will do in problems.

We are to minimize

$$\int_{x_1}^{x_2} \sqrt{1 + y'^2}\,dx,$$

so we have $F = \sqrt{1 + y'^2}$. Then

$$\frac{\partial F}{\partial y'} = \frac{y'}{\sqrt{1 + y'^2}}, \qquad \frac{\partial F}{\partial y} = 0,$$

and the Euler equation gives

$$\frac{d}{dx}\left(\frac{y'}{\sqrt{1 + y'^2}}\right) = 0,$$

as we had before.

We have used x and y as our variables. But the mathematics is just the same if we use some other letters, for example r and θ. To find $r = r(\theta)$ which makes stationary the integral

$$\int F(\theta, r, r')\,d\theta, \qquad \text{where} \quad r' = \frac{dr}{d\theta},$$

we solve the Euler equation

(3.1) $$\frac{d}{d\theta}\frac{\partial F}{\partial r'} - \frac{\partial F}{\partial r} = 0.$$

To minimize $\int F(t, x, \dot{x})\, dt$ where $\dot{x} = dx/dt$, we solve

$$(3.2) \qquad \frac{d}{dt}\frac{\partial F}{\partial \dot{x}} - \frac{\partial F}{\partial x} = 0.$$

In all these examples there is an independent variable (x, or θ, or t) which is the variable of integration; in all the general discussion of the theory we call this x. Then there is a dependent variable [$y(x)$, or $r(\theta)$, or $x(t)$] which we want to find as a function of the independent variable; we usually call this $y(x)$; and finally there is a derivative $y' = dy/dx$. To use the Euler equation (2.16) in problems with variables other than x and y, you must identify the independent variable with x and the dependent variable with y in (2.16).

Example 2. Find the geodesics on a sphere.

We shall use spherical coordinates r, θ, ϕ. In spherical coordinates the element of arc length is given by (see Chapter 4, Section 14)

$$ds^2 = dr^2 + r^2\, d\theta^2 + r^2 \sin^2 \theta\, d\phi^2.$$

If the equation of the sphere is $r = a$, then on the sphere $dr = 0$, so

$$ds^2 = a^2\, d\theta^2 + a^2 \sin^2 \theta\, d\phi^2.$$

We want to minimize

$$I = \int ds = \int \sqrt{a^2\, d\theta^2 + a^2 \sin^2 \theta\, d\phi^2}.$$

Either θ or ϕ may be chosen as the independent variable. If we choose ϕ as the independent variable, then we want to find the function $\theta(\phi)$ which minimizes I. We write

$$(3.3) \qquad I = a \int_{\phi_1}^{\phi_2} \sqrt{(\theta'^2 + \sin^2 \theta)}\, d\phi, \qquad \text{where} \quad \theta' = \frac{d\theta}{d\phi}.$$

The Euler equation in these variables is

$$(3.4) \qquad \frac{d}{d\phi}\frac{\partial F}{\partial \theta'} - \frac{\partial F}{\partial \theta} = 0,$$

and the function F from (3.3) is

$$(3.5) \qquad F(\phi, \theta, \theta') = \sqrt{\theta'^2 + \sin^2 \theta}.$$

(Note that we can ignore the constant factor a in I since minimizing a multiple of I is the same as minimizing I.) Substituting (3.5) into (3.4), we get

$$\frac{d}{d\phi}\left(\frac{\theta'}{\sqrt{\theta'^2 + \sin^2 \theta}}\right) - \frac{\sin \theta \cos \theta}{\sqrt{\theta'^2 + \sin^2 \theta}} = 0.$$

We differentiate the first term by the quotient formula:

$$\frac{\sqrt{\theta'^2 + \sin^2\theta}\;\theta'' - \dfrac{\theta'(\theta'\theta'' + \sin\theta\cos\theta\;\theta')}{\sqrt{\theta'^2 + \sin^2\theta}}}{\theta'^2 + \sin^2\theta} - \frac{\sin\theta\cos\theta}{\sqrt{\theta'^2 + \sin^2\theta}} = 0.$$

Next multiply the equation by $(\theta'^2 + \sin^2\theta)^{3/2}$ to get

$$\theta''(\theta'^2 + \sin^2\theta) - (\theta'^2\theta'' + \sin\theta\cos\theta\;\theta'^2) - \sin\theta\cos\theta(\theta'^2 + \sin^2\theta) = 0.$$

Collect terms and cancel $\sin\theta$ (since $\sin\theta$ is different from zero everywhere except at the north and south poles, we can cancel it):

$$\theta'' \sin\theta - 2\cos\theta\;\theta'^2 - \sin^2\theta\cos\theta = 0.$$

This is a standard type of differential equation (independent variable ϕ missing—see Chapter 7, Section 7) and the usual method of solving it is to put

$$\theta' = p,$$

$$\theta'' = \frac{dp}{d\phi} = \frac{dp}{d\theta}\frac{d\theta}{d\phi} = \frac{dp}{d\theta}\,p.$$

Substituting these into the differential equation, we get

$$p\frac{dp}{d\theta}\sin\theta - 2\cos\theta\;p^2 - \sin^2\theta\cos\theta = 0$$

or

$$\frac{dp}{d\theta} - 2\cot\theta\cdot p = p^{-1}\sin\theta\cos\theta.$$

This is again a standard equation (Bernoulli—Chapter 7, Section 4). To solve it, we make the change of variable $u = p^{1-n}$, where n is the exponent -1 in the power of p on the right-hand side. Thus we put

$$u = p^2,$$

$$\frac{du}{d\theta} = 2p\frac{dp}{d\theta}.$$

The differential equation then becomes

$$\frac{du}{d\theta} - 4u\cot\theta = 2\sin\theta\cos\theta.$$

This is a linear first-order equation (see Chapter 7, Section 3); the integrating factor is

$$e^{-\int 4\cot\theta\,d\theta} = e^{-4\ln\sin\theta} = \frac{1}{\sin^4\theta}.$$

Then we can write the solution for u, and so for p (which is $d\theta/d\phi$), and finally find the relation between θ and ϕ as follows:

$$\frac{u}{\sin^4 \theta} = \int \frac{2 \sin \theta \cos \theta}{\sin^4 \theta}\, d\theta = \int \frac{2 \cos \theta}{\sin^3 \theta}\, d\theta = -\frac{1}{\sin^2 \theta} + c,$$

$$u = c \sin^4 \theta - \sin^2 \theta,$$

$$p = \frac{d\theta}{d\phi} = \sqrt{u} = \sqrt{c \sin^4 \theta - \sin^2 \theta},$$

$$d\phi = \frac{d\theta}{\sqrt{c \sin^4 \theta - \sin^2 \theta}} = \frac{\csc^2 \theta\, d\theta}{\sqrt{c - \csc^2 \theta}},$$

$$\phi = \int \frac{\csc^2 \theta\, d\theta}{\sqrt{c - 1 - \cot^2 \theta}}.$$

If we call $c - 1$ a new constant k^2 and put $w = \cot \theta$, this integral becomes

$$\int \frac{-dw}{\sqrt{k^2 - w^2}} = -\text{arc} \sin \frac{w}{k} + \alpha,$$

where α is an integration constant. Then we have

$$\phi = -\text{arc} \sin \left(\frac{1}{k} \cot \theta\right) + \alpha$$

or

$$\cot \theta = k \sin (\alpha - \phi) = k \sin \alpha \cos \phi - k \cos \alpha \sin \phi.$$

Multiplying the last equation by $a \sin \theta$, where a is the radius of the sphere, we get

$$a \cos \theta = (a \sin \theta \cos \phi)k \sin \alpha - (a \sin \theta \sin \phi)k \cos \alpha.$$

To recognize what this means, we put it into rectangular coordinates and get

$$z = xk \sin \alpha - yk \cos \alpha.$$

This is the equation of a plane through the origin; its intersection with the sphere is a great circle. Hence the geodesics on the sphere are great circles. (Also see Problems 11 and 13.)

4. THE BRACHISTOCHRONE PROBLEM; CYCLOIDS

We have already mentioned this problem in Section 1. We are given the points (x_1, y_1) and (x_2, y_2); we choose axes through the point 1 with the x-axis positive downward as shown in Fig. 4.1. Our problem is to find the curve joining the two points, down which a bead will slide (from rest) in the least time; that is, we want to minimize $\int dt$. Let $v = 0$ initially, and let $x = 0$ be our reference level for potential energy. Then at the point (x, y) we have

$$\text{kinetic energy} = \tfrac{1}{2}mv^2 = \tfrac{1}{2}m\left(\frac{ds}{dt}\right)^2,$$

$$\text{potential energy} = -mgx.$$

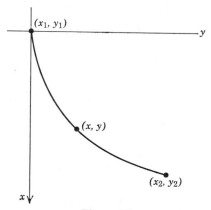

Figure 4.1

The sum of the two energies is zero initially and therefore zero at any time since the total energy is constant when there is no friction. Hence we have

$$\tfrac{1}{2}mv^2 - mgx = 0 \qquad \text{or} \quad v = \sqrt{2gx}.$$

Then the integral which we want to minimize is

$$\int dt = \int \frac{ds}{v} = \int \frac{ds}{\sqrt{2gx}} = \int_{x_1}^{x_2} \frac{\sqrt{1 + y'^2}\, dx}{\sqrt{2gx}} = \frac{1}{\sqrt{2g}} \int_{x_1}^{x_2} \frac{\sqrt{1 + y'^2}}{\sqrt{x}}\, dx.$$

The function F which we need in the Euler equation can be taken as

$$F = \frac{\sqrt{1 + y'^2}}{\sqrt{x}}.$$

(Since the constant $1/\sqrt{2g}$ would cancel out of the Euler equation anyway, we need not include it in F.) Then the Euler equation is

$$\frac{d}{dx}\frac{\partial F}{\partial y'} = \frac{d}{dx}\left(\frac{y'}{\sqrt{x}\sqrt{1 + y'^2}}\right) = 0$$

since $\partial F/\partial y = 0$. Integrating this we get

$$\frac{y'}{\sqrt{x}\sqrt{1+y'^2}} = \text{const.}$$

$$\frac{y'^2}{x(1+y'^2)} = \text{const.} = c.$$

Solving for y', we get

(4.1) $y' = \sqrt{\dfrac{cx}{1-cx}}$ or $dy = \sqrt{\dfrac{cx}{1-cx}}\, dx = \dfrac{x\, dx}{\sqrt{\dfrac{x}{c} - x^2}}.$

This can be integrated directly from tables to give

(4.2) $y = -\sqrt{\dfrac{x}{c} - x^2} + \dfrac{1}{2c}\arccos(1-2cx) + c'.$

This is the equation of the curve along which the particle slides in minimum time. Since we have chosen axes to make the curve pass through the origin, $x = y = 0$ must satisfy the equation, so $c' = 0$.

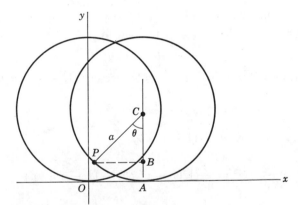

Figure 4.2

We can show that this is the equation of a cycloid. It is both customary and simpler to write parametric equations for a cycloid; we shall now derive these (using customary axes as shown in Fig. 4.2—*not* as in our brachistochrone problem, Fig. 4.1). Imagine a circle of radius a (say a wheel) in the (x, y) plane rolling along the x-axis. Let it start tangent to the x-axis at the origin O in Fig. 4.2. Place a mark on the *circle* at O. As the circle rolls, the mark traces out a cycloid as shown in Fig. 4.3. Let point P in Fig. 4.2 be the position of the mark when the circle is tangent to the x-axis at A; let (x, y) be the coordinates of P. Since the circle rolled, $OA = PA = a\theta$ with θ in radians. Then from Fig. 4.2 we have

(4.3)
$$x = OA - PB = a\theta - a \sin \theta = a(\theta - \sin \theta),$$
$$y = AB = AC - BC = a - a \cos \theta = a(1 - \cos \theta).$$

These are the parametric equations of a cycloid as usually stated.

In the brachistochrone problem above we have interchanged x- and y-axes; think of the circle rolling on the underside of the y-axis in Fig. 4.1. Then the parametric equations of the cycloid for Fig. 4.1 are obtained

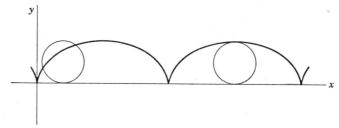

Figure 4.3

by interchanging x and y in (4.3). This gives

(4.4)
$$x = a(1 - \cos \theta),$$
$$y = a(\theta - \sin \theta).$$

We can write (4.2) in this form if we let arc cos $(1 - 2cx) = \theta$. Then we have

$$1 - 2cx = \cos \theta,$$

$$x = \frac{1}{2c}(1 - \cos \theta),$$

(4.5)
$$\frac{x}{c} - x^2 = \frac{1}{4c^2}[2(1 - \cos \theta) - (1 - \cos \theta)^2]$$

$$= \frac{1}{4c^2}(1 - \cos^2 \theta) = \frac{1}{4c^2} \sin^2 \theta,$$

and (4.2) with $c' = 0$ gives

(4.6)
$$y = -\frac{1}{2c} \sin \theta + \frac{1}{2c} \theta.$$

Thus from (4.5) and (4.6) we obtain

(4.7)
$$x = \frac{1}{2c}(1 - \cos \theta),$$

$$y = \frac{1}{2c}(\theta - \sin \theta)$$

as the parametric equations of the brachistochrone, which is therefore a cycloid.

Notice from either (4.4) or (4.7) that all cycloids are similar; that is, they differ from each other only in size (determined by a or c) and not in shape. Figure 4.4 is a sketch of a cycloid for arbitrary a. If the given endpoints for the wire along which the bead slides are O and P'', we see that the particle slides down to P and back up to P'' in minimum time! At point P the circle has rolled halfway around so $OA = \frac{1}{2} \cdot 2\pi a = \pi a$. For any

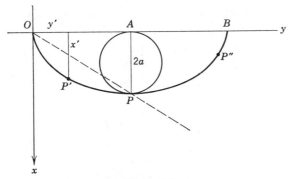

Figure 4.4

point P' on arc OP, P' is below the line OP, and the coordinates (x', y') of P' have

$$\frac{x'}{y'} > \frac{PA}{AO} = \frac{2a}{\pi a} = \frac{2}{\pi}$$

or $y'/x' < \pi/2$. For points like P'' on PB, $y''/x'' > \pi/2$, whereas *at* P, we have $y/x = \pi/2$ (Problem 7). Then if the right-hand endpoint is (x_2, y_2) and the origin is the left-hand endpoint, we can say that the bead just slides down, or slides down and back up, depending on whether y_2/x_2 is less than or greater than $\pi/2$.

5. FIRST INTEGRALS OF THE EULER EQUATION

In some problems the integrand F in I (1.1) does not contain y (that is, F does not contain the dependent variable). Then $\partial F/\partial y = 0$ and the Euler equation becomes

$$\frac{d}{dx}\frac{\partial F}{\partial y'} = 0, \qquad \frac{\partial F}{\partial y'} = \text{const.}$$

This happened in both the straight-line problem and the brachistochrone problem. Because $\partial F/\partial y$ was zero, we were able to integrate the Euler equation *once*; the equation $\partial F/\partial y' = $ const. is for this reason called a *first integral* of the Euler equation.

There is another less obvious case in which we can easily find a first integral of the Euler equation. Let us show this by an example (the soap film problem mentioned in Section 1).

Example.   Our problem is this: Given two points P_1 and P_2 (not too far apart), we are going to draw a curve joining P_1 and P_2 and revolve it about the x-axis to form a surface of revolution. We want the equation of the curve so that the surface area will be a minimum. That is, we want to minimize $I = \int 2\pi y \, ds$. We usually write $ds = \sqrt{1 + y'^2} \, dx$. Instead, let us write $ds = \sqrt{1 + x'^2} \, dy$, where $x' = dx/dy$. Then $I = \int 2\pi y \sqrt{1 + x'^2} \, dy$. Recall from Section 3 how to write the Euler equation in various sets of variables. Here y is the variable of integration, $F = y \sqrt{1 + x'^2}$, and the Euler equation is

(5.1)
$$\frac{d}{dy}\frac{\partial F}{\partial x'} - \frac{\partial F}{\partial x} = 0,$$

or

$$\frac{d}{dy}\left(\frac{yx'}{\sqrt{1 + x'^2}}\right) = 0.$$

This is the simplified equation we wanted. We integrate once, solve for x' and integrate again (using tables) as follows.

$$\frac{yx'}{\sqrt{1 + x'^2}} = c_1,$$

$$x' = \frac{c_1}{\sqrt{y^2 - c_1^2}},$$

$$dx = \frac{c_1 \, dy}{\sqrt{y^2 - c_1^2}},$$

$$x = c_1 \cosh^{-1}\frac{y}{c_1} + c_2,$$

$$y = c_1 \cosh\frac{x - c_2}{c_1}.$$

This is the equation of a catenary; the constants c_1 and c_2 are determined by making the curve pass through the two given points. For example, if the points are $(0,1)$ and $(\ln 2, \frac{5}{4})$, then $c_1 = 1$ and $c_2 = 0$, as you can

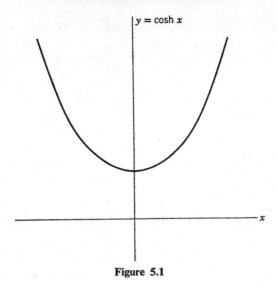

$y = \cosh x$

Figure 5.1

verify (Problem 8). We have, for this case, $y = \cosh x = \frac{1}{2}(e^x + e^{-x})$, with a graph as shown in Fig. 5.1.

Observe that the method used in this example will simplify any problem in which $I = \int F(y, y') \, dx$ does not have the independent variable x in the integrand. We change to y as the integration variable making the substitutions

$$x' = \frac{dx}{dy} = \left(\frac{dy}{dx}\right)^{-1}, \qquad y' = \frac{1}{x'}, \qquad dx = \frac{dx}{dy} \, dy = x' \, dy$$

in I. Then the integrand is a function of y and x', so the Euler equation [now (5.1)] simplifies since $\partial F/\partial x = 0$. (See also Problem 13.)

6. SEVERAL DEPENDENT VARIABLES

It is not necessary to restrict ourselves to problems with one dependent variable y. Recall that in ordinary calculus problems the necessary condition for a minimum point on $z = z(x)$ is $dz/dx = 0$; for a function of two variables $z = z(x, y)$, we have the two conditions $\partial z/\partial x = 0$ and $\partial z/\partial y = 0$. We have a somewhat analogous situation in the calculus of variations. Suppose that we are given an F which is a function of y, z, dy/dx, dz/dx, and x, and we want to find *two* curves $y = y(x)$ and $z = z(x)$ which make $I = \int F \, dx$ stationary. Then the value of the integral I depends on *both* $y(x)$ and $z(x)$ and you might very well guess that in this case we would have *two* Euler equations, one for y and one for z, namely

(6.1)
$$\frac{d}{dx}\left(\frac{\partial F}{\partial y'}\right) - \frac{\partial F}{\partial y} = 0,$$
$$\frac{d}{dx}\left(\frac{\partial F}{\partial z'}\right) - \frac{\partial F}{\partial z} = 0.$$

By carrying through calculations similar to those we used in deriving the single Euler equation for the one dependent variable case you can show (Problem 15) that this guess is correct. If there are still more dependent variables (but one independent variable), then we write an Euler equation for each dependent variable. (It is possible also to consider a problem with more than one independent variable, but the results are more complicated and less useful in applications, so we shall not do it here.)

There is a very important application of equations like (6.1) to mechanics. In elementary physics, Newton's second law $\mathbf{F} = m\mathbf{a}$ is a fundamental equation. In more advanced mechanics, it is often useful to start from a different assumption (which can be proved equivalent to Newton's law; see mechanics textbooks). This assumption is called *Hamilton's principle*. It says that any particle or system of particles always moves in such a way that $I = \int_{t_1}^{t_2} L\, dt$ is stationary, where $L = T - V$ is called the *Lagrangian*; T is the kinetic energy, and V is the potential energy of the particle or system.

Example 1. Use Hamilton's principle to find the equations of motion of a single particle of mass m moving (near the earth) under gravity.

We first write the formulas for the kinetic energy T and the potential energy V of the particle. (It is convenient to use a dot to mean a derivative with respect to t just as we use a prime to indicate a derivative with respect to x; thus $dx/dt = \dot{x}$, $dy/dt = \dot{y}$, $dy/dx = y'$, $d^2x/dt^2 = \ddot{x}$, etc.) The equations for T, V, and $L = T - V$, are:

(6.2)
$$T = \tfrac{1}{2}mv^2 = \tfrac{1}{2}m(\dot{x}^2 + \dot{y}^2 + \dot{z}^2),$$
$$V = mgz,$$
$$L = T - V = \tfrac{1}{2}m(\dot{x}^2 + \dot{y}^2 + \dot{z}^2) - mgz.$$

Here t is the independent variable; x, y, and z are the dependent variables, and L corresponds to what we have called F previously. Then to make $I = \int_{t_1}^{t_2} L\, dt$ stationary, we write the corresponding Euler equations. There are three Euler equations, one for x, one for y, and one for z. The

Euler equations are called *Lagrange's equations* in mechanics; these equations are:

(6.3)
$$\frac{d}{dt}\frac{\partial L}{\partial \dot{x}} - \frac{\partial L}{\partial x} = 0,$$
$$\frac{d}{dt}\frac{\partial L}{\partial \dot{y}} - \frac{\partial L}{\partial y} = 0,$$
$$\frac{d}{dt}\frac{\partial L}{\partial \dot{z}} - \frac{\partial L}{\partial z} = 0.$$

Substituting L in (6.2) into Lagrange's equations (6.3), we get

(6.4)
$$\begin{cases} \dfrac{d}{dt}(m\dot{x}) = 0, \\[2mm] \dfrac{d}{dt}(m\dot{y}) = 0, \\[2mm] \dfrac{d}{dt}(m\dot{z}) + mg = 0, \end{cases} \quad \text{or} \quad \begin{cases} \dot{x} = \text{const.}, \\[2mm] \dot{y} = \text{const.}, \\[2mm] \ddot{z} = -g. \end{cases}$$

These are just the familiar equations obtained from Newton's law; they say that in the gravitational field near the surface of the earth, the horizontal velocity is constant and the vertical acceleration is $-g$. In this problem you may say that it would have been simpler just to write the equations from Newton's law in the first place! This is true in simple cases, but in more complicated problems it may be much simpler to find one scalar function (that is, L) than to find six functions (that is, the components of the two vectors, force and acceleration). For example, the acceleration components in spherical coordinates are quite complicated to derive by elementary methods (see mechanics textbooks), but you should have no trouble deriving the equations of motion in spherical coordinates using the Lagrangian (Problem 17). We shall illustrate this for polar coordinates.

Example 2. Use Lagrange's equations to find the equations of motion of a particle in terms of the polar coordinate variables r and θ.

The element of arc in polar coordinates is

(6.5)
$$ds^2 = dr^2 + r^2\, d\theta^2.$$

The velocity of a moving particle is ds/dt; from (6.5) we get

(6.6)
$$v^2 = \left(\frac{ds}{dt}\right)^2 = \left(\frac{dr}{dt}\right)^2 + r^2\left(\frac{d\theta}{dt}\right)^2 = \dot{r}^2 + r^2\dot{\theta}^2.$$

The kinetic energy is $\frac{1}{2}mv^2$, so we have

(6.7)
$$T = \tfrac{1}{2}m(\dot{r}^2 + r^2\dot{\theta}^2),$$
$$L = T - V = \tfrac{1}{2}m(\dot{r}^2 + r^2\dot{\theta}^2) - V(r, \theta),$$

where $V(r, \theta)$ is the potential energy of the particle. Lagrange's equations in the variables r, θ are:

(6.8)
$$\frac{d}{dt}\frac{\partial L}{\partial \dot{r}} - \frac{\partial L}{\partial r} = 0,$$
$$\frac{d}{dt}\frac{\partial L}{\partial \dot{\theta}} - \frac{\partial L}{\partial \theta} = 0.$$

Substituting L from (6.7) into (6.8), we get

(6.9)
$$\frac{d}{dt}(m\dot{r}) - mr\dot{\theta}^2 + \frac{\partial V}{\partial r} = 0,$$
$$\frac{d}{dt}(mr^2\dot{\theta}) + \frac{\partial V}{\partial \theta} = 0.$$

The r equation of motion is, then,

(6.10)
$$m(\ddot{r} - r\dot{\theta}^2) = -\frac{\partial V}{\partial r}.$$

The θ equation is

$$m(r^2\ddot{\theta} + 2r\dot{r}\dot{\theta}) = -\frac{\partial V}{\partial \theta},$$

or, dividing by r,

(6.11)
$$m(r\ddot{\theta} + 2\dot{r}\dot{\theta}) = -\frac{1}{r}\frac{\partial V}{\partial \theta}.$$

Now the quantities $-\partial V/\partial r$ and $-(1/r)(\partial V/\partial \theta)$ are the components of the force on the particle in the r and θ directions. [See Chapter 5, equation (9.7).] Then equations (6.10) and (6.11) are just the components of $ma = F$; the acceleration components are then

$$a_r = \ddot{r} - r\dot{\theta}^2,$$
$$a_\theta = r\ddot{\theta} + 2\dot{r}\dot{\theta}.$$

The second term in a_r is a familiar one; it is just the centripetal accelera-tion v^2/r when $v = r\dot{\theta}$ (the minus sign indicates that it is toward the origin). The second term in a_θ is called the Coriolis acceleration.

7. ISOPERIMETRIC PROBLEMS

Recall that in ordinary calculus we sometimes want to maximize a quantity subject to a condition (for example, find the volume of the largest box you can make with given surface area). Also recall that the method of Lagrange multipliers was useful in such problems. There are similar problems in the calculus of variations. The original question which gave this class of problems its name was this: Of all the closed plane curves of given perimeter (isoperimetric = same perimeter), which one incloses the largest area? To solve this problem, we must maximize the area, $\int y \, dx$, subject to the condition that the arc, $\int ds$, is the given length l. In other words, we want to maximize an integral subject to the condition that another integral has a given (constant) value; any such problem is called an isoperimetric problem. Let

$$I = \int_{x_1}^{x_2} F(x, y, y') \, dx$$

be the integral we want to make stationary; at the same time,

$$J = \int_{x_1}^{x_2} G(x, y, y') \, dx,$$

with the same integration variable and the same limits, is to have a given constant value. (This means that the allowed varied paths must be paths for which J has the given value.) By using the Lagrange multiplier method (see Chapter 4, Section 9), it can be shown that the desired condition is that

$$\int_{x_1}^{x_2} (F + \lambda G) \, dx$$

should be stationary, that is, that $F + \lambda G$ should satisfy the Euler equation. The Lagrange multiplier λ is a constant. It will appear in the solution $y(x)$ of the Euler equation; having found $y(x)$, we can substitute it into $\int_{x_1}^{x_2} G(x, y, y') \, dx = $ const. and so find λ if we like. However, for many purposes we do not need to find λ.

Example 1. Given two points x_1 and x_2 on the x-axis, and an arc length $l > x_2 - x_1$, find the shape of the curve of length l joining the given points which, with the x-axis, incloses the largest area.

We want to maximize $I = \int_{x_1}^{x_2} y\, dx$ subject to the condition $J =$ $\int_{x_1}^{x_2} ds = l$. Here $F = y$ and $G = \sqrt{1 + y'^2}$ so

(7.1) $$F + \lambda G = y + \lambda\sqrt{1 + y'^2}.$$

We want the Euler equation for $F + \lambda G$. Since

$$\frac{\partial}{\partial y'}(F + \lambda G) = \frac{\lambda y'}{\sqrt{1 + y'^2}} \quad \text{and} \quad \frac{\partial}{\partial y}(F + \lambda G) = 1,$$

the Euler equation is

(7.2) $$\frac{d}{dx}\left(\frac{\lambda y'}{\sqrt{1 + y'^2}}\right) - 1 = 0.$$

We integrate (7.2), simplify the result, and integrate again as follows:

$$\frac{\lambda y'}{\sqrt{1 + y'^2}} = x + c,$$
$$\lambda^2 y'^2 = (x + c)^2(1 + y'^2),$$
$$y'^2[\lambda^2 - (x + c)^2] = (x + c)^2,$$
$$dy = \frac{(x + c)\, dx}{\sqrt{\lambda^2 - (x + c)^2}},$$
$$y + c' = -\sqrt{\lambda^2 - (x + c)^2},$$
$$(y + c')^2 = \lambda^2 - (x + c)^2,$$
(7.3) $$(x + c)^2 + (y + c')^2 = \lambda^2.$$

We see that the answer to our problem is a circle passing through the two given points. The center and radius of the circle are determined by the given points and the given arc length l. If l is not much larger than $x_2 - x_1$, the circle will look like Fig. 7.1a; if l is much larger than $x_2 - x_1$, the

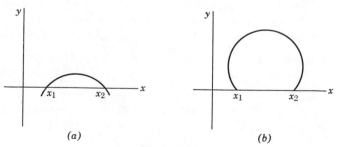

(a)   (b)

Figure 7.1

circle will look like Fig. 7.1*b*. In either case the Lagrange multiplier λ is the radius [see (7.3)].

A somewhat similar method can be used when there are two dependent variables and a constraint condition which is not an integral. Suppose we are to make stationary $\int_{x_1}^{x_2} F(x, y, z, y', z') \, dx$ subject to the condition $\phi(x, y, z) = $ const. It can be shown that the required condition is that

(7.4)
$$\int [F + \lambda(x)\phi] \, dx$$

should be stationary (here λ may depend on x but not on y and z). We shall illustrate the method by finding (again!) the geodesics on a sphere.

Example 2.   Minimize $\int ds$ subject to the condition $x^2 + y^2 + z^2 = a^2$.
Here

(7.5)
$$ds = \sqrt{dx^2 + dy^2 + dz^2} = \sqrt{1 + y'^2 + z'^2} \, dx$$

if we take x as the independent variable. Then we want to make stationary the integral

(7.6)
$$I = \int_{x_1}^{x_2} [\sqrt{1 + y'^2 + z'^2} + \lambda(x)(x^2 + y^2 + z^2)] \, dx.$$

There are two Euler equations:

(7.7)
$$\frac{d}{dx} \frac{y'}{\sqrt{1 + y'^2 + z'^2}} - \lambda \cdot 2y = 0,$$
$$\frac{d}{dx} \frac{z'}{\sqrt{1 + y'^2 + z'^2}} - \lambda \cdot 2z = 0.$$

To simplify the formulas we shall write just $\sqrt{}$ for $\sqrt{1 + y'^2 + z'^2}$ from now on. Eliminate λ between the two equations in (7.7):

(7.8)
$$z \frac{d}{dx}\left(\frac{y'}{\sqrt{}}\right) - y \frac{d}{dx}\left(\frac{z'}{\sqrt{}}\right) = 0.$$

You can easily show (Problem 23) that (7.8) can be written as

(7.9)
$$\frac{d}{dx}\left(z \frac{y'}{\sqrt{}} - y \frac{z'}{\sqrt{}}\right) = 0.$$

Integrating (7.9), we get

(7.10)
$$\frac{zy' - yz'}{\sqrt{}} = \text{const.} = c_1.$$

Since

$$\frac{d}{dx}\left(\frac{y}{z}\right) = \frac{zy' - yz'}{z^2},$$

we can write (7.10) as

(7.11)
$$\frac{z^2}{\sqrt{}} \frac{d}{dx} \frac{y}{z} = c_1.$$

Now from (7.5) we have $dx\sqrt{1 + y'^2 + z'^2} = ds$, so (7.11) can be written as

(7.12)
$$z^2 \frac{d}{ds}\left(\frac{y}{z}\right) = c_1.$$

Here we have changed to s instead of x as the independent variable. Now there is nothing special about x; we could just as well have chosen either y or z as the independent variable, so there are equations like (7.12) (with different constants) for any pair of the variables x, y, z. For the pair x and z, we have

(7.13)
$$z^2 \frac{d}{ds}\left(\frac{x}{z}\right) = c_2.$$

Combining (7.12) and (7.13), we have

(7.14)
$$c_2 \frac{d}{ds}\left(\frac{y}{z}\right) = c_1 \frac{d}{ds}\left(\frac{x}{z}\right).$$

Integrating (7.14), we get

$$c_2 \frac{y}{z} = c_1 \frac{x}{z} + c_3,$$

or

$$c_2 y = c_1 x + c_3 z.$$

This is the equation of a plane *through the origin*; its intersection with the sphere is a great circle. Thus we have shown that the geodesics on a sphere are great circles; this is the same result we had in Section 3.

8. VARIATIONAL NOTATION

The symbol δ was used in the early days of the development of the calculus of variations to indicate what we have called differentiation with respect to the parameter ϵ. It is just like the symbol d in a differential except that it warns you that ϵ and not x is the differentiation variable. The δ notation is not used much any more in mathematics, but you will find it in applications and so should understand its meaning. The quantity δI is just the differential

$$\delta I = \frac{dI}{d\epsilon} d\epsilon,$$

where $dI/d\epsilon$ is evaluated for $\epsilon = 0$. The symbol δ (read "the variation of") is also treated as a differential operator acting on F, y, and y'; we shall define δy, $\delta y'$, and δF in terms of our previous notation. We had in Section 2

$$(8.1) \qquad \begin{aligned} Y(x, \epsilon) &= y(x) + \epsilon \eta(x), \\ Y'(x, \epsilon) &= y'(x) + \epsilon \eta'(x). \end{aligned}$$

Then the meaning of δy is

$$(8.2) \qquad \delta y = \left(\frac{\partial Y}{\partial \epsilon} \right)_{\epsilon=0} d\epsilon = \eta(x)\, d\epsilon;$$

this is just like a differential dY if ϵ is the variable. The meaning of $\delta y'$ is

$$(8.3) \qquad \delta y' = \left(\frac{\partial Y'}{\partial \epsilon} \right)_{\epsilon=0} d\epsilon = \eta'(x)\, d\epsilon.$$

This is identical with

$$(8.4) \qquad \frac{d}{dx}\, (\delta y) = \frac{d}{dx}\, [\eta(x)\, d\epsilon\,] = \eta'(x)\, d\epsilon$$

since x and ϵ are independent variables; in other words, d and δ commute. The meaning of δF is

$$(8.5) \qquad \delta F = \frac{\partial F}{\partial y}\, \delta y + \frac{\partial F}{\partial y'}\, \delta y';$$

this is just a total differential $dF = (\partial F/\partial \epsilon)_{\epsilon=0}\, d\epsilon$ of the function $F[x, Y(x, \epsilon), Y'(x, \epsilon)]$ at $\epsilon = 0$ with ϵ considered the only variable. Then the variation in I is

$$(8.6) \qquad \begin{aligned} \delta I &= \delta \int_{x_1}^{x_2} F\, dx = \int_{x_1}^{x_2} \delta F\, dx \\ &= \int_{x_1}^{x_2} \left(\frac{\partial F}{\partial y}\, \delta y + \frac{\partial F}{\partial y'}\, \delta y' \right) dx \\ &= \int_{x_1}^{x_2} \left[\frac{\partial F}{\partial y}\, \eta(x)\, d\epsilon + \frac{\partial F}{\partial y'}\, \eta'(x)\, d\epsilon \right] dx. \end{aligned}$$

If you compare (8.6) with (2.13), you find that the following two statements about $I = \int F(x, y, y')\, dx$ mean the same thing:

(a) I is stationary; that is, $dI/d\epsilon = 0$ at $\epsilon = 0$ as in (2.13).
(b) The variation of I is zero; that is, $\delta I = 0$ as in (8.6).

REFERENCES

Some standard books on calculus of variations are Bliss, Forsyth, and Weinstock. You will also find chapters on the subject in some advanced calculus books and in some books on mathematics in physics and engineering. See the references at the end of the book identified for Chapter 8 by the figure [8] after the listing.

PROBLEMS

1. A simple (but inaccurate) statement of Fermat's principle was given in Section 1. A more accurate statement is that, of all the possible paths between two given points A and B, the one actually followed by a light beam is the one which makes the time of transit stationary. Use this principle to:

    (a) Derive the optical law of reflection. *Hint:* Given $P_1(x_1, y_1)$ and $P_2(x_2, y_2)$ (with a screen between them to stop the direct ray) and a mirror along the x-axis, write a formula for the distance P_1PP_2, where P is an arbitrary point on the mirror. Write the condition that P_1PP_2 should be a minimum (actually stationary) and show that it gives $\theta = \phi$.

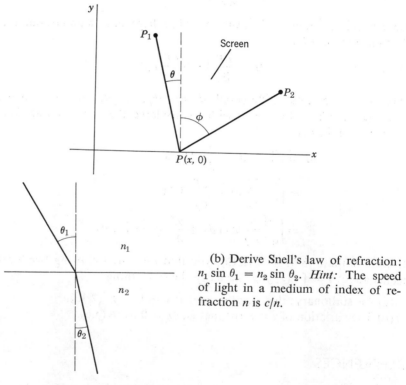

    (b) Derive Snell's law of refraction: $n_1 \sin \theta_1 = n_2 \sin \theta_2$. *Hint:* The speed of light in a medium of index of refraction n is c/n.

    (c) Show from the following experiment that the actual path is not necessarily one of minimum time. In the diagram L is a source of light; AB is

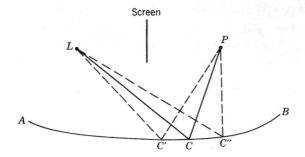

Screen

a cross section of a reflecting surface and P is a point to which a light ray is to be reflected. LCP is to be the actual path and $LC'P$, $LC''P$ represent varied paths. Show that the varied paths

(i) are the same length as the actual path if AB is an ellipse with L and P as foci;

(ii) are longer than the actual path if AB is a line tangent at C to the ellipse in (i);

(iii) are shorter than the actual path if AB is an arc of a curve tangent to the ellipse at C and lying inside it. Note that in this case the time is a *maximum*!

2. Find and solve the Euler equations for

(a) $\displaystyle\int_{x_1}^{x_2} \frac{ds}{y}$,

(b) $\displaystyle\int_{x_1}^{x_2} \sqrt{y}\, ds$,

(c) $\displaystyle\int_{x_1}^{x_2} y\sqrt{1 - y'^2}\, dx$,

(d) $\displaystyle\int_{x_1}^{x_2} e^x \sqrt{1 + y'^2}\, dx$.

Hint for (d): In the second integration of the differential equation, try the substitution $e^x = u$.

3. Use Fermat's principle to find the path followed by a light ray if the index of refraction is proportional to the given function.

Answers

(a) $\dfrac{1}{x}$ (a) circle

(b) $\sqrt{x}$ (b) parabola

(c) 1 (c) straight line

(d) $\dfrac{1}{\sqrt{y}}$ (d) cycloid

(e) y (e) catenary

(*Hint:* See hint in Problem 1b.)

4. Find the geodesics on a plane by using polar coordinates.

5. Show that the geodesics on a circular cylinder (with elements parallel to the z-axis) are helices $az + b\theta = 1$, where a and b are constants depending on the given endpoints. (*Hint:* Use cylindrical coordinates.) Note that the equation $az + b\theta = 1$ includes the circles $z = $ const. (for $b = 0$), and the straight lines $\theta = $ const. (for $a = 0$).

6. Find the geodesics on the cone $x^2 + y^2 = z^2$. *Hint:* Use cylindrical coordinates.

7. (a) Make the change of variable $x = u^2$ in (4.1) and integrate (using tables) to get

$$y = -\sqrt{x/c - x^2} + \frac{1}{c} \text{ arc sin } \sqrt{cx}.$$

Let $\sqrt{cx} = \sin \phi$ and $\theta = 2\phi$ to obtain (4.7).

(b) Show, in Fig. 4.4, that for a point like P'', $y''/x'' > \pi/2$ and for P, $y/x = \pi/2$.

8. Verify the numerical values in the example at the end of Section 5.

9. Taking the y-axis vertical, set up the brachistochrone problem with F a function of y and y'. Use the method of Section 5 to do the problem.

10. In the brachistochrone problem, show that if the particle is given an initial velocity $v_0 \neq 0$, the path of minimum time is still a cycloid.

11. Do the "geodesics on a sphere" problem with θ as the independent variable.

12. (a) Solve the soap film problem leaving x as the integration variable instead of changing to y as in Section 5. You should get the differential equation $yy'' - y'^2 - 1 = 0$. This is a standard type of differential equation usually solved by putting $y' = p$. Show that you get the same solution as in the text.

(b) Do the soap film problem again with the axes interchanged so that y is missing from the integrand.

13. (a) In Section 5, we showed how to obtain a first integral of the Euler equation when $F = F(y, y')$. There is an alternative method of handling this case. You can show that if $F = F(y, y')$, then $F - y' \, \partial F / \partial y' = $ const. To prove this, differentiate the left-hand side with respect to x, and show that the result is zero if F satisfies the Euler equation. Note that what you have is a first integral of the Euler equation.

(b) Use the method of (a) to do the "geodesics on a sphere" problem with ϕ as the independent variable; the brachistochrone problem with the y-axis vertical; the soap film problem with x as the independent variable.

(c) Consider the motion of a particle along the x-axis; then $L = T - V = \frac{1}{2}m\dot{x}^2 - V(x)$. Note that L does not contain the independent variable t; this corresponds to the case $F = F(y, y')$ in (a). Show that the first integral found in (a) is just the equation of conservation of energy for the mechanics problem.

14. In polar coordinates in the plane, $ds = \sqrt{dr^2 + r^2 d\theta^2}$. We can factor out either $d\theta$ or dr. In $I = \int ds$ which we want to minimize to find geodesics, the integrand F is a function of: (a) r and $r' = dr/d\theta$ if we factor out $d\theta$; (b) r and $\theta' = d\theta/dr$ if we factor out dr. In Problem 4 you found the geodesics in a plane using polar coordinates; probably you used (a) and the Euler equation (3.1). Do the problem in two more ways: using (a) and the first integral of the Euler equation as in Problem 13a; using (b) and the Euler equation (2.16). [*Note:* θ corresponds to y and r to x in part (b).]

15. Show that if $F = F(x, y, z, y', z')$, and we want to find $y(x)$ and $z(x)$ to make

$$I = \int_{x_1}^{x_2} F \, dx$$ stationary, then y and z should each satisfy an Euler equation as in (6.1). *Hint:* Construct a formula for a varied path Y for y as in Section 2 [$Y = y + \epsilon\eta(x)$ with $\eta(x)$ arbitrary] and construct a similar formula for z ($Z = z + \epsilon\zeta(x)$, where $\zeta(x)$ is *another* arbitrary function). Carry through the details of differentiating with respect to ϵ, putting $\epsilon = 0$, and integrating by parts as in Section 2; then use the fact that *both* $\eta(x)$ and $\zeta(x)$ are arbitrary to get (6.1).

16. Set up Lagrange's equations in cylindrical coordinates for a particle of mass m in a potential field $V(r, \theta, z)$. *Hint:* $v = ds/dt$; write ds in cylindrical coordinates.

17. Do Problem 16 in spherical coordinates.

18. Use Lagrange's equations to find the equation of motion of a simple pendulum (mass m suspended by a weightless string of length l, and swinging in a vertical plane; see Chapter 7, Problem 34).

19. Find the equation of motion of a particle moving in a straight line if the potential energy is $V = \frac{1}{2}kx^2$. (This is a simple harmonic oscillator.)

20. A particle moves on the surface of a sphere of radius a under the action of the earth's gravitational field. Find the θ, ϕ equations of motion. (*Comment:* This is called a spherical pendulum.)

21. Prove that a particle constrained to stay on a surface $\phi(x, y, z) = 0$, but subject to no other forces, moves along a geodesic of the surface. *Hint:* The potential energy V is constant, since constraint forces are normal to the surface and so do no work on the particle. Use Hamilton's principle and show that the problem of finding a geodesic and the problem of finding the path of the particle are identical problems.

22. Two particles each of mass m are connected by an (inextensible) string of length l. One particle moves on a horizontal table (assume no friction). The string passes through a hole in the table and the particle at the lower end moves up and down along a vertical line. Find the Lagrange equations of motion of the particles. *Hint:* Let the coordinates of the particle on the table be r and θ, and let the coordinate of the other particle be z. Eliminate one variable from L (using $r + z = l$) and write two Lagrange equations.

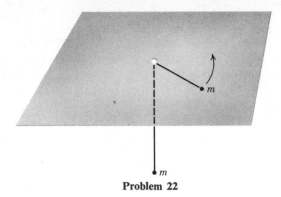

Problem 22

23. Show that (7.8) can be written as (7.9).

24. Given the area of a solid of revolution, find its shape to make its volume a maximum. *Hint:* Find a curve $y = y(x)$ which can be revolved about the x-axis to produce the solid of revolution. Use the fact that $y = 0$ must satisfy the equation of the curve (so that you do not have the complication of flat ends on the solid).

    In Problems 25 and 26, given the length l of a curve joining two given points, find the equation of the curve so that:

25. The surface of revolution formed by rotating the curve about the x-axis has minimum area.

26. The plane area between the curve and a straight line joining the points is a maximum.

27. Given 10 cc of lead, find how to form it into a solid of revolution of height 1 cm and minimum moment of inertia about its axis.

28. A uniform flexible chain of given length is suspended at given points (x_1, y_1) and (x_2, y_2). Find the curve in which it hangs. *Hint:* It will hang so that its center of gravity is as low as possible.

9

Gamma, Beta, and Error Functions; Asymptotic Series; Stirling's Formula; Elliptic Integrals and Functions

I. INTRODUCTION

The integrals and series and functions of this chapter arise in a variety of physical problems. Just as you learn about trigonometric functions, logarithms, etc., and use them in applied problems, so you should learn something about these special functions so that you can use them and understand their use as they come up in your more advanced work. An enormous amount of detail is known about these functions, and numerous formulas involving them exist and can be looked up. Our purpose is not to study them intensively, but to give definitions and some of the simpler relations so that you can then, if you need to, look up and understand and use the more complicated formulas.

2. THE FACTORIAL FUNCTION

Let us calculate the values of some integrals. For $\alpha > 0$,

$$(2.1) \qquad \int_0^\infty e^{-\alpha x}\, dx = -\frac{1}{\alpha} e^{-\alpha x}\Big|_0^\infty = \frac{1}{\alpha}.$$

Next differentiate both sides of this equation repeatedly with respect to α

(see Chapter 4, Section 12):

$$\int_0^\infty -xe^{-\alpha x}\,dx = -\frac{1}{\alpha^2} \quad \text{or} \quad \int_0^\infty xe^{-\alpha x}\,dx = \frac{1}{\alpha^2},$$

$$\int_0^\infty x^2 e^{-\alpha x}\,dx = \frac{2}{\alpha^3},$$

$$\int_0^\infty x^3 e^{-\alpha x}\,dx = \frac{3!}{\alpha^4},$$

or in general

(2.2) $$\int_0^\infty x^n e^{-\alpha x}\,dx = \frac{n!}{\alpha^{n+1}}.$$

Putting $\alpha = 1$, we get

(2.3) $$\int_0^\infty x^n e^{-x}\,dx = n!, \quad n = 1, 2, 3, \ldots.$$

Thus we have a definite integral whose value is $n!$ for positive integral n. We can use (2.3) to give a meaning to $0!$. Putting $n = 0$ in (2.3), we get

(2.4) $$0! = \int_0^\infty e^{-x}\,dx = -e^{-x}\Big|_0^\infty = 1.$$

(This agrees with our previous definition of $0!$ in Chapter 1.)

3. DEFINITION OF THE GAMMA FUNCTION; RECURSION RELATION

So far n has been a nonnegative integer; it is natural to *define* the factorial function for nonintegral n by the definite integral (2.3). There is no real objection to the notation $n!$ for nonintegral n (and we shall occasionally use it), but it is customary to reserve the factorial notation for integral n and to call the corresponding function for nonintegral n the gamma (Γ) function. It is also rather common practice to replace n by the letter p when we do not necessarily mean an integer. Following these conventions, we define, for *any* $p > 0$

(3.1) $$\Gamma(p) = \int_0^\infty x^{p-1} e^{-x}\,dx, \quad p > 0.$$

For $0 < p < 1$, this is an improper integral because x^{p-1} becomes infinite at the lower limit. However, it is a convergent integral for $p > 0$ (Problem 1). For $p \leq 0$, the integral diverges and so cannot be used to define $\Gamma(p)$; we shall see later how to define $\Gamma(p)$ when $p \leq 0$. Then from (3.1) and

(2.3) we have

$$\Gamma(n) = \int_0^\infty x^{n-1}e^{-x}\,dx = (n-1)!,$$

(3.2)

$$\Gamma(n+1) = \int_0^\infty x^n e^{-x}\,dx = n!.$$

Thus

$$\Gamma(1) = 0! = 1, \qquad \Gamma(2) = 1! = 1, \qquad \Gamma(3) = 2! = 2, \text{ etc.,}$$

with the usual meaning of factorial for integral n. The fact that $\Gamma(n) = (n-1)!$ and not $n!$ is unfortunate, but has to be learned in order to read the existing books and tables. Replacing p by $p+1$ in (3.1), we can write

(3.3) $$\Gamma(p+1) = \int_0^\infty x^p e^{-x}\,dx = p!, \qquad p > -1.$$

Some authors use the factorial notation

$$p! = \Gamma(p+1)$$

even though p is not an integer; this avoids the nuisance of the $p+1$. Another notation sometimes used is Gauss's function

$$\Pi(p) = \Gamma(p+1).$$

Let us integrate (3.3) by parts, calling $x^p = u$, $e^{-x}\,dx = dv$; then we get

$$du = px^{p-1}\,dx, \qquad v = -e^{-x},$$

$$\Gamma(p+1) = -x^p e^{-x}\,\Big|_0^\infty - \int_0^\infty (-e^{-x})px^{p-1}\,dx$$

$$= p\int_0^\infty x^{p-1}e^{-x}\,dx = p\Gamma(p).$$

This equation

(3.4) $$\Gamma(p+1) = p\Gamma(p)$$

is called the *recursion relation* for the Γ function. Given Γ of any number $p > 0$, we can use it to find $\Gamma(p+1)$. The Γ function is usually tabulated for p between 1 and 2. Using the recursion relation (3.4) we can then find $\Gamma(p)$ for p between 2 and 3; for example, $\Gamma(2.5) = 1.5\Gamma(1.5)$. Similarly, we have $\Gamma(3.5) = 2.5\Gamma(2.5) = (2.5)(1.5)\Gamma(1.5)$, and so on. To find $\Gamma(p)$ for p between 0 and 1 from the tabulated values between 1 and 2, we write the recursion equation as $\Gamma(p) = (1/p)\Gamma(p+1)$. Then, for example, $\Gamma(0.5) = (1/0.5)\Gamma(1.5)$.

4. THE GAMMA FUNCTION OF NEGATIVE NUMBERS

For $p \leq 0$, $\Gamma(p)$ has not so far been defined. We shall now define it by the recursion relation (3.4) solved for $\Gamma(p)$.

$$(4.1) \qquad \qquad \Gamma(p) = \frac{1}{p} \Gamma(p + 1)$$

defines $\Gamma(p)$ for $p < 0$. For example,

$$\Gamma(-0.5) = \frac{1}{-0.5} \Gamma(0.5), \qquad \Gamma(-1.5) = \frac{1}{-1.5} \frac{1}{-0.5} \Gamma(0.5),$$

and so on. Since $\Gamma(1) = 1$, we see that $\Gamma(p) = \dfrac{\Gamma(p + 1)}{p} \to \infty$ as $p \to 0$.

From this and successive use of (4.1), it follows that $\Gamma(p)$ becomes infinite not only at zero but also at all the negative integers. A sketch of the graph of the Γ function is left to the problems. For positive p, $\Gamma(p)$ is a continuous function passing through the points $p = n$, $\Gamma(p) = (n - 1)!$. For negative p, as we have seen, $\Gamma(p)$ is discontinuous at the negative integers. In the intervals between the integers it is alternatively positive and negative: negative from 0 to -1, positive from -1 to -2, and so on as you can see from computations like those for $\Gamma(-0.5)$ and $\Gamma(-1.5)$ above.

5. SOME IMPORTANT FORMULAS INVOLVING GAMMA FUNCTIONS

First we evaluate $\Gamma(\tfrac{1}{2})$. By definition

$$(5.1) \qquad \qquad \Gamma(\tfrac{1}{2}) = \int_0^\infty \frac{1}{\sqrt{t}} e^{-t} \, dt.$$

(Note that it does not matter what letter we use for the variable of integration in a definite integral; for this reason it is often called a *dummy* variable). Put $t = y^2$ in (5.1); then $dt = 2y \, dy$, and (5.1) becomes

$$\Gamma(\tfrac{1}{2}) = \int_0^\infty \frac{1}{y} e^{-y^2} 2y \, dy = 2 \int_0^\infty e^{-y^2} \, dy$$

or, if we like,

$$(5.2) \qquad \qquad \Gamma(\tfrac{1}{2}) = 2 \int_0^\infty e^{-x^2} \, dx.$$

Let us multiply these two integrals for $\Gamma(\tfrac{1}{2})$ together and write the result as a double integral:

$$[\Gamma(\tfrac{1}{2})]^2 = 4 \int_0^\infty \int_0^\infty e^{-(x^2 + y^2)} \, dx \, dy.$$

This is an integral over the first quadrant; it can be more easily evaluated in polar coordinates:

$$[\Gamma(\tfrac{1}{2})]^2 = 4 \int_{\theta=0}^{\pi/2} \int_{r=0}^{\infty} e^{-r^2} r \, dr \, d\theta = 4 \cdot \frac{\pi}{2} \cdot \frac{e^{-r^2}}{-2}\Big|_0^{\infty} = \pi.$$

Therefore

(5.3) $$\Gamma(\tfrac{1}{2}) = \sqrt{\pi}.$$

We state without proof another important formula involving Γ functions (see Chapter 11, Section 7, Example 5):

(5.4) $$\Gamma(p)\Gamma(1 - p) = \frac{\pi}{\sin \pi p}.$$

Notice that (5.4) also gives $\Gamma(\tfrac{1}{2}) = \sqrt{\pi}$ if we put $p = \tfrac{1}{2}$.

6. BETA FUNCTIONS

The *beta function* is also defined by a definite integral:

(6.1) $$B(p, q) = \int_0^1 x^{p-1}(1 - x)^{q-1} \, dx, \qquad p > 0, q > 0.$$

There are a number of simple transformations of (6.1) which are useful to know [see (6.3). (6.4), (6.5)]. It is easy to show that (Problem 9)

(6.2) $$B(p, q) = B(q, p).$$

The range of integration in (6.1) can be changed by putting $x = y/a$; then $x = 1$ corresponds to $y = a$, and (6.1) becomes

(6.3) $$B(p, q) = \int_0^a \left(\frac{y}{a}\right)^{p-1} \left(1 - \frac{y}{a}\right)^{q-1} \frac{dy}{a} = \frac{1}{a^{p+q-1}} \int_0^a y^{p-1}(a - y)^{q-1} \, dy.$$

To obtain the trigonometric form of the beta function, let $x = \sin^2 \theta$; then

$$dx = 2 \sin \theta \cos \theta \, d\theta,$$
$$(1 - x) = 1 - \sin^2 \theta = \cos^2 \theta,$$
$$x = 1 \text{ corresponds to } \theta = \pi/2.$$

With these substitutions, (6.1) becomes

(6.4) $$B(p, q) = \int_0^{\pi/2} (\sin^2\theta)^{p-1}(\cos^2\theta)^{q} {}^{-1} 2 \sin \theta \cos \theta \, d\theta$$
$$= 2 \int_0^{\pi/2} (\sin \theta)^{2p-1}(\cos \theta)^{2q-1} \, d\theta.$$

Finally, let $x = y/(1 + y)$; then we get (Problem 10)

(6.5) $$B(p, q) = \int_0^{\infty} \frac{y^{p-1} \, dy}{(1 + y)^{p+q}}.$$

Example.   Find

$$I = \int_0^\infty \frac{x^3 \, dx}{(1 + x)^5} .$$

This is (6.5) with $(p + q) = 5$, $p - 1 = 3$ or $p = 4$, $q = 1$. Then $I = B(4, 1)$.

7. THE RELATION BETWEEN THE BETA AND GAMMA FUNCTIONS

You will not find tables of B functions as you did tables of Γ functions. The reason is that B functions are easily expressed in terms of Γ functions. We shall show that

(7.1) $$B(p, q) = \frac{\Gamma(p)\Gamma(q)}{\Gamma(p + q)} .$$

Whenever you want to evaluate a B function, you use (7.1) first and then look up the Γ functions in the tables. In the integral above we had $B(4, 1)$. By (7.1), this is

$$\frac{\Gamma(4)\Gamma(1)}{\Gamma(5)} = \frac{3!}{4!} = \tfrac{1}{4}.$$

To prove (7.1), we start with

$$\Gamma(p) = \int_0^\infty t^{p-1}e^{-t} \, dt$$

and put $t = y^2$. Then we have

(7.2) $$\Gamma(p) = 2\int_0^\infty y^{2p-1}e^{-y^2} \, dy.$$

Similarly (the dummy integration variable can be any letter),

$$\Gamma(q) = 2\int_0^\infty x^{2q-1}e^{-x^2} \, dx.$$

Next we multiply these two equations together and change to polar coordinates:

(7.3) $$\Gamma(p)\Gamma(q) = 4\int_0^\infty \int_0^\infty x^{2q-1}y^{2p-1}e^{-(x^2+y^2)} \, dx \, dy$$

$$= 4\int_0^\infty \int_0^{\pi/2} (r \cos \theta)^{2q-1}(r \sin \theta)^{2p-1}e^{-r^2} r \, dr \, d\theta$$

$$= 4\int_0^\infty r^{2p+2q-1}e^{-r^2} dr \int_0^{\pi/2} (\cos \theta)^{2q-1}(\sin \theta)^{2p-1} d\theta.$$

The r integral in (7.3) is $\tfrac{1}{2}\Gamma(p + q)$ by (7.2). The θ integral in (7.3) is $\tfrac{1}{2}B(p, q)$ by (6.4). Then $\Gamma(p)\Gamma(q) = 4 \cdot \tfrac{1}{2}\Gamma(p + q) \cdot \tfrac{1}{2}B(p, q)$ and (7.1) follows.

8. THE SIMPLE PENDULUM

A simple pendulum means a mass m suspended by a string (or weightless rod) of length l so that it can swing in a plane, as shown in Fig. 8.1. The kinetic energy of m is then

$$(8.1) \qquad T = \tfrac{1}{2}mv^2 = \tfrac{1}{2}m(l\dot\theta)^2.$$

If the potential energy is zero when the string is horizontal, then at angle θ it is

$$V = -mgl\cos\theta.$$

Then the Lagrangian is (see Chapter 8, Section 6)

$$L = T - V = \tfrac{1}{2}ml^2\dot\theta^2 + mgl\cos\theta,$$

and the Lagrange equation of motion is

$$\frac{d}{dt}(ml^2\dot\theta) + mgl\sin\theta = 0$$

or

$$(8.2) \qquad \ddot\theta = -\frac{g}{l}\sin\theta.$$

Suppose the pendulum executes such small vibrations that $\sin\theta$ can be approximated by θ. Then (8.2) becomes the usual equation for the simple harmonic motion of a pendulum executing small vibrations, namely

$$(8.3) \qquad \ddot\theta = -\frac{g}{l}\theta.$$

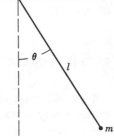

The solutions of (8.3) are $\sin\omega t$ and $\cos\omega t$ where $\omega = 2\pi\nu = \sqrt{g/l}$; the period of the motion is then

$$(8.4) \qquad T = \frac{1}{\nu} = 2\pi\sqrt{l/g}.$$

We now want to replace this approximate solution by one which is exact even for large θ.

Figure 8.1

Going back to the differential equation of motion (8.2), we multiply both sides of it by $\dot\theta$ and integrate, thus obtaining

$$\dot\theta\ddot\theta = -\frac{g}{l}\sin\theta\,\dot\theta \quad \text{or} \quad \dot\theta\,d\dot\theta = -\frac{g}{l}\sin\theta\,d\theta;$$

$$(8.5) \qquad \frac{1}{2}\dot\theta^2 = \frac{g}{l}\cos\theta + \text{const.}$$

We shall come back to the general solution of this equation when we discuss elliptic integrals; for the present let us find the period for 180° swings (back and forth from −90° to +90°). For this case, $\dot{\theta} = 0$ when $\theta = 90°$, so the constant in (8.5) is zero, and we have

$$\frac{1}{2}\dot{\theta}^2 = \frac{g}{l}\cos\theta,$$

$$\frac{d\theta}{dt} = \sqrt{\frac{2g}{l}}\sqrt{\cos\theta},$$

$$\frac{d\theta}{\sqrt{\cos\theta}} = \sqrt{\frac{2g}{l}}\,dt.$$

From $\theta = 0$ to $\theta = 90°$ is one-quarter of a period; hence the period for 180° swings is given by T in the equation

$$\int_0^{\pi/2} \frac{d\theta}{\sqrt{\cos\theta}} = \sqrt{\frac{2g}{l}} \int_0^{T/4} dt = \sqrt{\frac{2g}{l}} \cdot \frac{T}{4}.$$

Then the period is

(8.6) $$T = 4\sqrt{\frac{l}{2g}} \int_0^{\pi/2} \frac{d\theta}{\sqrt{\cos\theta}}.$$

We can see from (6.4) that this is a B function; evaluating it numerically is left to the problems. We can find the period for only this one special case (180° swings) by B functions; the general case gives an elliptic integral (Section 12).

9. THE ERROR FUNCTION

You will meet this function in probability theory (Chapter 15), and consequently in statistical mechanics and other applications of probability theory. If you have ever asked your instructor if he "grades on a curve," the "curve" you were talking about was $y = e^{-x^2}$; the error function is the area under a part of this curve. We define the error function as

(9.1) $$\text{erf}(x) = \frac{2}{\sqrt{\pi}} \int_0^x e^{-t^2}\,dt.$$

Although this is the usual definition of erf(x), there are other closely related integrals which are often used and tabulated and even sometimes referred to as the error function. Consequently, you must always look carefully at the form of the integral in the particular book or set of tables you are using. Here are some integrals you may find used and tabulated:

$$(9.2) \qquad \frac{1}{\sqrt{2\pi}} \int_0^x e^{-t^2/2}\, dt, \qquad \frac{2}{\sqrt{\pi}} \int_x^\infty e^{-t^2}\, dt, \qquad \sqrt{\frac{2}{\pi}} \int_x^\infty e^{-t^2/2}\, dt.$$

Let us see how to evaluate, say, erf(1.3) from a table of

$$(9.3) \qquad \frac{1}{\sqrt{2\pi}} \int_0^x e^{-t^2/2}\, dt.$$

Put $t = u/\sqrt{2}$ in (9.1); then the upper limit $t = x = 1.3$ becomes $u = x\sqrt{2} = 1.3\sqrt{2}$. Then we have

$$(9.4) \quad \operatorname{erf}(1.3) = \frac{2}{\sqrt{\pi}} \int_0^{1.3} e^{-t^2}\, dt = \frac{2}{\sqrt{\pi}} \int_0^{1.3\sqrt{2}} e^{-u^2/2}\, \frac{du}{\sqrt{2}}$$

$$= \frac{2}{\sqrt{2\pi}} \int_0^{1.3\sqrt{2}} e^{-u^2/2}\, du = 2 \cdot \frac{1}{\sqrt{2\pi}} \int_0^{1.3\sqrt{2}} e^{-t^2/2}\, dt$$

(since it doesn't matter what we call the dummy variable in a *definite* integral). Then we see from (9.4) that to find erf(1.3) from a table giving the integral (9.3), we would find the (area) entry corresponding to an upper limit of $1.3\sqrt{2}$, and then multiply by 2.

We next consider several useful facts about the error function. You can easily prove that the error function is odd; that is, $\operatorname{erf}(-x) = -\operatorname{erf}(x)$ (Problem 15). We can easily evaluate $\operatorname{erf}(\infty)$:

$$(9.5) \qquad \operatorname{erf}(\infty) = \frac{2}{\sqrt{\pi}} \int_0^\infty e^{-t^2}\, dt = \frac{2}{\sqrt{\pi}} \tfrac{1}{2}\Gamma(\tfrac{1}{2}) = \frac{2}{\sqrt{\pi}} \tfrac{1}{2}\sqrt{\pi} = 1$$

by (5.2) and (5.3). For very small values of x (below the range of the tables you have), $\operatorname{erf}(x)$ can be evaluated by expanding e^{-t^2} in a power series and integrating term by term. We get

$$(9.6) \qquad \operatorname{erf}(x) = \frac{2}{\sqrt{\pi}} \int_0^x e^{-t^2}\, dt = \frac{2}{\sqrt{\pi}} \int_0^x \left(1 - t^2 + \frac{t^4}{2!} - \cdots\right) dt \quad \text{small} \cdot x$$

$$= \frac{2}{\sqrt{\pi}} \left(x - \frac{x^3}{3} + \frac{x^5}{5 \cdot 2!} - \cdots\right).$$

For large x, say $x >$ about 3, $\operatorname{erf}(x)$ has (to four or more figures) the same value as for $x = \infty$. We are then usually interested in the difference between its values at x and at ∞. This is best obtained from an asymptotic series; we shall now discuss such expansions.

10. ASYMPTOTIC SERIES

Since you have spent some time learning to test series for convergence, it may surprise you to learn that there are divergent series which can be of practical use. We can show this best by an example. From (9.1) and (9.5) we can write

$$(10.1) \quad \mathrm{erf}(x) = \frac{2}{\sqrt{\pi}} \left[\int_0^\infty e^{-t^2} \, dt - \int_x^\infty e^{-t^2} \, dt \right] = 1 - \frac{2}{\sqrt{\pi}} \int_x^\infty e^{-t^2} \, dt.$$

We are going to expand the last integral in (10.1), namely

$$(10.2) \qquad\qquad \int_x^\infty e^{-t^2} \, dt,$$

in a series of inverse powers of x. To do this we write

$$e^{-t^2} = \frac{1}{t} \, t e^{-t^2} = \frac{1}{t} \frac{d}{dt} \left(-\tfrac{1}{2} e^{-t^2} \right)$$

and integrate (10.2) by parts. This gives

$$
\begin{aligned}
\int_x^\infty e^{-t^2} \, dt &= \int_x^\infty \frac{1}{t} \frac{d}{dt} \left(-\tfrac{1}{2} e^{-t^2} \right) dt \\
(10.3) \qquad &= \frac{1}{t} \left(-\tfrac{1}{2} e^{-t^2} \right) \Big|_x^\infty - \int_x^\infty \left(-\tfrac{1}{2} e^{-t^2} \right) \left(-\frac{1}{t^2} \right) dt \\
&= \frac{1}{2x} e^{-x^2} - \frac{1}{2} \int_x^\infty \frac{1}{t^2} e^{-t^2} \, dt.
\end{aligned}
$$

Now in the last integral in (10.3), write $(1/t^2)e^{-t^2} = (1/t^3)(d/dt)(-\tfrac{1}{2}e^{-t^2})$, and again integrate by parts:

$$
\begin{aligned}
\int_x^\infty \frac{1}{t^2} e^{-t^2} \, dt &= \int_x^\infty \frac{1}{t^3} \frac{d}{dt} \left(-\tfrac{1}{2} e^{-t^2} \right) dt \\
&= \frac{1}{t^3} \left(-\tfrac{1}{2} e^{-t^2} \right) \Big|_x^\infty - \int_x^\infty \left(-\tfrac{1}{2} e^{-t^2} \right) \left(-\frac{3}{t^4} \right) dt \\
&= \frac{1}{2x^3} e^{-x^2} - \frac{3}{2} \int_x^\infty \frac{1}{t^4} e^{-t^2} \, dt.
\end{aligned}
$$

Continuing this process, and substituting (10.3) and the steps following it back into (10.1) (Problem 18), we would obtain the series

$$(10.4) \quad \mathrm{erf}(x) \sim 1 - \frac{e^{-x^2}}{x\sqrt{\pi}} \left(1 - \frac{1}{2x^2} + \frac{1 \cdot 3}{(2x^2)^2} - \frac{1 \cdot 3 \cdot 5}{(2x^2)^3} + \cdots \right).$$

(We shall explain the exact meaning of the symbol $\sim$ shortly.) This series diverges for every x because of the factors in the numerator. However, suppose we stop after a few terms and keep the integral at the end so that we have an exact equation. If we stop after the third term, we have

$$(10.5) \qquad \operatorname{erf}(x) = 1 - \frac{e^{-x^2}}{x\sqrt{\pi}}\left(1 - \frac{1}{2x^2}\right) - \frac{3}{2\sqrt{\pi}}\int_x^\infty t^{-4}e^{-t^2}\,dt.$$

There is no approximation here. This is not an infinite series so there is no question of convergence. However, we shall show that the integral at the end is negligible for large enough x; this will then make it possible for us to use the rest of (10.5) [that is, the first three terms of (10.4)] as a good approximation for $\operatorname{erf}(x)$ for large x. This is the meaning of an asymptotic series. As an infinite series it may diverge, but we do not use the infinite series. Instead, using an exact equation [like (10.5) for this example], we show that the first few terms which we *do* use give a good approximation if x is large.

Now let us look at the integral in (10.5); we want to estimate its size for large x. The t in the integrand takes values from x to ∞; therefore $t \geq x$ or $1/x \geq 1/t$ for all values of t from x to ∞. Let us write the integral as

$$\int_x^\infty t^{-4}e^{-t^2}\,dt = \int_x^\infty \frac{1}{t^5}(te^{-t^2})\,dt.$$

We *increase* the value of this integral if we replace $1/t^5$ by $1/x^5$ since $1/x \geq 1/t$. Thus

$$\int_x^\infty t^{-4}e^{-t^2}\,dt < \int_x^\infty \frac{1}{x^5}(te^{-t^2}\,dt) = \frac{1}{x^5}\int_x^\infty te^{-t^2}\,dt$$

$$= \frac{1}{x^5}\left(-\tfrac{1}{2}e^{-t^2}\right)\Big|_x^\infty = \frac{e^{-x^2}}{2x^5}.$$

When we stop in (10.5) with the term in e^{-x^2}/x^3, the error is of the order of e^{-x^2}/x^5, which becomes much smaller than e^{-x^2}/x^3 as x increases.

It is interesting to consider calculating, say $\operatorname{erf}(10)$, from (10.4) and from (9.6). (See Problem 19.) The series in (9.6) converges, and would (after much work!) give the answer to any desired accuracy. But (10.4)—even though the infinite series diverges—gives quickly far more accuracy than one ever needs in practical work:

$$\operatorname{erf}(10) = 1 \text{ with an error of the order of } \frac{e^{-100}}{10},$$

or about 45 decimal place accuracy!

Of more interest is $1 - \mathrm{erf}(x)$; for $x = 10$, we have

$$1 - \mathrm{erf}(10) = \frac{e^{-100}}{10\sqrt{\pi}}(1 - \tfrac{1}{200})$$

with an error of the order of $e^{-100}/10^5$ or about 10^{-4} times the first term. The larger x is, the better the approximation given by the asymptotic series.

We can make the above discussion more precise. For (10.4), we have seen that if we stop after the term in $x^{-3}e^{-x^2}$, the error is of the order of $x^{-5}e^{-x^2}$. Then the ratio of the error to the last term kept (namely $x^{-5}e^{-x^2} \div x^{-3}e^{-x^2} = x^{-2}$) tends to zero as x tends to infinity, that is, the approximation becomes increasingly good for larger x as we have said. The "error" in an asymptotic expansion means in general the difference between the function being expanded and a partial sum (first N terms) of the series. A series is called an asymptotic expansion (about ∞) of a function $f(x)$ if, for each fixed N, the ratio of the error to the last (nonzero) term kept, tends to zero as $x \to \infty$. In symbols

$$f(x) \sim \sum_{n=0}^{\infty} \phi_n(x)$$

(10.6) $$\left(\text{read } \sum_{n=0}^{\infty} \phi_n(x) \text{ is an asymptotic expansion of } f(x)\right)$$

if for each fixed N

$$\left| f(x) - \sum_{n=0}^{N} \phi_n(x) \right| \div \phi_N(x) \to 0 \qquad \text{as } x \to \infty.$$

Frequently, the terms of an asymptotic series (about ∞) are inverse powers of x. [We could write (10.4) this way by multiplying through by e^{x^2}.] Then (10.6) becomes

$$f(x) \sim \sum_{n=0}^{\infty} \frac{a_n}{x^n}$$

(10.7)   if for each fixed N

$$\left| f(x) - \sum_{n=0}^{N} \frac{a_n}{x^n} \right| \cdot x^N \to 0 \qquad \text{as } x \to \infty.$$

We can also have asymptotic series about the origin (or any point— compare Taylor series). We say that

$$f(x) \sim \sum_{n=0}^{\infty} a_n x^n$$

(10.8)   if for each fixed N

$$\left| f(x) - \sum_{n=0}^{N} a_n x^n \right| \div x^N \to 0 \qquad \text{as } x \to 0.$$

Although we have discussed the particularly interesting case of a *divergent* asymptotic series, it is not necessary for such series to diverge. Note that to test a series for convergence, we fix x and let n tend to infinity; to see if a series is asymptotic, we fix n and let x tend to a limit. A given series may meet both tests, or only one or the other.

11. STIRLING'S FORMULA

Formulas involving $n!$ or $\Gamma(p)$ are not very convenient to simplify algebraically or to differentiate. There is an approximate formula for the factorial or Γ function known as Stirling's formula which can be used to simplify formulas involving factorials. It is

$$(11.1) \qquad n! \sim n^n e^{-n} \sqrt{2\pi n} \qquad \text{or} \quad \Gamma(p+1) \sim p^p e^{-p} \sqrt{2\pi p}.$$

The sign $\sim$ (read "is asymptotic to") means that the ratio of the two sides

$$\frac{n!}{n^n e^{-n} \sqrt{2\pi n}}$$

tends to 1 as $n \to \infty$. Thus we get better approximations to $n!$ as n becomes large. Actually the absolute error (difference between the Stirling approximation and the correct value) *increases*, but the relative error (ratio of the error to the value of $n!$) tends to zero as n increases. To get some idea of how this formula arises, we outline what could, with a little more detail, be a derivation of it. (For more detail, see, for example, Buck, p. 216.) Start with

$$(11.2) \qquad \Gamma(p+1) = p! = \int_0^\infty x^p e^{-x}\, dx = \int_0^\infty e^{p \ln x - x}\, dx.$$

Substitute a new variable y such that

$$x = p + y\sqrt{p}.$$

Then

$$dx = \sqrt{p}\, dy,$$

$$x = 0 \text{ corresponds to } y = -\sqrt{p},$$

and (11.2) becomes

$$(11.3) \qquad p! = \int_{-\sqrt{p}}^\infty e^{p \ln (p+y\sqrt{p})-p-y\sqrt{p}} \sqrt{p}\, dy.$$

For large p, the logarithm can be expanded in the following power series:

$$(11.4) \quad \ln (p + y\sqrt{p}) = \ln p + \ln \left(1 + \frac{y}{\sqrt{p}}\right) = \ln p + \frac{y}{\sqrt{p}} - \frac{y^2}{2p} + \cdots.$$

Substituting (11.4) into (11.3), we get

$$p! \sim \int_{-\sqrt{p}}^{\infty} e^{p \ln p + y\sqrt{p} - (y^2/2) - p - y\sqrt{p}} \sqrt{p} \, dy$$

$$= e^{p \ln p - p} \sqrt{p} \int_{-\sqrt{p}}^{\infty} e^{-y^2/2} \, dy$$

$$= p^p e^{-p} \sqrt{p} \left[\int_{-\infty}^{\infty} e^{-y^2/2} \, dy - \int_{-\infty}^{-\sqrt{p}} e^{-y^2/2} \, dy \right].$$

The first integral is easily shown to be $\sqrt{2\pi}$ (Problem 16). The second integral tends to zero as $p \to \infty$, and we have

$$p! \sim p^p e^{-p} \sqrt{2\pi p}$$

which is (11.1). With more work, it is possible to find an asymptotic expansion for $\Gamma(p + 1)$:

(11.5) $$\Gamma(p + 1) = p! = p^p e^{-p} \sqrt{2\pi p} \left(1 + \frac{1}{12p} + \frac{1}{288p^2} + \cdots \right).$$

This is another example of an asymptotic series which is divergent as an infinite series; however, the first term alone (Stirling's formula) is a good approximation for large p, and the second term can be used to estimate the relative error. Approximately, the relative error in (11.1) is:

$$\text{for } p > 1, \qquad \frac{1}{12p} < \frac{1}{10}, \qquad \text{error} < 10\%;$$

$$\text{for } p > 10, \qquad \frac{1}{12p} < \frac{1}{100}, \qquad \text{error} < 1\%;$$

$$\text{for } p > 100, \qquad \frac{1}{12p} < 10^{-3}, \quad \text{error} < 0.1\%.$$

12. ELLIPTIC INTEGRALS AND FUNCTIONS

These are another group of integrals and related functions which have been extensively studied and tabulated. Since they may arise in applied problems, it is worth while to know enough about them to be able to use the readily available tables, to recognize when you probably have an elliptic integral, and to be able to look up and use known properties and transformations when you need them. We shall merely summarize briefly the basic definitions and properties—there are whole books on the subject!

Legendre forms.   The *Legendre* forms of the elliptic integrals of the first and second kind are:

(12.1)
$$F(k, \phi) = \int_0^{\phi} \frac{d\phi}{\sqrt{1 - k^2 \sin^2 \phi}}, \qquad \begin{cases} 0 \le k \le 1, \\ \text{or} \\ k = \sin \theta, \ \ 0 \le \theta \le \dfrac{\pi}{2}. \end{cases}$$

$$E(k, \phi) = \int_0^{\phi} \sqrt{1 - k^2 \sin^2 \phi} \, d\phi,$$

(There is also an elliptic integral of the third kind, but this occurs less frequently.) Here k is called the *modulus* and ϕ the *amplitude* of the elliptic integral. The quantity $k' = \sqrt{1 - k^2}$ is called the *complementary modulus*. These integrals are tabulated for values of $\theta = $ arc sin k and ϕ between 0 and $\pi/2$; given a value of k^2 in an integral you want to evaluate, you will have to take its square root to get k, then look up $\theta = $ arc sin k in the ordinary natural sine table, and then find $F(k, \phi)$ or $E(k, \phi)$ from the tables of elliptic integrals.

Complete elliptic integrals.   The *complete* elliptic integrals of the first and second kind are the values of F and E (as functions of k) for $\phi = \pi/2$; we define

(12.2)
$$K \quad \text{or} \quad K(k) = F\left(k, \frac{\pi}{2}\right) = \int_0^{\pi/2} \frac{d\phi}{\sqrt{1 - k^2 \sin^2 \phi}},$$

$$E \quad \text{or} \quad E(k) = E\left(k, \frac{\pi}{2}\right) = \int_0^{\pi/2} \sqrt{1 - k^2 \sin^2 \phi} \, d\phi.$$

These are usually tabulated separately and to higher accuracy than $F(k, \phi)$ and $E(k, \phi)$.

Since k is restricted to the $(0, 1)$ interval, θ need take values only on $(0, \pi/2)$. However ϕ is not so restricted and may have any positive or negative value. Since the tables list only values of ϕ between 0 and $\pi/2$, we need to know how to find integrals with other ϕ values. To see this consider the *integrands* $\sqrt{1 - k^2 \sin^2 \phi}$ or $1/\sqrt{1 - k^2 \sin^2 \phi}$; these are both functions of $\sin^2 \phi$, so we shall just discuss $f(\sin^2 \phi)$, where f is some arbitrary function. Suppose we have a graph (say as in Fig. 12.1) of $f(\sin^2 \phi)$ between 0 and $\pi/2$. Then since $\sin \phi$ takes on the same values in the second quadrant as in the first, the graph of $f(\sin^2 \phi)$ from $\pi/2$ to π is just a reflection (in the $\phi = \pi/2$ line) of the graph from 0 to $\pi/2$. From 0 to π is one period of $\sin^2 \phi$, hence a period of $f(\sin^2 \phi)$, so the rest of the graph is just a repetition of the part from $\phi = 0$ to $\phi = \pi$. Now the area under the curve is $\int f(\sin^2 \phi) \, d\phi$; for either $F(k, \phi)$ or $E(k, \phi)$, the integral for $\phi > \pi/2$ can be made up of one or more areas equal to that from 0

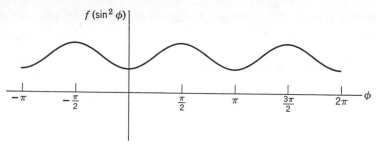

Figure 12.1

to π plus (or minus) an area which is equivalent to an integral from 0 to an angle less than $\pi/2$.

Example.

$$\int_0^{9\pi/4} = \int_0^{2\pi} + \int_0^{\pi/4} = 2\int_0^{\pi} + \int_0^{\pi/4} = 4\int_0^{\pi/2} + \int_0^{\pi/4}$$

and

$$\int_0^{7\pi/4} = \int_0^{2\pi} - \int_0^{\pi/4} = 4\int_0^{\pi/2} - \int_0^{\pi/4}.$$

Note carefully (Fig. 12.1), however, that $\int_0^{7\pi/4}$ is *not* equal to $\int_0^{3\pi/2} + \int_0^{\pi/4}$ since $\int_0^{\pi/4}$ and $\int_{\pi/2}^{3\pi/4}$ are not equal. We must always integrate over a number of π (not $\pi/2$) intervals and then add or subtract the correct integral over an interval of length less than $\pi/2$. Using the definitions of complete elliptic integrals, we have:

(12.3)
$$F(k, n\pi \pm \phi) = 2nK \pm F(k, \phi),$$
$$E(k, n\pi \pm \phi) = 2nE \pm E(k, \phi).$$

If the lower limit is not zero, we can write

$$\int_{\phi_1}^{\phi_2} \frac{d\phi}{\sqrt{1 - k^2 \sin^2 \phi}} = \int_0^{\phi_2} \frac{d\phi}{\sqrt{1 - k^2 \sin^2 \phi}} - \int_0^{\phi_1} \frac{d\phi}{\sqrt{1 - k^2 \sin^2 \phi}}$$

$$= F(k, \phi_2) - F(k, \phi_1),$$

and a similar formula for $E(k, \phi)$. If one of the limits is negative, we can use the fact that $F(k, \phi)$ and $E(k, \phi)$ are odd functions of ϕ, that is,

$$F(k, -\phi) = \int_0^{-\phi} \frac{d\phi}{\sqrt{1 - k^2 \sin^2 \phi}} = -\int_0^{\phi} \frac{d\phi}{\sqrt{1 - k^2 \sin^2 \phi}} = -F(k, \phi)$$

and $E(k, -\phi) = -E(k, \phi)$. You can see this also from Fig. 12.1; the integrand is unchanged, but we are integrating in the negative direction in $\int_0^{-\phi}$.

Since $k^2 \sin^2 \phi < 1$ (for $k < 1$), we get convergent infinite series for the elliptic integrals by expanding the integrands by the binomial theorem and integrating term by term (Problem 29). For small k these series converge rapidly and provide a good method for evaluating the elliptic integrals for k values below the range of the tables.

Jacobi forms.   If we put $\sin \phi = x$ in the *Legendre* forms (12.1), we obtain the *Jacobi* forms of the elliptic integrals of the first and second kind:

$$x = \sin \phi,$$

$$dx = \cos \phi \, d\phi \quad \text{or} \quad d\phi = \frac{dx}{\cos \phi} = \frac{dx}{\sqrt{1 - x^2}},$$

$$\phi = \pi/2 \text{ corresponds to } x = 1.$$

Then

$$F(k, \phi) = \int_0^\phi \frac{d\phi}{\sqrt{1 - k^2 \sin^2 \phi}} = \int_0^x \frac{dx}{\sqrt{(1 - x^2)(1 - k^2 x^2)}},$$

$$E(k, \phi) = \int_0^\phi \sqrt{1 - k^2 \sin^2 \phi} \, d\phi = \int_0^x \sqrt{\frac{1 - k^2 x^2}{1 - x^2}} \, dx,$$

(12.4)

$$K = F\left(k, \frac{\pi}{2}\right) = \int_0^1 \frac{dx}{\sqrt{(1 - x^2)(1 - k^2 x^2)}},$$

$$E = \int_0^1 \sqrt{\frac{1 - k^2 x^2}{1 - x^2}} \, dx.$$

Many integrals can be reduced to one or a combination of these forms. The necessary transformations for many cases can be found in the references given; we shall do one case which is of interest (Example 2 below). You know from integral tables that when the integrand is the square root of a quadratic, the indefinite integral is given in terms of elementary functions. When the integrand involves a square root of a cubic or a quartic, the integral will probably involve elliptic functions. Some simple transformations of such integrals to put them in forms (12.1) or (12.4), you should be able to do yourself; others are best looked up. For example,

$$\int_0^x \sqrt{\frac{10 - 5x^2}{1 - x^2}} \, dx$$

is easily found by factoring out $\sqrt{10}$; then this integral is $\sqrt{10}E(k, \phi)$ in (12.4) with $k^2 = \frac{1}{2}$.

Example 1. Find the arc length of an ellipse. This is the problem that gave elliptic integrals their name. We write the equation of the ellipse in the parametric form

$$x = a \sin \phi,$$
$$y = b \cos \phi.$$

for the case $a > b$. (If $b > a$, use the form $x = a \cos \phi$, $y = b \sin \phi$; see Problem 32.) Then for $a > b$, we have

$$ds^2 = dx^2 + dy^2 = (a^2 \cos^2 \phi + b^2 \sin^2 \phi) \, d\phi^2.$$

Since $a^2 - b^2 > 0$, we can write

$$\int ds = \int \sqrt{a^2 - (a^2 - b^2) \sin^2 \phi} \, d\phi = a \int \sqrt{1 - \frac{a^2 - b^2}{a^2} \sin^2 \phi} \, d\phi.$$

This is an elliptic integral of the second kind where $k^2 = (a^2 - b^2)/a^2 = e^2$ (e is the eccentricity of the ellipse in analytic geometry). If we want the complete circumference, ϕ goes from 0 to 2π, and the answer is $4aE(k, \pi/2)$. For a smaller arc, we can put the proper limits ϕ_1 to ϕ_2 on the integral and obtain $E(k, \phi_2) - E(k, \phi_1)$. For any given ellipse (that is, given a and b), we can then find the numerical value of the desired arc length by using a table of elliptic functions $E(k, \phi)$.

Example 2. We shall now continue the problem of the motion of a pendulum for large angles. We had in Section 8

$$(12.5) \qquad\qquad \dot\theta^2 = \frac{2g}{l} \cos \theta + \text{const.}$$

In our previous discussion we had $\dot\theta = 0$ at $\theta = \pi/2$, so the constant was zero (this corresponded to 180° swings, that is, of amplitude 90°). Now we want to consider swings of any amplitude, say α; then $\dot\theta = 0$ when $\theta = \alpha$, and (12.5) becomes

$$(12.6) \qquad\qquad \dot\theta^2 = \frac{2g}{l} (\cos \theta - \cos \alpha).$$

Integrating (12.6), we get

$$(12.7) \qquad\qquad \int_0^\alpha \frac{d\theta}{\sqrt{\cos \theta - \cos \alpha}} = \sqrt{\frac{2g}{l}} \frac{T_\alpha}{4},$$

where T_α is the period for swings from $-\alpha$ to $+\alpha$ and back. This integral can be changed to either of the standard forms for F; we shall find the

Jacobi form. Write

$$\cos\theta = 1 - 2\sin^2\frac{\theta}{2}, \qquad \cos\alpha = 1 - 2\sin^2\frac{\alpha}{2},$$

(12.8) $$\cos\theta - \cos\alpha = 2\left(\sin^2\frac{\alpha}{2} - \sin^2\frac{\theta}{2}\right)$$

$$= 2\sin^2\frac{\alpha}{2}\left(1 - \frac{\sin^2\dfrac{\theta}{2}}{\sin^2\dfrac{\alpha}{2}}\right).$$

Next let

(12.9) $$x = \frac{\sin\dfrac{\theta}{2}}{\sin\dfrac{\alpha}{2}}.$$

(Remember that α is a constant equal to the amplitude of the motion, that is, the largest value of θ.) Then

$$dx = \frac{\cos\dfrac{\theta}{2}\dfrac{d\theta}{2}}{\sin\dfrac{\alpha}{2}},$$

(12.10)

$$d\theta = \frac{2\,dx\sin\dfrac{\alpha}{2}}{\cos\dfrac{\theta}{2}} = \frac{2\sin\dfrac{\alpha}{2}\,dx}{\sqrt{1 - x^2\sin^2\dfrac{\alpha}{2}}}.$$

Substituting (12.8), (12.9), and (12.10) into (12.7), we have

$$\int_0^\alpha \frac{d\theta}{\sqrt{\cos\theta - \cos\alpha}} = \frac{2\sin\dfrac{\alpha}{2}}{\sqrt{2}\sin\dfrac{\alpha}{2}}\int_0^1 \frac{dx}{\sqrt{1 - x^2\sin^2\dfrac{\alpha}{2}}\sqrt{1 - x^2}}$$

$$= \sqrt{2}\,K\!\left(\sin\frac{\alpha}{2}\right).$$

Then (12.7) gives for the period

$$T_\alpha = 4\sqrt{\frac{l}{2g}}\,\sqrt{2}\,K\!\left(\sin\frac{\alpha}{2}\right) = 4\sqrt{\frac{l}{g}}\,K\!\left(\sin\frac{\alpha}{2}\right).$$

For α not too large (say $\alpha < 90°$, $\tfrac{1}{2}\alpha < 45°$, so that $\sin^2(\alpha/2) < \tfrac{1}{2}$), we can get a good approximation to T_α by series (Problem 29):

$$(12.11) \quad T_\alpha = 4\sqrt{\frac{l}{g}}\frac{\pi}{2}\left(1 + \left(\frac{1}{2}\right)^2\sin^2\frac{\alpha}{2} + \left(\frac{1\cdot 3}{2\cdot 4}\right)^2\sin^4\frac{\alpha}{2} + \cdots\right).$$

For α small enough so that $\sin\alpha/2$ can be approximated by $\alpha/2$, we can write

$$(12.12) \qquad\qquad T_\alpha = 2\pi\sqrt{\frac{l}{g}}\left(1 + \frac{\alpha^2}{16} + \cdots\right).$$

For very small α, we get the familiar formula for simple harmonic motion, $T = 2\pi\sqrt{l/g}$ independent of α. For somewhat larger α, say $\alpha = \frac{1}{2}$ radian (about 30°), we get

$$(12.13) \qquad\qquad T_{\alpha=1/2} = 2\pi\sqrt{\frac{l}{g}}\left(1 + \frac{1}{64} + \cdots\right).$$

This would mean that a pendulum started at 30° would get exactly out of phase with one of very small amplitude in about 32 periods.

Elliptic functions.   Recall that

$$u = \int_0^x \frac{dx}{\sqrt{1 - x^2}} = \sin^{-1} x$$

defines u as a function of x, or x as a function of u; in fact, $x = \sin u$. In a similar way $u = F(k, \phi)$ in (12.4) defines u as a function of ϕ (or of $x = \sin\phi$) or it defines x or ϕ as functions of u (we are assuming k fixed). We write

$$(12.14) \qquad\qquad u = \int_0^x \frac{dx}{\sqrt{1 - x^2}\sqrt{1 - k^2 x^2}} = \text{sn}^{-1} x,$$

$$x = \text{sn } u \qquad \text{(read ess-en of } u\text{)}.$$

Since $\phi = \text{amp } u$ is the amplitude of the elliptic integral $u = F(k, \phi)$, and $x = \sin\phi$, we have

$$(12.15) \qquad\qquad \text{sn } u = \sin\phi = \sin(\text{amp } u).$$

The function sn u is an elliptic function. There are other elliptic functions, related to sn u; you will notice [in (12.16)] that they have some resemblance to the trigonometric functions. We define

$$\text{cn } u = \cos\phi = \cos(\text{amp } u) = \sqrt{1 - \sin^2(\text{amp } u)}$$
$$= \sqrt{1 - \text{sn}^2 u} = \sqrt{1 - x^2},$$

$$(12.16)$$

$$\text{dn } u = \frac{d\phi}{du} = \frac{1}{\dfrac{du}{d\phi}} = \sqrt{1 - k^2\sin^2\phi} = \sqrt{1 - k^2\text{sn}^2 u} = \sqrt{1 - k^2 x^2}.$$

[The value of $du/d\phi$ is found from $u = F(k, \phi)$ in (12.1) or (12.4).] There are many formulas relating these functions, for example, addition formulas, integrals, derivatives, etc. These can be looked up in the references given, or in some cases easily worked out. For example, since sn $u = \sin \phi$, we have

$$\frac{d}{du}(\text{sn } u) = \frac{d}{du}(\sin \phi) = \cos \phi \frac{d\phi}{du} = \text{cn } u \text{ dn } u.$$

REFERENCES

Discussion of the various topics of this chapter will be found in some advanced calculus books and in some books on mathematics in physics and engineering. (See references identified by a [9] after the listing at the end of the book.) Short tables of Γ and error functions and elliptic integrals may be found in the CRC Handbook. For much more detail, see specialized references, such as Abramowitz and Stegun, National Bureau of Standards Handbook (tables and formulas); Byrd and Friedman (elliptic integrals, tables and formulas); Erdélyi, Higher Transcendental Functions (formulas); Erdélyi, Asymptotic Expansions; Jahnke-Emde (tables and formulas); Oberhettinger and Magnus (elliptic functions, applications and tables).

PROBLEMS

1. The integral in (3.1) is improper because of the infinite upper limit and it is also improper for $0 < p < 1$ because x^{p-1} becomes infinite at the lower limit. However, the integral is convergent for any $p > 0$. Prove this.

2. Evaluate the following Γ functions using tables and the recursion relation (3.4).

(a) $\Gamma(1.7)$ (b) $\Gamma(5.7)$ (c) $\Gamma(-0.3)$

(d) $\Gamma(-1.7)$ (e) $\Gamma(2.7)$ (f) $\Gamma(0.7)$

(g) $\Gamma(-1.3)$

3. Using a table of Γ functions, sketch the Γ function between 1 and 2; then compute a few points and sketch it from -4 to $+4$.

4. Express the following integrals as Γ functions and evaluate them using a table of Γ functions.

(a) $\int_0^\infty x^{2/3} e^{-x}\, dx$ (b) $\int_0^\infty \sqrt{x}\, e^{-x}\, dx$

(c) $\displaystyle\int_0^\infty x^{-\frac{1}{2}}e^{-x}\,dx$ (d) $\displaystyle\int_0^\infty x^2 e^{-x^2}\,dx$ (*Hint:* put $x^2 = u$.)

(e) $\displaystyle\int_0^\infty xe^{-x^3}\,dx$ (f) $\displaystyle\int_0^1 x^2\left(\ln\frac{1}{x}\right)^3 dx$ (*Hint:* put $x = e^{-u}$.)

(g) $\displaystyle\int_0^1 \sqrt[3]{\ln x}\,dx$

5. Prove that, for positive integral n:

$$\Gamma(n + \tfrac{1}{2}) = \frac{1\cdot 3\cdot 5\cdots(2n-1)}{2^n}\sqrt{\pi} = \frac{(2n)!}{4^n n!}\sqrt{\pi}.$$

6. Use (5.4) to show that

(a) $\Gamma(\tfrac{1}{2} - n)\Gamma(\tfrac{1}{2} + n) = (-1)^n \pi$ if $n = $ a positive integer;

(b) $(z!)(-z)! = \pi z/\sin \pi z$, where z is not necessarily an integer; see comment after equation (3.3).

7. Prove that

$$\frac{d}{dp}\Gamma(p) = \int_0^\infty x^{p-1}e^{-x}\ln x\,dx,$$

$$\frac{d^n}{dp^n}\Gamma(p) = \int_0^\infty x^{p-1}e^{-x}(\ln x)^n\,dx.$$

8. A particle starting from rest at $x = 1$ moves along the x-axis toward the origin. Its potential energy is $V = \tfrac{1}{2}m \ln x$. Write the Lagrange equation and integrate it to find the time required for the particle to reach the origin. *Caution:* $dx/dt < 0$. *Answer:* $\Gamma(\tfrac{1}{2})$.

9. Prove that $B(p, q) = B(q, p)$. *Hint:* Put $x = 1 - y$.

10. Prove equation (6.5).

11. Express the following integrals as B functions, hence in terms of Γ functions, and evaluate using a table of Γ functions.

(a) $\displaystyle\int_0^1 \frac{x^4\,dx}{\sqrt{1 - x^2}}$ (b) $\displaystyle\int_0^{\pi/2}\sqrt{\sin^3 x \cos x}\,dx$

(c) $\displaystyle\int_0^1 \frac{dx}{\sqrt{1 - x^3}}$ (d) $\displaystyle\int_0^1 x^2(1 - x^3)^{3/2}\,dx$

(e) $\displaystyle\int_0^\infty \frac{y^3\,dy}{(1 + y)^5}$ (f) $\displaystyle\int_0^\infty \frac{y\,dy}{(1 + y^3)^2}$

(g) $\displaystyle\int_0^{\pi/2} \frac{d\theta}{\sqrt{\sin\theta}}$ (h) $\displaystyle\int_0^2 \frac{x^2}{\sqrt{2 - x}}$

12. Prove $B(n, n) = B(n, \tfrac{1}{2})/2^{2n-1}$. *Hint:* In (6.4), use the identity $2\sin\theta\cos\theta = \sin 2\theta$ and put $2\theta = \phi$. Use this result and (5.3) to derive the *duplication* *formula* for Γ functions:

$$\Gamma(2n) = \frac{1}{\sqrt{\pi}} 2^{2n-1}\Gamma(n)\Gamma(n + \tfrac{1}{2}).$$

Check this formula for the case $n = \tfrac{1}{4}$ by using (5.4).

13. Complete the pendulum problem to find the period for 180° swings as a multiple of $\sqrt{l/g}$ [that is, evaluate the integral in (8.6)].

14. Sketch $x^3 + y^3 = 8$. Write the integrals for the following quantities and evaluate them as B functions:

    (a) the first quadrant area bounded by the curve,
    (b) the centroid of this area,
    (c) the volume generated when the area is revolved about the y-axis,
    (d) the moment of inertia of this volume about its axis.

15. Prove that erf (x) is an odd function of x. *Hint:* Put $t = -s$ in (9.1).

16. Show that $\displaystyle\int_{-\infty}^{\infty} e^{-y^2/2}\,dy = \sqrt{2\pi}$ by

    (a) using (9.5);
    (b) reducing it to a Γ function and using (5.3).

17. Express each of the integrals in (9.2) in terms of erf (x).

18. Carry through the algebra to get equation (10.4).

19. The value of erf (2) is 0.995 to three decimal places. Compare the work involved in calculating this from the convergent power series (9.6) or from the asymptotic series (10.4). Approximate the error in each case after two terms; after ten terms. *Hint:* (9.6) is an alternating series; see Chapter 1, Section 15, just after Example 2, page 26.

20. Evaluate the following, using either power series, a table of error functions, or asymptotic series, whichever is appropriate.

    (a) $\displaystyle\int_0^2 e^{-x^2}\,dx$
             (b) $\displaystyle\int_{0.001}^{0.002} e^{-x^2}\,dx$

    (c) $1 - \mathrm{erf}\,(5)$
                (d) $\displaystyle\frac{2}{\sqrt{\pi}}\int_{1.5}^{\infty} e^{-x^2}\,dx$

    (e) $\displaystyle\frac{2}{\sqrt{\pi}}\int_5^{10} e^{-x^2}\,dx$
         (f) $1 - \mathrm{erf}\,(100)$

    (g) erf (0.7)
                   (h) $\displaystyle\int_1^{1.5} e^{-x^2/2}\,dx$

    (i) $\displaystyle\sqrt{\frac{2}{\pi}}\int_1^{\infty} e^{-x^2/2}\,dx$

21. By repeated integration by parts, find several terms of the asymptotic series for

$$\int_x^{\infty} t^{n-1}e^{-t}\,dt.$$

[Note that if $x = 0$, this integral is $\Gamma(n)$; for $x \neq 0$, it is called an *incomplete* Γ function, $\Gamma(n, x)$.]

22. Express the error function as an incomplete Γ function (see Problem 21) and show that the asymptotic expansion (10.4) agrees with your result in Problem 21.

23. The integral $\displaystyle\int_x^\infty \frac{e^{-t}}{t}\, dt$ is called an *exponential integral*.

   (a) Find the asymptotic series for the exponential integral.
   (b) Express the exponential integral as an incomplete Γ function.

24. Compare the exact values of $n!$ and the Stirling's formula approximation for $n = 2, 5, 10, 50, 100$. (Find the percentage error.)

$$(50! = 3.04141 \times 10^{64}, \qquad 100! = 9.33262 \times 10^{157}).$$

25. In statistical mechanics, we frequently use $\ln N! = N \ln N - N$, where N is of the order of Avogadro's number. Write out $\ln N!$ using Stirling's formula, compute the approximate value of each term for $N = 10^{26}$, and so justify the above approximation.

26. Use Stirling's formula to evaluate $\displaystyle\lim_{n\to\infty} \frac{(2n)!\,\sqrt{n}}{2^{2n}(n!)^2}$.

27. The following expression occurs in statistical mechanics:

$$P = \frac{n!}{(np + u)!\,(nq - u)!}\, p^{np+u} q^{nq-u}.$$

Use Stirling's formula to show that

$$\frac{1}{P} \sim x^{npx} y^{nqy} \sqrt{2\pi npqxy},$$

where $x = 1 + \dfrac{u}{np}$, $y = 1 - \dfrac{u}{nq}$, and $p + q = 1$. *Hint:* Show that

$$(np)^{np+u}(nq)^{nq-u} = n^n p^{np+u} q^{nq-u}$$

and divide numerator and denominator of P by this expression.

28. Sketch a graph of $y = \ln x$. Show that $\ln n!$ is between the values of the integrals $\displaystyle\int_2^{n+1} \ln x\, dx$ and $\displaystyle\int_1^n \ln x\, dx$. (*Hint:* $\ln n! = \ln 1 + \ln 2 + \ln 3 + \cdots$ is the sum of the areas of rectangles of width 1 and height up to the $\ln x$ curve at $x = 1, 2, 3$, etc.) By considering the values of the two integrals for large n as in Problem 25, show that $\ln n! = n \ln n - n$ approximately for large n.

29. Expand $F(k, \phi)$ and $E(k, \phi)$ in power series in $k^2 \sin^2 \phi$ for small k and integrate term by term. From these series find the series for the complete elliptic integrals K and E.

30. Find from tables or (for small k) from the power series of Problem 29, the values of each of the following elliptic integrals.

(a) $K(0.13)$

(b) $E(0.001)$

(c) $F\left(0.13, \dfrac{\pi}{3}\right)$

(d) $E\left(0.13, \dfrac{7\pi}{3}\right)$

(e) $\displaystyle\int_{-1/2}^{3/4} \sqrt{\dfrac{9 - 4x^2}{1 - x^2}}\, dx$

(f) $\displaystyle\int_{0}^{\pi/4} \dfrac{d\phi}{\sqrt{1 - 0.25 \sin^2 \phi}}$

(g) $\displaystyle\int_{0}^{5\pi/4} \sqrt{1 - 0.037 \sin^2 \phi}\, d\phi$

(h) $\displaystyle\int_{0}^{0.8} \dfrac{dx}{\sqrt{(1 - x^2)(1 - 0.16x^2)}}$

(i) $\displaystyle\int_{-\pi/2}^{3\pi/8} \dfrac{d\phi}{\sqrt{1 - 0.87 \sin^2 \phi}}$

(j) $\displaystyle\int_{-7\pi/8}^{11\pi/4} \sqrt{1 - 0.64 \sin^2 \phi}\, d\phi$

(k) $\displaystyle\int_{0}^{1/2} \sqrt{\dfrac{100 - x^2}{1 - x^2}}\, dx$

31. Find the circumference of the ellipse $4x^2 + 9y^2 = 36$.

32. Find the length of arc of the ellipse $x^2 + (y^2/4) = 1$ between $(0, 2)$ and $(\tfrac{1}{2}, \sqrt{3})$. (Note that here $b > a$; see Example 1, Section 12, page 414.)

33. Find the arc length of one arch of $y = \sin x$.

34. Sketch a graph of sn u as a function of u for $k = \tfrac{1}{2}$. Use the table for the elliptic integral $u = \displaystyle\int_{0}^{\phi} \dfrac{d\phi}{\sqrt{1 - k^2 \sin^2 \phi}}$ and remember that sn $u = \sin \phi$. Note that you are plotting the sine of the upper limit as a function of the value of the integral. From your graph of sn u, sketch rough graphs of cn u and dn u.

35. If $u = \ln (\sec \phi + \tan \phi)$, then ϕ is a function of u called the *gudermannian of u*, $\phi = $ gd u. Prove that:

$$u = \ln \tan \left(\dfrac{\pi}{4} + \dfrac{\phi}{2}\right),$$

$$\tan \text{ gd } u = \sinh u,$$

$$\sin \text{ gd } u = \tanh u,$$

$$\dfrac{d}{du} \text{ gd } u = \text{sech } u.$$

36. Show that for $k = 0$:

$$u = F(0, \phi) = \phi, \qquad \text{sn } u = \sin u, \qquad \text{cn } u = \cos u, \qquad \text{dn } u = 1;$$

and for $k = 1$:

$$u = F(1, \phi) = \ln (\sec \phi + \tan \phi) \qquad \text{or} \quad \phi = \text{gd } u \quad \text{(Problem 35)},$$

$$\text{sn } u = \tanh u,$$

$$\text{cn } u = \text{dn } u = \text{sech } u.$$

37. By transforming $\displaystyle\int_0^{\pi/2} \frac{d\phi}{\sqrt{\cos \phi}}$ to one of the standard forms for an elliptic integral of the first kind, show that

$$B\left(\frac{1}{4},\frac{1}{2}\right) = 2\sqrt{2}F\left(\frac{1}{\sqrt{2}},\frac{\pi}{2}\right) = 2\sqrt{2}K\left(\frac{1}{\sqrt{2}}\right)$$

and so

$$K\left(\frac{1}{\sqrt{2}}\right) = \frac{1}{4\sqrt{\pi}}\left[\Gamma\left(\frac{1}{4}\right)\right]^2.$$

Evaluate these expressions (from Γ and K tables) to check the result.

38. In the pendulum problem, $\theta = \alpha \sin\sqrt{g/l}\,t$ is one solution when the amplitude α is small enough for the motion to be considered simple harmonic. Show that the corresponding exact solution when α is not small is

$$\sin\frac{\theta}{2} = \sin\frac{\alpha}{2}\, \text{sn}\sqrt{\frac{g}{l}}\,t$$

where $k = \sin(\alpha/2)$ is the modulus of the elliptic function. Show that this reduces to the simple harmonic motion solution for small amplitude α.

10

Coordinate Transformations; Tensor Analysis

1. INTRODUCTION

One of the first tasks in solving a physical problem is to choose a suitable coordinate system; often a skillful choice of this reference system simplifies the work. Another way of expressing this is to say that we select a set of variables which is appropriate to the problem at hand. Recall that in setting up multiple integrals for volumes, moments, etc., the work is usually easier in the "right" coordinate system. In solving differential equations, we often make changes of variables to make the problem easier to do. In describing the motion of a projectile near the earth we would probably use rectangular coordinates and write

$$\ddot{x} = 0, \qquad \ddot{y} = 0, \qquad \ddot{z} = -g,$$

but for the motion of a particle moving around a circle we would use polar coordinates and write

$$r = \text{const.}, \qquad \ddot{\theta} = \text{the angular acceleration.}$$

In this chapter we want to consider transformations from one coordinate system to another. Whether we use geometric language and say "change of coordinate system" or algebraic language and say "change of variables," the basic mathematics involved is the same.

There is another important point here. The physical facts described by the answer to a physical problem do not depend upon which coordinate system we decide to use. For example, the temperature at a point is the same whether we use rectangular or spherical coordinates to locate the point, although, to be sure, the temperature is not the same function of x, y, z as of r, θ, ϕ. Or, if we consider a block sliding down an inclined plane, the equation $\mathbf{F} = m\mathbf{a}$ is correct whether we take the x-axis horizontal or along the incline; the x-components of $\mathbf{F}$ and $\mathbf{a}$ are, of course, different in the two cases. In fact, vectors are useful and important in applications just because a vector equation is true in any coordinate system. We shall see that this is also true for tensors, which are a generalization of vectors.

To understand this thoroughly, and to be able to express vector equations in other coordinate systems than rectangular, we are going to consider in this chapter transformations from one coordinate system to another and also some basic properties of the most frequently used coordinate systems. We shall then use our knowledge to define tensors and discuss some of their uses.

2. LINEAR TRANSFORMATIONS

A linear transformation is one in which each new variable is some linear combination of the old variables. In two dimensions the linear transformation equations are

$$(2.1) \qquad \begin{aligned} x' &= ax + by, \\ y' &= cx + dy, \end{aligned}$$

where a, b, c, d are constants. As an explicit numerical example, we shall consider

$$(2.2) \qquad \begin{aligned} x' &= 5x - 2y, \\ y' &= -2x + 2y. \end{aligned}$$

These equations can be interpreted geometrically in two ways.

First way (Fig. 2.1). Let $\mathbf{r}$ and $\mathbf{r}'$ be the vectors

$$(2.3) \qquad \begin{aligned} \mathbf{r} &= x\mathbf{i} + y\mathbf{j}, \\ \mathbf{r}' &= x'\mathbf{i} + y'\mathbf{j}. \end{aligned}$$

Then the equations (2.1) and (2.2) tell how to get the vector $\mathbf{r}'$ when we are given $\mathbf{r}$. Equations (2.1) can be written in matrix notation as

$$(2.4) \qquad \begin{pmatrix} x' \\ y' \end{pmatrix} = \begin{pmatrix} a & b \\ c & d \end{pmatrix} \begin{pmatrix} x \\ y \end{pmatrix} \qquad \text{or} \quad r' = Mr,$$

where r', M and r stand for matrices.* The matrix M, called the matrix of the transformation, contains all the information necessary to obtain r' from r. We could say that multiplication of r by matrix M changes it into another vector. (We shall see later that a second-order tensor has the same effect.)

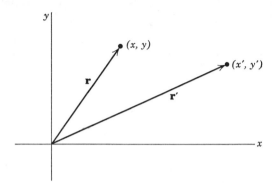

Figure 2.1

Second way of interpreting (2.1) and (2.2) (Fig. 2.2).   In order to avoid confusion later, let us call the new variables here X, Y instead of x', y'. Then the equations (2.1) are

(2.5)
$$X = ax + by,$$
$$Y = cx + dy.$$

Here we consider *two* sets of coordinate axes, (x, y) and (X, Y), and *one* vector $\mathbf{r} = \mathbf{R}$ with coordinates relative to each set of axes:

(2.6) $$\mathbf{r} = x\mathbf{i} + y\mathbf{j} = \mathbf{R} = X\mathbf{I} + Y\mathbf{J},$$

where $\mathbf{I}$ and $\mathbf{J}$ are unit vectors along the X- and Y-axes. This time the matrix M of the transformation tells us how to get the components of the vector $\mathbf{r} = \mathbf{R}$ relative to axes X and Y when we know its components relative to axes x and y.

---

* Notice that the components x, y of a vector can be displayed in the vector form $\mathbf{i}x + \mathbf{j}y$, or in the matrix form $\begin{pmatrix} x \\ y \end{pmatrix}$, or in the analytic geometry form (x, y). Following customary notation, we shall use $\mathbf{r}$ to mean $\mathbf{i}x + \mathbf{j}y$ or (x, y), and r to mean the column matrix $\begin{pmatrix} x \\ y \end{pmatrix}$. Note carefully that r as used here is *not* $|\mathbf{r}|$ as in Chapter 5, but instead stands for the column matrix $\begin{pmatrix} x \\ y \end{pmatrix}$.

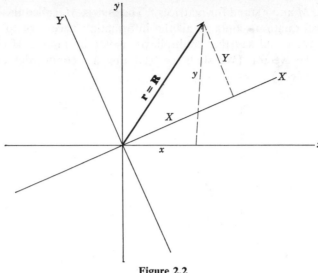

Figure 2.2

3. ORTHOGONAL TRANSFORMATIONS

In general the axes X and Y in (2.5) and Fig. 2.2 are not perpendicular. When they are, the equations (2.5) are the rotation equations and a, b, c, d can be written in terms of the rotation angle θ so that the equations (2.5) become

(3.1)
$$X = x \cos \theta + y \sin \theta,$$
$$Y = -x \sin \theta + y \cos \theta.$$

We shall be particularly interested in this special case of a linear transformation, which is called an *orthogonal transformation*. By definition, an orthogonal transformation is a linear transformation from x, y to X, Y such that

(3.2)
$$x^2 + y^2 = X^2 + Y^2.$$

Or, in Fig. 2.1, equations (2.1) represent an orthogonal transformation if

(3.3)
$$x^2 + y^2 = x'^2 + y'^2.$$

You can see from the figures that the requirements (3.2) and (3.3) say that the length of a vector is not changed by an orthogonal transformation. In Fig. 2.1, the vector is rotated (or perhaps reflected) with its length held fixed. In Fig. 2.2, the axes are rotated (or reflected), while the vector stays fixed. The matrix M of an orthogonal transformation is called an *orthogonal matrix*. We want to find a simple condition satisfied by any orthogonal matrix. We shall prove that the inverse of an orthogonal matrix equals its transpose; in symbols [see (9.8) of Chapter 3]*

(3.4) $$M^T = M^{-1} \qquad (M \text{ orthogonal}).$$

From (3.2) and (2.5) we have

$$\begin{aligned} X^2 + Y^2 &= (ax + by)^2 + (cx + dy)^2 \\ &= (a^2 + c^2)x^2 + 2(ab + cd)xy + (b^2 + d^2)y^2 \\ &\equiv x^2 + y^2. \end{aligned}$$

Then we must have

$$a^2 + c^2 = 1, \qquad ab + cd = 0, \qquad b^2 + d^2 = 1.$$

Hence we get

$$M^T M = \begin{pmatrix} a & c \\ b & d \end{pmatrix} \begin{pmatrix} a & b \\ c & d \end{pmatrix} = \begin{pmatrix} a^2 + c^2 & ab + cd \\ ab + cd & b^2 + d^2 \end{pmatrix}$$
$$= \begin{pmatrix} 1 & 0 \\ 0 & 1 \end{pmatrix}.$$

Thus $M^T M$ is the unit matrix, so M^T and M are inverse matrices as claimed in (3.4).

We have defined an orthogonal transformation in two dimensions [if (3.2) holds, (2.5) is an orthogonal transformation], and we have proved (3.4) for the two-dimensional case. However, a square matrix of any order is called orthogonal if it satisfies (3.4). (See Problems 1 and 15 for a discussion of the three-dimensional case.)

In three dimensions as in two dimensions, we can think of an orthogonal transformation as a rotation of axes. However, there are many problems in mathematical physics involving more than three variables. In such a problem, we cannot represent the variables as coordinates of a point in *physical* space since physical space has only three dimensions. But it is convenient and customary to extend our geometrical *terminology* anyway. Thus we use the terms *variables* and *coordinates* interchangeably and

---

* In this chapter we shall use M^T rather than M' to indicate the transpose of a matrix M in order to avoid confusion when prime indicates a new set of variables. For example, in (2.1),

$$r = \begin{pmatrix} x \\ y \end{pmatrix}, \qquad r^T = (x \quad y), \qquad r' = \begin{pmatrix} x' \\ y' \end{pmatrix}.$$

speak, for example, of a "point in five-dimensional space," meaning a set of values of five variables, and similarly for any number of variables. In three dimensions, we often think of the coordinates of a point as the components of a vector from the origin to the point; thus we may call an ordered set of three numbers a vector in three-dimensional space. By analogy, we may call an ordered set of five numbers a "vector in five-dimensional space" or an ordered set of n numbers a "vector in n-dimensional space." (See Section 11 for a more careful discussion of the meaning of a vector.) A great deal of the geometrical terminology which is familiar in two and three dimensions can be extended to problems in n dimensions (that is, n variables) by using the algebra which parallels the geometry. For example, the distance from the origin to the point (x, y, z) is $\sqrt{x^2 + y^2 + z^2}$. By analogy, in a problem in the five variables x, y, z, u, v, we define the "distance" from the "origin" $(0, 0, 0, 0, 0)$ to the "point" (x, y, z, u, v) as $\sqrt{x^2 + y^2 + z^2 + u^2 + v^2}$. By using the algebra which goes with the geometry, we can easily extend such ideas as the length of a vector, the dot product of two vectors (and therefore the angle between the vectors and the idea of orthogonality), etc. (Problem 2.) We saw above that an orthogonal transformation in two or three dimensions corresponds to a rotation of axes. Thus we might say, in a problem in n variables, that a linear transformation (that is, a linear change of variables) satisfying "sum of squares of new variables = sum of squares of old variables" [compare (3.2)] corresponds to a "rotation in n-dimensional space."

4. EIGENVALUES AND EIGENVECTORS; DIAGONALIZING MATRICES

We can give the following physical interpretation to Fig. 2.1 and equations (2.1) or (2.4). Suppose the (x, y) plane is covered by an elastic membrane which can be stretched, shrunk, or rotated (with the origin fixed). Then any point (x, y) of the membrane becomes some point (x', y') after the deformation and we can say that the matrix M describes the deformation. Notice that we use interchangeably "the point (x, y)" and "the vector $\mathbf{r}$" and similarly for $\mathbf{r}'$ [see (2.3)]. Let us now ask whether there are any vectors which are not changed in direction by the deformation, that is, vectors such that $\mathbf{r}' = \mu\mathbf{r}$ where $\mu = \text{const}$. Such vectors are called *eigenvectors* (or *characteristic* vectors) of the transformation, and the values of μ are called the *eigenvalues* (or characteristic values) of the matrix M of the transformation.

Eigenvalues. To illustrate finding eigenvalues we use equations (2.2) which in matrix form become

$$(4.1) \qquad \begin{pmatrix} x' \\ y' \end{pmatrix} = \begin{pmatrix} 5 & -2 \\ -2 & 2 \end{pmatrix} \begin{pmatrix} x \\ y \end{pmatrix}.$$

The eigenvector condition, $\mathbf{r}' = \mu \mathbf{r}$, is, in matrix notation,

$$\begin{pmatrix} x' \\ y' \end{pmatrix} = \begin{pmatrix} 5 & -2 \\ -2 & 2 \end{pmatrix} \begin{pmatrix} x \\ y \end{pmatrix} = \mu \begin{pmatrix} x \\ y \end{pmatrix} = \begin{pmatrix} \mu x \\ \mu y \end{pmatrix},$$

or written out in equation form:

$$(4.2) \qquad \begin{array}{ll} 5x - 2y = \mu x, & (5 - \mu)x - 2y = 0, \\ -2x + 2y = \mu y, & \text{or} \qquad -2x + (2 - \mu)y = 0. \end{array}$$

If we tried to solve such a set of homogeneous equations by determinants, we would get $x = 0$, $y = 0$ (because the constants on the right-hand side are zero) unless the determinant of the coefficients were equal to zero (see Chapter 3, end of Section 7). In the latter case the equations would be dependent and we would get an infinite set of solutions. The condition then for there to be solutions of (4.2) other than $x = y = 0$ is that

$$(4.3) \qquad \begin{vmatrix} 5 - \mu & -2 \\ -2 & 2 - \mu \end{vmatrix} = 0.$$

This is called the *characteristic equation* of the matrix M. Note that to obtain it from M, we subtract μ from the elements on the main diagonal of M, and then set the determinant of the resulting matrix equal to zero. We solve (4.3) for μ to find the characteristic values of M:

$$(4.4) \qquad \begin{array}{l} (5 - \mu)(2 - \mu) - 4 = \mu^2 - 7\mu + 6 = 0, \\ \mu = 1 \quad \text{or} \quad \mu = 6. \end{array}$$

Eigenvectors. Substituting the μ values from (4.4) into (4.2), we get:

$$(4.5) \qquad \begin{array}{ll} 2x - y = 0 & \text{from either of the equations (4.2) when } \mu = 1; \\ x + 2y = 0 & \text{from either of the equations (4.2) when } \mu = 6. \end{array}$$

We were looking for vectors $\mathbf{r} = \mathbf{i}x + \mathbf{j}y$ such that the transformation (2.2) would give an $\mathbf{r}'$ parallel to $\mathbf{r}$. What we have found is that *any* vector $\mathbf{r}$ with x- and y-components satisfying either of the equations (4.5) has this property. Since equations (4.5) are equations of straight lines through the origin, such vectors lie along these lines (Fig. 4.1). Then equations (4.5) show that any vector $\mathbf{r}$ from the origin to a point on $x + 2y = 0$ is changed by the transformation (2.2) to a vector in the same direction but six times as long, and any vector from the origin to a point on $2x - y = 0$ is unchanged by the transformation (2.2). These vectors (along $x + 2y = 0$ and $2x - y = 0$) are the eigenvectors of the transformation. Along these

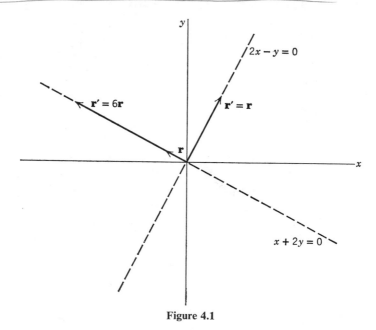

Figure 4.1

two directions (and only these), the deformation of the elastic membrane was a pure stretch with no shear (rotation).

Diagonalizing a matrix. We next write (4.2) once with $\mu = 1$, and again with $\mu = 6$, using subscripts 1 and 2 to identify the corresponding eigenvectors:

$$
\begin{array}{ll}
5x_1 - 2y_1 = x_1, & 5x_2 - 2y_2 = 6x_2, \\
-2x_1 + 2y_1 = y_1, & -2x_2 + 2y_2 = 6y_2.
\end{array}
$$

(4.6)

These four equations can be written as one matrix equation, as you can easily verify by multiplying out both sides:

$$
(4.7) \qquad \begin{pmatrix} 5 & -2 \\ -2 & 2 \end{pmatrix} \begin{pmatrix} x_1 & x_2 \\ y_1 & y_2 \end{pmatrix} = \begin{pmatrix} x_1 & x_2 \\ y_1 & y_2 \end{pmatrix} \begin{pmatrix} 1 & 0 \\ 0 & 6 \end{pmatrix}.
$$

All we really can say about (x_1, y_1) is that $2x_1 - y_1 = 0$; however, it is convenient to pick numerical values of x_1 and y_1 to make $\mathbf{r}_1 = (x_1, y_1)$ a unit vector, and similarly for $\mathbf{r}_2 = (x_2, y_2)$. Then we have

$$x_1 = \frac{1}{\sqrt{5}}, \qquad y_1 = \frac{2}{\sqrt{5}}, \qquad x_2 = \frac{-2}{\sqrt{5}}, \qquad y_2 = \frac{1}{\sqrt{5}},$$

and (4.7) becomes

$$\begin{pmatrix} 5 & -2 \\ -2 & 2 \end{pmatrix} \begin{pmatrix} \dfrac{1}{\sqrt{5}} & \dfrac{-2}{\sqrt{5}} \\ \dfrac{2}{\sqrt{5}} & \dfrac{1}{\sqrt{5}} \end{pmatrix} = \begin{pmatrix} \dfrac{1}{\sqrt{5}} & -\dfrac{2}{\sqrt{5}} \\ \dfrac{2}{\sqrt{5}} & \dfrac{1}{\sqrt{5}} \end{pmatrix} \begin{pmatrix} 1 & 0 \\ 0 & 6 \end{pmatrix}$$

Representing these matrices by letters we can write

$$MC = CD, \qquad \text{where}$$

(4.8)

$$M = \begin{pmatrix} 5 & -2 \\ -2 & 2 \end{pmatrix}, \qquad C = \begin{pmatrix} \dfrac{1}{\sqrt{5}} & -\dfrac{2}{\sqrt{5}} \\ \dfrac{2}{\sqrt{5}} & \dfrac{1}{\sqrt{5}} \end{pmatrix}, \qquad D = \begin{pmatrix} 1 & 0 \\ 0 & 6 \end{pmatrix}.$$

If, as here, the determinant of C is not zero, then C has an inverse C^{-1}; let us multiply (4.8) by C^{-1} and remember that $C^{-1}C$ is the unit matrix:

(4.9) $$C^{-1}MC = C^{-1}CD = D.$$

The matrix D has elements different from zero only down the main diagonal; it is called a *diagonal matrix*. The matrix D is called *similar* to M, and when we obtain D given M, we say that we have *diagonalized M by a similarity transformation.* We shall see shortly that this amounts physically to a simplification of the problem by a better choice of variables. For example, in the problem of the membrane, we shall find it simpler to describe the deformation if we use axes along the eigenvectors. We shall see later several more examples of the use of the diagonalization process.

Observe that it is easy to find D; we need only solve the characteristic equation of M. Then D is a matrix with these characteristic values down the main diagonal and zeros elsewhere. We can also find C (with more work), but for many purposes only D is needed.

Note that the order of the eigenvalues down the main diagonal of D is arbitrary; for example, we could write (4.6) as

(4.10)

$$\begin{pmatrix} 5 & -2 \\ -2 & 2 \end{pmatrix} \begin{pmatrix} x_2 & x_1 \\ y_2 & y_1 \end{pmatrix} = \begin{pmatrix} x_2 & x_1 \\ y_2 & y_1 \end{pmatrix} \begin{pmatrix} 6 & 0 \\ 0 & 1 \end{pmatrix}$$

instead of as (4.7). Then (4.9) still holds, with a different C, of course, and with $D = \begin{pmatrix} 6 & 0 \\ 0 & 1 \end{pmatrix}$ instead of as in (4.8) (Problem 3).

Meaning of C and D. To see more clearly the meaning of (4.9) let us find what the matrices C and D mean physically. We consider two sets of axes (x, y) and (X, Y) with (X, Y) rotated through θ from (x, y) (Fig. 4.2). The (x, y) and (X, Y) coordinates of *one* point (or components

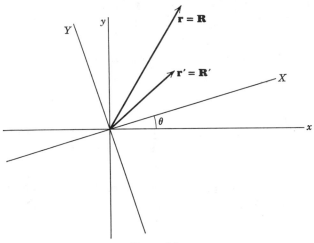

Figure 4.2

of one vector $\mathbf{r} = \mathbf{R}$) relative to the two systems are related by (3.1). Solving (3.1) for x and y, we have

$$(4.11) \qquad \begin{aligned} x &= X \cos \theta - Y \sin \theta, \\ y &= X \sin \theta + Y \cos \theta, \end{aligned}$$

or in matrix notation

$$(4.12) \qquad r = CR \qquad \text{where} \quad C = \begin{pmatrix} \cos \theta & -\sin \theta \\ \sin \theta & \cos \theta \end{pmatrix}.$$

This equation is true for *any* single vector with components given in the two systems. Suppose we have another vector $\mathbf{r}' = \mathbf{R}'$ (Fig. 4.2) with components x', y' and X', Y'; these components are related by

$$(4.13) \qquad r' = CR'.$$

Now let M be a matrix which describes a deformation of the plane in the (x, y) system. Then the equation

$$(4.14) \qquad r' = Mr$$

says that the vector **r** becomes the vector **r**′ after the deformation, both vectors given relative to the (x, y) axes. Let us ask how we can describe the deformation in the (X, Y) system, that is, what matrix carries **R** into **R**′? We substitute (4.12) and (4.13) into (4.14) and find $CR' = MCR$ or

$$(4.15) \qquad\qquad R' = C^{-1}MCR.$$

Thus the answer to our question is that $D = C^{-1}MC$ is the matrix which describes in the (X, Y) system the same deformation that M describes in the (x, y) system.

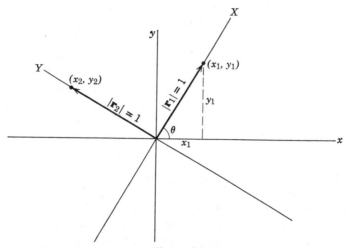

Figure 4.3

Next we want to show that if the matrix C is chosen to make $D = C^{-1}MC$ a diagonal matrix, then the new axes (X, Y) are along the directions of the eigenvectors of M. From (4.9) and the discussion before it we recall that the C which diagonalizes M is the matrix whose columns are the components of the *unit* eigenvectors of M. We can see from Fig. 4.3 that the C in (4.8) and the rotation matrix C in (4.12) are the same if the axes (X, Y) are along the eigenvectors. For we have from Fig. 4.3 (since $|\mathbf{r}_1| = 1$ and $|\mathbf{r}_2| = 1$)

$$x_1 = |\mathbf{r}_1| \cos \theta = \cos \theta, \qquad x_2 = -|\mathbf{r}_2| \sin \theta = -\sin \theta,$$
$$y_1 = |\mathbf{r}_1| \sin \theta = \sin \theta, \qquad y_2 = |\mathbf{r}_2| \cos \theta = \cos \theta;$$

$$(4.16) \qquad C = \begin{pmatrix} x_1 & x_2 \\ y_1 & y_2 \end{pmatrix} = \begin{pmatrix} \cos \theta & -\sin \theta \\ \sin \theta & \cos \theta \end{pmatrix},$$

which is (4.12). Thus the new axes (X, Y) are along the eigenvectors of M.

Relative to these new axes the diagonal matrix D describes the deformation. For our example we have

$$(4.17) \qquad R' = DR \quad \text{or} \quad \begin{pmatrix} X' \\ Y' \end{pmatrix} = \begin{pmatrix} 1 & 0 \\ 0 & 6 \end{pmatrix} \begin{pmatrix} X \\ Y \end{pmatrix} \quad \text{or}$$

$$X' = X, \qquad Y' = 6Y.$$

In words, (4.17) says that [in the (X, Y) system] each point (X, Y) has its X coordinate unchanged by the deformation and its Y coordinate multiplied by 6, that is, the deformation is simply a stretch in the Y direction. This is a simpler description of the deformation and clearer physically than the description given by (4.1).

You can see now why the order of eigenvalues down the main diagonal in D is arbitrary and why (4.10) is just as satisfactory as (4.7). The new axes (X, Y) are along the eigenvectors, but it is unimportant which eigenvector we call X and which we call Y. In doing a problem we simply select a D with the eigenvalues of M in some (arbitrary) order down the main diagonal. Our choice of D then determines which eigenvector direction is called the X-axis and which is called Y.

It was unnecessary in the above discussion to have the X- and Y-axes perpendicular, although this is the most useful case. If $r = CR$ but C is just any (nonsingular) matrix [not necessarily the orthogonal rotation matrix as in (4.12)], then (4.15) still follows. That is, $C^{-1}MC$ describes the deformation in the (X, Y) system. In this case, however, the (X, Y) axes are not necessarily perpendicular (Fig 4.4), and $x^2 + y^2 \neq X^2 + Y^2$, that

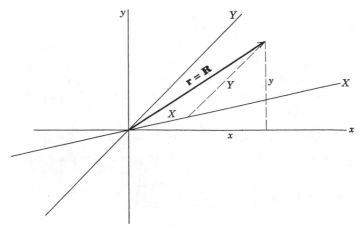

Figure 4.4

is, the transformation C is not orthogonal. Recall that C is the matrix of eigenvectors; if these are perpendicular (and unit vectors), then C is an orthogonal matrix (see Problem 4).

5. APPLICATIONS OF DIAGONALIZATION

We next consider some simple examples of the use of the diagonalization process. A central conic section (ellipse or hyperbola) with center at the origin has the equation

$$(5.1) \qquad Ax^2 + 2Hxy + By^2 = K,$$

where A, B, H, and K are constants. In matrix form this can be written

$$(5.2) \qquad (x \ \ y)\begin{pmatrix} A & H \\ H & B \end{pmatrix}\begin{pmatrix} x \\ y \end{pmatrix} = K \qquad \text{or} \qquad (x \ \ y)M\begin{pmatrix} x \\ y \end{pmatrix} = K$$

if we call $\begin{pmatrix} A & H \\ H & B \end{pmatrix} = M$ (as you can verify by multiplying out the matrices). We want to choose the principal axes of the conic as our reference axes in order to write the equation in simpler form. Consider Fig. 4.2; let the axes (X, Y) be rotated by some angle θ from (x, y). Then the (x, y) and (X, Y) coordinates of a point are related by (4.11) or (4.12):

$$(5.3) \qquad \begin{pmatrix} x \\ y \end{pmatrix} = \begin{pmatrix} \cos\theta & -\sin\theta \\ \sin\theta & \cos\theta \end{pmatrix}\begin{pmatrix} X \\ Y \end{pmatrix} \qquad \text{or} \qquad \begin{pmatrix} x \\ y \end{pmatrix} = C\begin{pmatrix} X \\ Y \end{pmatrix}.$$

Remembering that the transpose of a product of two matrices is the product of the transposes in inverse order (Problem 42a, Chapter 3), we can write

$$(5.4) \qquad (x \ \ y) = (X \ \ Y)\begin{pmatrix} \cos\theta & \sin\theta \\ -\sin\theta & \cos\theta \end{pmatrix} \qquad \text{or}$$

$$(x \ \ y) = (X \ \ Y)C^T = (X \ \ Y)C^{-1}$$

since C is an orthogonal matrix. Substituting (5.3) and (5.4) into (5.2), we get

$$(5.5) \qquad (X \ \ Y)C^{-1}MC\begin{pmatrix} X \\ Y \end{pmatrix} = K.$$

If C is the matrix which diagonalizes M, then (5.5) is the equation of the conic relative to its principal axes.

Example 1.   Consider the conic

(5.6) $$5x^2 - 4xy + 2y^2 = 30.$$

In matrix form this can be written

(5.7) $$(x \ \ y)\begin{pmatrix} 5 & -2 \\ -2 & 2 \end{pmatrix}\begin{pmatrix} x \\ y \end{pmatrix} = 30.$$

We have here the same matrix, $M = \begin{pmatrix} 5 & -2 \\ -2 & 2 \end{pmatrix}$, whose eigenvalues we found in Section 4. In that section we found a C such that

$$C^{-1}MC = \begin{pmatrix} 1 & 0 \\ 0 & 6 \end{pmatrix}.$$

Then the equation (5.5) of the conic relative to principal axes is

(5.8) $$(X \ \ Y)\begin{pmatrix} 1 & 0 \\ 0 & 6 \end{pmatrix}\begin{pmatrix} X \\ Y \end{pmatrix} = X^2 + 6Y^2 = 30.$$

Observe that interchanging the order of 1 and 6 in D would give $6X^2 + Y^2 = 30$ as the new equation of the ellipse instead of (5.8). This amounts simply to interchanging the X- and Y-axes.

By comparing the matrix C of the unit eigenvectors [see (4.8)] with the rotation matrix (4.12), we see that the rotation angle θ (Fig. 4.3) from the original axes (x, y) to the principal axes (X, Y) is

(5.9) $$\theta = \text{arc cos}\ \frac{1}{\sqrt{5}}.$$

Notice that in writing the conic section equation in matrix form (5.2) and (5.7), we split the xy term evenly between the two nondiagonal elements of the matrix; this made M symmetric. It can be proved that M can be diagonalized by a similarity transformation $C^{-1}MC$ with C an orthogonal matrix (that is, by a rotation of axes) if and only if M is symmetric. We choose M symmetric (by splitting the xy term in half) to make our process work.

Although for simplicity we have been working in two dimensions, the same ideas apply to three (or more) dimensions (that is, three or more variables). As we have said (end of Section 3), although we can represent only three coordinates in physical space, it is very convenient to use the same geometrical terminology even though the number of variables is greater than three. Thus if we diagonalize a matrix of any order, we still use the terms eigenvalues, eigenvectors, principal axes, rotation to principal axes, etc.

Example 2. Rotate to principal axes the quadric surface

$$x^2 + 6xy - 2y^2 - 2yz + z^2 = 24.$$

In matrix form this equation is

$$(x \quad y \quad z) \begin{pmatrix} 1 & 3 & 0 \\ 3 & -2 & -1 \\ 0 & -1 & 1 \end{pmatrix} \begin{pmatrix} x \\ y \\ z \end{pmatrix} = 24.$$

The characteristic equation of this matrix is

$$\begin{vmatrix} 1-\mu & 3 & 0 \\ 3 & -2-\mu & -1 \\ 0 & -1 & 1-\mu \end{vmatrix} = 0 = -\mu^3 + 13\mu - 12$$
$$= -(\mu - 1)(\mu + 4)(\mu - 3).$$

The characteristic values are

$$\mu = 1, \qquad \mu = -4, \qquad \mu = 3.$$

Relative to the principal axes (X, Y, Z) the quadric surface equation becomes

$$(X \quad Y \quad Z) \begin{pmatrix} 1 & 0 & 0 \\ 0 & -4 & 0 \\ 0 & 0 & 3 \end{pmatrix} \begin{pmatrix} X \\ Y \\ Z \end{pmatrix} = 24$$

or

$$X^2 - 4Y^2 + 3Z^2 = 24.$$

From this equation we can identify the quadratic surface (hyperboloid of one sheet) and sketch its size and shape using (X, Y, Z) axes without finding their relation to the original (x, y, z) axes. However, if we do want to know the relation between the two sets of axes, we find the C matrix in the following way. Recall from Section 4 that C is the matrix whose columns are the components of the unit eigenvectors. One of the eigenvectors can be found by substituting the eigenvalue $\mu = 1$ into the equations

$$\begin{pmatrix} 1 & 3 & 0 \\ 3 & -2 & -1 \\ 0 & -1 & 1 \end{pmatrix} \begin{pmatrix} x \\ y \\ z \end{pmatrix} = \begin{pmatrix} \mu x \\ \mu y \\ \mu z \end{pmatrix}$$

and solving for x, y, z. Then $\mathbf{i}x + \mathbf{j}y + \mathbf{k}z$ is an eigenvector corresponding to $\mu = 1$, and by dividing it by its magnitude we get a *unit* eigenvector. Repeating this process for each of the other values of μ, we get the following three unit eigenvectors:

$$\left(\frac{1}{\sqrt{10}}, 0, \frac{3}{\sqrt{10}} \right) \qquad \text{when} \quad \mu = 1;$$

$$\left(-\frac{3}{\sqrt{35}}, \frac{5}{\sqrt{35}}, \frac{1}{\sqrt{35}} \right) \qquad \text{when} \quad \mu = -4;$$

$$\left(\frac{3}{\sqrt{14}}, \frac{2}{\sqrt{14}}, -\frac{1}{\sqrt{14}} \right) \qquad \text{when} \quad \mu = 3.$$

Then the rotation matrix C is

$$C = \begin{pmatrix} \dfrac{1}{\sqrt{10}} & -\dfrac{3}{\sqrt{35}} & \dfrac{3}{\sqrt{14}} \\[2mm] 0 & \dfrac{5}{\sqrt{35}} & \dfrac{2}{\sqrt{14}} \\[2mm] \dfrac{3}{\sqrt{10}} & \dfrac{1}{\sqrt{35}} & -\dfrac{1}{\sqrt{14}} \end{pmatrix}.$$

The numbers in C are the cosines of the nine angles between the (x, y, z) and (X, Y, Z) axes. (Compare Fig. 4.3 and the discussion of it.)

A useful physical application of this method occurs in discussing vibrations. We illustrate this with a simple problem.

Example 3.   Find the characteristic vibration frequencies for the system of masses and springs shown in Fig. 5.1.

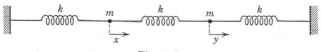

Figure 5.1

Let x and y be the coordinates of the two masses at time t relative to their equilibrium positions. Then the kinetic energy T and the potential energy V of the system are:

$$T = \tfrac{1}{2}m(\dot{x}^2 + \dot{y}^2),$$

(5.10)
$$V = \tfrac{1}{2}kx^2 + \tfrac{1}{2}ky^2 + \tfrac{1}{2}k(x - y)^2$$

$$= \tfrac{1}{2}k(2x^2 + 2y^2 - 2xy).$$

We can write T and V in (5.10) in the following matrix forms [compare writing (5.6) as (5.7)]:

(5.11)
$$T = \tfrac{1}{2}m(\dot{x} \quad \dot{y})\begin{pmatrix} 1 & 0 \\ 0 & 1 \end{pmatrix}\begin{pmatrix} \dot{x} \\ \dot{y} \end{pmatrix},$$

$$V = \tfrac{1}{2}k(x \quad y)\begin{pmatrix} 2 & -1 \\ -1 & 2 \end{pmatrix}\begin{pmatrix} x \\ y \end{pmatrix}.$$

We find the eigenvalues of the square matrix in V.

$$\begin{vmatrix} 2 - \mu & -1 \\ -1 & 2 - \mu \end{vmatrix} = \mu^2 - 4\mu + 3 = (\mu - 1)(\mu - 3) = 0,$$

$$\mu = 1, \qquad \mu = 3.$$

Then if we make the change of variables

(5.12)
$$\begin{pmatrix} x \\ y \end{pmatrix} = C\begin{pmatrix} X \\ Y \end{pmatrix},$$

where C is an orthogonal matrix such that

(5.13)
$$C^{-1}\begin{pmatrix} 2 & -1 \\ -1 & 2 \end{pmatrix}C = \begin{pmatrix} 1 & 0 \\ 0 & 3 \end{pmatrix},$$

the potential energy in the new variables is

(5.14)
$$V = \tfrac{1}{2}k(X^2 + 3Y^2).$$

We also want T in the new variables. Since C is a matrix of constants, (5.12) gives

$$\begin{pmatrix} \dot{x} \\ \dot{y} \end{pmatrix} = C\begin{pmatrix} \dot{X} \\ \dot{Y} \end{pmatrix},$$

that is, the transformation equations for $\dot{x}$, $\dot{y}$ are the same as for x, y. The square matrix in T in (5.11) is the unit matrix U; it is not changed by the transformation because

$$C^{-1}UC = C^{-1}C = U.$$

Thus in the new variables the kinetic energy is

$$T = \tfrac{1}{2}m(\dot{X}^2 + \dot{Y}^2).$$

The equations of motion are then given by Lagrange's equations:

$$m\ddot{X} = -kX,$$
$$m\ddot{Y} = -3kY.$$

The solutions of these equations are

(5.15)
$$X = A \sin (\omega_X t + \alpha),$$
$$Y = B \sin (\omega_Y t + \beta),$$

where A, B, α, and β are constants depending on the initial conditions, and the frequencies of the X and Y vibrations are

(5.16)
$$\omega_X = \sqrt{\frac{k}{m}}, \qquad \omega_Y = \sqrt{\frac{3k}{m}}.$$

By finding the orthogonal transformation matrix C (see Problem 16) and using (5.12), we get

(5.17)
$$x = \frac{1}{\sqrt{2}} (X - Y),$$
$$y = \frac{1}{\sqrt{2}} (X + Y).$$

In general, the motion of each of the masses is some combination of the two vibrations of frequencies ω_X and ω_Y. However, suppose the initial conditions make $B = 0$; then from (5.15) and (5.17) we have $Y = 0$ and

(5.18)
$$x = y = \frac{X}{\sqrt{2}} = \frac{A}{\sqrt{2}} \sin (\omega_X t + \alpha).$$

Equations (5.18) show that in this case the two masses oscillate back and forth together like this $\rightarrow\rightarrow$ and then this $\leftarrow\leftarrow$, with frequency ω_X. Alternatively, suppose the initial conditions make $A = 0$; then we have $X = 0$ and

(5.19)
$$x = -y = -\frac{Y}{\sqrt{2}} = -\frac{B}{\sqrt{2}} \sin (\omega_Y t + \beta).$$

In this case the two masses oscillate in opposite directions like this $\leftarrow \rightarrow$, and then this $\rightarrow \leftarrow$, with frequency ω_Y. These two especially simple ways in which the system can vibrate, each involving just one vibration frequency, are called the *characteristic* (or *normal*) *modes* of vibration, and the corresponding frequencies (5.16) are called the *characteristic* (or *normal*) *frequencies* of the system.

The problem we have just done shows an important method which can be used in many different applications. There are numerous examples of vibration problems in physics—in acoustics: the vibrations of strings of musical instruments, of drumheads, of the air in organ pipes or in a room; in mechanics and its engineering applications: vibrations of mechanical systems all the way from the simple pendulum to complicated structures like bridges and airplanes; in electricity: the vibrations of radio waves, of electric currents and voltages as in a tuned radio, etc. In such problems, it is often useful to find the characteristic vibration frequencies of the system under consideration and the characteristic modes of vibration. More complicated vibrations can then be discussed as combinations of these simpler normal modes of vibration.

6. CURVILINEAR COORDINATES

Before we continue further with our discussion of *changes* of variable or coordinate transformations, we need to talk about some properties of a single coordinate system. To make the discussion concrete, we shall

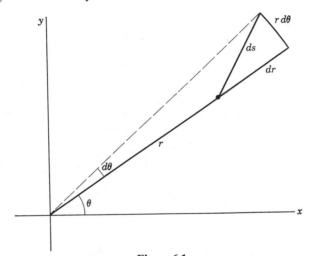

Figure 6.1

illustrate the ideas involved by using two familiar coordinate systems— the ordinary rectangular system (x, y, z) and the cylindrical system (r, θ, z). The elements of arc length in the rectangular and cylindrical systems are given by

(6.1)
$$ds^2 = dx^2 + dy^2 + dz^2 \qquad \text{(rectangular coordinates)},$$
$$ds^2 = dr^2 + r^2\, d\theta^2 + dz^2 \qquad \text{(cylindrical coordinates)}.$$

These expressions for ds are what the geometer calls the line element; they have much greater significance than just their use in computing arc lengths. First consider how we can find ds^2 for a given coordinate system. In the case of a well-known coordinate system, the answer may be obvious from the geometry. For example, in polar coordinates in the plane, we have (from Fig. 6.1 and the Pythagorean theorem)

(6.2)
$$ds^2 = dr^2 + r^2\, d\theta^2.$$

For an unfamiliar or complicated change of variables, however, we need a systematic method of finding ds; we illustrate the method by finding the value of ds^2 for cylindrical coordinates as given in (6.1). From the equations

$$
\begin{aligned}
x &= r \cos \theta, \\
y &= r \sin \theta, \\
z &= z,
\end{aligned}
$$

(6.3)

we get

$$
\begin{aligned}
dx &= \cos \theta \, dr - r \sin \theta \, d\theta, \\
dy &= \sin \theta \, dr + r \cos \theta \, d\theta, \\
dz &= dz.
\end{aligned}
$$

(6.4)

Squaring each equation in (6.4) and adding the results, we get

$$
(6.5) \qquad ds^2 = dx^2 + dy^2 + dz^2 = dr^2 + r^2 \, d\theta^2 + dz^2.
$$

Notice particularly here that all the cross products ($dr \, d\theta$, etc.) canceled out. This will not always happen, but it often does; when it does we call the coordinate system *orthogonal*. Such coordinate systems have some particularly simple and useful properties. Geometrically an orthogonal system means that the *coordinate surfaces* are mutually perpendicular.

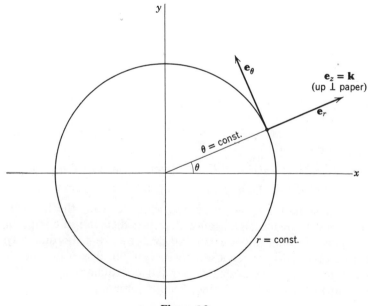

Figure 6.2

For the cylindrical system, the coordinate surfaces are $r = $ const. (set of concentric cylinders), $\theta = $ const. (set of half-planes), and $z = $ const. (set of planes). The three coordinate surfaces through a given point intersect at right angles. The three curves of intersection of the coordinate surfaces in pairs intersect at right angles; these curves are called the *coordinate* "*lines*" or directions. We draw unit (or *base*) vectors tangent to the co-ordinate directions; for the cylindrical system (Fig. 6.2) we might call them $\mathbf{e}_r, \mathbf{e}_\theta, \mathbf{e}_z$ ($\mathbf{e}_z$ is identical with $\mathbf{k}$). These unit vectors form an orthogonal triad like $\mathbf{i}, \mathbf{j}, \mathbf{k}$. We refer to such coordinate systems as <u>*curvilinear coordinate sys-tems*</u> when the coordinate surfaces (or some of them) are not planes and the coordinate lines are curves rather than straight lines. We shall be princi-pally interested in orthogonal curvilinear coordinate systems.

7. SCALE FACTORS AND BASE VECTORS FOR ORTHOGONAL SYSTEMS

In the rectangular system, if x, y, z are the coordinates of a particle and x changes by dx with y and z constant, then the distance the particle moves is $ds = dx$. However, in the cylindrical system, if θ changes by $d\theta$ with r and z constant, the distance the particle moves is <u>*not $d\theta$,*</u> but $ds = r\,d\theta$. Factors like the r in $r\,d\theta$ which must multiply the differentials of the coordinates to get distances are known as <u>*scale factors*</u> and are very im-portant as we shall see. A straightforward way to get them is to calculate ds^2 as we did in (6.5); if the transformation is orthogonal, then the scale factors can be read off from ds^2. From (6.5), we see that the scale factors for cylindrical coordinates are $1, r, 1$.

It is also useful to consider a vector $d\mathbf{s}$ which has components $dr, r\,d\theta$, and dz in the coordinate directions, that is, in the directions $\mathbf{e}_r, \mathbf{e}_\theta, \mathbf{e}_z$:

$$(7.1) \qquad\qquad d\mathbf{s} = \mathbf{e}_r\,dr + \mathbf{e}_\theta r\,d\theta + \mathbf{e}_z\,dz.$$

Then $ds^2 = d\mathbf{s} \cdot d\mathbf{s}$ which gives (6.1), since the $\mathbf{e}$ vectors are orthogonal and of unit length.

We can find the relations between the base or unit vectors of a curvi-linear coordinate system ($\mathbf{e}_r, \mathbf{e}_\theta, \mathbf{e}_z$ in cylindrical coordinates) and $\mathbf{i}, \mathbf{j}, \mathbf{k}$. This is useful when we want to differentiate a vector which is expressed in terms of the curvilinear coordinate base vectors; $\mathbf{i}, \mathbf{j}, \mathbf{k}$ are constant in magnitude *and direction*, but $\mathbf{e}_r$ and $\mathbf{e}_\theta$ are not fixed in direction, so their derivatives are not zero. We illustrate an algebraic method of finding the relations between the two sets of base vectors by finding them for the cylindrical system. (Compare the geometrical method shown in Chapter 5,

Section 7.) We write

(7.2) $ds = \mathbf{i}\, dx + \mathbf{j}\, dy + \mathbf{k}\, dz$

$$= \mathbf{i}\left(\frac{\partial x}{\partial r}\, dr + \frac{\partial x}{\partial \theta}\, d\theta\right) + \mathbf{j}\left(\frac{\partial y}{\partial r}\, dr + \frac{\partial y}{\partial \theta}\, d\theta\right) + \mathbf{k}\, dz.$$

Comparing (7.2) with (7.1), and using $x = r \cos\theta$, $y = r \sin\theta$, we find

$$\mathbf{e}_r = \mathbf{i}\frac{\partial x}{\partial r} + \mathbf{j}\frac{\partial y}{\partial r} = \mathbf{i} \cos\theta + \mathbf{j} \sin\theta,$$

(7.3) $$r\mathbf{e}_\theta = \mathbf{i}\frac{\partial x}{\partial \theta} + \mathbf{j}\frac{\partial y}{\partial \theta} = -\mathbf{i} r \sin\theta + \mathbf{j} r \cos\theta,$$

$$\mathbf{e}_z = \mathbf{k}.$$

Notice that $\mathbf{e}_r$ is a unit vector since $\sin^2\theta + \cos^2\theta = 1$. However, $r\mathbf{e}_\theta$ obtained by a similar formula must be divided by the scale factor r to get the unit vector $\mathbf{e}_\theta$. It is often convenient to use base vectors which we shall call $\mathbf{a}_r$, $\mathbf{a}_\theta$, which are not necessarily of unit length, given by the right-hand sides of (7.3). It is not necessary then to go back to (7.1) to get the $\mathbf{e}$ vectors; we only have to divide each $\mathbf{a}$ vector by its magnitude to get the corresponding $\mathbf{e}$ vector. Thus from (7.3):

$\mathbf{a}_r = \mathbf{e}_r$ is already a unit vector;

$\mathbf{a}_\theta = -\mathbf{i} r \sin\theta + \mathbf{j} r \cos\theta$ has magnitude $|\mathbf{a}_\theta| = r$,

so

$$\mathbf{e}_\theta = \frac{1}{r}\, \mathbf{a}_\theta = -\mathbf{i} \sin\theta + \mathbf{j} \cos\theta.$$

We can use these formulas to find the velocity and acceleration of a particle in cylindrical coordinates, and similar formulas for any co-ordinate system. The displacement of a particle from the origin at time t is, in cylindrical coordinates (Fig. 7.1),

$$\mathbf{s} = r\mathbf{e}_r + z\mathbf{e}_z.$$

Then

$$\frac{d\mathbf{s}}{dt} = \frac{dr}{dt}\mathbf{e}_r + r\frac{d}{dt}(\mathbf{e}_r) + \frac{dz}{dt}\mathbf{e}_z.$$

By (7.3),

$$\frac{d}{dt}(\mathbf{e}_r) = -\mathbf{i} \sin\theta\, \frac{d\theta}{dt} + \mathbf{j} \cos\theta\, \frac{d\theta}{dt} = \mathbf{e}_\theta\, \frac{d\theta}{dt},$$

so

$$\frac{d\mathbf{s}}{dt} = \dot{r}\mathbf{e}_r + r\dot{\theta}\mathbf{e}_\theta + \dot{z}\mathbf{e}_z.$$

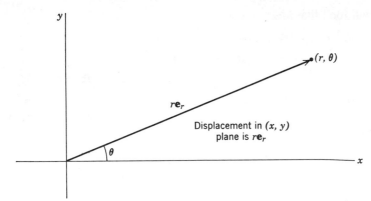

Figure 7.1

By differentiating again with respect to t and using (7.3) to find $(d/dt)(\mathbf{e}_\theta)$, we can find the acceleration $d^2\mathbf{s}/dt^2$ in cylindrical coordinates (Problem 21).

8. GENERAL CURVILINEAR COORDINATES

In general, let x_1, x_2, x_3 be the set of variables or coordinates we are considering (for example, for the rectangular system $x_1 = x$, $x_2 = y$, $x_3 = z$; for the cylindrical system $x_1 = r$, $x_2 = \theta$, $x_3 = z$). Then the three sets of coordinate surfaces are $x_1 = \text{const.}$, $x_2 = \text{const.}$, $x_3 = \text{const.}$ The three coordinate surfaces through a given point intersect in three co-ordinate lines. Given x, y, z as functions of x_1, x_2, x_3, we first find ds^2 as we did for the cylindrical system [see the derivation of (6.5) from (6.3)]. If the system is orthogonal, ds^2 will be of the form

$$(8.1) \qquad ds^2 = h_1^2\, dx_1^2 + h_2^2\, dx_2^2 + h_3^2\, dx_3^2 = \sum_{i=1}^{3} h_i^2\, dx_i^2.$$

The h's are the scale factors. We can write the vector displacement $d\mathbf{s}$ [compare (7.1)] as

$$(8.2) \qquad d\mathbf{s} = \mathbf{e}_1 h_1\, dx_1 + \mathbf{e}_2 h_2\, dx_2 + \mathbf{e}_3 h_3\, dx_3 = \sum_{i=1}^{3} \mathbf{e}_i h_i\, dx_i,$$

where the $\mathbf{e}$'s are unit vectors in the coordinate directions. It is also worth noticing that the volume element in an orthogonal system is $h_1 h_2 h_3\, dx_1\, dx_2\, dx_3$ (volume of a small rectangular parallelepiped with edges $h_1\, dx_1$, $h_2\, dx_2$, $h_3\, dx_3$, like $dx\, dy\, dz$). For example, in cylindrical coordinates the volume element is $dr \cdot r\, d\theta \cdot dz = r\, dr\, d\theta\, dz$.

If the coordinate system is not orthogonal, then ds^2 will not have the simple form (8.1). In general (that is, not assuming an orthogonal system)

ds^2 will look like this:

(8.3) $ds^2 = g_{11} \, dx_1^2 + g_{12} \, dx_1 \, dx_2 + g_{13} \, dx_1 \, dx_3$

$$+ g_{21} \, dx_2 \, dx_1 + g_{22} \, dx_2^2 + g_{23} \, dx_2 \, dx_3$$

$$+ g_{31} \, dx_3 \, dx_1 + g_{32} \, dx_3 \, dx_2 + g_{33} \, dx_3^2,$$

where the g_{ij}'s represent the coefficients which arise in computing $dx^2 + dy^2 + dz^2$. This is usually written in more compact form with summation signs:

$$ds^2 = \sum_{i=1}^{3} \sum_{j=1}^{3} g_{ij} \, dx_i \, dx_j.$$

It is also useful to write it in matrix form:

(8.4) $ds^2 = (dx_1 \quad dx_2 \quad dx_3) \begin{pmatrix} g_{11} & g_{12} & g_{13} \\ g_{21} & g_{22} & g_{23} \\ g_{31} & g_{32} & g_{33} \end{pmatrix} \begin{pmatrix} dx_1 \\ dx_2 \\ dx_3 \end{pmatrix}.$

We shall see later that the quantities g_{ij} form a tensor known as the *metric tensor*. Now if the coordinate system is orthogonal,

(8.5) $ds^2 = g_{11} \, dx_1^2 + g_{22} \, dx_2^2 + g_{33} \, dx_3^2$

(in matrix language g_{ij} is a diagonal matrix). In terms of the scale factors, we have from (8.1)

(8.6) $g_{11} = h_1^2, \qquad g_{22} = h_2^2, \qquad g_{33} = h_3^2,$

$$g_{12} = g_{21} = g_{13} = g_{31} = g_{23} = g_{32} = 0,$$

for an orthogonal coordinate system.

9. VECTOR OPERATORS IN ORTHOGONAL CURVILINEAR COORDINATES

We have previously (Chapter 5) defined the gradient (∇u), the divergence ($\nabla \cdot \mathbf{V}$), the curl ($\nabla \times \mathbf{V}$), and the Laplacian ($\nabla^2 u$) in rectangular coordinates x, y, z. Since in many practical problems it is better to use some other coordinate system (cylindrical or spherical, for example), we need to see how to express the vector operators in terms of general orthogonal coordinates x_1, x_2, x_3. (We consider only orthogonal coordinate systems here; see Section 14 for the more general case.) We shall outline proofs of the formulas; some of the details of the proofs are left to the problems.

Gradient, ∇u. In vector analysis we showed that the directional derivative du/ds in a given direction is the component of ∇u in that direction. In cylindrical coordinates, if we go in the r direction (θ and z constant), then by (6.5) $ds = dr$. Thus the r-component of ∇u is du/ds when $ds = dr$, that is, $\partial u/\partial r$. Similarly, the θ-component of ∇u is du/ds when $ds = r\,d\theta$, that is, $(1/r)(\partial u/\partial\theta)$. Thus ∇u in cylindrical coordinates is

$$(9.1) \qquad \nabla u = e_r \frac{\partial u}{\partial r} + e_\theta \frac{1}{r}\frac{\partial u}{\partial\theta} + e_z \frac{\partial u}{\partial z}.$$

Now in general orthogonal coordinates x_1, x_2, x_3, the component of ∇u in the x_1 direction (x_2 and x_3 constant) is du/ds if $ds = h_1\,dx_1$ [from (8.1)]; that is, the component of ∇u in the direction e_1 is $(1/h_1)(\partial u/\partial x_1)$. Similar formulas hold for the other components and we have

$$(9.2) \qquad \nabla u = e_1 \frac{1}{h_1}\frac{\partial u}{\partial x_1} + e_2 \frac{1}{h_2}\frac{\partial u}{\partial x_2} + e_3 \frac{1}{h_3}\frac{\partial u}{\partial x_3}$$
$$= \sum_{i=1}^{3} \frac{e_i}{h_i}\frac{\partial u}{\partial x_i}.$$

Divergence, $\nabla \cdot V$. Let

$$(9.3) \qquad V = e_1 V_1 + e_2 V_2 + e_3 V_3$$

be a vector with components V_1, V_2, V_3 in an orthogonal system. We can prove (Problem 25) that

$$(9.4) \qquad \nabla \cdot \left(\frac{e_3}{h_1 h_2}\right) = 0, \qquad \nabla \cdot \left(\frac{e_2}{h_1 h_3}\right) = 0, \qquad \nabla \cdot \left(\frac{e_1}{h_2 h_3}\right) = 0.$$

Let us write (9.3) as

$$(9.5) \qquad V = \frac{e_1}{h_2 h_3}(h_2 h_3 V_1) + \frac{e_2}{h_1 h_3}(h_1 h_3 V_2) + \frac{e_3}{h_1 h_2}(h_1 h_2 V_3).$$

We find $\nabla \cdot V$ by taking the divergence of each term on the right side of (9.5). Using (10.6) of Chapter 5, namely

$$(9.6) \qquad \nabla \cdot (\phi v) = v \cdot (\nabla\phi) + \phi \nabla \cdot v,$$

with $\phi = h_2 h_3 V_1$ and $v = e_1/h_2 h_3$, we find that the divergence of the first term on the right side of (9.5) is

$$(9.7) \quad \nabla \cdot \left(h_2 h_3 V_1 \frac{e_1}{h_2 h_3}\right) = \frac{e_1}{h_2 h_3}\cdot\nabla(h_2 h_3 V_1) + h_2 h_3 V_1 \nabla \cdot \left(\frac{e_1}{h_2 h_3}\right).$$

By (9.4), the second term in (9.7) is zero. In the first term of (9.7), the dot product of e_1 with $\nabla(h_2 h_3 V_1)$ is the first component of $\nabla(h_2 h_3 V_1)$. By

(9.2), this is $(1/h_1)(\partial/\partial x_1)(h_2 h_3 V_1)$. Calculating the divergence of the other terms of (9.5) in a similar way, we get

(9.8) $\mathbf{\nabla \cdot V} = \dfrac{1}{h_2 h_3}\dfrac{1}{h_1}\dfrac{\partial}{\partial x_1}(h_2 h_3 V_1) + \dfrac{1}{h_1 h_3}\dfrac{1}{h_2}\dfrac{\partial}{\partial x_2}(h_1 h_3 V_2)$

$$+ \dfrac{1}{h_1 h_2}\dfrac{1}{h_3}\dfrac{\partial}{\partial x_3}(h_1 h_2 V_3)$$

$$= \dfrac{1}{h_1 h_2 h_3}\left[\dfrac{\partial}{\partial x_1}(h_2 h_3 V_1) + \dfrac{\partial}{\partial x_2}(h_1 h_3 V_2) + \dfrac{\partial}{\partial x_3}(h_1 h_2 V_3)\right].$$

In cylindrical coordinates, $h_1 = 1$, $h_2 = r$, $h_3 = 1$. By (9.8), the divergence in cylindrical coordinates is

(9.9) $$\mathbf{\nabla \cdot V} = \dfrac{1}{r}\left[\dfrac{\partial}{\partial r}(rV_r) + \dfrac{\partial}{\partial \theta}(V_\theta) + \dfrac{\partial}{\partial z}(rV_z)\right]$$

$$= \dfrac{1}{r}\dfrac{\partial}{\partial r}(rV_r) + \dfrac{1}{r}\dfrac{\partial V_\theta}{\partial \theta} + \dfrac{\partial V_z}{\partial z}.$$

Laplacian, $\nabla^2 u$. Since $\nabla^2 u = \mathbf{\nabla \cdot \nabla} u$ we can find $\nabla^2 u$ by combining (9.2) and (9.8) with $\mathbf{V} = \mathbf{\nabla} u$. We get

(9.10) $$\nabla^2 u = \dfrac{1}{h_1 h_2 h_3}\left[\dfrac{\partial}{\partial x_1}\left(\dfrac{h_2 h_3}{h_1}\dfrac{\partial u}{\partial x_1}\right) + \dfrac{\partial}{\partial x_2}\left(\dfrac{h_1 h_3}{h_2}\dfrac{\partial u}{\partial x_2}\right) + \dfrac{\partial}{\partial x_3}\left(\dfrac{h_1 h_2}{h_3}\dfrac{\partial u}{\partial x_3}\right)\right].$$

In cylindrical coordinates, the Laplacian is then

$$\nabla^2 u = \dfrac{1}{r}\left[\dfrac{\partial}{\partial r}\left(r\dfrac{\partial u}{\partial r}\right) + \dfrac{\partial}{\partial \theta}\left(\dfrac{1}{r}\dfrac{\partial u}{\partial \theta}\right) + \dfrac{\partial}{\partial z}\left(r\dfrac{\partial u}{\partial z}\right)\right]$$

$$= \dfrac{1}{r}\dfrac{\partial}{\partial r}\left(r\dfrac{\partial u}{\partial r}\right) + \dfrac{1}{r^2}\dfrac{\partial^2 u}{\partial \theta^2} + \dfrac{\partial^2 u}{\partial z^2}.$$

Curl, $\mathbf{\nabla \times V}$. By methods similar to those used in finding $\mathbf{\nabla \cdot V}$ we can find $\mathbf{\nabla \times V}$ (Problem 26). The result is

(9.11) $$\mathbf{\nabla \times V} = \dfrac{1}{h_1 h_2 h_3}\begin{vmatrix} h_1\mathbf{e}_1 & h_2\mathbf{e}_2 & h_3\mathbf{e}_3 \\ \dfrac{\partial}{\partial x_1} & \dfrac{\partial}{\partial x_2} & \dfrac{\partial}{\partial x_3} \\ h_1 V_1 & h_2 V_2 & h_3 V_3 \end{vmatrix}$$

$$= \dfrac{\mathbf{e}_1}{h_2 h_3}\left[\dfrac{\partial}{\partial x_2}(h_3 V_3) - \dfrac{\partial}{\partial x_3}(h_2 V_2)\right]$$

$$+ \dfrac{\mathbf{e}_2}{h_1 h_3}\left[\dfrac{\partial}{\partial x_3}(h_1 V_1) - \dfrac{\partial}{\partial x_1}(h_3 V_3)\right]$$

$$+ \dfrac{\mathbf{e}_3}{h_1 h_2}\left[\dfrac{\partial}{\partial x_1}(h_2 V_2) - \dfrac{\partial}{\partial x_2}(h_1 V_1)\right].$$

In cylindrical coordinates, we find

$$\nabla \times \mathbf{V} = \frac{1}{r} \begin{vmatrix} \mathbf{e}_r & r\mathbf{e}_\theta & \mathbf{e}_z \\ \dfrac{\partial}{\partial r} & \dfrac{\partial}{\partial \theta} & \dfrac{\partial}{\partial z} \\ V_r & rV_\theta & V_z \end{vmatrix}$$

$$= \mathbf{e}_r\left(\frac{1}{r}\frac{\partial V_z}{\partial \theta} - \frac{\partial V_\theta}{\partial z}\right) + \mathbf{e}_\theta\left(\frac{\partial V_r}{\partial z} - \frac{\partial V_z}{\partial r}\right) + \frac{1}{r}\mathbf{e}_z\left[\frac{\partial}{\partial r}(rV_\theta) - \frac{\partial V_r}{\partial \theta}\right].$$

10. TENSOR ANALYSIS—INTRODUCTION

Tensors are a generalization of scalars and vectors; let us look at some examples. Tensors of *order* (or *rank*)* zero are just scalars, and tensors of order one are just vectors; you are already familiar with these. In three-dimensional space a scalar has one (or 3^0) "component" and a vector has 3 (or 3^1) components; a second-order tensor has 9 (or 3^2) components; and in general a tensor of order n has 3^n components. After scalars and vectors, second-order tensors are the most useful in applications, so we shall consider a physical example of such a tensor.

Think of a beam carrying a load; there are stresses and strains in the material of the beam. If we imagine cutting the beam in two by a plane perpendicular to the x direction, we realize that there is a force per unit area exerted *by* the material on one side of our imaginary cut *on* the material on the other side. This is a vector, so it has three components P_{xx}, P_{xy}, P_{xz}, where the first subscript x is to emphasize that this is a force across a plane perpendicular to the x direction. Similarly, if we consider a plane perpendicular to the y direction, there is a force per unit area across this plane with components P_{yx}, P_{yy}, P_{yz}; and finally across a plane perpendicular to the z direction there is a force per unit area with components P_{zx}, P_{zy}, P_{zz}. At a point in the material, then, we have a set of nine quantities which could be displayed as a matrix:

(10.1)
$$\begin{pmatrix} P_{xx} & P_{xy} & P_{xz} \\ P_{yx} & P_{yy} & P_{yz} \\ P_{zx} & P_{zy} & P_{zz} \end{pmatrix}.$$

This is a second-order tensor known as the stress tensor. The forces (per unit area) P_{xx}, P_{yy}, P_{zz} are pressures or tensions; the others are shear

* Some authors use the term *order* and some use the term *rank;* the two terms are equivalent.

forces (per unit area). For example, P_{zy} is a force per unit area in the y direction acting across a plane perpendicular to the z direction; this force tends to shear the beam.

So far, we have simply indicated the number of components that tensors of various orders have. This is not the whole story. To see what else is required, let us talk about first-order tensors, that is, vectors, which are already somewhat familiar. In elementary work a vector is usually defined either as a magnitude and a direction, or as a set of three components. To see that we need to give a more careful definition, consider this example. Let us draw an arrow to represent a given rotation of a rigid body in the following way. Draw the arrow along the axis of rotation, make its length equal to the rotation angle in radians, and let its sense be given by the right-hand rule. Then, apparently, a rotation is a vector according to the magnitude-plus-direction definition. But this is not so! Take a book and rotate it 90° about the x-axis, then 90° about the y-axis. Repeat, rotating this time first about the y-axis and then about the x-axis. The final positions of the book are different. But the sum of two vectors does not depend on the order in which they are added (in mathematical language, vector addition is commutative). The arrows associated with rotations are not vectors.

Now let us consider the idea of a vector as a set of three components. In order to talk about components, we must have a coordinate system. There are infinitely many coordinate systems [even for rectangular axes (x, y, z) there are infinitely many sets of rotated axes]; thus we must say that a vector consists of a set of three components *in each coordinate system*. If the components of a vector relative to one set of axes are given, we know from elementary vector analysis that the component of the vector in any direction, or its components relative to any rotated set of axes, can be found by taking projections. Then the new components are definite combinations of the old components. This statement is the basis for the really careful mathematical definition of a vector which we are going to consider. A similar fact is true for tensors, for example the second-order stress tensor we have described. We could imagine cutting the beam by a plane oriented in any given direction and ask for the force per unit area acting across this plane. It can be shown that each component of this force is a certain combination of the nine components of the stress tensor (10.1). Thus the components of the stress tensor in any other coordinate system are definite combinations of the nine components of the stress tensor relative to the (x, y, z) axes. In other words, tensors of all orders, like vectors, have a physical meaning which is independent of the reference coordinate system and there are definite mathematical laws which relate their components in two systems.

You may wonder why we cannot make just any set of components (3 for a vector, 9 for a second-order tensor, etc.), given in *one* coordinate system, a tensor by *defining* its components in other systems by the correct transformation laws. Mathematically, we could! But if we are discussing a physical entity, we are not free to define its components in various coordinate systems; they are determined by physical fact. We merely give a mathematical description of the entity and identify it as a scalar, a vector, a second-order tensor, etc. (or perhaps none of these). We can see again now why an arrow associated with a rotation is not a vector. If we treat the arrow as a vector and take components of it, these component vectors do not represent rotations which can be combined to give the original rotation. Thus a vector which looks superficially like the arrow we have defined is not a correct mathematical representation of the physical entity (a rotation) we are trying to describe.

11. CARTESIAN TENSORS

We shall now investigate the effect of coordinate transformations on vectors (that is, find how the components in one coordinate system are related to the components in another system) and then use our results to define tensors. A rotation of axes is a useful simple example to illustrate the ideas involved. Let (x, y, z) be a set of rectangular axes and (x', y', z') another set obtained by rotating the axes in any manner keeping the origin fixed (Fig. 11.1). In the table (11.1) we list the cosines of the nine angles between the (x, y, z) axes and the (x', y', z') axes.

	x	y	z
x'	l_1	m_1	n_1
y'	l_2	m_2	n_2
z'	l_3	m_3	n_3

(11.1)

(In the table, l_2 means the cosine of the angle between the x-axis and the y'-axis, etc.). A vector $\mathbf{r}$ (Fig. 11.1) has components x, y, z or x', y', z' relative to the two coordinate systems; we want to find the relations between the two sets of components. Let $\mathbf{i}, \mathbf{j}, \mathbf{k}$ be unit vectors along the (x, y, z) axes and $\mathbf{i}', \mathbf{j}', \mathbf{k}'$ be unit vectors along the (x', y', z') axes. Then the vector $\mathbf{r}$ can be written in terms of either set of components and unit vectors as follows:

(11.2) $$\mathbf{r} = \mathbf{i}x + \mathbf{j}y + \mathbf{k}z = \mathbf{i}'x' + \mathbf{j}'y' + \mathbf{k}'z'.$$

Taking the dot product of this equation with $\mathbf{i}'$, we get

(11.3) $$\mathbf{r} \cdot \mathbf{i}' = \mathbf{i} \cdot \mathbf{i}'x + \mathbf{j} \cdot \mathbf{i}'y + \mathbf{k} \cdot \mathbf{i}'z = x',$$

(since $\mathbf{i}' \cdot \mathbf{i}' = 1$ and $\mathbf{i}' \cdot \mathbf{j}' = \mathbf{i}' \cdot \mathbf{k}' = 0$). Now $\mathbf{i} \cdot \mathbf{i}'$ is the cosine of the angle between $\mathbf{i}$ and $\mathbf{i}'$, that is, between the x-axis and the x'-axis, since $\mathbf{i}$ and $\mathbf{i}'$ are unit vectors; thus $\mathbf{i} \cdot \mathbf{i}' = l_1$ from the table (11.1). Similarly, $\mathbf{j} \cdot \mathbf{i}' = m_1$ and $\mathbf{k} \cdot \mathbf{i}' = n_1$ and (11.3) becomes

$$(11.4) \qquad\qquad x' = l_1 x + m_1 y + n_1 z.$$

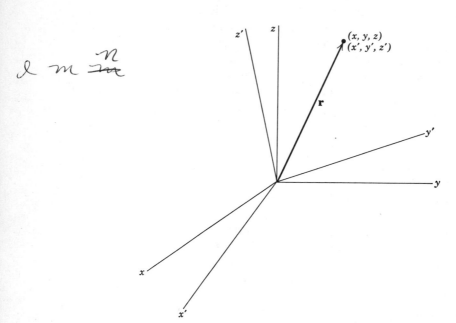

Figure 11.1

Similarly, dotting $\mathbf{r}$ into $\mathbf{j}'$ and $\mathbf{k}'$, and using (11.1) we get

$$(11.5) \qquad \begin{aligned} y' &= l_2 x + m_2 y + n_2 z, \\ z' &= l_3 x + m_3 y + n_3 z. \end{aligned}$$

The equations (11.4) and (11.5) are called the transformation equations from the coordinate system (x, y, z) to (x', y', z').

In the same way, dotting $\mathbf{r}$ with $\mathbf{i}$, $\mathbf{j}$, $\mathbf{k}$ in turn, we get equations for x, y, z in terms of x', y', z':

$$(11.6) \qquad \begin{aligned} x &= l_1 x' + l_2 y' + l_3 z', \\ y &= m_1 x' + m_2 y' + m_3 z', \\ z &= n_1 x' + n_2 y' + n_3 z'. \end{aligned}$$

These transformation equations may be written more concisely in matrix notation. Equations (11.4) and (11.5) become the matrix equation:

$$(11.7) \qquad \begin{pmatrix} x' \\ y' \\ z' \end{pmatrix} = \begin{pmatrix} l_1 & m_1 & n_1 \\ l_2 & m_2 & n_2 \\ l_3 & m_3 & n_3 \end{pmatrix} \begin{pmatrix} x \\ y \\ z \end{pmatrix} \qquad \text{or} \quad r' = Mr,$$

where r', M, and r stand for the matrices in (11.7). [Compare (2.4) for the two-dimensional case.] Similarly, (11.6) becomes

$$(11.8) \qquad\qquad r = M^{\mathrm{T}} r'$$

where M^{T} is the transpose of M.

So far we have been talking about **r** as a displacement vector. In elementary physics and vector analysis, we take it for granted that other vectors (say force, or velocity, or electric field) are treated mathematically just like displacement vectors. We shall now make this idea more precise by including it as part of our definition of a vector. Since we are considering only rectangular (often called Cartesian) coordinate systems here, we may call the vectors and tensors we define *Cartesian* vectors and tensors.

Definition of Cartesian vectors. A Cartesian vector **V** consists of a set of three numbers (components) in *every* rectangular coordinate system; if V_x, V_y, V_z are the components in one system and V'_x, V'_y, V'_z are the components in a rotated system, these two sets of components are related by an equation similar to (11.7), namely,

$$(11.9) \qquad \begin{pmatrix} V'_x \\ V'_y \\ V'_z \end{pmatrix} = M \begin{pmatrix} V_x \\ V_y \\ V_z \end{pmatrix} \qquad \text{or} \quad V' = MV,$$

where M is the rotation matrix in (11.7).

We can simplify our notation by making the following changes:

Replace x, y, z	by	x_1, x_2, x_3;
Replace x', y', z'	by	x'_1, x'_2, x'_3;
Replace V_x, V_y, V_z	by	V_1, V_2, V_3;
(11.10) Replace V'_x, V'_y, V'_z	by	V'_1, V'_2, V'_3;

$$\text{Replace } M \text{ in (11.7) by } \begin{pmatrix} a_{11} & a_{12} & a_{13} \\ a_{21} & a_{22} & a_{23} \\ a_{31} & a_{32} & a_{33} \end{pmatrix}.$$

In this notation (11.7) becomes

(11.11) $$x_i' = \sum_{j=1}^{3} a_{ij} x_j, \qquad i = 1, 2, 3,$$

and (11.9) becomes

(11.12) $$V_i' = \sum_{j=1}^{3} a_{ij} V_j, \qquad i = 1, 2, 3.$$

Using this more compact notation, it is easy to define tensors.

Definition of Cartesian tensors. A tensor of first order is just a vector. A Cartesian tensor of second order has nine components (in three dimensions) in every rectangular coordinate system; if we call the components in one system T_{ij}, where i and j each take the values 1, 2, 3, the components T_{kl}' in a rotated system are

(11.13) $$T_{kl}' = \sum_{i=1}^{3} \sum_{j=1}^{3} a_{ki} a_{lj} T_{ij}, \qquad k, l = 1, 2, 3,$$

where the a's are the direction cosines in the rotation matrix M.

We can give a very simple example of a second-order tensor. Let **U** and **V** be vectors; we form the following array (in each coordinate system) from the components U_1, U_2, U_3 and V_1, V_2, V_3 of **U** and **V** (in that coordinate system):

(11.14)
$$\begin{array}{ccc} U_1V_1 & U_1V_2 & U_1V_3 \\ U_2V_1 & U_2V_2 & U_2V_3 \\ U_3V_1 & U_3V_2 & U_3V_3. \end{array}$$

We can show that these nine quantities are the components of a second-order tensor which we shall denote by **UV** (*note:* no dot or cross). Since **U** and **V** are vectors, their components in a rotated coordinate system are, by (11.12):

$$U_k' = \sum_{i=1}^{3} a_{ki} U_i, \qquad V_l' = \sum_{j=1}^{3} a_{lj} V_j.$$

Hence the components of the second-order tensor **UV** are

(11.15) $$U_k' V_l' = \sum_{i=1}^{3} a_{ki} U_i \sum_{j=1}^{3} a_{lj} V_j = \sum_{i,j=1}^{3} a_{ki} a_{lj} U_i V_j,$$

which is just (11.13) with $T_{ij} = U_i V_j$ and $T_{kl}' = U_k' V_l'$.

Equation (11.13) generalizes immediately. For example, a fourth-order Cartesian tensor is defined as a set of 3^4 or 81 components T_{ijkl}, in every rectangular coordinate system, which transform to a rotated coordinate system by the equations

$$(11.16) \qquad T'_{\alpha\beta\gamma\delta} = \sum_{i,j,k,l} a_{\alpha i} a_{\beta j} a_{\gamma k} a_{\delta l} T_{ijkl},$$

where i, j, k, l take the values 1, 2, 3.

Tensors of zero order.   By analogy with the tensor transformation equations (11.12) for first order, (11.13) for second order and (11.16) for fourth order, the transformation equation for a tensor S of zero order is

$$(11.17) \qquad\qquad S' = S.$$

In other words, a zero-order tensor has one component which is un-changed by a rotation of axes; it is called an *invariant* or a *scalar*. Simple examples are the length of a vector, and the dot product of two vectors.

Summation convention.   As a further simplification of notation, it is customary to omit the summation signs in equations like (11.12), (11.13), (11.15), and (11.16) and simply understand a summation over any *repeated* subscript. For example, according to this convention

$$a_i a_i \quad \text{or} \quad a_j a_j \quad \text{or} \quad a_k a_k \quad \text{means} \quad a_1^2 + a_2^2 + a_3^2;$$

$$a_{ij} b_{jk} \quad \text{means} \quad a_{i1} b_{1k} + a_{i2} b_{2k} + a_{i3} b_{3k};$$

and so on. The repeated index which is summed over is called a dummy index; like a variable of integration, it does not matter what letter is used for it.

Vectors and tensors in n dimensions.   Now that we have given a more careful definition of a vector in three dimensions [(11.9) and the sentence containing it], we can go back to the discussion of n dimensions (Sections 3 and 5) and extend the definition (11.9) to a vector with n components. It will be especially convenient in n dimensions to use the new notation introduced in (11.10). We are talking about a problem in n variables which, in geometrical language, we call n coordinates; let these coordinates be $x_1, x_2, x_3, \ldots, x_n$. Suppose we make a change of variables— in geometrical language, a change to a new coordinate system. Let us call the new coordinates (variables) $x'_1, x'_2, x'_3, \ldots, x'_n$. By analogy with (11.7), we consider for the present only linear changes of variables for which the matrix M of the transformation is an orthogonal matrix. Recall (Section 3) that a matrix M of any order is called orthogonal if $M^T = M^{-1}$. We could then write the n equations which give the change of variables from the x coordinates to the x' coordinates in exactly the same abbreviated matrix form (11.7) used in the three-dimensional case, namely $r' = Mr$. In the new notation of (11.10), we could write the n-dimensional change of variables in the same form (11.11) we used in the three-dimensional case; we need only replace the sum over j from 1 to 3 in (11.11) by a sum from 1 to n. Note that, just as for the three-dimensional case, there are infinitely many sets of variables with each two sets related by an orthogonal matrix; the sets of variables $x_1, x_2, x_3, \ldots, x_n$, and $x'_1, x'_2, x'_3, \ldots, x'_n$ represent *any* two sets of variables (in geometric language, any two coordinate systems). Having observed how easy it is to extend (11.11) to n dimensions, we can now easily extend (11.12) to n dimensions and so define a vector in n dimensions. A vector in n dimensions then consists of an ordered set of n numbers in each coordinate system (that is, one set of vector components $V_1, V_2, V_3, \ldots, V_n$ to each set of variables $x_1, x_2, x_3, \ldots, x_n$); the components of the vector in two coordinate systems must be related by the matrix equation $V' = MV$ with the same M which relates the coordinates in the equation $r' = Mr$. The same statement in different notation is given by (11.12) and (11.11) with the sum over j from 1 to n. Notice how the algebra goes on to more variables than three with no more trouble than replacing a 3 by an n; it is simply a matter of convenience to continue the parallel geometrical terminology. The defining equations for tensors of any order may be similarly extended to any number of dimensions merely by summing from 1 to n instead of from 1 to 3. This means, of course, that in using the summation convention, we must state the number of dimensions in which we are working.

12. USES OF TENSORS; DYADICS

If a rigid body is rotating about a fixed axis, then $\mathbf{L} = I\boldsymbol{\omega}$ is a correct vector equation where $\mathbf{L}$ is the angular momentum, I is the moment of inertia of the body about the rotation axis, and $\boldsymbol{\omega}$ is the angular velocity. As indicated by the equation, $\mathbf{L}$ and $\boldsymbol{\omega}$ are parallel vectors and I is a scalar. But, in general, when the rotation axis is not fixed, the angular velocity and the angular momentum are not parallel. If the equation $\mathbf{L} = I\boldsymbol{\omega}$ is to be true, I cannot be a scalar; it must be some quantity which, multiplied times $\boldsymbol{\omega}$, gives a vector in a different direction. We shall see that I is, in fact, a second-order tensor. First let us look at some other similar physical examples. In an isotropic medium the electric polarization $\mathbf{P}$ is a vector parallel to the electric field $\mathbf{E}$, that is, $\mathbf{P} = \chi\mathbf{E}$ where χ is a constant. In a nonisotropic medium this may no longer be true, and again we need a mathematical quantity which, multiplied times a vector,

gives a vector in a different direction. A similar equation relates the magnetic polarization and the magnetic field. As another example: In elementary physics, we say that for materials within the elastic limit, stress =
Young's modulus times strain, where stress and strain are parallel and Y
is a scalar. In a general case, not only are stress and strain not parallel,
they are not even vectors, but are themselves second-order tensors (recall
the stress tensor in Section 10) and the quantity which replaces Y is a
fourth-order tensor. (See Problem 42.)

Let us now investigate how we can turn one vector into another by
multiplying it by something. (You might think first of a cross product,
but this would give only vectors perpendicular to the one you started
with.) First recall (Section 11) that $\mathbf{UV}$ is a second-order tensor. Now in
elementary vector analysis, we often write vectors in terms of $\mathbf{i}$, $\mathbf{j}$, and
$\mathbf{k}$, say $\mathbf{V} = \mathbf{i} - \mathbf{j}$, and $\mathbf{U} = \mathbf{i} + 3\mathbf{k}$. We can write tensors in a similar
form. Note carefully that $\mathbf{UV}$ is not a dot or cross product; this is what
it means [compare (11.14)]:

$$(12.1) \qquad \mathbf{UV} = (\mathbf{i} + 3\mathbf{k})(\mathbf{i} - \mathbf{j}) = \mathbf{ii} - \mathbf{ij} + 3\mathbf{ki} - 3\mathbf{kj}.$$

Such an expression is called a *dyadic*. It is merely one way of writing down
or identifying the components of a second-order tensor. Another very
good way of exhibiting the components of a second-order tensor is as a
matrix. Because a second-order tensor has just the right number of components to fill a 3 by 3 matrix, there is a very close correspondence between
the mathematics of matrices and of second-order tensors. The dyadic in
(12.1) could be displayed as the matrix

$$(12.2) \qquad \begin{pmatrix} 1 & -1 & 0 \\ 0 & 0 & 0 \\ 3 & -3 & 0 \end{pmatrix}.$$

Now suppose we take the dot product of the tensor (dyadic) in (12.1)
with a vector, say $\mathbf{i}$. It makes a difference whether we multiply by $\mathbf{i}$ from
the right or the left—we speak of pre-multiplication and post-multiplica-
tion. We get

$$
\begin{aligned}
(\mathbf{UV}) \cdot \mathbf{i} &= (\mathbf{ii} - \mathbf{ij} + 3\mathbf{ki} - 3\mathbf{kj}) \cdot \mathbf{i} \\
&= \mathbf{i}(\mathbf{i} \cdot \mathbf{i}) - \mathbf{i}(\mathbf{j} \cdot \mathbf{i}) + 3\mathbf{k}(\mathbf{i} \cdot \mathbf{i}) - 3\mathbf{k}(\mathbf{j} \cdot \mathbf{i}) \\
&= \mathbf{i} + 3\mathbf{k},
\end{aligned}
$$

$$
\begin{aligned}
(12.3) \qquad \mathbf{i} \cdot (\mathbf{UV}) &= \mathbf{i} \cdot (\mathbf{ii} - \mathbf{ij} + 3\mathbf{ki} - 3\mathbf{kj}) \\
&= (\mathbf{i} \cdot \mathbf{i})\mathbf{i} - (\mathbf{i} \cdot \mathbf{i})\mathbf{j} + 3(\mathbf{i} \cdot \mathbf{k})\mathbf{i} - 3(\mathbf{i} \cdot \mathbf{k})\mathbf{j} \\
&= \mathbf{i} - \mathbf{j}.
\end{aligned}
$$

[We can also write (12.3) in matrix form; see Problem 40a.] Thus we have found a mathematical quantity which can change one vector into another vector, and we see that such a quantity is a second-order tensor or dyadic.

Because second-order tensors (next to vectors) are of particular importance in applications, it is useful to be able to work with them in dyadic form or in matrix form as well as in component form (see Problems 37, 39, 40, 41, and 42). Recall that in Section 11, we started with a vector written using unit vector notation (11.2), and we wrote the transformation equations first in matrix form (11.9) and then in component form (11.12). We can carry out a similar calculation for second order tensors. If we write a dyadic $\mathbf{T}$ in terms of its components and the unit vectors in two coordinate systems [compare (11.2) for vectors],

$$(12.4) \quad \mathbf{T} = \mathbf{ii}T_{11} + \mathbf{ij}T_{12} + \mathbf{ik}T_{13} + \mathbf{ji}T_{21} + \mathbf{jj}T_{22} + \cdots$$
$$= \mathbf{i'i'}T'_{11} + \mathbf{i'j'}T'_{12} + \mathbf{i'k'}T'_{13} + \mathbf{j'i'}T'_{21} + \mathbf{j'j'}T'_{22} + \cdots,$$

we can show (Problem 37a) that the components satisfy (11.13), that is, $\mathbf{T}$ is a second-order tensor. We also find (Problem 37c) that the matrix form of the transformation equations (11.13) for a second-order tensor [compare (11.9) for vectors] is

$$(12.5) \qquad\qquad T' = MTM^{-1}$$

where T and T' are matrices whose elements are the components of $\mathbf{T}$ in the two coordinate systems, and M is the rotation matrix in (11.10).

13. GENERAL COORDINATE SYSTEMS

So far we have considered only a very special coordinate transformation, namely a rotation of rectangular axes; let us generalize this to include any change of variables, for example to spherical coordinates r, θ, ϕ:

$$(13.1) \quad \begin{aligned} x &= r \sin \theta \cos \phi, \\ y &= r \sin \theta \sin \phi, \\ z &= r \cos \theta. \end{aligned}$$

This is not a linear transformation, and we cannot write equations like (11.4) to (11.9) for the relations between the *variables*. However, we *can* write such equations for relations between the *differentials* of the variables. From (13.1), we find dx, dy, and dz in terms of dr, $d\theta$, and $d\phi$:

$$(13.2) \quad \begin{pmatrix} dx \\ dy \\ dz \end{pmatrix} = \begin{pmatrix} \sin \theta \cos \phi & r \cos \theta \cos \phi & -r \sin \theta \sin \phi \\ \sin \theta \sin \phi & r \cos \theta \sin \phi & r \sin \theta \cos \phi \\ \cos \theta & -r \sin \theta & 0 \end{pmatrix} \begin{pmatrix} dr \\ d\theta \\ d\phi \end{pmatrix}.$$

For general coordinates x_1, x_2, x_3, and x_1', x_2', x_3', if we are given the relations [like (13.1)] between the two sets of variables, we can write the relations between the two sets of differentials as follows:

(13.3)
$$\begin{pmatrix} dx_1' \\ dx_2' \\ dx_3' \end{pmatrix} = \begin{pmatrix} \dfrac{\partial x_1'}{\partial x_1} & \dfrac{\partial x_1'}{\partial x_2} & \dfrac{\partial x_1'}{\partial x_3} \\[2ex] \dfrac{\partial x_2'}{\partial x_1} & \dfrac{\partial x_2'}{\partial x_2} & \dfrac{\partial x_2'}{\partial x_3} \\[2ex] \dfrac{\partial x_3'}{\partial x_1} & \dfrac{\partial x_3'}{\partial x_2} & \dfrac{\partial x_3'}{\partial x_3} \end{pmatrix} \begin{pmatrix} dx_1 \\ dx_2 \\ dx_3 \end{pmatrix}.$$

In simpler notation, (13.3) becomes

(13.4)
$$dr' = J\, dr,$$

where dr', J, and dr stand for the matrices in (13.3). The determinant of J is called the Jacobian of the transformation (see Chapter 4, Section 14) and is often written*

$$\det J = \frac{\partial(x_1', x_2', x_3')}{\partial(x_1, x_2, x_3)}.$$

We can also write (13.3) and (13.4) as

(13.5)
$$dx_i' = \sum_j \frac{\partial x_i'}{\partial x_j}\, dx_j.$$

From equations (11.4) to (11.12), we can see that for transformations between rectangular axes (that is, rotations)

$$\frac{\partial x_i'}{\partial x_j} = \frac{\partial x_j}{\partial x_i'} = a_{ij},$$

since both partial derivatives are equal to the cosine of the angle between the x_i'-axis and the x_j-axis. Thus, for Cartesian systems, we could write (11.12) in two new forms using $a_{ij} = \partial x_i'/\partial x_j$ or $a_{ij} = \partial x_j/\partial x_i'$. These two forms would be the same for rectangular coordinates, but not for more general coordinates. For example, from (13.1) you can show that $\partial x/\partial \theta \neq \partial \theta/\partial x$ (Problem 45). Thus in general there are two possible definitions of a vector, which become identical when we consider only transformations between rectangular coordinate systems as in Section 11.

Covariant and contravariant vectors. By definition, **V** is a *covariant vector* if its components transform like this:

(13.6)
$$V_i' = \sum_j \frac{\partial x_j}{\partial x_i'} V_j,$$

---

* In Chapter 4, we used J to mean the Jacobian; here J is a matrix whose determinant is the Jacobian.

and **V** is a *contravariant vector* if its components transform like this:

$$(13.7) \qquad\qquad V_i' = \sum_j \frac{\partial x_i'}{\partial x_j} V_j.$$

By comparing (13.5) and (13.7), you can see that the differentials of the coordinates are the components of a contravariant vector. An example of a covariant vector is the gradient ∇u (Problem 49).

It is interesting to see the physical or geometrical meaning of contravariant and covariant vectors. Strictly speaking we should speak of contravariant and covariant *components* rather than vectors, but the former terminology is customary. In orthogonal curvilinear coordinate systems, any vector has three kinds of components: contravariant, covariant, and what we might call ordinary components. It is simplest to discuss this in two dimensions. We consider a transformation from rectangular coordinates x, y to polar coordinates r, θ. We can write

$$(13.8) \qquad d\mathbf{s} = \mathbf{i}\, dx + \mathbf{j}\, dy = \mathbf{e}_r\, dr + \mathbf{e}_\theta r\, d\theta = \mathbf{a}_r\, dr + \mathbf{a}_\theta\, d\theta.$$

We know from (13.5) and (13.7) that dr, $d\theta$ (*not* $r\, d\theta$) form a contravariant vector, or in other words they are the contravariant components of $d\mathbf{s}$; using the **a** vectors as base vectors, we have written the vector $d\mathbf{s}$ in terms of its contravariant components. We can then in a similar way write some other vector **V** in terms of its ordinary components and the unit **e** vectors, or in terms of its contravariant components and the **a** vectors as follows:

$$\mathbf{V} = V_r \mathbf{e}_r + V_\theta \mathbf{e}_\theta = V_r \mathbf{a}_r + \frac{V_\theta}{r} \mathbf{a}_\theta,$$

(where V_r and V_θ are ordinary components). Thus the contravariant components are the ordinary components divided by the scale factors. By considering grad u, we can show that covariant components are ordinary components multiplied by the scale factors; we can then write a vector in terms of its covariant components and the base vectors $\mathbf{e}_r$ ind $(1/r)\mathbf{e}_\theta$ (Problem 50). Note that the **a** vectors are the unit vectors multiplied by the scale factors, and the covariant components of a vector are the ordinary components multiplied by the scale factors. The **a** vectors are considered basic and the term covariant (vary *with*) is used to mean "vary in the same way as the **a** vectors." Then contravariant means to vary in the opposite way; the contravariant components are ordinary components divided by the scale factors. The components of the vector and the base vectors to be used with them always vary in opposite ways so that the scale factors cancel.

Definition of tensors.   It is now straightforward to define tensors of any kind. Tensors may be covariant of any order, contravariant of any order, or mixed. One further point is necessary here in notation. It is customary to write the indices for contravariant vectors and tensors as superscripts rather than subscripts; they must not be confused with exponents. We have not done this so far and it is not really essential for vectors; in this notation however, the condition (13.7) for a contravariant vector becomes

$$(13.9) \qquad V'^{i} = \sum_{j} \frac{\partial x'_i}{\partial x_j} V^{j}.$$

(In fact, to be strictly consistent, since the differentials dx_i are contravariant, we should write dx^i and $\partial x^i / \partial x'^j$; for our purposes this seems unnecessary so we shall leave the notation as it is.) Here are some sample tensor definitions; you should be able to write the corresponding definitions for tensors of any order or kind in a similar way.

$$T'_{ij} = \sum_{k,l} T_{kl} \frac{\partial x_k}{\partial x'_i} \frac{\partial x_l}{\partial x'_j} \qquad \text{second-order covariant tensor,}$$

$$(13.10) \quad T'^{ijk} = \sum_{l,m,n} T^{lmn} \frac{\partial x'_i}{\partial x_l} \frac{\partial x'_j}{\partial x_m} \frac{\partial x'_k}{\partial x_n} \qquad \begin{array}{l}\text{third-order contravariant} \\ \text{tensor,}\end{array}$$

$$T'^{ij}_{k} = \sum_{l,m,n} T^{lm}_{n} \frac{\partial x'_i}{\partial x_l} \frac{\partial x'_j}{\partial x_m} \frac{\partial x_n}{\partial x'_k} \qquad \begin{array}{l}\text{third-order mixed tensor with} \\ \text{one covariant and two} \\ \text{contravariant indices.}\end{array}$$

Contravariant and covariant components of a vector (or tensor) may have very peculiar units. For example, in polar coordinates, the θ contravariant component $d\theta$ of the displacement ds is unitless, and the covariant component of ds, namely, $r^2 d\theta$, has units (length)^2. You may wonder why there should be any interest in these peculiar components and why we should not always use the ordinary components. The reason lies in the simplicity of the transformation equations (13.6) and (13.9); a vector usually has a simpler form and simpler transformation equations in terms of its contravariant or covariant components. When we say that a vector is covariant (or contravariant), what we really mean is that its covariant components (or contravariant components) are simplest. For example, in polar coordinates the contravariant components of ds are dr, $d\theta$; the ordinary components are dr, $r\,d\theta$; the covariant components are dr, $r^2 d\theta$. Thus we call ds contravariant, and its (contravariant) components obey the simple transformation equations (13.9). After the necessary mathematical manipulations are done in the simpler form, it is easy enough to change tensor equations back to equations involving ordinary components to get a physical interpretation of the results.

In this section we have not indicated the range of our summations. Equations (13.6), (13.7), (13.9), and (13.10) apply to three-dimensional problems if we sum from 1 to 3, or they can just as well apply to n-dimensional problems for any n, if we sum from 1 to n. In Section 11 we defined Cartesian vectors or tensors in three or more dimensions. The equations of this section (13) now give more general definitions of vectors and tensors because there is no longer the restriction to linear transformations. Thus the definitions of this section include those of Section 11 as a special case.

14. VECTOR OPERATIONS IN TENSOR NOTATION

In (8.3) and (8.4) we used g_{ij} to represent the coefficients in ds^2 for a general coordinate system. We also [in (8.4)] used a matrix whose elements were g_{ij}. Given the g_{ij} matrix, we can find the matrix which is its reciprocal; let g^{ij} represent the elements of this reciprocal matrix. Also let g represent the determinant of the g_{ij} matrix. It is not hard to prove that for orthogonal systems with scale factors h_1, h_2, h_3, the following relations hold:

$$(14.1) \qquad g_{ij} = \begin{cases} 0 & i \neq j, \\ h_i^2 & i = j, \end{cases} \qquad g^{ij} = \begin{cases} 0 & i \neq j, \\ \dfrac{1}{h_i^2} & i = j, \end{cases}$$

$$g = h_1^2 h_2^2 h_3^2, \qquad \sqrt{g} = h_1 h_2 h_3$$

[see (8.6) and Problem 53]. From the general tensor definitions [(13.10) and similar formulas], it can be shown (Problem 54) that the quantities g_{ij} are the components of a second-order covariant tensor (called the metric tensor) and the quantities g^{ij} are the components of a second-order contravariant tensor.

We state without proof the following tensor expressions for ∇u, $\nabla \cdot \mathbf{V}$, and $\nabla^2 u$, which are compact and simple to remember. They are correct for any coordinate system, orthogonal or not. You can easily specialize them to orthogonal coordinate systems and so obtain the expressions given in Section 9. To do this use (14.1) and the relations (in terms of the scale factors) among the contravariant, covariant, and ordinary components of a vector in orthogonal systems. (See Section 13.)

The covariant components of ∇u are $\partial u / \partial x_i$;

$$\nabla \cdot \mathbf{V} = \frac{1}{\sqrt{g}} \sum_i \frac{\partial}{\partial x_i} (\sqrt{g}\, V^i),$$

where V^i are contravariant components of $\mathbf{V}$;

$$\nabla^2 u = \frac{1}{\sqrt{g}} \sum_{ij} \frac{\partial}{\partial x_i} \left(\sqrt{g}\, g^{ij} \frac{\partial u}{\partial x_j} \right).$$

REFERENCES

See books on matrices such as Finkbeiner, Fuller, or Wade, and books on vectors and tensors such as Brand, Jeffreys, Sokolnikoff, or Spiegel. You will also find discussion of these topics in some books on mathematics in physics and engineering. (See references at the end of the book identified for Chapter 10 by a [10] after the listing.)

PROBLEMS

1. (a) Prove (3.4) in three dimensions; that is, show that if M is the matrix of a linear transformation from x, y, z to X, Y, Z for which $x^2 + y^2 + z^2 = X^2 + Y^2 + Z^2$, then M satisfies (3.4).

   (b) Also prove the converse of (a), that is, that if $M^T = M^{-1}$, then the length of a vector is not changed by the transformation M. *Hint:* The matrix r and its transpose r^T are:

   $$r = \begin{pmatrix} x \\ y \\ z \end{pmatrix}, \qquad r^T = (x \quad y \quad z).$$

   Show that $r^T r = x^2 + y^2 + z^2$; then use $R = Mr$ and Problem 42a of Chapter 3.

   (c) From (3.4), show that if M is orthogonal, then det $M = +1$ or -1. (When det $M = 1$, the transformation is called a *proper* rotation; when det $M = -1$, one or all three axes have been reflected, in addition to rotation.) *Hint:* Find det (MM^T); how is a determinant affected by interchanging rows and columns?

2. (a) By extending familiar definitions in two and three dimensions to the required number of dimensions, find:
   the "distance" between the "points"

   $$(4, -1, 2, 7) \quad \text{and} \quad (2, 3, 1, 9),$$
   $$(-1, 5, -3, 2, 4) \quad \text{and} \quad (2, 6, 2, 7, 6);$$

   the "length" of the "vectors"

   $$(2, -1, 5, 1, -3), \quad (-5, 1, 5, 3, -2);$$

   the "cosine of the angle" between the two "vectors" just given. *Hint:* Generalize the dot product.

   (b) Show that the following "vectors" are orthogonal:

   $$(1, -5, 7, 2, 3) \quad \text{and} \quad (2, 1, -2, 7, 1).$$

   (*Hint:* Consider the "dot product.")

(c) In three-dimensional space, the unit vectors **i**, **j**, **k** are vectors with components $(1, 0, 0)$, $(0, 1, 0)$, and $(0, 0, 1)$. In, say five-dimensional space, we can define the unit vectors as vectors with components $(1, 0, 0, 0, 0)$, $(0, 1, 0, 0, 0)$, $(0, 0, 1, 0, 0)$, etc. Show that the five unit vectors in five dimensions are all mutually orthogonal. Generalize to n dimensions. Show that any vector in n dimensions can be written in terms of the n unit vectors.

(d) Using the ideas of linear dependence of sets of numbers discussed in Chapter 3, Section 6, show that $n + 1$ vectors in n dimensions are linearly dependent.

3. Verify (4.7). Also verify (4.10) and find the corresponding different C in (4.9). Hint for finding C: Start with (4.10) instead of (4.7) and follow through the method of getting (4.8) from (4.7).

4. (a) Show that if C is a matrix whose columns are the components of mutually perpendicular unit vectors, then C satisfies the condition (3.4) for an orthogonal matrix.

(b) Generalize this to n dimensions (see Problem 2c).

(c) Verify that the matrix of the transformation (3.1) (called a rotation matrix) is orthogonal, that is, that it satisfies (3.4).

5. Show that under the transformation (4.1), all points (x, y) on a given straight line through the origin go into points (x', y') on another straight line through the origin. *Hint:* Solve (4.1) for x and y in terms of x' and y' and substitute into the equation $y = mx$ to get an equation $y' = m'x'$, where m' is a constant. *Further hint:* If $r' = Mr$, then $r = M^{-1}r'$; (9.8) of Chapter 3 tells how to find M^{-1}.

6. Show that the C matrix in (4.8) does represent a rotation and write out the equations (3.1) and (4.11). Verify equation (5.9).

7. Consider a succession of linear transformations [like (2.1)] from x, y to x', y', and from x', y', to x'', y'', say $x'' = a'x' + b'y'$, $y'' = c'x' + d'y'$. Show that the resultant transformation from x, y to x'', y'' is a linear transformation whose matrix is the product of the matrices of the individual transformations.

8. Prove that the product of two orthogonal matrices is orthogonal. It then follows from Problem 7 that the net result of two successive orthogonal transformations is an orthogonal transformation. Note that the corresponding geometrical statement is that two successive rotations are equivalent to a single rotation.

9. Find the inverse of the transformation

$$x' = 2x - 3y,$$

$$y' = x + y,$$

that is, find x, y in terms of x', y'. (*Hint:* Use matrices.) Is the transformation orthogonal?

10. Verify that (5.2) multiplied out is (5.1).

11. Find the eigenvalues and eigenvectors of the following matrices. Observe that the eigenvectors are orthogonal if and only if M is symmetric.

(a) $\begin{pmatrix} 1 & 3 \\ 2 & 2 \end{pmatrix}$

(b) $\begin{pmatrix} 2 & 2 \\ 2 & -1 \end{pmatrix}$

(c) $\begin{pmatrix} 1 & 3 & 1 \\ 0 & 5 & 0 \\ 1 & 3 & 0 \end{pmatrix}$

(d) $\begin{pmatrix} 4 & 3 & 0 \\ 3 & 2 & 0 \\ 0 & 0 & 1 \end{pmatrix}$

(e) $\begin{pmatrix} 2 & 1 & 2 \\ 1 & 5 & -1 \\ 2 & -1 & 4 \end{pmatrix}$

(f) $\begin{pmatrix} 3 & 1 & 2 \\ 1 & 3 & -1 \\ 2 & -1 & 3 \end{pmatrix}$

(g) $\begin{pmatrix} -1 & 1 & 3 \\ 1 & 2 & 0 \\ 3 & 0 & 2 \end{pmatrix}$

(h) $\begin{pmatrix} 1 & 2 & 2 \\ 2 & 3 & 0 \\ 2 & 0 & 3 \end{pmatrix}$

(i) $\begin{pmatrix} -1 & 2 & 1 \\ 2 & 3 & 0 \\ 1 & 0 & 3 \end{pmatrix}$

(j) $\begin{pmatrix} 1 & 1 & 1 \\ 1 & -1 & 1 \\ 1 & 1 & -1 \end{pmatrix}$

(k) $\begin{pmatrix} -3 & 2 & 2 \\ 2 & 1 & 3 \\ 2 & 3 & 1 \end{pmatrix}$

(l) $\begin{pmatrix} 13 & 4 & -2 \\ 4 & 13 & -2 \\ -2 & -2 & 10 \end{pmatrix}$

12. Let each of the following matrices M describe a deformation of the (x, y) plane. For each given M find: the eigenvalues and eigenvectors of the transformation, the matrix C which diagonalizes M and specifies the rotation to new axes (X, Y) along the eigenvectors, and the matrix D which gives the deformation relative to the new axes. Describe the deformation relative to the new axes.

(a) $\begin{pmatrix} 2 & -1 \\ -1 & 2 \end{pmatrix}$

(b) $\begin{pmatrix} 5 & 2 \\ 2 & 2 \end{pmatrix}$

(c) $\begin{pmatrix} 3 & 4 \\ 4 & 9 \end{pmatrix}$

(d) $\begin{pmatrix} 3 & 1 \\ 1 & 3 \end{pmatrix}$

(e) $\begin{pmatrix} 3 & 2 \\ 2 & 3 \end{pmatrix}$

13. The characteristic equation for a second-order matrix M is a quadratic equation. We have considered the case in which the roots of this quadratic equation (that is, the eigenvalues) are real, positive, and unequal. Discuss the other possibilities as follows (assume M real and symmetric):

(a) Complex roots: Show that all vectors are rotated, that is, there are no (real) eigenvectors which are unchanged in direction by the deformation. Consider the characteristic equation of a rotation matrix as a special case.

(b) One real negative root: Show that the deformation involves a reflection of the plane in one of the eigenvector lines. Consider the transformation given by $\begin{pmatrix} 1 & 0 \\ 0 & -1 \end{pmatrix}$ as a simple special case.

(c) Two real equal roots: Show that in this case the deformation consists of a dilation or shrinkage in the radial direction (the same in all directions) with no rotation (and reflection in the origin if the root is negative).

14. Rotate to principal axes each of the following conics and quadric surfaces.

(a) $2x^2 + 4xy - y^2 = 24$

(b) $8x^2 + 8xy + 2y^2 = 35$

(c) $3x^2 + 8xy - 3y^2 = 8$

(d) $5x^2 + 3y^2 + 2z^2 + 4xz = 14$

(e) $x^2 + y^2 + z^2 + 4xy + 2xz - 2yz = 12$

(f) $x^2 + 3y^2 + 3z^2 + 4xy + 4xz = 30$

(g) Solve Problems 77 and 78 of Chapter 4 by rotating to principal axes.

15. (a) Carry through the details of Example 2 in Section 5 to find the unit eigenvectors. Prove that the resulting rotation matrix C is orthogonal. *Hint:* Find CC^{T}.

(b) Any rotation of axes in three dimensions can be described by giving the nine direction cosines of the angles between the (x, y, z) and (x', y', z') axes. Show that the 3 by 3 matrix of these direction cosines [arranged as in the table in (11.1)] is an orthogonal matrix. *Hint:* Find MM^{T}.

16. In Example 3 of Section 5, find C and verify (5.17). *Hint:* Find the unit eigenvectors and so construct C.

17. Find the characteristic frequencies and the two characteristic modes of vibration if the central spring constant is $2k$ in Fig. 5.1.

18. Find the characteristic frequencies and the characteristic modes of vibration for small vibrations of the coupled pendulums shown. Assume the spring unstretched when both pendulums hang vertically, and take the spring constant as $k = mg/l$ to simplify the algebra. *Hint:* For small vibrations $x = l \sin \theta = l\theta$, $1 - \cos \theta = \frac{1}{2}\theta^2$, and there are similar equations for ϕ and y.

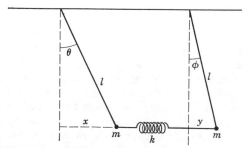

19. Using the equations for x, y, z in terms of the spherical coordinates r, θ, ϕ, find ds^2 in spherical coordinates by the method used in finding (6.5). From ds^2 find the scale factors, the vector $d\mathbf{s}$, the volume element, the base vectors $\mathbf{a}_r$, $\mathbf{a}_\theta$, $\mathbf{a}_\phi$, and the corresponding unit base vectors $\mathbf{e}_r$, $\mathbf{e}_\theta$, $\mathbf{e}_\phi$.

20. As in Problem 19, find ds^2, the scale factors, the vector $d\mathbf{s}$, the volume element, the $\mathbf{a}$ vectors, and the $\mathbf{e}$ vectors for each of the following coordinate systems. Also sketch or describe the coordinate surfaces.

(a) Parabolic cylinder coordinates u, v, z:

$$x = \tfrac{1}{2}(u^2 - v^2),$$
$$y = uv,$$
$$z = z.$$

(b) Elliptic cylinder coordinates u, v, z:

$$x = a \cosh u \cos v,$$
$$y = a \sinh u \sin v,$$
$$z = z.$$

(c) Paraboloidal coordinates u, v, ϕ:

$$x = uv \cos \phi,$$
$$y = uv \sin \phi,$$
$$z = \tfrac{1}{2}(u^2 - v^2).$$

(d) Bipolar coordinates u, v:

$$x = \frac{a \sinh u}{\cosh u + \cos v},$$

$$y = \frac{a \sin v}{\cosh u + \cos v}.$$

21. In the problem at the end of Section 7, note that a simpler way to find the velocity ds/dt is to divide the vector ds in (7.1) by dt. Complete the problem to find the acceleration components in cylindrical coordinates.

22. Use the results of Problem 19 to find the velocity and acceleration components in spherical coordinates. Find the velocity in two ways: starting with ds and starting with $\mathbf{s} = r\mathbf{e}_r$.

23. Using the expressions you have found for ds, and for the $\mathbf{e}$ vectors, find the velocity and acceleration components in each of the coordinate systems of Problem 20.

24. In the text and problems so far, we have found the $\mathbf{e}$ vectors for various coordinate systems in terms of $\mathbf{i}$ and $\mathbf{j}$ (or $\mathbf{i}$, $\mathbf{j}$, $\mathbf{k}$ in three dimensions). We can solve these equations to find $\mathbf{i}$ and $\mathbf{j}$ in terms of the $\mathbf{e}$ vectors, and so express a vector given in rectangular form in terms of the base vectors of another coordinate system. Carry out this process to express in cylindrical coordinates the vector $\mathbf{V} = 2y\mathbf{i} - x\mathbf{j} + \mathbf{k}$. *Hint:* Use matrices (as in Chapter 3) to solve the set of equations for $\mathbf{i}$ and $\mathbf{j}$.

25. Prove (9.4) in the following way. Using (9.2) with $u = x_1$, show that $\nabla x_1 = \mathbf{e}_1/h_1$. Similarly, show that $\nabla x_2 = \mathbf{e}_2/h_2$ and $\nabla x_3 = \mathbf{e}_3/h_3$. Let $\mathbf{e}_1$, $\mathbf{e}_2$, $\mathbf{e}_3$ in that order form a right-handed triad (so that $\mathbf{e}_1 \times \mathbf{e}_2 = \mathbf{e}_3$, etc.) and show that $\nabla x_1 \times \nabla x_2 = \mathbf{e}_3/(h_1 h_2)$. Take the divergence of this equation and using the vector identities (h) and (b) of Chapter 5, show that $\nabla \cdot (\mathbf{e}_3/h_1 h_2) = 0$. The other parts of (9.4) are proved similarly.

26. Derive the expression (9.11) for curl $\mathbf{V}$ in the following way. Show that $\nabla x_1 = \mathbf{e}_1/h_1$ and $\nabla \times (\nabla x_1) = \nabla \times (\mathbf{e}_1/h_1) = 0$. Write $\mathbf{V}$ in the form

$$\mathbf{V} = \frac{\mathbf{e}_1}{h_1}(h_1 V_1) + \frac{\mathbf{e}_2}{h_2}(h_2 V_2) + \frac{\mathbf{e}_3}{h_3}(h_3 V_3)$$

and use vector identities from Chapter 5 to complete the derivation.

27. Using cylindrical coordinates write the Lagrange equations for the motion of a particle acted on by a force $\mathbf{F} = -\nabla V$, where V is the potential energy. Divide each Lagrange equation by the corresponding scale factor so that the components of $\mathbf{F}$ (that is, of $-\nabla V$) appear in the equations. Thus write the equations as the component equations of $\mathbf{F} = m\mathbf{a}$, and so find the components of the acceleration $\mathbf{a}$. Compare the results with Problem 21.

28. Do Problem 27 in spherical coordinates; compare the results with Problem 22.

29. Do Problem 27 in each of the coordinate systems of Problem 20; compare the results with Problem 23.

30. Write out ∇U, $\nabla \cdot \mathbf{V}$, $\nabla^2 U$, and $\nabla \times \mathbf{V}$ in spherical coordinates.

31. Do Problem 30 for each of the coordinate systems of Problem 20.

32. Verify equations (11.6).

33. Use (11.9) or (11.12) to show that the sum of two vectors is a vector.

34. Show that the dot product of two vectors is a scalar, that is, a single number which is the same in the primed and unprimed systems. *Hint:* The dot product is $\sum_i U_i V_i$ which you can write in matrix form as

$$(U_1 \quad U_2 \quad U_3)\begin{pmatrix} V_1 \\ V_2 \\ V_3 \end{pmatrix}.$$

Use (11.9) or (11.12) to find $\sum_i U_i' V_i'$, and remember that M is orthogonal.

35. Write the transformation equation for a third-order tensor. Use it to show that the sum of two third-order tensors is a third-order tensor.

36. Write out in detail the following expressions which are written here using summation convention:

(a) $\dfrac{\partial u}{\partial x_i}\dfrac{\partial x_i}{\partial x_j'}$ (b) $a_j x^j$ (c) $a_{ij} x_i x_j$

(d) $a_{ij} b_{jk} = a_{ij} c_{jk}$

Observe that it is *not* correct to cancel a_{ij} in (d); this example shows how careful you must be in using the summation convention.

37. (a) Show that a dyadic is a second-order tensor, that is, show that if $\mathbf{T}$ is given by (12.4) in any two coordinate systems, then the components of $\mathbf{T}$ in the two systems are related by (11.13). *Hint:* Evaluate, say, $\mathbf{i}' \cdot \mathbf{T} \cdot \mathbf{j}'$ using both expressions for **T** in (12.4); you should get T'_{12} from the second line of (12.4) and a sum of nine terms from the first line [compare (11.3) for vectors]. Evaluate the dot products $\mathbf{i} \cdot \mathbf{i}'$, etc., as we did in getting (11.4) and (11.5) [but use the notation of (11.10)]. Similarly evaluate all other double dot products $\mathbf{i}' \cdot \mathbf{T} \cdot \mathbf{i}'$, etc.

(b) Let the array in (11.14) be a 3 by 3 matrix; show that it is UV^{T}, where U and V are column matrices as in (11.9) (so V^{T} is a row matrix). Write the transformation equations for the vectors **U** and **V** in matrix form (11.9) and obtain (11.15) in matrix form. Your result should agree with (12.5).

(c) Verify that (12.5) is equivalent to (11.13).

38. A second-order tensor is *symmetric* if $T_{ij} = T_{ji}$ and *skew-symmetric* if $T_{ij} = -T_{ji}$. Notice that these are the same definitions as for matrices with elements T_{ij}. Show that a skew-symmetric tensor in two dimensions has one independent nonzero component, and in three dimensions it has three independent nonzero components. Observe that this is just the right number of components to form a vector in three dimensions. Let **A** and **B** be two given vectors in three dimensions. Define nine quantities T_{ij} by the equations $T_{ij} = A_i B_j - A_j B_i$. Show that T_{ij} is a skew-symmetric tensor and that its three nonzero components are just the components of $\mathbf{A} \times \mathbf{B}$. Thus the cross product of two vectors is really a skew-symmetric second-order tensor; it is often called a *pseudo-vector* or an *axial* vector. It behaves like a *true* vector (also called a *polar* vector) unless we change from a right-handed to a left-handed coordinate system, in which case there is a sign difference between a true vector and a pseudo-vector. For example, if we reflect the z-axis (leaving x and y alone), then the true vector **k** is reflected, but the pseudo-vector $\mathbf{i} \times \mathbf{j}$ is unchanged and we no longer have $\mathbf{i} \times \mathbf{j} = \mathbf{k}$. Show what happens to the unit vectors (true vectors) and their cross products (pseudo-vectors) if the x-axis is reflected; if all three axes are reflected.

39. (a) Show that a symmetric second-order tensor T_{ij} can be diagonalized, that is, that there is a coordinate system in which only the components T_{11}, T_{22}, T_{33} are different from zero. *Hint:* Display the components T_{ij} in matrix form. In Section 4, you learned how to diagonalize symmetric matrices by a rotation of axes. Write out the equations for the elements of the diagonal matrix obtained from the T_{ij} matrix (in terms of the elements of the rotation matrix) and show that the transformation equations are the same as the tensor transformation equations (11.13).

(b) Interpret the elements of the matrices (g), (h), and (j) in Problem 11 as components of stress tensors. In each case diagonalize the matrix and so find the principal axes of the stress (along which the stress is pure tension or compression). Describe the stress relative to these axes.

(c) Show that the stress tensor **P** defined in (10.1) is a second-order tensor, that is, that it obeys the transformation law (11.13). Suggested outline of proof: The problem is to find the components of **P** relative to rotated axes (x', y', z'), in terms of the components of **P** relative to (x, y, z), and see that the results agree with (11.13). Draw a slanted plane, as shown, perpendicular to the x'-axis (that is, perpendicular to the unit vector $\mathbf{i}'$) and consider the forces on the small volume bounded by the coordinate planes and the slanted plane. Let the area of the slanted face be A and find the areas of the faces in the coordinate planes in terms of A and the unit vectors, that is, in

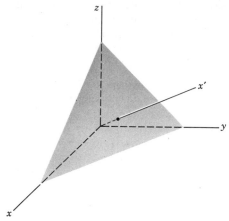

terms of a_{ij} in (11.10). The force acting *on* the volume element across the (x, y) face is [see definition of $\mathbf{P}$ in (10.1)]

(force per unit area)(area of face) $= (\mathbf{i}P_{zx} + \mathbf{j}P_{zy} + \mathbf{k}P_{zz})(A\mathbf{k} \cdot \mathbf{i}')$.

Similarly, write the forces on the (x, z) and (y, z) faces. For equilibrium of the volume, the total vector force on these three faces must equal the vector force acting across the slanted face *on* the neighboring material. Write this latter force as a pressure times the area of the slanted face. Now (using the cosines of the angles between the old and new axes, that is, the a_{ij} in M), take components of this force across A in the x', y', z' directions to get $P_{x'x'}$, $P_{x'y'}$, $P_{x'z'}$. (We have neglected any body forces, for example, gravity; to see why this is justified, let the small volume shrink to a point and compare the orders of magnitude of volume and of surface area when the sides are small.)

40. (a) In Section 12 we found the values of $\mathbf{UV} \cdot \mathbf{i}$ and $\mathbf{i} \cdot \mathbf{UV}$. Write these two problems in matrix notation, remembering that a vector can be represented by either a row or a column matrix.

   (b) The expression $\mathbf{1} = \mathbf{ii} + \mathbf{jj} + \mathbf{kk}$ is called the unit dyadic. Show that $\mathbf{1} \cdot \mathbf{V} = \mathbf{V} \cdot \mathbf{1} = \mathbf{V}$ for any vector $\mathbf{V}$.

   (c) Let $\boldsymbol{\Phi}$ be the dyadic $\mathbf{ii}a^2 + \mathbf{jj}b^2 + \mathbf{kk}c^2$. Find $\mathbf{r} \cdot \boldsymbol{\Phi} \cdot \mathbf{r}$. What does $\mathbf{r} \cdot \boldsymbol{\Phi} \cdot \mathbf{r} = 1$ represent geometrically? Write the equation $\mathbf{r} \cdot \boldsymbol{\Phi} \cdot \mathbf{r} = 1$ in matrix notation.

41. (a) If a body is rotating about a fixed axis, then its angular momentum $\mathbf{L}$ and its angular velocity $\boldsymbol{\omega}$ are parallel vectors and $\mathbf{L} = I\boldsymbol{\omega}$, where I is the (scalar) moment of inertia of the body about the axis. However, in general,

L and **ω** are not parallel and I in the equation must be a second-order tensor; let us call it **I**. Find **I** in dyadic form in the following way: For simplicity, first consider a point mass m at the point **r**. The angular momentum of m about the origin is by definition $m\mathbf{r} \times \mathbf{v}$, where **v** is the linear velocity. From Chapter 5, $\mathbf{v} = \boldsymbol{\omega} \times \mathbf{r}$. Write out the triple vector product for **L** and from it write each component of **L** in terms of the three components of **ω**. Write your results in matrix form

$$\begin{pmatrix} L_x \\ L_y \\ L_z \end{pmatrix} = \begin{pmatrix} I_{xx} & I_{xy} & I_{xz} \\ I_{yx} & I_{yy} & I_{yz} \\ I_{zx} & I_{zy} & I_{zz} \end{pmatrix} \begin{pmatrix} \omega_x \\ \omega_y \\ \omega_z \end{pmatrix}$$

and in dyadic form

$$\mathbf{L} = \mathbf{I} \cdot \boldsymbol{\omega} = (\mathbf{ii}I_{xx} + \mathbf{ij}I_{xy} + \cdots) \cdot \boldsymbol{\omega}$$

You should have

$$I_{xx} = m(y^2 + z^2),$$
$$I_{xy} = -mxy,$$
$$\text{etc.}$$

For a set of masses m_i or an extended body, replace the expressions for I_{xx}, etc., by the corresponding sums or integrals:

$$I_{xx} = \sum m_i(y_i^2 + z_i^2) \quad \text{or} \quad \int (y^2 + z^2)\, dm,$$

$$I_{xy} = -\sum m_i x_i y_i \quad \text{or} \quad -\int xy\, dm, \quad \text{etc.}$$

(b) Show that **I** is a second-order (Cartesian) tensor by expressing its components relative to a rotated system $[I_{x'x'} = m(y'^2 + z'^2)$, etc.] in terms of x, y, z using (11.7) or (11.11), and hence in terms of I_{xx}, etc., to show that **I** obeys the transformation equations (11.13).

(c) Show that if **n** is a unit vector, the expression $\mathbf{n} \cdot \mathbf{I} \cdot n$ gives the moment of inertia about an axis through the origin parallel to **n**. *Hint:* Consider **I** rotated to a system in which one of the axes is along **n**.

(d) Observe that the **I** matrix is symmetric and recall that a symmetric matrix may be diagonalized by a rotation of axes. The eigenvalues of the **I** matrix are called the principal moments of inertia. Show by part (c) that they are moments of inertia about the new axes (x', y', z') relative to which **I** is diagonal. These new axes are called the principal axes of inertia. For the mass distribution consisting of point masses m at $(1, 1, 1)$ and $(1, 1, -1)$, find the nine components of **I**, and find the principal moments of inertia and the principal axes.

42. (a) Let **T** be a second-order tensor (dyadic) and let **A** be a vector. Then we have seen (Section 12) that $\mathbf{T} \cdot \mathbf{A}$ is another vector, say **B**. Write the equations giving each of the three components of **B** as linear combinations of the three components of **A**; write these equations in matrix form, dyadic form, and

summation form. Observe that the nine coefficients in these linear combinations are just the nine components of **T**.

(b) Now let **P** and **Q** be second-order tensors and show that 81 coefficients are required to write each component of **P** as a linear combination of the components of **Q**. Show that 81 is the number of components in a fourth-order tensor (in three dimensions). If the components of the fourth-order tensor are A_{ijkl}, show that the equations

$$P_{ij} = \sum_{k,l} A_{ijkl} Q_{kl}$$

give the components of the second-order tensor **P** in terms of the components of the second-order tensor **Q**. Show that if **P** and **Q** are both symmetric, then there are only 36 instead of 81 independent nonzero components A_{ijkl}. *Hint:* Consider the number of independent components in **P** and **Q** when they are symmetric. *Comment:* If **P** is the stress tensor (10.1) and **Q** is a second-order tensor known as the strain tensor which specifies the deformation of a solid body under stress, then the equation above relating **P** and **Q** is a generalized form of Hooke's law. The components of the fourth-order tensor A_{ijkl} depend on the kind of substance under stress and are called the elastic constants of the substance. The stress and strain tensors are both symmetric.

(c) If **u** is a vector specifying the displacement under stress of each point of a deformable medium, then ∇**u** is a second-order (Cartesian) tensor which describes the strain at each point. Write out the components of ∇**u** in dyadic form. Show that any dyadic can be written as a symmetric dyadic plus an antisymmetric dyadic and write ∇**u** as such a sum. The symmetric part of ∇**u** is called the *strain tensor*, and the antisymmetric part the *rotation tensor*. *Comment:* These are Cartesian tensors, that is, they obey tensor transformation equations under rotation of rectangular axes; they do not (in this simple form) obey the general tensor transformation equations of Section 13—see Problem 49.

(d) Show that if for every vector V_j, the quantities $U_i = \sum_j T_{ij} V_j$ are the components of a vector, then the quantities T_{ij} are the components of a second-order tensor. (This fact is an example of the *quotient rule*). *Hint:* Use the transformation (11.12) for a vector to show that T_{ij} satisfies the transformation (11.13). Similarly, show that A_{ijkl} in the equation of part (b) is a fourth-order (Cartesian) tensor if, for every second-order (Cartesian) tensor Q_{kl}, P_{ij} is a second-order (Cartesian) tensor. Generalize the proof to show that if $U_i = \sum_j T_{ij} V^j$, where U_i is a covariant vector (satisfying (13.6)) and V^j is an arbitrary contravariant vector [satisfying (13.7)], then T_{ij} is a second-order covariant tensor. Generalize further to tensors of any order and kind.

(e) Let S_0 be a given rectangular coordinate system. In each rotated system S let a_{ij} be the elements of the rotation matrix (11.10) relating S and

S_0. Use your results in part (d) to show that a_{ij} is a second-order (Cartesian) tensor.

43. (a) In three-dimensional rectangular coordinates

$$ds^2 = dx^2 + dy^2 + dz^2.$$

Show that ds^2 is invariant under a rotation of axes, that is, show that the change of variables $r' = Mr$ with M the rotation matrix gives

$$ds^2 = dx'^2 + dy'^2 + dz'^2.$$

Hint: Differentiate (11.6) and find ds^2.

(b) Repeat part (a) in the notation of (11.10) to show that $ds^2 = \Sigma \, dx_i^2 = \Sigma \, dx_i'^2$. Use matrix notation; if $dr = \begin{pmatrix} dx_1 \\ dx_2 \\ dx_3 \end{pmatrix}$ and $dr' = M \, dr$, $dr = M^{\mathrm{T}} \, dr'$,

etc., then $ds^2 = dr^{\mathrm{T}} \, dr$.

(c) Part (b) generalizes to four dimensions simply by including a fourth variable x_4. Write out the details. M is a 4 by 4 orthogonal matrix; by analogy with three dimensions, we could call the transformation $r' = Mr$ a rotation of axes in four-dimensional space.

(d) In special relativity, the quantity

$$d\sigma^2 = dx^2 + dy^2 + dz^2 - c^2 \, dt^2$$

(x, y, z = space coordinates, t = time, c = velocity of light) is invariant under the changes of variables allowed by special relativity theory. (The allowed changes of variable are called the Lorentz transformations, and $d\sigma$ is called the space-time interval.) It is customary in special relativity to use the variables $x_1 = x$, $x_2 = y$, $x_3 = z$, $x_4 = ict$ ($i = \sqrt{-1}$). Show that in the variables x_i, $d\sigma$ becomes indentical with the four-dimensional ds of part (c). Thus we could say that the Lorentz transformations correspond to rotations in four-dimensional space (also called four-dimensional space-time in recognition of the fact that $x_4 = ict$).

(e) Consider a special case of a four-dimensional rotation $r' = Mr$ in which $x_2' = x_2$, $x_3' = x_3$, and the (x_1', x_4') axes are rotated by an angle θ from the (x_1, x_4) axes. Write the matrix M in terms of θ. Show that if $x_1' = 0$ when $x_1 = -i(v/c)x_4$, then

$$\cos \theta = \left(1 - \frac{v^2}{c^2}\right)^{-\frac{1}{2}}, \qquad \sin \theta = \frac{iv}{c}\left(1 - \frac{v^2}{c^2}\right)^{-\frac{1}{2}}$$

(Of course θ is imaginary, but this need not worry us; the algebra is carrying the weight of proof, and the geometrical language is used purely by analogy with three dimensions.) Write the matrix M, and the four transformation equations for x_i' in terms of x_i. Replace x_i and x_i' by their values in terms of

x, y, z, t to get

$$x' = \left(1 - \frac{v^2}{c^2}\right)^{-\frac{1}{2}}(x - vt), \qquad t' = \left(1 - \frac{v^2}{c^2}\right)^{-\frac{1}{2}}\left(t - \frac{vx}{c^2}\right),$$

$$y' = y, \qquad z' = z.$$

(These are the Lorentz transformation equations.)

44. Show that for a linear transformation an equation like (11.7) also implies an equation like (13.3) for the relations between the differentials. Thus (13.3) is a general equation for any kind of transformation, linear or not. Show that for the linear transformation given by (11.11), equations (13.6) and (13.7) both become (11.12), and the first of equations (13.10) becomes (11.13). Write several general equations defining a fourth-order tensor (with various combinations of contravariant and covariant indices) and show that they all reduce to (11.16) for the special case of the linear transformation (11.11).

45. From (13.1) find $\partial\theta/\partial x = (1/r)\cos\theta\cos\phi$ and show that $\partial x/\partial\theta \neq \partial\theta/\partial x$. Note carefully that $\partial x/\partial\theta$ means that r and ϕ are constant, but $\partial\theta/\partial x$ means that y and z are constant. (See Chapter 4 for further discussion.)

46. (a) If J represents the 3 by 3 matrix in (13.2), show that $\det J = r^2\sin\theta$. We call $\det J$ the Jacobian of the transformation (13.1). Observe that the spherical coordinate volume element is $(\det J)\, dr\, d\theta\, d\phi$ (Chapter 4, Section 14). *Hint:* Show that

$$J^{\mathrm{T}}J = \begin{pmatrix} 1 & 0 & 0 \\ 0 & r^2 & 0 \\ 0 & 0 & r^2\sin^2\theta \end{pmatrix},$$

where J^{T} is the transpose of J.

(b) In equation (13.3), if x_1', x_2', x_3' are ordinary rectangular coordinates, and x_1, x_2, x_3 are orthogonal coordinates, so that

$$ds^2 = dx_1'^2 + dx_2'^2 + dx_3'^2 = h_1^2\, dx_1^2 + h_2^2\, dx_2^2 + h_3^2\, dx_3^2,$$

show that $\det J$ is $h_1 h_2 h_3$. *Hint:* Find $J^{\mathrm{T}}J$ as in part (a). To evaluate the partial derivative expressions you get, observe that the same expressions arise in finding ds^2. Hence show that

$$J^{\mathrm{T}}J = \begin{pmatrix} h_1^2 & 0 & 0 \\ 0 & h_2^2 & 0 \\ 0 & 0 & h_3^2 \end{pmatrix}.$$

47. It is true in general that when you make a change of variables in a multiple integral, the product of the differentials of the old variables becomes the product of the new differentials times the Jacobian of the transformation. You have verified this for one special case in Problem 46a. Using the result of Problem 46b, now verify it for a change of variables from rectangular coordinates to any orthogonal system. *Hint:* Recall that the volume element in an orthogonal system is

$$h_1 h_2 h_3 \, dx_1 \, dx_2 \, dx_3.$$

48. Show that the velocity components dx_i/dt form a contravariant vector. *Hint:* See (13.5) and (13.7).

49. (a) Show that the components $\partial u/\partial x_j$ of ∇u form a covariant vector. *Hint:* By partial differentiation, find $\partial u/\partial x_i'$ in terms of the partial derivatives of u with respect to the x_j's and compare your results with (13.6).

(b) Show that the nine quantities $T_{ij} = \partial v_i/\partial x_j$ (which are the Cartesian components of $\nabla \mathbf{V}$, where $\mathbf{V}$ is a vector) satisfy the transformation equations (11.12) for a Cartesian second-order tensor. Show that they do *not* satisfy the general tensor transformation equations (Section 13). *Hint:* Differentiate (13.6) or (13.7) partially with respect to, say x_k', to find $\partial V_i'/\partial x_k'$ in terms of $\partial V_i/\partial x_l$. You should get the expected terms [as in (13.10)] plus some extra terms; these extraneous terms show that $\partial V_i/\partial x_j$ is not a tensor under general transformations. *Comment:* It is possible to express the components of $\nabla \mathbf{V}$ correctly in curvilinear coordinates by taking into account the variation of the unit vectors and scale factors as we did in Section 9. See, for example, Morse and Feshbach, p. 48.

50. Write ∇u in a familiar coordinate system (say polar coordinates) in terms of its ordinary components and in terms of its covariant components (see Problem 49). Deduce the relation between ordinary and covariant components of a vector (in orthogonal systems) as we did for ordinary and contravariant components from (13.8).

51. If U_i are the components of a covariant vector and V^j are the components of a contravariant vector, prove that $U_i V^j$ are the components of a mixed second-order tensor with one covariant index and one contravariant index. *Hint:* Write the correct transformation equations for U_i and V^j; then look at the proof of (11.15).

52. The Kronecker δ is $\delta_j^i = \begin{cases} 0, & i \neq j, \\ 1, & i = j. \end{cases}$ Prove that it is a second-order mixed tensor with one contravariant and one covariant index as indicated.

53. The quantities g^{ij} are defined as the elements of the matrix which is the reciprocal of the g_{ij} matrix. Show for orthogonal coordinate systems with scale factors h_1, h_2, h_3, that g_{ij} is diagonal with $g_{ii} = h_i^2$, and g^{ij} is also diagonal with $g^{ii} = 1/h_i^2$. Also show that $g = \det g_{ij} = h_1^2 h_2^2 h_3^2$ so that $\sqrt{g} = h_1 h_2 h_3$.

54. Using the fact that ds^2 is invariant, prove that g_{ij} is a second-order covariant tensor.

55. V_i and V^i, which are the covariant and contravariant components of a vector, are called *associated vectors* (or tensors) and the process of getting one from the other is called *raising* or *lowering indices*. It is true in general that $V^i = \sum_j g^{ij} V_j$ and $V_i = \sum_j g_{ij} V^j$. Show that, for the case of orthogonal curvilinear coordinates, these equations give the same relation we had in Section 13 between contravariant and covariant components of a vector. *Hint:* Write g_{ij} and g^{ij} in terms of the scale factors.

56. Verify that the tensor expressions for grad u, div V, and $\nabla^2 u$ in Section 14 are, for orthogonal systems, the same as those given in Section 9.

11

Functions of a Complex Variable

1. INTRODUCTION

   In Chapter 2 we discussed plotting complex numbers $z = x + iy$ in the complex plane (see Fig. 1.1) and finding values of the elementary functions of z such as roots, trigonometric functions, logarithms, etc. Now we want to discuss the calculus of functions of z, differentiation, integration, power series, etc. As you know from such topics as differential equations, Fourier series and integrals, mechanics, electricity, etc., it is often very convenient to use complex expressions. The basic facts and theorems about functions of a complex variable not only simplify many calculations but often lead to a better understanding of a problem and consequently to a more efficient method of solution. We are going to state

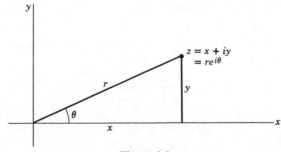

Figure 1.1

some of the basic definitions and theorems of the subject (omitting the longer proofs), and show some of their uses.

As we saw in Chapter 2, the value of a function of z for a given z is a complex number. Consider a simple function of z, namely $f(z) = z^2$. We may write

$$f(z) = z^2 = (x + iy)^2 = x^2 - y^2 + 2ixy = u(x, y) + iv(x, y),$$

where $u(x, y) = x^2 - y^2$ and $v(x, y) = 2xy$. In Chapter 2, we observed that a complex number $z = x + iy$ is equivalent to a pair of real numbers x, y. Here we may note that a function of z is equivalent to a pair of real functions, $u(x, y)$ and $v(x, y)$, of the real variables x and y. In general, we write

(1.1) $$f(z) = f(x + iy) = u(x, y) + iv(x, y),$$

where it is understood that u and v are real functions of the real variables x and y.

Recall that functions are customarily *single-valued*, that is, $f(z)$ has just one (complex) value for each z. Does this mean that we cannot define a function by a formula such as $\ln z$ or arc $\tan z$? By Chapter 2, we have

$$\ln z = \ln |z| + i(\theta + 2n\pi),$$

where $\tan \theta = y/x$. For each z, $\ln z$ has an infinite set of values. But if θ is allowed a range of only 2π, then $\ln z$ has one value for each z and this single-valued function is called a *branch* of $\ln z$. Thus in using formulas such as $\sqrt{z}$, $\ln z$, arc $\tan z$, to define functions, we always discuss a single branch at a time so that we have a single-valued function. (As a matter of terminology, however, you should know that the whole collection of branches is often called a "multiple-valued function.")

2. ANALYTIC FUNCTIONS

Definition: The derivative of $f(z)$ is defined (just as for a function of a real variable) by the equation

(2.1) $$f'(z) = \frac{df}{dz} = \lim_{\Delta z \to 0} \frac{\Delta f}{\Delta z},$$

where

$$\Delta f = f(z + \Delta z) - f(z),$$

$$\Delta z = \Delta x + i\Delta y.$$

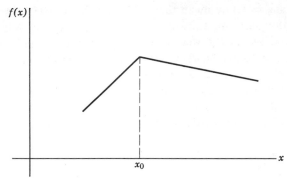

$f(x)$

x_0

x

Figure 2.1

Definition: A function $f(z)$ is *analytic* (or *regular* or *holomorphic* or *monogenic*) in a region* of the complex plane if it has a (unique) derivative at every point of the region. The statement "$f(z)$ is analytic *at a point* $z = a$" means that $f(z)$ has a derivative at every point inside some small circle about $z = a$.

Let us consider what it means for $f(z)$ to have a derivative. First think about a function $f(x)$ of a real variable x; it is possible for the limit of $\Delta f/\Delta x$ to have two values at a point x_0, as shown in Fig. 2.1—one value when we approach x_0 from the left and a different value when we approach x_0 from the right. When we say that $f(x)$ has a derivative at $x = x_0$, we mean that these two values are equal. However, for a function $f(z)$ of a complex variable z, there are an infinite number of ways we can approach a point z_0; a few ways are shown in Fig. 2.2. When we say that $f(z)$ has

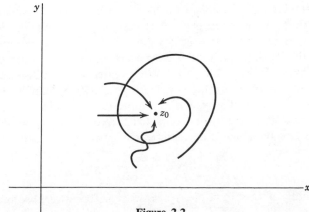

y

z_0

x

Figure 2.2

* Isolated points and curves are not regions; a region must be two-dimensional.

a derivative at $z = z_0$, we mean that $f'(z)$ [as defined by (2.1)] has the same value no matter how we approach z_0. This is an amazingly stringent requirement and we might well wonder whether there *are* any analytic functions. On the other hand, it is hard to imagine making any progress in calculus unless we can find derivatives!

Let us immediately reassure ourselves that there *are* analytic functions by using the definition (2.1) to find the derivatives of some simple functions. For example, let us show that $(d/dz)(z^2) = 2z$. By (2.1) we have

$$\frac{d}{dz}(z^2) = \lim_{\Delta z \to 0} \frac{(z + \Delta z)^2 - z^2}{\Delta z} = \lim_{\Delta z \to 0} \frac{z^2 + 2z\,\Delta z + (\Delta z)^2 - z^2}{\Delta z}$$

$$= \lim_{\Delta z \to 0} (2z + \Delta z) = 2z.$$

We see that the result is independent of *how* Δz tends to zero; thus z^2 is an analytic function. By the same method it follows that $(d/dz)(z^n) = nz^{n-1}$ if n is a positive integer. (Problem 3).

Now what we have just been doing is nothing but the familiar Δ-process! We observe that the definition (2.1) of a derivative is of exactly the same form as the corresponding definition for a function of a real variable. Because of this similarity, many familiar formulas can be proved by the same methods used in the real case, as we have just discovered in differentiating z^2. You can easily show (Problem 3) that derivatives of sums, products, and quotients follow the familiar rules and that the chain rule holds [if $f = f(g)$ and $g = g(z)$, then $df/dz = (df/dg)(dg/dz)$]. Then derivatives of rational functions of z follow the familiar real-variable formulas. If we assume the definitions and theorems of Chapters 1 and 2, we can see that the derivatives of the other elementary functions also follow the familiar formulas; for example, $(d/dz)(\sin z) = \cos z$, etc. (Problem 4).

Now you may be wondering what is new here since all our results so far seem to be just the same as for functions of a real variable. [The reason for this is that we have been discussing only functions $f(z)$ that *have* derivatives.] In Figs. 2.1 and 2.2 we pointed out the essential difference between finding $(d/dx)f(x)$ and finding $(d/dz)f(z)$, namely that there are an infinite number of ways we can approach z_0 in Fig. 2.2. To see an example of this let us try to find $(d/dz)(|z|^2)$. (Note that $|x|^2 = x^2$, and its derivative is $2x$.) If $|z|^2$ has a derivative, it is given by (2.1), that is, by

$$\lim_{\Delta z \to 0} \frac{\Delta f}{\Delta z} = \lim_{\Delta z \to 0} \frac{|z + \Delta z|^2 - |z|^2}{\Delta z}.$$

The numerator of this fraction is always real (because absolute values are real—recall $|z| = \sqrt{x^2 + y^2} = r$). Consider the denominator $\Delta z = \Delta x + i\,\Delta y$. As we approach z_0 in Fig. 2.2 (that is, let $\Delta z \to 0$), Δz has different values depending on our method of approach. For example, if we come in along a horizontal line, then $\Delta y = 0$ and $\Delta z = \Delta x$; along a vertical line $\Delta x = 0$ so $\Delta z = i\Delta y$, and along other directions Δz is some complex number; in general, Δz is neither real nor pure imaginary. Since the numerator of $\Delta f/\Delta z$ is real and the denominator may be real or imaginary (in general, complex), we see that $\lim\limits_{\Delta z \to 0} \dfrac{\Delta f}{\Delta z}$ has different values for different directions of approach to z_0, that is, $|z|^2$ is not analytic.

Now we have seen examples of both analytic and nonanalytic functions, but we still do not know how to tell whether a function has a derivative [except to appeal to (2.1)]. The following theorems answer this question.

Theorem I (which we shall prove). If $f(z) = u(x, y) + iv(x, y)$ is analytic in a region, then in that region

(2.2)
$$\frac{\partial u}{\partial x} = \frac{\partial v}{\partial y},$$
$$\frac{\partial v}{\partial x} = -\frac{\partial u}{\partial y}.$$

Cauchy–Riemann Conditions

These equations are called the *Cauchy-Riemann conditions.*

Proof. Remembering that $f = f(z)$, where $z = x + iy$, we find by the rules of partial differentiation (see Chapter 4 and Problem 3)

(2.3)
$$\frac{\partial f}{\partial x} = \frac{df}{dz}\frac{\partial z}{\partial x} = \frac{df}{dz} \cdot 1,$$
$$\frac{\partial f}{\partial y} = \frac{df}{dz}\frac{\partial z}{\partial y} = \frac{df}{dz} \cdot i.$$

Since $f = u(x, y) + iv(x, y)$ by (1.1), we also have

(2.4)
$$\frac{\partial f}{\partial x} = \frac{\partial u}{\partial x} + i\frac{\partial v}{\partial x} \quad \text{and} \quad \frac{\partial f}{\partial y} = \frac{\partial u}{\partial y} + i\frac{\partial v}{\partial y}.$$

Notice that if f has a derivative with respect to z, then it also has partial derivatives with respect to x and y by (2.3). Since a complex function has a derivative with respect to a real variable if and only if its real and imaginary parts do [see (1.1)], then by (2.4) u and v also have partial derivatives with respect to x and y. Combining (2.3) and (2.4) we have

$$\frac{df}{dz} = \frac{\partial f}{\partial x} = \frac{\partial u}{\partial x} + i\frac{\partial v}{\partial x} \quad \text{and}$$

$$\frac{df}{dz} = \frac{1}{i}\frac{\partial f}{\partial y} = \frac{1}{i}\left(\frac{\partial u}{\partial y} + i\frac{\partial v}{\partial y}\right) = \frac{\partial v}{\partial y} - i\frac{\partial u}{\partial y}.$$

Since we assumed that df/dz exists and is unique (this is what analytic means), these two expressions for df/dz must be equal. Taking real and imaginary parts, we get the Cauchy-Riemann equations (2.2).

Theorem II (which we state without proof).   If $u(x, y)$ and $v(x, y)$ and their partial derivatives with respect to x and y are continuous and satisfy the Cauchy-Riemann conditions in a region, then $f(z)$ is analytic at all points inside the region (not necessarily on the boundary).

Although we shall not prove this (for proof see texts on complex variable) we can make it plausible by showing that it is true when we approach z_0 along any straight line. We shall calculate df/dz assuming that we approach z_0 along a straight line of slope m, and we shall show that df/dz does not depend on m if u and v satisfy (2.2). The equation of the straight line of slope m through the point $z_0 = x_0 + iy_0$ is

$$y - y_0 = m(x - x_0)$$

and along this line we have $dy/dx = m$. Then we find

$$\frac{df}{dz} = \frac{du + i\,dv}{dx + i\,dy} = \frac{\dfrac{\partial u}{\partial x}\,dx + \dfrac{\partial u}{\partial y}\,dy + i\left(\dfrac{\partial v}{\partial x}\,dx + \dfrac{\partial v}{\partial y}\,dy\right)}{dx + i\,dy}$$

$$= \frac{\dfrac{\partial u}{\partial x} + \dfrac{\partial u}{\partial y}\,m + i\left(\dfrac{\partial v}{\partial x} + \dfrac{\partial v}{\partial y}\,m\right)}{1 + im}$$

Using the Cauchy-Riemann equations (2.2), we get

$$\frac{df}{dz} = \frac{\dfrac{\partial u}{\partial x} - \dfrac{\partial v}{\partial x}\,m + i\left(\dfrac{\partial v}{\partial x} + \dfrac{\partial u}{\partial x}\,m\right)}{1 + im}$$

$$= \frac{\dfrac{\partial u}{\partial x}(1 + im) + i\dfrac{\partial v}{\partial x}(1 + im)}{1 + im} = \frac{\partial u}{\partial x} + i\frac{\partial v}{\partial x}.$$

Thus df/dz has the same value when calculated for approach along *any* straight line. The theorem states that it also has the same value for approach along *any curve*.

Some definitions:

A *regular point* of $f(z)$ is a point at which $f(z)$ is analytic.

A *singular point* or *singularity* of $f(z)$ is a point at which $f(z)$ is not analytic. It is called an *isolated* singular point if $f(z)$ is analytic everywhere else inside some small circle about the singular point.

Theorem III (which we state without proof).   If $f(z)$ is analytic in a region (R in Fig. 2.3), then it has derivatives of all orders at points inside the region and can be expanded in a Taylor series about any point z_0 inside the region. The power series converges inside the circle about z_0 that extends to the nearest singular point (C in Fig. 2.3).

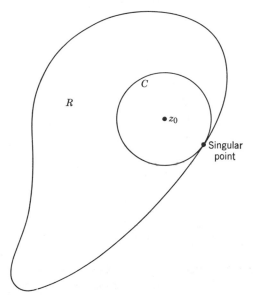

C

R

$\bullet\, z_0$

Singular
point

Figure 2.3

Notice again what a strong condition it is on $f(z)$ to say that it has a derivative. It is quite possible for a function of a real variable $f(x)$ to have a first derivative but not higher derivatives. But if $f(z)$ has a first derivative with respect to z, then it has derivatives of all orders.

This theorem also explains a fact about power series which may have puzzled you. The function $f(x) = 1/(1 + x^2)$ does not have anything peculiar about its behavior at $x = \pm 1$. Yet if we expand it in a power series

$$(2.5) \qquad \frac{1}{1 + x^2} = 1 - x^2 + x^4 - x^6 + \cdots$$

we see that the series converges only for $|x| < 1$. We can see why this happens if we consider instead

$$(2.6) \qquad f(z) = \frac{1}{1 + z^2} = 1 - z^2 + z^4 - z^6 + \cdots .$$

When $z = \pm i$, $f(z)$ and its derivatives become infinite; that is, $f(z)$ is not analytic in any region containing $z = \pm i$. The point z_0 of the theorem is the origin and the circle C (Fig. 2.4) of convergence of the series extends to the nearest singular points $\pm i$. The series converges *inside* C. Since a power series in z always converges inside its circle of convergence and diverges outside (Chapter 2, Problem 13), we see that (2.5) [which is (2.6) for $y = 0$] can converge only for $|x| < 1$.

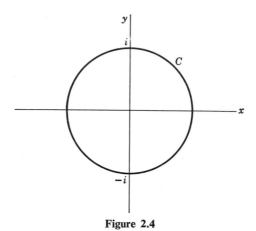

Figure 2.4

A function $\phi(x, y)$ which satisfies Laplace's equation, $\nabla^2\phi = \partial^2\phi/\partial x^2 + \partial^2\phi/\partial y^2 = 0$, is called a *harmonic* function. A great many physical problems lead to Laplace's equation, and consequently we are very much interested in finding solutions of it. (See Section 10 and Chapter 14.) The following theorem should then give you a clue as to one reason why the theory of functions of a complex variable is important in applications.

Theorem IV.   Part 1 (to be proved in Problem 6). If $f(z) = u + iv$ is analytic in a region, then u and v satisfy Laplace's equation in the region.

    Part 2 (which we state without proof). Any function u (or v) satisfying Laplace's equation in a region, is the real or imaginary part of an analytic function $f(z)$.

Thus we can find solutions of Laplace's equation simply by taking the real or imaginary parts of an analytic function of z. It is also often possible, starting with a simple function which satisfies Laplace's equation, to find the explicit function $f(z)$ of which it is, say, the real part. For example, consider the function $u(x, y) = x^2 - y^2$. We find that

$$\nabla^2 u = \frac{\partial^2 u}{\partial x^2} + \frac{\partial^2 u}{\partial y^2} = 2 - 2 = 0,$$

that is, u satisfies Laplace's equation (or u is a harmonic function). Let us find the function $v(x, y)$ such that $u + iv$ is an analytic function of z. By the Cauchy-Riemann equations

$$\frac{\partial v}{\partial y} = \frac{\partial u}{\partial x} = 2x.$$

Integrating partially with respect to y, we get

$$v(x, y) = 2xy + g(x),$$

where $g(x)$ is a function of x to be found. Differentiating partially with respect to x and again using the Cauchy-Riemann equations, we have

$$\frac{\partial v}{\partial x} = 2y + g'(x) = -\frac{\partial u}{\partial y} = 2y.$$

Thus we find

$$g'(x) = 0, \quad \text{or} \quad g = \text{const.}$$

Then

$$f(z) = u + iv = x^2 - y^2 + 2ixy + \text{const.} = z^2 + \text{const.}$$

The pair of functions u, v are called *conjugate harmonic functions*.

3. CONTOUR INTEGRALS

Theorem V. Cauchy's theorem (which we shall prove). Let C be a simple* closed curve with a continuously turning tangent except possibly at a finite number of points (that is, we allow a finite number of corners, but otherwise the curve must be "smooth"). If $f(z)$ is analytic on and inside C, then

$$(3.1) \qquad\qquad \oint_{\text{around } C} f(z)\, dz = 0.$$

(This is a line integral as in vector analysis; it is called a *contour integral* in the theory of complex variables.)

Proof.

$$(3.2) \qquad \oint_C f(z)\, dz = \oint_C (u + iv)(dx + i\, dy)$$

$$= \oint_C (u\, dx - v\, dy) + i \oint_C (v\, dx + u\, dy).$$

Green's theorem (which is Stokes' theorem when the surface area is plane; see Chapter 5, Problem 75) says that if $P(x, y)$ and $Q(x, y)$ and

---

* A simple curve is one which does not cross itself.

their partial derivatives are continuous in a simply-connected region R, then

$$(3.3) \qquad \oint_C P \, dx + Q \, dy = \iint_{\substack{\text{area inside } C}} \left(\frac{\partial Q}{\partial x} - \frac{\partial P}{\partial y} \right) dx \, dy,$$

where C is a simple closed curve in R. The curve C is traversed in a direction so that the area inclosed is always to the left. The area integral is over the area inside C, with C and the area entirely in R. Applying (3.3) to the first integral in (3.2), we get

$$(3.4) \qquad \oint_C (u \, dx - v \, dy) = \iint_{\substack{\text{area inside } C}} \left(-\frac{\partial v}{\partial x} - \frac{\partial u}{\partial y} \right) dx \, dy.$$

Since $f(z)$ is analytic, u and v and their derivatives are continuous; by the Cauchy-Riemann equations the integrand on the right of (3.4) is zero at every point of the area of integration, so the integral is equal to zero. In the same way the second integral in (3.2) is zero; thus (3.1) is proved.

Theorem VI. Cauchy's integral formula (which we shall prove). If $f(z)$ is analytic on and inside a simple closed curve C, the value of $f(z)$ at a point $z = a$ inside C is given by the following contour integral along C:

$$f(a) = \frac{1}{2\pi i} \oint \frac{f(z)}{z - a} \, dz.$$

Proof. Let a be a fixed point inside the simple closed curve C (Fig. 3.1) and consider the function

$$(3.5) \qquad \phi(z) = \frac{f(z)}{z - a},$$

where $f(z)$ is analytic on and inside C. Let C' be a small circle (inside C) with center at a and radius ρ. Make a cut between C and C' along AB (Fig. 3.1); two cuts are shown to make the picture clear, but later we shall make them coincide. We are now going to integrate along the path shown in Fig. 3.1 (in the direction shown by the arrows) from A, around C, to B, around C', and back to A. Notice that the area between the curves C and C' is always to the left of the path of integration and is inclosed by it. In this area between C and C', the function $\phi(z)$ is analytic; we have cut out a small circle about the point $z = a$ at which $\phi(z)$ is not analytic. Cauchy's theorem then applies to the integral along the combined path consisting of C counterclockwise, C' clockwise, and the two cuts. The two integrals, in opposite directions along the cuts, cancel when

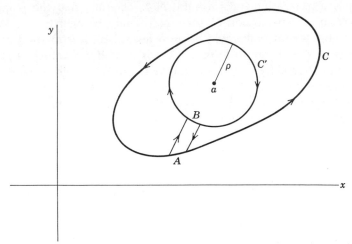

Figure 3.1

the cuts are made to coincide. Thus we have

$$\oint_{C \text{ counterclockwise}} \phi(z)\, dz + \oint_{C' \text{ clockwise}} \phi(z)\, dz = 0 \qquad \text{or}$$

(3.6)

$$\oint_{C} \phi(z)\, dz = \oint_{C'} \phi(z)\, dz \qquad \text{where both are counterclockwise.}$$

Along the circle C', $z = a + \rho e^{i\theta}$, $dz = \rho i e^{i\theta}\, d\theta$, and (3.6) becomes

(3.7)

$$\oint_{C} \phi(z)\, dz = \oint_{C'} \phi(z)\, dz = \oint_{C'} \frac{f(z)}{z - a}\, dz$$

$$= \int_{0}^{2\pi} \frac{f(z)}{\rho e^{i\theta}} \rho i e^{i\theta}\, d\theta = \int_{0}^{2\pi} f(z) i\, d\theta.$$

Since our calculation is valid for any (sufficiently small) value of ρ, we shall let $\rho \to 0$ (that is, $z \to a$) to simplify the formula. Because $f(z)$ is continuous at $z = a$ (it is analytic inside C), $\lim_{z \to a} f(z) = f(a)$. Then (3.7) becomes

(3.8)

$$\oint_{C} \phi(z)\, dz = \oint_{C} \frac{f(z)}{z - a}\, dz = \int_{0}^{2\pi} f(z) i\, d\theta$$

$$= \int_{0}^{2\pi} f(a) i\, d\theta = 2\pi i f(a)$$

or

(3.9)

$$f(a) = \frac{1}{2\pi i} \oint_{C} \frac{f(z)}{z - a}\, dz, \qquad a \text{ inside } C.$$

This is Cauchy's integral formula. Note carefully that the point a is inside C; if a were outside C, then $\phi(z)$ would be analytic everywhere inside C and the integral would be zero instead of $2\pi i f(a)$ (by Cauchy's theorem). A useful way to look at (3.9) is this: If the values of $f(z)$ are given on the boundary of a region (curve C), then (3.9) gives the value of $f(z)$ at any point a inside C. With this interpretation you will find Cauchy's integral formula written with a replaced by z, and z replaced by some different dummy integration variable, say w:

$$(3.10) \qquad f(z) = \frac{1}{2\pi i} \oint_C \frac{f(w)}{w - z} \, dw, \qquad z \text{ inside } C.$$

(See Problem 51 for an important use of this theorem.)

4. LAURENT SERIES

Theorem VII. Laurent's theorem [equation (4.1)] (which we shall state without proof). Let C_1 and C_2 be two circles with center at z_0. Let $f(z)$ be analytic in the region R between the circles. Then $f(z)$ can be expanded in a series of the form

$$(4.1)$$

$$f(z) = a_0 + a_1(z - z_0) + a_2(z - z_0)^2 + \cdots + \frac{b_1}{z - z_0} + \frac{b_2}{(z - z_0)^2} + \cdots$$

convergent in R.

Such a series is called a *Laurent series*. The "b" series in (4.1) is called the *principal part* of the Laurent series.

Example. Consider the Laurent series

$$(4.2) \qquad f(z) = 1 + \frac{z}{2} + \frac{z^2}{4} + \frac{z^3}{8} + \cdots + \left(\frac{z}{2}\right)^n + \cdots$$

$$+ \frac{1}{z^2} + \frac{1}{z^3} + \cdots + \frac{1}{z^n} + \cdots.$$

Let us see where this series converges. First consider the series of positive powers; by the ratio test (see Chapters 1 and 2), this series converges for $|z/2| < 1$, that is, for $|z| < 2$. Similarly, the series of negative powers converges for $|1/z| < 1$, that is, $|z| > 1$. Then both series converge (and so the Laurent series converges) for $|z|$ between 1 and 2, that is, in a ring between two circles of radii 1 and 2.

We expect this result in general. The "a" series is a power series, and a power series converges *inside* some circle (say C_2 in Fig. 4.1). The "b" series is a series of inverse powers of z, and so converges for $|1/z| <$ some constant; thus the "b" series converges *outside* some circle (say C_1 in

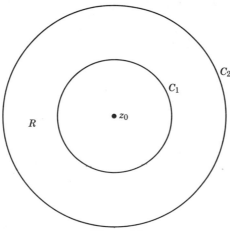

Figure 4.1

Fig. 4.1). Then a Laurent series converges between two circles (if it converges at all). (Note that the inner circle may be a point and the outer circle may have infinite radius.)

The formulas for the coefficients in (4.1) are (Problem 15)

$$(4.3) \quad a_n = \frac{1}{2\pi i} \oint_C \frac{f(z)\,dz}{(z - z_0)^{n+1}}, \qquad b_n = \frac{1}{2\pi i} \oint_C \frac{f(z)\,dz}{(z - z_0)^{-n+1}},$$

where C is any simple closed curve surrounding z_0 and lying in R. However, this is not usually the easiest way to find a Laurent series. Like power series about a point, the Laurent series (about z_0) for a function in a given annular ring (about z_0) where the function is analytic, is unique, and we can find it by any method we choose. (See examples below.) *Warning:* If $f(z)$ has several isolated singularities (Fig. 4.2), there are several annular rings, R_1, R_2, etc., in which $f(z)$ is analytic; then there are several different Laurent series for $f(z)$, one for each ring. The Laurent series which we usually want is the one that converges near z_0. If you have any doubt about the ring of convergence of a Laurent series, you can find out by testing the "a" series and the "b" series separately.

Example.   Let us find the Laurent series for the function $f(z)$ in (4.2) that converges for $0 < |z| < 1$. By summing the geometric progressions,

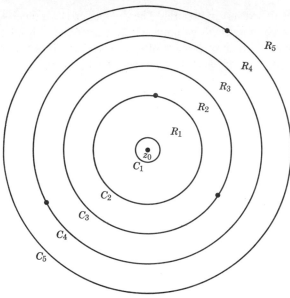

Figure 4.2

we find

(4.4) $$f(z) = \frac{1}{1 - z/2} + \frac{1/z^2}{1 - 1/z} = \frac{1}{1 - z/2} - \frac{1}{z}\frac{1}{1 - z}$$

$$= \frac{1}{1 - z/2} - \frac{1}{1 - z} - \frac{1}{z}.$$

The terms $1/(1 - z/2)$ and $1/(1 - z)$ can be expanded in power series which converge for $|z| < 1$ as required. The "b" series contains only one term, namely $-1/z$. We get

(4.5) $$f(z) = \left(1 + \frac{z}{2} + \frac{z^2}{4} + \cdots\right) - (1 + z + z^2 + \cdots) - \frac{1}{z}$$

$$= -\frac{z}{2} - \frac{3}{4}z^2 - \cdots - \frac{1}{z}.$$

Both (4.2) and (4.5) are Laurent series for the function $f(z)$ in (4.4); (4.5) is valid for $0 < |z| < 1$, whereas (4.2) is valid for $1 < |z| < 2$. (See Problem 16.)

Let z_0 in Fig. 4.1 be either a regular point or an isolated singular point and assume that there are no other singular points inside C_1. Let $f(z)$ (which is analytic between C_1 and C_2) be expanded in the Laurent series about $z = z_0$ which converges between C_1 and C_2. (Note that C_1 may be as small a circle as we like since there are no singularities inside C_1 except possibly z_0; thus we may say that we expand $f(z)$ in the Laurent series which converges near z_0.) Then we have the following definitions.

Definitions:

If all the b's are zero, $f(z)$ is analytic at $z = z_0$, and we call z_0 a *regular point*. (See Problem 18.)

If $b_n \neq 0$, but all the b's after b_n are zero, $f(z)$ is said to have a *pole of order n* at $z = z_0$. If $n = 1$, we say that $f(z)$ has a *simple pole*.

If there are an infinite number of b's different from zero, $f(z)$ has an *essential singularity* at $z = z_0$.

The coefficient b_1 of $1/(z - z_0)$ is called the *residue* of $f(z)$ at $z = z_0$.

Examples:

$$e^z = 1 + z + \frac{z^2}{2!} + \frac{z^3}{3!} + \cdots$$

is analytic at $z = 0$; the residue of e^z at $z = 0$ is 0.

$$\frac{e^z}{z^3} = \frac{1}{z^3} + \frac{1}{z^2} + \frac{1}{2!\, z} + \frac{1}{3!} + \cdots$$

has a pole of order 3 at $z = 0$; the residue of e^z/z^3 at $z = 0$ is $1/2!$.

$$e^{1/z} = 1 + \frac{1}{z} + \frac{1}{2!\, z^2} + \cdots$$

has an essential singularity at $z = 0$; the residue of $e^{1/z}$ at $z = 0$ is 1.

5. THE RESIDUE THEOREM

Let z_0 be an isolated singular point of $f(z)$. We are going to find the value of $\oint_C f(z)\, dz$ around a simple closed curve C surrounding z_0 but inclosing no other singularities. Let $f(z)$ be expanded in the Laurent series (4.1) about $z = z_0$ that converges near $z = z_0$. By Cauchy's theorem (V), the integral of the "a" series is zero since this part is analytic. To evaluate the integrals of the terms in the "b" series in (4.1), we replace the integrals around C by integrals around a circle C' with center at z_0 and radius ρ as in (3.6), (3.7), and Fig. 3.1. Along C', $z = z_0 + \rho e^{i\theta}$; calculating the integral of the b_1 term in (4.1), we find

(5.1) $$\oint_C \frac{b_1\, dz}{(z - z_0)} = b_1 \int_0^{2\pi} \frac{\rho i e^{i\theta}\, d\theta}{\rho e^{i\theta}} = 2\pi i b_1.$$

It is straightforward to show (Problem 15) that the integrals of all the other b_n terms are zero. Then $\oint_C f(z)\,dz = 2\pi i b_1$, or since b_1 is called the residue of $f(z)$ at $z = z_0$, we can say

$$\oint_C f(z)\,dz = 2\pi i \cdot \text{residue of } f(z) \text{ at the singular point inside } C.$$

The only term of the Laurent series which has survived the integration process is the b_1 term; you can see the reason for the term "residue." If

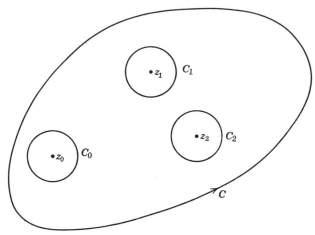

Figure 5.1

there are several isolated singularities inside C, say at $z_0, z_1, z_2, \ldots$, we draw small circles about each as shown in Fig. 5.1 so that $f(z)$ is analytic in the region between C and the circles. Then, introducing cuts as in the proof of Cauchy's integral formula, we find that the integral around C counterclockwise, plus the integrals around the circles clockwise, is zero (since the integrals along the cuts cancel), or the integral along C is the sum of the integrals around the circles (all counterclockwise). But by (5.1), the integral around each circle is $2\pi i$ times the residue of $f(z)$ at the singular point inside. Thus we have the *residue theorem*:

$$(5.2) \qquad \oint_C f(z)\,dz = 2\pi i \cdot \text{sum of the residues of } f(z) \text{ inside } C,$$

where the integral around C is in the counterclockwise direction.

This theorem is very useful in evaluating many definite integrals. In order to use it, we need to have some techniques for finding residues.

6. METHODS OF FINDING RESIDUES

A. Laurent series. If it is easy to write down the Laurent series for $f(z)$ about $z = z_0$ that is valid near z_0, then the residue is just the coefficient b_1 of the term $1/(z - z_0)$. *Caution:* Be sure you have the expansion about $z = z_0$; the series you have memorized for e^z, $\sin z$, etc., are expansions about $z = 0$ and so can be used only for finding residues at the origin (see the examples at the end of Section 4). Here is another example: Given $f(z) = e^z/(z - 1)$, find the residue, $R(1)$, of $f(z)$ at $z = 1$. We want to expand e^z in powers of $z - 1$; we write

$$\frac{e^z}{z - 1} = \frac{e \cdot e^{z-1}}{z - 1} = \frac{e}{z - 1}\left[1 + (z - 1) + \frac{(z - 1)^2}{2!} + \cdots\right]$$

$$= \frac{e}{z - 1} + e + \cdots.$$

Then the residue is the coefficient of $1/(z - 1)$, that is,

$$R(1) = e.$$

B. Simple pole. If $f(z)$ has a simple pole at $z = z_0$, we find the residue by multiplying $f(z)$ by $(z - z_0)$ and evaluating the result at $z = z_0$ (Problem 21a).

Example 1.   Find $R(0)$ for $f(z) = (\cos z)/z$.
Since $zf(z) = \cos z$, we have

$$R(0) = (\cos z)_{z=0} = \cos 0 = 1.$$

To use this method, we may in some problems have to evaluate an indeterminate form, so in general we write

(6.1) $R(z_0) = \lim_{z \to z_0} (z - z_0)f(z)$ when z_0 is a simple pole.

Example 2.   Find the residue of $\cot z$ at $z = 0$.
By (6.1),

$$R(0) = \lim_{z \to 0} \frac{z \cos z}{\sin z} = \cos 0 \cdot \lim_{z \to 0} \frac{z}{\sin z} = 1 \cdot 1 = 1.$$

If, as often happens, $f(z)$ can be written as $g(z)/h(z)$, where $g(z)$ is analytic and not zero at z_0 and $h(z_0) = 0$, then (6.1) becomes

(6.2) $R(z_0) = \lim_{z \to z_0} \frac{(z - z_0)g(z)}{h(z)} = g(z_0) \lim_{z \to z_0} \frac{z - z_0}{h(z)}$

$$= g(z_0) \lim_{z \to z_0} \frac{1}{h'(z)} = \frac{g(z_0)}{h'(z_0)}$$

FUNCTIONS OF A COMPLEX VARIABLE

by l'Hospital's rule or the definition of $h'(z)$ (Problem 21b). Often (6.2) gives the most convenient way of finding the residue at a simple pole.

Example 3. Find the residue of $(\sin z)/(1 - z^4)$ at $z = i$.
By (6.2) we have

$$R(i) = \frac{\sin z}{-4z^3}\Bigg|_{z=i} = \frac{\sin i}{-4i^3} = \frac{e^{-1} - e}{(2i)(4i)}$$

$$= \tfrac{1}{8}(e - e^{-1}) = \tfrac{1}{4}\sinh 1.$$

Now you may ask how you know, without finding the Laurent series, that a function has a simple pole. Perhaps the simplest answer is that if the limit we calculated above is some constant (not 0 or ∞), then $f(z)$ *does* have a simple pole and the constant is the residue. However, you can usually recognize a simple pole in advance. Suppose $f(z)$ is written in the form $g(z)/h(z)$, where $g(z)$ and $h(z)$ are analytic. Then you can think of $g(z)$ and $h(z)$ as power series in $(z - z_0)$. If the denominator has the factor $(z - z_0)$ to *one* higher power than the numerator, then $f(z)$ has a simple pole at z_0. For example,

$$\frac{\sin z}{z^2} = \frac{z - \dfrac{z^3}{3!} + \cdots}{z^2} = \frac{1}{z} - \frac{z}{3!} + \cdots$$

has a simple pole at $z = 0$. By the same method we can see whether a function has a pole of any order.

C. Multiple poles. When $f(z)$ has a pole of order n, we can use the following method of finding residues. Multiply $f(z)$ by $(z - z_0)^m$, where m is an integer greater than or equal to the order n of the pole, differentiate the result $m - 1$ times, divide by $(m - 1)!$, and evaluate the resulting expression at $z = z_0$. It is easy to prove that this rule is correct (Problem 21c) by using the Laurent series (4.1) for $f(z)$ and showing that the result of the outlined process is b_1.

Example. Find the residue of $f(z) = (z \sin z)/(z - \pi)^3$ at $z = \pi$.
We take $m = 3$ to eliminate the denominator before differentiating; this is an allowed choice for m because the order of the pole of $f(z)$ at π is not greater than 3 since $z \sin z$ is finite at π. (The pole is actually of order 2, but we do not need this fact.) Then following the rule stated, we get

$$R(\pi) = \frac{1}{2!}\frac{d^2}{dz^2}(z \sin z)\Bigg|_{z=\pi} = \tfrac{1}{2}[-z \sin z + 2 \cos z]_{z=\pi} = -1.$$

(To compute the derivative quickly, use Leibniz' rule for differentiating a product; see Chapter 12, Section 3.)

7. EVALUATION OF DEFINITE INTEGRALS BY USE OF THE RESIDUE THEOREM

We are going to use (5.2) and the techniques of Section 6 to evaluate several different types of definite integrals. The methods are best shown by examples.

Example 1.   Find $I = \displaystyle\int_0^{2\pi} \frac{d\theta}{5 + 4\cos\theta}$.

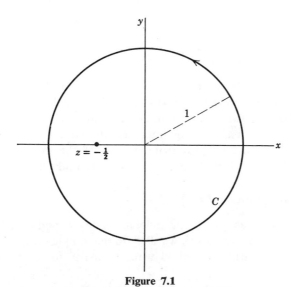

Figure 7.1

If we make the change of variable $z = e^{i\theta}$, then as θ goes from 0 to 2π, z traverses the unit circle $|z| = 1$ (Fig. 7.1) in the counterclockwise direction, and we have a contour integral. We shall evaluate this integral by the residue theorem. If $z = e^{i\theta}$, we have

$$dz = ie^{i\theta}\, d\theta = iz\, d\theta \qquad \text{or} \quad d\theta = \frac{1}{iz}\, dz,$$

$$\cos\theta = \frac{e^{i\theta} + e^{-i\theta}}{2} = \frac{z + \dfrac{1}{z}}{2}.$$

Making these substitutions in I, we get

$$I = \oint_C \frac{\frac{1}{iz}\, dz}{5 + 2(z + 1/z)} = \frac{1}{i} \oint_C \frac{dz}{5z + 2z^2 + 2}$$

$$= \frac{1}{i} \oint_C \frac{dz}{(2z + 1)(z + 2)},$$

where C is the unit circle. The integrand has poles at $z = -\frac{1}{2}$ and $z = -2$; only $z = -\frac{1}{2}$ is inside the contour C. The residue of $\dfrac{1}{(2z + 1)(z + 2)}$ at $z = -\frac{1}{2}$ is

$$R(-\tfrac{1}{2}) = \lim_{z \to -\frac{1}{2}} (z + \tfrac{1}{2}) \cdot \frac{1}{(2z + 1)(z + 2)} = \frac{1}{2(z + 2)}\bigg|_{z=-\frac{1}{2}} = \frac{1}{3}.$$

Then by the residue theorem

$$I = \frac{1}{i}\, 2\pi i R(-\tfrac{1}{2}) = 2\pi \cdot \frac{1}{3} = \frac{2\pi}{3}.$$

This method can be used to evaluate the integral of any rational function of $\sin\theta$ and $\cos\theta$ between 0 and 2π, provided the denominator is never zero for any value of θ. You can also find an integral from 0 to π if the integrand is even, since the integral from 0 to 2π of an even periodic function is twice the integral from 0 to π of the same function. (See Chapter 6, Section 9 for discussion of even and odd functions.)

Example 2.   Evaluate $I = \displaystyle\int_{-\infty}^{\infty} \frac{dx}{1 + x^2}$.

Here we could easily find the indefinite integral and so evaluate I by elementary methods. However, we shall do this simple problem by contour integration to illustrate a method which is useful for more complicated problems.

This time we are not going to make a change of variable in I. We are going to start with a different integral and show how to find I from it. We consider $\displaystyle\oint_C \frac{dz}{1 + z^2}$, where C is the closed boundary of the semicircle shown in Fig. 7.2. For any $\rho > 1$, the semicircle incloses the singular point $z = i$ and no others; the residue of the integrand at $z = i$ is

$$R(i) = \lim_{z \to i} (z - i) \frac{1}{(z - i)(z + i)} = \frac{1}{2i}.$$

Then the value of the contour integral is $2\pi i(1/2i) = \pi$. Let us write the integral in two parts: (1) an integral along the x-axis from $-\rho$ to ρ; for this part $z = x$; (2) an integral along the semicircle, where $z = \rho e^{i\theta}$. Then we have

(7.1)
$$\int_c \frac{dz}{1+z^2} = \int_{-\rho}^{\rho} \frac{dx}{1+x^2} + \int_0^{\pi} \frac{\rho i e^{i\theta}\, d\theta}{1+\rho^2 e^{2i\theta}}.$$

We know that the value of the contour integral is π no matter how large ρ becomes since there are no other singular points besides $z = i$ in the upper half-plane. Let $\rho \to \infty$; then the second integral on the right in (7.1) tends to zero since the numerator contains ρ and the denominator ρ^2.

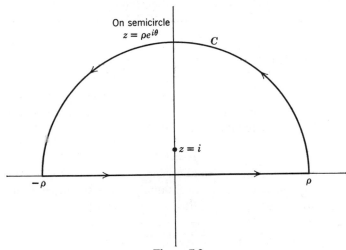

Figure 7.2

Thus the first term on the right tends to π (the value of the contour integral) as $\rho \to \infty$ and we have

$$I = \int_{-\infty}^{\infty} \frac{dx}{1+x^2} = \pi.$$

This method can be used to evaluate any integral of the form

$$\int_{-\infty}^{\infty} \frac{P(x)}{Q(x)}\, dx$$

if $P(x)$ and $Q(x)$ are polynomials with the degree of Q at least two greater than the degree of P, and if $Q(z)$ has no real zeros (that is, zeros on the x-axis). If the integrand $P(x)/Q(x)$ is an even function, then we can also find the integral from 0 to ∞.

Example 3. Evaluate $I = \displaystyle\int_0^{\infty} \frac{\cos x\, dx}{1+x^2}$.

We consider the contour integral

$$\oint_C \frac{e^{iz}\, dz}{1 + z^2},$$

where C is the same semicircular contour as in Example 2. The singular point inclosed is again $z = i$, and the residue there is

$$\lim_{z \to i} (z - i) \frac{e^{iz}}{(z - i)(z + i)} = \frac{e^{-1}}{2i} = \frac{1}{2ie}.$$

The value of the contour integral is $2\pi i(1/2ie) = \pi/e$. As in Example 2 we write the contour integral as a sum of two integrals:

$$(7.2) \qquad \oint_C \frac{e^{iz}\, dz}{1 + z^2} = \int_{-\rho}^{\rho} \frac{e^{ix}\, dx}{1 + x^2} + \underset{\substack{\text{along upper half} \\ \text{of } z = \rho e^{i\theta}}}{\int} \frac{e^{iz}\, dz}{1 + z^2}.$$

As before, we want to show that the second integral on the right of (7.2) tends to zero as $\rho \to \infty$. This integral is the same as the corresponding integral in (7.1) except for the e^{iz} factor. Now

$$|e^{iz}| = |e^{ix-y}| = |e^{ix}|\,|e^{-y}| = e^{-y} \le 1$$

since $y \ge 0$ on the contour we are considering. Since $|e^{iz}| \le 1$, this factor does not change the proof given in Example 2 that the integral along the semicircle tends to zero as the radius $\rho \to \infty$. We have then

$$\int_{-\infty}^{\infty} \frac{e^{ix}}{1 + x^2}\, dx = \frac{\pi}{e},$$

or taking the real part of both sides of this equation,

$$\int_{-\infty}^{\infty} \frac{\cos x}{1 + x^2}\, dx = \frac{\pi}{e}.$$

Since the integrand $(\cos x)/(1 + x^2)$ is an even function, the integral from 0 to ∞ is half the integral from $-\infty$ to ∞. Hence we have

$$I = \int_{0}^{\infty} \frac{\cos x\, dx}{1 + x^2} = \frac{\pi}{2e}.$$

Observe that the same proof would work if we replaced e^{iz} by e^{imz} ($m > 0$) in the above integrals. At the point where we said $e^{-y} \le 1$ (since $y \ge 0$) we would then want $e^{-my} \le 1$ for $y \ge 0$, which is true if $m > 0$. [For $m < 0$, we *could* use a semicircle in the lower half-plane ($y < 0$); then we would have $e^{my} \le 1$ for $y \le 0$. This is an unnecessary complication, however, in evaluating integrals containing $\sin mx$ or $\cos mx$ since we *can* then choose m to be positive.] Although we have assumed here that (as in Example 2) $Q(x)$ is of degree at least 2 higher than $P(x)$, a more detailed proof (see books on complex variable) shows that degree at least one higher is enough to make the integral

$$\int \frac{P(z)}{Q(z)} e^{imz} \, dz$$

around the semicircle tend to zero as $\rho \to \infty$. Thus

$$\int_{-\infty}^{\infty} \frac{P(x)}{Q(x)} e^{imx} \, dx = 2\pi i \cdot \text{sum of the residues of } \frac{P(z)}{Q(z)} e^{imz}$$

in the upper half-plane if all the following requirements are met:

$P(x)$ and $Q(x)$ are polynomials, and

$Q(x)$ has no real zeros, and

the degree of $Q(x)$ is at least 1 greater than the degree of $P(x)$, and

$m > 0$.

By taking real and imaginary parts, we then find the integrals

$$\int_{-\infty}^{\infty} \frac{P(x)}{Q(x)} \cos mx \, dx, \qquad \int_{-\infty}^{\infty} \frac{P(x)}{Q(x)} \sin mx \, dx.$$

Example 4. Evaluate $\displaystyle\int_{-\infty}^{\infty} \frac{\sin x}{x} \, dx$.

Here we remove the restriction of Examples 2 and 3 that $Q(x)$ has no real zeros. As in Example 3, we consider $\displaystyle\int \frac{e^{iz}}{z} \, dz$; to avoid the singular point at $z = 0$, we integrate around the contour shown in Fig. 7.3. We then let the radius r shrink to zero so that in effect we are integrating straight through the simple pole at the origin. We are going to show (later in this section and Problem 25) that the net result of integrating in the counterclockwise direction around a closed contour which passes straight* through one or more simple poles is $2\pi i \cdot$ (sum of the residues at interior points plus one-half the sum of the residues at the simple poles on the boundary). (*Warning:* this rule does not hold in general for a multiple pole on a boundary.) You might expect this result. If a pole is inside a contour, it contributes $2\pi i \cdot$ residue, to the integral; if it is outside, it contributes nothing; if it is *on* the straight line boundary, its contribution is just halfway between zero and $2\pi i \cdot$ residue. Using this fact, and observing that, as in Example 3, the integral along the large semicircle tends to zero as R tends to infinity, we have

$$\int_{-\infty}^{\infty} \frac{e^{ix}}{x} \, dx = 2\pi i \cdot \tfrac{1}{2}\left(\text{residue of } \frac{e^{iz}}{z} \text{ at } z = 0\right)$$

$$= 2\pi i \cdot \tfrac{1}{2} \cdot 1 = i\pi.$$

* By "straight" we mean that the contour curve has a tangent at the pole, that is, it does not turn a corner there.

To show more carefully that our result is correct, let us return to the contour of Fig. 7.3. Since e^{iz}/z is analytic inside this contour, the integral around the whole contour is zero. As we have said, the integral along C

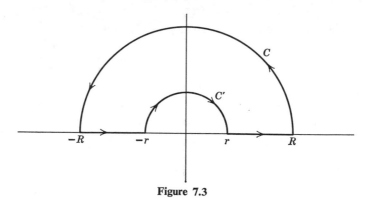

Figure 7.3

tends to zero as $R \to \infty$ by the theorem at the end of Example 3. Along the small semicircle C', we have

$$z = re^{i\theta}, \qquad dz = re^{i\theta}i\,d\theta, \qquad \frac{dz}{z} = i\,d\theta,$$

$$\int_{C'} \frac{e^{iz}\,dz}{z} = \int_{C'} e^{iz}i\,d\theta.$$

As $r \to 0$, $z \to 0$, $e^{iz} \to 1$, and the integral (along C' in the direction indicated in Fig. 7.3) tends to

$$\int_\pi^0 i\,d\theta = -i\pi.$$

Then we have as $R \to \infty$, and $r \to 0$,

$$\int_{-\infty}^\infty \frac{e^{ix}}{x}\,dx - i\pi = 0$$

or

$$\int_{-\infty}^\infty \frac{e^{ix}}{x}\,dx = i\pi$$

as before.

Principal value. Taking real and imaginary parts of this equation (using $e^{ix} = \cos x + i \sin x$), we get

$$\int_{-\infty}^\infty \frac{\cos x}{x}\,dx = 0, \qquad \int_{-\infty}^\infty \frac{\sin x}{x}\,dx = \pi.$$

Since $(\sin x)/x$ is an even function, we have

$$\int_0^\infty \frac{\sin x}{x}\, dx = \frac{1}{2}\int_{-\infty}^\infty \frac{\sin x}{x}\, dx = \frac{\pi}{2}\,.$$

However, $\displaystyle\int_0^\infty \frac{\cos x}{x}\, dx$ is a divergent integral since the integrand $(\cos x)/x$ is approximately $1/x$ near $x = 0$. The value zero which we found for $I = \displaystyle\int_{-\infty}^\infty \frac{\cos x}{x}\, dx$ is called the *principal value* (or Cauchy principal value) of I. To see what this means, consider a simpler integral, namely $\displaystyle\int_0^5 \frac{dx}{x-3}$. The integrand becomes infinite at $x = 3$, and both $\displaystyle\int_0^3 \frac{dx}{x-3}$ and $\displaystyle\int_3^5 \frac{dx}{x-3}$ are divergent. Suppose we cut out a small symmetric interval about $x = 3$, and integrate from 0 to $3 - r$ and from $3 + r$ to 5. We find

$$\int_0^{3-r} \frac{dx}{x-3} = \Big[\ln|x-3|\Big]_0^{3-r} = \ln r - \ln 3,$$

$$\int_{3+r}^5 \frac{dx}{x-3} = \ln 2 - \ln r.$$

The sum of these two integrals is

$$\ln 2 - \ln 3 = \ln \tfrac{2}{3};$$

this sum is independent of r. Thus, if we let $r \to 0$, we get the result $\ln \tfrac{2}{3}$ which is called the principal value of

$$\int_0^5 \frac{dx}{x-3} \quad \left(\text{often written } PV \int_0^5 \frac{dx}{x-3} = \ln \tfrac{2}{3}\right).$$

The terms $\ln r$ and $-\ln r$ have been allowed to cancel each other; graphically an infinite area above the x-axis and a corresponding infinite area below the x-axis have been canceled. In computing the contour integral, we integrated along the x-axis from $-\infty$ up to $-r$, and from $+r$ to $+\infty$, and then let $r \to 0$; this is just the process we have described for finding principal values, so the result we found for the improper integral $\displaystyle\int_{-\infty}^\infty \frac{\cos x}{x}\, dx$, namely zero, was the principal value of this integral.

Example 5. Evaluate $\displaystyle\int_0^\infty \frac{r^{p-1}}{1+r}\, dr$, $0 < p < 1$, and use the result to prove (5.4) of Chapter 9.

We first find

(7.3) $$\oint \frac{z^{p-1}}{1+z}\,dz, \qquad 0 < p < 1, \quad \text{around } C \text{ in Fig. 7.4.}$$

Before we can evaluate this integral, we must ask what z^{p-1} means, since for each z there may be more than one value of z^{p-1}. (See discussion of branches at the end of Section 1.) For example, consider the case $p = \tfrac{1}{2}$;

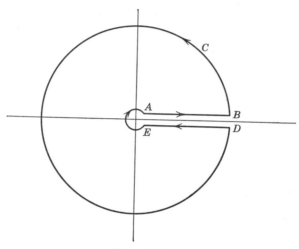

Figure 7.4

then $z^{p-1} = z^{-\frac{1}{2}}$. Recall from Chapter 2, Section 10, that there are two square roots of any complex number. At a point where $\theta = \pi/4$, say, we have $z = re^{i\pi/4}$, $z^{-\frac{1}{2}} = \dfrac{1}{\sqrt{r}}\,e^{-i\pi/8}$. But if θ increases by 2π (we think of following a circle around the origin and back to our starting point), we have $z = re^{i(\pi/4+2\pi)}$, $z^{-\frac{1}{2}} = \dfrac{1}{\sqrt{r}}\,e^{-i(\pi/8+\pi)} = -\dfrac{1}{\sqrt{r}}\,e^{-i\pi/8}$. Similarly, for any starting point (with $r \neq 0$), we find that $z^{-\frac{1}{2}}$ or z^{p-1} comes back to a different value (different branch) when θ increases by 2π and we return to our starting point. If we want to use the formula z^{p-1} to define a (single-valued) function, we must decide on some interval of length 2π for θ (that is, we must select one branch of z^{p-1}). Let us agree to restrict θ to the values of 0 to 2π in evaluating the contour integral (7.3). We may imagine an artificial barrier or cut (which we agree not to cross) along the positive x-axis; this is called a *branch cut*. A point which we cannot encircle (on an arbitrarily small circle) without crossing a branch cut (thus changing to another branch) is called a *branch point*; the origin is a branch point here.

In Fig. 7.4, then, $\theta = 0$ along AB (upper side of the positive x-axis); when we follow C around to DE, θ increases by 2π, so $\theta = 2\pi$ on the lower side of the positive x-axis. Note that the contour in Fig. 7.4 never takes us outside the 0 to 2π interval, so the factor z^{p-1} in (7.3) is a single-valued function. The integrand in (7.3), namely $z^{p-1}/(1 + z)$, is now an analytic function inside the closed curve C in Fig. 7.4 except for the pole at $z = -1 = e^{i\pi}$. The residue there is $(e^{i\pi})^{p-1} = -e^{i\pi p}$. Then we have

$$(7.4) \qquad \oint_C \frac{z^{p-1}}{1 + z}\, dz = -2\pi i e^{i\pi p}, \qquad 0 < p < 1.$$

Along either of the two circles in Fig. 7.4 we have $z = re^{i\theta}$ and the integral is

$$\int \frac{r^{p-1}e^{i(p-1)\theta}}{1 + re^{i\theta}}\, rie^{i\theta}\, d\theta = i\int \frac{r^p e^{ip\theta}}{1 + re^{i\theta}}\, d\theta.$$

This integral tends to zero if $r \to 0$ or if $r \to \infty$. (Verify this; note that the denominator is approximately 1 for small r, and approximately $re^{i\theta}$ for large r.) Thus the integrals along the circular parts of the contour tend to zero as the little circle shrinks to a point and the large circle expands indefinitely. We are left with the two integrals along the positive x-axis with AB now extending from 0 to ∞ and DE from ∞ to 0. Along AB we agreed to have $\theta = 0$, so $z = re^{i \cdot 0} = r$, and this integral is

$$\int_{r=0}^{\infty} \frac{r^{p-1}}{1 + r}\, dr.$$

Along DE, we have $\theta = 2\pi$, so $z = re^{2\pi i}$ and this integral is

$$\int_{r=\infty}^{0} \frac{(re^{2\pi i})^{p-1}}{1 + re^{2\pi i}}\, e^{2\pi i}\, dr = -\int_0^{\infty} \frac{r^{p-1}e^{2\pi i p}}{1 + r}\, dr.$$

Adding the AB and DE integrals, we get

$$(1 - e^{2\pi i p})\int_0^{\infty} \frac{r^{p-1}}{1 + r}\, dr = -2\pi i e^{i\pi p}$$

by (7.4). Then the desired integral is

$$(7.5) \qquad \int_0^{\infty} \frac{r^{p-1}}{1 + r}\, dr = \frac{-2\pi i e^{i\pi p}}{1 - e^{2\pi i p}} = \frac{\pi \cdot 2i}{e^{i\pi p} - e^{-i\pi p}} = \frac{\pi}{\sin \pi p}.$$

Let us use (7.5) to obtain (5.4) of Chapter 9. Putting $q = 1 - p$ in (6.5) and (7.1) of Chapter 9, we have

$$B(p, 1 - p) = \int_0^\infty \frac{y^{p-1}}{1 + y}\, dy \qquad \text{and}$$

(7.6)

$$B(p, 1 - p) = \Gamma(p)\Gamma(1 - p) \qquad \text{since } \Gamma(1) = 1.$$

Combining (7.5) and (7.6) gives (5.4) of Chapter 9, namely

$$\Gamma(p)\Gamma(1 - p) = B(p, 1 - p) = \int_0^\infty \frac{y^{p-1}}{1 + y}\, dy = \frac{\pi}{\sin \pi p}.$$

Example 6. Since $w = f(z)$ is a complex number for each z, we can write $w = Re^{i\Theta}$ (just as we write $z = re^{i\theta}$) where $R = |w|$ and Θ is the angle of w [or we could call it the angle of $f(z)$]. As z changes, $w = f(z)$ also changes and so R and Θ vary as we go from point to point in the complex (x, y) plane. We want to show that

(a) if $f(z)$ is analytic on and inside a simple closed curve C and $f(z) \neq 0$ on C, then the number of zeros of $f(z)$ inside C is equal to $(1/2\pi) \cdot$ (change in the angle of $f(z)$ as we traverse the curve C);

(b) if $f(z)$ has a finite number of poles inside C, but otherwise meets the requirements stated,* then the change in the angle of $f(z)$ around C is equal to $(2\pi) \cdot$ (the number of zeros minus the number of poles).

(Just as we say that a quadratic equation with equal roots has *two* equal roots, so here we mean that a zero of order n counts as n zeros and a pole of order n counts as n poles.)

To show this we consider $\oint_C \dfrac{f'(z)}{f(z)}\, dz$. By the residue theorem, the integral is equal to $2\pi i \cdot$ (sum of the residues at singularities inside C). It is straightforward to show (Problem 34) that the residue of $F(z) = f'(z)/f(z)$ at a zero of $f(z)$ of order n is n, and the residue of $F(z)$ at a pole of $f(z)$ of order p is $-p$. Then if N is the number of zeros and P the number of poles of $f(z)$ inside C, the integral is $2\pi i(N - P)$. Now by direct integration, we have

(7.7)
$$\oint_C \frac{f'(z)}{f(z)}\, dz = \ln f(z)\Big|_C = \ln Re^{i\Theta}\Big|_C = \ln R\Big|_C + i\Theta\Big|_C,$$

where $R = |f(z)|$ and Θ is the angle of $f(z)$. Recall from Chapter 2, Section 13, that $\ln R$ means the ordinary real logarithm (to the base e) of the positive number R, and is single-valued; $\ln f(z)$ is multiple-valued because Θ is multiple-valued. Then if we integrate from a point A on C all the way around the curve and back to A, $\ln R$ has the same value at A both at the beginning and at the end, so the term $\ln R|_C$ is $\ln R$ at A minus $\ln R$ at A; this is zero. The same result may not be true for Θ;

---

* A function which is analytic except for poles is called *meromorphic*.

that is, the angle may have changed as we go from point A all the way around C and back to A. (Think, for example, of the angle of z as we go from $z = 1$ around the unit circle and back to $z = 1$; the angle of z has increased from 0 to 2π.) Collecting our results, we have

$$(7.8) \qquad N - P = \frac{1}{2\pi i} \oint_C \frac{f'(z)}{f(z)} \, dz = \frac{1}{2\pi i} i\Theta_C$$

$$= \frac{1}{2\pi} \cdot (\text{change in the angle of } f(z) \text{ around } C),$$

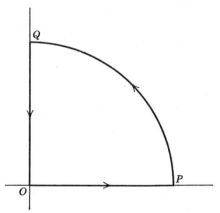

Figure 7.5

where N is the number of zeros and P the number of poles of $f(z)$ inside C, with poles of order n counted as n poles and similarly for zeros of order n. Equation (7.8) is known as the *argument principle* (recall from Chapter 2 that *argument* means *angle*).

This principle is often used to find out how many zeros (or poles) a given function has in a given region. For example, let us show that $f(z) = z^3 + 4z + 1 = 0$ at exactly one point in the first quadrant. The closed curve C in (7.8) is, for this problem, the contour OPQ in Fig. 7.5, where PQ is a large quarter circle. We first observe that $x^3 + 4x + 1 > 0$ for $x > 0$ and $(iy)^3 + 4iy + 1 \neq 0$ for any y (since its real part, namely 1, $\neq 0$); then $f(z) \neq 0$ on OP or OQ. Also $f(z) \neq 0$ on PQ if we choose a circle large enough to inclose all zeros. We now want to find the change in the angle Θ of $f(z) = Re^{i\Theta}$ as we go around C. Along OP, $z = x$; then $f(z) = f(x)$ is real and so $\Theta = 0$. Along PQ, $z = re^{i\theta}$, with r constant and very large. For very large r, the z^3 term in $f(z)$ far outweighs the other terms, and we have $f(z) \cong z^3 = r^3 e^{3i\theta}$. As θ goes from 0 to $\pi/2$ along PQ,

$\Theta = 3\theta$ goes from 0 to $3\pi/2$. On QO, $z = iy$, $f(z) = -iy^3 + 4iy + 1$; then

$$\tan \Theta = \frac{\text{imaginary part of } f(z)}{\text{real part of } f(z)} = \frac{4y - y^3}{1}.$$

For very large y (that is, at Q), we had $\Theta \simeq 3\pi/2$ (for $y = \infty$, we would have $\tan \Theta = -\infty$, and Θ would be exactly $3\pi/2$). Now as y decreases along QO, the value of $\tan \Theta = 4y - y^3$ decreases in magnitude but remains negative until it becomes 0 at $y = 2$. This means that Θ changes from $3\pi/2$ to 2π. Between $y = 2$ and $y = 0$, the tangent becomes positive, but then decreases to zero again without becoming infinite. This means that the angle Θ increases beyond 2π but not as far as $2\pi + \pi/2$, and then decreases again to 2π. Thus the total change in Θ around C is 2π, and by (7.8), the number of zeros of $f(z)$ in the first quadrant is $\dfrac{1}{2\pi} \cdot 2\pi = 1$.

If we realize that (for a polynomial with real coefficients) the zeros always occur in conjugate pairs, we see that there must also be one zero for z in the fourth quadrant, and the third zero must be on the negative x-axis.

8. THE POINT AT INFINITY; RESIDUES AT INFINITY

It is often useful to think of the complex plane as corresponding to the surface of a sphere in the following way. In Fig. 8.1, the sphere is tangent to the plane at the origin O. Let O be the south pole of the sphere, and N be the north pole of the sphere. If a line through N intersects the sphere at P and the plane at Q, we say that the point P on the sphere and the point Q on the plane are corresponding points. Then we have a one-to-one correspondence between points on the sphere (except N) and points of the plane (at finite distances from O). Imagine point Q moving farther and farther out away from O; then P moves nearer and nearer to N. If $z = x + iy$ is the complex coordinate of Q, then as Q moves out farther and farther from O, we would say $z \to \infty$. It is customary to say that the point N corresponds to the *point at infinity* in the complex plane. Observe that straight lines through the origin in the plane correspond to meridians of the sphere. The meridians all pass through both the north pole and the south pole. Corresponding to this, straight lines through the origin in the complex plane pass through the point at infinity. Circles in the complex plane with center at O correspond to parallels of latitude on the sphere. This mapping of the complex plane onto a sphere (or the mapping of the sphere onto a tangent plane) is called a *stereographic projection.*

To investigate the behavior of a function at infinity, we replace z by $1/z$ and consider how the new function behaves at the origin. We then say that infinity is a regular point, a pole, etc., of the original function, depending on what the new function does at the origin. For example, consider z^2 at infinity; $1/z^2$ has a pole of order 2 at the origin, so z^2 has a pole of order 2 at infinity. Or consider $e^{1/z}$; since e^z is analytic at $z = 0$, $e^{1/z}$ is analytic at ∞.

Next we want to see how to find the residue of a function at ∞. To do this, we are going to want to replace z by $1/z$ and work around the origin.

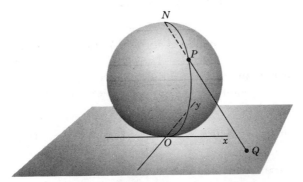

Figure 8.1

In order to keep our notation straight, let us use two variables, namely Z which takes on values near ∞, and $z = 1/Z$ which takes on values near 0. The residue of a function at ∞ is defined so that the residue theorem holds, that is,

$$(8.1) \qquad \oint_C f(Z)\, dZ = 2\pi i \cdot (\text{residue of } f(Z) \text{ at } Z = \infty)$$

if C is a closed path around the point at ∞ but inclosing no other singular points. Now what does it mean to integrate "around ∞"? Recall that we have agreed to traverse contours so that the area inclosed always lies to our left. The area we wish to "inclose" is the area "around ∞"; if C is a circle, this area would lie *outside* the circle in our usual terminology. Figure 8.1 may clarify this. Imagine a small circle about the north pole; the area inside this circle (that is, the area including N) corresponds to points in the plane which are outside a large circle C. We must go around C in the clockwise direction in order to have the area "around ∞" to our left. This is indicated by the arrow on the integral sign in (8.1). Note that if $Z = Re^{i\Theta}$, then in going clockwise around C, we are going in the direction of *decreasing* Θ. Let us make the following change of variable in the integral (8.1):

$$Z = \frac{1}{z}, \qquad dZ = -\frac{1}{z^2}\, dz.$$

If $Z = Re^{i\Theta}$ traverses a circle C of radius R in the direction of decreasing Θ, then $z = 1/Z = (1/R)e^{-i\Theta} = re^{i\theta}$ traverses a circle C' of radius $r = 1/R$ in the counterclockwise direction (that is, $\theta = -\Theta$ increases as Θ decreases). Thus (8.1) becomes

(8.2) $$\oint_{C'} -\frac{1}{z^2} f\!\left(\frac{1}{z}\right) dz = 2\pi i \cdot (\text{residue of } f(Z) \text{ at } Z = \infty).$$

The integral in (8.2) is an integral about the origin and so can be evaluated by calculating the residue of $(-1/z^2)f(1/z)$ at the origin. (There are no other singular points of $f(1/z)$ inside C' because we assumed that there were no singular points of $f(Z)$ outside C except perhaps ∞.) Thus we have

(8.3)   (residue of $f(Z)$ at $Z = \infty$) $= -\left(\text{residue of } \dfrac{1}{z^2} f\!\left(\dfrac{1}{z}\right) \text{ at } z = 0\right)$

and we can use the methods we already know for computing residues at the origin.

Note that a function may be analytic at ∞ and still have a residue there. For example, $f(Z) = 1/Z$ is analytic at ∞ because z is analytic at the origin. But the residue of $f(Z) = 1/Z$ at $Z = \infty$ is

$$-\left(\text{residue of } \frac{1}{z^2} \cdot z \text{ at } z = 0\right) = -1.$$

9. MAPPING

We often find it useful to sketch a graph of a given function $y = f(x)$ of a real variable x. Imagine trying to make a similar sketch for a function $w = f(z)$ of a complex variable z. We need a plane to plot values of z and another plane to plot values of $w = f(z)$, that is, we need a four-dimensional space. Lacking this, we must resort to a different method. Imagine trying to "graph" $y = f(x)$ using only two straight lines, but not a plane. A "graph" of $y = x^2$ might look like Fig. 9.1. Given a point on the x-axis, we can locate a corresponding point $y = f(x)$ on the y-axis and label the two points with the same letter to indicate this correspondence. (Note

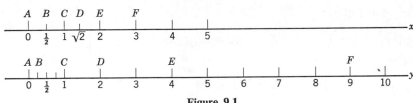

Figure 9.1

that to finish our "graph," we really need a second positive y-axis to hold the y points corresponding to negative values of x.)

Now consider a similar method of representing a function of a complex variable $w = f(z)$. We use a z-plane and a w-plane; a given point in the z-plane (that is, a value of z) determines a corresponding value of w, that is, a point in the w-plane. The pair of points, one z and one w, are called *images* of each other. Although we *could* label pairs of corresponding z and w points (as we did corresponding x and y points in Fig. 9.1), it is usually more interesting to sketch corresponding curves or regions in the two planes. The correspondence between a point (or curve or region) in the z-plane, and the image point (or curve or region) in the w-plane, is called a *mapping* or a *transformation*.

Example 1.   Consider the function $w = i + ze^{i\pi/4}$, and let us map the grid of coordinate lines $x = $ const., $y = $ const. (z-plane in Fig. 9.2) into the w-plane. You may be able to see at once that this transformation amounts to a rotation of the grid through an angle of $\pi/4$ (since $ze^{i\pi/4} = re^{i(\theta + \pi/4)}$) plus a translation i (the image of $z = 0$ is $w = i$), giving the result shown in the w-plane in Fig. 9.2. Alternatively, we can compute u

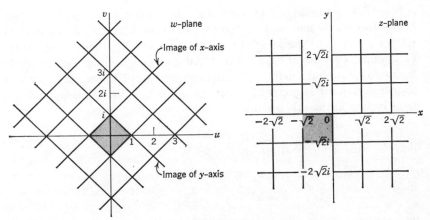

Figure 9.2

and v as follows:

$$w = i + ze^{i\pi/4} = i + (x + iy)\left(\cos\frac{\pi}{4} + i\sin\frac{\pi}{4}\right)$$

$$= i + (x + iy)\left(\frac{1+i}{\sqrt{2}}\right) = \frac{x-y}{\sqrt{2}} + i\left(1 + \frac{x+y}{\sqrt{2}}\right).$$

Since $w = u + iv$, we have

$$(9.1) \qquad u = \frac{x-y}{\sqrt{2}}, \qquad v = 1 + \frac{x+y}{\sqrt{2}}.$$

Then (eliminating x and y in turn), we have

$$(9.2) \qquad u - v = -1 - y\sqrt{2}, \qquad u + v = 1 + x\sqrt{2}.$$

The image of the x-axis $(y = 0)$ is, from the first equation in (9.2), $u - v = -1$; the image of the y-axis $(x = 0)$ is, from the second equation in (9.2), $u + v = 1$. Plotting these lines in the w-plane, and also plotting the images of $x = \pm\sqrt{2}$, $x = \pm 2\sqrt{2}$, $y = \pm\sqrt{2}$, $y = \pm 2\sqrt{2}$ [using the equations (9.2)], we get Fig. 9.2. (Verify that the shaded squares are images of each other.)

If the elimination [to get (9.2)] is not easy, we can use equations (9.1) directly. Suppose that we want the image of $y = 0$. With $y = 0$, equations (9.1) become $u = x/\sqrt{2}$, $v = 1 + x/\sqrt{2}$; these are a pair of parametric equations for a curve in the (u, v) plane, with x as the parameter. Similarly, to find the image of $x = $ const., we substitute the value of x into (9.2); we then have a pair of parametric equations with y as the parameter.

Note that we could just as easily have found the images in the z-plane of the lines $u = $ const., and $v = $ const. For example, letting $u = 0$ in (9.1), we get $x - y = 0$; the image of the v-axis $(u = 0)$ is the 45° line in the (x, y) plane. (We might have guessed that going back to the z-plane would involve a rotation through $-45°$.) In any given problem, we may start with simple curves (or regions) in either the z-plane or the w-plane, and find their images in the other plane.

Example 2. Let us map the coordinate grid $u = $ const., $v = $ const., into the z-plane by the function $w = z^2$. We have

$$(9.3) \qquad \begin{aligned} w &= z^2 = (x + iy)^2 = x^2 - y^2 + 2ixy, \\ u &= x^2 - y^2, \qquad v = 2xy. \end{aligned}$$

Then the images of $u = $ const. are hyperbolas $x^2 - y^2 = $ const., and the

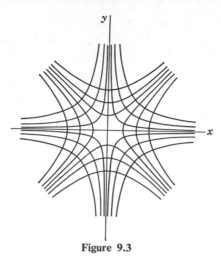

Figure 9.3

images of $v = $ const. are also hyperbolas $xy = $ const. (Fig. 9.3). Alternatively, we could map the lines $x = $ const., $y = $ const. into the w-plane (Problem 44); this gives two sets of parabolas in the (u, v) plane.

Example 3. Let us consider still another useful way of discussing the mapping by $w = z^2$. Using polar coordinates, we have

$$(9.4) \qquad\qquad z = re^{i\theta}, \qquad w = z^2 = r^2 e^{2i\theta}.$$

Consider the region inside the circle $r = 1$ in the (x, y) plane. If $r = 1$ in (9.4), we have $z = e^{i\theta}$, $w = e^{2i\theta}$. The angle of w is twice the angle of z; thus the first-quadrant part of the circle $r = 1$ in the z-plane maps into a semicircle in the w-plane as indicated by the shading in Fig. 9.4. The second quadrant of the z-plane circle (θ between $\pi/2$ and π) maps into the lower half of the circle in the w-plane (angle of w between π and 2π) as indicated. We have now used up the whole w-plane and only half of the z-plane. (Compare Fig. 9.1 and the comment about a second y-axis.) In order to have a one-to-one correspondence between points in the z-plane and their images in the w-plane, we draw a second w-plane (w-plane II in Fig. 9.4) to contain the images of points in the lower half of the z-plane. (Convince yourself that the two lower quarter-circles in the z-plane and their images in w-plane II are correctly indicated by the shading.) We agree that as we reach the angle 2π in w-plane I, we go over to w-plane II, and as we reach the angle 4π in w-plane II, we go back to w-plane I. The two w-planes joined in this way are called a *Riemann surface*; each plane is called a *sheet* of the Riemann surface. Note that the line along which the sheets of the Riemann surface are joined (positive real axis here) is a branch cut, and the origin is a branch point (see Example 5, Section 7).

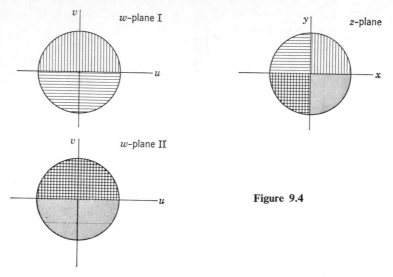

Figure 9.4

Here the branch cut and Riemann surface are in the w-plane because $z = \sqrt{w}$ has two branches; for $w = \sqrt{z}$, the Riemann surface would be in the z-plane (as in Section 7).

Conformal mapping. We have been discussing mappings or transformations. We used the term *transformation* in Chapter 10, meaning a change of variables or a change of coordinate system; let us see the connection between the two discussions. In Chapter 10 we used only one plane [the (x, y) plane]; we located a point in the (x, y) plane by giving its rectangular coordinates (x, y), or its polar coordinates (r, θ), or some other coordinates (u, v). The circles $r = $ const. and the rays $\theta = $ const. were sketched in the (x, y) plane. Similarly, for any coordinate system (u, v) (see Section 6 and Problem 20 of Chapter 10), we sketched the curves $u = $ const., $v = $ const. in the (x, y) plane. In the complex-variable language we are now using, this amounts to mapping the w-plane lines $u = $ const., $v = $ const. into the z-plane. In Chapter 10 we were particularly interested in transformations to orthogonal curvilinear coordinates. Let us see that any analytic function $w = f(z) = u + iv$ gives us a transformation to an orthogonal coordinate system (u, v). We have

$$(9.5) \qquad \begin{aligned} dz &= dx + i\,dy, & dw &= du + i\,dv, \\ |dz|^2 &= dx^2 + dy^2, & |dw|^2 &= du^2 + dv^2. \end{aligned}$$

Then the square of the arc length element in the (x, y) plane is

$$(9.6) \quad ds^2 = dx^2 + dy^2 = |dz|^2 = \left| \frac{dz}{dw} \right|^2 |dw|^2 = \left| \frac{dz}{dw} \right|^2 (du^2 + dv^2).$$

Since there is no $du\,dv$ term in ds^2, the (u, v) coordinate system is orthogonal (Chapter 10, Section 6). By this we mean that if we obtain $u(x, y)$ and $v(x, y)$ from $f(z) = u + iv$ and plot the curves $u(x, y) = $ const., $v(x, y) = $ const. in the (x, y) plane, we have two sets of mutually orthogonal curves. These are the coordinate curves for the (u, v) coordinate system as in Chapter 10. If we solve the equations $u = u(x, y)$, $v = v(x, y)$ for x and y in terms of u and v, we have the transformation equations from the variables x, y to the variables u, v as in Problem 20 of Chapter 10, and

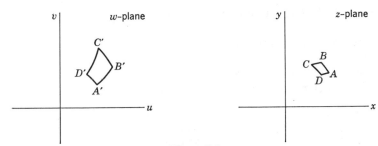

Figure 9.5

by (9.6) we know that the coordinate system (u, v) is an orthogonal system [if $f(z)$ is analytic]. We see an example of this in Fig. 9.3 (two orthogonal sets of hyperbolas). Note from (9.6) that the two scale factors in a (u, v) coordinate system obtained this way are equal.

Although we used only one plane in Chapter 10, in complex variable we find it useful to consider both the z-plane [that is the (x, y) plane] and the w-plane [that is, the (u, v) plane]. In the (x, y) plane, the arc length element ds is given by $ds^2 = dx^2 + dy^2$. Similarly, in the (u, v) plane, the arc length element (which we shall call dS) is given by $dS^2 = du^2 + dv^2$. From (9.5) we see that $ds = |dz|$ and $dS = |dw|$. Then the ratio of dS to ds is $|dw/dz|$. Consider a point z (and its image w) at which $w(z)$ is analytic and dw/dz is not zero. If we stay near z, the value of dw/dz is almost constant, and the ratio dS/ds is nearly constant. This says that if we consider a small area in the z-plane ($ABCD$ in Fig. 9.5) and its image ($A'B'C'D'$ in Fig. 9.5) in the w-plane, then

$$\frac{A'B'}{AB} = \frac{B'C'}{BC} = \frac{C'D'}{CD} = \frac{D'A'}{DA} = \frac{dS}{ds} = \left| \frac{dw}{dz} \right|,$$

that is, the two small areas are similar figures (since corresponding sides are proportional). Because of this property of any mapping by an analytic function, we call the mapping or transformation *conformal* (same form or shape). Corresponding angles are equal ($A = A'$, etc.) and the net result of the transformation is to magnify (or minify) and rotate each infinitesimal area. Note that the conformal property is a local one; since the value of dw/dz changes from point to point, each tiny bit of a figure is magnified and rotated by a different amount, and so a large figure will not have the same shape after mapping. Also note that we do not have conformality in the neighborhood of a point where $dw/dz = 0$; for example, in Fig. 9.4 a tiny quarter-circle about the origin in the z-plane maps into a tiny semicircle in the w-plane.

10. SOME APPLICATIONS OF CONFORMAL MAPPING

Many different physical problems require solution of Laplace's equation. We are going to show how to solve a few such problems by conformal mapping. First consider a very simple problem for which we know the answer from elementary physics.

Example 1. In Fig. 10.1, the shaded area in the (u, v) plane represents a rectangular plate. The ends and faces of the plate are insulated, the bottom edge is held at temperature $T = 0°$, and the top edge at $T = 100°$. Then we know from elementary physics that the temperature increases linearly from the bottom edge ($v = 0$) to the top edge ($v = \pi$), that is, $T = (100/\pi)v$ at any point of the plate. Let us also derive this answer by a more advanced method. It is known from the theory of heat that the temperature T of a body satisfies Laplace's equation in regions where there is no source of heat. In our problem we want a solution of Laplace's equation which satisfies the *boundary conditions*, that is, $T = 100°$ when $v = \pi$, $T = 0°$ when $v = 0$, and $\partial T/\partial u = 0$ on the ends. This last condition is the mathematical way of saying that the surface is insulated; in the theory of heat, the rate of flow of heat across a surface is proportional to the rate of change of temperature along the normal (perpendicular) to the surface. Here the normal direction is the u direction, and the rate of heat flow is zero across an insulated surface. You should verify that $T = 100v/\pi$ satisfies $\partial^2 T/\partial u^2 + \partial^2 T/\partial v^2 = 0$, and satisfies all the boundary conditions. Also note that an easy way to know that v satisfies Laplace's equation is to observe that it is the imaginary part of $w = u + iv$, and use Theorem IV of Section 2 which says that the real and imaginary parts of an analytic function of a complex variable satisfy Laplace's equation.

Now let us use our results to solve a harder problem.

Example 2. Consider the mapping of the rectangle in the w-plane into the z-plane by the function $w = \ln z$ (Fig. 10.1, z-plane). We have

$$w = \ln z = \ln (re^{i\theta}) = \ln r + i\theta = u + iv,$$

(10.1)

$$u = \ln r, \qquad v = \theta.$$

Then $v = 0$ maps into $\theta = 0$, that is, the positive x-axis; $v = \pi$ maps into $\theta = \pi$, that is, the negative x-axis (z-plane, Fig. 10.1). The insulated end of the rectangle at $u = 0$ maps into $\ln r = 0$ or $r = 1$; the left-hand end of the rectangle maps into a small semicircle about the origin which we can think of as a bit of insulation at the origin separating the $0°$ and $100°$ parts of the x-axis. (If the left-hand end of the rectangle is at $u = -\infty$, we have $\ln r = -\infty$, $r = 0$, and the image is just the origin; for finite

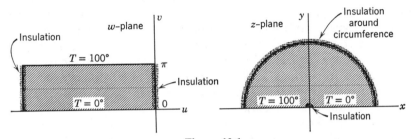

Figure 10.1

negative u, the image is a semicircle with $r < 1$.) We can now solve the problem indicated by the picture in the z-plane of Fig. 10.1. A semicircular plate has its faces and its curved boundary insulated, and has half its flat boundary at $0°$ and the other half at $100°$ (with a bit of insulation at the center). Find the temperature T at any point of the plate. To solve this problem we need only transform our solution in the (u, v) plane to the variables x, y by using (10.1). Thus we find

$$(10.2) \qquad T = \frac{100}{\pi} v = \frac{100}{\pi} \theta = \frac{100}{\pi} \arctan \frac{y}{x}, \qquad 0 \le \theta \le \pi.$$

It is not hard to justify our method; we need to show that our solution satisfies Laplace's equation and that it satisfies the boundary conditions. It is straightforward to show (Problem 49) that if a function $\phi(u, v)$ satisfies Laplace's equation $\partial^2\phi/\partial u^2 + \partial^2\phi/\partial v^2 = 0$, then the function of x and y obtained by substituting $u = u(x, y)$, $v = v(x, y)$ in ϕ satisfies Laplace's equation in x and y, where u and v are the real and imaginary parts of an analytic function $w = f(z)$. Thus we know that (10.2) satisfies Laplace's equation (or in this case you can easily verify the fact directly). We must also know that the transformed T satisfies the boundary conditions; this is where conformal mapping is so useful. Observe in Fig. 10.1 that we had a transformation which took the boundaries of a simple region (a rectangle) for which we knew the solution of our temperature problem, into the boundaries of a more complicated region for which we wanted the solution. This is the basic method of conformal mapping—to transform from a simple region where you know the answer to a given problem, to the region in which you want the solution. The temperature at any (x, y) point is the same as the temperature at the (u, v) image point, since we obtain the temperature as a function of x and y by the same substitution $u = u(x, y)$, $v = v(x, y)$ that we use to obtain image points. Thus the temperatures on the boundaries of the transformed region are the same as the temperatures on the corresponding boundaries of the simpler (u, v) region. Similarly, isothermals (curves of constant temperature) transform into isothermals; in this problem the (u, v) isothermals are the lines $v =$ const., and so the (x, y) isothermals are $\theta =$ const. You can show that the rate of change of T in a direction perpendicular to a boundary in the (u, v) plane is proportional to the corresponding rate of change of T in a direction perpendicular to the image boundary in the (x, y) plane (Problem 48b). Thus insulated boundaries (across which the rate of change of T is zero) map into insulated boundaries. The lines (or curves) perpendicular to the isothermals give the direction of flow of heat; in Fig. 10.1 heat flows along the lines $u =$ const. in the w-plane, and along the circles $r =$ const. (which are the images of $u =$ const.) in the z-plane.

Using the same mapping function $w = \ln z$, we can solve a number of other physical problems. Observe first that if we think of Fig. 10.1 as representing a cross section of a three-dimensional problem (with all parallel cross sections identical), then (10.2) gives the solution of the three-dimensional problem also. In Fig. 10.1 the (u, v) diagram would be the cross section of a slab with faces at $T = 100°$ and $T = 0°$ and all other surfaces insulated (or extending to infinity); the (x, y) diagram would similarly represent half a cylinder. Now let us do a three-dimensional problem in electrostatics.

Example 3.   In Fig. 10.2 the (u, v) diagram represents (the cross section of) two infinite parallel plates, one at potential $V = 0$ volts and one at potential $V = 100$ volts. The (x, y) diagram represents (the cross section of) one plane with its right-hand half at potential $V = 0$ volts and its

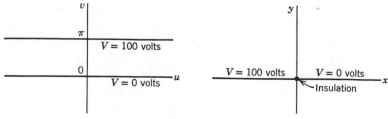

Figure 10.2

left-hand half at $V = 100$ volts. From electricity we know that the electrostatic potential V satisfies Laplace's equation in regions where there is no free charge. You should convince yourself that the mapping by (10.1) gives the result shown in Fig. 10.2, and that the potential is given by

$$V = \frac{100}{\pi} v = \frac{100}{\pi} \theta = \frac{100}{\pi} \arctan \frac{y}{x}, \qquad 0 \le \theta \le \pi$$

as in (10.2). The equipotentials ($V = $ const.) in the (x, y) plane are the lines $\theta = $ const. Recall that the electric field is given by $\mathbf{E} = -\nabla V$, and that the gradient of V is perpendicular to $V = $ const. (Chapter 5, Section 9). Then the direction of the electric field at any point is perpendicular to the equipotential through that point. Thus if we sketch the curves $r = $ const. which are perpendicular to the equipotentials $\theta = $ const., then the tangent to a circle at a point gives the direction of the electric field $\mathbf{E}$ at that point. Note the correspondence between the isothermals of the temperature problem and the equipotentials here, and between the lines of electric flux (curves tangent to $\mathbf{E}$) and the lines or curves along which heat flows.

We can also solve problems in hydrodynamics (see Chapter 5, Section 12) by conformal mapping. We consider a two-dimensional flow of water by which we mean either that we think of the water as flowing in a thin sheet over the (x, y) [or (u, v)] plane, or if it has depth, the flow is the same in all planes parallel to the (x, y) [or (u, v)] plane. Although it is convenient to talk about water, what we actually require is an irrotational flow (see Chapter 5, Section 13) of a nonviscous incompressible fluid. For then (see Problem 50) the velocity $\mathbf{V}$ of the liquid is given by $\mathbf{V} = \nabla\Phi$, where Φ (called the *velocity potential*) satisfies Laplace's equation. Water approximately meets these requirements.

Example 4. Figure 10.3 shows two simple flow patterns related by the same transformation we have used in the heat problem and the electrostatics problem, namely $w = \ln z$. In the w-plane of Fig. 10.3, we picture water flowing in the u direction at constant speed V_0 down a channel between $v = 0$ and $v = 2\pi$. (Note that v is the imaginary part of $w = u + iv$ and has nothing to do with velocity.) The velocity potential is $\Phi = V_0 u$; for then the velocity, $\mathbf{V} = \nabla\Phi$, has components $\partial\Phi/\partial u = V_0$ in the u direction and $\partial\Phi/\partial v = 0$ in the v direction as we have assumed. The function $\Phi + i\Psi = V_0 w = V_0(u + iv)$ is called the *complex potential*; the function Ψ (conjugate to Φ; see Section 2) is called the *stream function*. The lines $\Psi = $ const. (that is, $v = $ const. in the w-plane) are the lines along which the water flows and are called *streamlines*. Observe that the lines $\Phi = $ const. and the lines $\Psi = $ const. are mutually perpendicular

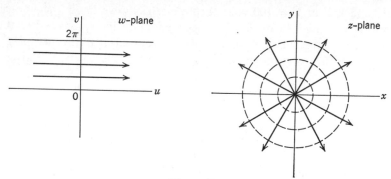

Figure 10.3

sets of lines. The water flows across lines of constant Φ and along stream-lines (constant Ψ); boundaries of the channel ($v = 0$ and $v = 2\pi$) must then be streamlines. The water comes from the left (Fig. 10.3, w-plane) and goes off to the right; we say that there is a *source* at the left and a *sink* at the right.

Now consider the mapping of the w-plane flow of Fig. 10.3 into the z-plane by the function $w = \ln z$. The complex potential is

$$\Phi + i\Psi = V_0 w = V_0 \ln z = V_0 (\ln r + i\theta).$$

The streamlines are $\Psi = $ const., or $\theta = $ const., that is, radial lines; the curves $\Phi = $ const. are circles $r = $ const. and are perpendicular to the streamlines. The velocity is given by

$$\mathbf{V} = \nabla\Phi = V_0 \nabla(\ln r) = V_0 \left(\mathbf{e}_r \frac{\partial}{\partial r} + \mathbf{e}_\theta \frac{1}{r} \frac{\partial}{\partial \theta} \right) \ln r = \mathbf{e}_r \frac{V_0}{r}.$$

What we are describing, then, is the flow of water from a source at the origin out along radial lines. Since the same amount of water crosses a small circle (about the origin) or a large one, the velocity of the water decreases with r as we have found ($|\mathbf{V}| = V_0/r$).

We can obtain another flow pattern from any given one by interchanging the equipotentials and the streamlines. In Fig. 10.3, z-plane, this new flow would have the circles $r = $ const. as streamlines and would correspond to a whirlpool motion of the water about the origin (called a *vortex*). There are still other applications of this diagram. The circles $r = $ const. give the direction of the magnetic field about a long current-carrying wire perpendicular to the (x, y) plane and passing through the origin. The radial lines $\theta = $ const. give the direction of the electric field about a similar long wire with a static charge on it. The radial lines give the direction of heat flow from a small hot object at the origin, and the circles $r =$ const. are then the isothermals. By starting with problems like these to which we know the answers and using various conformal transformations, we can solve many other physical problems involving fluid flow, electricity, heat, etc. Some examples are outlined in the problems and you will find many more in books on complex variable.

Example 5.   Let us consider one somewhat more complicated example of the use of conformal mapping. We shall be able to solve two interesting physical problems in this example: (1) to find the flow pattern for water

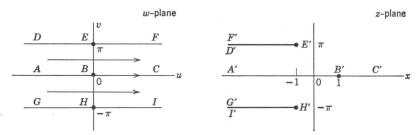

Figure 10.4

flowing out of the end of a straight channel into the open, and (2) to find the edge effect (fringing) at the ends of a parallel-plate capacitor.

We consider the mapping function

(10.3)
$$z = w + e^w = u + iv + e^u e^{iv} = u + iv + e^u(\cos v + i \sin v),$$
$$x = u + e^u \cos v, \quad y = v + e^u \sin v.$$

In Fig. 10.4, w-plane, we picture a parallel flow of water at constant velocity in the region between the lines DEF and GHI; this is just like the flow of Fig. 10.3, w-plane. Now let us map the w-plane streamlines into the z-plane using (10.3). On the u-axis, $v = 0$; putting $v = 0$ in (10.3), we find $y = 0$, and $x = u + e^u$. Thus the u-axis maps into the x-axis $(y = 0)$ with $u = -\infty$ corresponding to $x = -\infty$, $u = 0$ corresponding to $x = 1$, and $u = +\infty$ corresponding to $x = +\infty$ as shown in Fig. 10.4 (line ABC maps into $A'B'C'$). Now on DEF, $v = \pi$; substituting $v = \pi$ into (10.3), we find $y = \pi$, $x = u + e^u \cos \pi = u - e^u$. However, the image of $v = \pi$ is not the entire line $y = \pi$. To see this consider $x = u - e^u$. We find the maximum value of x for $dx/du = 1 - e^u = 0$, $d^2x/du^2 = -e^u < 0$. These equations are satisfied for $u = 0$, $x = -1$. The point $E(u = 0, v = \pi)$ maps into the point $E'(x = -1, y = \pi)$. Thus DE in the w-plane maps into the part of the line $y = \pi$ in the z-plane up to $x = -1$ with $u = -\infty$ corresponding to $x = -\infty$ and $u = 0$ corresponding to $x = -1$. To see how to map EF, we realize that x has its largest value at $u = 0$ and so decreases as u increases; for very large positive u, $x = u - e^u$ is negative and of large absolute value since $e^u \gg u$. Thus the positive part of $v = \pi$ (EF) maps into the same line segment ($y = \pi$, $x \leq -1$) that we obtained for the mapping of the negative part (DE), but this time the line segment ($E'F'$, z-plane) is traversed backward. It is as if the line $y = \pi$ were broken at $x = -1$ and bent back upon itself through an angle of 180°. By a

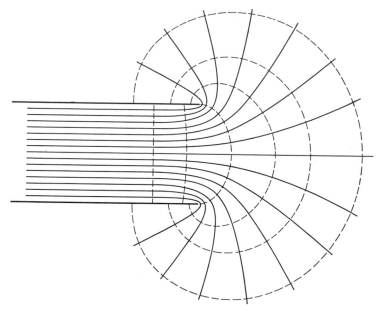

Figure 10.5

parallel discussion of the line GHI, we find that it maps as shown in Fig. 10.4 into $G'H'I'$. Other streamlines in the w-plane are given by $v = $ const. for any v between $-\pi$ and π. If we substitute $v = $ const. into the x and y equations in (10.3), we have parametric equations (with u as the parameter) for the streamlines in the z-plane. For any value of v, these streamlines can be plotted in the z-plane: some of them are shown by the solid curves in Fig. 10.5. Think of $D'E'$ and $G'H'$ as boundaries of a channel (in the z-plane) down which water flows coming from $x = -\infty$. The boundaries stop at $x = -1$ and the water flows out of the channel spreading over the whole plane, including spreading back along the outsides ($E'F'$ and $H'I'$) of the channel boundaries. This is correct according to our mapping, for the boundary streamline DEF mapped into the broken-and-folded-back line $D'E'F'$, and similarly for GHI to $G'H'I'$.

For the electrical application, let *DEF* and *GHI* represent (the cross section of) a large parallel plate capacitor. Then the lines $v = $ const. are the equipotentials and the lines $u = $ const. give the direction of the electric field **E**. The image in the z-plane represents (a cross section of) the end of a parallel plate capacitor. The images of the equipotentials $v = $ const. are the equipotentials in the z-plane (same as the streamlines, shown as solid curves in Fig. 10.5). The images of the lines $u = $ const. (shown as dotted curves in Fig. 10.5) give the direction of the electric field at the end of a parallel-plate capacitor. Well inside the plates the **E** lines are vertical, but at the end they bulge out; this effect is known as *fringing*.

REFERENCES

For more detail and for proofs of theorems, see books on complex variable such as Churchill, Kaplan, Nehari, Phillips, and Spiegel. There are also chapters on the subject in some books on advanced calculus or on mathematics in physics and engineering. See references at the end of the book identified as Chapter 11 references by the figure [11] after the listing.

PROBLEMS

1. Find the real and imaginary parts $u(x, y)$ and $v(x, y)$ of the following functions.

(a) z^3 (b) z •(c) $\bar{z}$

(d) $|z|$ (e) $\operatorname{Re} z$ (f) e^z

•(g) $\cosh z$ (h) $\sin z$ •(i) $\dfrac{1}{z}$

(j) $\dfrac{2z + 3}{z + 2}$ (k) $\dfrac{2z - i}{iz + 2}$ (l) $\dfrac{z}{z^2 + 1}$

•(m) $\ln z$ (Use $0 < \theta < 2\pi$.)   (n) $(1 + 2i)z^2 + (i - 1)z + 3$

•(o) $\sqrt{z}$

•(p) e^{iz} (Careful; $\cos z$ and $\sin z$ are *not* u and v.)

2. Use the Cauchy-Riemann conditions to find out whether the following functions are analytic.

*(a) z (b) z^3 (c) $|z|$

◀(d) Re z ◀(e) $\bar{z}$ *(f) e^z

(g) $\dfrac{1}{z}$ (h) $\sin z$ (i) $\cosh z$

(j) e^{iz} •(k) $x^2 - y^2 + 2ixy$ (l) $\cos \bar{z}$

3. Using the definition (2.1) of $(d/dz)f(z)$, show that the following familiar formulas hold. *Hint:* Use the same methods as for functions of a real variable.

(a) $\dfrac{d}{dz}[Af(z) + Bg(z)] = A\dfrac{df}{dz} + B\dfrac{dg}{dz}$.

(b) $\dfrac{d}{dz}[f(z)g(z)] = f(z)\dfrac{dg}{dz} + g(z)\dfrac{df}{dz}$.

(c) $\dfrac{d}{dz}\left(\dfrac{f(z)}{g(z)}\right) = \dfrac{gf' - fg'}{g^2}$, $g(z) \neq 0$.

(d) $\dfrac{d}{dz}f[g(z)] = \dfrac{df}{dg}\dfrac{dg}{dz}$

(chain rule for the derivative of a function of a function). *Hint:* Assume that df/dg and dg/dz exist, and write equations like (3.5) of Chapter 4 for Δf and Δg; substitute Δg into Δf, divide by Δz, and take limits.

(e) $\dfrac{d}{dz}(z^3) = 3z^2$.

(f) $\dfrac{d}{dz}(z^n) = nz^{n-1}$.

(g) $\dfrac{d}{dz}\ln z = \dfrac{1}{z}$, $z \neq 0$. *Hint:* Expand $\ln\left(1 + \dfrac{\Delta z}{z}\right)$ in series.

4. (a) Using the definition of e^z by its power series [(8.1) of Chapter 2], and the theorem (Chapters 1 and 2) that power series may be differentiated term by term (within the interval of convergence), and the result of Problem 3f, show that $(d/dz)(e^z) = e^z$.

(b) Using the definitions of $\sin z$ and $\cos z$ [Chapter 2, equation (11.4)], find their derivatives. Then using Problem 3c, find $(d/dz)(\cot z)$, $z \neq n\pi$.

5. Using series you know from Chapter 1, write the power series (about the origin) of the following functions. Use Theorem III to find the circle of convergence of each series. What you are looking for is the point (anywhere in the complex plane) nearest the origin, at which the function does not have a derivative. Then the circle of convergence has center at the origin and extends to that point. The series converges *inside* the circle.

(a) $\ln(1-z)$ (b) $\cos z$ (c) $\sqrt{1+z^2}$

(d) $\tanh z$ (e) $\dfrac{1}{2i+z}$ (f) $\dfrac{z}{z^2+9}$

*6. (a) Prove Theorem IV, Part 1. *Hint:* Recall the equality of the second cross partial derivatives; see Chapter 4, end of Section 1.

•(b) Let $f(z) = u + iv$ be an analytic function, and let **F** be the vector $\mathbf{F} = v\mathbf{i} + u\mathbf{j}$. Show that the equations div $\mathbf{F} = 0$ and curl $\mathbf{F} = 0$ are equivalent to the Cauchy-Riemann equations.

(c) Find the Cauchy-Riemann equations in polar coordinates. *Hint:* $z = re^{i\theta}$, $f(z) = u(r, \theta) + iv(r, \theta)$. Follow the method of equations (2.3) and (2.4).

•(d) Using your results in (c) and the method of (a), show that u and v satisfy Laplace's equation in polar coordinates (see Chapter 10, Section 9) if $f(z) = u + iv$ is analytic.

7. Using polar coordinates (Problem 6c), find out whether the following functions satisfy the Cauchy-Riemann equations.

(a) $\sqrt{\bar{z}}$ (b) $|z|$ (c) $\ln z$

(d) z^n (e) $|z|^2$ (f) $|z|^{1/2}e^{(1/2)i\theta}$

8. Show that the following functions are harmonic, that is, that they satisfy Laplace's equation, and find for each the function $f(z)$ of which the given function is the real part. Show that the function $v(x, y)$ which you find also satisfies Laplace's equation.

•(a) y (b) $3x^2y - y^3$ (c) xy (d) $x + y$

(e) $\cosh y \cos x$ ▸(f) $e^x \cos y$ (g) $\ln(x^2 + y^2)$

9. Evaluate the following line integrals in the complex plane by direct integration, that is, as in Chapter 5, Section 11, *not* using theorems from this chapter. (If you see that a theorem applies, use it to check your result.)

(a) $\displaystyle\int_{i}^{1+i} z\,dz$ along a straight line parallel to the x-axis.

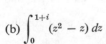

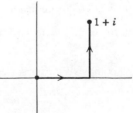

(b) $\displaystyle\int_{0}^{1+i} (z^2 - z)\,dz$

(i) along the line $y = x$;

(ii) along the indicated broken line.

(c) $\oint_C z^2\,dz$ along the indicated paths:

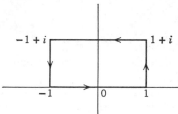 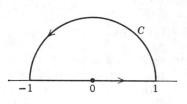

(d) $\int \dfrac{dz}{1-z^2}$ along the whole positive imaginary axis, that is, the y-axis; this

is frequently written as $\displaystyle\int_0^{i\infty} \dfrac{dz}{1-z^2}$.

(e) $\displaystyle\int e^{-z}\,dz$ along the positive part of the line $y = \pi$; this is frequently

written as $\displaystyle\int_{i\pi}^{\infty+i\pi} e^{-z}\,dz$.

10. Evaluate $\oint_C \bar{z}\,dz$ where C is the indicated closed curve along the first quadrant part of the circle $|z| = 2$, and the indicated parts of the x- and y-axes. *Hint:* Don't try to use Cauchy's theorem! (Why not? *Further hint:* See Problem 2e.)

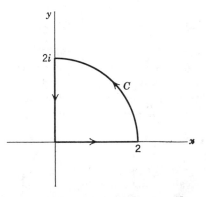

11. In Chapter 5, Section 13, we showed that a necessary condition for $\displaystyle\int_a^b \mathbf{F} \cdot d\mathbf{r}$

to be independent of the path of integration, that is, for $\oint_C \mathbf{F} \cdot d\mathbf{r}$ around a simple closed curve C to be zero, was curl $\mathbf{F} = 0$, or in two dimensions, $\partial F_y/\partial x = \partial F_x/\partial y$. By considering (3.2), show that the corresponding condition for $\oint_C f(z)\,dz$ to be zero is that the Cauchy-Riemann conditions hold.

12. In finding complex Fourier series in Chapter 6, we showed that

$$\oint_0^{2\pi} e^{inx}e^{-imx}\,dx = 0, \qquad n \neq m.$$

Show this by applying Cauchy's theorem to

$$\oint_C z^{n-m-1} \, dz, \qquad n > m,$$

where C is the circle $|z| = 1$. (Note that although we take $n > m$ to make z^{n-m-1} analytic at $z = 0$, an identical proof using z^{m-n-1} with $n < m$ completes the proof for all $n \neq m$.)

13. If $f(z)$ is analytic on and inside the circle $|z| = 1$, show that

$$\int_0^{2\pi} e^{i\theta} f(e^{i\theta}) \, d\theta = 0.$$

14. Use Cauchy's theorem or integral formula to evaluate

$$\oint_C \frac{\sin z \, dz}{2z - \pi}$$

when
   (a) C is a circle of radius 1 and center at the origin;
   (b) C is a circle of radius 2 and center at the origin.

15. (a) If C is a circle of radius ρ about z_0, show that

$$\oint_C \frac{dz}{(z - z_0)^n} = 2\pi i \qquad \text{if} \quad n = 1,$$

but for any other integral value of n, positive or negative, the integral is zero. *Hint:* Use the fact that $z = z_0 + \rho e^{i\theta}$ on C.
   (b) Verify the formulas (4.3) for the coefficients in a Laurent series. *Hint:* To get a_n, divide equation (4.1) by $(z - z_0)^{n+1}$ and use the results of part (a) to evaluate the integrals of the terms of the series. Use a similar method to find b_n.

16. For each of the following functions find the first few terms of each of the Laurent series about the origin, that is, one series for each annular ring between singular points. Find the residue of each function at the origin. (*Warning:* To find the residue, you must use the Laurent series which converges near the origin.)

(a) $\dfrac{1}{z(z - 1)}$.

Hint: Expand $1/(z - 1) = -1/(1 - z)$ in powers of z and divide the result by z; show that this series converges for $0 < |z| < 1$. Then expand $\dfrac{1}{1 - \dfrac{1}{z}}$ in powers of $1/z$ and divide by z^2; show that this series converges for $|z| > 1$. See top of page 526 for hint on parts (b) to (d).

(b) $\dfrac{1}{z(z - 1)(z - 2)}$,   (c) $\dfrac{z^3}{(z - 1)(z - 2)^2}$,   (d) $\dfrac{z - 1}{z^3(z - 2)}$.

FUNCTIONS OF A COMPLEX VARIABLE

Hint: Use partial fractions as in (4.4). Expand a term $1/(z - a)$ in powers of z to get a series convergent for $|z| < a$, and in powers of $1/z$ to get a series convergent for $|z| > a$.

17. Find the Laurent series for the following functions about the indicated points; hence find the residue of the function at the point. (Be sure you have the Laurent series which converges near the point.)

(a) $\dfrac{1}{z(z+1)}$, $z = 0$;   (b) $\dfrac{1}{z(z-1)}$, $z = 1$;   (c) $\dfrac{\sin z}{z^4}$, $z = 0$;

(d) $\dfrac{\cosh z}{z^2}$, $z = 0$;   (e) $\dfrac{e^z}{z^2 - 1}$, $z = 1$;   (f) $\sin \dfrac{1}{z}$, $z = 0$.

18. Show that the sum of a power series which converges in a circle C is an analytic function inside C. *Hint:* See Chapter 2, Section 7, and Chapter 1, Section 11, and the definition of an analytic function.

19. For each of the following functions, say whether the indicated point is regular, an essential singularity, or a pole, and if a pole of what order it is.

(a) $\dfrac{\cos z}{z}$, $z = 0$;   (b) $\dfrac{\sin z}{z}$, $z = 0$;

(c) $\dfrac{e^z}{z - 1}$, $z = 1$;   (d) $\dfrac{z^2 - 1}{z^2 + 1}$, $z = i$;

(e) $\dfrac{\sin z}{z^2}$, $z = 0$;   (f) $\dfrac{z^2 - 1}{(z - 1)^2}$, $z = 1$;

(g) $\tan^2 z$, $z = \dfrac{\pi}{2}$;   (h) $ze^{1/z}$, $z = 0$.

20. Obtain Cauchy's integral formula (3.9) from the residue theorem (5.2).

21. (a) Show that rule B in Section 6 is correct by applying it to (4.1).

(b) Derive (6.2) by using the limit definition of the derivative $h'(z_0)$ instead of using l'Hospital's rule. Remember that $h(z_0) = 0$ because we are assuming that $f(z)$ has a simple pole at z_0.

(c) Prove rule C in Section 6 for finding the residue at a multiple pole, by applying it to (4.1). Note that the rule is valid for $n = 1$ (simple pole) although we seldom use it for that case.

(d) Prove rule C in Section 6 by using (3.9). *Hints:* If $f(z)$ has a pole of order n at $z = a$, then $f(z) = g(z)/(z - a)^n$ with $g(z)$ analytic at $z = a$. By (3.9),

$$\int_C \frac{g(z)}{(z - a)} \, dz = 2\pi i g(a)$$

with C a contour inclosing a but no other singularities. Differentiate this equation $(n - 1)$ times with respect to a.

22. Find the residues of the following functions at the indicated points. Try to

select the easiest method.

(a) $\dfrac{z-2}{z(z-1)}$ at $z = 0$ and at $z = 1$.   (b) $\dfrac{z-2}{z^2(z-1)^2}$ at $z = 0$ and at $z = 1$.

(c) $\dfrac{z}{(z^2+1)^2}$ at $z = i$.   (d) $\dfrac{1-\cos 2z}{z^3}$ at $z = 0$.

(e) $\dfrac{z+2}{z^2+9}$ at $z = 3i$.   (f) $\dfrac{z+2}{(z^2+9)(z^2+1)}$ at $z = 3i$.

(g) $\dfrac{e^{3z}-3z-1}{z^4}$ at $z = 0$.   (h) $\dfrac{z^2}{z^4+16}$ at $z = \sqrt{2}\,(1+i)$.

(i) $\dfrac{\sin^2 z}{4+z}$ at $z = -4$.   (j) $\dfrac{e^{iz}}{z^2+4}$ at $z = 2i$.

(k) $\dfrac{e^{iz}}{(z^2+4)^2}$ at $z = 2i$.   (l) $\dfrac{1+\cos z}{(z-\pi)^3}$ at $z = \pi$.

(m) $\dfrac{e^{2z}}{1+e^z}$ at $z = i\pi$.   (n) $\dfrac{\cosh z - 1}{z^7}$ at $z = 0$.

23. Use the residue theorem to evaluate the contour integrals of each of the functions in Problem 22 around a circle of radius $\frac{3}{2}$ and center at the origin. Check carefully to see which singular points are inside the circle. You may use your results in Problem 22 as far as they go, but you may have to compute some more residues.

24. Using one of the methods discussed in Section 7, Examples 1, 2, and 3, evaluate the following definite integrals.

(a) $\displaystyle\int_0^{2\pi} \dfrac{d\theta}{13 + 5\sin\theta}$ (b) $\displaystyle\int_0^{2\pi} \dfrac{d\theta}{5 - 3\cos\theta}$

(c) $\displaystyle\int_0^{\pi} \dfrac{d\theta}{1 - 2r\cos\theta + r^2}$ $(0 \le r < 1)$ (d) $\displaystyle\int_0^{2\pi} \dfrac{\sin^2\theta\, d\theta}{5 + 3\cos\theta}$

(e) $\displaystyle\int_0^{2\pi} \dfrac{\cos 2\theta\, d\theta}{5 + 4\cos\theta}$ $z = e^{i\theta}$ (f) $\displaystyle\int_0^{\pi} \dfrac{d\theta}{(2 + \cos\theta)^2}$

(g) $\displaystyle\int_0^{2\pi} \dfrac{d\theta}{1 + \sin\theta\cos\alpha}$ $(\alpha = \text{const.})$ (h) $\displaystyle\int_{-\infty}^{\infty} \dfrac{dx}{x^2 + 4x + 5}$

(i) $\displaystyle\int_0^{\infty} \dfrac{x^2\, dx}{(x^2+4)(x^2+9)}$ (j) $\displaystyle\int_0^{\infty} \dfrac{x^2\, dx}{x^4 + 16}$

(k) $\displaystyle\int_0^{\infty} \dfrac{\cos 2x\, dx}{x^2 + 4}$ (l) $\displaystyle\int_{-\infty}^{\infty} \dfrac{\sin x\, dx}{x^2 + 4x + 5}$

(m) $\displaystyle\int_{-\infty}^{\infty} \dfrac{x\sin x\, dx}{x^2 + 4x + 5}$ (n) $\displaystyle\int_0^{\infty} \dfrac{x\sin x\, dx}{x^2 + 4}$

(o) $\displaystyle\int_0^{\infty} \dfrac{\cos 2x\, dx}{(x^2 + 9)^2}$ (p) $\displaystyle\int_0^{\infty} \dfrac{x\sin x\, dx}{1 + x^2 + x^4}$

25. In Example 4, Section 7, we stated a rule for evaluating a contour integral when the contour passes through simple poles. We proved that the result was correct for $\int_{\Gamma} \dfrac{e^{iz}}{z}\,dz$ around the contour Γ shown here.

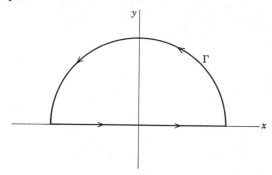

(a) By following the same method (integrating around C' of Fig. 7.3 and letting $r \to 0$) show that the result is correct if we replace e^{iz} by any $f(z)$ which is analytic at $z = 0$.

(b) Repeat the proof in (a) for $\int_{\Gamma} \dfrac{f(z)}{z - a}\,dz$, a real (that is, a pole on the x-axis), with $f(z)$ analytic at $z = a$.

26. Using the rule of Example 4, Section 7 (also see Problem 25), evaluate the following integrals. Find principal values if necessary.

(a) $\displaystyle\int_{-\infty}^{\infty} \frac{x \sin \pi x}{1 - x^2}\,dx$

(b) $\displaystyle\int_{0}^{\infty} \frac{\cos ax}{x^2 - b^2}\,dx$

(c) $\displaystyle\int_{0}^{\infty} \frac{x \sin ax}{x^2 - b^2}\,dx \quad (a > 0)$

(d) $\displaystyle\int_{0}^{\infty} \frac{\cos \pi x}{1 - 4x^2}\,dx$

(e) $\displaystyle\int_{0}^{\infty} \frac{dx}{1 - x^4}$

(f) $\displaystyle\int_{0}^{\infty} \frac{\sin ax}{x}\,dx$

27. (a) By the method of Example 2, Section 7, evaluate

$$\int_{0}^{\infty} \frac{dx}{1 + x^4}.$$

(b) Evaluate the same integral by using tables (say Dwight or Peirce) to get the indefinite integral; unless you are very careful you may get zero. Explain why.

(c) Make the change of variables $u = x^4$ in the integral in (a) and evaluate the u integral using (7.5).

(d) Use the method of part (c) to evaluate $\displaystyle\int_{0}^{\infty} \frac{dx}{1 + x^6}.$

(e) Use the method of part (c) and the contour and method of Example 5, Section 7, to evaluate $\displaystyle\int_{0}^{\infty} \frac{dx}{(1 + x^4)^2}.$

28. Evaluate the following integrals by the method of Example 5, Section 7.

(a) $\displaystyle\int_0^\infty \frac{\sqrt{x}\,dx}{1+x^2}$

(b) $\displaystyle\int_0^\infty \frac{\ln x}{x^{3/4}(1+x)}\,dx$

29. (a) Show that

$$\int_{-\infty}^\infty \frac{e^{px}}{1+e^x}\,dx = \frac{\pi}{\sin \pi p}$$

for $0 < p < 1$. *Hint:* Find $\displaystyle\int \frac{e^{pz}\,dz}{1+e^z}$ around the rectangular contour shown.

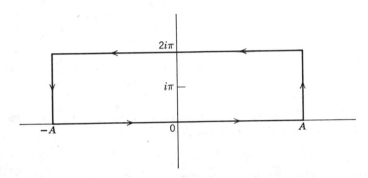

Show that the integrals along the vertical sides tend to zero as $A \to \infty$. Note that the integral along the upper side is a multiple of the integral along the x-axis.

(b) Make the change of variable $y = e^x$ in $\displaystyle\int_{-\infty}^\infty \frac{e^{px}}{1+e^x}$ of part (a), and using (6.5) of Chapter 9, show that this integral is the beta function, $B(p, 1-p)$. Then using (7.1) of Chapter 9, show that $\Gamma(p)\Gamma(1-p) = \pi/\sin \pi p$.

30. Using the same contour and method as in Problem 29a, evaluate $\displaystyle\int_{-\infty}^\infty \frac{e^{px}}{1-e^x}$, $0 < p < 1$. *Hint:* The only difference between this problem and Problem 29a is that you now have two simple poles on the contour instead of a pole inside. Use the rule of Section 7, Example 4.

31. Evaluate

$$\int_{-\infty}^\infty \frac{e^{2\pi x/3}}{\cosh \pi x}\,dx.$$

Hint: Use a rectangle as in Problem 29a, but of height 1 instead of 2π. Note that there is a pole at $i/2$.

32. Evaluate $\displaystyle\int_0^\infty \frac{x\,dx}{\sinh x}$. *Hint:* First find the $-\infty$ to ∞ integral. Use a rectangle of height π and note the simple pole at $i\pi$ on the contour.

33. The Fresnel integrals, $\int_0^u \sin u^2\, du$ and $\int_0^u \cos u^2\, du$, are important in

optics. For the case of infinite upper limits, evaluate these integrals as follows: Make the change of variable $x = u^2$; to evaluate the resulting integrals, find $\oint \dfrac{e^{iz}}{\sqrt{z}}\, dz$

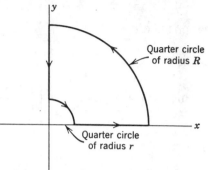

Quarter circle of radius R

Quarter circle of radius r

around the contour shown. Let $r \to 0$ and $R \to \infty$ and show that the integrals along these quarter-circles tend to zero. Recognize the integral along the y-axis as a Γ function and so evaluate it. Hence evaluate the integral along the x-axis; the real and imaginary parts of this integral are the integrals you are trying to find.

34. If $F(z) = f'(z)/f(z)$,

(a) show that the residue of $F(z)$ at an nth order zero of $f(z)$, is n. *Hint:* If $f(z)$ has a zero of order n at $z = a$, then

$$f(z) = a_n(z - a)^n + a_{n+1}(z - a)^{n+1} + \cdots.$$

(b) Also show that the residue of $F(z)$ at a pole of order p of $f(z)$, is $-p$. *Hint:* See the definition of a pole of order p at the end of Section 4.

35. By using theorem (7.8), show that $z^3 + z^2 + 9 = 0$ has exactly one root in the first quadrant. Recall that the roots of a polynomial equation with real coefficients are either real or occur in conjugate pairs $a \pm bi$ (think of the quadratic formula, for example). Hence show that since $z^3 + z^2 + 9 = 0$ has one root in the first quadrant, it has one in the fourth and one on the negative real axis.

36. The *fundamental theorem of algebra* says that every equation of the form $f(z) = a_n z^n + a_{n-1} z^{n-1} + \cdots + a_0 = 0$, $a_n \neq 0$, $n \geq 1$, has at least one root, from which it follows that an nth degree equation has n roots. Prove this by using the argument principle. *Hint:* Follow the increase in the angle of $f(z)$ around a very large circle $z = re^{i\theta}$; for sufficiently large r, all roots are inclosed, and $f(z)$ is approximately $a_n z^n$.

37. As in Problem 35, find out in which quadrants the roots of the following equations lie:

(a) $z^4 + z + 1 = 0$

(b) $z^3 + 3z^2 + 4z + 2 = 0$

(c) $z^3 + z^2 + z + 4 = 0$

(d) $z^4 + z^3 + 4z^2 + 2z + 3 = 0$

38. (a) Use (7.8) to evaluate $\oint_C \dfrac{f'(z)}{f(z)} \, dz, \quad f(z) = \dfrac{z^3(z+1)^2 \sin z}{(z^2+1)^2(z-3)}, \quad$ around the

circle $|z| = 2$; around $|z| = \frac{1}{2}$.

(b) Use (7.8) to evaluate $\oint \dfrac{z^3 \, dz}{1 + 2z^4}$ around $|z| = 1$.

39. Let $f(z)$ be expanded in the Laurent series that is valid for all z *outside* some circle, that is, $|z| > M$ (see Section 4 and Problem 16). This series is called the Laurent series "about infinity." Show that the result of integrating the Laurent series term by term around a very large circle (of radius $> M$) in the positive direction, is $2\pi i b_1$ (just as in the original proof of the residue theorem in Section 5). Remember (Section 8) that the integral "around ∞" is taken in the negative direction, and is equal to $2\pi i \cdot$ (residue at ∞). Conclude that $R(\infty) = -b_1$. *Caution:* In using this method of computing $R(\infty)$, you must be sure you have the Laurent series that converges for all sufficiently large z.

40. (a) Show that if $f(z)$ tends to a finite limit as z tends to infinity, then the residue of $f(z)$ at infinity is $\lim_{z \to \infty} z^2 f'(z)$.

(b) Also show that if $f(z)$ tends to zero as z tends to infinity, then the residue of $f(z)$ at infinity is $-\lim_{z \to \infty} z f(z)$.

41. Find out whether infinity is a regular point, an essential singularity, or a pole (and if a pole, of what order) for each of the following functions. Using Problem 39, or Problem 40, or (8.3), find the residue of each function at infinity.

(a) $\dfrac{z}{z^2 + 1}$

(b) $\dfrac{2z + 3}{(z + 2)^2}$

(c) $\sin \dfrac{1}{z}$

(d) $\dfrac{z^2 + 5}{z}$

(e) $\dfrac{4z^3 + 2z + 3}{z^2}$

(f) $\dfrac{z^2 + 2}{3z^2}$

(g) $\dfrac{z^2 - 1}{z^2 + 1}$

(h) $\dfrac{1 + z}{1 - z}$

(i) $\tan \dfrac{1}{z}$

(j) $\ln \dfrac{z + 1}{z - 1}$

42. Give another proof of the fundamental theorem of algebra (see Problem 36) as follows. Let $I = \oint \dfrac{f'(z)}{f(z)} \, dz$ about infinity, that is, in the negative direction around a very large circle C. Use the argument principle (7.8), and also evaluate I by finding the residue of $f'(z)/f(z)$ at infinity; thus show that $f(z)$ has n zeros inside C.

43. Evaluate the following integrals by computing residues at infinity (see Section 8 and Problems 39, 40, 41). Check your answers by computing residues at all the finite poles. (It is understood that $\oint$ means in the positive direction.)

(a) $\oint \dfrac{1 - z^2}{1 + z^2} \dfrac{dz}{z}$ around $|z| = 2$.

(b) $\oint \dfrac{z^2 \, dz}{(2z + 1)(z^2 + 9)}$ around $|z| = 5$.

(c) Observe that in parts (a) and (b) the sum of the residues at finite points plus the residue at infinity is zero. Prove that this is always true for a function which has a finite number of singularities.

44. Solve equations (9.3) for x and y in terms of u and v. Use your equations to sketch the images in the w-plane of the z-plane lines $x = $ const. (for several values of x) and similarly of $y = $ const.

45. For each of the following functions $w = f(z) = u + iv$, find u and v as functions of x and y. Sketch the graphs in the (x, y) plane of the images of $u = $ const. and $v = $ const. for several values of u and several values of v as was done for $w = z^2$ in Fig. 9.3. The curves $u = $ const. should be orthogonal to the curves $v = $ const.

(a) $w = \dfrac{z + 1}{2i}$ (b) $w = \dfrac{1}{z}$

(c) $w = e^z$ (d) $w = \dfrac{z - i}{z + i}$

(e) $w = \sqrt{z}$ *Hint:* This is equivalent to $w^2 = z$; find x and y in terms of u and v and then solve the pair of equations for u and v in terms of x and y. Note that this is really the same problem as Problem 44 with the z- and w-planes interchanged.

(f) $z = \sin w$.

46. Describe the Riemann surface for $w = z^3$; for $w = \sqrt{z}$; for $w = \ln z$.

47. (a) If $w = f(z) = u(x, y) + iv(x, y)$, $f(z)$ analytic, defines a transformation from the variables x, y to the variables u, v, show that the Jacobian of the transformation (see Chapter 10, Section 13) is $\partial(u, v)/\partial(x, y) = |f'(z)|^2$. *Hint:* To simplify the determinant, use the Cauchy-Riemann equations and the equations (Section 2) used in obtaining them.

(b) Verify the matrix equation $\begin{pmatrix} du \\ dv \end{pmatrix} = (J) \begin{pmatrix} dx \\ dy \end{pmatrix}$, where (J) is a matrix whose determinant is the Jacobian in part (a) (also see Chapter 10,

Section 13). Multiply the matrix equation by its transpose and use part (a) to obtain $dS/ds = |dw/dz|$ as in Section 9.

48. (a) In Section 9 we discussed the fact that a conformal transformation magnifies and rotates an infinitesimal geometrical figure. We showed that $|dw/dz|$ is the magnification factor. Show that the angle of dw/dz is the rotation angle. *Hint:* Consider the rotation and magnification of an arc $dz = dx + i\,dy$ (of length ds and angle arc tan dy/dx) which is required to obtain the image of dz, namely dw.

(b) Compare the directional derivative $d\phi/ds$ (Chapter 5, Section 9) in the direction given by dz in the z-plane, and the directional derivative $d\phi/dS$ in the direction in the w-plane given by the image dw of dz. Hence show (as claimed in the temperature problem of Section 10) that the rate of change of T in a given direction in the z-plane is proportional to the corresponding rate of change of T in the image direction in the w-plane.

49. Prove the theorem stated just after (10.2) as follows. Let $\phi(u, v)$ be a harmonic function (that is, $\partial^2\phi/\partial u^2 + \partial^2\phi/\partial v^2 = 0$). Show that there is then an analytic function $g(w) = \phi(u, v) + i\psi(u, v)$ (see Section 2). Let $w = f(z) = u + iv$ be another analytic function (this is the mapping function). Show that the function $h(z) = g(f(z))$ is analytic. (*Hint:* Show that $h(z)$ has a derivative. How do you find the derivative of a function of a function, for example, $\ln \sin z$?). Then (by Section 2), the real part of $h(z)$ is harmonic. Show that this real part is $\phi(u(x, y), v(x, y))$.

50. (a) A fluid flow is called irrotational if $\nabla \times \mathbf{V} = 0$ where $\mathbf{V} = $ velocity of fluid (Chapter 5, Section 13); then $\mathbf{V} = \nabla\Phi$. Use the equation of continuity [(12.9) of Chapter 5] to show that if the fluid is incompressible (that is, has constant density), then Φ satisfies Laplace's equation. (*Caution:* In Chapter 5, we used $\mathbf{V} = \mathbf{v}\rho$, with $\mathbf{v} = $ velocity; here $\mathbf{V} = $ velocity.)

(b) Similarly, assuming from electricity the equations $\nabla \cdot \mathbf{D} = \rho$, $\mathbf{E} = -\nabla V$, $\mathbf{D} = \epsilon\mathbf{E}$ ($\epsilon = $ const.), show that in regions where the free charge density ρ is zero, V satisfies Laplace's equation.

51. A (nonconstant) harmonic function (solution of Laplace's equation) takes its maximum value and its minimum value on the boundary of any region (not at an interior point). Thus, for example, the electrostatic potential V in a region containing no free charge takes on its largest and smallest values on the boundary of the region, and the temperature T of a body containing no sources of heat takes its largest and smallest values on the surface of the body. Prove this fact (for two-dimensional regions) as follows. In (3.9), let $z = a + re^{i\theta}$ (that is, C is a circle with center at a), and show that the average value of $f(z)$ on the circle is $f(a)$ (see Chapter 6, Section 4 for discussion of the average of a function). Take real and imaginary parts of $f(a) = [u(x, y) + iv(x, y)]_{z=a}$. Conclude that the value of $u(x, y)$ at $z = a$ lies between the maximum and minimum values of $u(x, y)$ on the circle. Now suppose that it is claimed that $u(x, y)$ has a maximum value at some interior point a, by which we would mean that at all points of some small circle about a,

$u(x, y)$ has smaller values than at a. Show that such a claim leads to a contradiction. Give a similar proof that $u(x, y)$ cannot have a minimum point except on a boundary. .

52. (a) Let a flat plate in the shape of a quarter-circle, as shown, have its faces and curved boundary insulated, and its two straight edges held at $0°$ and $100°$. Find the temperature distribution $T(x, y)$ in the plate, and the equations of the isothermals. *Hint:* Use the mapping function $w = \ln z$ as in Fig. 10.1; what w-plane line maps into the y-axis?

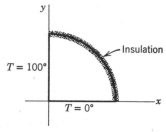

(b) Consider a capacitor made of two very large perpendicular plates. (Let the positive x- and y-axes in the diagram of part (a) represent a cross section of the capacitor.) Let one plate (x-axis) be held at potential $V = 0$, and the other plate (y-axis) be held at potential $V = 100$ volts. Find the potential $V(x, y)$ for $x > 0, y > 0$, and the equations of the equipotentials. *Hint:* This problem is mathematically identical with part (a).

53. Let the figure represent (the cross section of) a hot cylinder (say $T = 100°$) lying on a cold plane (say $T = 0°$). (Separate the two by a bit of insulation.) Find the temperature in the shaded region. Alternatively, let the cylinder and the plane be held at two different electrical potentials (with insulation between), and find the electrical potential in the shaded region. Find and sketch some of the isothermals (equipotentials) and some of the curves (perpendicular to the isothermals) along which heat flows (lines of flux for the electrical case). *Hint:* Use the mapping function $w = 1/z$, and consider the image of the w-plane region between $v = 0$ and $v = -1$.

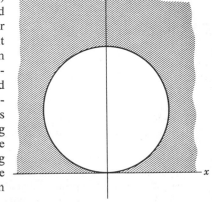

54. (a) Use the mapping function $w = z^2$ to find the streamlines for the flow of water around the inside of a right-angle boundary. Find the velocity potential Φ, the stream function Ψ, and the velocity $\mathbf{V} = \nabla\Phi$.

(b) Observe that the magnitude of the velocity in part (a) can be obtained from $V = V_0 |dw/dz|$. Show that this result holds in general as follows. Let $w = f(z)$ be an analytic mapping function such that the lines $v = $ const. map into the streamlines of the flow you want to consider in the z-plane. Then

$$V_0 w = V_0(u + iv) = \Phi(x, y) + i\Psi(x, y).$$

Show that

$$V_0 \frac{dw}{dz} = \frac{\partial \Phi}{\partial x} - i \frac{\partial \Phi}{\partial y} = V_x - iV_y$$

(this expression is called the *complex velocity*). Hence show that $V = V_0 |dw/dz|$.

55. Find and sketch the streamlines for the flow of water over a semicircular hump (say a half-buried log at the bottom of a stream) as shown. *Hint:* Use the mapping function $w = z + z^{-1}$. Show that the u-axis maps into the contour $ABCDE$ with the correspondence shown.

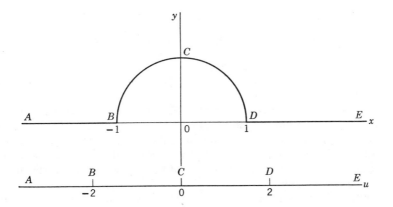

56. Find and sketch the streamlines for the indicated flow of water inside a rectangular boundary. *Hint:* Consider $w = \sin z$; map the u-axis into the boundary of the rectangle.

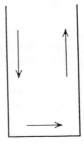

57. (a) For $w = \ln (z + 1)/(z - 1)$, show that the images of $u = $ const. and $v = $ const. are two orthogonal sets of circles. Find centers and radii of five or six circles of each set and sketch them. Include the circle with center at the origin. Use your results to solve the following physical problems.

(b) The figure represents the cross section of a long cylinder (assume it infinitely long) cut in half, with the two halves insulated from each other. Let the surface of the top half be held at temperature $T = 30°$ and the surface of the bottom half at $T = 10°$. Find the temperature $T(x, y)$ inside the

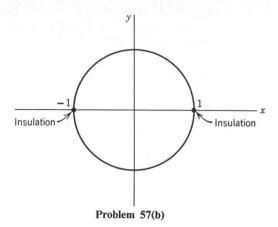

Problem 57(b)

cylinder. *Hint:* Show that the line $v = \pi/2$ maps into the lower half of the circle $|z| = 1$, and the line $v = 3\pi/2$ maps into the upper half of the circle.

(c) Let the figure in (b) represent (the cross section of) a capacitor with the lower half at potential V_1 and the upper half at potential V_2. Find the potential $V(x, y)$ between the plates (that is, inside the circle). *Hint:* This is almost like (b). Observe that in the text and in (b), the w-plane temperature is of the form Av, with A const.; here you need the potential of the form $Av + B$, A and B constants.

(d) In the figure in (b), let $z = -1$ be a source and $z = +1$ a sink, and let the water flow inside the circular boundary. Find Φ, Ψ, and V. Sketch the streamlines.

(e) In (d), the streamlines were the images of $v = $ const. Consider the flow (over the whole plane, that is, with no boundaries) with streamlines $u = $ const. This flow may be described as two vortices rotating in opposite directions. Sketch a number of streamlines indicating the direction of the velocity with arrows. Since a boundary is a streamline, a flow is not disturbed by inserting a boundary along a streamline. Insert two circular boundaries corresponding to $u = a$ and $u = -a$. Show that the velocity through the narrow neck (say at $z = 0$) is greater than the velocity elsewhere (say at $z = i$). You can simplify your calculation of the velocity by showing that the result in Problem 54b holds here also.

(f) Two long parallel cylinders form a capacitor. (Let their cross sections be the images of $u = a$ and $u = -a$.) If they are held at potentials V_0 and $-V_0$, find the potential $V(x, y)$ at points between them. Given that the charge (per unit length) on a cylinder is $q = V_0/(2a)$, show that the capacitance (per unit length), that is, $q/(2V_0)$, is given by $1\left/\left(4 \operatorname{arc cosh} \dfrac{d}{2r}\right)\right.$, where d is the distance between the centers of the two cylinders, and their radii are r.

(g) Other problems to consider using this same mapping function: (i) a capacitor consisting of two long cylinders one inside the other, but not concentric; (ii) the magnetic field in a plane perpendicular to two long parallel wires carrying equal but opposite currents; (iii) the electric field in a plane perpendicular to two long parallel wires, one charged positive and the other negative; (iv) other flow problems obtained by inserting boundaries along streamlines.

12

Series Solutions of Differential Equations; Legendre Polynomials; Bessel Functions; Sets of Orthogonal Functions

I. INTRODUCTION

By now you are well aware of the fact that physical problems in many fields lead to differential equations which must be solved. Some of these can be solved by standard methods, but when these methods do not apply we may resort to series solutions. Let us illustrate the method of series solution for the following simple equation (which can easily be solved by straightforward methods also!):

$$(1.1) \qquad\qquad y' = 2xy.$$

We assume a solution of this differential equation in the form of a power series, namely

$$(1.2) \qquad y = a_0 + a_1 x + a_2 x^2 + a_3 x^3 + \cdots + a_n x^n + \cdots$$
$$= \sum_{n=0}^{\infty} a_n x^n,$$

where the a's are to be found. Differentiating (1.2) term by term, we get

$$(1.3) \qquad y' = a_1 + 2a_2 x + 3a_3 x^2 + \cdots + na_n x^{n-1} + \cdots$$
$$= \sum_{n=1}^{\infty} na_n x^{n-1}.$$

We substitute (1.2) and (1.3) into the differential equation (1.1); we then have two power series equal to each other. Now the original differential equation is to be satisfied for all values of x, that is, y' and $2xy$ are to be the same function of x. Since a given function has only one series expansion in powers of x (see Chapter 1, Section 11), the two series must be identical, that is, the coefficients of corresponding powers of x must be equal. We get the following set of equations for the a's:

(1.4) $a_1 = 0, \quad a_2 = a_0, \quad a_3 = \frac{2}{3}a_1 = 0, \quad a_4 = \frac{1}{2}a_0,$

or in general:

(1.5) $na_n = 2a_{n-2}, \qquad a_n = \begin{cases} 0 & \text{odd } n, \\ \dfrac{2}{n} a_{n-2} & \text{even } n. \end{cases}$

Putting $n = 2m$ (since only even terms appear in this series), we get

(1.6) $a_{2m} = \dfrac{2}{2m} a_{2m-2}$

$\qquad = \dfrac{1}{m} a_{2m-2} = \dfrac{1}{m} \dfrac{1}{m-1} a_{2m-4} = \cdots = \dfrac{1}{m!} a_0.$

Substituting these values of the coefficients into the assumed solution (1.2) gives the solution

(1.7) $y = a_0 + a_0 x^2 + \dfrac{1}{2!} a_0 x^4 + \cdots + \dfrac{1}{m!} a_0 x^{2m} + \cdots$

$\qquad = a_0 \sum\limits_{m=0}^{\infty} \dfrac{x^{2m}}{m!}.$

Let us compare this with the solution by a standard method (in this case, separation of variables):

$$\frac{dy}{y} = 2x \, dx,$$

$$\ln y = x^2 + \ln c,$$

$$y = ce^{x^2}.$$

Expanding this in a series of powers of x^2, we get:

$$y = c\left(1 + x^2 + \frac{x^4}{2!} + \cdots\right) = c\sum_{n=0}^{\infty} \frac{x^{2n}}{n!}$$

which, with $c = a_0$, is the same as the series solution (1.7). You cannot always expect to find the closed form of a power series solution (that is, an elementary function for which your series solution is the power series expansion), but in simple cases you may recognize it. Of course, in that case, the problem could also have been done without series; the real need for series is in problems for which there is no closed form in terms of elementary functions. Also you should realize that not all solutions have series expansions in powers of x, for example, $\ln x$ or $1/x^2$. All we can say is that if there is a solution which can be represented by a convergent power series this method will find it. We shall discuss later (Section 21b) some theorems which tell us when we can expect to find such a solution.

Let us now consider some differential equations which occur frequently in applied problems and which are usually solved by series methods.

2. LEGENDRE'S EQUATION

Although the most useful solutions of this equation are polynomials (called the *Legendre polynomials*), one way to find them is to assume a series solution of the differential equation, and show that the series terminates after a finite number of terms. We shall see later some other ways of finding the Legendre polynomials (Sections 4 and 5).

The Legendre differential equation is

(2.1)
$$(1 - x^2)y'' - 2xy' + l(l + 1)y = 0,$$

where l is a constant. We assume the series solution (1.2) for y and differentiate it term by term twice to get y' and y'':

(2.2)
$$y = a_0 + a_1x + a_2x^2 + a_3x^3 + a_4x^4 + \cdots + a_nx^n + \cdots,$$
$$y' = a_1 + 2a_2x + 3a_3x^2 + 4a_4x^3 + \cdots + na_nx^{n-1} + \cdots,$$
$$y'' = 2a_2 + 6a_3x + 12a_4x^2 + 20a_5x^3 + \cdots + n(n-1)a_nx^{n-2} + \cdots.$$

We substitute (2.2) into (2.1) and collect the coefficients of the various powers of x; it is convenient to tabulate them as follows:

	const.	x	x^2	x^3	$\cdots x^n \cdots$
y''	$2a_2$	$6a_3$	$12a_4$	$20a_5$	$(n+2)(n+1)a_{n+2}$
$-x^2y''$			$-2a_2$	$-6a_3$	$-n(n-1)a_n$
$-2xy'$		$-2a_1$	$-4a_2$	$-6a_3$	$-2na_n$
$l(l+1)y$	$l(l+1)a_0$	$l(l+1)a_1$	$l(l+1)a_2$	$l(l+1)a_3$	$l(l+1)a_n$

Next we set the total coefficient of each power of x equal to zero [because, as discussed in Section 1, y must satisfy (2.1) identically]. For the first few powers of x we get

$$2a_2 + l(l+1)a_0 = 0 \quad \text{or} \quad a_2 = -\frac{l(l+1)}{2}a_0;$$

$$6a_3 + (l^2 + l - 2)a_1 = 0 \quad \text{or} \quad a_3 = -\frac{(l-1)(l+2)}{6}a_1;$$

(2.3)

$$12a_4 + (l^2 + l - 6)a_2 = 0 \quad \text{or} \quad a_4 = -\frac{(l-2)(l+3)}{12}a_2$$

$$= \frac{l(l+1)(l-2)(l+3)}{4!}a_0;$$

and from the x^n coefficient we get

(2.4) $\qquad (n+2)(n+1)a_{n+2} + (l^2 + l - n^2 - n)a_n = 0.$

The coefficient of a_n in (2.4) can be factored to give

(2.5) $\quad l^2 - n^2 + l - n = (l+n)(l-n) + (l-n) = (l-n)(l+n+1).$

Then we can write a general formula for a_{n+2} in terms of a_n. This formula (2.6) includes the formulas (2.3) for a_2, a_3, and a_4, and makes it possible for us to find any even coefficient as a multiple of a_0, and any odd coefficient as a multiple of a_1. Solving (2.4) for a_{n+2} and using (2.5), we have

(2.6) $\qquad\boxed{a_{n+2} = -\frac{(l-n)(l+n+1)}{(n+2)(n+1)}a_n.}$

The general solution of (2.1) is then a sum of two series containing (as the solution of a second-order differential equation should) two constants a_0 and a_1 to be determined by the given initial conditions:

(2.7)

$$y = a_0\left[1 - \frac{l(l+1)}{2!}x^2 + \frac{l(l+1)(l-2)(l+3)}{4!}x^4 - \cdots\right]$$

$$+ a_1\left[x - \frac{(l-1)(l+2)}{3!}x^3 + \frac{(l-1)(l+2)(l-3)(l+4)}{5!}x^5 - \cdots\right].$$

From equation (2.6) you can see by the ratio test that these series converge for $x^2 < 1$. It can be shown that, in general, they do not converge for $x^2 = 1$. As an example of this, consider the a_1 series for $l = 0$. If $x^2 = 1$, this series is $1 + \frac{1}{3} + \frac{1}{5} + \cdots$, that is, the harmonic series, which is divergent. Now in many applications x is the cosine of an angle θ, and l is a (nonnegative) integer. We want a solution which converges for all θ, that is, a solution which converges *at* $x = \pm 1$ as well as for $|x| < 1$. We can always find one (but not two) such solutions for integral l; let us see how.

Legendre polynomials. We have seen that for $l = 0$ the a_1 series in (2.7) diverges. But look at the a_0 series; it gives just $y = a_0$ for $l = 0$ since all the rest of the terms contain the factor l. If $l = 1$, the a_0 series is divergent at $x^2 = 1$, but the a_1 series stops with $y = a_1 x$ [since all the rest of the terms in the a_1 series contain the factor $(l - 1)$]. For any integral l, one series terminates giving a polynomial solution; the other series is divergent at $x^2 = 1$. (Negative integral values of l would simply give solutions already obtained for positive l's; for example, $l = -2$ gives the polynomial solution $y = a_1 x$ which is the same as the $l = 1$ solution. Consequently, it is customary to restrict l to nonnegative values.) Thus we obtain a set of polynomial solutions of the Legendre equation, one for each nonnegative integral l. Each solution contains an arbitrary constant factor (a_0 or a_1); for $l = 0$, $y = a_0$; for $l = 1$, $y = a_1 x$, etc. If the value of a_0 or a_1 in each polynomial is selected so that $y = 1$ when $x = 1$, the resulting polynomials are called the *Legendre polynomials*, written $P_l(x)$. From (2.6) and (2.7) and the requirement $P_l(1) = 1$, we find the following expressions for the first few Legendre polynomials:

$$(2.8) \qquad P_0(x) = 1, \qquad P_1(x) = x, \qquad P_2(x) = \tfrac{1}{2}(3x^2 - 1).$$

Finding a few more Legendre polynomials by this method and other methods will be left to the problems. Although $P_l(x)$ for any integral l may be found by this method, simpler ways of obtaining the Legendre polynomials for larger l values will be outlined in Sections 4 and 5.

Eigenvalue problems. In finding the Legendre polynomials as solutions of Legendre's equation (2.1), we have solved an *eigenvalue problem*. (See Chapter 3, end of Section 7 and Problem 22, and Chapter 10, Section 4.) Recall that in an eigenvalue problem we are given an equation or a set of equations containing a parameter, and we want solutions that satisfy some special requirement; in order to obtain such solutions we must choose particular values (called eigenvalues) for the parameter in the problem. In finding the Legendre polynomials, we asked for series solutions of Legendre's equation (2.1) which converged at $x = \pm 1$. We saw that we could obtain such solutions if the parameter l took on any integral value. The values of l, namely 0, 1, 2, . . . , are called *eigenvalues* (or *characteristic values*); the corresponding solutions $P_l(x)$ are called *eigenfunctions* (or *characteristic functions*). See Problems 64 and 65 for further examples of eigenvalues and eigenfunctions.

The Legendre polynomials are also called Legendre functions of the first kind. The second solution for each l, which is an infinite series (convergent for $x^2 < 1$), is called a Legendre function of the second kind and is denoted by $Q_l(x)$. The functions $Q_l(x)$ are not used as frequently as the polynomials $P_l(x)$. For fractional l both solutions are infinite series; these again occur less frequently in applications.

3. LEIBNIZ' RULE FOR DIFFERENTIATING PRODUCTS

Let us digress for a moment to mention a very useful method for finding a high order derivative of a product. We shall illustrate it with an example (also see Problem 5).

Example.   Find $(d^9/dx^9)(x \sin x)$.

We could, of course, calculate nine derivatives, but this is a lot of work. Leibniz' rule says that the answer is

$$(3.1) \quad x \frac{d^9}{dx^9}(\sin x) + 9 \frac{d}{dx}(x)\frac{d^8}{dx^8}(\sin x) + \frac{9 \cdot 8}{2!}\frac{d^2}{dx^2}(x)\frac{d^7}{dx^7}(\sin x) + \cdots.$$

This should remind you of a binomial expansion

$$(a + b)^9 = a^0 b^9 + 9ab^8 + \frac{9 \cdot 8}{2!}a^2 b^7 + \cdots.$$

The coefficients in (3.1) are, in fact, binomial coefficients, and the sum of the orders of the two derivatives in each term is nine. (You may find the second hint in Problem 5c useful in understanding and remembering this). Now if it happens, as here, that the derivatives of one factor become zero after the first few, the rule saves much work. In the example, $(d^2/dx^2)(x) = 0$ and all higher derivatives are zero. Then we get

$$\frac{d^9}{dx^9}(x \sin x) = x \frac{d^9}{dx^9}(\sin x) + 9 \frac{d^8}{dx^8}(\sin x)$$

$$= x \cos x + 9 \sin x.$$

4. RODRIGUES' FORMULA

We have obtained the Legendre polynomials as solutions of Legendre's equation for integral l; there are other ways of obtaining them. We shall prove that Rodrigues' formula

$$(4.1) \qquad\qquad P_l(x) = \frac{1}{2^l l!}\frac{d^l}{dx^l}(x^2 - 1)^l$$

gives correctly the Legendre polynomials $P_l(x)$. There are two parts to the proof. First we show that if

$$(4.2) \qquad v = (x^2 - 1)^l,$$

then $d^l v/dx^l$ is a solution of Legendre's equation; then we show that $P_l(1) = 1$ in (4.1). To prove the first part, find dv/dx in (4.2) and multiply it by $x^2 - 1$:

$$(4.3) \qquad (x^2 - 1)\frac{dv}{dx} = (x^2 - 1)l(x^2 - 1)^{l-1} \cdot 2x = 2lxv.$$

Differentiate (4.3) $l + 1$ times by Leibniz' rule:

$$(4.4) \quad (x^2 - 1)\frac{d^{l+2}v}{dx^{l+2}} + (l + 1)(2x)\frac{d^{l+1}v}{dx^{l+1}} + \frac{(l + 1)l}{2!} \cdot 2 \cdot \frac{d^l v}{dx^l}$$

$$= 2lx\frac{d^{l+1}v}{dx^{l+1}} + 2l(l + 1)\frac{d^l v}{dx^l}.$$

Simplifying (4.4), we get (Problem 6)

$$(4.5) \qquad (1 - x^2)\left(\frac{d^l v}{dx^l}\right)'' - 2x\left(\frac{d^l v}{dx^l}\right)' + l(l + 1)\frac{d^l v}{dx^l} = 0.$$

This is just Legendre's equation (2.1) with $y = d^l v/dx^l$; thus $d^l v/dx^l = (d^l/dx^l)(x^2 - 1)^l$ is a solution of Legendre's equation as we claimed. It *is* a polynomial of degree l, and since we have previously called the polynomial solution of degree l the Legendre polynomial $P_l(x)$, this must be it with the possible exception of the numerical factor which must be such as to give $P_l(1) = 1$. A simple method of showing that $P_l(1) = 1$ for the functions $P_l(x)$ in (4.1) is outlined in Problem 7.

5. GENERATING FUNCTION FOR LEGENDRE POLYNOMIALS

The expression

$$(5.1) \qquad \Phi(x, h) = (1 - 2xh + h^2)^{-\frac{1}{2}}, \qquad |h| < 1,$$

is called the generating function for Legendre polynomials. We shall show that

$$(5.2) \qquad \Phi(x, h) = P_0(x) + hP_1(x) + h^2 P_2(x) + \cdots = \sum_{l=0}^{\infty} h^l P_l(x),$$

where the functions $P_l(x)$ are the Legendre polynomials. (See Problem 10 for discussion of convergence of the series.) Let us first verify a few terms of (5.2). For simplicity put $2xh - h^2 = y$ in (5.1), expand $(1 - y)^{-\frac{1}{2}}$ in powers of y, then substitute back $y = 2xh - h^2$ and collect powers of h to get

(5.3) $\Phi = (1 - y)^{-\frac{1}{2}} = 1 + \frac{1}{2}y + \dfrac{\frac{1}{2} \cdot \frac{3}{2}}{2!} y^2 + \cdots$

$= 1 + \frac{1}{2}(2xh - h^2) + \frac{3}{8}(2xh - h^2)^2 + \cdots$

$= 1 + xh - \frac{1}{2}h^2 + \frac{3}{8}(4x^2h^2 - 4xh^3 + h^4) + \cdots$

$= 1 + xh + h^2(\frac{3}{2}x^2 - \frac{1}{2}) + \cdots$

$= P_0(x) + hP_1(x) + h^2P_2(x) + \cdots.$

This is not a proof that the functions called $P_l(x)$ in (5.2) are really Legendre polynomials, but merely a verification of the first few terms. To prove in general that the polynomials called $P_l(x)$ in (5.2) are Legendre polynomials we must show that they satisfy Legendre's equation and that they have the property $P_l(1) = 1$. The latter is easy to prove; putting $x = 1$ in (5.1) and (5.2), we get

(5.4) $\Phi(1, h) = (1 - 2h + h^2)^{-\frac{1}{2}} = \dfrac{1}{1 - h} = 1 + h + h^2 + \cdots$

$\equiv P_0(1) + P_1(1)h + P_2(1)h^2 + \cdots.$

Since this is an identity in h, the functions $P_l(x)$ in (5.2) have the property $P_l(1) = 1$. To show that they satisfy Legendre's equation, we shall use the following identity which can be verified from (5.1) by straightforward differentiation and some algebra (Problem 12):

(5.5) $(1 - x^2)\dfrac{\partial^2 \Phi}{\partial x^2} - 2x \dfrac{\partial \Phi}{\partial x} + h \dfrac{\partial^2}{\partial h^2}(h\Phi) = 0.$

Substituting the series (5.2) for Φ into (5.5), we get

(5.6) $(1 - x^2)\displaystyle\sum_{l=0}^{\infty} h^l P_l''(x) - 2x \sum_{l=0}^{\infty} h^l P_l'(x) + \sum_{l=0}^{\infty} l(l + 1)h^l P_l(x) = 0.$

This is an identity in h, so the coefficient of each power of h must be zero. Setting the coefficient of h^l equal to zero, we get

(5.7) $(1 - x^2)P_l''(x) - 2xP_l'(x) + l(l + 1)P_l(x) = 0.$

This is Legendre's equation, so we have proved that the functions $P_l(x)$ in (5.2) satisfy it as claimed.

Recursion relations.   We shall now use the generating function to derive one of the *recursion relations* (also called *recurrence relations*) for Legendre polynomials. (There are other recursion relations—see Problems 14 to 17 for some of them.) These recursion relations are identities in x and are used (as trigonometric identities are) to simplify work and to help in proofs and derivations.

From (5.1) we get

(5.8)
$$\frac{\partial \Phi}{\partial h} = -\tfrac{1}{2}(1 - 2xh + h^2)^{-3/2}(-2x + 2h);$$

$$(1 - 2xh + h^2)\frac{\partial \Phi}{\partial h} = (x - h)\Phi.$$

Substituting the series (5.2) and its derivative with respect to h into (5.8), we get

(5.9) $$(1 - 2xh + h^2) \sum_{l=1}^{\infty} lh^{l-1}P_l(x) = (x - h) \sum_{l=0}^{\infty} h^l P_l(x).$$

This is an identity in h; we set the coefficient of h^{l-1} equal to zero. Carefully adjusting indices so that we select the term in h^{l-1} each time, we find

$$lP_l(x) - 2x(l - 1)P_{l-1}(x) + (l - 2)P_{l-2}(x) = xP_{l-1}(x) - P_{l-2}(x)$$

or

(5.10) $$lP_l(x) = (2l - 1)xP_{l-1}(x) - (l - 1)P_{l-2}(x).$$

The recursion relation (5.10) gives the simplest way of finding any Legendre polynomial when we know the Legendre polynomials for smaller l.

Expansion of a potential.   The generating function is useful in problems dealing with the potential associated with any inverse square force. Recall that the gravitational force between two point masses separated by a distance d is proportional to $1/d^2$ and the associated potential energy is proportional to $1/d$. Similarly, the electrostatic force between two electric charges a distance d apart is proportional to $1/d^2$ and the associated electrostatic potential energy is proportional to $1/d$. In either case we can write the potential as

(5.11) $$V = \frac{K}{d},$$

where K is an appropriate constant. In Fig. 5.1, let the two masses (or charges) be at the heads of the vectors $\mathbf{r}$ and $\mathbf{R}$. Then the distance between them is

(5.12) $$d = |\mathbf{R} - \mathbf{r}|$$

$$= \sqrt{R^2 - 2Rr \cos \theta + r^2}$$

$$= R\sqrt{1 - 2\frac{r}{R} \cos \theta + \left(\frac{r}{R}\right)^2}$$

and the gravitational or electrical potential is

(5.13) $$V = \frac{K}{R}\left[1 - \frac{2r}{R} \cos \theta + \left(\frac{r}{R}\right)^2\right]^{-1/2}.$$

For $|\mathbf{r}| < |\mathbf{R}|$, we make the change of variables

(5.14)
$$h = \frac{r}{R}$$
$$w = \cos\theta$$

Then we have

(5.15)
$$d = R\sqrt{1 - 2hw + h^2}$$
$$V = \frac{K}{R}(1 - 2hw + h^2)^{-\frac{1}{2}} = \frac{K}{R}\Phi,$$

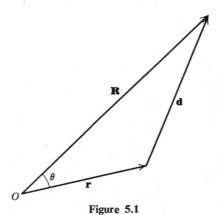

Figure 5.1

where Φ is the generating function (5.1). Then using (5.2), we can write the potential V as an infinite series

(5.16)
$$V = \frac{K}{R}\sum_{l=0}^{\infty} h^l P_l(w)$$

or in terms of r and θ [using (5.14)]

(5.17)
$$V = \frac{K}{R}\sum_{l=0}^{\infty}\frac{r^l P_l(\cos\theta)}{R^l} = K\sum_{l=0}^{\infty}\frac{r^l P_l(\cos\theta)}{R^{l+1}}.$$

In many applications the distance $|\mathbf{R}|$ is much larger than $|\mathbf{r}|$. Then the terms of the series (5.17) decrease rapidly in magnitude because of the factor $(r/R)^l$ and the potential can be approximated by using only a few terms of the series.

We can make (5.17) more general and useful by considering the following problem. (We shall discuss the electrical case for definiteness—the gravitational case could be discussed in parallel fashion.) Suppose there are a large number of charges q_i at points $\mathbf{r}_i$ (Fig. 5.2). The electrostatic potential V_i at the point $\mathbf{R}$ due to the charge q_i at $\mathbf{r}_i$ means the electrostatic potential energy of a pair of charges q_i at $\mathbf{r}_i$ and a *unit* charge at $\mathbf{R}$; this is given by (5.11) and (5.12), or by (5.17), with $r = r_i$, $\theta = \theta_i$, and

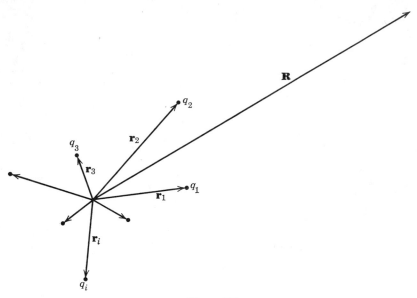

Figure 5.2

$K = q_i \cdot 1 \cdot K'$, where K' is a numerical constant depending on the choice of units:

$$(5.18) \qquad V_i = K' q_i \sum_{l=0}^{\infty} \frac{r_i^l P_l(\cos \theta_i)}{R^{l+1}}.$$

The total potential V at $\mathbf{R}$ due to all the charges q_i is then a sum over i of all the series (5.18), namely

$$(5.19) \quad V = \sum_i V_i = K' \sum_i q_i \sum_{l=0}^{\infty} \frac{r_i^l P_l(\cos \theta_i)}{R^{l+1}} = K' \sum_{l=0}^{\infty} \frac{\sum_i q_i r_i^l P_l(\cos \theta_i)}{R^{l+1}}.$$

If, instead of a set of discrete charges, we have a continuous charge distribution, then the sum over i becomes an integral, namely

$$(5.20) \qquad \int r^l P_l(\cos \theta) \, dq \qquad \text{or} \qquad \iiint r^l P_l(\cos \theta) \rho \, d\tau,$$

where ρ is the charge density and the integral is over the space occupied by the charge. Then (5.19) becomes

$$(5.21) \qquad V = K' \sum_{l} \frac{1}{R^{l+1}} \iiint r^l P_l(\cos \theta) \rho \, d\tau.$$

The terms of the series (5.21) can be interpreted physically. The $l = 0$ term is

$$(5.22) \qquad \frac{1}{R} \iiint \rho \, d\tau = \frac{1}{R} \cdot \text{(total charge)}.$$

Thus if R is large enough compared to all the r_i or all the values of r at points of the charge distribution, we can approximate the potential of

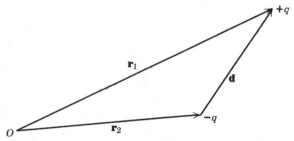

Figure 5.3

the distribution as that of a single charge at the origin of magnitude equal to the total charge of the distribution. The second term of the series (5.21) is

$$(5.23) \qquad \frac{1}{R^2} \iiint r \cos \theta \, \rho \, d\tau.$$

To interpret this recall that the *electric dipole moment* of a pair of charges $+q$ and $-q$ a distance d apart (as in Fig. 5.3) is defined as the vector $q\mathbf{d}$, where $\mathbf{d}$ is the vector from $-q$ to $+q$. Since the vector $q\mathbf{d}$ is equal to $q(\mathbf{r}_1 - \mathbf{r}_2) = q\mathbf{r}_1 - q\mathbf{r}_2$, we often call $q\mathbf{r}_1$ and $-q\mathbf{r}_2$ the dipole moments of $+q$ and $-q$ about O; then the total dipole moment due to the two charges is just the sum of the two moments. Suppose we calculate the dipole moment about O of all the charges q_i in Fig. 5.2; this is the vector sum $\sum_i q_i \mathbf{r}_i$. The component of this dipole moment in the $\mathbf{R}$ direction is then $\sum q_i r_i \cos \theta_i$, since θ_i is the angle between $\mathbf{R}$ and $\mathbf{r}_i$. In the case of a continuous charge distribution this sum becomes

$$(5.24) \qquad \iiint r \cos \theta \, \rho \, d\tau.$$

Thus we see from (5.23) and (5.24) that the second term of the series (5.21) is $1/R^2$ times the component in the $\mathbf{R}$ direction of the dipole moment of the charge distribution. If you consider the fact that the first term of (5.21) involves the total charge (a scalar, that is, a tensor of order zero) and the second term involves the dipole moment (a vector, that is, a tensor of order one), it may not surprise you to learn that the third term involves a second-order tensor known as the quadrupole moment of the charge distribution, the fourth term involves a third order tensor known as the octopole moment, etc. (See Problem 18 for more detail.)

Given a charge or mass distribution, the moments of various orders and the terms in (5.21) can be computed. The opposite process is often of great interest in applied problems. Consider a satellite circling the earth; it is moving in the gravitational field of the earth's mass. If the mass distribution of the earth were spherically symmetric, then only the first term would appear in the series for the gravitational potential [this series would be (5.21) with ρ a mass density instead of a charge density]. But since the earth is not a perfect sphere (equatorial bulge, etc.), other terms are present in (5.21) and the corresponding forces affect the motion of satellites. From accurate measurements of the satellite orbits, it is now possible to calculate several terms of the series (5.21). Similarly, in the electrical case, experimental measurements give us information about the distribution of electric charge inside atoms and nuclei; our discussion here and equation (5.21) provide the basis for the interpretation of such measurements, and the terminology used in discussing them.

6. COMPLETE SETS OF ORTHOGONAL FUNCTIONS

In order to see the reason for the terminology we shall use, let us recall some facts from Chapters 5 and 10. In elementary vector analysis we learned that two vectors $\mathbf{A}$ and $\mathbf{B}$ are orthogonal if their dot product is zero. We write

(6.1)
$$A_x B_x + A_y B_y = 0 \quad \text{in two dimensions,}$$
$$A_x B_x + A_y B_y + A_z B_z = 0 \quad \text{in three dimensions.}$$

In Chapter 10 we found it convenient to use the more general notation

$$A_x = A_1, \quad A_y = A_2, \quad A_z = A_3$$

and similarly for $\mathbf{B}$. In this notation we can write the orthogonality conditions (6.1) as

(6.2)
$$A_1 B_1 + A_2 B_2 = \sum_{i=1}^{2} A_i B_i = 0,$$
$$A_1 B_1 + A_2 B_2 + A_3 B_3 = \sum_{i=1}^{3} A_i B_i = 0.$$

Recall also that in Chapter 5 we thought of a vector as a geometrical entity (an arrow, say) with two or three components in two- or three-dimensional space. But in Chapter 10 we found a more satisfactory way of defining a vector; in three-dimensional space a vector consists of a set of three numbers (components) in each coordinate system with certain definite relations between the components in any two systems. This is an algebraic definition which frees us from our dependence upon a physical picture of a vector in three-dimensional space. Even the term "coordinate system" is not essential; we can instead talk about a "set of variables." Then a transformation from one coordinate system to another is simply an algebraic change of variables (say from x, y, z to x', y', z' or to r, θ, ϕ). Thus there is no reason why we cannot use our algebraic definition to define vectors of four components or more (see Chapter 10, end of Section 3). It is then convenient to continue the parallel geometrical language and refer to a vector with n components as a "vector in n-dimensional space." Using this terminology, we would then say by analogy with (6.1) and (6.2) that two vectors in n dimensions are orthogonal if

$$(6.3) \qquad \sum_{i=1}^{n} A_i B_i = 0.$$

Now let us consider two functions $A(x)$ and $B(x)$ for which it is true that

$$(6.4) \qquad \int_a^b A(x)B(x)\, dx = 0.$$

We often think of an integral as a kind of sum in which the summation variable (variable of integration) takes on a continuous set of values instead of a discrete set. Thus there is a close analogy between the equations (6.3) and (6.4). Because of this analogy we say that $A(x)$ and $B(x)$ are orthogonal on the interval (a, b) if they satisfy (6.4). This is a *definition* of the term *orthogonal functions*; the analogy simply explains why the terminology is used. If the functions $A(x)$ and $B(x)$ are complex, the definition of orthogonality is slightly different from (6.4). We then define $A(x)$ and $B(x)$ as orthogonal on (a, b) if they satisfy

$$(6.5) \qquad \int_a^b A^*(x)B(x)\, dx = 0,$$

where $A^*(x)$ is the complex conjugate of $A(x)$ (see Problem 19). Since (6.5) is identical with (6.4) if $A(x)$ and $B(x)$ are real, we can take (6.5) as the basic definition of orthogonality of $A(x)$ and $B(x)$ on (a, b).

If we have a whole set of functions $A_n(x)$ where $n = 1, 2, 3, \ldots$, and

$$(6.6) \qquad \int_a^b A_n^*(x)A_m(x)\, dx = \begin{cases} 0 & \text{if } m \neq n, \\ \text{const.} \neq 0 & \text{if } m = n, \end{cases}$$

we call the functions $A_n(x)$ a set of orthogonal functions. We have already used such sets of functions in Fourier series. Recall that

$$(6.7) \qquad \int_{-\pi}^{\pi} \sin nx \sin mx\, dx = \begin{cases} 0 & \text{if } m \neq n, \\ \pi & \text{if } m = n \neq 0. \end{cases}$$

Thus $\sin nx$ is a set of orthogonal functions on $(-\pi, \pi)$, or in fact on any other interval of length 2π. Similarly, the functions $\cos nx$ are orthogonal on $(-\pi, \pi)$. Also the whole set consisting of $\sin nx$ *and* $\cos nx$ is a set of orthogonal functions on $(-\pi, \pi)$ since

$$\int_{-\pi}^{\pi} \sin nx \cos mx\, dx = 0 \qquad \text{for } \textit{any } n \text{ and } m.$$

We have used complex functions also, namely the set e^{inx}. For this set the orthogonality property is given by (6.6), namely

$$(6.8) \qquad \int_{-\pi}^{\pi} (e^{inx})^* e^{imx}\, dx = \int_{-\pi}^{\pi} e^{-inx} e^{imx}\, dx = \begin{cases} 0, & m \neq n, \\ 2\pi, & m = n. \end{cases}$$

Recall that $\sin nx$ and $\cos nx$ (or e^{inx}) were the functions used in a Fourier series expansion on $(-\pi, \pi)$. You should now realize that it was the orthogonality property that we used in getting the coefficients. When we multiplied the equation $f(x) = \sum_{m=-\infty}^{\infty} c_m e^{imx}$ by e^{-inx} and integrated, the integrals of all the terms in the series except the c_n term were zero by the orthogonality property (6.8). There are many other sets of orthogonal functions besides the trigonometric or exponential ones. Just as we used the sine-cosine or exponential set to expand a function in a Fourier series, so we can expand a function in a series using other sets of orthogonal functions. We shall show this for the functions $P_l(x)$ after we prove that they are orthogonal.

There is another important point to consider when we want to expand a function in terms of a set of orthogonal functions. Again let us first consider the vector analogy. We write vectors in terms of their components and the unit vectors **i, j, k**. In two dimensions we need only two unit vectors, say **i** and **j**. But if we tried to write three-dimensional vectors in terms of just **i** and **j**, there would be some vectors we could not represent; we say that (in three dimensions) **i** and **j** are not a *complete* set of unit (or base) vectors. A simple way of expressing this (which generalizes to n dimensions) is to say that there is another vector (namely **k**) which is orthogonal to both **i** and **j**. Thus we define a set of orthogonal base vectors as complete if there is no other vector orthogonal to all of them (in the space of the number of dimensions we are considering). By analogy, we define a set of orthogonal functions as *complete* on a given interval if there is no other function orthogonal to all of them on that interval. Now it is easy to see that there are some vectors in three dimensions which we cannot represent using only **i** and **j**. Similarly, there are functions that cannot be represented by a series of orthogonal functions that is not complete. We have discussed one example of this in Fourier series (Chapter 6, Section 11). If we are trying to represent a sound wave by a Fourier series, we must not leave out any of the harmonics; that is, the set of functions $\sin nx$, $\cos nx$ on $(-\pi, \pi)$ would not be complete if we left out some values of n. As another example, the set of functions $\sin nx$ is an orthogonal set on $(-\pi, \pi)$. However, it is not complete; to have a complete set we must include also the functions $\cos nx$, and you should recall that this is what we did in Fourier series. On the other hand, $\sin nx$ is a complete set on $(0, \pi)$; we used this fact when we started with a function given on $(0, \pi)$, defined it on $(-\pi, 0)$ to make it odd, and then expanded it in a sine series. Similarly, $\cos nx$ is a complete set on $(0, \pi)$. In this chapter, we are particularly interested in the fact (which we state without proof) that the Legendre polynomials are a complete set on $(-1, 1)$.

7. ORTHOGONALITY OF THE LEGENDRE POLYNOMIALS

We are going to show that the Legendre polynomials are a set of orthogonal functions on $(-1, 1)$, that is, that

$$(7.1) \qquad \int_{-1}^{1} P_l(x) P_m(x)\, dx = 0 \qquad \text{unless} \quad l = m.$$

To prove this we rewrite the Legendre differential equation (2.1) in the form

$$(7.2) \qquad \frac{d}{dx}\left[(1 - x^2)P_l'(x)\right] + l(l + 1)P_l(x) = 0.$$

Write (7.2) for $P_l(x)$ and for $P_m(x)$; multiply the $P_l(x)$ equation by $P_m(x)$, and the $P_m(x)$ equation by $P_l(x)$, and subtract to get

$$(7.3) \quad P_m(x)\frac{d}{dx}\left[(1 - x^2)P_l'(x)\right] - P_l(x)\frac{d}{dx}\left[(1 - x^2)P_m'(x)\right]$$

$$+ \left[l(l + 1) - m(m + 1)\right]P_m(x)P_l(x) = 0.$$

The first two terms of (7.3) can be written as

$$(7.4) \qquad \frac{d}{dx}\left[(1 - x^2)(P_m P_l' - P_l P_m')\right]$$

where, for simplicity, we have used $P_l = P_l(x)$, etc. Integrating (7.3) between -1 and 1 and using (7.4), we get

$$(7.5) \quad (1 - x^2)(P_m P_l' - P_l P_m') \Big|_{-1}^{1}$$

$$+ [l(l + 1) - m(m + 1)] \int_{-1}^{1} P_m(x) P_l(x)\, dx = 0.$$

The integrated term is zero because $(1 - x^2) = 0$ at $x = \pm 1$, and $P_m(x)$ and $P_l(x)$ are finite. The bracket in front of the integral is not zero unless $m = l$. Therefore the integral must be zero for $l \neq m$ and we have (7.1).

The method we have used here is a standard one which can be used for many other sets of orthogonal functions to prove the orthogonality property by using the differential equation satisfied by the functions (see Problem 20).

8. NORMALIZATION OF THE LEGENDRE POLYNOMIALS

Just as we needed the value of $\int_{-\pi}^{\pi} \sin^2 nx\, dx = \pi$ in Fourier series, so we shall need the value of $\int_{-1}^{1} [P_l(x)]^2\, dx$ in expanding functions in Legendre series. It is common practice to divide each function of an orthogonal set by the correct number to make the integral of the square of each function equal to 1. We say then that the functions are *normalized*. A set of normalized orthogonal functions is called (by a combination of the two words) *orthonormal*. For example, $(1/\sqrt{\pi}) \sin nx$ is an orthonormal set on $(-\pi, \pi)$.

For the Legendre polynomials we shall prove that

$$(8.1) \qquad \int_{-1}^{1} [P_l(x)]^2\, dx = \frac{2}{2l + 1}.$$

Then the functions $\sqrt{(2l + 1)/2}\, P_l(x)$ form an orthonormal set of functions on $(-1, 1)$.

To prove (8.1), multiply (5.10) by $P_l(x)$ and integrate to get

$$(8.2) \quad \int_{-1}^{1} l[P_l(x)]^2\, dx$$

$$= (2l - 1) \int_{-1}^{1} x P_l(x) P_{l-1}(x)\, dx - (l - 1) \int_{-1}^{1} P_l(x) P_{l-2}(x)\, dx.$$

The last term is zero by (7.1). Write (5.10) with l replaced by $l + 1$, multiply by $P_{l-1}(x)$, and integrate to get

$$(8.3) \quad (l+1)\int_{-1}^{1} P_{l+1}(x)P_{l-1}(x)\,dx$$
$$= (2l+1)\int_{-1}^{1} xP_{l}(x)P_{l-1}(x)\,dx - l\int_{-1}^{1} [P_{l-1}(x)]^2\,dx.$$

The first integral is zero by (7.1). We eliminate the $xP_{l}(x)P_{l-1}(x)$ integral between (8.2) and (8.3) to get

$$\int_{-1}^{1} l[P_{l}(x)]^2\,dx = \frac{2l-1}{2l+1}\, l\int_{-1}^{1} [P_{l-1}(x)]^2\,dx$$

or

$$(8.4) \quad \int_{-1}^{1} [P_{l}(x)]^2\,dx = \frac{2l-1}{2l+1}\cdot\frac{2l-3}{2l-1}\cdots\frac{3}{5}\cdot\frac{1}{3}\int_{-1}^{1} [P_{0}(x)]^2\,dx = \frac{2}{2l+1}.$$

9. LEGENDRE SERIES

Since the Legendre polynomials form a complete orthogonal set on $(-1, 1)$, we can expand functions in Legendre series just as we expanded functions in Fourier series.

Example. Expand in a Legendre series the function $f(x)$ given by

$$(9.1) \qquad f(x) = \begin{cases} 0, & -1 < x < 0, \\ 1, & 0 < x < 1, \end{cases}$$

(see Fig. 9.1). We put

$$(9.2) \qquad f(x) = \sum_{l=0}^{\infty} c_l P_l(x).$$

Our problem is to find the coefficients c_l. We do this by a method parallel to the one we used in finding the formulas for the coefficients in a Fourier series. We multiply both sides of (9.2) by $P_m(x)$ and integrate from -1 to 1. Because the Legendre polynomials are orthogonal, all the integrals

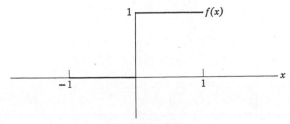

Figure 9.1

on the right are zero except the one containing c_m, and we can evaluate it by (8.4). Thus we get

$$(9.3) \quad \int_{-1}^{1} f(x) P_m(x) \, dx = \sum_{l=0}^{\infty} c_l \int_{-1}^{1} P_l(x) P_m(x) \, dx = c_m \cdot \frac{2}{2m+1} \, .$$

Using this result in our example (9.1), we find

$$\int_{-1}^{1} f(x) P_0(x) \, dx = c_0 \int_{-1}^{1} [P_0(x)]^2 \, dx \quad \text{or} \quad \int_{0}^{1} dx = c_0 \cdot 2, \quad c_0 = \tfrac{1}{2};$$

$$\int_{-1}^{1} f(x) P_1(x) \, dx = c_1 \int_{-1}^{1} [P_1(x)]^2 \, dx \quad \text{or} \quad \int_{0}^{1} x \, dx = c_1 \cdot \tfrac{2}{3}, \quad c_1 = \tfrac{3}{4};$$

$$\int_{-1}^{1} f(x) P_2(x) \, dx = c_2 \int_{-1}^{1} [P_2(x)]^2 \, dx \quad \text{or}$$

$$\int_{0}^{1} (\tfrac{3}{2} x^2 - \tfrac{1}{2}) \, dx = c_2 \cdot \tfrac{2}{5}, \quad c_2 = 0.$$

Continuing in this way we find for the function given in (9.1)

$$(9.4) \qquad f(x) = \tfrac{1}{2} P_0(x) + \tfrac{3}{4} P_1(x) - \tfrac{7}{16} P_3(x) + \tfrac{11}{32} P_5(x) + \cdots .$$

It is unnecessary for $f(x)$ to be continuous as it must be for expansion in a Maclaurin series. Just as for Fourier series, the Dirichlet conditions (see Chapter 6, Section 6) are a convenient set of sufficient conditions for a function $f(x)$ to be expandable in a Legendre series. If $f(x)$ satisfies the Dirichlet conditions on $(-1, 1)$, then at points inside $(-1, 1)$ (not necessarily at the endpoints), the Legendre series converges to $f(x)$ anywhere $f(x)$ is continuous and converges to the midpoint of the jump at discontinuities.

Here is an interesting fact about Legendre series. Sometimes we want to fit a given curve as closely as possible by a polynomial of a given degree, say a cubic. The criterion of "least squares" is often used to determine the best fit. This means that if, say, we want to fit a given $f(x)$ on $(-1, 1)$ by a cubic, we find a, b, c, d so that

$$\int_{-1}^{1} [f(x) - (ax^3 + bx^2 + cx + d)]^2 \, dx$$

is as small as possible. Then

$$f(x) = ax^3 + bx^2 + cx + d$$

is called the best approximation (by a cubic) in the least squares sense. It can be proved that an expansion (as far as the desired degree of the polynomial approximation) in Legendre polynomials gives this best least squares approximation (Problem 26).

10. THE ASSOCIATED LEGENDRE FUNCTIONS

A differential equation closely related to the Legendre equation is

$$(10.1) \qquad (1 - x^2)y'' - 2xy' + \left[l(l + 1) - \frac{m^2}{1 - x^2}\right]y = 0$$

with $m^2 \leq l^2$. We *could* solve this equation by series; however, it is more useful to know how the solutions are related to Legendre polynomials, so we shall simply verify the known solution. First we substitute

$$(10.2) \qquad\qquad\qquad y = (1 - x^2)^{m/2}u$$

into (10.1) and obtain (Problem 27)

$$(10.3) \quad (1 - x^2)u'' - 2(m + 1)xu' + [l(l + 1) - m(m + 1)]u = 0.$$

For $m = 0$, this is Legendre's equation with solutions $P_l(x)$. Differentiate (10.3), obtaining (Problem 27)

$$(10.4) \quad (1 - x^2)(u')'' - 2[(m + 1) + 1]x(u')' \\ + [l(l + 1) - (m + 1)(m + 2)]u' = 0.$$

But this is just (10.3) with u' in place of u, and $(m + 1)$ in place of m. In other words, if $P_l(x)$ is a solution of (10.3) with $m = 0$, $P_l'(x)$ is a solution of (10.3) with $m = 1$, $P_l''(x)$ is a solution with $m = 2$, and in general for any m, $(d^m/dx^m)P_l(x)$ is a solution of (10.3). Then

$$(10.5) \qquad\qquad y = (1 - x^2)^{m/2}\frac{d^m}{dx^m}P_l(x)$$

is a solution of (10.1). The functions in (10.5) are called *associated Legendre functions* and are denoted by

$$(10.6) \qquad\qquad P_l^m(x) = (1 - x^2)^{m/2}\frac{d^m}{dx^m}P_l(x).$$

They arise in many of the same problems in which Legendre polynomials appear; in fact, the Legendre polynomials are just the special case of the functions $P_l^m(x)$ when $m = 0$. (See also Problem 28.)

II. GENERALIZED POWER SERIES OR THE METHOD OF FROBENIUS

It may happen that the solution of a differential equation is not a power series $\sum_{n=0}^{\infty} a_n x^n$ but may either

(a) contain some negative powers of x, for example,

$$y = \frac{\cos x}{x^2} = \frac{1}{x^2} - \frac{1}{2!} + \frac{x^2}{4!} - \cdots$$

or

(b) have a fractional power of x as a factor, for example,

$$y = \sqrt{x}\, \sin x = x^{\frac{1}{2}}\left(x - \frac{x^3}{3!} + \cdots\right).$$

Both these cases are covered by a series of the form

(11.1) $$y = x^s \sum_{n=0}^{\infty} a_n x^n = \sum_{n=0}^{\infty} a_n x^{n+s},$$

where s is a number to be found to fit the problem; it may be either positive or negative and it may be a fraction. (In fact, it may even be complex, but we shall not consider this case.) Since $a_0 x^s$ is to be the first term of the series, we assume that a_0 is not zero. The series (11.1) is called a *generalized power series*. We shall consider some differential equations which can be solved by assuming a series of the form (11.1); this way of solving differential equations is called the *method of Frobenius*.

As an illustration of this method we solve the equation

(11.2) $$x^2 y'' + 4xy' + (x^2 + 2)y = 0.$$

From (11.1), we have

$$y = a_0 x^s + a_1 x^{s+1} + a_2 x^{s+2} + \cdots = \sum_{n=0}^{\infty} a_n x^{n+s},$$

$$y' = sa_0 x^{s-1} + (s + 1)a_1 x^s + (s + 2)a_2 x^{s+1} + \cdots$$

(11.3) $$= \sum_{n=0}^{\infty} (n + s)a_n x^{n+s-1},$$

$$y'' = s(s - 1)a_0 x^{s-2} + (s + 1)sa_1 x^{s-1} + (s + 2)(s + 1)a_2 x^s + \cdots$$

$$= \sum_{n=0}^{\infty} (n + s)(n + s - 1)a_n x^{n+s-2}.$$

We substitute (11.3) into (11.2) and set up a table of powers of x as for the Legendre equation:

	x^s	x^{s+1}	x^{s+2}	$\cdots$	x^{n+s}
$x^2 y''$	$s(s - 1)a_0$	$(s + 1)sa_1$	$(s + 2)(s + 1)a_2$		$(n + s)(n + s - 1)a_n$
$4xy'$	$4sa_0$	$4(s + 1)a_1$	$4(s + 2)a_2$		$4(n + s)a_n$
$x^2 y$			a_0		a_{n-2}
$2y$	$2a_0$	$2a_1$	$2a_2$		$2a_n$

The total coefficient of each power of x must be zero. From the coefficient of x^s we get $(s^2 + 3s + 2)a_0 = 0$, or since $a_0 \neq 0$ by hypothesis,

(11.4) $$s^2 + 3s + 2 = 0.$$

This equation for s is called the *indicial* equation. We solve it and find

$$s = -2, \qquad s = -1.$$

From here on we solve two separate problems, one for $s = -2$, and another for $s = -1$; a linear combination of the two solutions so obtained is then the general solution just as $A \sin x + B \cos x$ is the general solution of $y'' + y = 0$.

For $s = -1$, the coefficient of x^{s+1} in the table gives $a_1 = 0$. From the x^{s+2} column on, we can use the general formula given by the last column. Notice, however, that the first two columns in the table do not contain the a_{n-2} term, so you must be careful about using the general term at first (Problem 31). From the general column with $s = -1$, we have

$$a_n[(n-1)(n+2) + 2] = -a_{n-2}$$

or

$$a_n = -\frac{a_{n-2}}{n(n+1)} \qquad \text{for} \quad n \geq 2.$$

Since $a_1 = 0$, this gives all odd a's equal to zero. For even a's:

(11.5) $$a_2 = -\frac{a_0}{3!}, \qquad a_4 = \frac{a_0}{5!}, \qquad a_6 = -\frac{a_0}{7!}, \quad \text{etc.}$$

Then one solution of (11.2) is

(11.6) $$y = a_0 x^{-1} - \frac{a_0}{3!}x + \frac{a_0}{5!}x^3 - \cdots$$

$$= a_0 x^{-2}\left(x - \frac{x^3}{3!} + \frac{x^5}{5!} - \cdots\right) = \frac{a_0 \sin x}{x^2}.$$

The other solution, for $s = -2$, will be left to the problems.

12. BESSEL'S EQUATION

This is (like Legendre's equation) another of the "named" equations which have been studied extensively and whose solutions you will find tabulated. There are whole books on Bessel functions and almost any handbook or applied mathematics book will contain something about them (formulas and/or numerical tables). You can think of Bessel functions as being something like damped sines and cosines. In fact, if you had first learned about $\sin nx$ and $\cos nx$ as power series solutions of $y'' = -n^2 y$ instead of in elementary trigonometry, you would not feel that Bessel functions were appreciably more difficult or strange than trigonometric functions. Like sines and cosines, Bessel functions are solutions of a differential equation; they are tabulated and their graphs can be drawn; they can be represented as series; and a large number of formulas involving them are known. Of especial interest to science students is the fact that they occur in many applications. The following list of some of the problems in which they arise will give you an idea of the great range of topics which may involve Bessel functions: problems in electricity, heat, hydrodynamics, elasticity, wave motion, etc., involving cylindrical symmetry (for this reason Bessel functions are sometimes called cylinder functions); the motion of a pendulum whose length increases steadily; the small oscillations of a flexible chain; railway transition curves; the stability of a vertical wire or beam; Fresnel integrals in optics; the current distribution in a conductor; Fourier series for the arc of a circle. We shall discuss some of these applications later.

Bessel's equation in the usual standard form is

(12.1) $$x^2 y'' + xy' + (x^2 - p^2)y = 0,$$

where p is a constant (not necessarily an integer) called the *order* of the *Bessel function* y which is the solution of (12.1). You can easily verify that $x(xy')' = x^2 y'' + xy'$, so we can write (12.1) in the simpler form

(12.2) $$x(xy')' + (x^2 - p^2)y = 0.$$

We find a generalized power series solution for (12.2) in the same way that we solved (11.2). (In fact, (11.2) is a form of Bessel's equation! See Problems 38 and 40.) Writing only the general terms in the series for y and the derivatives we need in (12.2), we have

$$y = \sum_{n=0}^{\infty} a_n x^{n+s},$$

$$y' = \sum_{n=0}^{\infty} a_n (n+s) x^{n+s-1},$$

(12.3) $$xy' = \sum_{n=0}^{\infty} a_n (n+s) x^{n+s},$$

$$(xy')' = \sum_{n=0}^{\infty} a_n (n+s)^2 x^{n+s-1},$$

$$x(xy')' = \sum_{n=0}^{\infty} a_n (n+s)^2 x^{n+s}.$$

We substitute (12.3) into (12.2) and tabulate the coefficients of powers of x:

	x^s	x^{s+1}	x^{s+2}	$\cdots$	x^{s+n}
$x(xy')'$	$s^2 a_0$	$(1+s)^2 a_1$	$(2+s)^2 a_2$		$(n+s)^2 a_n$
$x^2 y$			a_0		a_{n-2}
$-p^2 y$	$-p^2 a_0$	$-p^2 a_1$	$-p^2 a_2$		$-p^2 a_n$

The coefficient of x^s gives the indicial equation and the two values of s:

$$s^2 - p^2 = 0, \qquad s = \pm p.$$

The coefficient of x^{s+1} gives $a_1 = 0$. The coefficient of x^{s+2} gives a_2 in terms of a_0, etc., but we may as well write the general formula from the last column at this point. We get

$$[(n+s)^2 - p^2]a_n + a_{n-2} = 0$$

or

(12.4) $$a_n = -\frac{a_{n-2}}{(n+s)^2 - p^2}.$$

First we shall find the coefficients for the case $s = p$. From (12.4) we have

(12.5) $$a_n = -\frac{a_{n-2}}{(n+p)^2 - p^2} = -\frac{a_{n-2}}{n^2 + 2np} = -\frac{a_{n-2}}{n(n+2p)}.$$

Since $a_1 = 0$, all odd a's are zero. For even a's it is convenient to replace n by $2n$; then from (12.5) we have

(12.6) $$a_{2n} = -\frac{a_{2n-2}}{2n(2n+2p)} = -\frac{a_{2n-2}}{2^2 n(n+p)}.$$

The formulas for the coefficients can be simplified by use of the Γ function notation as you can see by examining (12.7) below. Recall that $\Gamma(p+1) = p\Gamma(p)$ for any p, so $\Gamma(p+2) = (p+1)\Gamma(p+1)$, $\Gamma(p+3) = (p+2)\Gamma(p+2) = (p+2)(p+1)\Gamma(p+1)$, etc. Then from (12.6) we find

$$a_2 = -\frac{a_0}{2^2(1+p)} = -\frac{a_0\Gamma(1+p)}{2^2\Gamma(2+p)},$$

(12.7)
$$a_4 = -\frac{a_2}{2^3(2+p)} = \frac{a_0}{2!\,2^4(1+p)(2+p)} = \frac{a_0\Gamma(1+p)}{2!\,2^4\Gamma(3+p)},$$

$$a_6 = -\frac{a_4}{3!\,2(3+p)} = -\frac{a_0}{3!\,2^6(1+p)(2+p)(3+p)}$$

$$= -\frac{a_0\Gamma(1+p)}{3!\,2^6\Gamma(4+p)},$$

and so on. Then the series solution (for the $s = p$ case) is

$$(12.8) \quad y = a_0 x^p \Gamma(1 + p) \left[\frac{1}{\Gamma(1 + p)} - \frac{1}{\Gamma(2 + p)} \left(\frac{x}{2}\right)^2 \right.$$

$$+ \frac{1}{2!\,\Gamma(3 + p)} \left(\frac{x}{2}\right)^4 - \frac{1}{3!\,\Gamma(4 + p)} \left(\frac{x}{2}\right)^6 + \cdots \right]$$

$$= a_0 2^p \left(\frac{x}{2}\right)^p \Gamma(1 + p) \left[\frac{1}{\Gamma(1)\Gamma(1 + p)} - \frac{1}{\Gamma(2)\Gamma(2 + p)} \left(\frac{x}{2}\right)^2 \right.$$

$$+ \frac{1}{\Gamma(3)\Gamma(3 + p)} \left(\frac{x}{2}\right)^4 - \frac{1}{\Gamma(4)\Gamma(4 + p)} \left(\frac{x}{2}\right)^6 + \cdots \right].$$

We have inserted $\Gamma(1)$ and $\Gamma(2)$ which are both equal to 1 in the first two terms and written $x^p = 2^p(x/2)^p$ to make the series appear more systematic. If we take

$$a_0 = \frac{1}{2^p \Gamma(1 + p)} \quad \text{or} \quad \frac{1}{2^p p!},$$

then y is called the Bessel function of the first kind and order p, and written $J_p(x)$.

$$(12.9) \quad J_p(x) = \frac{1}{\Gamma(1)\Gamma(1 + p)} \left(\frac{x}{2}\right)^p - \frac{1}{\Gamma(2)\Gamma(2 + p)} \left(\frac{x}{2}\right)^{2+p}$$

$$+ \frac{1}{\Gamma(3)\Gamma(3 + p)} \left(\frac{x}{2}\right)^{4+p} - \frac{1}{\Gamma(4)\Gamma(4 + p)} \left(\frac{x}{2}\right)^{6+p} + \cdots$$

$$= \sum_{n=0}^{\infty} \frac{(-1)^n}{\Gamma(n + 1)\Gamma(n + p + 1)} \left(\frac{x}{2}\right)^{2n+p}$$

13. THE SECOND SOLUTION OF BESSEL'S EQUATION

We have just found one of the two solutions of Bessel's equation, that is, the one when $s = p$; we must next find the solution when $s = -p$. It is unnecessary to go through the details again; we can just replace p by $-p$ in (12.9). In fact, the solution when $s = -p$ is usually written as J_{-p}. From (12.9) we have

$$(13.1) \qquad J_{-p}(x) = \sum_{n=0}^{\infty} \frac{(-1)^n}{\Gamma(n + 1)\Gamma(n - p + 1)} \left(\frac{x}{2}\right)^{2n-p}.$$

If p is not an integer, $J_p(x)$ is a series starting with x^p and $J_{-p}(x)$ is a series starting with x^{-p}. Then $J_p(x)$ and $J_{-p}(x)$ are two independent solutions and a linear combination of them is a general solution. But if p is an integer, then the first few terms in J_{-p} are zero because $\Gamma(n - p + 1)$

in the denominator is Γ of a negative integer which is infinite. It can be shown (Problem 33) that $J_{-p}(x)$ starts with the term x^p (for integral p) just as $J_p(x)$ does, and that

$$(13.2) \qquad J_{-p}(x) = (-1)^p J_p(x) \qquad \text{for integral } p;$$

thus $J_{-p}(x)$ is not an independent solution when p is an integer. The second solution in this case is not a Frobenius series (11.1) but contains a logarithm. $J_p(x)$ is finite at the origin, but the second solution is infinite and so is useful only in applications in which $x \neq 0$.

Although $J_{-p}(x)$ is a satisfactory second solution for nonintegral p, it is not what you will usually find tabulated. What *is* tabulated is a combination of $J_p(x)$ and $J_{-p}(x)$. This is much as if $\sin x$ and $(2\sin x - 3\cos x)$ were tabulated, but not $\cos x$. For practical problems involving the differential equation $y'' + y = 0$ you want a linear combination of $\sin x$ and $\cos x$ with arbitrary coefficients. But

$$A \sin x + B(2\sin x - 3\cos x)$$

is just as good a linear combination as $c_1 \sin x + c_2 \cos x$. Similarly, any combination of $J_p(x)$ and $J_{-p}(x)$ is a satisfactory second solution of Bessel's equation. The combination that is tabulated is called either the Neumann function or the Weber function, and is denoted by either N_p or Y_p:

$$(13.3) \qquad N_p(x) = Y_p(x) = \frac{\cos(\pi p) J_p(x) - J_{-p}(x)}{\sin \pi p}.$$

For integral p this expression is an indeterminate form $0/0$. However, for any $x \neq 0$ it has a limit which is the correct second solution for integral p. (See, for example, Relton, p. 78.) This is why the special form (13.3) is used; it is valid for any p. The general solution of Bessel's equation (12.1) may then be written as

$$(13.4) \qquad y = AJ_p(x) + BN_p(x),$$

where A and B are arbitrary constants.

14. TABLES, GRAPHS, AND ZEROS OF BESSEL FUNCTIONS

Like trigonometric functions, Bessel functions are tabulated (for many different values of p). You will find values of $J_0(x)$ and $J_1(x)$ in a general handbook, but you will have to consult specialized references (for example, Jahnke-Emde, or Watson) for values of $J_p(x)$ for other p, and for $N_p(x)$. You can plot graphs of the Bessel functions from the tabulated values, and you will find graphs of some of them in various books. Except for $J_0(x)$, all the J's start at the origin and oscillate something like $\sin x$ but with decreasing amplitude. $J_0(x)$ is equal to 1 at $x = 0$ and so looks something like a damped cosine. All the N's are $\pm \infty$ at the origin, but away from it they also oscillate with decreasing amplitude.

The values of x for which $\sin x = 0$ (called the zeros of $\sin x$) do not need to be tabulated because they are just $x = n\pi$ for $n = 0$, 1, 2, etc. The zeros of the Bessel functions, however, do not occur at regular intervals; they have to be computed numerically and tabulated. As you will see, the zeros are very important in applications; you will find their values tabulated along with the values of the functions themselves. It is worth noticing that the difference between two successive zeros becomes approximately π (as it is for $\sin x$ and $\cos x$) when x is large. You can see this from tables, and also from the approximate formulas for Bessel functions when x is large (see Section 20).

15. RECURSION RELATIONS

The following useful relations hold among Bessel functions and their derivatives. Although we state them and outline proofs for $J_p(x)$, they also hold for $N_p(x)$.

(15.1) $\dfrac{d}{dx}[x^p J_p(x)] = x^p J_{p-1}(x). \Rightarrow \displaystyle\int x^p J_{p-1}(x)\,dx = x^p J_p(x) + C$

(15.2) $\dfrac{d}{dx}[x^{-p} J_p(x)] = -x^{-p} J_{p+1}(x).$

(15.3) $J_{p-1}(x) + J_{p+1}(x) = \dfrac{2p}{x} J_p(x).$

(15.4) $J_{p-1}(x) - J_{p+1}(x) = 2J_p'(x).$

(15.5) $J_p'(x) = -\dfrac{p}{x} J_p(x) + J_{p-1}(x) = \dfrac{p}{x} J_p(x) - J_{p+1}(x).$

To prove (15.1), first multiply (12.9) by x^p and differentiate to get

$$\frac{d}{dx}[x^p J_p(x)] = \frac{d}{dx} \sum_{n=0}^{\infty} \frac{(-1)^n}{\Gamma(n+1)\Gamma(n+p+1)} \frac{x^{2n+2p}}{2^{2n+p}}$$

$$= \sum_{n=0}^{\infty} \frac{(-1)^n(2n+2p)}{\Gamma(n+1)\Gamma(n+p+1)} \frac{x^{2n+2p-1}}{2^{2n+p}}.$$

Use the fact that $\Gamma(n + p + 1) = (n + p)\Gamma(n + p)$, and cancel the factors 2 and $(n + p)$ to get

$$\frac{d}{dx}[x^p J_p(x)] = \sum_{n=0}^{\infty} \frac{(-1)^n}{\Gamma(n + 1)\Gamma(n + p)} \frac{x^{2n+2p-1}}{2^{2n+p-1}} .$$

Divide by x^p and compare with (12.9); this gives

$$\frac{1}{x^p} \frac{d}{dx}[x^p J_p(x)] = \sum_{n=0}^{\infty} \frac{(-1)^n}{\Gamma(n + 1)\Gamma(n + p)} \left(\frac{x}{2}\right)^{2n+p-1} = J_{p-1}(x),$$

since this series is just (12.9) with p replaced by $p - 1$. Proofs of the other relations are outlined in Problems 35 to 37.

16. A GENERAL DIFFERENTIAL EQUATION HAVING BESSEL FUNCTIONS AS SOLUTIONS

Many differential equations occur in practice that are not of the standard form (12.1) but whose solutions can be written in terms of Bessel functions. It can be shown (Problem 39) that the differential equation

$$(16.1) \qquad y'' + \frac{1 - 2a}{x} y' + \left[(bcx^{c-1})^2 + \frac{a^2 - p^2c^2}{x^2}\right] y = 0$$

has the solution

$$(16.2) \qquad\qquad y = x^a Z_p(bx^c),$$

where Z stands for J or N or any linear combination of them, and a, b, c, p are constants. To see how to use this, let us "solve" the differential equation

$$(16.3) \qquad\qquad y'' + 9xy = 0.$$

If (16.3) is of the type (16.1), then we must have

$$1 - 2a = 0, \quad (bc)^2 = 9, \quad 2(c - 1) = 1, \quad a^2 - p^2c^2 = 0.$$

From these equations we find

$$a = \frac{1}{2}, \quad c = \frac{3}{2}, \quad b = 2, \quad p = \frac{a}{c} = \frac{1}{3}.$$

Then the solution of (16.3) is

$$y = x^{1/2} Z_{1/3}(2x^{3/2}).$$

This means that the general solution of (16.3) is

$$y = x^{1/2}[A J_{1/3}(2x^{3/2}) + B N_{1/3}(2x^{3/2})],$$

where A and B are arbitrary constants.

17. OTHER KINDS OF BESSEL FUNCTIONS

We have discussed $J_p(x)$ and $N_p(x)$ which are called *Bessel functions of the first and second kinds* respectively. Since Bessel's equation is of second order, there are, of course, only two independent solutions. However, there are a number of related functions which are also called Bessel functions. Here again there is a close analogy to sines and cosines. We may think of $\cos x$ and $\sin x$ as the basic solutions of $y'' + y = 0$. But $\cos x \pm i \sin x$ are also solutions which we usually write as $e^{\pm ix}$. If we replace x by ix, we get the functions e^x, e^{-x}, $\cosh x$, $\sinh x$, which are solutions of $y'' - y = 0$. We list a number of Bessel functions which are frequently used and their trigonometric analogues:

Hankel functions or Bessel functions of the third kind.

(17.1)
$$H_p^{(1)}(x) = J_p(x) + iN_p(x),$$
$$H_p^{(2)}(x) = J_p(x) - iN_p(x).$$

(Compare $e^{\pm ix} = \cos x \pm i \sin x$.)

Modified or hyperbolic Bessel functions.   The solutions of

(17.2)
$$x^2 y'' + xy' - (x^2 + p^2)y = 0$$

are, by (16.1), $Z_p(ix)$. (Compare this with the standard Bessel equation and by analogy consider the relation between $y'' + y = 0$ and $y'' - y = 0$.) The two independent solutions of (17.2) which are ordinarily used are

(17.3)
$$I_p(x) = i^{-p} J_p(ix),$$
$$K_p(x) = \frac{\pi}{2} i^{p+1} H_p^{(1)}(ix).$$

These should be compared with $\sinh x = -i \sin (ix)$ and $\cosh x = \cos (ix)$; because of the analogy, I and K are called hyperbolic Bessel functions. The i factors are adjusted to make I and K real for real x.

Spherical Bessel functions.   If $p = (2n + 1)/2 = n + \frac{1}{2}$, n an integer, then $J_p(x)$ and $N_p(x)$ are called Bessel functions of half odd integral order; they can be expressed in terms of $\sin x$, $\cos x$, and powers of x. The spherical Bessel functions are closely related to them as you can see from the formulas (17.4) below. Spherical Bessel functions arise in a variety of vibration problems especially when spherical coordinates are used. We define the spherical Bessel functions $j_n(x)$, $y_n(x)$, $h_n^{(1)}(x)$, $h_n^{(2)}(x)$, for

$n = 0, 1, 2, \ldots$, and state without proof their values in terms of elementary functions:

$$j_n(x) = \sqrt{\frac{\pi}{2x}}\, J_{n+\frac{1}{2}}(x) = x^n\left(-\frac{1}{x}\frac{d}{dx}\right)^n\left(\frac{\sin x}{x}\right),$$

(17.4)
$$y_n(x) = \sqrt{\frac{\pi}{2x}}\, Y_{n+\frac{1}{2}}(x) = -x^n\left(-\frac{1}{x}\frac{d}{dx}\right)^n\left(\frac{\cos x}{x}\right),$$

$$h_n^{(1)}(x) = j_n(x) + i y_n(x),$$
$$h_n^{(2)}(x) = j_n(x) - i y_n(x).$$

The ber, bei, ker, kei functions. A standard method of solution of vibration problems is to assume a solution involving $e^{i\omega t}$; the resulting equation may contain imaginary terms. As an example, the following equation arises in the problem of the distribution of alternating current in wires (skin effect) (Relton, p. 177):

(17.5)
$$y'' + \frac{1}{x}y' - iy = 0.$$

If we compare this with (16.1), we find

$$a = 0, \quad c = 1, \quad (bc)^2 = -i, \quad a^2 = p^2 c^2;$$
$$p = 0, \quad b = \sqrt{-i} = i^{3/2} \quad \text{since } i^3 = -i.$$

Then the solution of (17.5) is, by (16.2),

(17.6)
$$y = Z_0(i^{3/2}x).$$

This is complex and it is customary to separate it into its real and imaginary parts, called (for $Z = J$) ber and bei; these stand for Bessel-real and Bessel-imaginary. We define the ber, bei, ker, kei functions by

(17.7)
$$J_0(i^{3/2}x) = \text{ber } x + i\,\text{bei } x,$$
$$K_0(i^{1/2}x) = \text{ker } x + i\,\text{kei } x.$$

There are also similar functions for $n \neq 0$. These functions occur in problems in heat flow and in the theory of viscous fluids, as well as in electricity.

18. THE LENGTHENING PENDULUM

As an example of the use of Bessel functions we consider the following problem. Suppose that a simple pendulum (see Chapter 9, Section 8) has the length l of its string increased at a steady rate. Find the equation of motion and the solution for small oscillations.

The kinetic energy is

$$(18.1) \qquad T = \tfrac{1}{2}m(\dot{l}^2 + l^2\dot{\theta}^2)$$

and the potential energy is

$$(18.2) \qquad V = -mgl \cos \theta.$$

Then

$$(18.3) \qquad L = T - V = \tfrac{1}{2}m(\dot{l}^2 + l^2\dot{\theta}^2) + mgl \cos \theta$$

and the Lagrange equation of motion for the variable θ is

$$\frac{d}{dt}(ml^2\dot{\theta}) + mgl \sin \theta = 0.$$

Performing the differentiation and simplifying the algebra, we get

$$ml^2\ddot{\theta} + 2ml\dot{l}\dot{\theta} + mgl \sin \theta = 0$$

or

$$(18.4) \qquad l\ddot{\theta} + 2\dot{l}\dot{\theta} + g \sin \theta = 0.$$

Let the length of the string at time t be

$$(18.5) \qquad l = l_0 + vt,$$

where v is the constant rate at which the string is lengthening; then $\dot{l} = v$. For small oscillations we may replace $\sin \theta$ by θ. Substituting these values into (18.4), we get

$$(18.6) \qquad (l_0 + vt)\ddot{\theta} + 2v\dot{\theta} + g\theta = 0.$$

(This equation could also describe the damped vibration of a variable mass, or an *RLC* circuit with variable *L*.)

To find the solutions of (18.6) as Bessel functions, we make a change of variable from t to x, namely

$$(18.7) \qquad x = \frac{l_0 + vt}{v}.$$

Then we have

$$(18.8) \qquad dx = dt, \quad \dot{\theta} = \frac{d\theta}{dt} = \frac{d\theta}{dx} = \theta', \quad \ddot{\theta} = \theta''.$$

We make these substitutions in (18.6) and divide by vx. This gives the differential equation for θ with x as the independent variable:

$$(18.9) \qquad \theta'' + \frac{2}{x}\theta' + \frac{g}{v}\frac{1}{x}\theta = 0.$$

We compare (18.9) with the standard equation (16.1) and find

$$1 - 2a = 2, \quad a^2 = p^2 c^2, \quad (bc)^2 = \frac{g}{v}, \quad 2c - 2 = -1,$$

(18.10) $\quad a = -\frac{1}{2}, \quad p^2 = \frac{a^2}{c^2} = 1, \quad b = \frac{1}{c}\sqrt{\frac{g}{v}} = 2\sqrt{\frac{g}{v}}, \quad c = \frac{1}{2},$

$$\theta = x^{-\frac{1}{2}} Z_1\left(2\sqrt{\frac{g}{v}}\, x^{\frac{1}{2}}\right).$$

To simplify the notation, let us make the substitution

(18.11) $$u = 2\sqrt{\frac{g}{v}}\, x^{\frac{1}{2}}.$$

The general solution of (18.9) is then

(18.12) $$\theta = Au^{-1}J_1(u) + Bu^{-1}N_1(u).$$

We can find $d\theta/du$ from (18.12) using (15.2):

(18.13) $$\frac{d\theta}{du} = -[Au^{-1}J_2(u) + Bu^{-1}N_2(u)].$$

The constants A and B must be found from the starting conditions just as they are for the ordinary simple pendulum with constant l. For example, in the ordinary case, if $\theta = \theta_0$ and $\dot\theta = 0$ at $t = 0$, then the general solution $\theta = A\cos\omega t + B\sin\omega t$ becomes just $\theta = \theta_0\cos\omega t$. For the lengthening pendulum, let us take the same simple initial conditions, namely $\theta = \theta_0$ and $\dot\theta = 0$ at $t = 0$. Then at $t = 0$, we have

(18.14)

from (18.7): $\qquad x = \dfrac{l_0}{v}\,;$

from (18.11): $\qquad u = u_0 = \dfrac{2}{v}\sqrt{gl_0},$

$$\frac{du}{dx} = \sqrt{\frac{g}{v}}\, x^{-\frac{1}{2}} = \sqrt{\frac{g}{l_0}}\,;$$

from (18.8): $\qquad \dfrac{d\theta}{du} = \dfrac{d\theta}{dx}\Big/\dfrac{du}{dx} = \dot\theta\Big/\sqrt{\dfrac{g}{l_0}} = 0.$

Substituting the $t = 0$ values from (18.14) into (18.12) and (18.13), we get

(18.15)
$$\theta_0 = Au_0^{-1}J_1(u_0) + Bu_0^{-1}N_1(u_0),$$
$$0 = AJ_2(u_0) + BN_2(u_0).$$

It can be proved that

(18.16) $$J_1(u)N_2(u) - J_2(u)N_1(u) = -\frac{2}{\pi u}$$

(see Problems 50 to 52). Solving (18.15) for A and B and using (18.16), we have

$$u_0\theta_0 N_2(u_0) = A[J_1(u_0)N_2(u_0) - N_1(u_0)J_2(u_0)] = A\left(-\frac{2}{\pi u_0}\right),$$

(18.17) $$u_0\theta_0 J_2(u_0) = B[N_1(u_0)J_2(u_0) - N_2(u_0)J_1(u_0)] = B\left(\frac{2}{\pi u_0}\right),$$

$$A = -\frac{\pi u_0^2}{2}\,\theta_0 N_2(u_0), \quad B = \frac{\pi u_0^2}{2}\,\theta_0 J_2(u_0).$$

Then the general solution (18.12) becomes

(18.18) $$\theta = \frac{\pi}{2}\,u_0^2\theta_0 u^{-1}[-N_2(u_0)J_1(u) + J_2(u_0)N_1(u)].$$

This solution has a particularly simple form if we adjust the constants v and l_0 so that

(18.19) $$u_0 = \frac{2}{v}\sqrt{gl_0}\text{ is a zero of }J_2(u).$$

Then $B = 0$ and the second term of (18.18) is zero, so we have

(18.20) $$\theta = Au^{-1}J_1(u) = Cx^{-\frac{1}{2}}J_1\left(2\sqrt{\frac{gx}{v}}\right),$$

where

$$C = \frac{A}{2}\sqrt{\frac{v}{g}}, \quad x = \frac{l_0}{v} + t.$$

For this simple case, $\dot{\theta}$ is a multiple of $J_2(u)$ (Problem 48); thus $\theta = 0$ corresponds to zeros of $J_1(u)$ and $\dot{\theta} = 0$ corresponds to zeros of $J_2(u)$. A "quarter" period corresponds to the time from $\theta = 0$ to $\dot{\theta} = 0$, or $\dot{\theta} = 0$ to $\theta = 0$. These quarter periods can be found from the zeros of $J_1(u)$ and $J_2(u)$ (Problem 48).

19. ORTHOGONALITY OF BESSEL FUNCTIONS

You may expect here that we are going to prove that two J_p's for different p values are orthogonal. However, this is *not* what we are going to do—as a matter of fact it isn't true! To see what we *are* going to prove, look at the following comparison between Bessel functions and sines and cosines.

(19.1) Two functions: $\sin x$ and $\cos x$.	Two functions for each p: $J_p(x)$ and $N_p(x)$.

Consider just $\sin x$.   Consider just $J_p(x)$ for one value of p.

At the zeros of $\sin x$, namely, $x = n\pi$, $\sin x = 0$.   At the zeros of $J_p(x)$, say $x = a$, b, etc., $J_p(x) = 0$.

At $x = 1$, $\sin n\pi x = 0$.   At $x = 1$, $J_p(ax) = 0$, $J_p(bx) = 0$, etc.

The differential equation satisfied by $y = \sin n\pi x$ is $y'' + (n\pi)^2 y = 0$.   The differential equation satisfied by $J_p(ax)$ is $x(xy')' + (a^2x^2 - p^2)y = 0$ [see (19.2) below].

(In comparing the differential equations remember that p is a fixed constant. The correspondence is between the zeros of $\sin x$, namely $n\pi$, and the zeros of $J_p(x)$, namely a, b, etc.)

We have proved: We shall prove:

$$\int_0^1 \sin n\pi x \sin m\pi x \, dx = 0 \qquad \int_0^1 x J_p(ax) J_p(bx) \, dx = 0$$

for $n \neq m$.   for $a \neq b$.

First let us verify the differential equation satisfied by $J_p(ax)$, mentioned in (19.1). The differential equation (12.2) is satisfied by $y = J_p(x)$. If we replace x by ax, then $x(dy/dx)$ becomes $ax[dy/d(ax)] = x(dy/dx)$ and similarly $x(xy')'$ is unchanged. Then (12.2) becomes

$$(19.2) \qquad\qquad x(xy')' + (a^2x^2 - p^2)y = 0$$

and the solution of (19.2) is $J_p(ax)$. Similarly, the differential equation satisfied by $J_p(bx)$ is

$$(19.3) \qquad\qquad x(xy')' + (b^2x^2 - p^2)y = 0.$$

Let us for simplicity call $J_p(ax) = u$ and $J_p(bx) = v$; then (19.2) and (19.3) become

$$(19.4) \qquad \begin{aligned} x(xu')' + (a^2x^2 - p^2)u &= 0, \\ x(xv')' + (b^2x^2 - p^2)v &= 0. \end{aligned}$$

We are going to use equations (19.4) to prove the orthogonality of Bessel functions by a method parallel to that used in proving the orthogonality of Legendre polynomials (also see Problem 20). Multiply the first equation of (19.4) by v, the second by u, subtract the two equations and cancel an x to get

$$(19.5) \qquad v(xu')' - u(xv')' + (a^2 - b^2)xuv = 0.$$

The first two terms of (19.5) are equal to

$$(19.6) \qquad \frac{d}{dx}(vxu' - uxv').$$

Using (19.6) and integrating (19.5), we get

$$(19.7) \qquad (vxu' - uxv')\Big|_0^1 + (a^2 - b^2)\int_0^1 xuv\,dx = 0.$$

At the lower limit the integrated term is zero because $x = 0$ and u, v, u', v' are finite. To evaluate the integrated term at the upper limit, recall that $u = J_p(ax)$, $v = J_p(bx)$; then at $x = 1$, $u = J_p(a) = 0$, $v = J_p(b) = 0$ since a and b are zeros of J_p. The integrated term is therefore zero at the upper limit also. Thus (19.7) becomes

$$(19.8) \qquad (a^2 - b^2)\int_0^1 xuv\,dx = 0$$

or

$$(19.9) \qquad (a^2 - b^2)\int_0^1 xJ_p(ax)J_p(bx)\,dx = 0.$$

If $a \neq b$, that is, if a and b are different zeros of J_p, the integral must be zero. If $a = b$, the integral is not zero; it can be evaluated, but we shall just state the answer (see Problem 55):

(19.10)

$$\int_0^1 xJ_p(ax)J_p(bx)\,dx = \begin{cases} 0 & \text{if } a \neq b \\ \tfrac{1}{2}J_{p+1}^2(a) = \tfrac{1}{2}J_{p-1}^2(a) = \tfrac{1}{2}J_p'^2(a) & \text{if } a = b \end{cases}$$

[You can see that the three answers for the case $a = b$ are equal by equations (15.3) to (15.5), remembering that a is a zero of J_p.]

We can state (19.10) in words in two different ways; if a_n, $n = 1, 2, 3, \ldots$, are the zeros of $J_p(x)$, then we say either that

(a) the functions $\sqrt{x}J_p(a_nx)$ are orthogonal on $(0, 1)$;
or that
(b) the functions $J_p(a_nx)$ are orthogonal on $(0, 1)$ with respect to the *weight function* x.

You may meet other sets of functions which are orthogonal with respect to a weight function. In general, we say that $y_n(x)$ is a set of orthogonal functions on (x_1, x_2) with respect to a weight function $w(x)$ if

$$\int_{x_1}^{x_2} y_n(x)y_m(x)w(x)\,dx = 0 \qquad \text{for} \quad n \neq m.$$

The fact that the Bessel functions $J_p(a_n x)$ obey (19.10) makes it possible for us to expand a given function in a series of Bessel functions much as we expand functions in Fourier series and Legendre series. We shall do this later (Chapter 14) when we need it in a physical example.

20. APPROXIMATE FORMULAS FOR BESSEL FUNCTIONS

There are often cases in which it is useful to have an approximate formula giving the behavior of a Bessel function when x is near zero or when x is very large. We list some of these formulas for reference. The symbol $O(x^n)$ is read "terms of the order of x^n," and means that the error in the given approximation is less than a constant times x^n; thus $O(1)$ means bounded terms. Note that $p \geq 0$.

Function	Small x	Large x (asymptotic formulas)
$J_p(x)$	$\dfrac{1}{\Gamma(p+1)}\left(\dfrac{x}{2}\right)^p + O(x^{p+2})$	$\sqrt{\dfrac{2}{\pi x}}\cos\left(x - \dfrac{2p+1}{4}\,\pi\right) + O(x^{-3/2})$
$N_p(x)\begin{cases} p=0 \\[2em] p>0 \end{cases}$	$\dfrac{2}{\pi}\ln x + O(1)$ $-\dfrac{\Gamma(p)}{\pi}\left(\dfrac{2}{x}\right)^p + O\left(\dfrac{1}{x^{p-1}}\right)$	$\sqrt{\dfrac{2}{\pi x}}\sin\left(x - \dfrac{2p+1}{4}\,\pi\right) + O(x^{-3/2})$
$H_p^{(1)\,\text{or}\,(2)}$	$\pm iN_p(x) + O(x^p)$	$\sqrt{\dfrac{2}{\pi x}}\,e^{\pm i[x-(1/2)(p+1/2)\pi]} + O(x^{-3/2})$
$I_p(x)$	Just like $J_p(x)$	$\dfrac{1}{\sqrt{2\pi x}}\,e^x + O\left(\dfrac{e^x}{x}\right)$
$K_p(x)\begin{cases} p=0 \\[2em] p>0 \end{cases}$	$-\ln x + O(1)$ $\dfrac{1}{2}\Gamma(p)\left(\dfrac{2}{x}\right)^p + O\left(\dfrac{1}{x^{p-1}}\right)$	$\sqrt{\dfrac{\pi}{2x}}\,e^{-x} + O\left(\dfrac{e^{-x}}{x}\right)$

2I. SOME GENERAL COMMENTS ABOUT SERIES SOLUTIONS

We have discussed two examples of differential equations solvable by the Frobenius method (Legendre and Bessel equations). There are a good many more "named" equations and the corresponding "named" functions which are their solutions (see problems). All of them have much in common with our two examples and you should not hesitate to look them up and use them even without a formal introduction. You may discover any or all of the following things about such a new (to you) set of functions: that they are the set of solutions of a differential equation with one or more parameters (like the p in Bessel's equation); that the values of the functions, their derivatives, their zeros, etc., are tabulated; that there are recurrence and derivative relations, and many other known formulas which you can look up and use; that they have orthogonality properties, perhaps with respect to a weight function, and consequently (suitably restricted) functions can be expanded in series of them; that there is a generating function for the set of functions or some of them; that there are physical problems whose solutions involve the functions, often via the solution of a partial differential equation; etc.

In addition to the well-known equations, the method of series solutions is useful for solving any differential equation which *has* a Frobenius series solution and which you cannot solve any other way. To use series solutions intelligently you should know

(a) where to look for alternative methods;

(b) how to tell from the differential equation whether the Frobenius method will give a complete solution;

(c) how to find the complete solution of a second-order differential equation when you have found one solution.

We shall take these questions up in order.

(a) **Alternative methods.** There is a very complete compilation of a large number of differential equations in a book by Kamke. When you are unable to solve a differential equation by elementary methods, it is worth while to look for it in Kamke before you resort to series solution.

(b) **Fuchs's theorem.** A general theorem due to Fuchs tells when the method of Frobenius will work; we shall state it for second-order differential equations, which are the most important ones in applications. Write the differential equation as

$$(21.1) \qquad y'' + f(x)y' + g(x)y = 0.$$

If $xf(x)$ and $x^2 g(x)$ are expandable in convergent power series $\sum\limits_{n=0}^{\infty} a_n x^n$, we say that the differential equation (21.1) is regular (or has a nonessential singularity) at the origin. Let us call these the Fuchsian conditions. Fuchs's theorem says that these conditions are necessary and sufficient for the general solution of (21.1) to consist of either

(1) two Frobenius series, or

(2) one solution which is a Frobenius series, and a second solution which consists of the first solution multiplied by $\ln x$, plus another Frobenius series. Case (2) occurs only when the roots of the indicial equation are equal or differ by an integer, and not always then. See Problem 62 for further comment on this case.

Note the *necessary* condition: if the Fuchsian conditions are not met, one solution might be a Frobenius series, but the other will not be. For example, consider the differential equation

$$x^4 y'' + y = 0 \quad \text{or} \quad y'' + \frac{1}{x^4} y = 0.$$

Here $g(x) = 1/x^4$, $x^2 g(x) = 1/x^2$ which cannot be expanded in a series of nonnegative powers of x. This equation is then not Fuchsian, and so Fuchs's theorem tells us that there is *not more than one* Frobenius series solution. As a matter of fact, series methods give $y = 0$. The solution is (from Kamke)

$$y = x\left(c_1 \cos \frac{1}{x} + c_2 \sin \frac{1}{x}\right);$$

the Frobenius method failed because this solution cannot be expanded in a generalized power series (11.1).

(c) **Finding a second solution.** Sometimes you may know (by inspection, by series solution, etc.) one solution of a second-order equation. Given this one solution, we consider how to get the second solution. For a Fuchsian equation it may be that the two roots of the indicial equation give rise to two independent solutions. However, sometimes (as for Bessel functions of integral order) the two values of s lead to only one solution. In this case Fuchs's theorem says that the second solution is $\ln x$ times the first, plus another Frobenius series. A more general method (which applies to the non-Fuchsian case also) is to substitute in (21.1)

(21.2) $$y(x) = u(x)v(x),$$

where u is the solution already found and v is a new dependent variable. We illustrate both of these methods by solving the differential equation

(21.3) $$4x^2 y'' + y = 0.$$

Either by assuming a Frobenius series solution, or by trial and error, we may find that one solution of (21.3) is $y = \sqrt{x}$. Then observing that (21.3)

is Fuchsian, we know that a second solution is

$$(21.4) \qquad\qquad y = \sqrt{x} \ln x + \sum_{n=0}^{\infty} b_n x^{n+s}.$$

We calculate y' and y'' from (21.4):

$$(21.5) \qquad y' = \tfrac{1}{2} x^{-\frac{1}{2}} \ln x + \frac{\sqrt{x}}{x} + \sum_{n=0}^{\infty} b_n(n + s)x^{n+s-1},$$

$$y'' = -\tfrac{1}{4} x^{-\frac{3}{2}} \ln x + \tfrac{1}{2} x^{-\frac{3}{2}} - \tfrac{1}{2} x^{-\frac{3}{2}}$$

$$+ \sum_{n=0}^{\infty} b_n(n + s)(n + s - 1)x^{n+s-2}.$$

Substituting (21.4) and (21.5) into (21.3), we get

$$(21.6) \quad -\sqrt{x} \ln x + 4 \sum_{n=0}^{\infty} b_n(n + s)(n + s - 1)x^{n+s}$$

$$+ \sqrt{x} \ln x + \sum_{n=0}^{\infty} b_n x^{n+s} = 0.$$

For $n = 0$ we get the indicial equation

$$(21.7) \qquad \begin{array}{ll} 4b_0 s(s - 1) + b_0 = 0 & \text{or} \quad 4s^2 - 4s + 1 = 0, \\ (2s - 1)^2 = 0, & s = \tfrac{1}{2}. \end{array}$$

For any $n > 0$, (21.6) gives

$$(21.8) \qquad\qquad b_n[4(n + s)(n + s - 1) + 1] = 0,$$

or $b_n = 0$ for $n \ne 0$ since the bracket is different from zero for $s = \tfrac{1}{2}$ and $n > 0$. Then a second solution of (21.3) is

$$y = \sqrt{x} \ln x + b_0 \sqrt{x}$$

and the general solution is

$$y = c_1 \sqrt{x} + c_2(\sqrt{x} \ln x + b_0 \sqrt{x})$$

or more simply

$$(21.9) \qquad\qquad y = A\sqrt{x} + B\sqrt{x} \ln x.$$

We can illustrate the more general method using this same equation. Having found $\sqrt{x}$ as one solution, make the substitution (21.2) where $u = \sqrt{x}$, that is,

$$(21.10) \qquad\qquad y = v\sqrt{x}.$$

By Leibniz' rule,

$$y'' = v''\sqrt{x} + 2v' \cdot \tfrac{1}{2} x^{-\frac{1}{2}} + v(-\tfrac{1}{4} x^{-\frac{3}{2}}).$$

Substituting this into (21.3) and dividing by $\sqrt{x}$, we have

$$4x^2v'' + 4xv' - v + v = 0,$$
$$xv'' + v' = 0.$$

This is a (separable) first-order equation in v'; we solve it as follows:

$$\frac{dv'}{v'} + \frac{dx}{x} = 0, \qquad v' = \frac{1}{x}, \qquad v = \ln x.$$

Then the second solution of (21.3), namely (21.10), becomes $y = \sqrt{x} \ln x$ and the general solution is (21.9) as before.

REFERENCES

For discussion of the method of series solutions, see books on differential equations (for example, Kaplan, or Tenenbaum and Pollard) or on advanced calculus (for example, Hildebrand). Handbooks containing numerous formulas and tables for the functions discussed in this chapter and also many other functions are: Abramowitz and Stegun, National Bureau of Standards Handbook; Jahnke-Emde; Erdélyi, Higher Transcendental Functions. For detailed discussion of many of these functions, see Hochstadt, Morse and Feshbach, and Rainville. Books on Bessel functions are Gray, Mathews, and MacRobert; Relton; Watson. Less detailed discussions of the material of this chapter will be found in many other books; see references at the end of the book identified as Chapter 12 references by a [12] following the listing.

PROBLEMS

1. Solve the following differential equations by power series and also by a standard method. Verify that the series solution is the power series expansion of your other solution.

   (a) $y'' = -4y$

   (b) $y' = xy + x$

   (c) $y'' + y = 4x \sin x$

   (d) $xy' = xy + y$

   (e) $y' = 3x^2y$

   (f) $y'' - 5y' + 6y = 0$

2. Solve the following differential equations by power series.

   (a) $y'' - x^2y' - xy = 0$

   (b) $xy' - y = x^2$

   (c) $y'' + xy = 0$

   (d) $(x^2 + 1)y'' - 2xy' + 2y = 0$

   (e) $y'' - 2y = 4x^2e^{x^2}$

   (f) $y'' - (x^2 + 1)y = 0$

3. Using (2.6) and (2.7) and the requirement that $P_l(1) = 1$, find $P_3(x)$ and $P_4(x)$.

4. Sketch graphs of $P_0(x)$, $P_1(x)$, $P_2(x)$, and $P_3(x)$ from $x = -1$ to $x = 1$. *Hint:* When is $P_l(x)$ an even function and when is it an odd function?

5. (a) By Leibniz' rule, write the formula for $(d^n/dx^n)(uv)$.

   (b) Use (a) to find $(d^6/dx^6)(x^2 \sin x)$; $(d^{10}/dx^{10})(xe^x)$.

   (c) Verify part (a). *Hints:* One method is to use mathematical induction. Another method is to write

$$\frac{d}{dx}\,(uv) = D(uv) = (D_u + D_v)(uv),$$

where D_u acts only on u and D_v acts only on v, that is, $D_u(uv)$ means $v(du/dx)$, etc. Then

$$\frac{d^n}{dx^n}\,(uv) = (D_u + D_v)^n(uv).$$

Expand $(D_u + D_v)^n$ by the binomial theorem and interpret the terms to get Leibniz' rule.

6. Verify equations (4.4) and (4.5).

7. Show that $P_l(1) = 1$, with $P_l(x)$ given by (4.1), in the following way. Factor $(x^2 - 1)^l$ into $(x + 1)^l(x - 1)^l$ and differentiate the product l times by Leibniz' rule. Without writing out very many terms you should see that every term but one contains the factor $x - 1$ and so becomes zero when $x = 1$. Use this to evaluate $P_l(x)$ in (4.1) when $x = 1$ to get $P_l(1) = 1$.

8. Find $P_0(x)$, $P_1(x)$, $P_2(x)$, $P_3(x)$, and $P_4(x)$ from Rodrigues' formula (4.1). Compare your results with (2.8) and Problem 3.

9. Show that $\displaystyle\int_{-1}^{1} x^m P_l(x)\,dx = 0$ if $m < l$. *Hint:* Use Rodrigues' formula (4.1) and integrate repeatedly by parts, differentiating the power of x and integrating the derivative each time.

10. Recall from Chapter 11, Section 2, that the power series expansion of $f(z)$ about $z = 0$ converges in the circle $|z| < |z_0|$, where z_0 is the singularity of $f(z)$ nearest the origin. Also recall that the corresponding series when $z = x$ converges for $|x| < |z_0|$. Thus a convenient way of finding the interval of convergence of the series for $f(x)$ is to find the singularity of $f(z)$ nearest the origin. Apply this to show that the series in powers of h for $\Phi(x, h)$ in (5.2) converges for $|h| < 1$ and $-1 \le x \le 1$. Here h is the variable and x is a parameter; you should find the (complex) value of h which makes Φ infinite, and show that the absolute value of this complex number is 1 (independent of x). This proves that the series for real h converges for $|h| < 1$.

11. Find $P_3(x)$ by getting one more term in the generating function expansion (5.3).

12. Verify (5.5) using (5.1).

13. Use the recursion relation (5.10) and the values of $P_0(x)$ and $P_1(x)$ to find $P_2(x)$, $P_3(x)$, $P_4(x)$, $P_5(x)$, and $P_6(x)$. [After you have found $P_3(x)$, use it to find $P_4(x)$, etc.]

14. Show from (5.1) that

$$(x - h) \frac{\partial \Phi}{\partial x} = h \frac{\partial \Phi}{\partial h}.$$

Substitute the series (5.2) for Φ, and so prove the recursion relation

$$x P'_l(x) - P'_{l-1}(x) = l P_l(x).$$

15. Differentiate the recursion relation (5.10) and use the recursion relation of Problem 14 with l replaced by $l - 1$ to prove the recursion relation

$$P'_l(x) - x P'_{l-1}(x) = l P_{l-1}(x).$$

16. From the results of Problems 14 and 15, show that

$$(1 - x^2) P'_l(x) = l P_{l-1}(x) - l x P_l(x).$$

Differentiate this with respect to x and eliminate $P'_{l-1}(x)$ using Problem 14. Your result should be the Legendre equation. The derivation of Problems 14 to 16 constitutes an alternative proof [to that of equations (5.5) to (5.7)] that the functions $P_l(x)$ in (5.2) are Legendre polynomials.

17. Write the equation in Problem 15 with l replaced by $l + 1$ and use it to eliminate the $x P'_l(x)$ term in Problem 14. You should get

$$P'_{l+1}(x) = (2l + 1) P_l(x) + P'_{l-1}(x).$$

Multiply this by $P_l(x)$, integrate from -1 to 1, and show that

$$\int_{-1}^{1} P'_{l-1}(x) P_l(x)\, dx = 0.$$

(*Hint:* Use Problem 9; consider what powers of x are in P'_{l-1}.) Evaluate $\int_{-1}^{1} P_l(x) P'_{l+1}(x)\, dx$ by integrating by parts. Remember that $P_l(1) = 1$ and $P_l(x)$ is even or odd with l. Thus give an alternative proof of (8.4).

18. Expand the potential $V = K/d$ in (5.11) in the following way in order to see how the terms depend on the tensors mentioned at the end of Section 5. In Fig. 5.1 let $\mathbf{R}$ have coordinates X, Y, Z and $\mathbf{r}$ have coordinates x, y, z. [*Note:* The coordinate x here is *not* the x in (5.14).] Then

$$V = \frac{K}{d} = K[(X - x)^2 + (Y - y)^2 + (Z - z)^2]^{-\frac{1}{2}}.$$

Consider X, Y, Z as constants and expand $V(x, y, z)$ in a three-variable power series about the origin. (See Chapter 4, Section 2, for discussion of two-variable power series and generalize the method.) You should find

$$V = \frac{K}{R} + \frac{K}{R^2}\left(\frac{X}{R}x + \cdots\right)$$

$$+ \frac{K}{R^3}\left[\left(\frac{3}{2}\frac{X^2}{R^2} - \frac{1}{2}\right)x^2 + \cdots + \frac{3}{2}\frac{X}{R}\frac{Y}{R}2xy + \cdots\right] + \cdots$$

and similar terms in y, z, y^2, xz, etc. Now letting $\mathbf{r} = \mathbf{r}_i$ and $K = K'q_i$ for a charge distribution as in Fig. 5.2, and summing (or integrating) over the charge distribution, show that: the first term is just $(K'/R)\cdot$ total charge; the next group of terms (in x, y, z) involve the three components of the electric dipole moment; the sum of these terms is $(K'/R^2)\cdot$ component of the dipole moment in the $\mathbf{R}$ direction; the next group (quadratic terms) involve six quantities of the form

$$\iiint x^2\rho\, d\tau \qquad \text{and similar } y, z \text{ integrals,}$$

$$\iiint 2xy\rho\, d\tau \qquad \text{and similar } xz, yz \text{ integrals.}$$

If we split the $2xy$ term as $xy + yx$, these six terms give the nine components of a second-order tensor called the quadrupole moment. Use the method of Problem 41b in Chapter 10 to show that it *is* a second-order tensor. Just as two charges $+q$ and $-q$ form an electric dipole, so four charges like this $\begin{smallmatrix}+\bullet & \bullet- \\ -\bullet & \bullet+\end{smallmatrix}$ form an electric quadrupole and the quadratic terms in the V series give the potential of such a charge configuration. Without calculating the coefficients in the series, show that the third-order terms in x, y, z will contain the right number of terms for a third-order tensor; this is known as the octopole moment and can be represented physically by two quadrupoles side by side just as a quadrupole above was formed by two dipoles side by side.

19. Show that if $\displaystyle\int_a^b A^*(x)B(x)\, dx = 0$ [see (6.5)], then $\displaystyle\int_a^b A(x)B^*(x)\, dx = 0$ and vice versa.

20. (a) By a method similar to that used to show that the P_l's are an orthogonal set of functions on $(-1, 1)$, show that the solutions of $y_n'' = -n^2 y_n$ are an orthogonal set on $(-\pi, \pi)$. *Hint:* You should know what functions the solutions y_n are; do not use the functions themselves, but you may use their values and the values of their derivatives at $-\pi$ and π to evaluate the integrated part of your equation.

(b) The following differential equation is often called a Sturm-Liouville equation:

$$\frac{d}{dx}[A(x)y'] + [\lambda B(x) + C(x)]y = 0$$

(λ is a constant parameter). This equation includes many of the differential equations of mathematical physics as special cases. Show that the following equations can be written in the Sturm-Liouville form: the Legendre equation (7.2); Bessel's equation (19.2) for a *fixed p*, that is, with the parameter λ corresponding to a^2; the simple harmonic motion equation in part (a) of this problem; the differential equations in Problems 64 and 65. Show, as in part (a), that if y_1 and y_2 are two solutions of the Sturm-Liouville equation (corresponding to the two values λ_1 and λ_2 of the parameter λ), then y_1 and y_2 are orthogonal on (a, b) with respect to the weight function $B(x)$ under the assumptions $y(a) = y(b)$, $y'(a) = y'(b)$, and $A(x)$ a continuous function.

21. Use Problem 9 to show that $\int_{-1}^{1} P_m(x)P_l(x)\,dx = 0$ if $m < l$. *Comment:* This amounts to a different proof of orthogonality—via Rodrigues' formula instead of the differential equation.

22. Express each of the following polynomials as linear combinations of Legendre polynomials. *Hint:* Start with the highest power of x and work down in finding the correct combination.

   (a) $5 - 2x$ (b) $3x^2 + x - 1$

   (c) x^4 (d) $x - x^3$

   (e) Show that any polynomial of degree n can be written as a linear combination of Legendre polynomials with $l \leq n$.

23. Use Problem 22e and equation (7.1) to do Problem 9 without Rodrigues' formula.

24. Expand the following functions in Legendre series.

   (a) $f(x) = \begin{cases} -1, & -1 < x < 0, \\ 1, & 0 < x < 1. \end{cases}$

   (b) $f(x) = \begin{cases} 0, & -1 < x < 0, \\ x, & 0 < x < 1. \end{cases}$

   (c) $f(x) = P_n'(x)$. *Hint:* For $l \geq n$, $\int_{-1}^{1} P_n'(x)P_l(x)\,dx = 0$ (Why?); for $l < n$, integrate by parts.

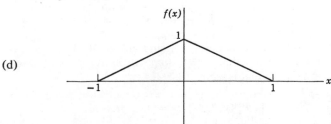

   (d)

   (e) The polynomials in Problem 22. *Comment:* You should get the same results as in Problem 22.

25. Find the best (in the least squares sense) second-degree polynomial approximation to $y = x^4$ for $-1 < x < 1$.

26. Prove the least squares approximation property of Legendre polynomials (stated at the end of Section 9) as follows. Let $f(x)$ be the given function to be approximated. Let the functions $p_l(x)$ be the normalized Legendre polynomials, that is, $p_l(x) = \sqrt{(2l + 1)/2}\,P_l(x)$ so that $\int_{-1}^{1} [p_l(x)]^2\, dx = 1$. Show that the Legendre series for $f(x)$ as far as the $p_2(x)$ term is

$$f(x) = c_0 p_0(x) + c_1 p_1(x) + c_2 p_2(x)$$

with

$$c_l = \int_{-1}^{1} f(x) p_l(x)\, dx.$$

Write the quadratic polynomial satisfying the least squares condition as $b_0 p_0(x) + b_1 p_1(x) + b_2 p_2(x)$ (by Problem 22e any quadratic polynomial can be written in this form). The problem is to find b_0, b_1, b_2 so that

$$I = \int_{-1}^{1} [f(x) - (b_0 p_0(x) + b_1 p_1(x) + b_2 p_2(x))]^2\, dx$$

is a minimum. Square the bracket and write I as a sum of integrals of the individual terms. Show that some of the integrals are zero by orthogonality, some are 1 because the p_l's are normalized, and others are equal to the coefficients c_l. Add and subtract $c_0^2 + c_1^2 + c_2^2$ and show that

$$I = \int_{-1}^{1} [f^2(x) + (b_0 - c_0)^2 + (b_1 - c_1)^2 + (b_2 - c_2)^2 - c_0^2 - c_1^2 - c_2^2]\, dx.$$

Now determine the values of the b's to make I as small as possible. (*Hint:* The smallest value the square of a real number can have is zero.) Generalize the proof to polynomials of degree n.

27. Verify equations (10.3) and (10.4).

28. (a) In applied problems, the equation for the associated Legendre functions (and for Legendre functions when $m = 0$) usually arises in the form

$$\frac{1}{\sin\theta}\frac{d}{d\theta}\left(\sin\theta\,\frac{dy}{d\theta}\right) + \left[l(l + 1) - \frac{m^2}{\sin^2\theta}\right]y = 0.$$

Make the change of variable $x = \cos\theta$, and obtain (10.1).

(b) Show that the functions $P_l^m(x)$ for each m are a set of orthogonal functions on $(-1, 1)$, that is, show that

$$\int_{-1}^{1} P_l^m(x) P_n^m(x)\, dx = 0, \qquad l \neq n.$$

Hint: Use the differential equation (10.1) and follow the method of Section 7.

29. Finish the solution of equation (11.2) for $s = -2$. Write your solution in closed form as in (11.6). To avoid confusion with the a_n values we found when $s = -1$, you may want to call the coefficients in your series a'_n or b_n; however, this is not essential as long as you realize that there are two separate problems, one for $s = -1$ and one for $s = -2$ and each series has its own coefficients.

30. Solve the following differential equations by the method of Frobenius (generalized power series).

(a) $x^2y'' - 6y = 0$ (b) $2xy'' + y' + 2y = 0$

(c) $3xy'' + (3x + 1)y' + y = 0$ (d) $x^2y'' - (x^2 + 2)y = 0$

(e) $x^2y'' + 2x^2y' - 2y = 0$

(f) $3xy'' - 2(3x - 1)y' + (3x - 2)y = 0$

(g) $2xy'' - y' + 2y = 0$ (h) $xy'' - y' + 9x^5y = 0$

(i) $36x^2y'' + (5 - 9x^2)y = 0$

31. Consider each of the following problems as illustrations showing that we must be cautious about using the general recursion relation between the coefficients in a power series solution for the first few terms of the series.

(a) Solve $y'' + y'/x^2 = 0$ by power series to find the relation

$$a_{n+1} = -\frac{n(n-1)}{n+1}a_n.$$

If, without thinking carefully, we test the series $\sum_{n=0}^{\infty} a_n x^n$ for convergence by the ratio test, we find

$$\lim_{n\to\infty} \frac{|a_{n+1}x^{n+1}|}{|a_n x^n|} = \infty. \quad \text{(Show this.)}$$

Thus we might conclude that the series diverges and that there is no power series solution of this equation. Show why this is wrong, and that the power series solution is $y = $ const.

(b) Solve $y'' = -y$ by the Frobenius method. You should find the roots $s = 0$ and $s = 1$ of the indicial equation. The value $s = 0$ leads to the solutions $\cos x$ and $\sin x$ as you would expect. For $s = 1$, call the series $y = \sum_{n=0}^{\infty} b_n x^{n+1}$, and find the relation

$$b_{n+2} = -\frac{b_n}{(n+3)(n+2)}.$$

Show that the b_0 series obtained from this relation is just $\sin x$, but that the b_1 series is *not* a solution of the differential equation. What is wrong?

32. Show by the ratio test that the infinite series (12.9) for $J_p(x)$ converges for all x.

33. (a) Using (12.9) write out the first four terms of $J_0(x)$; of $J_1(x)$; of $J_{-1}(x)$.

(b) Show that for integral p, $J_{-p}(x) = (-1)^pJ_p(x)$ and $J_p(-x) = (-1)^pJ_p(x)$.

(c) Using tables, sketch graphs of $J_0(x)$ and $J_1(x)$.

34. For complex z, $J_p(z)$ can be defined by the series (12.9) with x replaced by z. Use this definition to find the residue (see Chapter 11, Section 6) of $z^{-3}J_0(z)$ at $z = 0$.

35. Prove equation (15.2) by a method similar to the one used in the text to prove (15.1).

36. Solve equations (15.1) and (15.2) for $J_{p+1}(x)$ and $J_{p-1}(x)$. Add and subtract these two equations to get (15.3) and (15.4).

37. Carry out the differentiation in equations (15.1) and (15.2) to get (15.5).

38. Find the solutions of the following differential equations in terms of Bessel functions by using equations (16.1) and (16.2).

(a) Equation (11.2)   (b) $y'' + 4x^2 y = 0$

(c) $xy'' + 2y' + 4y = 0$ (d) $3xy'' + 2y' + 12y = 0$

(e) $y'' - \dfrac{1}{x}y' + \left(4 + \dfrac{1}{x^2}\right)y = 0$ (f) $4xy'' + y = 0$

(g) $xy'' + 3y' + x^3 y = 0$

39. Verify by direct substitution that the text solution of equation (16.3) and your solutions in Problem 38 are correct. Also prove in general that the solution (16.2) given for (16.1) is correct. *Hint:* These are exercises in partial differentiation. To verify the result in the example of Section 16, we would change variables from x, y to say z, u, where

$$y = \sqrt{x}\,u, \quad u = J_{\frac{1}{3}}(z), \quad z = 2x^{\frac{3}{2}},$$

and show that if x, y satisfy (16.3), then u, z satisfy (12.1), that is,

$$z^2\frac{d^2 u}{dz^2} + z\frac{du}{dz} + (z^2 - \tfrac{1}{9})u = 0.$$

40. Show directly from the series for $J_p(x)$ and $J_{-p}(x)$ that

$$J_{\frac{1}{2}}(x) = \sqrt{\frac{2}{\pi}}\frac{\sin x}{\sqrt{x}}, \qquad J_{-\frac{1}{2}}(x) = \sqrt{\frac{2}{\pi}}\frac{\cos x}{\sqrt{x}}.$$

Then use (15.2) to find $J_{\frac{3}{2}}(x)$. Also obtain the solutions (in terms of elementary functions) of (11.2) [see (11.6) and Problem 29] from Problem 38a and the above formulas.

41. Using the definition $j_n(x) = \sqrt{\pi/(2x)}J_{n+\frac{1}{2}}(x)$, show that

$$j_n(x) = x^n\left(-\frac{1}{x}\frac{d}{dx}\right)^n\left(\frac{\sin x}{x}\right)$$

for $n = 0$, 1 and 2. *Hint:* Use Problem 40 and equation (15.2). *Caution:*
$\left(-\dfrac{1}{x}\dfrac{d}{dx}\right)^2 u$ means $\left(-\dfrac{1}{x}\dfrac{d}{dx}\right)\left(-\dfrac{1}{x}\dfrac{du}{dx}\right)$.

42. Show either from the result of Problem 40 or directly from the series for $I_p(x)$ that

$$I_{\frac{1}{2}}(x) = \sqrt{\frac{2}{\pi}} \frac{\sinh x}{\sqrt{x}} \quad \text{and} \quad I_{-\frac{1}{2}}(x) = \sqrt{\frac{2}{\pi}} \frac{\cosh x}{\sqrt{x}}.$$

43. Using (16.1) and (17.4) show that the spherical Bessel functions satisfy the differential equation

$$x^2 y'' + 2xy' + [x^2 - n(n + 1)]y = 0.$$

44. Using (17.3) and (15.1) to (15.5), find the recursion relations for $I_p(x)$. In particular, show that $I_0' = I_1$.

45. Show from (13.3) that $N_{n+\frac{1}{2}}(x) = (-1)^{n+1} J_{-(n+\frac{1}{2})}(x)$.

46. Show from (17.4) that $h_n^{(1)}(x) = -ix^n \left(-\frac{1}{x} \frac{d}{dx} \right)^n \left(\frac{e^{ix}}{x} \right).$

47. Using tabulated values, sketch a graph of the hyperbolic Bessel function $I_0(x)$.

48. From (18.20) find θ using (15.2), (18.11) and (18.8), to see that for the simple case (18.20), $\theta = 0$ when $J_2(u) = 0$. Show that the successive (variable) quarter periods of the lengthening pendulum are $\dfrac{v}{4g} (r_2^2 - r_1^2)$ or $\dfrac{v}{4g} (r_1^2 - r_2^2)$, where r_1 and r_2 are successive zeros of J_1 and J_2. Look up and calculate several quarter periods (as multiples of $v/(4g)$), and observe that an inward swing takes longer than either the preceding or following outward swing.

49. Solve the differential equation $xy'' = y$ using (16.1), and then express the answer in terms of a function I_p by (17.3).

50. Prove

$$J_p(x)J_{-p}'(x) - J_{-p}(x)J_p'(x) = -\frac{2}{\pi x} \sin p\pi$$

as follows: Write Bessel's equation (12.1) with $y = J_p$ and with $y = J_{-p}$; multiply the J_p equation by J_{-p} and the J_{-p} equation by J_p and subtract to get

$$\frac{d}{dx} [x(J_p J_{-p}' - J_{-p} J_p')] = 0.$$

Then $J_p J_{-p}' - J_{-p} J_p' = c/x$. To find c, use (12.9) for each of the four functions and pick out the $1/x$ terms in the products. Then use (5.4) of Chapter 9.

51. Using (13.3) show that

$$J_p(x)N_p'(x) - J_p'(x)N_p(x) = \frac{J_p'(x)J_{-p}(x) - J_p(x)J_{-p}'(x)}{\sin p\pi}.$$

52. Use (15.1) or (15.2) (for N's as well as for J's) and Problems 50 and 51 to prove (18.16).

53. The differential equation for transverse vibrations of a string whose density increases linearly from one end to the other is $y'' + (a + bx)y = 0$, where a and b are constants. Find the general solution of this equation in terms of Bessel functions. *Hint:* Make a change of variable as in the lengthening pendulum problem.

SERIES SOLUTIONS OF DIFFERENTIAL EQUATIONS

54. Consider the "shortening pendulum" problem. Follow the method of the text but with $l = l_0 - vt$. Does the θ amplitude of the vibration increase or decrease as the pendulum shortens? Restate the result of Problem 48 about quarter periods for this case.

55. Prove equation (19.10) in the following way. First note that (19.2) and (19.3) and therefore (19.7) hold whether a and b are roots of $J_p(x)$ or not. Let a be a root but let b be just any number. From (19.7) show that then

$$\int_0^1 xuv\, dx = \frac{J_p(b)aJ_p'(a)}{b^2 - a^2}.$$

Now let $b \to a$ and evaluate the indeterminate form by l'Hospital's rule (that is, differentiate numerator and denominator with respect to b and let $b \to a$). Hence find

$$\int_0^1 xuv\, dx = \tfrac{1}{2}J_p'^2(a)$$

for $a = b$, that is, for $u = v = J_p(ax)$ as in (19.10). Use equations (15.3) to (15.5) to show that the other two expressions given in (19.10) are equivalent.

56. (a) The generating function for Bessel functions of integral order $p = n$ is

$$e^{\frac{1}{2}x(h-h^{-1})} = \sum_{n=-\infty}^{\infty} h^n J_n(x).$$

By expanding the exponential in powers of $x(h - h^{-1})$ show that the $n = 0$ term is $J_0(x)$ as claimed.

(b) Let $\Phi(x, h) = e^{\frac{1}{2}x(h-h^{-1})}$ be the generating function for Bessel functions of integral order. Show that

$$x^2 \frac{\partial^2 \Phi}{\partial x^2} + x \frac{\partial \Phi}{\partial x} + x^2 \Phi - \left(h \frac{\partial}{\partial h}\right)^2 \Phi = 0.$$

Use this result and $\Phi(x, h) = \sum_{n=-\infty}^{\infty} h^n J_n(x)$ to show that the functions $J_n(x)$ satisfy Bessel's equation. By considering the terms in h^n in the expansion of $e^{\frac{1}{2}x(h-h^{-1})}$ in part (a), show that the coefficient of h^n is a series starting with the term $(1/n!)(x/2)^n$. (You have then proved that the functions called $J_n(x)$ in the expansion of $\Phi(x, h)$ are indeed the Bessel functions of integral order previously defined by (12.9) and (13.1) with $p = n$.)

57. In the generating function equation of Problem 56, put $h = e^{i\theta}$ and separate real and imaginary parts to derive the equations

$$\cos (x \sin \theta) = J_0(x) + 2J_2(x) \cos 2\theta + 2J_4(x) \cos 4\theta + \cdots$$

$$= J_0(x) + 2 \sum_{n=1}^{\infty} J_{2n}(x) \cos 2n\theta,$$

$$\sin (x \sin \theta) = 2[J_1(x) \sin \theta + J_3(x) \sin 3\theta + \cdots]$$

$$= 2 \sum_{n=0}^{\infty} J_{2n+1}(x) \sin (2n + 1)\theta.$$

These are Fourier series with Bessel functions as coefficients. (In fact the J_n's for integral n are often called Bessel coefficients because they occur in many series like these.) Use the formulas for the coefficients in a Fourier series to find integrals representing J_n for even n, and for odd n. Show that these results can be combined to give

$$J_n(x) = \frac{1}{\pi} \int_0^\pi \cos(n\theta - x\sin\theta)\, d\theta$$

for *any* integral n. These series and integrals are of interest in astronomy and in the theory of frequency modulated waves (see Bronwell, p. 89).

58. In the generating function equation, Problem 56, put $x = iy$ and $h = -ik$ and show that

$$e^{\frac{1}{2}y(k+k^{-1})} = \sum_{n=-\infty}^{\infty} k^n I_n(y).$$

59. A straight wire clamped vertically at its lower end stands vertically if it is short, but bends under its own weight if it is long. It can be shown that the greatest length for vertical equilibrium is l, where $kl^{3/2}$ is the first zero of $J_{-1/3}$ and $k = \frac{4}{3r^2}\sqrt{\frac{\rho g}{\pi Y}}$, r = radius of the wire, ρ = linear density, g = acceleration of gravity, Y = Young's modulus. Find l for a steel wire of radius 1 mm; for a lead wire of the same radius.

60. Using the table in Section 20 and the definition of $j_n(x)$, find the asymptotic formula for $j_n(x)$.

61. Find the general solutions of the following differential equations by looking them up in Kamke.

(a) $y'' - (x^2 + 1)y = 0$ (b) $y'' + y' + 4e^{-2x}y = 0$

(c) $xy'' - y' + x^3(e^{x^2} - p^2)y = 0$ (d) $x^2 y'' + (3x - 1)y' + y = 0$

(e) $x^2 y'' - 2xy' + (9x^2 + 2)y = 0$ (f) $(x^2 + 1)y'' - xy' + y = 0$

(g) $x(x - 1)^2 y'' - 2y = 0$ (h) $(x^2 - 1)y'' + 8xy' + 12y = 0$

(i) $x^2 y'' + (x + 1)y' - y = 0$ (j) $x^2 y'' + x^2 y' - 2y = 0$

62. Solve each of the following differential equations by the Frobenius method; observe that you get only one solution. (Note, also, that the two values of s are equal or differ by an integer, and in the latter case the larger s gives the one solution.) Show that the conditions of Fuchs's theorem are satisfied. Knowing that the second solution is $\ln x$ times the solution you have, plus another Frobenius series, find the general solution. (It is convenient to note that the value of s in the second Frobenius series is always the same as the second value of s which did not give a solution in the first part of the problem.)

(a) $xy'' + y' = 0$ (b) $x(x + 1)y'' - (x - 1)y' + y = 0$

(c) $x^2 y'' - xy' + y = 0$ (d) $x(x - 1)^2 y'' - 2y = 0$

(e) $xy'' + xy' - 2y = 0$ (f) $x^2 y'' + (x^3 - 3x)y' + (4 - 2x)y = 0$

63. For each of the following equations, one solution u is given. Find the other solution by assuming $y = uv$.

(a) $xy'' - 2(x + 1)y' + (x + 2)y = 0;\ u = e^x;$

(b) $x^2 y'' - 3xy' + 4y = 0;\ u = x^2;$

(c) $x^3 y'' + xy' - y = 0;\ u = x;$

(d) $(x^2 + 1)y'' - xy' + y = 0;\ u = x.$

64. Solve the *Hermite* differential equation

$$y'' - 2xy' + 2py = 0$$

by power series. You should find an a_0 series and an a_1 series as for the Legendre equation in Section 2. Show that the a_0 series terminates when p is an even integer, and the a_1 series terminates when p is an odd integer. Thus for each integer n, the differential equation

(A) $y'' - 2xy' + 2ny = 0$

has one polynomial solution of degree n. These polynomials with a_0 or a_1 chosen so that the highest order term is $(2x)^n$ are called the *Hermite* polynomials and are denoted by $H_n(x)$. Find $H_0(x)$, $H_1(x)$, $H_2(x)$, and $H_3(x)$.

The Hermite polynomials are also given by the formula

(B) $H_n(x) = (-1)^n e^{x^2} \dfrac{d^n}{dx^n} e^{-x^2}.$

[Compare Rodrigues' formula (4.1) for $P_l(x)$; in fact, (B) is often called a Rodrigues' formula for Hermite polynomials.] Show that $y = H_n(x)$ given by (B) satisfies equation (A). *Hint:* Follow a method similar to that in Section 4. Let $v = e^{-x^2}$ and show that $v' = -2xv$. Differentiate this last equation $n + 1$ times by Leibniz' rule and then substitute $d^n v / dx^n = (-1)^n e^{-x^2} H_n(x)$ from (B). To complete the proof that the functions in (B) are Hermite polynomials, show that the highest term in (B) is $(2x)^n$. Find $H_0(x)$, $H_1(x)$, $H_2(x)$, and $H_3(x)$ from (B) and compare with your answers above.

The generating function for the Hermite polynomials is

(C) $\Phi(x, h) = e^{2xh - h^2} = \displaystyle\sum_{n=0}^{\infty} H_n(x) \dfrac{h^n}{n!}.$

Write the series for $e^{2xh - h^2}$ and collect powers of h to verify the first few terms of the series. Verify the identity

(D) $\dfrac{\partial^2 \Phi}{\partial x^2} - 2x \dfrac{\partial \Phi}{\partial x} + 2h \dfrac{\partial \Phi}{\partial h} = 0.$

Substitute the series in (C) into (D) to prove that the functions $H_n(x)$ in (C) satisfy Hermite's equation (A). Verify that the highest term in $H_n(x)$ is $(2x)^n$. (You have then proved that the functions called $H_n(x)$ in (C) are really the Hermite polynomials.)

Use the generating function to prove the following recursion relations.

$$H_n'(x) = 2nH_{n-1}(x).$$

(*Hint:* Differentiate (C) with respect to x and equate coefficients of h^n.)

$$H_{n+1}(x) - 2xH_n(x) + 2nH_{n-1}(x) = 0.$$

(*Hint:* Differentiate Φ with respect to h and equate coefficients of h^n.)

Prove that the functions $H_n(x)$ are orthogonal on $(-\infty, \infty)$ with respect to the weight function e^{-x^2}. *Hint:* Write the differential equation (A) as

$$e^{x^2} \frac{d}{dx}(e^{-x^2}y') + 2ny = 0.$$

Prove that $\displaystyle\int_{-\infty}^{\infty} e^{-x^2}[H_n(x)]^2 \, dx = \sqrt{\pi}\, 2^n n!$ by using (B) and the first recursion relation above, and integrating by parts.

The differential equation

(E) $$y'' + (2n + 1 - x^2)y = 0$$

arises in quantum mechanics. Verify that a solution of (E) is

$$y = e^{-x^2/2}H_n(x).$$

These functions are called *Hermite functions.*

Solve the following eigenvalue problem (see end of Section 2): Given the differential equation $y'' + (\epsilon - x^2)y = 0$, find the possible values of ϵ (eigenvalues) such that the solutions $y(x)$ of the given differential equation tend to zero as $x \to \pm\infty$; for these values of ϵ, find the eigenfunctions $y(x)$. *Hint:* Make the change of variable $y = e^{-x^2/2}u(x)$ and observe that the differential equation for $u(x)$ is just (A) if $\epsilon = 2n + 1$. The eigenfunctions $y(x)$ are then the Hermite functions; show that they *do* tend to zero as $x \to \pm\infty$, as required.

65. Solve the *Laguerre* differential equation

$$xy'' + (1 - x)y' + py = 0$$

by power series. Show that the a_0 series terminates if p is an integer. Thus for each integer n the differential equation

(A) $$xy'' + (1 - x)y' + ny = 0$$

has one solution which is a polynomial of degree n. These polynomials with $a_0 = n!$ are called the *Laguerre* polynomials and are denoted by $L_n(x)$. Find $L_0(x)$, $L_1(x)$, $L_2(x)$, and $L_3(x)$.

The Laguerre polynomials are also given by the following formula:

(B) $$L_n(x) = e^x \left(\frac{d}{dx}\right)^n (x^n e^{-x}).$$

[Compare (B) of Problem 64; again this may be called a Rodrigues' formula.] Show that $y = L_n(x)$ given by (B) satisfies (A), and verify that the constant term is $n!$ *Hint:* Follow a method similar to that used in Section 4. Let $v = x^n e^{-x}$ and show that $xv' = (n - x)v$. Differentiate this last equation $(n + 1)$ times by Leibniz' rule, and use $d^n v/dx^n = e^{-x}L_n(x)$ from (B).

The generating function for the Laguerre polynomials is

(C) $$\Phi(x, h) = \frac{1}{1-h} e^{\frac{xh}{h-1}} = \sum_{n=0}^{\infty} L_n(x) \frac{h^n}{n!}.$$

Write the series for the exponential and collect powers of h to verify the first few terms of the series. Verify the identity

(D) $$x \frac{\partial^2 \Phi}{\partial x^2} + (1-x) \frac{\partial \Phi}{\partial x} + h \frac{\partial \Phi}{\partial h} = 0.$$

Substitute the series in (C) into (D) to prove that the functions $L_n(x)$ in (C) satisfy Laguerre's equation (A). Verify that the constant term is $n!$ by putting $x = 0$ in the generating function. [You have then proved that the functions called $L_n(x)$ in (C) are really Laguerre polynomials.]

Use the generating function to prove the following recursion relations.

$$L_n'(x) - nL_{n-1}'(x) + nL_{n-1}(x) = 0.$$

[*Hint:* Differentiate (C) with respect to x to get $h\Phi = (h-1)(\partial\Phi/\partial x)$; equate coefficients of h^n.]

$$L_{n+1}(x) - (2n + 1 - x)L_n(x) + n^2 L_{n-1}(x) = 0.$$

(*Hint:* Differentiate Φ with respect to h.)

Prove that the functions $L_n(x)$ are orthogonal on $(0, \infty)$ with respect to the weight function e^{-x}. *Hint:* Write the differential equation (A) as

$$e^x \frac{d}{dx} (xe^{-x}y') + ny = 0.$$

Prove that

$$\int_0^\infty e^{-x} [L_n(x)]^2 \, dx = (n!)^2$$

by using (B).

The differential equation

(E) $$xy'' + (k + 1 - x)y' + (n - k)y = 0, \qquad k = \text{integer} \geq 0,$$

arises in the theory of the hydrogen atom in quantum mechanics. Show that a solution of (E) is

$$y = \frac{d^k}{dx^k} L_n(x).$$

These functions are called the *associated Laguerre polynomials.* *Hint:* Replace y by $L_n(x)$ in (A) and differentiate the equation k times by Leibniz' rule (Section 3).

Use the results above to solve the following eigenvalue problem. Given the differential equation $xy'' + (k + 1 - x)y' + (p - k)y = 0$ where k is an integer ≥ 0, find the values of p (eigenvalues) such that the solutions $y(x)$ have the property that $e^{-x/2}y(x) \to 0$ as $x \to +\infty$.

13

Integral Transforms

1. INTRODUCTION

If $f(t) = e^{-t}$, then the integral

$$\int_0^\infty f(t)t^p \, dt = \int_0^\infty t^p e^{-t} \, dt = F(p)$$

is a function of p [in fact, by Chapter 9, equation (3.3), we have $F(p) = p!$ or $\Gamma(p+1)$]. Starting with a function of t, we have multiplied it by a function of p and t, found the definite integral with respect to t, and so obtained a function of p. This function $F(p)$ is called an integral transform of $f(t)$. Integral transforms are used in a variety of applications, for example, in solving ordinary differential equations (Section 3) or partial differential equations (Chapter 14, Sections 9 and 10). There are many different kinds of integral transforms with different names, depending on what function of p and t we multiply by and what the range of integration is (the above example is called a Mellin transform). In this chapter, we shall consider two integral transforms (Laplace and Fourier) that are especially important in applications, and indicate some of their uses.

2. THE LAPLACE TRANSFORM

We define $L(f)$, the Laplace transform of $f(t)$ [also written $F(p)$ since it is a function of p], by the equation

$$(2.1) \qquad L(f) = \int_0^\infty f(t)e^{-pt}\,dt = F(p).$$

Some books and tables define $L(f)$ as p times the integral in (2.1); you need to watch for this in using a different book. There is a wide variation in notation used in writing (2.1); the variables x and p or t and s are often used instead of t and p and other letters are used instead of f and F. We shall consistently use the notation of a small letter for the function of t, and the corresponding capital letter for the transform which is a function of p, for example $f(t)$ and $F(p)$ or $g(t)$ and $G(p)$, etc. Note from (2.1) that since we integrate from 0 to ∞, $L(f)$ is the same no matter how $f(t)$ is defined for negative t. However, as we shall see later (Section 6), it is desirable to define $f(t) = 0$ for $t < 0$.

It is very convenient to have a table of corresponding $f(t)$ and $F(p)$ when we are using the Laplace transform to solve problems. Let us calculate some of the entries in the short table of Laplace transforms given on pages 594 to 596. To obtain $L1$ in the table, we substitute $f(t) = 1$ into (2.1) and find

$$(2.2) \qquad F(p) = \int_0^\infty 1 \cdot e^{-pt}\,dt = -\frac{1}{p}e^{-pt}\Big|_0^\infty = \frac{1}{p}, \qquad p > 0.$$

We have assumed $p > 0$ to make e^{-pt} zero at the upper limit; if p is complex, as it may be, then the real part of p (Re p) must be positive, and this is the restriction we have stated in the table for $L1$. For $L2$, we have

$$(2.3) \qquad \begin{aligned} &f(t) = e^{-at}, \\ &F(p) = \int_0^\infty e^{-(a+p)t}\,dt = \frac{1}{p+a}, \qquad \text{Re}\,(p+a) > 0. \end{aligned}$$

We could continue in this way to obtain the function $F(p)$ corresponding to each $f(t)$ by using (2.1) and evaluating the integral. However, there are some easier methods which we now illustrate. First observe that the Laplace transform of a sum of two functions is the sum of their Laplace transforms; also the transform of $cf(t)$ is $cL(f)$ when c is a constant:

$$L[f(t) + g(t)] = \int_0^\infty [f(t) + g(t)]e^{-pt}\, dt$$

(2.4)
$$= \int_0^\infty f(t)e^{-pt}\, dt + \int_0^\infty g(t)e^{-pt}\, dt = L(f) + L(g),$$

$$L[cf(t)] = \int_0^\infty cf(t)e^{-pt}\, dt = c \int_0^\infty f(t)e^{-pt}\, dt = cL(f).$$

In mathematical language, we say that the Laplace transform is *linear* (or is a *linear operator*). Now let us verify $L3$. In (2.3), replace a by $-ia$; then we have

(2.5)
$$f(t) = e^{iat} = \cos at + i \sin at,$$

$$F(p) = \frac{1}{p - ia} = \frac{p + ia}{p^2 + a^2}, \qquad \operatorname{Re}(p - ia) > 0.$$

Remembering (2.4), we can write (2.5) as

$$L(\cos at + i \sin at) = L(\cos at) + iL(\sin at)$$

(2.6)
$$= \frac{p}{p^2 + a^2} + i\,\frac{a}{p^2 + a^2}.$$

Similarly, replacing a by ia in (2.3), we get

(2.7) $$L(\cos at - i \sin at) = \frac{p}{p^2 + a^2} - i\,\frac{a}{p^2 + a^2}, \qquad \operatorname{Re}(p + ia) > 0.$$

Adding (2.6) and (2.7), we get $L4$; by subtracting, we get $L3$.
    To verify $L11$, start with $L4$, namely

(2.8) $$L(\cos at) = \int_0^\infty e^{-pt} \cos at\, dt = \frac{p}{p^2 + a^2}.$$

Differentiate (2.8) with respect to the parameter a to get

$$\int_0^\infty e^{-pt}(-t \sin at)\, dt = \frac{p(-2a)}{(p^2 + a^2)^2}$$

or

$$\int_0^\infty e^{-pt} t \sin at\, dt = \frac{2pa}{(p^2 + a^2)^2},$$

which is $L11$. Ways of finding other entries in the table are outlined in the problems.

A SHORT TABLE OF LAPLACE TRANSFORMS

	$y = f(t), t > 0$ $(y = f(t) = 0, t < 0)$	$Y = L(y) = F(p) = \displaystyle\int_0^\infty e^{-pt} f(t)\, dt$	
L1	1	$\dfrac{1}{p}$	$\operatorname{Re} p > 0$
L2	e^{-at}	$\dfrac{1}{p+a}$	$\operatorname{Re}(p+a) > 0$
L3	$\sin at$	$\dfrac{a}{p^2+a^2}$	$\operatorname{Re} p > \lvert\operatorname{Im} a\rvert$
L4	$\cos at$	$\dfrac{p}{p^2+a^2}$	$\operatorname{Re} p > \lvert\operatorname{Im} a\rvert$
L5	$t^k, \quad k > -1$	$\dfrac{k!}{p^{k+1}} \quad\text{or}\quad \dfrac{\Gamma(k+1)}{p^{k+1}}$	$\operatorname{Re} p > 0$
L6	$t^k e^{-at}, \quad k > -1$	$\dfrac{k!}{(p+a)^{k+1}} \quad\text{or}\quad \dfrac{\Gamma(k+1)}{(p+a)^{k+1}}$	$\operatorname{Re}(p+a) > 0$
L7	$\dfrac{e^{-at} - e^{-bt}}{b - a}$	$\dfrac{1}{(p+a)(p+b)}$	$\operatorname{Re}(p+a) > 0$
L8	$\dfrac{ae^{-at} - be^{-bt}}{a - b}$	$\dfrac{p}{(p+a)(p+b)}$	and $\operatorname{Re}(p+b) > 0$
L9	$\sinh at$	$\dfrac{a}{p^2-a^2}$	$\operatorname{Re} p > \lvert\operatorname{Re} a\rvert$
L10	$\cosh at$	$\dfrac{p}{p^2-a^2}$	$\operatorname{Re} p > \lvert\operatorname{Re} a\rvert$
L11	$t \sin at$	$\dfrac{2ap}{(p^2+a^2)^2}$	$\operatorname{Re} p > \lvert\operatorname{Im} a\rvert$
L12	$t \cos at$	$\dfrac{p^2-a^2}{(p^2+a^2)^2}$	$\operatorname{Re} p > \lvert\operatorname{Im} a\rvert$
L13	$e^{-at} \sin bt$	$\dfrac{b}{(p+a)^2+b^2}$	$\operatorname{Re}(p+a) > \lvert\operatorname{Im} b\rvert$
L14	$e^{-at} \cos bt$	$\dfrac{p+a}{(p+a)^2+b^2}$	$\operatorname{Re}(p+a) > \lvert\operatorname{Im} b\rvert$
L15	$1 - \cos at$	$\dfrac{a^2}{p(p^2+a^2)}$	$\operatorname{Re} p > \lvert\operatorname{Im} a\rvert$

A SHORT TABLE OF LAPLACE TRANSFORMS (continued)

	$\begin{aligned}&y = f(t), \ t > 0\\&(y = f(t) = 0, \ t < 0)\end{aligned}$	$Y = L(y) = F(p) = \displaystyle\int_0^\infty e^{-pt} f(t)\, dt$	
$L16$	$at - \sin at$	$\dfrac{a^3}{p^2(p^2 + a^2)}$	$\operatorname{Re} p > |\operatorname{Im} a|$
$L17$	$\sin at - at \cos at$	$\dfrac{2a^3}{(p^2 + a^2)^2}$	$\operatorname{Re} p > |\operatorname{Im} a|$
$L18$	$e^{-at}(1 - at)$	$\dfrac{p}{(p + a)^2}$	$\operatorname{Re}(p + a) > 0$
$L19$	$\dfrac{\sin at}{t}$	$\arctan \dfrac{a}{p}$	$\operatorname{Re} p > |\operatorname{Im} a|$
$L20$	$\dfrac{1}{t} \sin at \cos bt,$ $a > 0, \ b > 0$	$\dfrac{1}{2}\left(\arctan \dfrac{a + b}{p}\right.$ $\left. + \arctan \dfrac{a - b}{p}\right)$	$\operatorname{Re} p > 0$
$L21$	$\dfrac{e^{-at} - e^{-bt}}{t}$	$\ln \dfrac{p + b}{p + a}$	$\operatorname{Re}(p + a) > 0$ and $\operatorname{Re}(p + b) > 0$
$L22$	$1 - \operatorname{erf}\left(\dfrac{a}{2\sqrt{t}}\right), \quad a > 0$	$\dfrac{1}{p} e^{-a\sqrt{p}}$	$\operatorname{Re} p > 0$
$L23$	$J_0(at)$	$(p^2 + a^2)^{-\frac{1}{2}}$	$\operatorname{Re} p > |\operatorname{Im} a|$
$L24$	$f(t) = \begin{cases} 1, & t > a > 0 \\ 0, & t < a \end{cases}$ [unit step, often written $f(t) = u(t - a)$]	$\dfrac{1}{p} e^{-pa}$	$\operatorname{Re} p > 0$
$L25$	$f(t) = u(t - b) - u(t - a)$ 	$\dfrac{e^{-ap} - e^{-bp}}{p}$	All p
$L26$		$\dfrac{1}{p} \tanh \dfrac{1}{2} ap$	$\operatorname{Re} p > 0$

A SHORT TABLE OF LAPLACE TRANSFORMS (continued)

$$y = f(t), \, t > 0$$
$$(y = f(t) = 0, \, t < 0)$$
$$Y = L(y) = F(p) = \int_0^\infty e^{-pt} f(t) \, dt$$

L27	$\delta(t - a), \quad a \geq 0$ (See Section 7.)	e^{-pa}
L28	$f(t) = \begin{cases} g(t - a), & t > a > 0 \\ 0, & t < a \end{cases}$ $= g(t - a)u(t - a)$	$e^{-pa} G(p)$ $[G(p) \text{ means } L(g).]$
L29	$e^{-at} g(t)$	$G(p + a)$
L30	$g(at), \quad a > 0$	$\dfrac{1}{a} G\left(\dfrac{p}{a}\right)$
L31	$\dfrac{g(t)}{t} \quad$ (if integrable)	$\displaystyle\int_p^\infty G(u) \, du$
L32	$t^n g(t)$	$(-1)^n \dfrac{d^n G(p)}{dp^n}$
L33	$\displaystyle\int_0^t g(\tau) \, d\tau$	$\dfrac{1}{p} G(p)$
L34	$\displaystyle\int_0^t g(t - \tau)h(\tau) \, d\tau =$ $\displaystyle\int_0^t g(\tau)h(t - \tau) \, d\tau$	$G(p)H(p)$

(convolution of g and h, often written as $g * h$; see Section 5)

L35   Transforms of derivatives of y (see Section 3):

$$L(y') = pY - y_0$$
$$L(y'') = p^2 Y - py_0 - y_0'$$
$$L(y''') = p^3 Y - p^2 y_0 - py_0' - y_0'', \text{ etc.}$$
$$L(y^{(n)}) = p^n Y - p^{n-1} y_0 - p^{n-2} y_0' - \cdots - y_0^{(n-1)}$$

3. SOLUTION OF DIFFERENTIAL EQUATIONS BY LAPLACE TRANSFORMS

We are going to discuss the solution of linear differential equations with constant coefficients (see Chapter 7, Sections 5 and 6). You already know how to solve such equations; why, then, should you bother to learn another method? Recall two things: (1) When the right-hand side of a differential equation is not zero, it is sometimes quite a lot of work to find the particular solution. (2) What you find by standard methods is a general solution, containing arbitrary constants; you must make a further calculation of the values of the constants satisfying given initial conditions in order to solve a particular problem. The Laplace transform method simplifies both these difficulties. When you use a table of Laplace transforms (much as you would use integral tables), you may avoid some of the algebra; also, the Laplace transform method gives directly the final solution satisfying given initial conditions. Thus, although you *can* get along without using Laplace transforms to solve differential equations, in practice they are very useful.

We are going to take the Laplace transforms of the terms in differential equations; to do this we need to know the transforms of derivatives $y' = dy/dt$, $y'' = d^2y/dt^2$, etc. To find $L(y')$, we use the definition (2.1) and integrate by parts, as follows.

$$(3.1) \quad L(y') = \int_0^\infty y'(t)e^{-pt}\,dt = e^{-pt}y(t)\Big|_0^\infty - (-p)\int_0^\infty y(t)e^{-pt}\,dt$$

$$= -y(0) + pL(y) = pY - y_0,$$

where for simplicity we have written $L(y) = Y$ and $y(0) = y_0$. To find $L(y'')$, we think of y'' as $(y')'$, and substitute y' for y in (3.1) to get

$$L(y'') = pL(y') - y'(0).$$

Using (3.1) again to eliminate $L(y')$, we finally have

$$(3.2) \quad L(y'') = p^2L(y) - py(0) - y'(0) = p^2Y - py_0 - y_0'.$$

Continuing this process, we obtain the transforms of the higher-order derivatives (Problem 10, and L35).

We are now ready to solve a differential equation. The process is much like the use of logarithms in doing arithmetic: first you look up logarithms, then you do a simple process (addition, say) instead of a harder one (multiplication), and then you take antilogarithms. Here we shall take the Laplace transform of each term of a differential equation; then we shall do a simple process (solving an *algebraic* equation) instead of a hard one (solving a *differential* equation); then we shall find the inverse Laplace transform (like taking antilogarithms).

Example 1. Find the solution of

$$y'' + 4y' + 4y = t^2e^{-2t}$$

which satisfies the initial conditions $y_0 = 0$, $y_0' = 0$.

We take the Laplace transform of each term in the equation, using $L35$ and $L6$ in the table of Laplace transforms. We get

$$p^2 Y - p y_0 - y_0' + 4pY - 4y_0 + 4Y = L(t^2 e^{-2t}) = \frac{2}{(p+2)^3}.$$

But the initial conditions are $y_0 = y_0' = 0$. Thus we have

$$(p^2 + 4p + 4)Y = \frac{2}{(p+2)^3} \quad \text{or} \quad Y = \frac{2}{(p+2)^5}.$$

Note that we solved an *algebraic* equation for Y. Now we want y, which is the inverse Laplace transform of Y. We look in the table for the inverse transform of $2/(p+2)^5$. By $L6$, we get

$$y = \frac{2t^4 e^{-2t}}{4!} = \frac{t^4 e^{-2t}}{12}.$$

This is much simpler than the general solution; we have obtained just the solution satisfying the given initial conditions.

Example 2.   Solve $y'' + 4y = \sin 2t$, subject to the initial conditions $y_0 = 10$, $y_0' = 0$.

Using the table, we take the Laplace transform of each term of the equation to get

$$p^2 Y - p y_0 - y_0' + 4Y = L(\sin 2t) = \frac{2}{p^2 + 4}.$$

Then we substitute the initial conditions and solve for Y as follows:

$$(p^2 + 4)Y - 10p = \frac{2}{p^2 + 4},$$

$$Y = \frac{10p}{p^2 + 4} + \frac{2}{(p^2 + 4)^2}.$$

Finally, taking the inverse transform using $L4$ and $L17$, we have the desired solution:

$$y = 10 \cos 2t + \tfrac{1}{8}(\sin 2t - 2t \cos 2t)$$

$$= 10 \cos 2t + \tfrac{1}{8} \sin 2t - \tfrac{1}{4}t\cos 2t.$$

The process of finding y from Y is not always as simple as in these two examples. In Sections 5 and 6 we shall consider some more advanced techniques for finding inverse transforms, but right now we can see some fairly simple things to try if the inverse transform we want is not in the table. If Y contains several terms, we can try to find the inverse transforms of the separate terms; alternatively, we can try combining the terms first. Suppose, for example, that we had added together the two fractions in Y in Example 2 and so had $Y = (10p^3 + 40p + 2)/(p^2 + 4)^2$. The inverse transform of this expression is not in the table and obviously the thing to do is to leave the two fractions not combined as we did in Example 2. On the other hand, sometimes we get a simpler expression for Y if we do combine terms. For example, consider

$$Y = \frac{1}{p^2 - 1}\left(\frac{4}{p+3} - 1\right) = \frac{1}{p^2 - 1}\left(\frac{4-p-3}{p+3}\right)$$

$$= \frac{1}{(p-1)(p+1)}\frac{1-p}{p+3} = \frac{-1}{(p+1)(p+3)}.$$

Here Y simplified because of the cancellation of the factor $(p-1)$ and the inverse transform of the final expression for Y is in the table. (In general, Y will not simplify this way, but if it does, this is the simplest method of completing the problem.) However, let us suppose that Y contains a fairly complicated fraction (which arises naturally in the problem, *not* because we combined simpler fractions) and that combining terms in Y does not simplify it. By the technique of partial fractions (see a calculus text) we may break the complicated fraction into several simpler fractions whose inverse transforms are in the table. It is unnecessary to use a partial fractions expansion with all linear denominators, however, since we can find the inverse transform of any fraction with a quadratic denominator from the table (see Problem 6b). We may want to use partial fractions when the denominator is of the forms *linear times quadratic* or *quadratic times quadratic*.

Example 3.   Solve $y'' + 4y' + 13y = 20e^{-t}$, $y_0 = 1$, $y_0' = 3$.
We take the transform of each term and solve for Y as follows.

$$p^2Y - p - 3 + 4pY - 4 + 13Y = \frac{20}{p+1},$$

$$Y = \frac{1}{p^2 + 4p + 13}\left(\frac{20}{p+1} + p + 7\right) = \frac{p^2 + 8p + 27}{(p+1)(p^2 + 4p + 13)}.$$

Using partial fractions, we write

$$\frac{p^2 + 8p + 27}{(p+1)(p^2 + 4p + 13)} \equiv \frac{A}{p+1} + \frac{Bp + C}{p^2 + 4p + 13}$$

or, after clearing fractions,

$$p^2 + 8p + 27 \equiv (A + B)p^2 + (4A + B + C)p + (13A + C).$$

Since this is an identity, we equate powers of p to get

$$A + B = 1, \qquad 4A + B + C = 8, \qquad 13A + C = 27.$$

We solve these equations simultaneously to find $A = 2$, $B = -1$, $C = 1$. Then we have

$$Y = \frac{2}{p+1} + \frac{-p+1}{p^2 + 4p + 13} = \frac{2}{p+1} + \frac{3}{(p+2)^2 + 9} - \frac{p+2}{(p+2)^2 + 9},$$

and by L2, L13, and L14,

$$y = 2e^{-t} + e^{-2t} \sin 3t - e^{-2t} \cos 3t.$$

A set of simultaneous differential equations can also be solved by using Laplace transforms (if there is a solution; see Hildebrand, *Advanced Calculus for Engineers*, p. 80). Here is an example.

Example 4. Solve the set of equations

$$y' - 2y + z = 0,$$
$$z' - y - 2z = 0,$$

subject to the initial conditions $y_0 = 1$, $z_0 = 0$.

We shall call $L(z) = Z$ and $L(y) = Y$ as before. We take the Laplace transform of each of the equations to get

$$pY - y_0 - 2Y + Z = 0,$$
$$pZ - z_0 - Y - 2Z = 0.$$

After substituting the initial conditions and collecting terms, we have

$$(p - 2)Y + Z = 1,$$
$$Y - (p - 2)Z = 0.$$

We solve this set of algebraic equations simultaneously for Y and Z (by any of the methods usually used for a pair of simultaneous equations— elimination, determinants, etc.). For example, we may multiply the first equation by $(p - 2)$ and add the second to get

$$[(p - 2)^2 + 1]Y = p - 2 \qquad \text{or} \qquad Y = \frac{p-2}{(p-2)^2 + 1}.$$

We find y by looking up the inverse transform of Y using L14. We get

$$y = e^{2t} \cos t.$$

Similarly, solving for Z and looking up the inverse transform, we find

$$Z = \frac{1}{(p-2)^2 + 1},$$
$$z = e^{2t} \sin t.$$

Alternatively, we could find z from the first differential equation by substituting the y solution:

$$z = 2y - y' = 2e^{2t} \cos t + e^{2t} \sin t - 2e^{2t} \cos t = e^{2t} \sin t.$$

Solving linear differential equations with constant coefficients is not the only use of Laplace transforms. As you will see in Chapter 14, we may solve some kinds of partial differential equations by Laplace transforms. Also a table of Laplace transforms can be used to evaluate definite integrals of the type $\int_0^\infty e^{-pt} f(t)\, dt$. For example, by $L15$ with $a = 3$ and $p = 2$, we have

$$\int_0^\infty e^{-2t}(1 - \cos 3t)\, dt = \frac{3^2}{2(2^2 + 3^2)} = \frac{9}{26}.$$

Actually, there is more to the subject than this. Although we are discussing in this chapter the use of Laplace transforms as a tool, they also can play a more theoretical role in applied problems. It is often possible to find desired information about a problem directly from the Laplace transform of the solution without ever finding the solution. Thus the use of Laplace transforms may lead to a better understanding of a problem or a simpler method of solution. (Compare the use of matrices, for example, or the use of log-log paper.)

4. FOURIER TRANSFORMS

In Chapter 6, we expanded *periodic* functions in series of sines, cosines, and complex exponentials. Physically, we could think of the terms of these Fourier series as representing a set of harmonics. In music these would be an infinite set of frequencies nv, $n = 1, 2, 3, \ldots$; notice that this set, although infinite, does not by any means include all possible frequencies. In electricity, a Fourier series could represent a periodic voltage; again we could think of this as made up of an infinite but discrete (that is, not continuous) set of a-c voltages of frequencies $n\omega$. Similarly, in discussing light, a Fourier series could represent light consisting of a discrete set of wavelengths λ/n, $n = 1, 2, \ldots$, that is, a discrete set of colors. Two related questions might occur to us here. First, is it possible to represent a function which is *not* periodic by something analogous to a Fourier series? Second, can we somehow extend or modify Fourier series to cover the case of a continuous spectrum of wavelengths of light, or a sound wave containing a continuous set of frequencies?

If you recall that an integral is a limit of a sum, it may not surprise you very much to learn that the Fourier *series* (that is, a *sum* of terms) is replaced by a Fourier *integral* in the above cases. The Fourier integral can be used to represent nonperiodic functions, for example a single voltage pulse not repeated, or a flash of light, or a sound which is not repeated. The Fourier integral also represents a continuous set (spectrum) of frequencies, for example a whole range of musical tones or colors of light rather than a discrete set.

Recall from Chapter 6, Section 8, the following complex Fourier series formulas.

(4.1)
$$f(x) = \sum_{-\infty}^{\infty} c_n e^{in\pi x/l},$$

$$c_n = \frac{1}{2l} \int_{-l}^{l} f(x) e^{-in\pi x/l} \, dx.$$

The period of $f(x)$ is $2l$ and the frequencies of the terms in the series are $n/(2l)$. We now want to consider the case of continuous frequencies.

Definition of Fourier transforms. We state without proof the formulas corresponding to (4.1) for a continuous range of frequencies.

(4.2)
$$f(x) = \int_{-\infty}^{\infty} g(\alpha) e^{i\alpha x} \, d\alpha,$$

$$g(\alpha) = \frac{1}{2\pi} \int_{-\infty}^{\infty} f(x) e^{-i\alpha x} \, dx.$$

Compare (4.2) and (4.1); $g(\alpha)$ corresponds to c_n, α corresponds to n, and $\int_{-\infty}^{\infty}$ corresponds to $\sum_{-\infty}^{\infty}$. This agrees with our discussion of the physical meaning and use of Fourier integrals. The quantity α is a continuous analog of the integral-valued variable n, and so the set of coefficients c_n has become a function $g(\alpha)$; the sum over n has become an integral over α. The two functions $f(x)$ and $g(\alpha)$ are called a pair of *Fourier transforms*. Usually, $g(\alpha)$ is called the Fourier transform of $f(x)$, and $f(x)$ is called the inverse Fourier transform of $g(\alpha)$, but since the two integrals differ in form only in the sign in the exponent, it is rather common simply to call either a Fourier transform of the other. You should check the notation of any book or table you are using. Another point on which various books differ is the position of the factor $1/(2\pi)$ in (4.2); it is possible to have it multiply the $f(x)$ integral instead of the $g(\alpha)$ integral, or to have the factor $1/\sqrt{2\pi}$ multiply each of the integrals.

The *Fourier integral theorem* says that, if a function $f(x)$ satisfies the Dirichlet conditions (Chapter 6, Section 6) on every finite interval, and if $\displaystyle\int_{-\infty}^{\infty} |f(x)|\, dx$ is finite, then (4.2) is correct. That is, if $g(\alpha)$ is computed and substituted into the integral for $f(x)$ [compare the procedure of computing the c_n's for a Fourier series and substituting them into the series for $f(x)$], then the integral gives the value of $f(x)$ anywhere that $f(x)$ is continuous; at jumps of $f(x)$, the integral gives the midpoint of the jump (again compare Fourier series, Chapter 6, Section 6). The following discussion is not a mathematical proof of this theorem (for proof see Sneddon) but is intended to help you see more clearly how Fourier integrals are related to Fourier series.

It might seem reasonable to think of trying to represent a function which is not periodic by letting the period $(-l, l)$ increase to $(-\infty, \infty)$. Let us try to do this, starting with (4.1). If we call $n\pi/l = \alpha_n$ and $\alpha_{n+1} - \alpha_n = \pi/l = \Delta\alpha$, then $1/(2l) = \Delta\alpha/(2\pi)$ and (4.1) can be rewritten as

$$(4.3) \qquad f(x) = \sum_{-\infty}^{\infty} c_n e^{i\alpha_n x},$$

$$(4.4) \qquad c_n = \frac{1}{2l}\int_{-l}^{l} f(x)e^{-i\alpha_n x}\, dx = \frac{\Delta\alpha}{2\pi}\int_{-l}^{l} f(u)e^{-i\alpha_n u}\, du.$$

(We have changed the dummy integration variable in c_n from x to u to avoid later confusion.) Substituting (4.4) into (4.3), we have

$$
\begin{aligned}
f(x) &= \sum_{-\infty}^{\infty}\left[\frac{\Delta\alpha}{2\pi}\int_{-l}^{l} f(u)e^{-i\alpha_n u}\, du\right]e^{i\alpha_n x}\\[2mm]
(4.5)\qquad &= \sum_{-\infty}^{\infty}\frac{\Delta\alpha}{2\pi}\int_{-l}^{l} f(u)e^{i\alpha_n(x-u)}\, du = \frac{1}{2\pi}\sum_{-\infty}^{\infty} F(\alpha_n)\,\Delta\alpha,
\end{aligned}
$$

where

$$(4.6) \qquad F(\alpha_n) = \int_{-l}^{l} f(u)e^{i\alpha_n(x-u)}\, du.$$

Now $\displaystyle\sum_{-\infty}^{\infty} F(\alpha_n)\Delta\alpha$ looks rather like the formula in calculus for the sum whose limit, as $\Delta\alpha$ tends to zero, is an integral. If we let l tend to infinity [that is, let the period of $f(x)$ tend to infinity], then $\Delta\alpha = \pi/l \to 0$, and the sum $\displaystyle\sum_{-\infty}^{\infty} F(\alpha_n)\Delta\alpha$ goes over formally to $\displaystyle\int_{-\infty}^{\infty} F(\alpha)\, d\alpha$; we have dropped the subscript n on α now that it is a continuous variable. We also let l tend to infinity and $\alpha_n = \alpha$ in (4.6) to get

$$(4.7) \qquad F(\alpha) = \int_{-\infty}^{\infty} f(u)e^{i\alpha(x-u)}\, du.$$

Replacing $\sum\limits_{-\infty}^{\infty} F(\alpha_n)\Delta\alpha$ in (4.5) by $\int_{-\infty}^{\infty} F(\alpha)\, d\alpha$ and substituting from (4.7) for $F(\alpha)$ gives

(4.8)
$$f(x) = \frac{1}{2\pi}\int_{-\infty}^{\infty} F(\alpha)\, d\alpha = \frac{1}{2\pi}\int_{-\infty}^{\infty}\int_{-\infty}^{\infty} f(u)e^{i\alpha(x-u)}\, du\, d\alpha$$
$$= \frac{1}{2\pi}\int_{-\infty}^{\infty} e^{i\alpha x}\, d\alpha\int_{-\infty}^{\infty} f(u)e^{-i\alpha u}\, du.$$

If we define $g(\alpha)$ by

(4.9)
$$g(\alpha) = \frac{1}{2\pi}\int_{-\infty}^{\infty} f(x)e^{-i\alpha x}\, dx = \frac{1}{2\pi}\int_{-\infty}^{\infty} f(u)e^{-i\alpha u}\, du,$$

then (4.8) gives

(4.10)
$$f(x) = \int_{-\infty}^{\infty} g(\alpha)e^{i\alpha x}\, d\alpha.$$

These equations are the same as (4.2). Notice that the actual requirement for the factor $1/(2\pi)$ is that the *product* of the constants multiplying the two integrals for $g(\alpha)$ and $f(x)$ should be $1/(2\pi)$; this accounts for the fact that different books write the factors in various ways as we mentioned before.

Just as we have sine series representing odd functions and cosine series representing even functions (Chapter 6, Section 9), so we have sine and cosine Fourier integrals which represent odd or even functions respectively. Let us prove that if $f(x)$ is odd, then $g(\alpha)$ is odd too, and show that in this case (4.2) reduces to a pair of sine transforms. The corresponding proof for even $f(x)$ is similar (Problem 14). We substitute

$$e^{-i\alpha x} = \cos \alpha x - i \sin \alpha x$$

into (4.9) to get

(4.11)
$$g(\alpha) = \frac{1}{2\pi}\int_{-\infty}^{\infty} f(x)(\cos \alpha x - i \sin \alpha x)\, dx.$$

Since $\cos \alpha x$ is even and we are assuming that $f(x)$ is odd, the product $f(x)\cos \alpha x$ is odd. Recall that the integral of an odd function over a symmetric interval about the origin (here, $-\infty$ to $+\infty$) is zero, so the term $\int_{-\infty}^{\infty} f(x)\cos \alpha x\, dx$ in (4.11) is zero. The product $f(x)\sin \alpha x$ is even (product of two odd functions); recall that the integral of an even function over a symmetric interval is twice the integral over positive x.

Substituting these results into (4.11), we have

(4.12)
$$g(\alpha) = \frac{1}{2\pi} \int_{-\infty}^{\infty} f(x)(-i \sin \alpha x) \, dx$$

$$= -\frac{i}{\pi} \int_{0}^{\infty} f(x) \sin \alpha x \, dx.$$

From (4.12), we can see that replacing α by $-\alpha$ changes the sign of $\sin \alpha x$ and so changes the sign of $g(\alpha)$. That is, $g(-\alpha) = -g(\alpha)$ or $g(\alpha)$ is an odd function as we claimed. Then expanding the exponential in (4.10) and arguing as we did to obtain (4.12), we find

(4.13)
$$f(x) = \int_{-\infty}^{\infty} g(\alpha)e^{i\alpha x} \, d\alpha = \int_{-\infty}^{\infty} g(\alpha)(\cos \alpha x + i \sin \alpha x) \, d\alpha$$

$$= 2i \int_{0}^{\infty} g(\alpha) \sin \alpha x \, d\alpha.$$

If we substitute $g(\alpha)$ from (4.12) into (4.13) to obtain an equation like (4.8), the numerical factor is $(-i/\pi)(2i) = 2/\pi$; thus the imaginary factors are not needed. The factor $2/\pi$ may multiply either of the two integrals or each integral may be multiplied by $\sqrt{2/\pi}$. Let us make the latter choice in giving the following definition.

Fourier sine transforms. We define $f_s(x)$ and $g_s(\alpha)$, a pair of *Fourier sine transforms* representing *odd functions*, by the equations

(4.14)
$$f_s(x) = \sqrt{\frac{2}{\pi}} \int_{0}^{\infty} g_s(\alpha) \sin \alpha x \, d\alpha,$$

$$g_s(\alpha) = \sqrt{\frac{2}{\pi}} \int_{0}^{\infty} f_s(x) \sin \alpha x \, dx.$$

Fourier cosine transforms. We define $f_c(x)$ and $g_c(\alpha)$, a pair of *Fourier cosine transforms* representing *even functions*, in a similar way (Problem 14):

(4.15)
$$f_c(x) = \sqrt{\frac{2}{\pi}} \int_{0}^{\infty} g_c(\alpha) \cos \alpha x \, d\alpha,$$

$$g_c(\alpha) = \sqrt{\frac{2}{\pi}} \int_{0}^{\infty} f_c(x) \cos \alpha x \, dx.$$

Example. Let us represent a nonperiodic function as a Fourier integral. The function

$$f(x) = \begin{cases} 1, & -1 < x < 1, \\ 0, & |x| > 1, \end{cases}$$

shown in Fig. 4.1 might represent an impulse in mechanics (that is, a force applied only over a short time such as a bat hitting a baseball), or a sudden short surge of current in electricity, or a short pulse of sound or light which is not repeated. Since the given function is not periodic, it cannot be expanded in a Fourier *series*, since a Fourier series always represents a *periodic* function. Instead, we write $f(x)$ as a Fourier integral

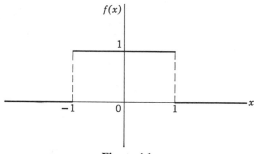

Figure 4.1

as follows. Using (4.9), we calculate $g(\alpha)$; this process is like finding the c_n's for a Fourier series. We find

(4.16)
$$g(\alpha) = \frac{1}{2\pi} \int_{-\infty}^{\infty} f(x)e^{-i\alpha x}\,dx = \frac{1}{2\pi} \int_{-1}^{1} e^{-i\alpha x}\,dx$$

$$= \frac{1}{2\pi} \frac{e^{-i\alpha x}}{-i\alpha}\Big|_{-1}^{1} = \frac{1}{\pi\alpha} \frac{e^{-i\alpha} - e^{i\alpha}}{-2i} = \frac{\sin \alpha}{\pi\alpha}.$$

We substitute $g(\alpha)$ in (4.16) into the formula (4.10) for $f(x)$ (this is like substituting the evaluated coefficients into a Fourier series). We get

(4.17)
$$f(x) = \int_{-\infty}^{\infty} \frac{\sin \alpha}{\pi\alpha} e^{i\alpha x}\,d\alpha$$

$$= \frac{1}{\pi} \int_{-\infty}^{\infty} \frac{\sin \alpha(\cos \alpha x + i \sin \alpha x)}{\alpha}\,d\alpha = \frac{2}{\pi} \int_{0}^{\infty} \frac{\sin \alpha \cos \alpha x}{\alpha}\,d\alpha$$

since $(\sin \alpha)/\alpha$ is an even function. We thus have an integral representing the function $f(x)$ shown in Fig. 4.1.

We can use (4.17) to evaluate a definite integral. We have

(4.18)
$$\int_{0}^{\infty} \frac{\sin \alpha \cos \alpha x}{\alpha}\,d\alpha = \frac{\pi}{2}f(x) = \begin{cases} \dfrac{\pi}{2} & \text{for } |x| < 1, \\[2mm] \dfrac{\pi}{4} & \text{for } |x| = 1, \\[2mm] 0 & \text{for } |x| > 1. \end{cases}$$

Notice that we have used the fact that the Fourier integral represents the midpoint of the jump in $f(x)$ at $|x| = 1$. If we let $x = 0$, we get

(4.19)
$$\int_0^\infty \frac{\sin \alpha}{\alpha}\, d\alpha = \frac{\pi}{2}.$$

(See Chapter 11, Section 7, Example 4, for another way of evaluating this integral.) Notice that we could have done this problem by observing that $f(x)$ is an even function and so can be represented by a cosine transform. The final results (4.17) to (4.19) would be just the same (Problem 15).

5. CONVOLUTION; PARSEVAL'S THEOREM

In solving differential equations by Laplace transforms in Section 3, we found Y and then looked in the table for the inverse transform y. If we were lucky, we found it; if not, and we were clever, we could sometimes obtain it from a combination of the given inverse transforms. However, we had no way of getting the inverse transform except to go backward from computed direct transforms. We want to consider in this section (and the next) more general ways of finding inverse transforms.

Let us first see why the method we are going to discuss in this section is useful. Consider differential equations of the kind discussed in Chapter 7, Sections 5 and 6, namely linear second-order equations with constant coefficients. Recall that such equations describe the vibrations or oscillations of either a mechanical or an electrical system. If the right-hand side of the equation is a function of t, called the *forcing function*, then the differential equation describes forced vibrations. Let us solve the following representative equation by Laplace transforms, assuming that the system is initially at rest and that the force $f(t)$ starts being applied at $t = 0$.

(5.1)
$$Ay'' + By' + Cy = f(t), \qquad y_0 = y_0' = 0.$$

We take the Laplace transform of each term, substitute the initial conditions, and solve for Y as follows.

(5.2)
$$Ap^2Y + BpY + CY = L(f) = F(p),$$

$$Y = \frac{1}{Ap^2 + Bp + C}\, F(p).$$

Note that Y is a product of two functions of p. We know the inverse transform of $F(p)$, namely $f(t)$. The factor

$$T(p) = \frac{1}{Ap^2 + Bp + C}$$

(called the *transfer function*) can always be written as

$$T(p) = \frac{1}{A(p + a)(p + b)}$$

by factoring the quadratic expression in the denominator. Hence by $L7$ (or $L6$ if $a = b$) we can find the inverse transform of $T(p)$ for any problem. Then y [the inverse transform of Y in (5.2)] is the inverse transform of a product of two functions whose inverse transforms we know. We are going to show how to write y as an integral (that is, we are going to verify $L34$ in the table).

Let $G(p)$ and $H(p)$ be the transforms of $g(t)$ and $h(t)$. We want the inverse transform of the product $G(p)H(p)$. By the definition (2.1)

$$(5.3) \qquad G(p)H(p) = \int_0^\infty e^{-pt}g(t)\, dt \cdot \int_0^\infty e^{-pt}h(t)\, dt.$$

Let us rewrite (5.3) replacing t by different dummy variables of integration so that we can write the product of the two integrals as a double integral. We then have

$$\begin{aligned} G(p)H(p) &= \int_0^\infty e^{-p\sigma}g(\sigma)\, d\sigma \cdot \int_0^\infty e^{-p\tau}h(\tau)\, d\tau \\ (5.4) \\ &= \int_0^\infty \int_0^\infty e^{-p(\sigma+\tau)}g(\sigma)h(\tau)\, d\sigma\, d\tau. \end{aligned}$$

Now we make a change of variables; in the σ integral (that is, with τ fixed), let $\sigma + \tau = t$. Then $\sigma = t - \tau$, $d\sigma = dt$, and the range of integration with respect to t is from $t = \tau$ (corresponding to $\sigma = 0$) to $t = \infty$ (corresponding to $\sigma = \infty$). Making these substitutions in (5.4), we get

$$(5.5) \qquad G(p)H(p) = \int_{\tau=0}^\infty \int_{t=\tau}^\infty e^{-pt}g(t - \tau)h(\tau)\, dt\, d\tau.$$

Next we want to change the order of integration. From Fig. 5.1, we see that the double integral in (5.5) is over the triangle in the first quadrant below the line $t = \tau$. The t integral ranges from the line $t = \tau$ to $t = \infty$ (indicated by a horizontal strip of width $d\tau$ from $t = \tau$ to ∞) and then the τ integral sums over the horizontal strips from $\tau = 0$ to $\tau = \infty$ covering the whole infinite triangle. Let us integrate with respect to τ first; τ then ranges from 0 to the line $\tau = t$ [indicated by a vertical strip in Fig. 5.1] and then the t integral sums over the vertical strips from

$t = 0$ to ∞. Making this change in (5.5), we get

(5.6)
$$
\begin{aligned}
G(p)H(p) &= \int_{t=0}^{\infty} \int_{\tau=0}^{t} e^{-pt} g(t - \tau) h(\tau)\, d\tau\, dt \\
&= \int_{0}^{\infty} e^{-pt} \left[\int_{0}^{t} g(t - \tau) h(\tau)\, d\tau \right] dt \\
&= L\left[\int_{0}^{t} g(t - \tau) h(\tau)\, d\tau \right].
\end{aligned}
$$

The last step follows from the definition (2.1) of a Laplace transform.

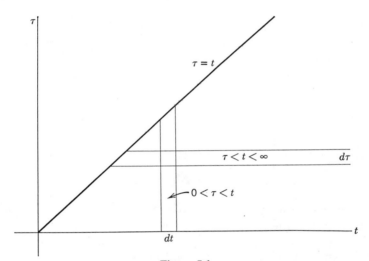

Figure 5.1

Definition of convolution. The integral

(5.7)
$$
\int_{0}^{t} g(t - \tau) h(\tau)\, d\tau = g * h
$$

is called the *convolution* of g and h (or the *resultant* or the *Faltung*); note the abbreviation $g * h$ for the convolution integral, and do not confuse the symbol $*$, written *on* the line, with a star used as a superscript meaning complex conjugate. It is easy to show (Problem 23) that $g * h = h * g$; this result and (5.6) and (5.7) give $L34$ in the table.

Now let us see how to use (5.6) or $L34$ to solve the kind of problem indicated in (5.1) and (5.2).

Example. Solve $y'' + 3y' + 2y = e^{-t}$, $y_0 = y_0' = 0$.

Taking the Laplace transform of each term, substituting the initial conditions, and solving for Y, we get

$$p^2 Y + 3pY + 2Y = L(e^{-t}),$$

$$Y = \frac{1}{p^2 + 3p + 2} L(e^{-t}).$$

Since we are intending to use the convolution integral, we do not bother to look up the transform of e^{-t}. We do want, however, the inverse transform of $1/(p^2 + 3p + 2)$; by $L7$, this is $e^{-t} - e^{-2t}$, so we have

$$Y = L(e^{-t} - e^{-2t})L(e^{-t}) = G(p)H(p),$$

with $g(t) = e^{-t} - e^{-2t}$ and $h(t) = e^{-t}$. We now use $L34$ to find y. Observe from $L34$ that we may use either $g(t - \tau)h(\tau)$ or $g(\tau)h(t - \tau)$ in the integral. It is well to choose whichever form is easier to integrate; usually it is best to put $(t - \tau)$ in the simpler function [here $h(t)$]. Then we have

$$y = \int_0^t g(\tau)h(t - \tau)\, d\tau = \int_0^t (e^{-\tau} - e^{-2\tau})e^{-(t-\tau)}\, d\tau$$

$$= e^{-t}\int_0^t (1 - e^{-\tau})\, d\tau = e^{-t}(\tau + e^{-\tau})\Big|_0^t$$

$$= e^{-t}(t + e^{-t} - 1) = te^{-t} + e^{-2t} - e^{-t}.$$

It is not always as easy to evaluate the convolution integral as it was in this example. However, let us observe that, at the very worst, we can always write the solution to a forced vibrations problem [equation (5.1)] as an integral (which can, if necessary, be evaluated numerically). This is true because, as we showed just after (5.2), we can always find the inverse transform of the transfer function $T(p)$, and so have Y as a product of two functions whose inverse transforms we know. Then y is given by the convolution (5.7) of the forcing function $f(t)$ and the inverse transform of the transfer function. Also note (Problem 24) that a combination of $L6$, $L7$, and $L8$ will handle any terms arising in a problem with nonzero initial conditions.

Fourier transform of a convolution. We have shown that the Laplace transform of the convolution of two functions is the product of their Laplace transforms. There is a similar theorem for Fourier transforms; let us see what it says. Let $g_1(\alpha)$ and $g_2(\alpha)$ be the Fourier transforms of $f_1(x)$ and $f_2(x)$. By analogy with equations (5.3), (5.4), (5.5), and (5.6), we might expect the product $g_1(\alpha) \cdot g_2(\alpha)$ to be the Fourier transform of something. Let us investigate this idea. By the definition (4.2) of a Fourier transform, we have

(5.8)
$$g_1(\alpha) \cdot g_2(\alpha) = \frac{1}{2\pi} \int_{-\infty}^{\infty} f_1(v)e^{-i\alpha v}\, dv \cdot \frac{1}{2\pi} \int_{-\infty}^{\infty} f_2(u)e^{-i\alpha u}\, du$$

$$= \left(\frac{1}{2\pi}\right)^2 \int_{-\infty}^{\infty}\int_{-\infty}^{\infty} e^{-i\alpha(v+u)}f_1(v)f_2(u)\, dv\, du.$$

[We have used different dummy integration variables as in (5.4).] Next we make the change of variables $x = v + u$, $dx = dv$, in the v integral, to get

(5.9)
$$g_1(\alpha)g_2(\alpha) = \left(\frac{1}{2\pi}\right)^2 \int_{-\infty}^{\infty}\int_{-\infty}^{\infty} e^{-i\alpha x}f_1(x-u)f_2(u)\, dx\, du$$

$$= \left(\frac{1}{2\pi}\right)^2 \int_{-\infty}^{\infty} e^{-i\alpha x}\left[\int_{-\infty}^{\infty} f_1(x-u)f_2(u)\, du\right] dx.$$

If we define the convolution of $f_1(x)$ and $f_2(x)$ by

(5.10)
$$f_1 * f_2 = \int_{-\infty}^{\infty} f_1(x-u)f_2(u)\, du, \dagger$$

then (5.9) becomes

(5.11)
$$g_1 \cdot g_2 = \frac{1}{2\pi}\left[\frac{1}{2\pi}\int_{-\infty}^{\infty} f_1 * f_2 e^{-i\alpha x}\, dx\right]$$

$$= \frac{1}{2\pi} \cdot \text{Fourier transform of } f_1 * f_2.$$

In other words,

(5.12) $g_1 \cdot g_2$ and $\dfrac{1}{2\pi} f_1 * f_2$ are a pair of Fourier transforms.

Because of the symmetry of the $f(x)$ and $g(\alpha)$ integrals, there is a similar result relating $f_1 \cdot f_2$ and the convolution of g_1 and g_2. We find that (Problem 28)

(5.13) $g_1 * g_2$ and $f_1 \cdot f_2$ are a pair of Fourier transforms.

[As discussed after (4.2) and after (4.10), the position of the factor $1/(2\pi)$ differs from book to book. Some authors include factors of $1/(2\pi)$ or $1/\sqrt{2\pi}$ in the convolution definition (5.10); this definition as well as (4.2) affects (5.12) and (5.13). Check the notation in any book you are using.]

Parseval's theorem.   Let us use our results to prove Parseval's theorem for Fourier integrals. Recall (Chapter 6, Section 11) that Parseval's

---

† Note that (5.10) is really the same as (5.7) since in our work with Laplace transforms we agreed that our functions were to be zero for negative t; thus in (5.7) $h(\tau) = 0$ for $\tau < 0$ and $g(t - \tau) = 0$ for $\tau > t$, so the integral would not really be different if written with infinite limits (in fact, it is sometimes written that way).

theorem for a Fourier series $f(x) = \sum\limits_{n=-\infty}^{\infty} c_n e^{in\pi x/l}$ relates $\int_{-l}^{l} |f|^2\, dx$ and $\sum\limits_{n=-\infty}^{\infty} |c_n|^2$. In physical applications (see Chapter 6, Section 11), Parseval's theorem says that the total energy (say in a sound wave, or in an electrical signal) is equal to the sum of the energies associated with the various harmonics. Remember that a Fourier integral represents a continuous spectrum of frequencies and that $g(\alpha)$ corresponds to c_n. Then we might expect that $\sum\limits_{n=-\infty}^{\infty} |c_n|^2$ would be replaced by $\int_{-\infty}^{\infty} |g(\alpha)|^2\, d\alpha$ (that is, a "sum" over a continuous rather than a discrete spectrum) and that Parseval's theorem would relate $\int_{-\infty}^{\infty} |f|^2\, dx$ and $\int_{-\infty}^{\infty} |g|^2\, d\alpha$. This is correct; let us find the relation.

First we need to know the Fourier transform of $\bar{f}(x)$ [complex conjugate of $f(x)$] if $g(\alpha)$ is the transform of $f(x)$. We have by (4.2)

$$(5.14) \qquad g(\alpha) = \frac{1}{2\pi} \int_{-\infty}^{\infty} f(x) e^{-i\alpha x}\, dx.$$

Taking the complex conjugate of (5.14), we get

$$\bar{g}(\alpha) = \frac{1}{2\pi} \int_{-\infty}^{\infty} \bar{f}(x) e^{i\alpha x}\, dx.$$

Next replacing α by $-\alpha$, we have

$$(5.15) \qquad \bar{g}(-\alpha) = \frac{1}{2\pi} \int_{-\infty}^{\infty} \bar{f}(x) e^{-i\alpha x}\, dx$$

which we recognize by (5.14) as the Fourier transform of $\bar{f}(x)$. Hence the Fourier transform of $\bar{f}(x)$ is $\bar{g}(-\alpha)$. In (5.13), let us replace $f_1(x)$ by $\bar{f}_1(x)$, and $g_1(\alpha)$ by the transform of $\bar{f}_1(x)$, namely [by (5.15)] $\bar{g}_1(-\alpha)$. Then (5.13) says that if

$$f(x) = \bar{f}_1(x) f_2(x) \qquad \text{and} \qquad g(\alpha) = \bar{g}_1(-\alpha) * g_2(\alpha),$$

then $f(x)$ and $g(\alpha)$ are a pair of Fourier transforms. Using (5.14) and the definition (5.10) of a convolution, we have

$$g(\alpha) = \bar{g}_1(-\alpha) * g_2(\alpha) = \int_{-\infty}^{\infty} \bar{g}_1[-(\alpha - \beta)] g_2(\beta)\, d\beta$$

$$= \frac{1}{2\pi} \int_{-\infty}^{\infty} f(x) e^{-i\alpha x}\, dx = \frac{1}{2\pi} \int_{-\infty}^{\infty} \bar{f}_1(x) f_2(x) e^{-i\alpha x}\, dx.$$

Letting $\alpha = 0$, we get

$$(5.16) \qquad \int_{-\infty}^{\infty} \bar{g}_1(\beta) g_2(\beta)\, d\beta = \frac{1}{2\pi} \int_{-\infty}^{\infty} \bar{f}_1(x) f_2(x)\, dx.$$

This is a generalized form of Parseval's theorem (see Problem 35, Chapter 6). If $f_1 = f_2 = f$ and $g_1 = g_2 = g$, we have the result we expected, namely

(5.17) $$\int_{-\infty}^{\infty} |g(\alpha)|^2 \, d\alpha = \frac{1}{2\pi} \int_{-\infty}^{\infty} |f(x)|^2 \, dx.$$

6. INVERSE LAPLACE TRANSFORM (BROMWICH INTEGRAL)

In Section 3, we were completely dependent on our table of Laplace transforms to find inverse transforms. In Section 5, we discussed one method of finding inverse transforms, but this covered only the one special case of a product of two functions whose inverse transforms we knew. By analogy with Fourier transforms, where we have similar integrals for the direct and inverse transforms, we might reasonably wonder whether an inverse Laplace transform could be given by an integral. If we compare the Laplace transform (2.1) with the Fourier transform [$g(\alpha)$ in (4.2)], we observe that if p were imaginary, the integrals would be almost the same. This suggests that we should consider complex p, and that the integral we want for the inverse Laplace transform might be an integral in the complex p-plane (that is, a contour integral). Let us investigate this idea.

In the definition (2.1) of the Laplace transform of $f(t)$, let p be complex, say $p = z = x + iy$. (Note that this possibility has already been considered in Section 2.) Then (2.1) becomes

(6.1)
$$F(p) = F(z) = F(x + iy) = \int_0^{\infty} e^{-pt} f(t) \, dt$$
$$= \int_0^{\infty} e^{-(x+iy)t} f(t) \, dt = \int_0^{\infty} e^{-xt} f(t) e^{-iyt} \, dt, \qquad x = \operatorname{Re} p > k.$$

[Recall that we must have some restriction on $\operatorname{Re} p$ to make the integral converge at infinity—see (2.2) and (2.3), for example. The restriction depends on what the function $f(t)$ is, but is always of the form $\operatorname{Re} p > k$, for *some* real k, as you can see in the table of Laplace transforms.] Now (6.1) is of the form of a Fourier transform. To see this, compare (6.1) with (4.2) making the following correspondences: $e^{-iyt} \, dt$ corresponds to $e^{-i\alpha x} \, dx$, that is, y corresponds to α and t to x [the x in (6.1) is just a constant parameter in this discussion]; the function,

(6.2) $$\phi(t) = \begin{cases} e^{-xt} f(t), & t > 0, \\ 0, & t < 0, \end{cases}$$

corresponds to $f(x)$ in (4.2) and $F(p) = F(x + iy)$ corresponds to $g(\alpha)$; and finally we recall that the $1/(2\pi)$ factor may be in either integral in (4.2). Then, assuming that $\phi(t)$ satisfies the required conditions for a function to have a Fourier transform (see Section 4: Dirichlet conditions, and $\int_{-\infty}^{\infty} |\phi(t)| \, dt$ finite), we can write the inverse transform to get

$$(6.3) \qquad \phi(t) = \frac{1}{2\pi} \int_{-\infty}^{\infty} F(x + iy)e^{iyt} \, dy.$$

Using the definition (6.2) of $\phi(t)$, we find

$$(6.4) \quad f(t) = e^{xt} \cdot \frac{1}{2\pi} \int_{-\infty}^{\infty} F(x + iy)e^{iyt} \, dy = \frac{1}{2\pi} \int_{-\infty}^{\infty} F(x + iy)e^{(x+iy)t} \, dy$$

for $t > 0$. Since x is constant, say $x = c$, we have $dz = d(x + iy) = i \, dy$, and we can write (6.4) as

$$(6.5) \qquad f(t) = \frac{1}{2\pi i} \int_{c-i\infty}^{c+i\infty} F(z)e^{zt} \, dz, \qquad t > 0,$$

where the notation means (see Chapter 11, Problem 9) that we integrate along a vertical line $x = c$ in the z-plane. [This can be *any* vertical line on which $x = c > k$ as required by the restriction on Re p in (6.1).] The integral (6.5) for the inverse Laplace transform is known as the *Bromwich integral*.

Now let us consider an example of the use of (6.5) in evaluating $f(t)$ for a given $F(p)$ [which we call $F(z)$ since we consider complex p]. You may recall from Chapter 11 that it is often convenient to evaluate integrals in the complex plane by using the residue theorem. Now the integral in (6.5) is along a vertical line. We evaluated integrals along a straight line, namely the x-axis, in Chapter 11, Section 7, Examples 2 and 3, by considering the contour made up of the x-axis and a large semicircle inclosing the upper half plane. If we should rotate this contour 90°, we would have a contour consisting of a vertical straight line and a semicircle inclosing a left half-plane (that is, the area to the left of $x = c$). Let us consider evaluating (6.5) by using this contour. We restrict $F(z)$ to be of the form $[P(z)/Q(z)]e^{-az}$, $a > 0$, with $P(z)$ and $Q(z)$ polynomials, and $Q(z)$ of degree at least one higher than $P(z)$ (compare the conditions in Example 3, Section 7 of Chapter 11). Then it can be shown that, as in the Chapter 11 examples, the integral along the semicircle tends to zero as the radius tends to infinity. Thus the integral along the straight line is equal to $2\pi i$ times the sum of the residues of $F(z)e^{zt}$ at its poles, or, canceling the factor $2\pi i$ in (6.5),

$$(6.6) \qquad f(t) = \text{sum of residues of } F(z)e^{zt} \text{ at all poles.}$$

We must include *all* poles in (6.6); to see this we can argue as follows. We know that (6.5) is correct for any value of $c > k$. Suppose we use a value of c which is large enough so that all poles lie to the left of $x = c$; then we know our answer is correct. Turning the argument around, we can say that since we would get a different answer if we did not take $x = c$ to the right of all poles, we *must* integrate along a vertical line such that all poles of $F(z)e^{zt}$ are included in the contour to the left of the line.

Example. Find the inverse transform of $F(p) = 1/[(p + a)(p^2 + b^2)]$. We first find the poles of $F(z)e^{zt}$ and factor the denominator to get

$$F(z)e^{zt} = \frac{e^{zt}}{(z + a)(z + ib)(z - ib)}.$$

Evaluating the residues at the three simple poles (see Chapter 11, Section 6, method B), we find

$$\text{residue at } z = -a \quad \text{is} \quad \frac{e^{-at}}{a^2 + b^2},$$

$$\text{residue at } z = ib \quad \text{is} \quad \frac{e^{ibt}}{(a + ib)(2ib)},$$

$$\text{residue at } z = -ib \quad \text{is} \quad \frac{e^{-ibt}}{(a - ib)(-2ib)}.$$

Then by (6.6) we have

$$f(t) = \frac{e^{-at}}{a^2 + b^2} + \frac{a(e^{ibt} - e^{-ibt}) - ib(e^{ibt} + e^{-ibt})}{(a^2 + b^2)(2ib)}$$

$$= \frac{e^{-at}}{a^2 + b^2} + \frac{a \sin bt}{b(a^2 + b^2)} - \frac{\cos bt}{a^2 + b^2}.$$

7. THE DIRAC DELTA FUNCTION

In mechanics we consider the idea of an impulsive force such as a hammer blow which lasts for a very short time. We usually do not know the exact shape of the force function $f(t)$, and so we proceed as follows. Let the impulsive force $f(t)$ lasting from $t = t_0$ till $t = t_1$ be applied to a mass m; then by Newton's second law we have

$$(7.1) \qquad \int_{t_0}^{t_1} f(t)\, dt = \int_{t_0}^{t_1} m\, \frac{dv}{dt}\, dt = \int_{v_0}^{v_1} m\, dv = m(v_1 - v_0).$$

This says that the integral of $f(t)$ [called the impulse of $f(t)$] is equal to the change in the momentum of m, and we note that the result is independent of the shape of $f(t)$ but depends only on the area under the $f(t)$

curve. If this area is 1, we call the impulse a *unit impulse*. If $t_1 - t_0$ is very small, we may simply ignore the motion of m during this small time, and say only that the momentum jumped from mv_0 to mv_1 during the time $t_1 - t_0$. If $v_0 = 0$, the graph of the momentum as a function of time would be as in Fig. 7.1, where we have simply omitted the (unknown) part of the graph between t_0 and t_1. We note that if $t_1 - t_0$ is very small, the graph in Fig. 7.1 is almost the unit step function ($L24$). Let us imagine making $t_1 - t_0$ smaller and smaller while keeping the jump in mv always 1.

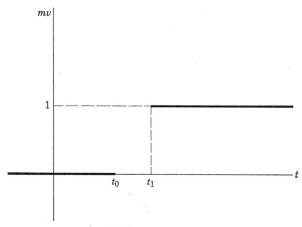

Figure 7.1

In Figs. 7.2, 7.3, and 7.4 we have sketched some possible sequences of functions $f_n(t)$ which would do this (for simplicity in writing formulas we have taken $t_0 = 0$ in Figs. 7.3 and 7.4). We could draw many other similar sets of graphs; the essential requirement is that $f(t)$ should become taller and narrower (that is, that the force should become more intense but act over a shorter time) in such a way that the impulse [area under the $f(t)$ curve] remains 1. We might then consider the limiting case in which Fig. 7.1 has a jump of 1 at t_0; the force $f(t)$ required to produce this result would have to be infinite and act instantaneously. Also, from equation (7.1), we see that the function $f(t)$ is the slope of the mv graph; thus we are asking for $f(t)$ to be the derivative of a step function at the jump. We see immediately that no ordinary function has these properties. However, we also note that we are not so much interested in $f(t)$ as in the results it produces. Figure 7.1 with a jump at t_0 makes perfectly good sense; for any $t > t_0$ we could choose a sufficiently tall and narrow $f_n(t)$ so that mv would already have its final value. We shall see that it is convenient to introduce a symbol $\delta(t - t_0)$ to represent the force which produces a jump of 1 in mv at t_0; $\delta(t - t_0)$ is called the _Dirac delta function_ although it is not an ordinary function as we have seen. (It may properly be called a generalized function and is one of a whole class of such functions; see, for example, Lighthill.) Introducing and using this symbol is much like introducing and using the symbol ∞. It is convenient to write equations

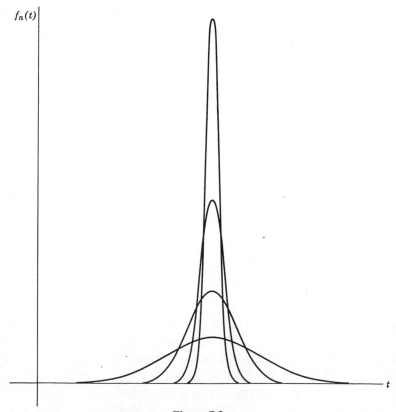

Figure 7.2

like $1/\infty = 0$, but we must not write $\infty/\infty = 1$; that is, such symbolic equations must be abbreviations for correct limiting processes. We must investigate, then, how we can use the δ function correctly.

Consider the differential equation

(7.2) $$y'' + \omega^2 y = f(t), \qquad y_0 = y_0' = 0.$$

This equation might describe the oscillations of a mass suspended by a spring, or a simple series electric circuit with negligible resistance. Let us assume that the system is initially at rest ($y_0 = y_0' = 0$); then suppose that, at $t = 0$, the mass is struck a sharp blow, or a sudden short surge of current is sent through the electric circuit. The function $f(t)$ may be one of those shown in Figs. 7.2 to 7.4 or another similar function. Let us solve (7.2) with $f(t)$ equal to one of the functions in Fig. 7.4, that is,

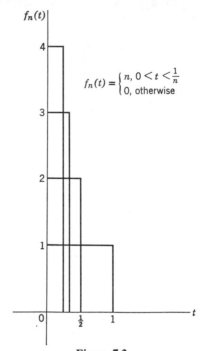

$$f_n(t) = \begin{cases} n, & 0 < t < \frac{1}{n} \\ 0, & \text{otherwise} \end{cases}$$

Figure 7.3

$f(t) = ne^{-nt}$. Using Laplace transforms, we find

(7.3)
$$(p^2 + \omega^2)Y = L(ne^{-nt}) = n \cdot \frac{1}{p + n},$$

$$Y = n \cdot \frac{1}{(p + n)(p^2 + \omega^2)}.$$

The example at the end of Section 6 gives the inverse transform (put $a = n$, $b = \omega$)

(7.4)
$$y = n\left(\frac{e^{-nt}}{n^2 + \omega^2} + \frac{n \sin \omega t}{(n^2 + \omega^2)\omega} - \frac{\cos nt}{n^2 + \omega^2}\right).$$

By making $f(t)$ sufficiently narrow and peaked (that is, by making n large enough), we can make the first and third terms in y negligible, and the

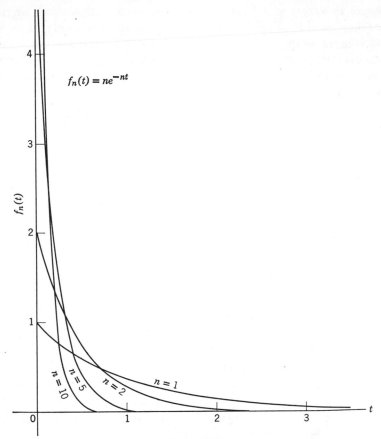

Figure 7.4

coefficient of $\sin \omega t$ approximately equal to $1/\omega$. Thus the solution is approximately

(7.5) $$y = \frac{1}{\omega} \sin \omega t$$

for a unit impulse of very short duration at $t = 0$. (We have shown this only for the functions of Fig. 7.4; however, the same result would be found for other sets of functions, such as those in Fig. 7.3, for example— see Problem 33.)

Now we would like to be able to find (7.5) without finding (7.4), in fact, without specifying the functions $f_n(t)$. Our discussion above suggests that we try using the symbol $\delta(t)$ for $f(t)$ on the right-hand side of (7.2). In solving the equation, we would then like to take the Laplace transform of $\delta(t)$.

Laplace transform of a δ function.   Let us investigate whether we can make sense out of the Laplace transform of $\delta(t)$. More generally, let us try to attach meaning to the integral $\int \phi(t)\, \delta(t - t_0)\, dt$, where $\phi(t)$ is any continuous function and $\delta(t - t_0)$ is the symbol indicating an impulse at t_0. We consider the integrals $\int \phi(t) f_n(t - t_0)\, dt$, where the functions $f_n(t - t_0)$ are more and more strongly peaked at t_0 as n increases (Fig. 7.5), but the area under each graph is 1. When $f_n(t - t_0)$ is so narrow that $\phi(t)$ is essentially constant [equal to $\phi(t_0)$] over the width of $f_n(t - t_0)$, the integral

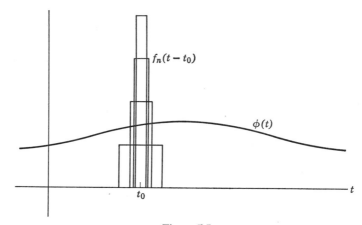

Figure 7.5.

becomes nearly $\phi(t_0) \int f_n(t - t_0)\, dt = \phi(t_0) \cdot 1 = \phi(t_0)$; that is, the sequence of integrals $\int \phi(t) f_n(t - t_0)\, dt$ tends to $\phi(t_0)$ as n tends to infinity. It then seems reasonable to say that

$$(7.6) \qquad \int \phi(t)\, \delta(t - t_0)\, dt = \phi(t_0)$$

provided the range of integration includes t_0. Equation (7.6) might well be called the defining property of the δ function; whenever we operate with δ functions, we always use them in integrals using (7.6).

We can now easily find the Laplace transform of $\delta(t)$. In the notation used in $L27$ (which we are about to derive), we have, using (2.1),

$$(7.7) \qquad L[\delta(t - a)] = \int_0^\infty \delta(t - a) e^{-pt}\, dt = e^{-pa}, \qquad a > 0,$$

since, by (7.6), the integral of the product of $\delta(t - a)$ and a function "picks out" the value of the function at $t = a$. Now let us use our results to obtain (7.5) more easily.

Example. Solve

(7.8) $$y'' + \omega^2 y = \delta(t), \qquad y_0 = y_0' = 0.$$

Taking Laplace transforms and using (7.7), we get

(7.9) $$(p^2 + \omega^2)Y = L(\delta(t)) = 1$$

since $e^{-pa} = 1$ if $a = 0$. Then

(7.10) $$Y = \frac{1}{p^2 + \omega^2}$$

and, by $L3$,

(7.11) $$y = \frac{1}{\omega} \sin \omega t$$

as in (7.5).

Fourier transform of a δ function. Using (4.2) and (7.6), we may write

(7.12) $$g(\alpha) = \frac{1}{2\pi} \int_{-\infty}^{\infty} \delta(x - a)e^{-i\alpha x}\, dx = \frac{1}{2\pi} e^{-i\alpha a}.$$

Formally, then, (4.2) would give for the inverse transform

(7.13) $$\delta(x - a) = \frac{1}{2\pi} \int_{-\infty}^{\infty} e^{i\alpha(x-a)}\, d\alpha.$$

We say "formally" because the integral in (7.13) does not converge. However, if we replace the limits $-\infty$, ∞ by $-n$, n, we obtain a set of functions (Problem 36) which, like the functions $f_n(t)$ in Figs. 7.2 to 7.4, are increasingly peaked around $x = a$ as n increases, but all have area 1. In this sense, then, (7.13) is a representation of the δ function. Equations (7.12) and (7.13) are useful in quantum mechanics.

REFERENCES

The following are useful references on the subjects indicated.

Laplace transforms: Holl, Maple, and Vinograde; LePage; Spiegel; Thomson.

Fourier transforms: Sneddon.

Fourier and Laplace transforms (operational methods): Churchill, Kaplan.

Integral transform tables: Erdélyi.

Fourier transform tables: Oberhettinger.

Delta functions: Jones, Lighthill.

For less detailed discussions, see other books in the list of references at the end of the book identified as Chapter 13 references by a [13] after the listing.

PROBLEMS

1. Using the definition of the Γ function (Chapter 9, Section 3), verify $L5$ and $L6$ in the Laplace transform table. Show that $L(1/\sqrt{t}) = \sqrt{\pi/p}$.

2. By using $L2$, verify $L7$ and $L8$ in the Laplace transform table.

3. Using either $L2$, or $L3$ and $L4$, verify $L9$ and $L10$.

4. (a) By differentiating the appropriate formula with respect to a, verify $L12$.
   (b) By integrating the appropriate formula with respect to a, verify $L19$.

5. By replacing a in $L2$ by $a + ib$ and then by $a - ib$, and adding and subtracting the results [as in (2.6) and (2.7)], verify $L13$ and $L14$.

6. (a) Verify $L15$, $L16$, $L17$, and $L18$, by combining appropriate preceding formulas using (2.4).
   (b) Show that a combination of entries $L3$ to $L10$, $L13$, $L14$, and $L18$ in the table, will give the inverse transform of any function of the form

$$\frac{(Ap + B)}{(Cp^2 + Dp + E)}.$$

As examples, find the inverse transforms of

$$\frac{1 + p}{(p + 2)^2}, \qquad \frac{5 - 2p}{p^2 + p - 2}, \qquad \frac{2p - 1}{p^2 - 2p + 10}.$$

Hints: For the second example, use $L7$ and $L8$. For the third, you *can* use $L7$ and $L8$ with complex a and b, but $L13$ and $L14$ are more direct.)

7. (a) Prove the general formula $L29$ using (2.1).
   (b) Use $L29$ to verify $L6$, $L13$, $L14$, and $L18$.
   (c) Use $L29$ and $L11$ to obtain $L(te^{-at} \sin bt)$ which is not in the table.
   (d) Prove $L32$ for $n = 1$. (*Hint:* Integrate by parts.) Then use $L32$ with $L13$ to check your answer in (c).
   (e) Obtain $L(te^{-at} \cos bt)$ as in (c) or (d) and use your results with (c) to find the inverse transform of $(p^2 + 2p - 1)/(p^2 + 4p + 5)^2$.

8. (a) Using $L28$ and $L4$, find the inverse transform of $pe^{-pb}/(p^2 + a^2)$.
   (b) Find the transform of $f(t) = \begin{cases} \sin(x - vt), & t > x/v, \\ 0, & t < x/v, \end{cases}$ where x and v are constants.

9. (a) Use $L31$ to derive $L21$.
   (b) Use $L34$ and $L2$ to find the inverse transform of $G(p)H(p)$ when $G(p) = 1/(p + a)$ and $H(p) = 1/(p + b)$; your result should be $L7$.

10. Continuing the method used in deriving (3.1) and (3.2), verify the Laplace transforms of higher-order derivatives of y given in the table ($L35$).

11. By using Laplace transforms, solve the following differential equations subject to the given initial conditions.

(a) $y'' - 4y = 4e^{2t}$, $y_0 = 0$, $y_0' = 1$.

(b) $y' - y = 2e^t$, $y_0 = 3$.

(c) $y'' - y = e^{-t} - 2te^{-t}$, $y_0 = 1$, $y_0' = 2$.

(d) $y'' + y = 5 \sinh 2t$, $y_0 = 0$, $y_0' = 2$.

(e) $y'' + y = \sin t$, $y_0 = 1$, $y_0' = 0$.

(f) $y'' - 4y' = -4te^{2t}$, $y_0 = 0$, $y_0' = 1$.

(g) $y'' + 4y' + 4y = e^{-2t}$, $y_0 = 0$, $y_0' = 4$.

(h) $y'' + 5y' + 6y = 12$, $y_0 = 2$, $y_0' = 0$.

(i) $y'' - 4y = 3e^{-t}$, $y_0 = 1$, $y_0' = -3$.

(j) $y'' + 16y = 8 \cos 4t$, $y_0 = y_0' = 0$.

(k) $y'' + 16y = 8 \cos 4t$, $y_0 = 0$, $y_0' = 8$.

(l) $y'' + 2y' + 5y = 10 \cos t$, $y_0 = 0$, $y_0' = 3$.

(m) $y'' + y' - 5y = e^{2t}$, $y_0 = 1$, $y_0' = 2$.

12. Solve the following sets of equations by the Laplace transform method.

(a) $y' + z' - 3z = 0$, $y_0 = y_0' = 0$,
    $y'' + z' = 0$, $z_0 = \frac{4}{3}$.

(b) $y' + z = 2 \cos t$, $y_0 = -1$,
    $z' - y = 1$, $z_0 = 1$.

(c) $y' + z' - 2y = 1$, $y_0 = z_0 = 1$.
    $z - y' = t$,

(d) $y' + 2z = 1$, $y_0 = 0$,
    $2y - z' = 2t$, $z_0 = 1$.

13. Evaluate each of the following definite integrals by using the Laplace transform table.

(a) $\int_0^\infty e^{-2t} \sin 3t \, dt = \frac{3}{13}$.

Hint: This is (2.1) with $p = 2$, $f(t) = \sin 3t$; use L3 with $a = 3$.

(b) $\int_0^\infty te^{-t} \sin 5t \, dt$.

(c) $\int_0^\infty \frac{\sin 2t \, e^{-3t}}{t} \, dt$.

(d) $\int_0^\infty t^5 e^{-2t} \, dt$.

(e) $\int_0^\infty tJ_0(2t)e^{-t} \, dt$.

(f) $\int_0^\infty \frac{e^{-t} - e^{-2t}}{t} \, dt$.

(g) $f(t) = \int_0^\infty \sin(t - \tau)e^{-\tau} \, d\tau$.

Hint for (g): In L34, let $g(t) = \sin t$ and $h(t) = e^{-t}$, and find $G(p)H(p)$ which is the Laplace transform of the integral you want. Break the result into partial fractions and look up the inverse transforms.

14. Following a method similar to that used in obtaining equations (4.11) to (4.14), show that if $f(x)$ is even, then $g(\alpha)$ is even too. Show that in this case $f(x)$ and $g(\alpha)$ can be written as Fourier cosine transforms and obtain (4.15).

15. Do the example at the end of Section 4 by using cosine transforms (4.15). Obtain (4.17).

16. Let $f(x) = \begin{cases} -1, & -1 < x < 0, \\ +1, & 0 < x < 1. \end{cases}$

   (a) Sketch the *periodic* function of period 2 which is equal to $f(x)$ on $(-1, 1)$. Expand this periodic function in an exponential Fourier *series* and in a Fourier sine *series*. Verify that your results are the same.

   (b) Sketch the *nonperiodic* function which is equal to $f(x)$ on $(-1, 1)$ and is zero for $|x| > 1$. Find the exponential Fourier transform of this function [that is, find $g(\alpha)$ from (4.2)]. Hence represent $f(x)$ as a Fourier integral [that is, substitute your $g(\alpha)$ into (4.10)].

   (c) Since $f(x)$ in (b) is an odd function, it can be represented as a Fourier sine transform. Do this [use (4.14)] and verify that your result is the same as in (b).

   (d) Using your result in either (b) or (c), show that

$$\int_0^\infty \frac{(1 - \cos \alpha) \sin \alpha x}{\alpha} \, d\alpha = \begin{cases} \pi/2, & 0 < x < 1, \\ \pi/4, & x = 1, \\ 0, & x > 1 \quad \text{and} \quad x = 0, \end{cases}$$

and the negatives of these values for corresponding negative x.

17. Let $f(x)$ be defined by $f(x) = \begin{cases} x, & |x| < 1, \\ 0, & |x| > 1. \end{cases}$

   (a) Find the exponential Fourier transform of $f(x)$ [that is, find $g(\alpha)$]. Hence represent $f(x)$ as a Fourier integral [that is, substitute your $g(\alpha)$ into (4.10)].

   (b) Find the same result as in (a) by using sine transforms (4.14).

   (c) From (a) or (b) and (17.4) of Chapter 12, show that

$$\int_0^\infty \sin \alpha x \, j_1(\alpha) \, d\alpha = \begin{cases} \dfrac{\pi x}{2}, & -1 < x < 1, \\ 0, & |x| > 1. \end{cases}$$

18. (a) Find the exponential Fourier transform of $f(x) = e^{-|x|}$ and write the inverse transform. You should find

$$\int_0^\infty \frac{\cos \alpha x}{\alpha^2 + 1} \, d\alpha = \frac{\pi}{2} e^{-|x|}.$$

(b) Also obtain the result in (a) by using the Fourier cosine transform equations (4.15).

(c) Find the Fourier cosine transform of $f(x) = 1/(1 + x^2)$. *Hint:* Write your result in (b) with x and α interchanged.

19. (a) Represent as an exponential Fourier transform the function

$$f(x) = \begin{cases} \sin x, & 0 < x < \pi, \\ 0, & \text{otherwise.} \end{cases}$$

Hint: Write $\sin x$ in complex exponential form.

(b) Show that your result can be written as

$$f(x) = \frac{1}{\pi} \int_0^\infty \frac{\cos \alpha x + \cos \alpha(x - \pi)}{1 - \alpha^2} \, d\alpha.$$

20. Let $f(x)$ be defined by the graph. Represent $f(x)$ by a Fourier cosine transform.

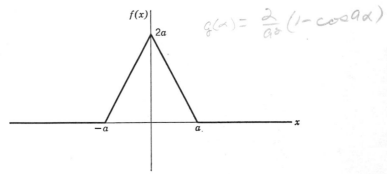

$$g(\alpha) = \frac{2}{a\alpha^2}(1 - \cos a\alpha)$$

21. Let $f(x) = \begin{cases} \cos x, & -\pi/2 < x < \pi/2, \\ 0, & |x| > \pi/2. \end{cases}$

Represent $f(x)$ by a Fourier exponential transform and reduce your result to a Fourier cosine transform. (See hint in 19a.)

22. Find the Fourier transform of $f(x) = e^{-x^2/(2\sigma^2)}$. *Hint:* Complete the square in the x terms in the exponent and make the change of variable $y = x + \sigma^2 i\alpha$. See Chapter 9, equation (9.5), to evaluate the definite integral.

23. Make the substitution $u = t - \tau$ in (5.7) to show that $g * h = h * g$ as claimed in $L34$.

24. Consider solving an equation like (5.1) but with nonzero initial conditions.

(a) Write the corrected form of (5.2), writing the transfer function in factored form as indicated just after (5.2). Consider the extra terms in Y which arise from the initial conditions; show that the inverse transforms of such terms can always be found from $L6$, $L7$, and $L8$.

(b) Find the explicit form of the inverse transform of the transfer function for $a \neq b$ (use $L7$), and so write the general solution of (5.2) with nonzero initial conditions as a convolution integral plus the terms which you found in (a).

25. Solve the differential equation $y'' - a^2 y = f(t)$, where

$$f(t) = \begin{cases} 0, & t < 0, \\ 1, & t > 0, \end{cases} \quad \text{and} \quad y_0 = y_0' = 0.$$

Hint: Use the convolution integral as in the example of Section 5.

26. Use the convolution integral to find the inverse transforms of

(a) $\dfrac{p}{(p^2 - 1)^2} = \dfrac{p}{p^2 - 1} \cdot \dfrac{1}{p^2 - 1}$,

(b) $\dfrac{p}{(p^2 + a^2)(p^2 + b^2)}$,

(c) $\dfrac{1}{p(p^2 + a^2)(p^2 + b^2)}$.

Hint for (b) *and* (c)*:* $2 \sin \theta \cos \phi = \sin(\theta + \phi) + \sin(\theta - \phi)$.

27. A mechanical or electrical system is described by the differential equation $y'' + \omega^2 y = f(t)$. Find y if

$$f(t) = \begin{cases} 1, & 0 < t < a, \\ 0, & \text{otherwise,} \end{cases} \quad \text{and} \quad y_0 = y_0' = 0.$$

Hint: Use the convolution integral carefully. Consider $t < a$ and $t > a$ separately, remembering that $f(t) = 0$ for $t > a$. Show that

$$y = \begin{cases} \dfrac{1}{\omega^2} (1 - \cos \omega t), & t < a, \\ \dfrac{1}{\omega^2} [\cos \omega(t - a) - \cos \omega t], & t > a. \end{cases}$$

Sketch the motion if $a = \frac{1}{3}T$ where T is the period for free vibrations of the system; if $a = \frac{3}{2}T$; if $a = \frac{1}{10}T$.

28. Following the method of equations (5.8) to (5.12), show that $f_1 f_2$ and $g_1 * g_2$ are a pair of Fourier transforms.

29. Verify Parseval's theorem (5.17) for the following special cases.
   (a) $f(x)$ as in Fig. 4.1. *Hint:* Integrate by parts and use (4.18) to evaluate

$$\int_{-\infty}^{\infty} |g(\alpha)|^2 \, d\alpha.$$

   (b) $f(x)$ and $g(\alpha)$ as in Problem 18a.
   (c) $f(x)$ and $g(\alpha)$ as in Problem 22.

30. (a) Show that if (4.2) is written with the factor $1/\sqrt{2\pi}$ multiplying each integral, then the corresponding form of Parseval's theorem (5.17) is

$$\int_{-\infty}^{\infty} |f(x)|^2 \, dx = \int_{-\infty}^{\infty} |g(\alpha)|^2 \, d\alpha.$$

(b) Starting with the symmetrized integrals as in (a), make the substitutions $\alpha = 2\pi p/h$ (p is the new variable, h is a constant), $f(x) = \psi(x)$, $g(\alpha) = \sqrt{h/2\pi}\phi(p)$; show that then

$$\psi(x) = \frac{1}{\sqrt{h}} \int_{-\infty}^{\infty} \phi(p)e^{2\pi i p x/h} \, dp,$$

$$\phi(p) = \frac{1}{\sqrt{h}} \int_{-\infty}^{\infty} \psi(x)e^{-2\pi i p x/h} \, dx,$$

$$\int_{-\infty}^{\infty} |\psi(x)|^2 \, dx = \int_{-\infty}^{\infty} |\phi(p)|^2 \, dp.$$

This notation is often used in quantum mechanics.

(c) Normalize $f(x)$ in Problem 22; that is, find the factor N so that $\int_{-\infty}^{\infty} |Nf(x)|^2 = 1$. Let $\psi(x) = Nf(x)$, and find $\phi(p)$ as given in part (b). Verify Parseval's theorem, that is, show that $\int_{-\infty}^{\infty} |\phi(p)|^2 \, dp = 1$.

31. Find the inverse Laplace transforms of the following functions by using (6.6).

(a) $\dfrac{p^3}{p^4 + 4}$ [*Hint:* Use (6.2) of Chapter 11.]

(b) $\dfrac{(p - 1)^2}{p(p + 1)^2}$

(c) $\dfrac{p}{p^4 - 1}$

(d) $\dfrac{p^2}{(p^2 - 1)(p^2 - 4)}$

(e) $\dfrac{p}{(p + 1)(p^2 + 4)}$

32. Show that $\int_{-\infty}^{\infty} f_n(t) \, dt = 1$ for the functions $f_n(t)$ in Figs. 7.3 and 7.4.

33. Solve the differential equation $y'' + \omega^2 y = f(t)$, $y_0 = y_0' = 0$, with $f(t)$ given by the functions in Fig. 7.3 (see hint in Problem 27). Let $n \to \infty$ and show that your solution tends to the same solution (7.5) obtained using the functions of Fig. 7.4; that is, either set of functions gives, in the limit, the same solution (7.11) obtained using the δ function.

34. (a) Let a mechanical or electrical system be described by the differential equation $Ay'' + By' + Cy = f(t)$, $y_0 = y_0' = 0$. As in Problem 24b, write the solution as a convolution (assume $a \neq b$). Let $f(t)$ be one of the functions in Fig. 7.3 and Problem 33. Find y and then let $n \to \infty$.

(b) Also solve the problem with $f(t) = \delta(t)$; your result should be the same as in (a).

(c) The solution y as found in (a) and (b) is called the *response* of the system to a unit impulse. Show that the response of a system to a unit impulse is the inverse Laplace transform of the transfer function.

35. Using the δ function method, find the response (see Problem 34c) of each of the following systems to a unit impulse.

(a) $y'' + 2y' + y = \delta(t)$

→(b) $y'' + 4y' + 5y = \delta(t)$

(c) $y'' + 2y' + 10y = \delta(t)$

→(d) $y'' - 9y = \delta(t)$.

36. Evaluate the functions $f_n(x - a)$ defined by the integral in (7.13) with limits $-n$, n. Show that $\displaystyle\int_{-\infty}^{\infty} f_n(x - a)\, dx = 1$ for all n. Sketch graphs of several f_n's to show that as n increases, the functions $f_n(x)$ are increasingly peaked around $x = a$, and that as $|x - a|$ increases, they oscillate with decreasing amplitude.

14

Partial Differential Equations

1. INTRODUCTION

Many of the problems of mathematical physics involve the solution of partial differential equations. The same partial differential equation may apply to a variety of physical problems; thus the mathematical methods which you will learn in this chapter apply to many more problems than those we shall discuss in the illustrative examples. Let us outline the partial differential equations we shall consider, and the kinds of physical problems which lead to each of them.

(1.1) **Laplace's equation** $\nabla^2 u = 0.$

The function u may be the gravitational potential in a region containing no matter, the electrostatic potential in a charge-free region, the steady-state temperature (that is, temperature not changing with time) in a region containing no source of heat, or the velocity potential for an incompressible fluid with no vortices and no sources or sinks.

(1.2) **Poisson's equation** $\nabla^2 u = f(x, y, z).$

The function u may represent the same physical quantities listed for Laplace's equation, but in a region containing matter, electric charge, or sources of heat or fluid, respectively, for the various cases. The function $f(x, y, z)$ is called the source density; for example, in electricity it is proportional to the density of electric charge.

(1.3)   The diffusion or heat flow equation $\nabla^2 u = \dfrac{1}{\alpha^2} \dfrac{\partial u}{\partial t}$.

Here u may be the non-steady-state temperature (that is, temperature varying with time) in a region with no heat sources; or it may be the concentration of a diffusing substance (for example, a chemical, or particles such as neutrons). The quantity α^2 is a constant known as the diffusivity.

(1.4)   Wave equation $\nabla^2 u = \dfrac{1}{v^2} \dfrac{\partial^2 u}{\partial t^2}$.

Here u may represent the displacement from equilibrium of a vibrating string or membrane or (in acoustics) of the vibrating medium (gas, liquid, or solid); in electricity u may be the current or potential along a transmission line; or u may be a component of $\mathbf{E}$ or $\mathbf{H}$ in an electromagnetic wave (light, radio waves, etc.). The quantity v is the speed of propagation of the waves; for example, for light waves in a vacuum it is c, the velocity of light, and for sound waves it is the speed at which sound travels in the medium under consideration.

(1.5)   Helmholtz equation $\nabla^2 F + k^2 F = 0$.

As you will see later, the function F here represents the space part (that is, the time-independent part) of the solution of either the diffusion or the wave equation.

We shall be principally concerned with the solution of these equations rather than their derivation. If you like, you could say that it is true experimentally that the physical quantities mentioned above satisfy the given equations. However, it is also true that the equations can be derived from somewhat simpler experimental assumptions. Let us indicate briefly an example of how this can be done. In Chapter 5, Sections 12 and 13, we considered the flow of fluid. With $\mathbf{V} = \rho\mathbf{v}$, where ρ is the density and $\mathbf{v}$ the velocity of the fluid, we showed that $\nabla \cdot \mathbf{V} = 0$ for an incompressible fluid in a region containing no sources or sinks. If it is also true that there are no vortices (that is, the flow is irrotational), then curl $\mathbf{V} = 0$, and $\mathbf{V}$ can be written as the gradient of a scalar function: $\mathbf{V} = \nabla u$. Combining these two equations, we have $\nabla \cdot \nabla u = \nabla^2 u = 0$. The function u is called the velocity potential and we see that (under the given conditions) it satisfies Laplace's equation as we claimed.

We shall next consider a number of physical problems to illustrate the very useful method of solving partial differential equations known as *separation of variables.* The examples will also show how to solve equations of the kinds listed above when we use various coordinate systems (rectangular, spherical, etc.). At the end of the chapter, we shall consider the solution of partial differential equations by integral transforms.

2. LAPLACE'S EQUATION; STEADY-STATE TEMPERATURE IN A RECTANGULAR PLATE

We want to solve the following problem: A long rectangular metal plate has its two long sides and the far end at 0° and the base at 100° (Fig. 2.1). The width of the plate is 10 cm. Find the steady-state temperature distribution inside the plate.

To simplify the problem, we shall assume at first that the plate is so long compared to its width that we may make the mathematical approximation that it extends to infinity in the y direction. It is then called a semi-infinite plate. This is a good assumption if we are interested in temperatures not too near the far end.

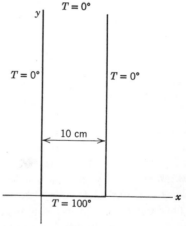

The temperature T satisfies Laplace's equation inside the plate where there are no sources of heat, that is,

(2.1)

$$\nabla^2 T = 0 \quad \text{or} \quad \frac{\partial^2 T}{\partial x^2} + \frac{\partial^2 T}{\partial y^2} = 0.$$

We have written ∇^2 in rectangular coordinates because the boundary of the plate is rectangular and we have

Figure 2.1

omitted the z term because the plate is in two dimensions. To solve this equation, we are going to *try* a solution of the form

(2.2) $T(x, y) = X(x) Y(y),$

where, as indicated, X is a function only of x, and Y is a function only of y. Immediately you may raise the question: But how do we know that the solution is of this form? The answer is that it is not! However, as you will see, once we have solutions of the form (2.2) we can combine them to get the solution we want. [Note that a sum of solutions of (2.1) is a solution of (2.1).] Substituting (2.2) into (2.1), we have

(2.3)
$$Y \frac{d^2 X}{dx^2} + X \frac{d^2 Y}{dy^2} = 0.$$

(Ordinary instead of partial derivatives are now correct since X depends only on x, etc.) Divide (2.3) by XY to get

(2.4)
$$\frac{1}{X} \frac{d^2 X}{dx^2} + \frac{1}{Y} \frac{d^2 Y}{dy^2} = 0.$$

The next step is really the key to the process of *separation of variables*. We are going to say that each of the terms in (2.4) is a constant because the first term is a function of x alone and the second term is a function of y alone. Why is this correct? Recall that when we say $y = \sin x$ is a *solution* of $y'' = -y$, we mean it satisfies the differential equation identically, that is, for every x. Although we speak of an *equation*, when we substitute the solution into a differential equation, we have an *identity* in the independent variable. (We made use of this fact in series solutions of differential equations in Chapter 12.) In (2.1) to (2.4) we have two independent variables, x and y. Saying that (2.2) is a solution of (2.1) means that (2.4) is an identity in the two independent variables x and y [recall that (2.4) was obtained by substituting (2.2) into (2.1)]. In other words, if (2.2) is a solution of (2.1), then (2.4) must be true for any and all values of the two independent variables x and y. Since X is a function only of x and Y of y, the first term of (2.4) is a function only of x and the second term is a function only of y. Suppose we substitute a particular x into the first term; that term is then some numerical constant. To have (2.4) satisfied, the second term must be minus the same constant. While x remains fixed, let y vary (remember that x and y are independent).We have said that (2.4) is an identity; it is then true for our fixed x and *any* y. Thus the second term remains constant as y varies. Similarly, if we fix y and let x vary, we see that the first term of (2.4) is a constant. To say this more concisely, the equation $f(x) = g(y)$, with x and y independent variables, is an identity only if both functions are the same constant; this is the basis of the process of separation of variables. From (2.4) we then write

(2.5)
$$\frac{1}{X} \frac{d^2 X}{dx^2} = -\frac{1}{Y} \frac{d^2 Y}{dy^2} = \text{const.} = -k^2, \quad \text{or}$$
$$X'' = -k^2 X \quad \text{and} \quad Y'' = k^2 Y.$$

The constant k^2 is called the *separation constant*. The solutions of (2.5) are

(2.6)
$$X = \begin{cases} \sin kx, \\ \cos kx, \end{cases} \quad Y = \begin{cases} e^{ky}, \\ e^{-ky}, \end{cases}$$

and the solutions of (2.1) of the form (2.2) are

(2.7)
$$T = XY = \begin{cases} e^{ky} \sin kx, \\ e^{-ky} \sin kx, \\ e^{ky} \cos kx, \\ e^{-ky} \cos kx. \end{cases}$$

None of these four basic solutions satisfies the given boundary temperatures. What we must do now is to take a combination of the solutions (2.7), with the constant k properly selected, which *will* satisfy the given boundary conditions. [Any linear combination of solutions of (2.1) is a solution of (2.1) because the differential equation (2.1) is *linear*; see Chapter 7, Sections 1 and 6.] We first discard the solutions containing e^{ky} since we are given $T \to 0$ as $y \to \infty$. (We are assuming $k > 0$; see Problem 4.) Next we discard solutions containing $\cos kx$ since $T = 0$ when $x = 0$. This leaves us just $e^{-ky} \sin kx$, but the value of k is still to be determined. When $x = 10$, we are to have $T = 0$; this will be true if $\sin(10k) = 0$, that is, if $k = n\pi/10$ for $n = 1, 2, \ldots$. Thus for any integral n, the solution

(2.8)
$$T = e^{-n\pi y/10} \sin \frac{n\pi x}{10}$$

satisfies the given boundary conditions on the three $T = 0$ sides.

Finally, we must have $T = 100$ when $y = 0$; this condition is not satisfied by (2.8) for any n. But a linear combination of solutions like (2.8) is a solution of (2.1); let us try to find such a combination which does satisfy $T = 100$ when $y = 0$. In order to allow all possible n's we write an infinite series for T, namely

(2.9)
$$T = \sum_{n=1}^{\infty} b_n e^{-n\pi y/10} \sin \frac{n\pi x}{10}.$$

For $y = 0$, we must have $T = 100$; from (2.9) with $y = 0$ we get

(2.10)
$$T_{y=0} = \sum_{n=1}^{\infty} b_n \sin \frac{n\pi x}{10} = 100.$$

But this is just the Fourier sine series (Chapter 6, Section 9) for $f(x) = 100$ with $l = 10$. We can find the coefficients b_n as we did in Chapter 6; we get
(2.11)

$$b_n = \frac{2}{l} \int_0^l f(x) \sin \frac{n\pi x}{l} \, dx = \frac{2}{10} \int_0^{10} 100 \sin \frac{n\pi x}{10} \, dx$$

$$= 20 \cdot \frac{10}{n\pi} \left(-\cos \frac{n\pi x}{10} \right) \Big|_0^{10} = -\frac{200}{n\pi} [(-1)^n - 1] = \begin{cases} \dfrac{400}{n\pi}, & \text{odd } n, \\ 0, & \text{even } n. \end{cases}$$

Then (2.9) becomes

$$(2.12) \qquad T = \frac{400}{\pi}\left(e^{-\pi y/10}\sin\frac{\pi x}{10} + \frac{1}{3}e^{-3\pi y/10}\sin\frac{3\pi x}{10} + \cdots\right).$$

This is the final solution; we have found a function $T(x, y)$ which satisfies (2.1) and all the given boundary conditions. It is an experimental fact (and it can also be proved mathematically) that there is only one $T(x, y)$ satisfying Laplace's equation and the given boundary conditions; therefore (2.12) is the solution.

Equation (2.12) can be used for computation if $\pi y/10$ is not too small since then the series converges rapidly. (See also Problem 6a.) For example at $x = 5$ (central line of the plate) and $y = 5$, we find

$$
\begin{aligned}
T &= \frac{400}{\pi}\left(e^{-\pi/2}\sin\frac{\pi}{2} + \frac{1}{3}e^{-3\pi/2}\sin\frac{3\pi}{2} + \cdots\right) \\
&= \frac{400}{\pi}(0.208 - 0.003 + \cdots) = 26.1°.
\end{aligned}
$$

(2.13)

If the temperature on the bottom edge is any function $f(x)$ instead of $100°$ (with the other three sides at $0°$ as before), we can do the problem by the same method. We have only to expand the given $f(x)$ in a Fourier sine series and substitute the coefficients into (2.9).

If we want to consider the finite plate, we must not discard the solutions (2.7) containing e^{ky}. Instead of using just e^{-ky} we take a linear combination of e^{-ky} and e^{ky} which is zero at the top edge of the plate. For example, if the plate is 30 cm long (and 10 cm wide, as before) we may use the combination $e^{-ky} + Ae^{ky}$ with A determined to make the combination zero at $y = 30$. Thus we want $e^{-30k} + Ae^{30k} = 0$ or $A = -e^{-60k}$. Then in place of $e^{-ky}\sin kx$ from (2.7) we use $(e^{-ky} - e^{-60k}e^{ky})\sin kx$; we proceed as before to find $k = n\pi/10$ and to find a series solution of the problem. The result is (Problem 6)

$$(2.14) \qquad T = \sum_{\text{odd } n}\frac{400}{n\pi(1 - e^{-6n\pi})}(e^{-n\pi y/10} - e^{-6n\pi}e^{n\pi y/10})\sin\frac{n\pi x}{10}.$$

Note that we could just as well have used any constant times the combination $(e^{-ky} - e^{-60k}e^{ky})$, say

$$e^{30k}(e^{-ky} - e^{-60k}e^{ky}) = e^{30k}e^{-ky} - e^{-30k}e^{ky};$$

the Fourier series coefficients would then contain compensating factors so that the result would still be (2.14).

It may have occurred to you to wonder why we took the constant in (2.5) to be $-k^2$ and what would happen if we took $+k^2$ instead. As far as getting solutions of the differential equation is concerned it would be perfectly correct to use $+k^2$; we would get instead of (2.7):

(2.15)
$$T = XY = \begin{cases} e^{kx} \sin ky, \\ e^{-kx} \sin ky, \\ e^{kx} \cos ky, \\ e^{-kx} \cos ky. \end{cases}$$

[We are assuming that k is real; an imaginary k in (2.15) would simply give combinations of the solutions (2.7) over again. Also see Problem 4.] The solutions (2.15) would not be of any use for the problem we have just done since none of them tends to zero as $y \to \infty$, and a linear combination of e^{kx} and e^{-kx} cannot be zero both at $x = 0$ and at $x = 10$. However, if we had considered a semi-infinite plate with its long sides parallel to the x-axis instead of the y-axis, and $T = 100°$ along the short end on the y-axis, the solutions (2.15) would have been the ones needed. Or, for the finite plate, if the $100°$ side were along the y-axis, then we would want (2.15).

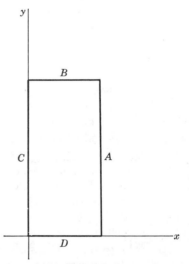

Figure 2.2

Finally, let us see how to find the temperature distribution in a plate if two adjacent sides are held at $100°$ and the other two at $0°$ (or, in general, if any values are given for the four sides). We can find the solution to this problem by a combination of the results we have already obtained. Let us call the sides of the rectangular plate A, B, C, D (Fig. 2.2). If sides A, B, and C are held at $0°$, and D at $100°$, we can find the temperature distribution by the same method we used in finding (2.14) if we take the x-axis along D. Next suppose that for the same plate (Fig. 2.2) sides A, B, and D are held at $0°$ and C at $100°$. This is the same kind of problem over again, but this time we want to use the basic solutions (2.15). [Or to shortcut the work, we could write the solution like (2.14) with the x-axis taken along C and then interchange x and y in the result to agree with Fig. 2.2.] Having obtained the two solutions (one for C at $100°$ and one for D at $100°$), let us add these two answers. The result is a solution of the differential equation (2.1) (linearity: the sum of any two solutions is a solution). The temperatures on the boundary (as well as inside) are the sums of the temperatures in the two solutions we added, that is, $0°$ on A,

$0°$ on B, $0° + 100°$ on C, and $100° + 0°$ on D. These are the given boundary conditions we wanted to satisfy. Thus the sum of the solutions of two simple problems gives the answer to the more complicated one.

Before solving more problems, let us stop for a moment to summarize this process of separation of variables which is basically the same for all the partial differential equations we shall discuss. We first assume a solution which is a product of functions of the independent variables [like (2.2)], and separate the partial differential equation into several ordinary differential equations [like (2.5)]. We solve these ordinary differential equations; the solutions may be exponential functions, trigonometric functions, powers (positive or negative), Bessel functions, Legendre polynomials, etc. Any linear combination of these basic solutions, with any values of the separation constants, is a solution of the differential equation. The problem is to determine both the values of the separation constants and the correct linear combination to fit the given boundary or initial conditions.

The problem of finding the solution of a given differential equation subject to given boundary conditions is called a *boundary value problem*. Such problems often lead to *eigenvalue problems*. Recall (Chapter 3, Problem 22, and Chapter 12, end of Section 2) that in an eigenvalue (or characteristic value) problem, there is a parameter whose values are to be selected so that the solutions of the problem meet some given requirements. The separation constants we have been using are just such parameters; their values are determined by demanding that the solutions satisfy some of the boundary conditions. [For example, we found $k = n\pi/10$ just before (2.8) by requiring that $T = 0$ when $x = 10$.] The resulting values of the separation constants are called *eigenvalues* and the basic solutions of the differential equation [for example, (2.8)] corresponding to the eigenvalues are called *eigenfunctions*. It may also happen that in addition to the separation constants there is a parameter in the original partial differential equation (see, for example, the Schrödinger equation in Problem 36). Again, the possible values of this parameter for which the equation has solutions meeting specified requirements, are called eigenvalues, and the corresponding solutions are called eigenfunctions.

3. THE DIFFUSION OR HEAT FLOW EQUATION; HEAT FLOW IN A BAR OR SLAB

The heat flow equation is

$$(3.1) \qquad \nabla^2 u = \frac{1}{\alpha^2} \frac{\partial u}{\partial t},$$

where u is the temperature and α^2 is a constant characteristic of the material through which the heat is flowing. It is worth while to do first a partial separation of (3.1) into a space equation and a time equation; the space equation in more than one dimension then must be further separated into ordinary differential equations in x and y, or x, y, and z, or r, θ, ϕ, etc. We assume a solution of (3.1) of the form

$$(3.2) \qquad\qquad u = F(x, y, z)T(t).$$

(Note the change in meaning of T; we have previously used it for temperature; here u is temperature and T is the time-dependent factor in u.) Substitute (3.2) into (3.1); we get

$$(3.3) \qquad\qquad T\nabla^2 F = \frac{1}{\alpha^2} F \frac{dT}{dt}.$$

Next divide (3.3) by FT to get

$$(3.4) \qquad\qquad \frac{1}{F}\nabla^2 F = \frac{1}{\alpha^2}\frac{1}{T}\frac{dT}{dt}.$$

The left side of this identity is a function only of the space variables x, y, z, and the right side is a function only of time. Therefore both sides are the same constant and we can write

$$\frac{1}{F}\nabla^2 F = -k^2 \qquad \text{or} \quad \nabla^2 F + k^2 F = 0 \qquad \text{and}$$

$$(3.5)$$

$$\frac{1}{\alpha^2}\frac{1}{T}\frac{dT}{dt} = -k^2 \qquad \text{or} \quad \frac{dT}{dt} = -k^2\alpha^2 T.$$

The time equation can be integrated to give

$$(3.6) \qquad\qquad T = e^{-k^2\alpha^2 t}.$$

We can see a physical reason here for choosing the separation constant $(-k^2)$ to be negative. As t increases, the temperature of a body might decrease to zero as in (3.6), but it could not increase to infinity as it would if we had used $+k^2$ in (3.5) and (3.6). The space equation in (3.5) is the Helmholtz equation (1.5) as promised. You will find (Problem 11) that the space part of the wave equation is also the Helmholtz equation.

Let us now consider the flow of heat through a slab of thickness l (for example, the wall of a refrigerator). We shall assume that the faces of the slab are so large that we may neglect any end effects and assume that heat flows only in the x direction. This problem is then identical with the problem of heat flow in a bar of length l with insulated sides, because in

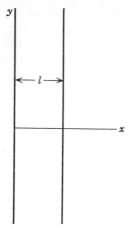

Figure 3.1

both cases the heat flow is just in the x direction. Suppose the slab has initially a steady-state temperature distribution with the $x = 0$ wall at $0°$ and the $x = l$ wall at $100°$. From $t = 0$ on, let the $x = l$ wall (as well as the $x = 0$ wall) be held at $0°$. We want to find the temperature at any x (in the slab) at any later time.

First, we find the initial steady-state temperature distribution. You probably already know that this is linear, but it is interesting to see this from our equations. The initial steady-state temperature u_0 satisfies Laplace's equation, which in this one-dimensional case is $\dfrac{d^2u_0}{dx^2} = 0$. The solution of this equation is $u_0 = ax + b$, where a and b are constants which must be found to fit the given conditions. Since $u_0 = 0$ at $x = 0$ and $u_0 = 100$ at $x = l$, we have

$$(3.7) \qquad\qquad u_0 = \frac{100}{l}\,x. \qquad \text{before } t = 0$$

From $t = 0$ on, u satisfies the heat flow equation (3.1). We have already separated this; the solutions are (3.2) where $T(t)$ is given by (3.6) and $F(x)$ satisfies the first of equations (3.5), namely

$$(3.8) \qquad \nabla^2 F + k^2 F = 0 \qquad \text{or} \qquad \frac{d^2F}{dx^2} + k^2 F = 0.$$

(For this one-dimensional problem, F is a function only of x.) The solutions of (3.8) are

$$(3.9) \qquad\qquad F(x) = \begin{cases} \sin kx, \\ \cos kx, \end{cases}$$

and the basic solutions (3.2) are

$$(3.10) \qquad\qquad u = \begin{cases} e^{-k^2\alpha^2 t}\sin kx, \\ e^{-k^2\alpha^2 t}\cos kx. \end{cases}$$

We discard the $\cos kx$ solution for this problem because we are given $u = 0$ at $x = 0$. Also we want $u = 0$ at $x = l$; this will be true if $\sin kl = 0$, that is, $kl = n\pi$, or $k = n\pi/l$ (eigenvalues). Our basic solutions (or eigenfunctions) are then

$$(3.11) \qquad\qquad u = e^{-(n\pi\alpha/l)^2 t}\sin\frac{n\pi x}{l}$$

and the solution of our problem will be the series

$$(3.12) \qquad u = \sum_{n=1}^{\infty} b_n e^{-(n\pi\alpha/l)^2 t} \sin \frac{n\pi x}{l}.$$

At $t = 0$, we want $u = u_0$ as in (3.7), that is,

$$(3.13) \qquad u = \sum_{n=1}^{\infty} b_n \sin \frac{n\pi x}{l} = u_0 = \frac{100}{l} x.$$

This means finding the Fourier sine series for $(100/l)x$ on $(0, l)$; the result (from Problem 5) for the coefficients is

$$(3.14) \qquad b_n = \frac{100}{l} \frac{2l}{\pi} \frac{1}{n} (-1)^{n-1} = \frac{200}{\pi} \frac{(-1)^{n-1}}{n}.$$

Then we get the final solution by substituting (3.14) into (3.12); this gives

(3.15)

$$u = \frac{200}{\pi} \left[e^{-(\pi\alpha/l)^2 t} \sin \frac{\pi x}{l} - \frac{1}{2} e^{-(2\pi\alpha/l)^2 t} \sin \frac{2\pi x}{l} + \frac{1}{3} e^{-(3\pi\alpha/l)^2 t} \sin \frac{3\pi x}{l} + \cdots \right].$$

We can now do some variations of this problem. Suppose the final temperatures of the faces are given as two different constant values different from zero. Then, as for the initial steady state, the final steady state is a linear function of distance. The series (3.12) tends to a final steady state of zero; to obtain a solution tending to some other final steady state, we add to (3.12) the linear function u_f representing the correct final steady state. Thus we write instead of (3.12)

$$(3.16) \qquad u = \sum_{n=1}^{\infty} b_n e^{-(n\pi\alpha/l)^2 t} \sin \frac{n\pi x}{l} + u_f.$$

Then for $t = 0$, the equation corresponding to (3.13) is

$$(3.17) \qquad u_0 = \sum_{n=1}^{\infty} b_n \sin \frac{n\pi x}{l} + u_f$$

or

$$(3.18) \qquad u_0 - u_f = \sum_{n=1}^{\infty} b_n \sin \frac{n\pi x}{l}.$$

Thus when $u_f \neq 0$, it is $u_0 - u_f$ rather than u_0 which must be expanded in a Fourier series.

So far we have had the boundary temperatures given. We could, instead, have the faces insulated; then no heat flows in or out of the body. This will be true if the normal derivative $\partial u/\partial n$ (see Problem 10) of the temperature is zero at the boundary. (When the boundary values of u are given, the problem is called a *Dirichlet problem*; when the boundary values of the normal derivative $\partial u/\partial n$ are given, the problem is called a *Neumann problem*.) For the one-dimensional case we have considered, we replace the condition $u = 0$ at $x = 0$ and l by the condition $\partial u/\partial x = 0$ at $x = 0$ and l if the faces are insulated. This means that the useful basic solution in (3.10) is now the one containing $\cos kx$; note carefully that we must include the constant term (corresponding to $k = 0$). See Problem 14.

4. THE WAVE EQUATION; THE VIBRATING STRING

Let a string (for example, a piano or violin string) be stretched tightly and its ends fastened to supports at $x = 0$ and $x = l$. When the string is vibrating, its vertical displacement y from its equilibrium position along the x-axis depends on x and t. We assume that the displacement y is always very small and that the slope $\partial y/\partial x$ of the string at any point at any time is small. In other words, we assume that the string never gets very far away from its stretched equilibrium position; in fact, we do not distinguish between the length of the string and the distance between the supports, although it is clear that the string must stretch a little as it vibrates out of its equilibrium position. Under these assumptions, the displacement y satisfies the (one-dimensional) wave equation

$$(4.1) \qquad \frac{\partial^2 y}{\partial x^2} = \frac{1}{v^2}\frac{\partial^2 y}{\partial t^2}.$$

The constant v depends on the tension and the linear density of the string; it is called the wave velocity because it is the velocity with which a disturbance at one point of the string would travel along the string. To separate the variables, we substitute

$$(4.2) \qquad y = F(x)T(t)$$

into (4.1), and get (Problem 11)

$$\frac{1}{F}\frac{d^2 F}{dx^2} = \frac{1}{v^2}\frac{1}{T}\frac{d^2 T}{dt^2} = -k^2,$$

or

$$(4.3) \qquad \begin{aligned} F'' + k^2 F &= 0, \\ \ddot{T} + k^2 v^2 T &= 0. \end{aligned}$$

We can see from the physical problem why we use a negative separation constant here; the solutions are to describe vibrations which are represented by sines and cosines, not by real exponentials. Of course, if we tried taking $+k^2$, we would also discover mathematically that we could not satisfy the boundary conditions for real k.

Recall the following notation used in discussing wave phenomena (see Chapter 6, Section 2 and Problem 1f).

ν = frequency (sec^{-1}), $\omega = 2\pi\nu$ = angular frequency (radians),
λ = wavelength,
$v = \lambda\nu$, $k = \dfrac{2\pi}{\lambda} = \dfrac{2\pi\nu}{v} = \dfrac{\omega}{v}$ = wave number.

The solutions of the two equations in (4.3) are

$$
(4.4) \qquad F = \begin{cases} \sin kx, \\ \cos kx, \end{cases} \qquad T = \begin{cases} \sin kvt = \sin \omega t, \\ \cos kvt = \cos \omega t. \end{cases}
$$

The basic solutions (4.2) for y are

$$
(4.5) \qquad y = \begin{cases} \sin kx \sin \omega t, \\ \sin kx \cos \omega t, \\ \cos kx \sin \omega t, \\ \cos kx \cos \omega t. \end{cases}
$$

Since the string is fastened at $x = 0$ and $x = l$, we must have $y = 0$ for these values of x and all t. This means that we want only the sin kx terms in (4.5), and also we select k so that $\sin kl = 0$, or $k = n\pi/l$. The solutions (4.5) then become

$$
(4.6) \qquad y = \begin{cases} \sin \dfrac{n\pi x}{l} \sin \dfrac{n\pi vt}{l}, \\ \sin \dfrac{n\pi x}{l} \cos \dfrac{n\pi vt}{l}. \end{cases}
$$

The particular combination of solutions (4.6) that we should take to solve a given problem depends on the initial conditions. For example, suppose the string is started vibrating by plucking (that is, pulling it aside a small distance h at the center and letting go). Then we are given the shape of the string at $t = 0$, namely $y_0 = f(x)$ as in Fig. 4.1, and also the fact

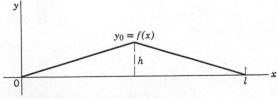

Figure 4.1

that the velocity $\partial y/\partial t$ of points on the string is zero at $t = 0$. (Do not confuse $\partial y/\partial t$ with the wave velocity v; there is no relation between them.) In (4.6), we must then discard the term containing $\sin(n\pi vt/l)$ since its time derivative is not zero when $t = 0$. We then write the solution for this problem in the form

$$(4.7) \qquad y = \sum_{n=1}^{\infty} b_n \sin \frac{n\pi x}{l} \cos \frac{n\pi vt}{l}.$$

The coefficients b_n are to be determined so that at $t = 0$ we have $y_0 = f(x)$, that is,

$$(4.8) \qquad y_0 = \sum_{n=1}^{\infty} b_n \sin \frac{n\pi x}{l} = f(x).$$

As in previous problems, we find the coefficients in the Fourier sine series for the given $f(x)$ and substitute them into (4.7). The result is (Problem 15)

$$(4.9) \qquad y = \frac{8h}{\pi^2}\left(\sin \frac{\pi x}{l} \cos \frac{\pi vt}{l} - \frac{1}{9}\sin \frac{3\pi x}{l} \cos \frac{3\pi vt}{l} + \cdots\right).$$

Another way to start the string vibrating is to hit it (a piano string, for example). In this case the initial conditions would be $y = 0$ at $t = 0$, and the velocity $\partial y/\partial t$ at $t = 0$ given as a function of x (that is, the velocity of each point of the string is given at $t = 0$). This time we discard in (4.6) the term containing $\cos(n\pi vt/l)$ because it is not zero at $t = 0$. The solution of the problem is then of the form

$$(4.10) \qquad y = \sum_{n=1}^{\infty} a_n \sin \frac{n\pi x}{l} \sin \frac{n\pi vt}{l}.$$

Here the coefficients must be determined so that

$$(4.11) \qquad \left(\frac{\partial y}{\partial t}\right)_{t=0} = \sum_{n=1}^{\infty} a_n \frac{n\pi v}{l} \sin \frac{n\pi x}{l} = V(x),$$

that is, $V(x)$, the given initial velocity, must be expanded in a Fourier sine series (see Problems 16 and 18).

Suppose the string is vibrating in such a way that instead of an infinite series for y, we have just one of the solutions (4.6), say

$$(4.12) \qquad y = \sin \frac{n\pi x}{l} \sin \frac{n\pi vt}{l}$$

for some one value of n. The largest value of $\sin(n\pi vt/l)$, for any t, is 1, and the shape of the string then is

(4.13)
$$y = \sin \frac{n\pi x}{l}.$$

Graphs of (4.13) are sketched in Fig. 4.2 for $n = 1, 2, 3, 4$. (The graphs are exaggerated! Remember that the displacements are actually very small.) Consider a point x on the string; for this point $\sin (n\pi x/l)$ is some number, say A. Then the displacement of this point at time t is (from (4.12))

(4.14)
$$y = A \sin \frac{n\pi vt}{l}.$$

As time passes, this point of the string oscillates up and down with frequency ν_n given by $\omega_n = n\pi v/l = 2\pi \nu_n$ or $\nu_n = nv/(2l)$; the amplitude of

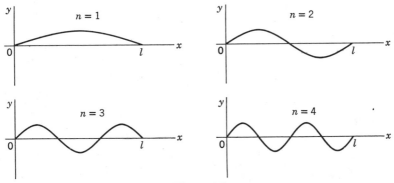

Figure 4.2

the oscillation at this point is $A = \sin (n\pi x/l)$ (see Fig. 4.2). Other points of the string oscillate with different amplitudes but the *same* frequency. This is the frequency of the musical note which the string is producing. If $n = 1$ (see Fig. 4.2), the frequency is $v/(2l)$; in music this tone is called the fundamental or first harmonic. If $n = 2$, the frequency is just twice that of the fundamental; this tone is called the first overtone or the second harmonic; etc. All the frequencies which this string can produce are multiples of the fundamental. These frequencies are called the *characteristic frequencies* of the string. (They are proportional to the *characteristic values* or *eigenvalues*, $k = n\pi/l$.) The corresponding ways in which the string may vibrate producing a pure tone of just one frequency [that is, with y given by (4.12) for one value of n)] are called the *normal modes of vibration*. The first four normal modes are indicated in Fig. 4.2. Any vibration is a combination of these normal modes [for example, (4.9) or (4.10)]. The solution (4.12) (for *one* n) describing one normal mode, is a *characteristic function* or *eigenfunction*.

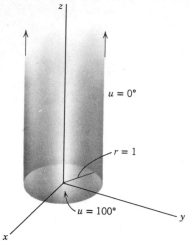

$u = 0°$

$r = 1$

$u = 100°$

Figure 5.1

5. STEADY-STATE TEMPERATURE IN A CYLINDER

Consider the following problem. Find the steady-state temperature distribution u in a semi-infinite solid cylinder (Fig. 5.1) of radius 1 if the base is held at 100° and the curved sides at 0°. This sounds very much like the problem of the temperature distribution in a semi-infinite plate. However, it is not convenient here to use the solutions in rectangular coordinates, because the boundary condition $u = 0$ is given for $r = 1$ rather than for constant values of x or y. The natural variables for the problem are the cylindrical coordinates r, θ, z. The temperature u inside the cylinder satisfies Laplace's equation since there are no sources of heat there.

Laplace's equation in cylindrical coordinates is (see Chapter 10, section 9)

$$(5.1) \qquad \nabla^2 u = \frac{1}{r}\frac{\partial}{\partial r}\left(r\frac{\partial u}{\partial r}\right) + \frac{1}{r^2}\frac{\partial^2 u}{\partial \theta^2} + \frac{\partial^2 u}{\partial z^2} = 0.$$

To separate the variables, we assume a solution of the form

$$(5.2) \qquad u = R(r)\Theta(\theta)Z(z).$$

Substitute (5.2) into (5.1) and divide by $R\Theta Z$ to get

$$(5.3) \qquad \frac{1}{R}\frac{1}{r}\frac{d}{dr}\left(r\frac{dR}{dr}\right) + \frac{1}{\Theta}\frac{1}{r^2}\frac{d^2\Theta}{d\theta^2} + \frac{1}{Z}\frac{d^2 Z}{dz^2} = 0.$$

The last term is a function only of z, while the other two terms do not contain z. Therefore the last term is a constant and the *sum* of the first two terms is minus the same constant. [Notice that neither of the first two terms is constant alone since both contain r. In order to say that a term is constant, we must be sure that: (1) it is a function of only one variable, and (2) that variable does not appear elsewhere in the equation.] Thus we have

$$(5.4) \qquad \frac{1}{Z}\frac{d^2 Z}{dz^2} = k^2, \qquad Z = \begin{cases} e^{kz}, \\ e^{-kz}. \end{cases}$$

Since we want the temperature u to tend to zero as z tends to infinity, we call the separation constant $+k^2$ (k positive) and then use only the e^{-kz} solution. The r, θ equation is

$$\frac{1}{R}\frac{1}{r}\frac{d}{dr}\left(r\frac{dR}{dr}\right) + \frac{1}{\Theta}\frac{1}{r^2}\frac{d^2\Theta}{d\theta^2} + k^2 = 0.$$

We can separate the variables by multiplying by r^2.

(5.5) $$\frac{r}{R}\frac{d}{dr}\left(r\frac{dR}{dr}\right) + \frac{1}{\Theta}\frac{d^2\Theta}{d\theta^2} + k^2r^2 = 0.$$

In (5.5) the second term is a function of θ only, and the other terms are independent of θ. Thus we have

(5.6) $$\frac{1}{\Theta}\frac{d^2\Theta}{d\theta^2} = -n^2, \qquad \Theta = \begin{cases} \sin n\theta, \\ \cos n\theta. \end{cases}$$

Here we must use $-n^2$ as the separation constant and then require n to be an integer for the following reason. When we locate a point using polar coordinates, we can choose the angle as θ or as $\theta + 2m\pi$ where m is any integer. But regardless of the value of m, there is one physical point and one temperature there. The mathematical formula for the temperature at the point must give the same value at θ as at $\theta + 2m\pi$, that is, the temperature must be a periodic function of θ with period 2π. This is true only if the Θ solutions are sines and cosines instead of exponentials (hence the negative separation constant) and the constant n is an integer (to give period 2π).

Finally, the r equation is

$$\frac{r}{R}\frac{d}{dr}\left(r\frac{dR}{dr}\right) - n^2 + k^2r^2 = 0$$

or

(5.7) $$r\frac{d}{dr}\left(r\frac{dR}{dr}\right) + (k^2r^2 - n^2)R = 0.$$

This is a Bessel equation with solutions $J_n(kr)$ and $N_n(kr)$ [see Chapter 12, equation (19.2); put $x = r$, and $a = k$]. Since the base of the cylinder we are considering contains the origin, we can use only the J_n and not the N_n solutions since N_n becomes infinite at the origin. Hence we have

(5.8) $$R(r) = J_n(kr).$$

We can determine the possible values of k from the condition that $u = 0$ on the curved surface of the cylinder, that is, $u = 0$ when $r = 1$ (for all θ and z) or $R(r) = 0$ for $r = 1$. From (5.8), we have

(5.9) $$R_{r=1} = J_n(k) = 0.$$

Thus the possible values of k are the zeros of J_n. The basic solutions for u are then

$$(5.10) \qquad u = \begin{cases} J_n(kr)\sin n\theta\, e^{-kz}, \\ J_n(kr)\cos n\theta\, e^{-kz}, \end{cases}$$

where k is a zero of J_n.

For our problem, the base of the cylinder is held at a constant temperature of $100°$. If we turn the cylinder through any angle the boundary conditions are not changed; thus the solution does not depend on the angle θ. This means that we use $\cos n\theta$ with $n = 0$ in (5.10). The possible values of k are the zeros of J_0; call these zeros k_m, where $m = 1, 2, 3$, etc. Then there are an infinite number of solutions of the form (5.10) (one corresponding to each zero of J_0), and we shall write the solution of our problem as a series of such solutions (eigenfunctions):

$$(5.11) \qquad u = \sum_{m=1}^{\infty} c_m J_0(k_m r) e^{-k_m z}.$$

When $z = 0$, we want $u = 100$, that is,

$$(5.12) \qquad u_{z=0} = \sum_{m=1}^{\infty} c_m J_0(k_m r) = 100.$$

This should remind you of Fourier series; here we want to expand 100 in a series of Bessel functions instead of a series of sines or cosines. We proved (see Chapter 12, Section 19) that the functions $J_0(k_m r)$ are orthogonal on $(0, 1)$ with respect to the weight function r. We can then find the coefficients c_m in (5.12) by the same method used in finding the coefficients in a Fourier sine or cosine series. (For this reason, series like (5.12) are often called Fourier-Bessel series.) Multiply (5.12) by $rJ_0(k_\mu r)$, $\mu = 1, 2, 3, \ldots$, and integrate term by term from $r = 0$ to $r = 1$. Because of the orthogonality [see Chapter 12, equation (19.10)], all terms of the series drop out except the term with $m = \mu$, and we have

$$(5.13) \qquad c_\mu \int_0^1 r[J_0(k_\mu r)]^2\, dr = \int_0^1 100 r J_0(k_\mu r)\, dr.$$

For each value of $\mu = 1, 2, 3, \ldots$, (5.13) gives one of the coefficients in (5.11) and (5.12); thus any c_m in (5.11) is given by (5.13) with μ replaced by m.

We need to evaluate the integrals in (5.13). Equation (19.10) of Chapter 12 gives

$$(5.14) \qquad \int_0^1 r[J_0(k_m r)]^2\, dr = \tfrac{1}{2}J_1^2(k_m).$$

By equation (15.1) of Chapter 12

$$\frac{d}{dx}\,[xJ_1(x)] = xJ_0(x).$$

If we put $x = k_m r$ in this formula, we get

$$\frac{1}{k_m}\frac{d}{dr}\,[k_m r J_1(k_m r)] = k_m r J_0(k_m r).$$

Canceling one k_m factor and integrating, we have

(5.15) $$\int_0^1 r J_0(k_m r)\,dr = \frac{1}{k_m}\,r J_1(k_m r)\Big|_0^1 = \frac{1}{k_m}\,J_1(k_m).$$

Now we write (5.13) for c_m, substitute the values of the integrals from (5.14) and (5.15), and solve for c_m. The result is

(5.16) $$c_m = \frac{100 J_1(k_m)}{k_m}\cdot\frac{2}{J_1^2(k_m)} = \frac{200}{k_m J_1(k_m)}.$$

Warning: Remember that k_m is a zero of J_0, not of J_1. In some tables you may find tabulated the values of J_1 at the zeros of J_0; if not, you can first find the values of k_m (zeros of J_0) and then interpolate in a J_1 table to find the values of $J_1(k_m)$. With the c's given by (5.16), (5.11) is the solution of our problem. The numerical value of the temperature at any point can be found by computing a few terms of the series (Problem 19).

Suppose the given temperature of the base of the cylinder is more complicated than just a constant value, say $f(r, \theta)$, some function of r and θ. Down to (5.10) we proceed as before. But now the series solution is more complicated than (5.11) since we must include all J_n's instead of just J_0. We need a double subscript on the numbers k which are the zeros of the Bessel functions; by k_{mn} we shall mean the mth positive zero of J_n, where $n = 0, 1, 2, \ldots$ and $m = 1, 2, 3, \ldots$. The temperature u is a double infinite series, summed over the indices m, n of all zeros of all the J_n's:

(5.17) $$u = \sum_{m=1}^{\infty}\sum_{n=0}^{\infty} J_n(k_{mn} r)(a_{mn}\cos n\theta + b_{mn}\sin n\theta)\,e^{-k_{mn}z}.$$

At $z = 0$, we want $u = f(r, \theta)$. Thus we write

(5.18) $$u_{z=0} = \sum_{m=1}^{\infty}\sum_{n=0}^{\infty} J_n(k_{mn} r)(a_{mn}\cos n\theta + b_{mn}\sin n\theta) = f(r, \theta).$$

To determine the coefficients a_{mn}, multiply this equation by $J_\nu(k_{\mu\nu} r)\cos \nu\theta$ and integrate over the whole base of the cylinder (0 to 2π for θ, 0 to 1 for r). Because of the orthogonality of the functions $\sin n\theta$ and $\cos n\theta$ on $(0, 2\pi)$, all the b_{mn} terms drop out, and only the a_{mn} terms for $n = \nu$

remain. Because of the orthogonality of the functions $J_n(k_{mn}r)$ (*one n, all m*), only the one term $a_{\mu\nu}$ remains. Thus we have

(5.19)

$$\int_0^1 \int_0^{2\pi} f(r,\theta)J_\nu(k_{\mu\nu}r)\cos\nu\theta\, r\, dr\, d\theta = a_{\mu\nu}\int_0^1\int_0^{2\pi} J_\nu^2(k_{\mu\nu}r)\cos^2\nu\theta\, r\, dr\, d\theta$$

$$= a_{\mu\nu}\cdot\tfrac{1}{2}J_{\nu+1}^2(k_{\mu\nu})\cdot\pi.$$

[The r integral is given by (19.10) of Chapter 12, and the θ integral by Chapter 6, Section 4.] Notice how the weight function r in the Bessel function integral arises here as part of the element of area in polar coordinates. Similarly, we can find

(5.20) $$b_{\mu\nu} = \frac{2}{\pi J_{\nu+1}^2(k_{\mu\nu})}\int_0^1\int_0^{2\pi} f(r,\theta)J_\nu(k_{\mu\nu}r)\sin\nu\theta\, r\, dr\, d\theta.$$

By substituting the values of the a and b coefficients from (5.19) and (5.20) into (5.17), we find the solution to the problem.

6. VIBRATION OF A CIRCULAR MEMBRANE

A circular membrane (for example, a drumhead) is attached to a rigid support along its circumference. Find the characteristic vibration frequencies and the corresponding normal modes of vibration.

Take the (x, y) plane to be the plane of the circular support and take the origin at its center. Let $z(x, y, t)$ be the displacement of the membrane from the (x, y) plane. Then z satisfies the wave equation

(6.1) $$\nabla^2 z = \frac{1}{v^2}\frac{\partial^2 z}{\partial t^2}.$$

Putting

(6.2) $$z = F(x,y)T(t),$$

we separate (6.1) into a space equation (Helmholtz) and a time equation (see Problem 11 and Section 3). We get the two equations

(6.3) $$\nabla^2 F + k^2 F = 0 \quad \text{and} \quad \ddot{T} + k^2 v^2 T = 0.$$

Because the membrane is circular we write ∇^2 in polar coordinates (see Chapter 10, Section 9); then the F equation is

(6.4) $$\frac{1}{r}\frac{\partial}{\partial r}\left(r\frac{\partial F}{\partial r}\right) + \frac{1}{r^2}\frac{\partial^2 F}{\partial\theta^2} + k^2 F = 0.$$

When we put

(6.5) $$F = R(r)\Theta(\theta),$$

(6.4) becomes (5.5), and the separated equations and their solutions are just (5.6), (5.7), and (5.8). The time equation in (6.3) is the same as in (4.3) and the solutions for T are the same as in (4.4). The basic solutions for z are then

$$(6.6) \qquad z = J_n(kr) \begin{cases} \sin n\theta \sin kvt, \\[6pt] \sin n\theta \cos kvt, \\[6pt] \cos n\theta \sin kvt, \\[6pt] \cos n\theta \cos kvt. \end{cases}$$

Just as in Section 5, n must be an integer. To find possible values of k, we use the fact that the membrane is attached to a rigid frame at $r = 1$, so we must have $z = 0$ at $r = 1$ for all values of θ and t. Thus $J_n(k) = 0$, and we see that the possible values (eigenvalues) of k for each J_n are k_{mn}, the zeros of J_n. For a given initial displacement or velocity of the membrane, we could find z as a double series as we found (5.17) in the cylinder temperature problem. However, here we shall do something different, namely investigate the separate normal modes of vibration and their frequencies.

Recall that for the vibrating string (Section 4), each n gives a different frequency and a corresponding normal mode of vibration (Fig. 4.2). The frequencies are $\nu_n = nv/(2l)$; all frequencies are integral multiples of the frequency $\nu_1 = v/(2l)$ of the fundamental. For the circular membrane, the frequencies are [from (6.6) or (4.4)]

$$\nu = \frac{\omega}{2\pi} = \frac{kv}{2\pi}.$$

The possible values of k are the zeros k_{mn} of the Bessel functions. Each value of k_{mn} gives a frequency $\nu_{mn} = (1/2\pi)k_{mn}v$, so we have a doubly infinite set of characteristic frequencies and the corresponding normal modes of vibration. All these frequencies are different, and they are not integral multiples of the fundamental as is true for the string. This is why a drum is less musical than a violin. It is left to a problem (26) to look up several k_{mn} values and find the frequencies as (nonintegral) multiples of the fundamental (which corresponds to k_{10}, the first zero of J_0). Let us sketch a few graphs (Fig. 6.1) of the normal vibration modes corresponding to those in Fig. 4.2 for the string, and write the corresponding formulas (eigenfunctions) for the displacement z given in (6.6). (For simplicity, we have used just the $\cos n\theta \cos kvt$ solutions in Fig. 6.1.) In the fundamental mode of vibration corresponding to k_{10}, the membrane vibrates as a whole. In the k_{20} mode, it vibrates in two parts as shown, the + part vibrating up while the − part vibrates down, and vice versa, with the circle between them at rest. We can show that there is such a circle (called a nodal line) and find its radius. Since $k_{20} > k_{10}$, the circle $r = k_{10}/k_{20}$ is a circle of radius less than 1; hence it is a circle on the membrane. For this value of r, $J_0(k_{20}r) = J_0(k_{20}k_{10}/k_{20}) = J_0(k_{10}) = 0$, so points on this circle are not displaced. For the k_{11} mode, $\cos \theta = 0$ for $\theta = \pm\pi/2$ and

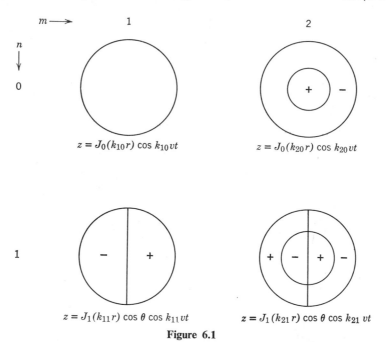

Figure 6.1

is positive or negative as shown. Continuing in this way you can sketch any normal mode (Problem 26).

It is difficult experimentally to obtain pure normal modes of a vibrating object. However, a complicated vibration will have nodal lines of some kind and it is easy to observe these. Fine sand sprinkled on the vibrating object will collect along the nodal lines (where there is no vibration) so that you can see them clearly.

7. STEADY-STATE TEMPERATURE IN A SPHERE

Find the steady-state temperature inside a sphere of radius 1 when the surface of the upper half is held at 100° and the surface of the lower half at 0°.

Inside the sphere, the temperature u satisfies Laplace's equation. In spherical coordinates this is (see Chapter 10, Section 9)

(7.1) $\quad \nabla^2 u = \dfrac{1}{r^2} \dfrac{\partial}{\partial r}\left(r^2 \dfrac{\partial u}{\partial r}\right) + \dfrac{1}{r^2 \sin \theta} \dfrac{\partial}{\partial \theta}\left(\sin \theta \dfrac{\partial u}{\partial \theta}\right) + \dfrac{1}{r^2 \sin^2 \theta} \dfrac{\partial^2 u}{\partial \phi^2} = 0.$

We separate this equation following our standard procedure. Substitute

(7.2) $\qquad\qquad\qquad u = R(r)\Theta(\theta)\Phi(\phi)$

into (7.1) and multiply by $r^2/(R\Theta\Phi)$ to get

(7.3) $\quad \dfrac{1}{R} \dfrac{d}{dr}\left(r^2 \dfrac{dR}{dr}\right) + \dfrac{1}{\Theta} \dfrac{1}{\sin \theta} \dfrac{d}{d\theta}\left(\sin \theta \dfrac{d\Theta}{d\theta}\right) + \dfrac{1}{\Phi} \dfrac{1}{\sin^2 \theta} \dfrac{d^2 \Phi}{d\phi^2} = 0.$

If we multiply (7.3) by $\sin^2 \theta$, the last term becomes a function of ϕ only and the other two terms do not contain ϕ. Thus we obtain the ϕ equation and its solutions:

(7.4) $\qquad\qquad \dfrac{1}{\Phi} \dfrac{d^2 \Phi}{d\phi^2} = -m^2, \qquad \Phi = \begin{cases} \sin m\phi, \\ \cos m\phi. \end{cases}$

The separation constant must be negative and m an integer to make Φ a periodic function of ϕ [see the discussion after (5.6)].

Equation (7.3) can now be written as

(7.5) $\quad \dfrac{1}{R} \dfrac{d}{dr}\left(r^2 \dfrac{dR}{dr}\right) + \dfrac{1}{\Theta} \dfrac{1}{\sin \theta} \dfrac{d}{d\theta}\left(\sin \theta \dfrac{d\Theta}{d\theta}\right) - \dfrac{m^2}{\sin^2 \theta} = 0.$

The first term is a function of r and the last two terms are functions of θ, so we have two equations

(7.6) $\qquad\qquad\qquad \dfrac{1}{R} \dfrac{d}{dr}\left(r^2 \dfrac{dR}{dr}\right) = k,$

(7.7) $\qquad\qquad \dfrac{1}{\sin \theta} \dfrac{d}{d\theta}\left(\sin \theta \dfrac{d\Theta}{d\theta}\right) - \dfrac{m^2}{\sin^2 \theta} \Theta + k\Theta = 0.$

If you compare (7.7) with the equation of Problem 28 in Chapter 12, you will see that (7.7) is the equation for the associated Legendre functions if $k = l(l + 1)$. Recall that l must be an integer in order for the solution of Legendre's equation to be finite at $x = \cos \theta = \pm 1$, that is, at $\theta = 0$ or π; the same statement is true for the equation for the associated Legendre functions. The corresponding result for (7.7) is that k must be a product of two successive integers; it is then convenient to replace k by $l(l + 1)$, where l is an integer. The solutions of (7.7) are then the associated Legendre functions (see Problem 28, Chapter 12)

(7.8) $\qquad\qquad\qquad \Theta = P_l^m(\cos \theta).$

In (7.6), we put $k = l(l + 1)$; you can then easily verify (Problem 21) that the solutions of (7.6) are

$$(7.9) \qquad R = \begin{cases} r^l, \\ r^{-l-1}. \end{cases}$$

Since we are interested in the interior of the sphere, we discard the solutions r^{-l-1} because they become infinite at the origin. If we were discussing a problem (say about water flow or electrostatic potential) outside the sphere, we would use these solutions and discard the solutions r^l because they become infinite at infinity.

The basic solutions for our problem are then

$$(7.10) \qquad u = r^l P_l^m(\cos \theta) \begin{cases} \sin m\phi, \\ \cos m\phi. \end{cases}$$

[The functions $P_l^m(\cos \theta) \sin m\phi$ and $P_l^m(\cos \theta) \cos m\phi$ are called *spherical harmonics*; also see Problems 35 and 36.] If the surface temperature at $r = 1$ were given as a function of θ and ϕ, we would have a double series (summed on l and m) as in Section 5. For the given surface temperatures in our problem ($100°$ on the top hemisphere and $0°$ on the lower hemisphere), the temperature is independent of ϕ; thus in (7.10) we must have $m = 0$, $\cos m\phi = 1$. The solutions (7.10) then reduce to $r^l P_l(\cos \theta)$. We write the solution of our problem as a series of such solutions:

$$(7.11) \qquad u = \sum_{l=0}^{\infty} c_l r^l P_l(\cos \theta).$$

We determine the coefficients c_l by using the given temperatures when $r = 1$; that is, we must have

$$(7.12) \quad u_{r=1} = \sum_{l=0}^{\infty} c_l P_l(\cos \theta) = \begin{cases} 100, & 0 < \theta < \dfrac{\pi}{2}, \quad 0 < \cos \theta < 1, \\ 0, & \dfrac{\pi}{2} < \theta < \pi, \; -1 < \cos \theta < 0, \end{cases}$$

or

$$(7.13) \qquad u_{r=1} = \sum_{l=0}^{\infty} c_l P_l(w) = 100 f(w),$$

where

$$f(w) = \begin{cases} 0, & -1 < w < 0, \\ 1, & 0 < w < 1. \end{cases}$$

In Section 9 of Chapter 12, we expanded this $f(w)$ in a series of Legendre polynomials and obtained:

$$(7.14) \qquad f(w) = \tfrac{1}{2} P_0(w) + \tfrac{3}{4} P_1(w) - \tfrac{7}{16} P_3(w) + \tfrac{11}{32} P_5(w) + \cdots.$$

The coefficients c_l in (7.13) are just these coefficients times 100. Substituting the c's into (7.11), we get the final solution:

$$(7.15) \quad u = 100[\tfrac{1}{2}P_0(\cos\theta) + \tfrac{3}{4}rP_1(\cos\theta) - \tfrac{7}{16}r^3P_3(\cos\theta)$$
$$+ \tfrac{11}{32}r^5P_5(\cos\theta) + \cdots].$$

We can do variations of this problem. Notice that we have not even mentioned so far what temperature scale we are using (Celsius, Fahrenheit, absolute, etc.). This is a very easy adjustment to make once we have a solution in any one scale. To see why, observe that if u is a solution of Laplace's equation $\nabla^2 u = 0$ or of the heat flow equation $\nabla^2 u = (1/\alpha^2)(\partial u/\partial t)$, then $u + C$ and Cu are also solutions for any constant C. If we add, say, $50°$ to the solution (7.15), we have the temperature distribution inside a sphere with the top half of the surface at $150°$ and the lower half at $50°$. If we multiply the solution (7.15) by 2, we find the temperature distribution with given surface temperatures of $200°$ and $0°$, and so on.

The temperature of the equatorial plane $\theta = \pi/2$ or $\cos\theta = 0$ as given by equations (7.11) to (7.15) is halfway between the top and bottom surface temperatures, because Legendre series, like Fourier series, converge to the midpoint of a jump in the function which was expanded to get the series. To solve the problem of the temperature in a hemisphere given the temperatures of the spherical surface and of the equatorial plane, we need only imagine the lower hemisphere in place and at the proper temperature to give the desired average on the equatorial plane. This amounts to defining the function $f(x)$ in (7.13) on $(-1, 0)$ to suit our purposes.

8. POISSON'S EQUATION

We are going to derive Poisson's equation for a simple problem whose answer we know in advance. Using our known solution, we shall be able to see a method of solving more difficult problems.

Recall from Chapter 5 (see Sections 11 and 13, and Problem 68) that the gravitational field is conservative, that is, curl $\mathbf{F} = 0$, and there is a potential function V such that $\mathbf{F} = -\nabla V$. If we consider the gravitational field at a point P due to a point mass m a distance r away (Fig. 8.1), we

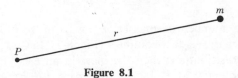

Figure 8.1

have

(8.1) $$V = -\frac{Gm}{r} \quad \text{and} \quad \mathbf{F} = -\frac{Gm}{r^2}\,\mathbf{u},$$

where $\mathbf{u}$ is a unit vector along r toward P. It is straightforward to show that div $\mathbf{F} = 0$ and V satisfies Laplace's equation (Problem 37), that is,

(8.2) $$\nabla \cdot \mathbf{F} = -\nabla \cdot \nabla V = -\nabla^2 V = 0.$$

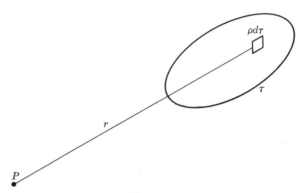

Figure 8.2

Now suppose there are many masses m_i at distances r_i from P. The total potential at P is the sum of the potentials due to the individual m_i, that is,

$$V = \sum_i V_i = -\sum_i \frac{Gm_i}{r_i}$$

and the total gravitational field at P is the vector sum of the fields $\mathbf{F}_i$, that is,

$$\mathbf{F} = -\sum_i \nabla V_i = -\nabla V.$$

Note that we are taking it for granted that none of the masses m_i are *at* P, that is, that no r_i is zero. Since

$$\nabla \cdot \mathbf{F}_i = -\nabla^2 V_i = 0,$$

we have also

$$\nabla \cdot \mathbf{F} = -\nabla^2 V = 0.$$

Instead of a number of masses m_i, we can consider a continuous distribution of mass inside a volume τ (Fig. 8.2). Let $\rho(x, y, z)$ be the mass density of the distribution; then the mass in an element $d\tau$ is $\rho\,d\tau$. The gravitational potential at P due to this mass $\rho\,d\tau$ is $-(G\rho/r)\,d\tau$. Then the total gravitational potential at P due to the whole mass distribution is the triple integral over the volume τ:

(8.3)
$$V = - \iiint_{\text{volume } \tau} \frac{G\rho \, d\tau}{r}.$$

As before, the contribution to V at P due to each bit of mass satisfies Laplace's equation and therefore V satisfies Laplace's equation. Also the

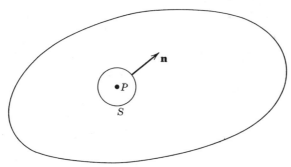

Figure 8.3

total field $\mathbf{F}$ at P is the vector sum of the fields due to the elements of mass, and as before we have

$$\mathbf{\nabla} \cdot \mathbf{F} = -\nabla^2 V = 0.$$

Again note that we are implicitly assuming that none of the mass distribution coincides with P, that is, that $r \neq 0$, which means that point P is not a point of the region τ.

Now let us investigate what happens if P *is* a point of τ. Can we find V from (8.3) and does V satisfy Laplace's equation? Let S be a small sphere of radius a about P; imagine all the mass removed from S (Fig. 8.3). Then our previous discussion holds at points inside S since these points are not in the mass distribution. If $\mathbf{F}'$ and V' are the new field and potential (with the matter in S removed), then $\mathbf{\nabla} \cdot \mathbf{F}' = -\nabla^2 V' = 0$ at points of S. Now restore the mass to S; let $\mathbf{F}$ and V represent the field and potential due to the whole distribution and let $\mathbf{F}_S$ and V_S represent the field and potential due to just the mass in S. Then

$$\mathbf{F} = \mathbf{F}' + \mathbf{F}_S$$

and at points inside S

(8.4)
$$\mathbf{\nabla} \cdot \mathbf{F} = \mathbf{\nabla} \cdot \mathbf{F}' + \mathbf{\nabla} \cdot \mathbf{F}_S = \mathbf{\nabla} \cdot \mathbf{F}_S$$

since $\mathbf{\nabla} \cdot \mathbf{F}' = 0$ in S.

By the divergence theorem (see Fig. 8.3 and Chapter 5, Section 12)

$$(8.5) \qquad \iiint_{\text{volume of } S} \mathbf{\nabla} \cdot \mathbf{F}_S \, d\tau = \iint_{\text{surface of } S} \mathbf{F}_S \cdot \mathbf{n} \, d\sigma.$$

If we let the radius a of S tend to zero, the density ρ of matter in S tends to its value at P; thus for small a, S contains a total mass M approximately equal to $\frac{4}{3}\pi a^3 \rho$, where ρ is evaluated at P. The gravitational field at the surface of S due to this mass is of magnitude.

$$F_S = \frac{GM}{a^2} = G \frac{4}{3} \pi a \rho$$

directed *toward* P. Thus in (8.5), $\mathbf{F}_S \cdot \mathbf{n} = -\frac{4}{3}G\pi a\rho$ because $\mathbf{F}_S$ and $\mathbf{n}$ are antiparallel. Since F_S is constant over the surface S, the right-hand side of (8.5) is $\mathbf{F}_S \cdot \mathbf{n}$ times the area of the sphere. The left-hand side is, for small a, approximately the value of $\mathbf{\nabla} \cdot \mathbf{F}_S$ at P times the volume of S. Then we have

$$(\mathbf{\nabla} \cdot \mathbf{F}_S)(\tfrac{4}{3}\pi a^3) = (-\tfrac{4}{3}G\pi a\rho)(4\pi a^2)$$

or

$$(8.6) \qquad \mathbf{\nabla} \cdot \mathbf{F}_S = -4\pi G\rho \qquad \text{at} \quad P.$$

Since

$$\mathbf{\nabla} \cdot \mathbf{F}_S = \mathbf{\nabla} \cdot \mathbf{F} = -\mathbf{\nabla} \cdot \mathbf{\nabla}V = -\nabla^2 V,$$

we have

$$(8.7) \qquad \nabla^2 V = 4\pi G\rho.$$

This is Poisson's equation; we see that the gravitational potential in a region containing matter satisfies Poisson's equation as claimed in (1.2). Note that if $\rho = 0$, (8.7) becomes (8.2) as it should.

Next we must consider whether our formula (8.3) for V is valid when P is a point of the mass distribution. The integral appears to diverge at $r = 0$, but this is not really so as we see most easily by using spherical coordinates. Then (8.3) becomes

$$V = -\iiint_{\text{volume } \tau} \frac{G\rho}{r} r^2 \sin\theta \, dr \, d\theta \, d\phi$$

and we see that there is no trouble when $r = 0$. Thus (8.3) is valid in general and gives a solution for (8.7).

Using the notation of (1.2) for Poisson's equation [that is, replacing $4\pi G\rho$ by f and V by u in (8.7) and (8.3)] we can write

$$(8.8) \qquad u = -\frac{1}{4\pi} \iiint \frac{f \, d\tau}{r} \qquad \text{is a solution of } \nabla^2 u = f.$$

In the more detaïled notation needed when we use this solution in a problem, (8.8) becomes (see Fig. 8.4)

(8.9)

$$u(x, y, z) = -\frac{1}{4\pi} \iiint \frac{f(x', y', z')}{\sqrt{(x - x')^2 + (y - y')^2 + (z - z')^2}} dx' \, dy' \, dz'$$

is a solution of

$$\nabla^2 u(x, y, z) = f(x, y, z).$$

In (8.9), the point (x, y, z) is the point at which we are calculating the potential u; the point (x', y', z') is a point in the mass distribution over

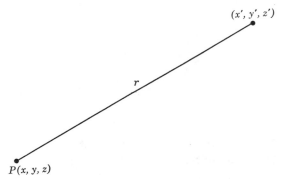

(x', y', z')

r

$P(x, y, z)$

Figure 8.4

which we integrate; r in (8.8) is the distance between these two points and is written out in full in (8.9).

·Equations (8.8) or (8.9) actually give a very special solution of Poisson's equation. Recall that it is customary to take the zero point for gravitational (and electrostatic) potential energy at infinity, and this is what we have done. Thus (8.8) or (8.9) gives a solution of Poisson's equation which tends to zero at infinity. In another problem this may not be what we want. For example, suppose we have an electrostatic charge distribution near a grounded plane. The electrostatic potential satisfies Poisson's equation, but here we want a solution which is zero on the grounded plane rather than at infinity. To see how we might find such a solution, observe that if u is a solution of Poisson's equation, and w is any solution of Laplace's equation ($\nabla^2 w = 0$), then

(8.10) $\nabla^2(u + w) = \nabla^2 u + \nabla^2 w = \nabla^2 u = f;$

thus $u + w$ is a solution of Poisson's equation. Then we can add to the solution (8.9) any solution of Laplace's equation; the combination must be adjusted to fit the given boundary conditions just as we have done in the problems in previous paragraphs.

Example.   Let us do the following simple problem to illustrate this process. In Fig. 8.5, a point charge q at $(0, 0, a)$ is outside a grounded sphere of radius R and center at the origin. Our problem is to find the

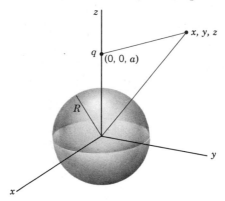

Figure 8.5

electrostatic potential V at points outside the sphere. The potential V and the charge density ρ are related by Poisson's equation

(8.11) $$\nabla^2 V = -4\pi\rho \qquad \text{(in Gaussian units).}$$

The potential at (x, y, z) due to a given charge distribution ρ is given by (8.8) with $f = -4\pi\rho$:

(8.12)

$$V(x, y, z) = -\frac{1}{4\pi} \iiint \frac{-4\pi\rho(x', y', z')}{\sqrt{(x - x')^2 + (y - y')^2 + (z - z')^2}} \, dx' \, dy' \, dz'.$$

For a given space-charge distribution, we would next evaluate this integral. For the single point charge q, we have $(x', y', z') = (0, 0, a)$ and we replace $\iiint \rho \, dx' \, dy' \, dz'$ (which is simply the total charge) by q to obtain

(8.13) $$V = \frac{q}{\sqrt{x^2 + y^2 + (z - a)^2}}.$$

[We could, of course, simply have written down (8.13) without using (8.8); (8.13) is just the electrostatic formula corresponding to the gravitational formula (8.1) with which we started.]

Now we want to add to (8.13) a solution of Laplace's equation such that the combination is zero on the given sphere (Fig. 8.5). It will be

convenient to change to spherical coordinates and to use solutions of
Laplace's equation in spherical coordinates. [Note a change in the meaning
of r from now on. We have been using r to mean the distance from q at
(x', y', z') to (x, y, z); from now on we want to use it to mean the distance
from $(0, 0, 0)$ to (x, y, z). See, for example, Figs. 8.4 and 8.5.] Writing V_q
for V in (8.13) (to distinguish it from our final answer which will be a
sum of V_q and a solution of Laplace's equation) and changing to spherical
coordinates, we get

$$(8.14) \qquad V_q = \frac{q}{\sqrt{r^2 - 2ar \cos \theta + a^2}}.$$

The basic solutions of Laplace's equation in spherical coordinates are
(Section 7):

$$(8.15) \qquad \begin{Bmatrix} r^l \\ r^{-l-1} \end{Bmatrix} P_l^m(\cos \theta) \begin{Bmatrix} \sin m\phi \\ \cos m\phi \end{Bmatrix}.$$

Since we are interested in the region outside the sphere, we want r solutions which do not become infinite at infinity; thus we use r^{-l-1} and discard
the r^l solutions. Because the physical problem is symmetric about the
z-axis, we look for solutions independent of ϕ; that is, we choose $m = 0$,
$\cos m\phi = 1$. Then our basic solutions are $r^{-l-1}P_l(\cos \theta)$ and we try to
find a solution of the form

$$(8.16) \qquad V = V_q + \sum_l c_l r^{-l-1} P_l(\cos \theta).$$

We must satisfy the boundary condition $V = 0$ when $r = R$. This gives

$$(8.17) \quad V_{r=R} = \frac{q}{\sqrt{R^2 - 2aR \cos \theta + a^2}} + \sum_l c_l R^{-l-1} P_l(\cos \theta) = 0.$$

Thus we want to expand V_q in a Legendre series. Since V_q is essentially
the generating function for Legendre polynomials, this is very easy.
Comparing (8.17) and the formulas of Chapter 12, Section 5 [(5.1) and
(5.2), or more simply, (5.12) and (5.17)], we find

$$(8.18) \qquad \frac{q}{\sqrt{R^2 - 2aR \cos \theta + a^2}} = q \sum_l \frac{R^l P_l(\cos \theta)}{a^{l+1}}.$$

Thus the coefficients c_l in (8.17) are given by

$$(8.19) \qquad c_l R^{-l-1} = -\frac{qR^l}{a^{l+1}} \quad \text{or} \quad c_l = -\frac{qR^{2l+1}}{a^{l+1}}.$$

Substituting (8.19) into (8.16), we obtain the final solution for V:

$$(8.20) \quad V = \frac{q}{\sqrt{r^2 - 2ar\cos\theta + a^2}} - q\sum_l \frac{R^{2l+1}r^{-l-1}P_l(\cos\theta)}{a^{l+1}}.$$

Since the second term in (8.20) is of the same general form as (8.18), we can simplify (8.20) by summing the series to get (Problem 38)

$$(8.21) \quad V = \frac{q}{\sqrt{r^2 - 2ar\cos\theta + a^2}} - \frac{(R/a)q}{\sqrt{r^2 + (R^2/a)^2 - 2r(R^2/a)\cos\theta}}.$$

Formula (8.21) has a very interesting physical interpretation. The second term is the potential of a charge $-(R/a)q$ at the point $(0, 0, R^2/a)$; thus we could replace the grounded sphere by this charge and have the same potential for $r > R$. This result can be shown also by elementary analytic geometry and is known as the "method of images." For problems with simple geometry (involving planes, spheres, circular cylinders), it may offer a simpler method of solution than the one we have discussed; however, our purpose was to illustrate the more general method.

9. SOLUTION BY USE OF LAPLACE TRANSFORMS

We have seen (Chapter 13, Section 3) that taking the Laplace transform of an ordinary differential equation converts it into an algebraic equation. Taking the Laplace transform of a partial differential equation reduces the number of independent variables by one, and so converts a two-variable partial differential equation into an ordinary differential equation. To illustrate this, we solve the following problem.

A semi-infinite bar (extending from $x = 0$ to $x = \infty$), with insulated sides, is initially at the uniform temperature $u = 0°$. At $t = 0$, the end at $x = 0$ is brought to $u = 100°$ and held there. Find the temperature distribution in the bar as a function of x and t.

The differential equation satisfied by u is

$$(9.1) \quad \frac{\partial^2 u}{\partial x^2} = \frac{1}{\alpha^2}\frac{\partial u}{\partial t}.$$

We are going to take the t Laplace transform of (9.1); the variable x will just be a parameter in this process. Let U be the Laplace transform of u, that is,

$$(9.2) \quad U(x, p) = \int_0^\infty u(x, t)\, e^{-pt}\, dt.$$

By (3.1) of Chapter 13, we have

$$L\left(\frac{\partial u}{\partial t}\right) = pU - u_{t=0} = pU$$

since $u = 0$ when $t = 0$. Also

$$L\left(\frac{\partial^2 u}{\partial x^2}\right) = \frac{\partial^2}{\partial x^2} L(u) = \frac{\partial^2 U}{\partial x^2}$$

(remember that x is just a parameter here; we are taking a t Laplace transform). The transform of (9.1) is then

(9.3)
$$\frac{\partial^2 U}{\partial x^2} = \frac{1}{\alpha^2} pU.$$

If we think of p as a constant here, this is an ordinary differential equation for U as a function of x. Its solutions are

(9.4)
$$U = \begin{cases} e^{(\sqrt{p}/\alpha)x}, \\ e^{-(\sqrt{p}/\alpha)x}. \end{cases}$$

To find the correct combination of these solutions to fit our problem, we need the Laplace transforms of the boundary conditions on u since these give the conditions on U. Using Chapter 13 to find the transforms, we have

(9.5)
$$u = 100 \text{ at } x = 0, \qquad U = L(100) = \frac{100}{p} \text{ at } x = 0;$$
$$u \to 0 \text{ as } x \to \infty, \qquad U \to L(0) = 0 \quad \text{as } x \to \infty.$$

Since $U \to 0$ as $x \to \infty$, we see that we must use the solution $e^{-(\sqrt{p}/\alpha)x}$ from (9.4) and discard the positive exponential solution. We determine the constant multiple of this solution which fits our problem from the condition that $U = 100/p$ at $x = 0$. Thus we find that the U solution satisfying the given boundary conditions is

(9.6)
$$U = \frac{100}{p} e^{-(\sqrt{p}/\alpha)x}.$$

We find u by looking up the inverse transform of (9.6); it is, by $L22$ of Chapter 13,

(9.7)
$$u = 100\left[1 - \text{erf} \frac{x}{2\alpha\sqrt{t}}\right]$$

and this is the solution of the problem.

10. SOLUTION BY USE OF FOURIER TRANSFORMS

In several of the examples we have done by separation of variables, we expanded a given function in a Fourier series. This was possible because the function was to be represented by the series over a finite interval. We could then take that interval as the basic period for the Fourier series. If we are dealing with a function which is given over an infinite interval

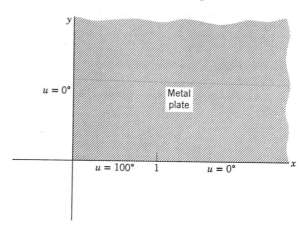

Figure 10.1

(and not periodic), then instead of representing it by a Fourier series we represent it by a Fourier integral (see Chapter 13, Section 4). Let us do this for a specific problem.

An infinite metal plate (Fig. 10.1) covering the first quadrant has the edge along the y-axis held at $0°$, and the edge along the x-axis held at

$$(10.1) \qquad u(x, 0) = \begin{cases} 100°, & 0 < x < 1, \\ 0°, & x > 1. \end{cases}$$

Find the steady-state temperature distribution as a function of x and y.

The differential equation and basic solutions are the same as in the problem of Section 2, equations (2.1), (2.6), and (2.7). As in that problem, we assume $u \to 0$ as $y \to \infty$, and use only the e^{-ky} terms. Since $u = 0$ when $x = 0$, we use only the sine solutions. The basic solutions are then $u = e^{-ky} \sin kx$. We do not have any requirement here which determines k as we did in Section 2. We must then allow all k's and try to find a solution in the form of an integral over k. Instead of coefficients b_n in a series, we have a coefficient function $B(k)$ to determine. Remember that $k > 0$ since e^{-ky} must tend to zero as $y \to \infty$. Thus we try to find a solution of the form

$$(10.2) \qquad u(x, y) = \int_0^\infty B(k) \sin kx \, e^{-ky} \, dk.$$

When $y = 0$, we have

$$(10.3) \qquad u(x, 0) = \int_0^\infty B(k) \sin kx \, dk.$$

This is the first of equations (4.14) of Chapter 13 if we identify k with α, $u(x, 0)$ with $f_s(x)$ and $B(k)$ with $\sqrt{2/\pi} \, g_s(\alpha)$. Thus the given temperature on the x-axis is a Fourier sine transform of the desired coefficient function, so $B(k)$ can be found as the inverse transform. Using the second of equations (4.14), Chapter 13, we get

$$(10.4) \quad B(k) = \sqrt{\frac{2}{\pi}} \, g_s(k) = \frac{2}{\pi} \int_0^\infty f_s(x) \sin kx \, dx = \frac{2}{\pi} \int_0^\infty u(x, 0) \sin kx \, dx.$$

For the given $u(x, 0)$ in (10.1), we find

$$(10.5) \quad B(k) = \frac{2}{\pi} \int_0^1 100 \sin kx \, dx = -\frac{200}{\pi} \frac{\cos kx}{k} \Big|_0^1 = \frac{200}{\pi k}(1 - \cos k).$$

Finding $B(k)$ corresponds to evaluating the coefficients in a Fourier series. Substituting (10.5) into (10.2), we get the solution to our problem in the form of an integral instead of a series as in Section 2:

$$(10.6) \qquad u(x, y) = \frac{200}{\pi} \int_0^\infty \frac{1 - \cos k}{k} \sin kx \, e^{-ky} \, dk.$$

An integral can, of course, be evaluated numerically just as a convergent series can be approximated by calculating a few terms. However, (10.6) can be integrated; a convenient way to do it is to recognize that it is a Laplace transform of $f(k) = [(1 - \cos k) \sin kx]/k$, where x is just a parameter and y corresponds to p and k to t in the notation of Chapter 13. From $L19$ and $L20$ of Chapter 13, we find

$$(10.7) \quad u(x, y) = \frac{200}{\pi} \left[\arctan \frac{x}{y} - \frac{1}{2} \arctan \frac{x+1}{y} - \frac{1}{2} \arctan \frac{x-1}{y} \right].$$

This can also be written in polar coordinates as

$$(10.8) \qquad u = \frac{100}{\pi} \left(\frac{\pi}{2} - \arctan \frac{r^2 - \cos 2\theta}{\sin 2\theta} \right).$$

REFERENCES

A useful textbook on this subject is Weinberger. See also chapters in some differential equations textbooks and in most books on mathematics in physics and engineering. (Some suggestions are given in the reference list at the end of the book; look for references with a [14] following the listing.)

PROBLEMS

1. Assume from electricity the equations $\nabla \cdot \mathbf{D} = \rho$ ($\mathbf{D}$ = electric displacement and ρ = charge density) and $\mathbf{D} = -\epsilon \nabla \phi$ (ϕ = electrostatic potential and ϵ = dielectric constant). Show that the electrostatic potential satisfies Laplace's equation (1.1) in a charge-free region and satisfies Poisson's equation (1.2) in a region of charge density ρ.

2. Show that the expression $u = \sin(x - vt)$ describing a sinusoidal wave, satisfies the wave equation. Show that in general

$$u = f(x - vt) \quad \text{and} \quad u = f(x + vt)$$

satisfy the wave equation (1.4), where f is any function with a second derivative.

3. Assume from electricity the following equations which are valid in free space. (They are called Maxwell's equations.)

$$\nabla \cdot \mathbf{E} = 0, \qquad \nabla \cdot \mathbf{H} = 0,$$

$$\nabla \times \mathbf{E} = -\mu \frac{\partial \mathbf{H}}{\partial t}, \qquad \nabla \times \mathbf{H} = \epsilon \frac{\partial \mathbf{E}}{\partial t}.$$

From them show that any component of $\mathbf{E}$ or $\mathbf{H}$ satisfies the wave equation (1.4) with $v = (\epsilon \mu)^{-\frac{1}{2}}$. *Hint:* Use vector identity (e) in the table at the end of Chapter 5.

4. In equation (2.5) and the discussion after it, we assumed k real and non-negative. Taking k pure imaginary in (2.5) amounts to interchanging k^2 and $-k^2$ in (2.5) and so leads to (2.15). Show that even if we assume that k may be complex, say $k = a + bi$, the boundary conditions still lead to (2.8).

5. Find the steady-state temperature distribution for the semi-infinite plate problem if the temperature of the bottom edge is $T = f(x) = x$ (in degrees; that is, the temperature at x cm is x degrees), the temperature of the other sides is $0°$, and the width of the plate is 10 cm.

6. (a) Show that the series in (2.12) can be summed to get

$$T = \frac{200}{\pi} \arctan\left(\frac{\sin(\pi x/10)}{\sinh(\pi y/10)}\right)$$

with the arc tangent in radians, or

$$T = \frac{10}{9} \text{ arc tan} \left(\frac{(\sin \pi x/10)}{\sinh (\pi y/10)} \right)$$

with the arc tangent in degrees. Use this last formula to check the value $T = 26.1°$ at $x = y = 5$. *Hint for summing the series:* Write the sines in (2.12) in terms of complex exponentials, and use equation (13.7) of Chapter 1.

(b) Complete the details to obtain equation (2.14). Also show that the answer can be written in the following more concise form:

$$T = \sum_{\text{odd } n} \frac{400}{n\pi \sinh 3n\pi} \sinh \frac{n\pi}{10} (30 - y) \sin \frac{n\pi x}{10}.$$

7. Find the steady-state temperature distribution in a metal plate 10 cm square if one side is held at $100°$ and the other three sides at $0°$. Find the temperature at the center of the plate.

8. Find the steady-state temperature distribution in the plate of Problem 7 if two adjacent sides are at $100°$ and the other two at $0°$. *Hint:* Use your solution of Problem 7. You should not have to do any calculation—just write the answer!

9. Complete the calculations in Section 2 to find the temperature distribution in a rectangular plate 10 cm by 30 cm if two adjacent sides are held at $100°$ and the other two sides at $0°$.

10. In the rectangular plate problem of Section 2, we have so far had the temperature specified all around the boundary. We could, instead, have some edges insulated. The heat flow across an edge is proportional to $\partial T/\partial n$, where n is a variable in the direction normal to the edge (see normal derivatives, Chapter 5, Section 9). For example, the heat flow across an edge lying along the x-axis is proportional to $\partial T/\partial y$. Since the heat flow across an insulated edge is zero, we must have not T, but a partial derivative of T, equal to zero on an insulated boundary. Use this fact to find the steady-state temperature distribution in a semi-infinite plate of width 10 cm if the two long sides are insulated, the far end (at ∞ as in Section 2) is at $0°$, and the bottom edge is at $T = f(x) = x - 5$.

Note that you used $T \to 0$ as $y \to \infty$ only to discard the solutions e^{+ky}; it would be just as satisfactory to say that T does not become infinite as $y \to \infty$. Actually, the temperature (assumed finite) as $y \to \infty$ in this problem is determined by the given temperature at $y = 0$. Let $T = f(x) = x$ at $y = 0$, repeat your calculations above to find the temperature distribution, and find the value of T for large y. Don't forget the $k = 0$ term in the series!

Next consider a finite plate, 10 cm by 30 cm as in Section 2, with two insulated sides, one end at $0°$ and the other at a given temperature $T = f(x)$. Try $f(x) = 100°$; $f(x) = x$. You should convince yourself that this problem cannot be done using just the solutions (2.7). To see what is wrong, go back to the differential equations (2.5) and solve them for $k = 0$. You should find solutions x, y, xy, and constant (the constant is already contained in (2.7) for $k = 0$, but the other three solutions are not). Now go back over each of the problems we have done so far and see why we could ignore these $k = 0$ solutions; then including the $k = 0$ solutions, finish the problem of the finite plate with insulated sides.

11. Separate the wave equation (1.4) into a space equation and a time equation as we did the heat flow equation, and show that the space equation is the Helmholtz equation for this case also.

12. A bar 10 cm long with insulated sides is initially at 100°. Starting at $t = 0$, the ends are held at 0°. Find the temperature distribution in the bar at time t.

13. In the initial steady state of an infinite slab of thickness l, the face $x = 0$ is at 0° and the face $x = l$ is at 100°. From $t = 0$ on, the $x = 0$ face is held at 100° and the $x = l$ face at 0°. Find the temperature distribution at time t.

14. A bar of length l with insulated sides has its ends also insulated from time $t = 0$ on. Initially the temperature is $u = x$, where x is the distance from one end. Determine the temperature distribution inside the bar at time t. *Hints and comments:* See Problem 10 and the end of Section 3. Show that the $k = 0$ solutions are x and constant (time independent). Note that here (unlike the example in Problem 10) you do not need the extra solution (namely x) for $k = 0$ since the final steady state is a constant and this is included in the solutions (3.10). Also note that we *did* need the $k = 0$ solutions in the discussion following (3.15) but were able to simplify the work by observing that these linear solutions simply give the final steady state. Show that the following problem is easily solved using (3.15): The ends of a bar are initially at 20° and 150°; at $t = 0$ the 150° end is changed to 50°. Find the time-dependent temperature distribution.

15. Complete the derivation of equation (4.9).

16. A string of length l is initially stretched straight; its ends are fixed for all t. At time $t = 0$, its points are given the *velocity* $V(x) = (\partial y / \partial t)_{t=0}$ as indicated in the diagram (for example, by hitting the string). Determine the shape of

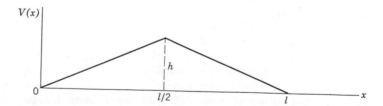

the string at time t, that is, find the displacement y as a function of x and t in the form of a series similar to (4.9). *Warning:* What functions do you need here?

17. A string of length l has a zero initial velocity and a displacement $y_0(x)$ as shown. (This initial displacement might be caused by stopping the string at the center and plucking half of it.) Find the displacement as a function of x and t.

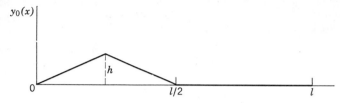

18. Do Problem 16 if the initial velocity $V(x) = (\partial y/\partial t)_{t=0}$ is as shown.

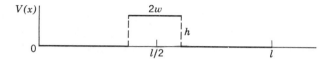

19. Compute numerically the coefficients (5.16) of the first three terms of the series (5.11) for the steady-state temperature in a solid semi-infinite cylinder when $u = 0$ at $r = 1$, and $u = 100$ at $z = 0$. Find u at $r = \frac{1}{2}$, $z = 1$.

20. Find the steady-state temperature distribution in a solid semi-infinite cylinder if the boundary temperatures are $u = 0$ at $r = 1$ and $u = y = r \sin \theta$ at $z = 0$. *Hints:* In (5.10) you want the solution containing $\sin \theta$; therefore you want the functions J_1. You will need to integrate $r^2 J_1$; follow the text method of integrating $r J_0$ just before (5.15).

21. The following two $R(r)$ equations arise in various separation of variables problems in polar, cylindrical, or spherical coordinates:

$$r \frac{d}{dr}\left(r \frac{dR}{dr} \right) = n^2 R,$$

$$\frac{d}{dr}\left(r^2 \frac{dR}{dr} \right) = l(l + 1)R.$$

There are various ways of solving them: They are a standard kind of equation (often called Euler or Cauchy equations—see Chapter 7, Section 7d); you could use power series methods; given the fact that the solutions are just powers of r, it is easy to find the powers. Choose any method you like, and solve the two equations for future reference. Consider the case $n = 0$ separately. Is this necessary for $l = 0$?

22. Separate Laplace's equation in two dimensions in polar coordinates and solve the r and θ equations. (See Problem 21.) Remember that for the θ equation, only periodic solutions are of interest. Use your results to solve the problem of the steady-state temperature in a circular plate if the upper semicircular boundary is held at $100°$ and the lower at $0°$.

Comment: Another physical problem whose mathematical solution is identical with this temperature problem is this: Find the electrostatic potential inside a capacitor formed by two half-cylinders, insulated from each other and maintained at potentials 0 and 100.

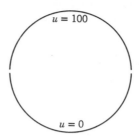

23. Find the steady-state distribution of temperature in the sector of a circular plate of radius 10 and angle $\pi/4$ if the temperature is maintained at 0° along the radii and at 100° along the curved edge. *Hint:* See Problem 22.

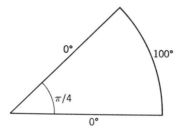

24. Water at 100° is flowing through a long pipe of radius 1 rapidly enough so that we may assume that the temperature is 100° at all points. At $t = 0$, the water is turned off and the surface of the pipe is maintained at 0° from then on (neglect the wall thickness of the pipe). Find the temperature distribution in the water as a function of r and t. (Neglect the fact that the water will freeze.) Note that you need only consider a cross section of the pipe since (for a long pipe) the temperature does not depend on z.

25. Find the steady-state temperature distribution in a circular annulus (shaded area) of inner radius 1 and outer radius 2 if the inner circle is held at 0° and the outer circle has half its circumference at 0° and half at 100°. *Hint:* Don't forget the r-solutions corresponding to $k = 0$.

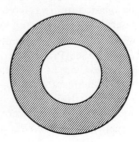

26. Find the first six frequencies of a vibrating circular membrane (Section 6) as multiples of the fundamental frequency. Sketch a diagram of each mode of vibration, and write under it the formula for the displacement z as a function of r, θ, t, that is, continue Fig. 6.1. *Hint:* It is not obvious which modes give the first six frequencies; look up several extras and select the six lowest.

27. Separate the wave equation in two-dimensional rectangular coordinates x, y. Consider a rectangular membrane as shown, rigidly attached to supports along its sides. Show that its characteristic frequencies are

$$\nu_{nm} = (v/2)\sqrt{(n/a)^2 + (m/b)^2},$$

where n and m are positive integers, and sketch the normal modes of vibration corresponding to the first few frequencies. That is, indicate the nodal lines as we did for the circular membrane in Fig. 6.1 and Problem 26.

Next suppose the membrane is square. Show that in this case there may be two or more normal modes of vibration corresponding to a single frequency. (*Hint for one example:* $7^2 + 1^2 = 1^2 + 7^2 = 5^2 + 5^2$.) This is an example of what is called *degeneracy*; we say that there is degeneracy when several different solutions of the wave equation correspond to the same frequency. Sketch several normal modes giving rise to the same frequency.

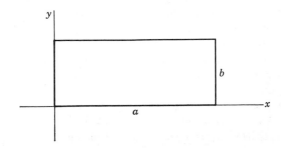

28. Find the steady-state distribution of temperature in a cube of side 10 if the temperature is 100° on the face $z = 0$ and 0° on the other five faces. *Hint:* Separate Laplace's equation in three dimensions in rectangular coordinates, and follow the methods of Section 2. You will want to expand 100 in the double Fourier series

$$\sum_{n=1}^{\infty} \sum_{m=1}^{\infty} a_{nm} \sin \frac{n\pi x}{l} \sin \frac{m\pi y}{l}.$$

The coefficients a_{nm} are determined by the orthogonality of the functions $\sin(n\pi x/l)\sin(m\pi y/l)$ over the square, that is,

$$\int_0^l \int_0^l \sin \frac{n\pi x}{l} \sin \frac{m\pi y}{l} \sin \frac{p\pi x}{l} \sin \frac{q\pi y}{l}\, dx\, dy = 0 \qquad \text{unless} \begin{cases} n = p, \\ m = q. \end{cases}$$

29. A square membrane of side l is distorted into the shape

$$f(x, y) = xy(l - x)(l - y)$$

and released. Express its shape at subsequent times as an infinite series. *Hint:* Use a double Fourier series as in Problem 28.

30. Find the steady-state temperature distribution inside a hemisphere if the spherical surface is held at 100° and the equatorial plane at 0°. *Hint:* See the end of Section 7.

31. Find the electrostatic potential outside a conducting sphere of radius a placed in an originally uniform electric field, and maintained at zero potential. *Hint:* Let the original field $\mathbf{E}$ be in the negative z direction so that $\mathbf{E} = -E_0\mathbf{k}$. Then since $\mathbf{E} = -\nabla\Phi$, where Φ is the potential, we have $\Phi = E_0 z = E_0 r \cos\theta$ (Verify this!) for the original potential. You then want a solution of Laplace's equation $\nabla^2 u = 0$ which is zero at $r = a$ and becomes $u \sim \Phi$ for large r (that is, far away from the sphere). Select the solutions of Laplace's equation in spherical coordinates which have the right θ and ϕ dependence (there are just two such solutions) and find the combination which reduces to zero for $r = a$.

32. Find the characteristic frequencies for sound vibration in a rectangular box (say a room) of sides a, b, c. *Hint:* Separate the wave equation in three dimensions in rectangular coordinates. This problem is like Problem 27 but for three dimensions instead of two. Discuss degeneracy (see Problem 27).

▫33. A cube is originally at 100°. From $t = 0$ on, the faces are held at 0°. Find the time-dependent temperature distribution. *Hint:* This problem leads to a triple Fourier series; see the double Fourier series in Problem 28 and generalize it to three dimensions.

34. A sphere initially at 0° has its surface kept at 100° from $t = 0$ on (for example, a frozen potato in boiling water!). Find the time-dependent temperature distribution. *Hint:* Subtract 100° from all temperatures and solve the problem; then add the 100° to the answer. Can you justify this procedure? Show that the Legendre function required for this problem is P_0 and the r solution is $(1/\sqrt{r})J_{1/2}$ or j_0 [see (17.4) in Chapter 12]. Since spherical Bessel functions can be expressed in terms of elementary functions, the series in this problem can be thought of as either a Bessel series or a Fourier series. Show that the results are identical.

35. Separate the wave equation in spherical coordinates, and show that the θ, ϕ solutions are the spherical harmonics $P_l^m(\cos\theta)e^{\pm im\phi}$ and the r solutions are spherical Bessel functions $j_l(kr)$ and $y_l(kr)$ [Chapter 12, equations (17.4)].

36. The (time-independent) Schrödinger equation in quantum mechanics is

$$\nabla^2\psi + (a - bV)\psi = 0,$$

where a and b are constants and V is a given function of r, θ, ϕ for each problem. In most simple cases V is a function of r only (no θ, ϕ dependence). (Physically, V is the potential energy, and the fact that it depends only on r implies that we are dealing with central forces, for example, electrostatic or gravitational forces.) Separate the Schrödinger equation in spherical coordinates for the case $V = V(r)$, and show that the θ, ϕ solutions are spherical harmonics (see Problem 35).

37. Show that the gravitational potential $V = -Gm/r$ satisfies Laplace's equation, that is, show that $\nabla^2(1/r) = 0$ where $r^2 = x^2 + y^2 + z^2$.

38. Using the formulas of Chapter 12, Section 5, sum the series in (8.20) to get (8.21).

39. Repeat the problem of Section 8 for the case of a charge q inside a grounded sphere to obtain the potential V inside the sphere. Sum the series solution and state the image method of solving this problem.

40. Do the two-dimensional analogue of the problem in Section 8. A "point charge" in a plane means physically a uniform charge along an infinite line perpendicular to the plane; a "circle" at zero potential means an infinitely long circular cylinder perpendicular to the plane. However, since all cross sections of the parallel line and cylinder are the same, the problem is a two-dimensional one. *Hint:* The potential must satisfy Laplace's equation in charge-free regions. What are the solutions of the two-dimensional Laplace equation?

Find the method of images for this problem.

41. Verify that (10.8) follows from (10.7). *Hint:* Use the formulas for $\tan(\alpha \pm \beta)$, $\tan 2\alpha$, etc., to condense (10.7) and then change to polar coordinates. You may find

$$u = \frac{100}{\pi} \arctan \frac{\sin 2\theta}{r^2 - \cos 2\theta}.$$

Show that if you use principal values of the arc tangent, this formula does not give the correct boundary conditions on the x-axis, whereas (10.8) does.

42. A metal plate covering the first quadrant has the edge which is along the y-axis insulated and the edge which is along the x-axis held at

$$u(x, 0) = \begin{cases} 100(2 - x) & \text{for } 0 < x < 2, \\ 0 & \text{for } x > 2. \end{cases}$$

Find the steady-state temperature distribution as a function of x and y. *Hint:* Follow the procedure of Section 10, but use a cosine transform (because $\partial u/\partial x = 0$ for $x = 0$). Leave your answer as an integral like (10.6).

43. Consider the heat flow problem of Section 3. Solve this by Laplace transforms (with respect to t) by starting as in Section 9. You should get

$$\frac{\partial^2 U}{\partial x^2} - \frac{p}{\alpha^2} U = -\frac{100}{\alpha^2 l} x \quad \text{and} \quad U(0, p) = U(l, p) = 0.$$

Solve this differential equation to get

$$U(x, p) = -\frac{100 \sinh(\sqrt{p}/\alpha)x}{p \sinh(\sqrt{p}/\alpha)l} + \frac{100}{pl} x.$$

Assume the following expansion, and find u by looking up the inverse Laplace transforms of the individual terms of U:

$$\frac{\sinh\left(\sqrt{p/\alpha}\right)x}{p\sinh\left(\sqrt{p/\alpha}\right)l} = \frac{x}{pl} - \frac{2}{\pi}\left[\frac{\sin\left(\pi x/l\right)}{p+(\pi^2\alpha^2/l^2)} - \frac{\sin\left(2\pi x/l\right)}{2[p+(4\pi^2\alpha^2/l^2)]}\right.$$
$$\left. + \frac{\sin\left(3\pi x/l\right)}{3[p+(9\pi^2\alpha^2/l^2)]}\cdots\right].$$

Your answer should be (3.15).

44. A semi-infinite bar is initially at temperature $100°$ for $0 < x < 1$, and $0°$ for $x > 1$. Starting at $t = 0$, the end $x = 0$ is maintained at $0°$ and the sides are insulated. Find the temperature in the bar at time t, as follows. Separate variables in the heat flow equation and get elementary solutions $e^{-\alpha^2 k^2 t}\sin kx$ and $e^{-\alpha^2 k^2 t}\cos kx$. Discard the cosines since $u = 0$ at $x = 0$. Look for a solution

$$u(x, t) = \int_0^\infty B(k)e^{-k^2\alpha^2 t}\sin kx\, dk$$

and proceed as in Section 10. Leave your answer as an integral.

45. A long wire occupying the x-axis is initially at rest. The end $x = 0$ is oscillated up and down so that

$$y(0, t) = 2\sin 3t, \qquad t > 0.$$

Find the displacement $y(x, t)$. The initial and boundary conditions are $y(0, t) = 2\sin 3t$, $y(x, 0) = 0$, $\partial y/\partial t|_{t=0} = 0$. Take Laplace transforms of these conditions and of the wave equation with respect to t as in Section 9. Solve the resulting differential equation to get

$$Y(x, p) = \frac{6e^{-(p/v)x}}{p^2 + 9}.$$

Use a table of Laplace transforms to find

$$y(x, t) = \begin{cases} 2\sin 3\left(t - \dfrac{x}{v}\right), & x < vt, \\ 0, & x > vt. \end{cases}$$

46. Continue the problem of Section 10 in the following way: Instead of using the explicit form of $B(k)$ from (10.5), leave it as an integral and write (10.6) in the form

$$u(x, y) = \frac{200}{\pi}\int_0^\infty e^{-ky}\sin kx\, dk\int_0^1 \sin kt\, dt.$$

Change the order of integration and evaluate the integral with respect to k first. (*Hint:* Write the product of sines as a difference of cosines.) Now do the t integration and get (10.7).

47. Continue with Problem 44 as in Problem 46.

15

Probability

I. INTRODUCTION; DEFINITION OF PROBABILITY

The theory of probability has many applications in the physical sciences. It is of basic importance in quantum mechanics, kinetic theory, and statistical mechanics. It is needed in any problem dealing with large numbers of particles or variables where it is impossible or impractical to have complete information, such as the shot effect in vacuum tubes, radioactive decay, turbulence in hydrodynamics, some electrical network problems, information theory, etc. Also, since physical measurements are always subject to error, probability theory is needed in the theory of errors. We shall discuss in this chapter some of the basic ideas of probability theory which are most useful in applications.

The word "probably" is frequently used in everyday life. We say "The test will probably be hard," "It will probably snow today," "We will probably win this game," etc. Such statements always imply a state of partial ignorance about the outcome of some event; we do not say "probably" about something whose outcome we know. The theory of probability tries to express more precisely just what our state of ignorance is. We say that the probability of getting a head in one toss of a coin is $\frac{1}{2}$, and similarly for a tail. We mean by this that there are two possible outcomes of the experiment (if we do not consider the possibility of the coin's standing on edge) and that we have no reason to expect one outcome more than the other; therefore we assign equal probabilities to the two possible outcomes. (See end of Section 2 for further discussion of this.)

Consider the following problem. You and a friend each toss a coin and look at your own coins but not each other's. The question is "What is the probability that both coins show heads?" Suppose you see that your coin shows tails; you say that the probability that both coins are heads is zero because you *know* that yours is tails. On the other hand, suppose your friend sees that his coin is heads; then he says that the probability of both heads is $\frac{1}{2}$ because he has no way of knowing whether your coin shows heads or tails. Now suppose neither of you looks at either coin, but a third person looks at both coins and gives you the information that at least one is heads. Without this information, there are four possibilities, namely

(1.1)   *hh   tt   th   ht*

to each of which we would ordinarily assign the probability $\frac{1}{4}$ (see end of Section 2, and Section 3). The information "at least one head" rules out *tt*, but gives no new information about the other three cases. Since *hh*, *th*, *ht* were equally likely before, we still consider them equally likely and say that the probability of *hh* is $\frac{1}{3}$.

Notice in the above discussion that the answer to a probability problem depends on the state of knowledge (or ignorance) of the person giving the answer. Notice also that in order to find the probability of an event, we consider all the different equally likely outcomes which are possible according to our information. We say that these are mutually exclusive (for example, if a coin is heads it cannot be tails), collectively exhaustive (we must consider *all* possibilities), and equally likely (we have no information which makes us expect one result more than another so we assume the same probability for each one of the set of outcomes). Let us now formalize this notion of probability as a definition (also see Section 2).

(1.2)   If there are several equally likely, mutually exclusive, and collectively exhaustive outcomes of an experiment, the probability
             of an event E is

$$p = \frac{\text{number of outcomes favorable to } E}{\text{total number of outcomes}}.$$

Example 1. Find the probability that a single card drawn from a shuffled deck of cards will be either a diamond or a king (or both).

There are 52 different possible outcomes of the drawing; since the deck is shuffled, we assume all cards equally likely. Of the 52 cards, 16 are favorable (13 diamonds and the other 3 kings); therefore by (1.2) the desired probability is $\frac{16}{52} = \frac{4}{13}$.

Example 2. A three-digit number (that is, a number from 100 to 999) is selected "at random." ("At random" means that we assume all numbers to have the same probability of being selected.) What is the probability that all three digits are the same?

There are 900 such numbers; 9 of them (namely 111, 222, ..., 999) have all three digits the same. Hence the desired probability is $\frac{9}{900} = \frac{1}{100}$.

2. SAMPLE SPACE

It is frequently convenient to make a list of the possible outcomes of an experiment [as we did in (1.1)]. Such a set of all possible mutually exclusive outcomes is called a *sample space*; each individual outcome is called a *point* of the sample space. There are many different sample spaces for any given problem. For example, instead of (1.1), we could say that a set of all mutually exclusive outcomes of two tosses of a coin is

(2.1)   2 heads,   1 head,   no heads.

Still another sample space for the same problem is

(2.2)   no heads,   at least 1 head.

(Can you list some more examples?) On the other hand, the set of outcomes
                 2 heads,   at least 1 head,   exactly 1 tail

cannot be used as a sample space, because these outcomes are not mutually exclusive. "At least 1 head" includes "2 heads" and also includes "exactly 1 tail" (which means also "exactly 1 head").

In order to use a sample space to solve problems, we need to have the probabilities corresponding to the different points of the sample space. We usually assign probability $\frac{1}{4}$ to each of the outcomes listed in (1.1). (See end of Section 2, and Section 3.) We call such a list of equally likely outcomes a *uniform* sample space. Either by using the uniform sample space (1.1) or in some other way (see Sections 3 and 4) you can verify that the probabilities associated with the points of (2.1) and (2.2) are:

(2.1) $2h$ $1h$ no h
                $\frac{1}{4}$ $\frac{1}{2}$ $\frac{1}{4}$

(2.2)   no h at least 1 h
                   $\frac{1}{4}$ $\frac{3}{4}$

The sample spaces (2.1) and (2.2) with different probabilities associated with different points are called *non-uniform* sample spaces. For some problems, there may be both uniform and non-uniform sample spaces;

for example, (1.1) is a uniform sample space and (2.1) and (2.2) are non-uniform sample spaces for a toss of two coins. But sometimes there *is* no uniform sample space; for example, consider a weighted coin which has probability $\frac{1}{3}$ for heads and $\frac{2}{3}$ for tails. In such cases, we cannot use the definition (1.2) of probability, and we need the following more general definition.

Definition of probability. Given any sample space (uniform or not) and the probabilities associated with the points, we find the probability of an event by adding the probabilities associated with all the sample points favorable to the event.

For a given non-uniform sample space, we must use this definition since (1.2) does not apply. If the given sample space is uniform, or if there is an underlying uniform sample space [for example, (1.1) is the uniform space underlying (2.1) and (2.2)], then this definition is consistent with the definition (1.2) by equally likely cases (Problems 15 and 16), and we may use either definition.

Example. Let us find from (2.1) the probability of at least one head; this is the probability of one head plus the probability of two heads or $\frac{1}{2} + \frac{1}{4} = \frac{3}{4}$. We get the same result from (1.1) and (2.1).

If we can easily construct several sample spaces for a given problem, we must choose an appropriate one for the question we want to answer. Suppose we ask the question: In two tosses of a coin, what is the probability that both are heads? From either (1.1) or (2.1) we find the answer $\frac{1}{4}$; (2.2) is not an appropriate sample space to use in answering this question. (Why not?) To find the probability of both tails, we could use any of the three listed sample spaces, and to find the probability that the first toss gave a head and the second a tail, we could use only (1.1) since the other sample spaces do not give enough information. Let us now consider some less trivial examples.

Example 1. A coin is tossed three times. A uniform sample space for this problem contains eight points,

(2.3) hhh hth ttt tht
         hht thh tth htt

and we attach probability $\frac{1}{8}$ to each. Now let us use this sample space to answer some questions.

What is the probability of at least two tails in succession? By actual count, we see that there are three such cases, so the probability is $\frac{3}{8}$.

What is the probability that two consecutive coins fall the same? Again by actual count, this is true in six cases, so the probability is $\frac{6}{8}$ or $\frac{3}{4}$.

If we know that there was at least one tail, what is the probability of all tails? The point *hhh* is now ruled out; we have a new sample space consisting of seven points. Since the new information (at least one tail) tells us nothing new about these seven outcomes, we consider them equally probable, each with probability $\frac{1}{7}$. Thus the probability of all tails when all heads is ruled out is $\frac{1}{7}$.

(See Problems 11 and 12 for further discussion of this example.)

Example 2. Let two dice be thrown; the first die can show any number from 1 to 6 and similarly for the second die. Then there are 36 possible outcomes or points in a uniform sample space for this problem; with each point we associate the probability $\frac{1}{36}$. We can indicate a 3 on the first die and a 2 on the second die by the symbol 3,2. Then the sample space is as shown in (2.4). (Ignore the circling of some points and the letters *a* and *b* right now; they are for use in the problems below.)

$$
(2.4) \quad
\begin{array}{cccccc}
1,1 & 1,2 & 1,3 & 1,4 & 1,5 & 1,6 \\
2,1 & 2,2 & 2,3 & 2,4 & 2,5 & 2,6 \\
3,1 & 3,2 & 3,3 & 3,4 & 3,5 & 3,6 \\
4,1 & 4,2 & 4,3 & 4,4 & 4,5 & 4,6 \\
5,1 & 5,2 & 5,3 & 5,4 & 5,5 & 5,6 \\
6,1 & 6,2 & 6,3 & 6,4 & 6,5 & 6,6 \\
\end{array}
$$

Let us now ask some questions and use the sample space (2.4) to answer them.

(a) What is the probability that the sum of the numbers on the dice will be 5? The sample space points circled and marked *a* in (2.4) give all the cases for which the sum is 5. There are four of these sample points; therefore the probability that the sum is 5 is $\frac{4}{36}$ or $\frac{1}{9}$.

(b) What is the probability that the sum on the dice is divisible by 5? This means a sum of 5 or 10, so we want to know the number of sample points for which the sum is either 5 or 10. The four points circled and marked *a* in (2.4) correspond to a sum of 5, and the three points circled and marked *b* correspond to a sum of 10. Thus there are seven points in the sample space corresponding to a sum divisible by 5, so the probability of a sum divisible by 5 is $\frac{7}{36}$ (7 favorable cases out of 36 possible cases, or 7 times the probability $\frac{1}{36}$ of each of the favorable sample points).

(c) Set up a sample space in which the points correspond to the possible sums of the two numbers on the dice, and find the probabilities associated with the points of this non-uniform sample space. The possible sums range from 2 (that is, $1 + 1$) to 12 (that is, $6 + 6$). From (2.4) we see that the points corresponding to any given sum lie on a diagonal (parallel to the diagonal elements marked *a* or *b*). There is one point corresponding to the sum 2; there are two points giving the sum 3, three points for sum 4, etc. Thus we have:

(2.5)

Sample space	2	3	4	5	6	7	8	9	10	11	12
Associated probabilities	$\frac{1}{36}$	$\frac{2}{36}$	$\frac{3}{36}$	$\frac{4}{36}$	$\frac{5}{36}$	$\frac{6}{36}$	$\frac{5}{36}$	$\frac{4}{36}$	$\frac{3}{36}$	$\frac{2}{36}$	$\frac{1}{36}$

(d) What is the most probable sum in a toss of two dice? Although we can answer this from the sample space (2.4) (Try it!), it is easier from (2.5). We see that the sum 7 has the largest probability, namely $\frac{6}{36} = \frac{1}{6}$.

(e) What is the probability that the sum on the dice is greater than or equal to 9? Using (2.5), we add the probabilities associated with the sums 9, 10, 11, and 12. Thus the desired probability is

$$\frac{4}{36} + \frac{3}{36} + \frac{2}{36} + \frac{1}{36} = \frac{10}{36} = \frac{5}{18}.$$

So far we have been talking as if it were perfectly obvious and un-questionable that heads and tails are equally likely in the toss of a coin. If you have felt skeptical about this, you are perfectly right. It is *not* obvious; it is not even necessarily true, as a bent or weighted coin would show. We must distinguish here between the mathematical theory of probability and its application to a problem about the physical world. Mathematical probability (like all of mathematics) starts with a set of assumptions and shows that *if* the assumptions are true, *then* various results follow. The basic assumptions in a mathematical probability problem are the probabilities associated with the points of the sample space. Thus in a coin tossing problem, we *assume* that for each toss the probability of heads and the probability of tails are both $\frac{1}{2}$, and then we show that the probability of both heads in two tosses is $\frac{1}{4}$. (See Section 3.) The question of whether the assumptions are correct is not a mathematical one. Here we must ask what physical problem we are trying to solve. If we are dealing with a weighted coin, and if we know or can somehow estimate experimentally the probability p of heads (and so $1 - p$ of tails), then the mathematical theory starts with these values instead of $\frac{1}{2}$, $\frac{1}{2}$. In the absence of any information as to whether heads or tails is more likely, we often make the "natural" or "intuitive" assumption that the probabilities are both $\frac{1}{2}$. The only possible answer to the question of

whether this is correct or not lies in experiment. If the results predicted
on the basis of our assumptions agree with experiment, then the assumptions are good; otherwise we must revise the assumptions. (See Section 4,
Example 5.)

In this chapter we shall consider mainly the mathematical methods of
calculating the probabilities of complicated happenings if we are given
the probabilities associated with the points of the sample space. For
simplicity, we shall often assume these probabilities to be the "natural"
ones; the mathematical theory we develop applies, however, if we replace
these "natural" probabilities ($\frac{1}{2}$, $\frac{1}{2}$ in the coin problem, etc.) by any set of
non-negative fractions whose sum is 1.

3. PROBABILITY THEOREMS

It is not always easy to make direct use of our definitions to calculate
probabilities. Definition (1.2) asks us to find a uniform sample space for
a problem, that is, a set of all the possible *equally likely*, mutually
exclusive outcomes of an experiment, and then determine how many of
these are favorable to a given event. The definition in Section 2 similarly
requires a sample space, that is, a list of the possible outcomes and their
probabilities. Such lists may be prohibitively long; we want to consider
some theorems which will shorten our work.

Suppose there are 5 black balls and 10 white balls in a box; we draw
one ball "at random" (this means we are assuming that each ball has
probability $\frac{1}{15}$ of being drawn), and then without replacing the first ball
we draw another. Let us ask for the probability that the first ball is white
and the second one is black. The probability of drawing a white ball the
first time is $\frac{10}{15}$ (10 of the 15 balls are white). The probability of *then*
drawing a black ball is $\frac{5}{14}$ since there are 14 balls left and 5 of them are
black. We are going to show that the probability of drawing first a white
ball and then (without replacement) a black ball is the product $\frac{10}{15} \cdot \frac{5}{14}$.
We reason in the following way, using a uniform sample space. Imagine
that the balls are numbered 1 to 15. The symbol 5,3 will mean that ball 5
was drawn the first time, and ball 3 the second time. In such pairs of two
(different) numbers representing a drawing of two balls in succession,
there are 15 choices for the first number and 14 for the second (the first
ball was not replaced). Thus the uniform sample space representing all
possible drawings consists of a rectangular array of symbols (like 5,3)
with 15 columns (for the 15 different choices for the first number) and
14 rows (for the 14 choices for the second number). Thus there are $15 \cdot 14$

points in the sample space. [See also (4.1)]. How many of these sample points correspond to drawing first a white ball and then a black ball? Ten numbers correspond to white balls and the other five to black balls. Thus to obtain a sample point corresponding to drawing first a white and then a black ball, we can choose the first number in 10 ways, and then the second number in 5 ways, and so choose the sample point in $10 \cdot 5$ ways; that is, there are $10 \cdot 5$ sample points favorable to the desired drawing. Then by the definition (1.2), the desired probability is $\dfrac{10 \cdot 5}{15 \cdot 14}$ as claimed.

Let us state in general the theorem we have just illustrated. We are interested in two successive events A and B. Let $P(A)$ be the probability

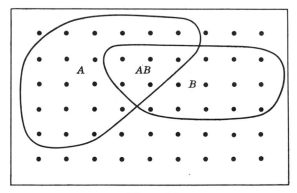

Figure 3.1

that A will happen, $P(AB)$ be the probability that both A and B will happen, and $P_A(B)$ be the probability that B will happen if we know that A has happened. Then

(3.1) $P(AB) = P(A) \cdot P_A(B)$

or in words, the probability of the compound event "A *and* B" is the product of the probability that A will happen times the probability that B will happen if A does. Using the idea of a uniform sample space, we can prove (3.1) by following the method in the ball drawing problem. Let N be the total number of sample points in a uniform sample space, $N(A)$ and $N(B)$ be the numbers of sample points corresponding to the events A and B respectively, and $N(AB)$ be the number of sample points corresponding to the compound event A *and* B. It is useful to picture the sample space geometrically (Fig. 3.1) as an array of N points [compare the sample space (2.4)]. We can then circle all points which correspond to A's happening and mark this region A; it contains $N(A)$ points. Similarly, we can circle the $N(B)$ points which correspond to B's happening and call this region B. The overlapping region we call AB; it is part of both A and B and contains $N(AB)$ points which correspond to the compound event A *and* B. Then by the definition (1.2):

$$P(AB) = \frac{N(AB)}{N},$$

(3.2) $$P(A) = \frac{N(A)}{N},$$

$$P_A(B) = \frac{N(AB)}{N(A)}.$$

Perhaps this last formula for $P_A(B)$ needs some discussion. Recall from Section 2, Example 1, the uniform sample space (2.3) for three tosses of a coin. To find the probability of all tails given that there was at least one tail, we reduced our sample space to seven points (eliminating *hhh*). We then assumed that the seven points of the new sample space had the same relative probability as before the deletion of the point *hhh*; thus each of the seven points had probability $\frac{1}{7}$. (This is no more and no less "obvious" than the original assumption that the eight points had equal probability; it is an additional assumption which we make in the absence of any information to the contrary; see end of Section 2.) Now let us look at the third equation of (3.2). $N(A)$ is the number of sample points corresponding to event A; the N points in the original sample space all had the same probability so we now assume that when we cross off all the points corresponding to A's *not* happening, the remaining $N(A)$ points also have equal probability. Thus we have a new uniform sample space consisting of $N(A)$ points. $N(AB)$ of these $N(A)$ points correspond to the event B (assuming A). Thus by (1.2), the probability of "B if A" is $N(AB)/N(A)$. From the three equations (3.2), we then have (3.1). In a similar way we can show that

(3.3) $$P(BA) = P(B) \cdot P_B(A) = P(AB)$$

(see Problem 23). [We have proved (3.1) assuming a uniform sample space. This assumption is not necessary; (3.1) is true whether or not we can construct a uniform sample space; see Problem 26.]

Suppose, now, in our example of 5 black and 10 white balls in a box, we draw a ball and replace it and then draw a second ball. The probability of a black ball on the second drawing is then $\frac{5}{15} = \frac{1}{3}$; this is exactly the same result we would get if we had not drawn and replaced the first ball. In the notation of the last paragraph

(3.4) $P(B) = P_A(B),$ A and B independent.

When (3.4) is true, we say that the event B is *independent* of event A and (3.1) becomes

(3.5) $P(AB) = P(A) \cdot P(B),$ A and B independent.

Because of the symmetry of (3.5), we may simply say that A and B are independent if (3.5) is true. (Also see Problem 31.)

Example 1.   (a) In three tosses of a coin, what is the probability that all three are heads? We found $p = \frac{1}{8}$ for this problem in Section 2 by seeing that one sample point out of eight corresponds to all heads. Now we can do the problem more simply by saying that the probability of heads on each toss is $\frac{1}{2}$, the tosses are independent, and therefore

$$p = \tfrac{1}{2} \cdot \tfrac{1}{2} \cdot \tfrac{1}{2} = \tfrac{1}{8}.$$

(b) If we should want the probability of all heads when a coin is tossed ten times, the sample space would be unwieldy; instead of using the sample space, we can say that since the tosses are independent, the desired probability is $p = (\frac{1}{2})^{10}$.

(c) To find the probability of at least one tail in ten tosses, we see that this event corresponds to all the rest of the sample space except the "all heads" point. Since the sum of the probabilities of all the sample points is 1, the desired probability is $1 - (\frac{1}{2})^{10}$.

Example 2.   (a) A loaded die has probabilities $\frac{1}{21}$, $\frac{2}{21}$, $\frac{3}{21}$, $\frac{4}{21}$, $\frac{5}{21}$, $\frac{6}{21}$, of showing 1, 2, 3, 4, 5, 6. What is the probability of throwing two 3's in succession? Since the throws are independent, $p = (\frac{3}{21})^2 = \frac{1}{49}$.

(b) What is the probability of throwing a 4 the first time and not a 4 the second time with a die loaded as in (a)? The probability of "not a 4" is, to be sure, the sum of the other five probabilities, but it is easier to find it as $1 - \frac{4}{21}$ since the sum of the probabilities of all possible cases is 1. Then the desired probability is $p = \frac{4}{21} \cdot \frac{17}{21}$.

(c) If two dice loaded as in (a) are thrown, and we know that the sum of the numbers on the faces is greater than or equal to 10, what is the probability that both are 5's? One way to do this problem is to set up the sample space (2.4) and find the probabilities associated with each of the points. Here we are interested only in the points for which the sum is ≥ 10, so let us list only these points [referring to (2.4) if necessary], and compute their probabilities as we did in (a) and (b).

	6,4	5,5	4,6	6,5	5,6	6,6
(3.6)	$\dfrac{6 \cdot 4}{21^2}$	$\dfrac{5 \cdot 5}{21^2}$	$\dfrac{4 \cdot 6}{21^2}$	$\dfrac{6 \cdot 5}{21^2}$	$\dfrac{5 \cdot 6}{21^2}$	$\dfrac{6 \cdot 6}{21^2}$

What we have listed here is a part of the total sample space (2.4). Now what we want is a new sample space consisting of just these points. Remember that we assume that the relative probabilities stay the same in the smaller sample space. We must multiply the probabilities in (3.6) all by the same number chosen so as to make their sum 1. You can verify that the sum of the probabilities in (3.6) is $169/21^2$, so we multiply each probability by $21^2/169$ to obtain the probabilities in the new sample space:

	6,4	5,5	4,6	6,5	5,6	6,6
(3.7)	$\dfrac{6 \cdot 4}{169}$	$\dfrac{5 \cdot 5}{169}$	$\dfrac{4 \cdot 6}{169}$	$\dfrac{6 \cdot 5}{169}$	$\dfrac{5 \cdot 6}{169}$	$\dfrac{6 \cdot 6}{169}$

In this sample space we want the probability that the numbers on the dice are both 5's. There is only one sample point corresponding to this requirement, so the desired probability is just the probability of that point, namely $\dfrac{5 \cdot 5}{169} = \left(\dfrac{5}{13}\right)^2$.

Another way to do this problem is to use (3.1) with A meaning "sum of numbers ≥ 10," and B meaning "both 5's." Then $P(AB)$ means the probability that the sum of the numbers is greater than or equal to 10 and the numbers are both 5's; this is $(\frac{5}{21})^2$. $P(A)$ means the probability that the sum of the numbers is greater than or equal to 10; this we found above to be $\dfrac{169}{21^2}$. The symbol $P_A(B)$ means the probability of B ("both are 5's") when we know A ("sum ≥ 10"); this is the desired probability and by (3.1) it is

$$P_A(B) = \frac{P(AB)}{P(A)} = \left(\frac{5}{21}\right)^2 \bigg/ \frac{169}{21^2} = \left(\frac{5}{13}\right)^2$$

as above. [When (3.1) is used in this way, it is often called Bayes' formula; see Goldberg, p. 91.]

(d) How many times must we throw a die loaded as in (a) to have probability greater than $\frac{1}{2}$ of getting an ace?

The probability of getting an ace at any throw is $\frac{1}{21}$, so the probability of not getting an ace is $\frac{20}{21}$. Then the probability of not getting an ace in any of n consecutive throws is $(\frac{20}{21})^n$. We want this probability to be less than $\frac{1}{2}$, for then the probability of getting an ace on at least one throw is greater than $\frac{1}{2}$. To solve $(\frac{20}{21})^n < \frac{1}{2}$, take logarithms of both sides of the inequality and find n as follows:

$$\log \left(\frac{20}{21}\right)^n = n \log \frac{20}{21} < \log \frac{1}{2} = -\log 2,$$

$$n \log \frac{21}{20} > \log 2,$$

$$n > \log 2/\log \frac{21}{20} = \frac{0.301}{0.021} = 14.3.$$

Thus we must toss the die 15 times.

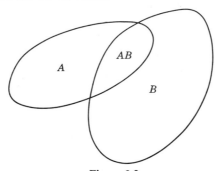

Figure 3.2

In Fig. 3.1 or Fig. 3.2 the region AB corresponds to the happening of *both* A and B. The whole region consisting of points in A or B or both corresponds to the happening of *either A or B or both*. We wrote $P(AB)$ for the probability that both A and B occur. We shall write $P(A + B)$ for the probability that either or both occur. Then we can prove that

$$(3.8) \qquad P(A + B) = P(A) + P(B) - P(AB).$$

To see why this is true, consider Fig. 3.2. To find $P(A + B)$ we add the probabilities of all the sample points in the region consisting of A or B or both. But if we add $P(A)$ and $P(B)$ we have included the probabilities of all the sample points in AB twice [once in $P(A)$ and once in $P(B)$]. Thus we must subtract $P(AB)$, which is the sum of the probabilities of all the sample points in AB. This is just what (3.8) says.

If the sample space diagram is like the one in Fig. 3.3, so that $P(AB) = 0$, we say that A and B are mutually exclusive. Then (3.8) becomes

$$(3.9) \quad P(A + B) = P(A) + P(B), \qquad A \text{ and } B \text{ mutually exclusive.}$$

Figure 3.3

Example 3. Two students are working separately on the same problem. If the first student has probability $\frac{1}{2}$ of solving it and the second student has probability $\frac{3}{4}$ of solving it, what is the probability that at least one of them solves it?

Let A be the event "first student succeeds," and B be the event "second student succeeds." Then $P(AB) = \frac{1}{2} \cdot \frac{3}{4} = \frac{3}{8}$ (we assume A and B independent since the students work separately). Then by (3.8) the probability that one or the other or both students solve the problem is

$$P(A + B) = \tfrac{1}{2} + \tfrac{3}{4} - \tfrac{3}{8} = \tfrac{7}{8}.$$

Example 4. A card is selected from a shuffled deck, and then a second card is selected (without replacement of the first). What is the probability that the second card is a spade? (Note that we have no information about the first card.)

Let A mean "first card spade and second card spade";

B mean "first card not spade and second card spade."

Then $P(A) = \frac{13}{52} \cdot \frac{12}{51}$ (that is, the probability of a spade the first time times the probability of then getting a spade again with 12 remaining spades and 51 remaining cards). Similarly, $P(B) = \frac{39}{52} \cdot \frac{13}{51}$. A and B are mutually exclusive since we cannot draw both "spade" and "not spade" on the first draw. Then, using (3.9), we find for the probability that the second card is a spade

$$P(A + B) = \frac{13 \cdot 12 + 39 \cdot 13}{52 \cdot 51} = \frac{1}{4}.$$

Note that this is the same as the probability that the first card is a spade. (If this seems unreasonable to you, imagine discarding one card after another without looking at them; what is the probability that the last card is a spade?)

Example 5. A preliminary test is customarily given to the students at the beginning of a certain course. The following data are accumulated after several years:

95% of the students pass the course, 5% fail.

96% of the students who pass the course also passed the preliminary test.

25% of the students who fail the course passed the preliminary test.

Given a student who has failed the preliminary test, what is the probability of his passing the course?

Let A be the event "fails preliminary test" and B be the event "passes course." The probability we want is then $P_A(B)$. By (3.1), $P_A(B) = P(AB)/P(A)$. $P(AB)$ is the probability that the student both fails the preliminary test and passes the course; this is $P(AB) = (0.95)(0.04) = 0.038$. (See Fig. 3.4; 95% of the students passed the course and of these 4% had

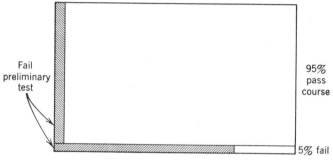

Figure 3.4

failed the preliminary test.) We also want $P(A)$, the probability that a student fails the preliminary test; this event corresponds to the shaded area in Fig. 3.4. Thus $P(A)$ is the sum of the probabilities of the two events "passes course after failing test," "fails course after failing test." Then

$$P(A) = (0.95)(0.04) + (0.05)(0.75) = 0.0755$$

(See Fig. 3.4; of the 95% of the students who passed the course, 4% failed the preliminary test; of the 5% of the students who failed the course, 75% failed the preliminary test since we are given that 25% passed.) By (3.1) we have

$$P_A(B) = \frac{P(AB)}{P(A)} = \frac{0.038}{0.0755} = 50\%,$$

that is, half the students who fail the preliminary test succeed in passing the course.

Note that in Fig. 3.4, the shaded area corresponds to event A (fails preliminary test). We are interested in event B (passes course) given event A. Thus instead of the original sample space (whole rectangle in Fig. 3.4) we consider a smaller sample space (shaded area in Fig. 3.4). We then want to know what part of this sample space corresponds to event B (passes course). This fraction is $P(AB)/P(A)$ which we computed.

4. METHODS OF COUNTING

Let us digress for a bit to review some ideas and formulas we need in computing probabilities in more complicated problems.

Let us ask how many two-digit numbers have either 5 or 7 for the tens digit, and either 3, 4, or 6 for the units digit. The answer becomes obvious if we arrange the possible numbers in a rectangle

$$53 \qquad 54 \qquad 56$$
$$73 \qquad 74 \qquad 76$$

with two rows corresponding to the two choices of the tens digit and three columns corresponding to the three choices of the units digit. This is an example of the *fundamental principle of counting*:

(4.1) If one thing can be done N_1 ways, and after that a second thing can be done in N_2 ways, the two things can be done in succession in that order in $N_1 \cdot N_2$ ways. This can be extended to doing any number of things one after the other, the first N_1 ways, the second N_2 ways, the third N_3 ways, etc. Then the total number of ways to perform the succession of acts is $N_1 N_2 N_3 \cdots$.

Now consider a set of n things lined up in a row; we ask how many ways we can arrange (permute) them. This result is called the number of *permutations* of n things n at a time, and is denoted by $_nP_n$ or $P(n, n)$ or P_n^n. To find this number, we think of seating n people in a row of n chairs. We can place anyone in the first chair, that is, we have n possible ways of filling the first chair. Once we have selected someone for the first chair, there are $(n - 1)$ choices left for the second chair, then $(n - 2)$ choices for the third chair, etc. Thus, by the fundamental principle, there are $n(n - 1)(n - 2) \cdots 2 \cdot 1 = n!$ ways of arranging the n people in the row of n chairs. The number of permutations of n things n at a time is

(4.2) $$P(n, n) = n!.$$

Next suppose there are n people but only $r < n$ chairs and we ask how many ways we can select groups of r people and seat them in the r chairs. The result is called the number of permutations of n things r at a time and is denoted by $_nP_r$ or $P(n, r)$ or P_r^n. Arguing as before, we find that there are n ways to fill the first chair, $(n - 1)$ ways to fill the second chair, $(n - 2)$ ways for the third [note that we could write this as $(n - 3 + 1)$], etc., and finally $(n - r + 1)$ ways of filling chair r. Thus we have for the number of permutations of n things r at a time

$$P(n, r) = n(n - 1)(n - 2) \cdots (n - r + 1).$$

By multiplying and dividing by $(n - r)!$ we can write this as

$$(4.3) \quad P(n, r) = n(n - 1)(n - 2) \cdots (n - r + 1) \frac{(n - r)!}{(n - r)!} = \frac{n!}{(n - r)!}.$$

So far we have been talking about arranging things in a definite order. Suppose, instead, that we ask how many committees of r people can be chosen from a group of n people $(n \geq r)$. Here the order of the people in the committee is not considered; the committee made up of people A, B, C, is the same as the committee made up of the people B, A, C. We call the number of such committees of r people which we can select from n people, the number of *combinations* or *selections* of n things r at a time, and denote this number by ${}_nC_r$ or $C(n, r)$ or $\binom{n}{r}$. To find $C(n, r)$, we go

back to the problem of selecting r people from a group of n and seating them in r chairs; we found that the number of ways of doing this is $P(n, r)$ as given in (4.3). We can perform this job by first selecting r people from the total n and then arranging the r people in r chairs. The selection of r people can be done in $C(n, r)$ ways (this is the number we are trying to find), and after r people are selected, they can be arranged in r chairs in $P(r, r)$ ways by (4.2). By the fundamental principle (4.1), the total number of ways $P(n, r)$ of selecting and seating r people out of n is the product $C(n, r) \cdot P(r, r)$. Thus we have

$$(4.4) \qquad\qquad P(n, r) = C(n, r) \cdot P(r, r).$$

We can solve this equation to find the value $C(n, r)$ which we wanted. Substituting the values of $P(n, r)$ and $P(r, r)$ from (4.3) and (4.2) into (4.4) and solving for $C(n, r)$, we find for the number of combinations of n things r at a time

$$(4.5) \qquad\qquad C(n, r) = \frac{P(n, r)}{P(r, r)} = \frac{n!}{(n - r)! \, r!}.$$

Each time we select r people to be seated, we leave $n - r$ people without chairs. Then there are exactly the same number of combinations of n things $n - r$ at a time as there are combinations of n things r at a time. Hence we write

$$(4.6) \qquad\qquad C(n, n - r) = C(n, r) = \frac{n!}{(n - r)! \, r!}.$$

We can also obtain (4.6) from (4.5) by replacing r by $(n - r)$.

Example 1. A club consists of 50 members. In how many ways can a president, vice-president, secretary, and treasurer be chosen? In how many ways can a committee of 4 members be chosen?

In the selection of officers, we must not only select 4 people, but decide which one is president, etc; we could think of seating the 4 people in chairs labeled president, vice-president, etc. Thus the number of ways of selecting the officers is

$$P(50, 4) = \frac{50!}{(50 - 4)!} = \frac{50!}{46!} = 50 \cdot 49 \cdot 48 \cdot 47.$$

The committee members, however, are all equivalent (we are neglecting the possibility that one is named chairman), so the number of ways of selecting committees of 4 people is

$$C(50, 4) = \frac{50!}{46! \, 4!} = \frac{50 \cdot 49 \cdot 48 \cdot 47}{24}.$$

Example 2. Find the coefficient of x^8 in the binomial expansion of $(1 + x)^{15}$.

Think of multiplying out

$$(1 + x)(1 + x)(1 + x) \cdots (1 + x), \qquad \text{(with 15 factors)}.$$

We obtain a term in x^8 each time we multiply 1's from seven of the parentheses by x's from eight of the parentheses. The number of ways of selecting 8 parentheses out of 15 is

$$C(15, 8) = \frac{15!}{8! \, 7!}.$$

This is the desired coefficient of x^8.

Generalizing this example, we see that in the expansion of $(a + b)^n$, the coefficient of $a^{n-r}b^r$ is $C(n, r)$, usually written $\binom{n}{r}$ when used in connection with a binomial expansion. Thus the expressions $C(n, r)$ are just the binomial coefficients, and we can write

$$(4.7) \qquad\qquad (a + b)^n = \sum_{r=0}^{n} \binom{n}{r} a^{n-r} b^r.$$

Example 3. A basic problem in statistical mechanics is this: Given N balls, and n boxes, in how many ways can the balls be put into the boxes so that there will be given numbers of balls in the boxes, say N_1 balls in the first box, N_2 balls in the second box, N_3 in the third, ..., N_n in the *n*th, and what is the probability that this given distribution will occur when the balls are put into the boxes? In statistical mechanics the "balls" may be molecules, electrons, photons, etc., and each "box" corresponds to a small range of values of position and momentum of a particle. We can state many other problems in this same language of putting balls into boxes. For example, in tossing a coin, we can equate heads with box 1, and tails with box 2; in tossing a die, there are six "boxes." In putting letters into envelopes, the letters are the balls, and the envelopes are the boxes. In dealing cards, the cards are the balls, and the players who receive them are the boxes. In an alpha-scattering experiment, the alpha particles are the balls, and the boxes are elements of area on the detecting screen which the particles hit after they are scattered. (Also see Problems 48 and 52, and Feller, pp. 10–11.)

Let us do a special case of this problem in which we have 15 balls and 6 boxes, and the numbers of balls we are to put into the various boxes are:

Number of balls:	3	1	4	2	3	2
In box number:	1	2	3	4	5	6

We first ask how many ways we can select 3 balls to go in the first box from the 15 balls; this is $C(15, 3)$. (Note that the order of the balls in the boxes is not considered; this is like the committee problem in Example 1.) Now we have 12 balls left, of which we are to select 1 for box 2; we can do this in $C(12, 1)$ ways. We can then select the 4 balls for box 3 from the remaining 11 balls in $C(11, 4)$ ways, the 2 balls for box 4 in $C(7, 2)$ ways, the 3 balls for box 5 in $C(5, 3)$ ways, and finally the balls for box 6 in $C(2, 2)$ ways (verify that this is 1). By the fundamental principle, the total number of ways of putting the required numbers of balls into the boxes is

$$C(15, 3) \cdot C(12, 1) \cdot C(11, 4) \cdot C(7, 2) \cdot C(5, 3) \cdot C(2, 2)$$

$$= \frac{15!}{3! \cdot 12!} \cdot \frac{12!}{1! \cdot 11!} \cdot \frac{11!}{4! \cdot 7!} \cdot \frac{7!}{2! \cdot 5!} \cdot \frac{5!}{3! \cdot 2!} \cdot \frac{2!}{2! \cdot 0!}$$

$$= \frac{15!}{3! \cdot 1! \cdot 4! \cdot 2! \cdot 3! \cdot 2!}.$$

(Remember from Chapters 1 and 9 that $0! = 1$.)

Next we want the probability of this particular distribution. Let us assume that the balls are distributed "at random" into the boxes; by this we mean that a ball has the same probability (namely $\frac{1}{6}$) of being put into any one box as into any other box. We can put the first ball into any one of the 6 boxes, the second ball into any one of the 6 boxes, etc.

Thus by the fundamental principle, the total number of ways of distributing the 15 balls into the 6 boxes is $6 \cdot 6 \cdot 6 \cdot 6 \cdots 6 = 6^{15}$ and we are assuming that these distributions are equally probable. Then the probability that, when 15 balls are distributed "at random" into 6 boxes, there will be 3 balls in box 1, 1 in box 2, etc., as given, is, by (1.2) (favorable cases ÷ total)

$$\frac{15!}{3! \cdot 1! \cdot 4! \cdot 2! \cdot 3! \cdot 2!} \div 6^{15}.$$

Example 4. In Example 3, we assumed that the 6^{15} possible distributions of 15 balls into 6 boxes were equally likely. This seems very reasonable if we think of putting the balls into the boxes by tossing a die for each ball; if the die shows 1 we put the ball into box 1, etc. However, we can think of situations to which this method and result do not apply. For example, suppose we are putting letters into envelopes or seating people in chairs; then we may reasonably require only one letter per envelope, not more than one person per chair, that is, one ball (or none) per box. Consider the problem of seating 4 people in 6 chairs, that is, of putting 4 balls into 6 boxes. If we number the chairs from 1 to 6 and let each person choose his chair by tossing a die, we may have two or more people choosing the same chair. The result 6^4 (which the method of Example 3 gives for the problem of 4 balls in 6 boxes) then does not apply to this problem. However, let us consider the uniform sample space of 6^4 points and select from it the points corresponding to our restriction (one ball or none per box). The new sample space contains $C(6, 4) \cdot 4!$ points (number of ways of selecting the 4 chairs to be occupied times the number of ways of then arranging 4 people in 4 chairs). Since these points were equally probable in the original (uniform) sample space, we still consider them equally probable. Now let us ask for the probability that the first two chairs are vacant when the 4 people are seated. The number of sample points corresponding to this event is 4! (the number of ways of arranging the 4 people in the last 4 chairs). Thus the desired probability is

$$\frac{4!}{C(6, 4) \cdot 4!} = \frac{1}{C(6, 4)}.$$

We can now see an easier way of doing problems of this kind. The factor 4!, which canceled in the probability calculation, was the number of rearrangements of the 4 people among the 4 occupied chairs. Since this is the same for any given set of 4 chairs, we can lump together all the sample points corresponding to each given set of 4 chairs and have a smaller (still uniform) sample space of $C(6, 4)$ points. Each point now corresponds to a given set of 4 occupied chairs; the quantity $C(6, 4)$ is just the number of ways of picking 4 occupied chairs out of 6. The probability that the first two chairs are vacant when 4 people are seated is $1/C(6, 4)$ since there is only one way to select 4 occupied chairs leaving the first 2 chairs vacant.

Another useful way of looking at this problem is to consider a set of 4 *identical* balls to be put into 6 boxes. Since the balls are identical, the 4! arrangements of the 4 balls in 4 given boxes all look alike. We can say that there are $C(6, 4)$ *distinguishable* arrangements of the 4 identical balls in 6 boxes (one ball or none per box). Since all these arrangements are equally probable, the probability of any one arrangement (say the first 2 boxes empty) is $1/C(6, 4)$ as we found previously.

Example 5. In Example 4 we found the same answer for the probability that two particular boxes were empty whether or not we considered the balls distinguishable. This was true because the allowed distinguishable arrangements were equally probable. Without the restriction of one ball or none per box, all distinguishable arrangements are not equally probable according to the methods of Examples 3 and 4. For example, the probability of all balls in box 1 is $1/6^4$; compare this with the probability of no balls in the first 2 boxes and one ball in each of the other 4 boxes, which is $1/C(6, 4) = 4! \cdot 2!/6! = \frac{1}{15}$. We see that the concentrated arrangements (all or several balls in one box) are less probable than the more uniform arrangements.

Now we are going to try to imagine a situation in which *all* distinguishable arrangements *are* equally probable. Suppose the 6 boxes are benches in a waiting room and the 4 balls are people who are going to come in and sit on the benches. Then if the people are friends, there will be a certain tendency for them to sit together and the probabilities we have been calculating will not apply—the probabilities of the concentrated arrangements will increase. Consider the following mathematical model. (This is a modification of Pólya's urn model.) We have 6 boxes labeled 1 to 6, and 4 balls. From 6 cards labeled 1 to 6 we draw one at random and place a ball in the box numbered the same as the card drawn. We then replace the card and also add another card of the same number so that there are now 7 cards, two with the number first drawn. We now select a card at random from these 7, put a ball in the corresponding box and again replace the card adding a duplicate to make 8 cards. We repeat this process two more times (until all balls are distributed). Then the probability that all balls are in box 1 is $\frac{1}{6} \cdot \frac{2}{7} \cdot \frac{3}{8} \cdot \frac{4}{9}$. The probability that one ball is in each of the first 4 boxes is $\frac{1}{6} \cdot \frac{1}{7} \cdot \frac{1}{8} \cdot \frac{1}{9} \cdot 4!$ (here $\frac{1}{6} \cdot \frac{1}{7} \cdot \frac{1}{8} \cdot \frac{1}{9}$ is the probability that the first ball is in box 1, the second in box 2, etc.; we must add to this the probability that the first ball is in box 3, the second in box 1, etc.; there are 4! such possibilities all giving one ball in each of the first 4 boxes). We see that the distributions "all balls in box 1" and "one ball in each of the first 4 boxes" are equally probable. Further calculation (Problem 51) shows that all distinguishable arrangements are equally probable.

To find the number of distinguishable arrangements, consider the following picture of the 4 balls in the 6 boxes.

$$| \text{o} | \quad | \text{oo} | \quad | \text{o} | \quad |$$

| Box number: | 1 | 2 | 3 | 4 | 5 | 6 |
| Number of balls: | 1 | 0 | 2 | 0 | 1 | 0 |

The lines mean the sides of the boxes and the circles are the balls; note that it requires 7 lines to picture the 6 boxes. This picture shows one of many possible arrangements of the 4 balls in 6 boxes. In any such picture there must be a line at the beginning and at the end, but the rest of the lines (5 of them) and the 4 circles can be arranged in any order. You should convince yourself that every arrangement of the balls in the boxes can be so pictured. Then the number of such distinguishable arrangements is just the number of ways we can select 4 positions for the 4 circles out of 9 positions for the 5 lines and 4 circles. Thus there are $C(9, 4)$ equally likely arrangements in this problem.

We see then that putting balls in boxes is not quite as simple as we thought; we must say *how* we propose to distribute them and even before that we must think what practical problem we are trying to solve; this is what determines the sample space and the probabilities to be associated with the sample points. Unfortunately, it may not always be clear what the sample space probabilities should be; then the best we can do is to try various assumptions. In statistical mechanics it is found that certain particles (for example, the molecules of a gas) are correctly described if we assume that they behave like the balls of Example 3 (all 6^{15} arrangements equally likely); we then say that they obey Maxwell-Boltzmann statistics. Other particles (for example, electrons) behave like the people to be seated in Example 4 (one particle or none per box); we say that such particles obey Fermi-Dirac statistics. Finally some particles (for example, photons) act something like the friends who want to sit near each other (all distinguishable arrangements of identical particles are equally likely); we say that these particles obey Bose-Einstein statistics. For the problem of 4 particles in 6 boxes, there are then 6^4 equally likely arrangements for Maxwell-Boltzmann particles, $C(6, 4)$ for Fermi-Dirac particles, and $C(9, 4)$ for Bose-Einstein particles. (See Problems 49 to 51.)

5. RANDOM VARIABLES

In the problem of tossing two dice (Example 2, Section 2, or Example 2 Section 3) we may be more interested in the value of the sum of the numbers on the two dice than we are in the individual numbers. Let us call this sum x; then for each point of the sample space in (2.4), x has a value. For example, for the point 2,1, we have $x = 2 + 1 = 3$; for the point 6,2, we have $x = 8$, etc. Such a variable, x, which has a definite value for each sample point, is called a *random variable*. We can easily construct many more examples of random variables for the sample space (2.4); here are a few (Can you construct some more?):

$x =$ number of first die minus number on second;

$x =$ number on second die;

$x =$ probability p associated with the sample point;

$$x = \begin{cases} 1 \text{ if the sum is 7 or 11,} \\ 0 \text{ otherwise.} \end{cases}$$

For each of these random variables x, we could set up a table listing all the sample points in (2.4) and, next to each sample point, the corresponding value of x. This table may remind you of the tables of values we often use in plotting the graph of a function. In analytic geometry or in a physics problem, knowing x as a function of t means that for any given t we can find the corresponding value of x. In probability, the sample point corresponds to the independent variable t; given the sample point, we can find the corresponding value of the random variable x if we are given a description of x (for example, $x =$ sum of numbers on dice). The "description" corresponds to the formula $x(t)$ that we use in plotting a graph in analytic geometry. Thus we may say that a *random variable x is a function defined on a sample space.*

Probability functions. Let us consider further the random variable $x =$ "sum of numbers on dice" for a toss of two dice [sample space (2.4)]. We note that there are several sample points for which $x = 5$, namely the points marked a in (2.4). Similarly, there are several sample points for most of the other values of x. It is then convenient to lump together all the sample points corresponding to a given value of x, and consider a new sample space in which each point corresponds to one value of x; this is the sample space (2.5). The probability associated with each point of the new sample space is obtained as in Section 2, by adding the probabilities associated with all the points in the original sample space corresponding to the particular value of x. Each value of x, say x_i, has a probability p_i of occurrence; we may write $p_i = f(x_i) =$ probability that $x = x_i$, and call the function $f(x)$ the *probability function* for the random variable x. In (2.5) we have listed on the first line the values of x and on the second line the values of $f(x)$. [In this problem, x and $f(x)$ take on only a finite number of discrete values; in some later problems they will take on a continuous set of values.] We could also exhibit these values graphically (Fig. 5.1).

Now that we have the table of values (2.5) or the graph (Fig. 5.1) to describe the random variable x and its probability function $f(x)$, we can

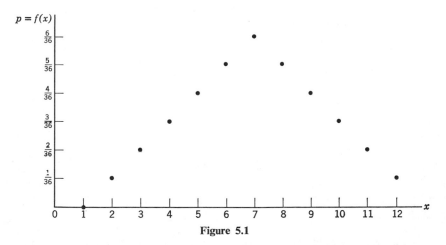

Figure 5.1

dispense with the original sample space (2.4). Since we used (2.4) in defining what is meant by a random variable, however, let us now give another definition using (2.5) or Fig. 5.1. We can say that *x is a random variable if it takes on various values x_i with probabilities $p_i = f(x_i)$*. This definition may explain the name random variable; x is called a variable since it takes on various values. A random (or stochastic) process is one whose outcome is not known in advance. The way the two dice fall is such an unknown outcome, so the value of x is unknown in advance, and we call x a *random* variable.

You may note that at first we thought of x as a dependent variable or function with the sample point as the independent variable. Although we didn't say much about it, there was also a value of the probability p attached to each sample point, that is, p and x were both functions of the sample point. In the last paragraph, we have thought of x as an independent variable with p as a function of x. This is quite analogous to having both x and p given as functions of t and eliminating t to obtain p as a function of x. We have here eliminated the sample point from the forefront

of our discussion in order to consider directly the probability function
$p = f(x)$.

As a second example, let $x =$ number of heads when three coins are
tossed. The uniform sample space is (2.3) and we could write the value
of x for each sample point in (2.3). Instead, let us go immediately to a
table of x and $p = f(x)$. [Can you verify this table by using (2.3), or
otherwise?]

(5.1)

x	0	1	2	3
$p = f(x)$	$\frac{1}{8}$	$\frac{3}{8}$	$\frac{3}{8}$	$\frac{1}{8}$

The probability function $p = f(x)$ of a random variable x is also called
the *frequency function*, or the *probability density*, or the *probability distribution* (caution: *not* distribution *function*, which means something else;
see Fig. 5.2). The origins of these terms will become clearer as we go on
(Sections 6 and 7) but we can get some idea of the terms frequency and
distribution from (5.1). Suppose we toss three coins repeatedly; we might
reasonably expect to get three heads in about $\frac{1}{8}$ of the tosses, two heads
in about $\frac{3}{8}$ of the tosses, etc. That is, each value of $p = f(x)$ is proportional to the *frequency* of occurrence of that value of x—hence the term
frequency function (see also Section 7). Again in (5.1), imagine four boxes
labeled $x = 0, 1, 2, 3$, and put a marble into the appropriate box for
each toss of three coins. Then $p = f(x)$ indicates approximately how the
marbles are distributed into the boxes after many tosses—hence the term
distribution.

Mean value; standard deviation.   The probability function $f(x)$ of a
random variable x gives us detailed information about it, but for many
purposes we want a simpler description. Suppose, for example, that x
represents experimental measurements of the length of a rod, and that we
have a large number N of measurements x_i. We might reasonably take
$p_i = f(x_i)$ proportional to the number of times N_i we obtained the value
x_i, that is, $p_i = N_i/N$. We are especially interested in two numbers,
namely a mean or average value of all our measurements, and some
number which indicates how widely the original set of values spreads out
about that average. Let us define two such quantities which are
customarily used to describe a random variable. To calculate the average
of a set of N numbers, we add them and divide by N. Instead of adding
the large number of measurements, we can multiply each measurement
by the number of times it occurs and add the results. This gives for the
average of the measurements, the value

$$\frac{1}{N} \cdot \sum_i N_i x_i = \sum_i p_i x_i.$$

By analogy with this calculation, we now define the *average* or *mean value μ of a random variable x* whose probability function is $f(x)$ by the equation

$$(5.2) \qquad \mu = \text{average of } x = \sum_i x_i p_i = \sum_i x_i f(x_i).$$

To obtain a measure of the spread of our measurements, we might first list how much each measurement differs from the average. Some of these deviations are positive and some are negative; if we average them, we get zero (Problem 57). Instead, let us square each deviation and average the squares. We define the *variance* of a random variable x by the equation

$$(5.3) \qquad \text{Var}(x) = \sum_i (x_i - \mu)^2 f(x_i).$$

If nearly all the measurements x_i are very close to μ, then $\text{Var}(x)$ is small; if the measurements are widely spread, $\text{Var}(x)$ is large. Thus we have a number which indicates the spread of the measurements; this is what we wanted. The square root of $\text{Var}(x)$, called the *standard deviation* of x, is often used instead of $\text{Var}(x)$:

$$(5.4) \qquad \sigma_x = \text{standard deviation of } x = \sqrt{\text{Var}(x)}.$$

The mean or average value of a random variable x is also called its *expectation* or its *expected value* or (especially in quantum mechanics) its *expectation value*. Instead of μ, the symbols $\bar{x}$ or $E(x)$ may be used to denote the mean value of x.

$$(5.5) \qquad \bar{x} = E(x) = \mu = \sum_i x_i f(x_i).$$

The term expectation comes from games of chance. For example, suppose you will be paid \$5 if a die shows a 5, \$2 if it shows a 2 or a 3, and nothing otherwise. Let x represent your gain in playing the game. Then the possible values of x and the corresponding probabilities are $x = 5$ with $p = \frac{1}{6}$, $x = 2$ with $p = \frac{1}{3}$, and $x = 0$ with $p = \frac{1}{2}$. We find for the average or expectation of x:

$$E(x) = \sum x_i p_i = \$5 \cdot \tfrac{1}{6} + \$2 \cdot \tfrac{1}{3} + \$0 \cdot \tfrac{1}{2} = \$1.50.$$

If you play the game many times, this is a reasonable estimate of your average gain per game; this is what your expectation means. It is also a reasonable amount to pay as a fee for each game you play. The term *expected value* (which means the same as *expectation* or *average*) may be somewhat confusing and misleading if you try to interpret "expected" in an everyday sense. Note that the expected value (\$1.50) of x is not one of the possible values of x, so you cannot ever "expect" to have

$x = \$1.50$. If you think of expected value as a technical term meaning the same as average, then there is no difficulty. Of course, in some cases, it makes reasonable sense with its everyday meaning; for example, if a coin is tossed n times, the expected number of heads is $n/2$ (Problem 58) and it is true that we may reasonably "expect" a fair approximation to this result (see Section 7).

Distribution functions. So far we have been using the probability (or frequency) function $f(x)$ which gives the probability $p_i = f(x_i)$ that x is exactly x_i. In some problems we may be more interested in the probability that x is less than some particular value. For example, in an election

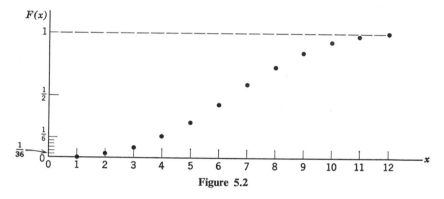

Figure 5.2

we would like to know the probability that less than half the votes would be cast for the opposing candidate, that is, that our candidate would win. In an experiment on radioactivity, we would like to know the probability that the background radiation always remains below a certain level. Given the probability function $f(x)$, we can obtain the probability that x is less than or equal to a certain value x_i by adding all the probabilities of values of x less than or equal to x_i. For example, consider the sum of the numbers on two dice; the probability function $p = f(x)$ is plotted in Fig. 5.1. The probability that x is, say, less than or equal to 4 is the sum of the probabilities that x is 2 or 3 or 4, that is, $\frac{1}{36} + \frac{2}{36} + \frac{3}{36} = \frac{1}{6}$. Similarly, we could find the probability that x is less than or equal to any given number. The resulting function of x is plotted in Fig. 5.2. Such a function $F(x)$ is called a *distribution function*; we can write

$$(5.6) \qquad F(x_i) = (\text{probability that } x \leq x_i) = \sum_{x_j \leq x_i} f(x_j).$$

Note carefully that, although the probability or frequency function $f(x)$ is sometimes referred to as a distribution, the term distribution *function* always means $F(x)$.

6. CONTINUOUS DISTRIBUTIONS

In Section 5, we discussed random variables x which took on a discrete set of values x_i. It is not hard to think of cases in which a random variable takes on a continuous set of values.

Example 1. Consider a particle moving back and forth along the x-axis from $x = 0$ to $x = l$, rebounding elastically at the turning points so that its speed is constant. (This could be a simple-minded model of an alpha particle in a radioactive nucleus, or of a gas molecule bouncing back and forth between the walls of a container.) Let the position x of the particle be the random variable; then x takes on a continuous set of values from $x = 0$ to $x = l$. Now suppose that, following Section 5, we ask for the probability that the particle is *at* a particular point x; this probability must be the same, say k, for all points (because the speed is constant). But there are an infinite number of points x, so for any nonzero value of k the total probability for the particle to be at *some* x (k times the number of values of x) would not be 1 as it should be, and we see that k (probability that particle is *at* a given point) must be zero. But this is not a very useful result. Let us instead consider several small intervals dx, all of the same length, on $(0, l)$; since the particle has constant speed, it spends the same time in each dx, and we can say that the probability of finding the particle in any particular dx is proportional to the length dx. In fact, since the particle spends the fraction $(dx)/l$ of the time in a given interval dx, the probability of finding it in dx is just $(dx)/l$.

To see how to define a probability function for the continuous case and to correlate this discussion with the discrete case, let us return for a moment to Fig. 5.1. There we plotted a vertical *distance* to represent the probability $p = f(x)$ of each value of x. Instead of a dot (as in Fig. 5.1) to indicate p for each x, let us now draw a horizontal line segment of length 1 centered on each dot, as in Fig. 6.1. Then the *area* under the horizontal line segment at a particular x_i is $f(x_i) \cdot 1 = f(x_i) = p_i$ (since the length of each horizontal line segment is 1), and we could use this *area* instead of the ordinate as a measure of the probability. Such a graph is called a *histogram*.

Now let us apply this area idea to the problem of the particle moving at constant speed between 0 and l. Consider Fig. 6.2. We have plotted the function

$$f(x) = \begin{cases} \dfrac{1}{l}, & 0 < x < l, \\[2mm] 0, & x < 0 \quad \text{and} \quad x > l. \end{cases}$$

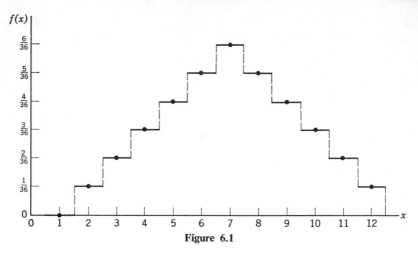

Figure 6.1

If we consider any interval x to $x + dx$ on $(0, l)$, the area under the curve $f(x) = 1/l$ for this interval is $(1/l)\,dx$ or $f(x)\,dx$, and this is just the probability that the particle is in this interval. The probability that the particle is in some longer subinterval of $(0, l)$, say (a, b), is $(b - a)/l$ or $\int_a^b f(x)\,dx$, that is, the area under the curve from a to b. If the interval (a, b) is outside $(0, l)$, then $\int_a^b f(x)\,dx = 0$ since $f(x)$ is zero, and again this is the correct value of the probability of finding the particle on the given interval.

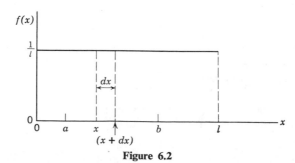

Figure 6.2

When $f(x)$ is constant over an interval (as in Fig. 6.2), we say that x is *uniformly* distributed on that interval. Let us consider an example in which $f(x)$ is not constant.

Example 2. This time suppose the particle of our last example is sliding up and down an inclined plane (no friction), rebounding elastically (no energy loss) against a spring at the bottom and reaching zero speed at height $h = l$ (Fig. 6.3). The total energy, $\frac{1}{2}mv^2 + mgh$, is constant and equal to mgl since $v = 0$ at $h = l$. Thus we have

$$(6.1) \qquad v^2 = \frac{2}{m}(mgl - mgh) = 2g(l - h).$$

The probability of finding the particle within an interval dh at a given height h is proportional to the time dt spent in that interval. From $v = ds/dt$, we have $dt = (ds)/v$; from Fig. 6.3, we find $ds = (dh)\csc\alpha$. Substituting for v from (6.1), we get

$$dt = \frac{ds}{v} = \frac{dh\,\csc\alpha}{v} = \frac{\csc\alpha}{\sqrt{2g}} \cdot \frac{dh}{\sqrt{l - h}}\,.$$

Since the probability $f(h)\,dh$ of finding the particle in the interval dh at

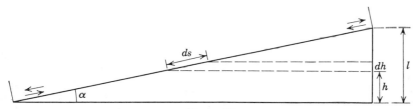

Figure 6.3

height h is proportional to dt, we can drop the constant factor $(\csc\alpha)/\sqrt{2g}$ and say that $f(h)\,dh$ is proportional to $(dh)/\sqrt{l - h}$. In order to find $f(h)$, we must multiply by a constant factor which makes the total probability $\int_0^l f(h)\,dh$ equal to 1, since this is the probability that the particle is *somewhere*. You can easily verify that

$$f(h)\,dh = \frac{1}{2\sqrt{l}}\frac{dh}{\sqrt{l - h}} \qquad \text{or} \quad f(h) = \frac{1}{2\sqrt{l}\sqrt{l - h}}\,.$$

A graph of $f(h)$ is plotted in Fig. 6.4. Note that although $f(h)$ becomes infinite at $h = l$, the area under the $f(h)$ curve for any interval is finite; this area represents the probability that the particle is in that height interval.

We can now extend the ideas of mean (expectation), variance, standard deviation, and distribution function to the continuous case. The average of a random variable x with probability function $f(x)$ is given by

$$(6.2) \qquad \mu = \bar{x} = E(x) = \int_{-\infty}^{\infty} xf(x)\,dx.$$

(In writing the limits $-\infty$, ∞ here, we assume that $f(x)$ is defined to be zero on intervals where the probability is zero.) Note that (6.2) is a natural extension of the sum in (5.5). Having found the mean of x, we now define the variance as in Section 5 as the average of $(x - \mu)^2$, that is,

$$(6.3) \qquad \text{Var}\,(x) = \int_{-\infty}^{\infty} (x - \mu)^2 f(x)\, dx = \sigma_x^2.$$

As before, the standard deviation σ_x is the square root of the variance. Finally, the distribution function $F(x)$ gives for each x the probability that

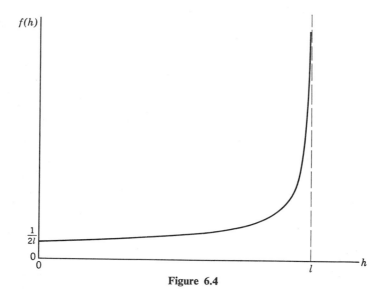

Figure 6.4

the random variable is less than or equal to that x. But this probability is just the area under the $f(x)$ curve from $-\infty$ up to the point x. Thus we have

$$(6.4) \qquad F(x) = \int_{-\infty}^{x} f(u)\, du.$$

In Section 5, we mentioned that the probability function $f(x)$ is often called the *probability density*; we can now explain why. Consider (6.2); if $f(x)$ represents the density (mass per unit length) of a thin rod, then the center of mass of the rod is given by [see Chapter 4, (13.3)]

$$(6.5) \qquad \bar{x} = \int xf(x)\, dx \Big/ \int f(x)\, dx,$$

where the integrals are over the length of the rod, or from $-\infty$ to ∞ as in (6.2) with $f(x) = 0$ outside the rod. But in (6.2), $\int f(x)\, dx$ is the total probability that x has *some* value, and so this integral is equal to 1. Then (6.5) and (6.2) are really the same; we see that it is reasonable to call $f(x)$ a density, and also that the mean of x corresponds to the center of mass of a linear mass distribution of density $f(x)$. In a similar way, we can interpret (6.3) as giving the moment of inertia of the mass distribution about the center of mass (see Chapter 4, Section 13).

We can easily generalize the ideas and formulas we have discussed to two (or more) dimensions. Suppose we have two random variables x and y; we define their joint probability or density function $f(x, y)$ so that $f(x_i, y_j)\, dx\, dy$ is the probability that the point (x, y) is in an element of area $dx\, dy$ at $x = x_i$, $y = y_j$. Then the probability that the point (x, y) is in a given region of the (x, y) plane, is the integral of $f(x, y)$ over that area. The average or expected values of x and y, and the variances and standard deviations of x and y, are given by

$$\bar{x} = \int_{-\infty}^{\infty} \int_{-\infty}^{\infty} xf(x, y)\, dx\, dy,$$

$$\bar{y} = \int_{-\infty}^{\infty} \int_{-\infty}^{\infty} yf(x, y)\, dx\, dy,$$

(6.6)

$$\text{Var}(x) = \int_{-\infty}^{\infty} \int_{-\infty}^{\infty} (x - \bar{x})^2 f(x, y)\, dx\, dy = \sigma_x^2,$$

$$\text{Var}(y) = \int_{-\infty}^{\infty} \int_{-\infty}^{\infty} (y - \bar{y})^2 f(x, y)\, dx\, dy = \sigma_y^2.$$

You should see that these are generalizations of (6.2) and (6.3); that (6.6) can be interpreted as giving the coordinates of the center of mass and the moments of inertia of a two-dimensional mass distribution; and that similar formulas can be written for three (or more) random variables (that is, in three or more dimensions). Also note that the formulas in (6.6) could be written in terms of polar coordinates r, θ; similarly, in three dimensions, we may use cylindrical or spherical coordinates (see Problems 63 and 64).

7. BINOMIAL DISTRIBUTION

Example 1. Let a coin be tossed 5 times; what is the probability of exactly 3 heads out of the 5 tosses? We can represent any sequence of 5 tosses by a symbol such as *thhtt*. The probability of this particular sequence (or any other particular sequence) is $(\frac{1}{2})^5$ since the tosses are independent (see Example 1 of Section 3). The number of such sequences containing 3 heads and 2 tails is the number of ways we can select 3 positions out of 5 for heads (or 2 for tails), namely $C(5, 3)$. Hence the probability of exactly

3 heads in 5 tosses of a coin is $C(5, 3)(\frac{1}{2})^5$. Suppose a coin is tossed repeatedly, say n times; let x be the number of heads in the n tosses. We want to find the probability function $p = f(x)$ which gives the probability of exactly x heads in n tosses. By generalizing the case of 3 heads in 5 tosses, we see that

$$(7.1) \qquad\qquad f(x) = C(n, x)(\tfrac{1}{2})^n.$$

Example 2. Let us do a similar problem with a die, asking this time for the probability of exactly 3 aces in 5 tosses of the die. If A means ace and N not ace, the probability of a particular sequence such as $ANNAA$ is $\frac{1}{6} \cdot \frac{5}{6} \cdot \frac{5}{6} \cdot \frac{1}{6} \cdot \frac{1}{6}$ since the probability of A is $\frac{1}{6}$, the probability of N is $\frac{5}{6}$, and the tosses are independent. The number of such sequences containing 3 A's and 2 N's is $C(5, 3)$; thus the probability of exactly 3 aces in 5 tosses of a die is $C(5, 3)(\frac{1}{6})^3(\frac{5}{6})^2$. Generalizing this, we find that the probability of exactly x aces in n tosses of a die is

$$(7.2) \qquad\qquad f(x) = C(n, x)(\tfrac{1}{6})^x(\tfrac{5}{6})^{n-x}.$$

In the two problems we have just done, we have been concerned with repeated independent trials, each trial having two possible outcomes (h or t, A or N) of given probability. There are many examples of such problems; let us consider a few. A manufactured item is good or defective; given the probability of a defect we want the probability of x defectives out of n items. A marksman has probability p of hitting a target; we ask for the probability of x hits out of n tries. Each atom of a radioactive substance has probability p of emitting an alpha particle during the next minute; we are to find the probability that x alpha particles will be emitted in the next minute from the n atoms in the sample. A particle moves back and forth along the x-axis in unit jumps; it has, at each step, equal probabilities of jumping forward or backward. (This motion is called a *random walk*; it can be used as a model of a diffusion process.) We want to know the probability that, after n jumps, the particle is at a distance

d = number x of positive jumps − number $(n - x)$ of negative jumps,

from its starting point; this probability is the probability of x positive jumps out of a total of n.

Binomial probability functions. In all these problems, something is tried repeatedly; at each trial there are two possible outcomes of probabilities p (usually called the probability of "success") and $q = 1 - p$ (q = probability of "failure"). Such repeated independent trials with constant probabilities p and q are called *Bernoulli trials*. Let us generalize (7.1) and (7.2) to obtain a formula which applies to any such problem, namely the probability $f(x)$ of exactly x successes in n trials. Reasoning as we did to obtain (7.1) and (7.2), we find that

(7.3) $f(x) = C(n, x)p^x q^{n-x}.$

We might also ask for the probability of *not more than* x successes in n trials; this is the sum of the probabilities of $0, 1, 2, \ldots, x$ successes, that

Graphs of the binomial distribution, $f(x) = C(n,x)p^x q^{n-x}$

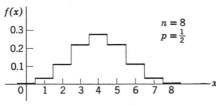

Figure 7.1

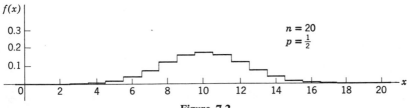

Figure 7.2

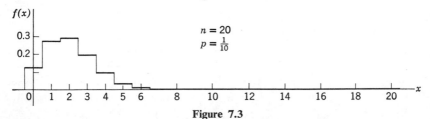

Figure 7.3

is, it is the distribution function $F(x)$ for the random variable x whose probability function is (7.3) [see (5.6)]. We can write

(7.4) $F(x) = f(0) + f(1) + \cdots + f(x)$
        $= C(n, 0)p^0 q^n + C(n, 1)p^1 q^{n-1} + \cdots + C(n, x)p^x q^{n-x}.$

Observe that (7.3) is one term of the binomial expansion of $(p + q)^n$ and (7.4) is a sum of several terms of this expansion (see Example 2, Section 4). For this reason, the functions $f(x)$ in (7.1), (7.2), or (7.3) are called *binomial probability* (or *frequency* or *density*) *functions* or *binomial distributions*, and the function $F(x)$ in (7.4) is called a *binomial distribution function*.

We shall find it very useful to sketch graphs of the binomial probability function $f(x)$ for several values of p and n. (See Figs. 7.1, 7.2, 7.3, and

Problems 65, 66.) Instead of a point at $y = f(x)$ for each x, we draw a horizontal line segment of length 1 centered on each x as in Fig. 6.1; the probabilities are then represented by the *area* under the broken line, rather than by ordinates. From Figs. 7.1 to 7.3 and similar graphs, we can draw a number of conclusions. The most probable value of x [corresponding to the largest value of $f(x)$] is approximately $x = np$ (Problems 68, 69); for example, for $p = \frac{1}{2}$, the most probable value of x is $\frac{1}{2}n$ for even n; for odd n, there are two consecutive values of x, namely $\frac{1}{2}(n \pm 1)$,

Binomial distribution graphs of $nf(x)$ plotted against x/n

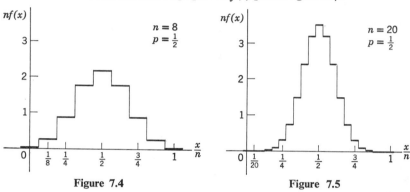

Figure 7.4   Figure 7.5

for which the probability is largest. The graphs for $p = \frac{1}{2}$ are symmetric about $x = \frac{1}{2}n$. For $p \neq \frac{1}{2}$, the curve is asymmetric, favoring small x values for small p and large x values for large p. As n increases, the graph of $f(x)$ becomes wider and flatter (the total area under the graph must remain 1). The probability of the most probable value of x decreases with n. For example, the most probable number of heads in 8 tosses of a coin is 4 with probability 0.27; the most probable number of heads in 20 tosses is 10 with probability 0.17; for 10^6 tosses, the probability of exactly 500,000 heads is less than 10^{-3}.

Let us redraw Figs. 7.1 and 7.2 plotting $nf(x)$ against the relative number of successes x/n (Figs. 7.4 and 7.5). Since this change of scale (ordinate times n, abscissa divided by n) leaves the area unchanged, we can still use the area to represent probability. Note that now the curves become narrower and taller as n increases. This means that values of the ratio x/n tend to cluster about their most probable value, namely $np/n = p$. For example, if we toss a coin repeatedly, the difference "number of heads $-\frac{1}{2}$ number of tosses" is apt to be large and to increase with n (Figs. 7.1 and 7.2), but the ratio "number of heads $\div$ number of tosses" is apt to be closer and closer to $\frac{1}{2}$ as n increases (Figs. 7.4 and 7.5). It is for this reason that we can use experimentally determined values of x/n as a reasonable estimate of p.

Law of large numbers.   Statements and proofs which make the ideas of the last paragraph more precise are known as *laws of large numbers*. Let us state and prove one such law. First we want a simple but very general result called *Chebyshev's inequality*. We consider a random variable x with probability function $f(x)$, and let μ be the mean value and σ the standard deviation of x. We are going to prove that if we select any number t, the probability that x differs from its mean value μ by more than t, is less than σ^2/t^2. This means that x is unlikely to differ from μ by more than a few standard deviations; for example, if t is twice the standard deviation σ, we find that the probability for x to differ from μ by more than 2σ is less than $\sigma^2/t^2 = \sigma^2/(2\sigma)^2 = \frac{1}{4}$. The proof is simple. By definition of σ, we have

$$\sigma^2 = \sum (x - \mu)^2 f(x)$$

where the sum is over all x. Then if we sum just over values of x for which $|x - \mu| \geq t$, we get less than σ^2:

$$(7.5) \qquad \sigma^2 > \sum_{|x-\mu|\geq t} (x - \mu)^2 f(x).$$

If we replace each $x - \mu$ by the number t in (7.5), the sum is decreased, so we have

$$(7.6) \quad \sigma^2 > \sum_{|x-\mu|\geq t} t^2 f(x) = t^2 \sum_{|x-\mu|\geq t} f(x) \quad \text{or} \quad \sum_{|x-\mu|\geq t} f(x) < \frac{\sigma^2}{t^2}.$$

But $\displaystyle\sum_{|x-\mu|\geq t} f(x)$ is just the sum of all the probabilities of x values which differ from μ by more than t, and (7.6) says that this probability is less than σ^2/t^2, as we claimed.

Let us apply Chebyshev's inequality to a random variable x whose probability function is the binomial distribution (7.3). From Problems 67 and 72 we have $\mu = np$ and $\sigma = \sqrt{npq}$. Then by Chebyshev's inequality,

$$(7.7) \qquad (\text{probability of } |x - np| \geq t) \quad \text{is less than} \quad npq/t^2.$$

Let us choose the arbitrary value of t in (7.7) proportional to n, that is, $t = n\epsilon$, where ϵ is now arbitrary. Then (7.7) becomes

$$(7.8) \qquad (\text{probability of } |x - np| \geq n\epsilon) \quad \text{is less than} \quad npq/n^2\epsilon^2,$$

or, when we divide the first inequality by n,

$$(7.9) \qquad \left(\text{probability of } \left|\frac{x}{n} - p\right| \geq \epsilon\right) \quad \text{is less than} \quad \frac{pq}{n\epsilon^2}.$$

Recall that x/n is the relative number of successes; we intuitively expect x/n to be near p for large n. Now (7.9) says that the probability for x/n to differ from p by any arbitrarily small number ϵ, is less than $pq/(n\epsilon^2)$; that is, as n tends to infinity, this probability tends to zero. (Note, however, that $(x/n) - p$ need not tend to zero.) This is one form of the law of large numbers and justifies our intuitive ideas.

8. THE NORMAL OR GAUSSIAN DISTRIBUTION

As you may discover in doing some of the problems, a great deal of computation is involved in calculating the binomial distribution for any but very small values of n. Although calculated tables exist, it is usually

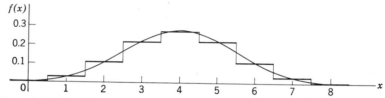

Figure 8.1. Binomial distribution for $n = 8$, $p = \frac{1}{2}$, and the normal approximation.

more satisfactory to use an approximation to the binomial distribution for large n. We shall consider two such approximations in this section and Section 9.

Using Stirling's formula to approximate the factorials in $C(n, x)$ in (7.3) and making other suitable approximations for large n, we can show that when n and np are both large, the following formula gives a good approximation to the binomial distribution (7.3):

$$(8.1) \qquad f(x) \sim \frac{1}{\sqrt{2\pi npq}}\, e^{-(x-np)^2/(2npq)}.$$

The sign $\sim$ means (as in Chapter 9, Section 11) that the ratio of the exact binomial distribution (7.3) and the right-hand side of (8.1) tends to 1 as $n \to \infty$. (An outline of a derivation of (8.1) is given in Problem 73.) The right-hand side of (8.1) is called the *normal* (or *Gaussian*) approximation to the binomial distribution (7.3), and a graph of this function is often called the *normal error curve*. Although we have said that this is an approximation valid for large n, the agreement is quite good even for fairly small values of n. The graph (Fig. 8.1) shows this for the case $n = 8$. The binomial distribution $f(x)$ is defined only for integral x; you should compare the values of $f(x)$ with the values of the approximating normal curve at integral values of x. When n is very large (Fig. 8.2), a graph of the exact binomial distribution is very close to the normal approximation.

The probability of exactly x successes in n Bernoulli trials is given approximately by (8.1) for large n. We may be more interested in the probability that the number x of successes is between x_1 and x_2 ($x_1 \leq x \leq x_2$), for example, the probability of getting between 45 and 55 heads in 100 tosses of a coin. Such a probability is given exactly by the appropriate area under a binomial $f(x)$ graph (such as in Figs. 7.1, 7.2, 8.1, and 8.2).

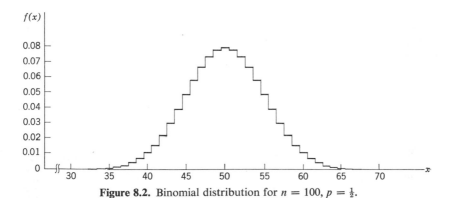

Figure 8.2. Binomial distribution for $n = 100$, $p = \frac{1}{2}$.

For large n, we can more easily obtain an approximation to the desired probability by finding the area under the normal approximation curve. Thus we have

$$(8.2) \quad \text{(Probability that } x_1 \leq x \leq x_2) \sim \frac{1}{\sqrt{2\pi npq}} \int_{x_1}^{x_2} e^{-(x-np)^2/(2npq)} \, dx.$$

The statement that the ratio of the two sides of (8.2) tends to 1 as $n \to \infty$ is called the *Laplace-DeMoivre limit theorem*. (See Feller, p. 172.)

The mean value μ and standard deviation σ of a random variable whose probability function is the binomial distribution (7.3) are (Problems 67 and 72)

$$(8.3) \qquad \mu = np, \qquad \sigma = \sqrt{npq}.$$

It is straightforward to show (Problem 74) that the normal approximation satisfies the requirement for a probability density function, that its integral from $-\infty$ to ∞ must be 1, and that if a random variable x has the normal approximation as its probability density function, then the mean value and standard deviation of x are given by (8.3). Substituting

(8.3) into (8.1), we can write:

(8.4)   Normal density function for a random variable of mean μ and

standard deviation σ is $\dfrac{1}{\sigma\sqrt{2\pi}}\, e^{-(x-\mu)^2/(2\sigma^2)}$.

The corresponding normal distribution function is given by:

(8.5)   Normal distribution function $= \dfrac{1}{\sigma\sqrt{2\pi}}\displaystyle\int_{-\infty}^{x} e^{-(t-\mu)^2/(2\sigma^2)}\, dt$.

In solving problems, we will want to use (8.1), (8.2), (8.4), and (8.5). These are not what you will find in tables, however; tabulated values are for the case $\mu = 0$, $\sigma = 1$, so we need to see how to use the tables to solve actual problems. We define the *standard* normal (or Gaussian) density function $\phi(x)$ by

(8.6) $\phi(x) = \dfrac{1}{\sqrt{2\pi}}\, e^{-x^2/2}$.

From a table of $\phi(x)$, we can obtain the functions in (8.1) or (8.4) by finding $\dfrac{1}{\sigma}\,\phi\!\left(\dfrac{x-\mu}{\sigma}\right)$.

Example 1. Find the approximate probability of exactly 52 heads in 100 tosses of a coin.

From (8.3), we find

$$\mu = np = 100\cdot\tfrac{1}{2} = 50, \qquad \sigma = \sqrt{npq} = \sqrt{100\cdot\tfrac{1}{2}\cdot\tfrac{1}{2}} = 5.$$

Then the desired probability is

$$\frac{1}{\sigma}\,\phi\!\left(\frac{x-\mu}{\sigma}\right) = \frac{1}{5}\,\phi\!\left(\frac{52-50}{5}\right) = \frac{1}{5}\,\phi(0.4) = \frac{1}{5}(0.36) = 0.07$$

from tables.

We shall also use the function

(8.7) $\Phi(x) = \displaystyle\int_{0}^{x}\phi(t)\, dt = \frac{1}{\sqrt{2\pi}}\int_{0}^{x} e^{-t^2/2}\, dt$,

which is often tabulated; adding 0.5 to $\Phi(x)$ gives the *standard* normal distribution function [which is by definition $\displaystyle\int_{-\infty}^{x}\phi(t)\, dt$] since

$$\int_{-\infty}^{0}\phi(t)\, dt = \tfrac{1}{2}\int_{-\infty}^{\infty}\phi(t)\, dt = \tfrac{1}{2}.$$

Note that $\Phi(-x) = -\Phi(x)$; also note that $\Phi(x)$ is closely related to the error function (Chapter 9, Section 9); in fact (Problem 75),

$$(8.8) \qquad \Phi(x) = \tfrac{1}{2} \, \text{erf} \left(\frac{x}{\sqrt{2}} \right).$$

(The notation used here is quite common but not universal; some authors call our $\Phi(x)$ the error function, and there are other notations. Check carefully the definitions in books and tables you use.) You will usually find tabulated either $\Phi(x)$ or $\text{erf}(x)$. Let us see how to use a table of $\Phi(x)$. Think of shifting the vertical axis in a graph of the density function (8.4) (for example, in Fig. 8.1), so that it passes through the peak of the curve $(x = \mu)$; the curve is then symmetric about the new axis. This amounts to taking $(x - \mu)$ as a new variable in (8.4). Let us also change the scale on the x-axis so as to measure $(x - \mu)$ in multiples of the standard deviation σ, that is, let us take as a new variable

$$(8.9) \qquad t = \frac{x - \mu}{\sigma}.$$

Making this substitution in (8.2) [and remembering (8.3)], we get

$$(\text{Probability that } x_1 \le x \le x_2) \sim \frac{1}{\sigma\sqrt{2\pi}} \int_{t_1}^{t_2} e^{-t^2/2} \sigma \, dt$$

$$(8.10) \qquad\qquad\qquad = \Phi(t_2) - \Phi(t_1)$$

$$\text{where} \quad t_1 = \frac{x_1 - \mu}{\sigma}, \qquad t_2 = \frac{x_2 - \mu}{\sigma}.$$

Example 2. Let us use (8.10) to estimate the probability that in 100 tosses of a coin, we get between 45 and 55 heads, that is, $45 \le x \le 55$. From Example 1, we have $\mu = 50$, $\sigma = 5$. Then

$$t_1 = \frac{45 - 50}{5} = -1, \qquad t_2 = \frac{55 - 50}{5} = 1.$$

From (8.10), the desired probability is approximately

$$\Phi(t_2) - \Phi(t_1) = \Phi(1) - \Phi(-1) = 2\,\Phi(1) = 2(0.34) = 0.68$$

from tables. [We could get a slightly more accurate result—see Feller, p. 173—by integrating from 44.5 to 55.5; this would correspond more closely to the appropriate area under the exact binomial graph in Fig. 8.2 by including the whole steps at $x = 45$ and $x = 55$. You can verify that this would give $2\Phi(1.1) = 2(0.36) = 0.72$.]

9. THE POISSON DISTRIBUTION

Let us consider an experiment in which we observe and count the particles emitted by a radioactive substance. We shall assume that our period of observation is much less than the half-life of the substance, so that the average counting rate does not decrease during the experiment. Then the probability that one particle is emitted during a small time interval dt is $\mu \, dt$, $\mu = $ const., if dt is short enough so that the probability of two particles during dt is negligible. We want to find the probability $P_n(t)$ of observing exactly n counts during a time interval t. The probability $P_n(t + \Delta t)$ is the probability of observing n counts in the time interval $t + \Delta t$. For $n > 0$, this is the sum of the probabilities of the two mutually exclusive events, "n particles in t, none in Δt" and "$(n - 1)$ particles in t, one in Δt"; in symbols,

$$(9.1) \qquad P_n(t + \Delta t) = P_n(t)P_0(\Delta t) + P_{n-1}(t)P_1(\Delta t).$$

Now $P_1(\Delta t)$ is the probability of one particle in Δt; this, by assumption, is $\mu \Delta t$. Then the probability of no particles in Δt is $1 - P_1(\Delta t) = 1 - \mu \Delta t$. Substituting these values into (9.1), we get

$$(9.2) \qquad P_n(t + \Delta t) = P_n(t)(1 - \mu \Delta t) + P_{n-1}(t)\mu \Delta t$$

or

$$(9.3) \qquad \frac{P_n(t + \Delta t) - P_n(t)}{\Delta t} = \mu P_{n-1}(t) - \mu P_n(t).$$

Letting $\Delta t \to 0$, we have

$$(9.4) \qquad \frac{dP_n(t)}{dt} = \mu P_{n-1}(t) - \mu P_n(t).$$

For $n = 0$, (9.1) simplifies since the only possible event is "no particles in t, no particles in Δt," and (9.4) becomes, for $n = 0$,

$$(9.5) \qquad \frac{dP_0}{dt} = -\mu P_0.$$

Then, since $P_0(0) = $ "probability that no particle is emitted during a zero time interval" $= 1$, integration of (9.5) gives

$$(9.6) \qquad P_0 = e^{-\mu t}.$$

Substituting (9.6) into (9.4) with $n = 1$ gives a differential equation for $P_1(t)$; its solution (Problem 81) is $P_1(t) = \mu t \, e^{-\mu t}$. Solving (9.4) successively

(Problem 81) for $P_2, P_3, \ldots, P_n$, we obtain

(9.7)
$$P_n(t) = \frac{(\mu t)^n}{n!} e^{-\mu t}.$$

Putting $t = 1$, we get for the probability of exactly n counts per unit time

(9.8)
$$P_n = \frac{\mu^n}{n!} e^{-\mu}.$$

The meaning of μ is important for applications of this formula; a proof is outlined in Problem 82 that μ is just $\bar{n}$, the average number of counts

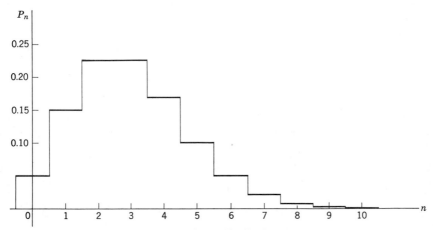

Figure 9.1. Poisson distribution, $\mu = 3$.

per unit time. The probability function (9.8) is called the *Poisson distribution*.

The Poisson distribution is useful in a great variety of problems in which the probability of some occurrence is small and constant (see Problems 83 to 86, and Parratt, Chapter 5).

Example 1. The number of particles emitted each minute by a radioactive source is recorded for a period of 10 hours; a total of 1800 counts are registered. During how many 1-minute intervals should we expect to observe no particles; exactly one; etc.?

The average number of counts per minute is $1800/(10 \cdot 60) = 3$ counts per minute; this is the value of μ. Then by (9.8), the probability of n counts per minute is

$$P_n = \frac{3^n}{n!} e^{-3}.$$

A graph of this probability function is shown in Fig. 9.1. For $n = 0$, we find $P_0 = e^{-3} = 0.05$; then we should expect to observe no particles in about 5% of the 600 1-minute intervals, that is, during 30 1-minute intervals. Similarly, we could compute the expected number of 1-minute intervals during which 1, 2, etc., particles would be observed.

In Section 8, we discussed the fact that the binomial distribution can be approximated by the normal distribution for large n and large np. If p is very small so that np is very much less than n (say, for example, $p = 10^{-3}$, $n = 2000$, $np = 2$), the normal approximation is not good. In this case you can show (Problem 87) that the Poisson distribution gives a good approximation to the binomial distribution (7.3) that is, that

$$(9.9) \qquad C(n,\, x)p^x q^{n-x} \sim \frac{(np)^x e^{-np}}{x!}, \qquad \text{large } n, \text{ small } p.$$

[The exact meaning of (9.9) is that, for any fixed x, the ratio of the two sides approaches 1 as $n \to \infty$ and $p \to 0$ with np remaining constant.]

Example 2. If 1000 people each select a number at random between 1 and 500, what is the probability that 3 people selected the number 29?

The answer is given by the binomial distribution with $n = 1000$, $p = 1/500$, $x = 3$; this gives

$$\frac{1000!}{3!\,997!}\left(\frac{1}{500}\right)^3\left(\frac{499}{500}\right)^{997}.$$

It is simpler to compute the Poisson approximation! By (9.9), we have $2^3\, e^{-2}/3! = 0.17$.

The Poisson distribution is used mainly for small values of $\mu = np$. For large values of μ, the Poisson distribution (as well as the binomial) is fairly well approximated by the normal distribution as in (9.10):

$$(9.10) \qquad \frac{\mu^x e^{-\mu}}{x!} \cong \frac{1}{\sqrt{2\pi\mu}}\, e^{-(x-\mu)^2/(2\mu)}, \qquad \mu \text{ large.}$$

Recall that the peak of the Poisson graph is at $x = \mu$, and note that the approximating normal curve in (9.10) is shifted to have its center at $x = \mu$; (9.10) gives a good approximation in the central region (around $x = \mu$) where the probability is large. Also note from Problem 82 that $\sigma^2 = \mu$ for the Poisson distribution.

10. APPLICATIONS TO EXPERIMENTAL MEASUREMENTS

So far we have been discussing principally situations in which we know or can reasonably assume some density function (normal, Poisson, etc.).

Let us suppose that, instead, we have only a table of data, say a set of measurements of some physical quantity. Presumably, if we spent more time, we could enlarge this table of data as much as we liked. We can then imagine an infinite set of measurements of which we have only a sample. The infinite set is called the *parent population* or *universe*. What we would really like to know is the probability function for the parent population, or at least the average value μ (often thought of as the "true" value of the quantity being measured) and the standard deviation σ for the parent population. We must content ourselves with the best estimates we can make of these quantities using our available sample, that is, the set of measurements which we have made.

First we want to estimate μ, the population average, from our finite sample. As a quick estimate we might take the *median* of our measurements (a value such that there are equal numbers of larger and smaller measurements), or the *mode* (the measurement we obtained the most times, that is, the most probable measurement). The most frequently used estimate of μ is, however, the *arithmetic mean* (or average) of the measurements. This choice is easily justified for a large set of measurements as follows (also see Problem 88). Think of each measurement as a selection of one member of the parent population. Then the probability for the measurement to have a particular value is given by the population density function $f(x)$. That is, a single measurement x is a random variable with probability function $f(x)$; the expected value of x is μ, and the variance of x is σ^2. Let $\bar{x} = (1/n) \sum_{i=1}^{n} x_i$ be the average of n measurements x_i (we call $\bar{x}$ the *sample average* to distinguish it from the *population average* μ). We want the expected value and the variance of this sample average; these are theoretical quantities computed for samples containing n measurements, using the population density function $f(x)$. It is easy to show (Problem 89) that the expected value of $\bar{x}$ is μ, and the variance of $\bar{x}$ is σ^2/n, so the standard deviation of $\bar{x}$ is $\sigma/\sqrt{n}$. Now Chebyshev's inequality (Section 7) says that a random variable is unlikely to differ from its expected value by more than a few standard deviations. For our problem, this says that $\bar{x}$ is unlikely to differ from μ by more than a few multiples of $\sigma/\sqrt{n}$ which becomes small as n increases. Thus $\bar{x}$ becomes an increasingly good estimate of μ as we increase the number n of measurements.

Next we want to obtain from our sample an estimate of the *population variance* σ^2. Our first guess might be to use the *sample variance*, which is

$$(10.1) \qquad\qquad s^2 = \frac{1}{n} \sum_{i=1}^{n} (x_i - \bar{x})^2.$$

To see if this is reasonable, we compute the expected value of the sample variance. We find (Problem 89b) that $E(s^2) = [(n - 1)/n]\,\sigma^2$. We conclude that a reasonable estimate of σ^2 is

$$(10.2) \qquad \sigma^2 \cong \frac{n}{n - 1}\, s^2 = \frac{\sum\limits_{i=1}^{n} (x_i - \bar{x})^2}{n - 1}.$$

The only difference between this value and the sample variance is that we divide by $n - 1$ instead of n.

The quantity σ which we have just estimated is the standard deviation for the parent population whose probability function is $f(x)$. Consider just a single measurement x. The function $f(x)$ (if we knew it) would give us the probabilities of the different possible values of x, the population mean μ would tell us approximately the value we are apt to find for x, and the standard deviation σ would tell us roughly the spread of x values about μ. Since σ tells us something about a single measurement, it is often called the *standard deviation of a single measurement*. Instead of a single measurement, let us consider the average $\bar{x}$ of a set of n measurements. We have seen (Problem 89a) that $\mathrm{Var}(\bar{x}) = \sigma^2/n$. The quantity

$$(10.3) \qquad \sigma_m = \sqrt{\mathrm{Var}\,(\bar{x})} = \frac{\sigma}{\sqrt{n}}$$

gives us an estimate of the spread of values of $\bar{x}$ about μ. We can think of a new density function for $\bar{x}$ which is much more peaked about the value μ because the standard deviation $\sigma/\sqrt{n}$ is much smaller than σ. We call $\sigma_m = \sigma/\sqrt{n}$ the *standard deviation in the mean* or the *standard error*. Collecting formulas (10.2) and (10.3), we have

$$(10.4) \qquad \sigma_m \cong \sqrt{\frac{\sum\limits_{i=1}^{n} (x_i - \bar{x})^2}{n(n - 1)}}.$$

We have discussed finding the sample average $\bar{x} = \dfrac{1}{n}\sum\limits_{i=1}^{n} x$ and the sample variance $s^2 = \dfrac{1}{n}\sum\limits_{i=1}^{n} (x_i - \bar{x})^2$ for a set of measurements x_1, x_2, $x_3, \ldots, x_n$. Now suppose we want to measure, say, a velocity $v = x/t$, by measuring x and t and computing v; we then ask how to compute a sample average and variance for v from the measurements of x and t. We could, of course, obtain a set of measurements of v by computing $v_1 = x_1/t_1$, $v_2 = x_2/t_2$, etc.; then we could calculate the sample average and variance for v just as we did before for x. However, there is an easier way if we may assume that the differences (errors) $x - \bar{x}$, $t - \bar{t}$, and $v - \bar{v}$ are all small (compared to the corresponding values $\bar{x}$, $\bar{t}$, and $\bar{v}$). For then we can approximate $\bar{v}$ by $\bar{x}/\bar{t}$ (Problem 90), and we can approximate the difference

$\Delta x = x - \bar{x}$ by dx, etc. (see Chapter 4, Section 4). We write

$$dv = \frac{\bar{t}\, dx - \bar{x}\, dt}{\bar{t}^2} = \frac{\bar{x}}{\bar{t}}\left(\frac{dx}{\bar{x}} - \frac{dt}{\bar{t}}\right) = \bar{v}\left(\frac{dx}{\bar{x}} - \frac{dt}{\bar{t}}\right).$$

Then the variance $\dfrac{1}{n}\displaystyle\sum_{i=1}^{n}(v_i - \bar{v})^2$ is approximately

$$\frac{1}{n}\sum_{i=1}^{n} dv_i^2 = \frac{\bar{v}^2}{n}\sum_{i=1}^{n}\left(\frac{dx_i}{\bar{x}} - \frac{dt_i}{\bar{t}}\right)^2 = \frac{\bar{v}^2}{n}\sum_{i=1}^{n}\left(\frac{dx_i^2}{\bar{x}^2} - \frac{2\, dx_i\, dt_i}{\bar{x}\bar{t}} + \frac{dt_i^2}{\bar{t}^2}\right)$$

$$= \bar{v}^2\left(\frac{s_x^2}{\bar{x}^2} + \frac{s_t^2}{\bar{t}^2}\right)$$

since $(1/n)\displaystyle\sum_{i=1}^{n} dx_i^2 = s_x^2$ (by definition of s_x^2), $(1/n)\displaystyle\sum_{i=1}^{n} dt_i^2 = s_t^2$, and $\displaystyle\sum_{i=1}^{n} dx_i\, dt_i = 0$ (average of deviations from average $= 0$, and average of product $=$ product of averages for independent variables; see Problems 57 and 70). Thus the *fractional standard deviation* $s_v/\bar{v}$ is given by

$$(10.5) \qquad\qquad \frac{s_v}{\bar{v}} = \sqrt{\frac{s_x^2}{\bar{x}^2} + \frac{s_t^2}{\bar{t}^2}}.$$

Similarly, we can find the standard deviation for a sum, or a difference, or a product of two variables, or for any function of two (or more) variables. (See Problem 91.)

So far we have not assumed any special form (such as normal, etc.) for the density function $f(x)$ of the parent population, so that our results for computation of approximate values of μ, σ, and σ_m from a set of measurements apply whether or not the parent distribution is normal. (And, in fact, in actual practice it may not be; for example, Poisson distributions are quite common.) You will find, however, that most discussions of experimental errors are based on an assumed normal distribution. Let us discuss the justification for this. We have seen above that we can think of $\bar{x} = \dfrac{1}{n}\displaystyle\sum_{i=1}^{n} x_i$ as a random variable with average μ and standard deviation $\sigma/\sqrt{n}$. We have said that we might think of a density function for $\bar{x}$, and that it would be more strongly peaked about μ than the density function $f(x)$ for a single measurement, but we have so far not said anything about the form of this new density function. There is a basic theorem in probability (which we shall quote without proof) which gives us some information about the probability function for $\bar{x}$. The *central limit theorem* [(8.2) is a special case of this theorem] says that no matter what the parent probability function $f(x)$ is (provided μ and σ exist), the probability function for $\bar{x} = \dfrac{1}{n} \sum\limits_{i=1}^{n} x_i$ is approximately the normal distribution with standard deviation $\sigma/\sqrt{n}$, if n is large.

If we assume normally distributed errors, we can then give a more specific meaning to σ_m (the standard deviation in the mean) than our vague statement that it gives us an estimate of the spread of $\bar{x}$ values about μ. Since the probability for a normally distributed variable to have values between $\mu - \sigma$ and $\mu + \sigma$ is $2\Phi(1) = 0.68$, we can say that (for normally distributed errors) the probability is 0.68 for a measurement of $\bar{x}$ to lie between $\mu - \sigma_m$ and $\mu + \sigma_m$. (This interval is called the 68 % confidence interval.) In the reporting of scientific data, it is customary to give an interval $\mu \pm r$ such that the probability is $\frac{1}{2}$ that a new measurement of $\bar{x}$ would lie in this interval (and so also probability $\frac{1}{2}$ that it would lie outside!), that is, a 50 % confidence interval. Assuming a normal distribution, we find $r = 0.67\sigma_m$ (Problem 92). The quantity r is called the *probable error*.

REFERENCES

Some useful reference books on probability are Feller, Goldberg, Parratt, and Parzen. See also chapters on probability and statistics in texts such as Evans; Kemeny, Mirkil, Snell, and Thompson; May; Sokolnikoff and Redheffer. (For complete references, see the list at the end of the book.)

PROBLEMS

1. Find the probability that a single throw of a die will give a number less than 3; an even number; a 6.

2. Three coins are tossed; what is the probability that two are heads and one tails? That the first two are heads and the third tails?

3. In a box there are 2 white, 3 black, and 4 red balls. If a ball is drawn at random, what is the probability that it is black? That it is *not* red?

4. A single card is drawn at random from a shuffled deck. What is the probability that it is red? That it is the ace of hearts? That it is either a three or a five? That it is either an ace or red or both?

5. Given a family of two children (assume boys and girls equally likely, that is, probability $\frac{1}{2}$ for each), what is the probability that both are boys? That at least one is a girl? Given that at least one is a girl, what is the probability that both are girls? Given that the first two are girls, what is the probability that an expected third child will be a boy?

6. A trick deck of cards is printed with the hearts and diamonds black, and the spades and clubs red. A card is chosen at random from this deck (after it is shuffled). Find the probability that it is either a red card or the queen of hearts. That it is either a red face card or a club. That it is either a red ace or a diamond.

7. A letter is selected at random from the alphabet. What is the probability that it is one of the letters in the word "probability?" What is the probability that it occurs in the first half of the alphabet? What is the probability that it is a letter after x?

8. An integer N is chosen at random with $1 \leq N \leq 100$. What is the probability that N is divisible by 11? That $N > 90$? That $N \leq 3$? That N is a perfect square?

9. You are trying to find instrument A in a laboratory. Unfortunately, someone has put both instruments A and another kind (which we shall call B) away in identical unmarked boxes mixed at random on a shelf. You know that the laboratory has 3 A's and 7 B's. If you take down one box, what is the probability that you get an A? If it is a B and you put it on the table and take down another box, what is the probability that you get an A this time?

10. Set up an appropriate sample space for each of Problems 1 to 9 and use it to solve the problem. Use either a uniform or a non-uniform sample space or try both.

11. Set up several non-uniform sample spaces for the problem of three tosses of a coin (Example 1, Section 2).

12. Use the sample space of Example 1, Section 2, or one or more of your sample spaces in Problem 11 to answer the following questions.

  (a) If there were more heads than tails, what is the probability of one tail?

  (b) If two heads did not appear in succession, what is the probability of all tails?

  (c) If the coins did not all fall alike, what is the probability that two in succession were alike?

  (d) If N_t = number of tails, and N_h = number of heads, what is the probability that $|N_h - N_t| = 1$?

13. (a) Three typed letters and their envelopes are piled on a desk. If someone puts the letters into the envelopes at random (one letter in each), what is the probability that each letter gets into its own envelope? Call the envelopes A, B, C, and the corresponding letters a, b, c, and set up the sample space. Note that "a in C, b in B, c in A" is *one* point in the sample space.

  (b) What is the probability that at least one letter gets into its own envelope? *Hint:* What is the probability that no letter gets into its own envelope?

  (c) Let A mean that a got into envelope A, etc. Find the probability $P(A)$ that a got into A. Find $P(B)$ and $P(C)$. Find the probability $P(A + B)$ that either a or b or both got into their correct envelopes, and the probability $P(AB)$ that both got into their correct envelopes. Verify equation (3.8).

14. Two dice are thrown. Use the sample space (2.4) to answer the following questions.

(a) What is the probability of being able to form a two-digit number greater than 33 with the two numbers on the dice? (Note that the sample point 1, 4 yields the two-digit number 41 which is greater than 33, etc.)

(b) Repeat part (a) for the probability of being able to form a two-digit number greater than or equal to 42.

(c) Can you find a two-digit number (or numbers) such that the probability of being able to form a larger number is the same as the probability of being able to form a smaller number? [See note, part (a).]

15. Use both the sample space (2.4) and the sample space (2.5) to answer the following questions about a toss of two dice.
(a) What is the probability that the sum is ≤ 4?
(b) What is the probability that the sum is even?
(c) What is the probability that the sum is divisible by 3?

16. Given a non-uniform sample space and the probabilities associated with the points, we defined the probability of an event A as the sum of the probabilities associated with the sample points favorable to A. [You used this definition in Problem 15 with the sample space (2.5).] Show that this definition is consistent with the definition by equally likely cases if there is also a uniform sample space for the problem (as there was in Problem 15). *Hint:* Let the uniform sample space have N points each with probability N^{-1}. Let the non-uniform sample space have $n < N$ points, the first point corresponding to N_1 points of the uniform space, the second to N_2 points, etc. What is

$$N_1 + N_2 + \cdots + N_n?$$

What are $p_1, p_2, \ldots$, the probabilities associated with the first, second, etc., points of the non-uniform space? What is $p_1 + p_2 + \cdots + p_n$? Now consider an event for which several points, say i, j, k, of the non-uniform sample space are favorable. Then using the non-uniform sample space, we have, by definition of the probability p of the event, $p = p_i + p_j + p_k$. Write this in terms of the N's and show that the result is the same as that obtained by equally likely cases using the uniform space. Refer to Problem 15 as a specific example if you need to.

17. Two dice are thrown. Given the information that the number on the first die is even, and the number on the second is <4, set up an appropriate sample space and answer the following questions.
(a) What are the possible sums and their probabilities?
(b) What is the most probable sum?
(c) What is the probability that the sum is even?

18. Are the following correct non-uniform sample spaces for a throw of two dice? If so, find the probabilities of the given sample points. If not show what is wrong. *Suggestion:* Copy sample space (2.4) and circle on it the regions corresponding to the points of the proposed non-uniform spaces.

(a) First die shows an even number.
First die shows an odd number.
(b) Sum of two numbers on dice is even.
First die is even and second odd.
First die is odd and second even.
(c) First die shows a number ≤ 3.
At least one die shows a number >3.

19. Repeat the third part of Problem 5 by using (3.1). Let event A mean "at least one girl," and B mean "both girls." Solve for $P_A(B)$.

20. What is the probability of getting the sequence *hhhttt* in six tosses of a coin? If you know the first three are heads, what is the probability that the last three are tails? If you don't know anything about the first three, what is the probability that the last three are tails?

21. (a) A weighted coin has probability $\frac{2}{3}$ of showing heads and $\frac{1}{3}$ of showing tails. Find the probabilities of *hh*, *ht*, *th*, and *tt* in two tosses of the coin. Set up the sample space and the associated probabilities. Do the probabilities add to 1 as they should? What is the probability of at least one head? What is the probability of two heads if you know there was at least one head?

(b) For the coin in (a), set up the sample space for three tosses, find the associated probabilities, and use it to answer the questions in Problem 12.

22. A die, loaded as in Example 2 of Section 3, is thrown twice. What is the probability that the number on the die is even the first time and >4 the second time?

23. (a) Set up a sample space for the 5 black and 10 white balls in a box discussed in Section 3 assuming the first ball is not replaced. *Suggestions:* Number the balls, say 1 to 5 for black and 6 to 15 for white. Then the sample points form an array something like (2.4), but the point 3,3 for example is not allowed. (Why? What other points are not allowed?) You might find it helpful to write the numbers for black balls and the numbers for white balls in different colors.

(b) Let A be the event "first ball is white," and B be the event "second ball is black." Circle the region of your sample space containing points favorable to A and mark this region A. Similarly, circle and mark region B. Count the number of sample points in A and in B; these are $N(A)$ and $N(B)$. The region AB is the region inside both A and B; the number of points in this region is $N(AB)$. Use the numbers you have found to verify (3.2) and (3.1). Also find $P(B)$ and $P_B(A)$ and verify (3.3) numerically.

(c) Use Fig. 3.1 and the ideas of part (b) to prove (3.3) in general.

24. For the loaded dice in Example 2 of Section 3, find the probability that the dice show one 4 if the sum is 10; the probability that the two numbers on the dice are equal.

25. (a) A candy vending machine is out of order. The probability that you get a candy bar (with or without the return of your dime) is $\frac{1}{2}$, the probability that you get your dime back (with or without candy) is $\frac{1}{3}$, and the probability

that you get both the candy and your money back is $\frac{1}{12}$. What is the probability that you get nothing at all? *Suggestion:* Sketch a geometric diagram similar to Fig. 3.1, indicate regions representing the various possibilities and their probabilities; then set up a four-point sample space and the associated probabilities of the points.

(b) Suppose you put another dime into the candy vending machine of part (a). Set up the 16-point sample space corresponding to the possible results of your two attempts to buy a candy bar, and find the probability that you get two candy bars (and no money back); that you get no candy and lose both dimes; that you just get your money back both times.

26. Prove (3.1) for a non-uniform sample space. *Hints:* Remember that the probability of an event is the sum of the probabilities of the sample points favorable to it. Using Fig. 3.1, let the points in A but not in AB have probabilities $p_1, p_2, \ldots, p_n$, the points in AB have probabilities $p_{n+1}, p_{n+2}, \ldots, p_{n+k}$, and the points in B but not in AB have probabilities $p_{n+k+1}, p_{n+k+2}, \ldots, p_{n+k+l}$. Find each of the probabilities in (3.1) in terms of the p's and show that you then have an identity.

27. What is the probability that a number n, $1 \le n \le 99$, is divisible by *both* 6 and 10? By *either* 6 *or* 10 or both?

28. A card is selected from a shuffled deck. What is the probability that it is either a king or a club? That it is both a king and a club?

29. There are 3 red and 5 black balls in one box and 6 red and 4 white balls in another. If you pick a box at random, and then pick a ball from it at random, what is the probability that it is red? Black? White? That it is either red or white? Suppose the first ball selected is red and is not replaced before a second ball is drawn. What is the probability that the second ball is red also?

30. A basketball player succeeds in making a basket 3 tries out of 4. How many times must he try for a basket in order to have probability >0.99 of making at least one basket?

31. (a) Note that (3.4) assumes $P(A) \ne 0$ since $P_A(B)$ is meaningless if $P(A) = 0$. Assuming both $P(A) \ne 0$ and $P(B) \ne 0$, show that if (3.4) is true, then $P(A) = P_B(A)$; that is, if B is independent of A, then A is independent of B. If either $P(A)$ or $P(B)$ is zero, then we use (3.5) to define independence.

(b) When is an event E independent of itself? When is E independent of "not E"?

32. Show that

$$P(A + B + C) = P(A) + P(B) + P(C) - P(AB) - P(AC)$$
$$- P(BC) + P(ABC).$$

Hint: Start with Fig. 3.2 and sketch in a region C overlapping some of the points of each of the regions A, B, and AB.

33. A laboratory assistant has stored some vacuum tubes of two different kinds (call them A and B) in two drawers in identical unlabeled boxes. You know only that he put 6 A's in one drawer and 2 A's and 3 B's in another drawer.

A student brings you a tube which he has selected at random from a drawer and you find that it is an A tube. What is the probability that it came from the drawer with 6 A's? From the other drawer? If another tube is picked from the same drawer, what is the probability that it is also an A tube?

34. Suppose it is known that 1 % of the population have a certain kind of cancer. It is also known that a test for this kind of cancer is positive in 99 % of the people who have it but is also positive in 2 % of the people who do not have it. If an individual has a positive test, what is the probability that he has cancer of this type?

35. Two people are taking turns tossing a pair of coins; the first person to toss two alike wins. What are the probabilities of winning for the first player and for the second player? *Hint:* Although there are an infinite number of possibilities here (win on first turn, second turn, third turn, etc.), the sum of the probabilities is a geometric series which can be summed; see Chapter 1 if necessary.

36. Repeat Problem 35 if the players toss a pair of dice trying to get a double (that is, both dice showing the same number).

37. Two cards are drawn at random from a shuffled deck and laid aside without being examined. Then a third card is drawn. Show that the probability that the third card is a spade is $\frac{1}{4}$ just as it was for the first card. *Hint:* Consider all the (mutually exclusive) possibilities (two discarded cards spades, third card spade or not spade, etc.).

38. (a) There are ten chairs in a row and eight people to be seated. In how many ways can this be done?

(b) There are ten questions on a test and you are to do eight of them. In how many ways can you choose them?

(c) In part (a) what is the probability that the first two chairs in the row are vacant?

(d) In part (b), what is the probability that you omit the first two problems in the test?

(e) Explain why the answers to parts (a) and (b) are different, but the answers to (c) and (d) are the same.

39. In the expansion of $(a + b)^n$ (see Example 2, Section 4) let $a = b = 1$, and interpret the terms of the expansion to show that the total number of combinations of n things taken 1, 2, 3, ..., n at a time, is $2^n - 1$.

40. A bank allows one person to have only one savings account insured to $10,000. However, a larger family may have accounts for each individual, and also accounts in the names of any 2 people, any 3, etc. How many accounts are possible for a family of 2? Of 3? Of 5? Of n? *Hint:* See Problem 39.

41. Five cards are dealt from a shuffled deck. What is the probability that they are all of the same suit? That they are all diamonds? That they are all face cards? That the five cards are a sequence in the same suit (for example, 3, 4, 5, 6, 7 of hearts)?

42. In a family of five children, what is the probability that there are two boys and three girls? That the two oldest are boys and the other three, girls?

43. A so-called 7-way lamp has three 60 watt bulbs which may be turned on one or two or all three at a time, and a large bulb which may be turned to 100 watts, 200 watts, or 300 watts. How many different light intensities can the lamp be set to give if the completely off position is not included? (The answer is *not* 7.)

44. What is the probability that the 2 and 3 of clubs are next to each other in a shuffled deck? *Hint:* Imagine the two cards accidentally stuck together and shuffled as one card.

45. Two cards are drawn from a shuffled deck. What is the probability that both are aces? If you know that at least one is an ace, what is the probability that both are aces? If you know that one is the ace of spades, what is the probability that both are aces?

46. What is the probability that you and a friend have different birthdays? (For simplicity, let a year have 365 days.) What is the probability that three people have three different birthdays? Show that the probability that n people have n different birthdays is

$$p = \left(1 - \frac{1}{365}\right)\left(1 - \frac{2}{365}\right)\left(1 - \frac{3}{365}\right) \cdots \left(1 - \frac{n-1}{365}\right).$$

Estimate this for $n \ll 365$ by calculating $\ln p$ [recall that $\ln(1+x)$ is approximately x for $x \ll 1$]. Find the smallest (integral) n for which $p < \frac{1}{2}$. Hence show that for a group of 23 people or more, the probability is greater than $\frac{1}{2}$ that two of them have the same birthday. (Try it with a group of friends or a list of people such as the presidents of the United States.)

47. Generalize Example 3 of Section 4 to show that the number of ways of putting N balls in n boxes with N_1 in box 1, N_2 in box 2, etc., is

$$\left(\frac{N!}{N_1! \cdot N_2! \cdot N_3! \cdots N_n!}\right).$$

48. (a) Find the probability that in two tosses of a coin, one is heads and one tails. That in six tosses of a die, all six of the faces show up. That in 12 tosses of a 12-sided die, all 12 faces show up. That in n tosses of an n-sided die, all n faces show up.

(b) The last problem in (a) is equivalent to finding the probability that, when n balls are distributed at random into n boxes, each box contains exactly one ball. Show that for large n, this is approximately $e^{-n}\sqrt{2\pi n}$.

49. (a) Set up the uniform sample spaces for the problem of putting 2 particles in 3 boxes: for Maxwell-Boltzmann particles, for Fermi-Dirac particles, and for Bose-Einstein particles. See Example 5, Section 4. (You should find 9 sample points for MB, 3 for FD, and 6 for BE.)

(b) Repeat part (a) for 2 particles in 2 boxes. Using the model discussed in Example 5, Section 4, find the probability of each of the three sample points in the Bose-Einstein case. (You should find that each has probability $\frac{1}{3}$, that is, they are equally probable.)

50. (a) Following the methods of Examples 3, 4, 5, Section 4, show that the number of equally likely ways of putting N particles in n boxes, $n > N$, is n^N for Maxwell-Boltzmann particles, $C(n, N)$ for Fermi-Dirac particles, and $C(n - 1 + N, N)$ for Bose-Einstein particles.

    (b) Show that if n is much larger than N (think, for example, of $n = 10^6$, $N = 10$), then both the Bose-Einstein and the Fermi-Dirac results in part (a) contain products of N numbers, each number approximately equal to n. Thus show that for $n \gg N$, both the BE and the FD results are approximately equal to $n^N/N!$, which is $1/N!$ times the MB result.

51. (a) In Example 5, Section 4, a mathematical model is discussed which claims to give a distribution of identical balls into boxes in such a way that all distinguishable arrangements are equally probable (Bose-Einstein statistics). Prove this by showing that the probability of a distribution of N balls into n boxes (according to this model) with N_1 balls in the first box, N_2 in the second, ..., N_n in the nth, is $1/C(n - 1 + N, N)$ for any set of numbers N_i such that $\sum_{i=1}^{n} N_i = N$.

    (b) Show that the model in (a) leads to Maxwell-Boltzmann statistics if the drawn card is replaced (but no extra card added) and to Fermi-Dirac statistics if the drawn card is not replaced. *Hint:* Calculate in each case the number of possible arrangements of the balls in the boxes. Do first the problem of 4 particles in 6 boxes as in the example, and.then do N particles in n boxes ($n > N$) to get the results in Problem 50.

52. The following problem arises in quantum mechanics. Find the number of ordered triples of nonnegative integers a, b, c whose sum $a + b + c$ is a given positive integer n. (For example, if $n = 2$, we could have $(a, b, c) = (2, 0, 0)$ or $(0, 2, 0)$ or $(0, 0, 2)$ or $(0, 1, 1)$ or $(1, 0, 1)$ or $(1, 1, 0)$.) *Hint:* Show that this is the same as the number of distinguishable distributions of n identical balls in 3 boxes, and follow the method of Example 5, Section 4, or use Problem 50a.

53. Set up sample spaces for each of the following problems and list next to each sample point the value of the indicated random variable x, and the probability associated with the sample point. Make a table of the different values x_i of x and the corresponding probabilities $p_i = f(x_i)$.

    (a) Three coins are tossed; $x =$ number of heads minus number of tails.

    (b) Two dice are thrown; $x =$ product of the numbers on the dice.

    (c) A coin is tossed repeatedly; $x =$ number of the toss at which a head first appears.

    (d) One card is drawn from a shuffled deck; $x =$ the number on the card unless it is a face card; $x = 10$ for face cards.

    (e) A weighted coin with probability p of coming down heads is tossed three times; $x =$ number of heads minus number of tails.

54. Compute the mean, the variance, and the standard deviation for each of the random variables in Problem 53.

55. Using the results of Problem 54, decide whether you would pay $10 per throw of two dice if you were to receive a number of dollars equal to the product of the numbers on the dice. *Hint:* What is your expectation? If it is more than $10, then the game would be favorable for you.

56. (a) Show that the expectation of the sum of two random variables defined over the same sample space is the sum of the expectations. *Hint:* Let $p_1, p_2, p_3, \ldots, p_n$ be the probabilities associated with the n sample points; let $x_1, x_2, \ldots, x_n$, and $y_1, y_2, \ldots, y_n$, be the values of the random variables x and y for the n sample points. Write out $E(x)$, $E(y)$, and $E(x + y)$.

(b) Do (a) for a continuous distribution.

57. (a) Let μ be the average of the random variable x. Then the quantities $(x_i - \mu)$ are the deviations of x from its average. Show that the average of these deviations is zero. *Hint:* Use Problem 56 (average and expectation mean the same thing).

(b) Repeat (a) for a continuous distribution.

58. Show that the expected number of heads in a single toss of a coin is $\frac{1}{2}$. Show in two ways that the expected number of heads in two tosses of a coin is 1: (a) Let x = number of heads in two tosses and find $\bar{x}$. (b) Let x = number of heads in toss 1 and y = number of heads in toss 2; find the average of $x + y$ by Problem 56.

Use method (b) to show that the expected number of heads in n tosses of a coin is $\frac{1}{2}n$.

59. For each of the probability functions $f(x)$ in Problem 53, find and plot the distribution function $F(x)$.

60. Show that adding a constant K to a random variable increases the average by K but does not change the variance. Show that multiplying a random variable by K multiplies both the average and the standard deviation by K. Do this problem for both the discrete and the continuous case.

61. (a) Find the probability function $f(x)$ for the position x of a particle which is executing simple harmonic motion on $(-a, a)$ along the x-axis. (See Chapter 6, Section 2, for a discussion of simple harmonic motion.) *Hint:* The value of x at time t is $x = a \cos \omega t$. Find the velocity dx/dt; then the probability of finding the particle in a given dx is proportional to the time it spends there which is inversely proportional to its speed there. Don't forget that the total probability of finding the particle *somewhere* must be 1.

(b) Sketch the probability function $f(x)$ found in part (a) and also the distribution function $F(x)$ [see (6.4)].

(c) Find the average and the standard deviation of x in part (a).

62. It is shown in the kinetic theory of gases that the probability for the distance a molecule travels between collisions to be between x and $x + dx$, is proportional to $e^{-x/\lambda} \, dx$, where λ is a constant. Show that the average distance between collisions (called the "mean free path") is λ.

63. Given that a particle is inside a sphere of radius 1, and that it has equal probabilities of being found in any two volume elements of the same size, find the distribution function $F(r)$ for the spherical coordinate r, and from it find the density function $f(r)$. *Hint:* $F(r)$ is the probability that the particle is inside a sphere of radius r.

64. A hydrogen atom consists of a proton and an electron. According to the Bohr theory, the electron revolves about the proton in a circle of radius a ($a = 5 \cdot 10^{-9}$ cm for the ground state). According to quantum mechanics, the electron may be at any distance r (from 0 to ∞) from the proton; for the ground state, the probability that the electron is in a volume element dV, at a distance r to $r + dr$ from the proton, is proportional to $e^{-2r/a}\, dV$, where a is the Bohr radius. Write dV in spherical coordinates (see Chapter 4, Section 14) and find the density function $f(r)$ so that $f(r)\, dr$ is the probability that the electron is at a distance between r and $r + dr$ from the proton. (Remember that the probability for the electron to be somewhere must be 1.) Sketch $f(r)$ and show that its maximum value is at $r = a$; we then say that the most probable value of r is a. Also show that the average value of r^{-1} is a^{-1}.

65. (a) Find the probabilities of x heads in n tosses of a coin and plot graphs (as in Figs. 7.1 and 7.2) of the frequency function $f(x)$ [equation (7.1)] for the cases $n = 4$, 5, 6, and 10. Also draw graphs of $nf(x)$ as a function of x/n and of the distribution function $F(x)$ in equation (7.4).

(b) Use your calculations and graphs to answer these questions for the values of n you have used in (a): What is the probability of exactly 3 heads? Of at most 3 heads? [*Hint:* Consider $F(x)$.] Of at least 3 heads? What is the most probable number of heads? The expected number of heads?

66. Plot a graph of the binomial frequency function $f(x)$ for the case $n = 6$, $p = \frac{1}{6}, q = \frac{5}{6}$, representing the probability of, say, x aces in 6 throws of a die. Also draw graphs of $nf(x)$ as a function of x/n, and of $F(x)$. What is the probability of at least 2 aces out of 6 tosses of a die? *Hint:* Can you read the probability of at most one ace from one of your graphs?

67. Use the second method of Problem 58 to show that the expected number of successes in n Bernoulli trials with probability p of success is $\bar{x} = np$. *Hint:* What is the expected number of successes in one trial?

68. Show that the most probable number of heads in n tosses of a coin is $\frac{1}{2}n$ for even n [that is, $f(x)$ in (7.1) has its largest value for $x = n/2$] and that for odd n, there are two equal "largest" values of $f(x)$, namely for $x = \frac{1}{2}(n + 1)$ and $x = \frac{1}{2}(n - 1)$. *Hint:* Simplify the fraction $f(x + 1)/f(x)$, and then find the values of x for which it is greater than 1 [that is, $f(x + 1) > f(x)$], and less than or equal to 1 [that is, $f(x + 1) \le f(x)$]. Remember that x must be an integer.

69. Use the method of Problem 68 to show that for the binomial distribution (7.3), the most probable value of x is approximately np (actually within 1 of this value).

70. (a) Recall that two events A and B are called independent if $p(AB) = p(A) \cdot p(B)$. Similarly, two random variables x and y with probability functions $f(x)$ and $g(y)$ are called independent if the probability of $x = x_i$ and $y = y_j$ is $f(x_i) \cdot g(y_j)$ for every pair of values of x and y, that is, if the joint probability function for x, y is $f(x)g(y)$. Show that if x and y are independent, then the expectation or average of xy is $E(xy) = E(x) \cdot E(y) = \mu_x \mu_y$.

(b) Use the result of part (a) and Problem 56 to show that for two independent random variables x and y,

$$E[(x - \mu_x)(y - \mu_y)] = E(xy) - \mu_x E(y) - \mu_y E(x) + \mu_x \mu_y = 0,$$

and hence show that

$$\text{Var}(x + y) = E\{[(x + y) - (\mu_x + \mu_y)]^2\} = \text{Var } x + \text{Var } y.$$

71. Let $x =$ number of heads in one toss of a coin. What are the possible values of x and their probabilities? What is μ_x? Hence show that $\text{Var } x =$ [average of $(x - \mu_x)^2] = \frac{1}{4}$, so the standard deviation is $\frac{1}{2}$. Now use the result "variance of a sum of independent random variables $=$ sum of their variances" to show that if $x =$ number of heads in n tosses of a coin, $\text{Var}(x) = \frac{1}{4}n$ and the standard deviation $\sigma_x = \frac{1}{2}\sqrt{n}$.

72. Generalize Problem 71 to show that for the general binomial distribution (7.3), $\text{Var}(x) = npq$, and $\sigma = \sqrt{npq}$.

73. Carry through the following details of a derivation of (8.1). Start with (7.3); we want an approximation to (7.3) for large n. First approximate the factorials in $C(n, x)$ by Stirling's formula (Chapter 9, Section 11) and simplify to get

$$f(x) \sim \left(\frac{np}{x}\right)^x \left(\frac{nq}{n - x}\right)^{n-x} \sqrt{\frac{n}{2\pi x(n - x)}}.$$

Show that if $\delta = x - np$, then $x = np + \delta$ and $n - x = nq - \delta$. Make these substitutions for x and $n - x$ in the approximate $f(x)$. To evaluate the first two factors in $f(x)$ (ignore the square root for now): Take the logarithm of the first two factors; show that

$$\ln \frac{np}{x} = -\ln\left(1 + \frac{\delta}{np}\right)$$

and a similar formula for $\ln[nq/(n - x)]$; expand the logarithms in a series of powers of $\delta/(np)$, collect terms and simplify to get

$$\ln\left(\frac{np}{x}\right)^x \left(\frac{nq}{n - x}\right)^{n-x} \sim -\frac{\delta^2}{2npq}\left(1 + \text{powers of } \frac{\delta}{n}\right).$$

Hence

$$\left(\frac{np}{x}\right)^x \left(\frac{nq}{n - x}\right)^{n-x} \sim e^{-\delta^2/(2npq)}.$$

for large n. [We really want δ/n small, that is, x near enough to its average value np so that $\delta/n = (x - np)/n$ is small. This means that our approximation is valid for the central part of the graph (see Figs. 7.1 to 7.3) around $x = np$ where $f(x)$ is large. Since $f(x)$ is negligibly small anyway for x far from np, we ignore the fact that our approximation may not be good there. For more detail on this point, see Feller, p. 168.] Returning to the square root factor in $f(x)$, approximate x by np and $n - x$ by nq (assuming $\delta \ll np$ or nq) and obtain (8.1).

74. (a) Show that the factor $1/\sqrt{2\pi npq}$ in (8.1) is correct to make the normal approximation to the binomial distribution a probability density function, that is, to make its integral from $-\infty$ to ∞ give a total probability of 1. *Hint:* Make the change of variables $t = (x - np)/\sqrt{npq}$ and use Chapter 9, Section 5.

   (b) In the normal approximation [right-hand side of (8.1)] np and $\sqrt{npq}$ are the mean value μ and standard deviation σ of x for the binomial distribution (Problems 67 and 72). Show that they are also the mean value and standard deviation of x for the normal approximation. (*Hint:* Write and evaluate the appropriate integrals.)

75. Show that $\Phi(x) = \frac{1}{2} \operatorname{erf}(x/\sqrt{2})$ [see (8.7) for $\Phi(x)$ and Chapter 9, Section 9, for erf x.]

76. (a) Write out a proof of Chebyshev's inequality for the case of a continuous probability function $f(x)$.

   (b) Prove the law of large numbers using (a) and the normal approximation to the binomial distribution. *Hint:* Show that the probability of $|(x - np)/n| \geq \epsilon$, which is the same as the probability of $|(x - np)/\sqrt{npq}| \geq \epsilon \sqrt{n}/\sqrt{pq}$, is approximately $1 - 2\Phi(\epsilon\sqrt{n}/\sqrt{pq})$ which tends to zero as $n \to \infty$.

77. Using tables, sketch a graph of the error curve (8.6).

78. Using tables, find the probability that:
   (a) In 100 tosses of a coin, exactly 50 are heads.
   (b) In 720 tosses of a die, 120 are aces.
   (c) In 720 tosses of a die, between 100 and 140 are aces.
   (d) In 10^6 tosses of a coin, the number of heads is between 499,000 and 501,000.

79. Find the probabilities for a normally distributed random variable to differ by more than σ, 2σ, 3σ, 4σ, from its mean value. Your answers should satisfy Chebyshev's inequality (for example, the probability of a deviation of more than 2σ is less than $\frac{1}{4}$). You will find, however, that for the normal distribution, the probabilities are actually much smaller than Chebyshev's inequality requires.

80. An instructor who grades "on the curve" computes the mean and standard deviation of the grades, and then, assuming a normal distribution with this μ and σ, he sets the border lines between the grades at: C from $\mu - \frac{1}{2}\sigma$ to

$\mu + \frac{1}{2}\sigma$, B from $\mu + \frac{1}{2}\sigma$ to $\mu + \frac{3}{2}\sigma$, A from $\mu + \frac{3}{2}\sigma$ up, etc. Find the percentages of the students receiving the various grades. Where should the border lines be set to give the percentages: A and F, 10%; B and D, 20%; C, 40%?

81. Solve the sequence of differential equations (9.4) for successive n values [as started in (9.5) and (9.6)] to obtain (9.7).

82. Show that the average value of a random variable n whose probability function is the Poisson distribution (9.8) is the number μ in (9.8). Also show that the standard deviation of the random variable is $\sqrt{\mu}$. *Hint:* Write the infinite series for e^x, differentiate it and multiply by x to get $xe^x = \Sigma\,(nx^n/n!)$; put $x = \mu$. To find σ^2 differentiate the xe^x series again, etc.

83. In an alpha-particle counting experiment the number of alpha particles is recorded each minute for 50 hours. The total number of particles is 6000. In how many 1-minute intervals would you expect no particles? Exactly n particles, for $n = 1, 2, 3, 4, 5$? Plot the Poisson distribution.

84. Suppose you receive an average of 4 phone calls per day. What is the probability that on a given day you receive no phone calls? Just one call? Exactly 4 calls?

85. Suppose that you have 5 exams during the 5 days of exam week. Find the probability that on a given day you have no exams; just 1 exam; 2 exams; 3 exams.

86. If you receive, on the average, 5 letters per day, in how many days out of a year would you expect to receive no mail? Exactly 5 letters? Exactly 10 letters?

87. Derive (9.9) as follows: In $C(n, x)$, show that $n!/(n - x)! \sim n^x$ for fixed x and large n [write $n!/(n - x)!$ as a product of x factors, divide by n^x, and show that the limit is 1 as $n \to \infty$]. Then write $q^{n-x} = (1 - p)^{n-x}$ as $(1 - p)^n(1 - p)^{-x} = (1 - np/n)^n(1 - p)^{-x}$; evaluate the limit of the first factor as $n \to \infty$, np fixed; the limit of the second factor as $p \to 0$ is 1. Collect your results to obtain (9.9).

88. Let $m_1, m_2, \ldots, m_n$ be a set of measurements, and define the values x_i by $x_1 = m_1 - a$, $x_2 = m_2 - a, \ldots, x_n = m_n - a$, where a is some number (as yet unspecified, but the same for all x_i). Show that in order to minimize $\sum_{i=1}^{n} x_i^2$, we should choose $a = (1/n)\sum_{i=1}^{n} m_i$. *Hint:* Differentiate $\sum_{i=1}^{n} x_i^2$ with respect to a. You have shown that the arithmetic mean is the "best" average in the least squares sense, that is, that if the sum of the squares of the deviations of the measurements from their "average" is a minimum, the "average" is the arithmetic mean (rather than, say, the median or mode).

89. (a) Let $x_1, x_2, \ldots, x_n$ be independent random variables, each with density function $f(x)$, expected value μ, and variance σ^2. Define the sample mean by $\bar{x} = (1/n)\sum_{i=1}^{n} x_i$. Show that $E(\bar{x}) = \mu$, and Var $\bar{x} = \sigma^2/n$. (See Problems 56 and 60.)

(b) Define the sample variance by $s^2 = (1/n) \sum\limits_{i=1}^{n} (x_i - \bar{x})^2$. Show that the expected value of s^2 is $[(n-1)/n]\sigma^2$. *Hints:* Write

$$(x_i - \bar{x})^2 = [(x_i - \mu) - (\bar{x} - \mu)]^2$$
$$= (x_i - \mu)^2 - 2(x_i - \mu)(\bar{x} - \mu) + (\bar{x} - \mu)^2.$$

Find the average value of the first term from the definition of σ^2 and the average value of the third term from part (a). To find the average value of the middle term write

$$(\bar{x} - \mu) = \left(\frac{x_1 + x_2 + \cdots + x_n}{n} - \mu \right) = \frac{1}{n} [(x_1 - \mu)$$
$$+ (x_2 - \mu) + \cdots + (x_n - \mu)];$$

show by Problem 70 that

$$E[(x_i - \mu)(x_j - \mu)] = E(x_i - \mu)E(x_j - \mu) = 0 \qquad \text{for} \quad i \neq j,$$

and evaluate $E[(x_i - \mu)^2]$ (same as the first term). Collect terms to find

$$E(s^2) = \frac{n-1}{n} \sigma^2.$$

90. Suppose that we measure a velocity v by measuring x and t repeatedly to find $v_1 = x_1/t_1$, $v_2 = x_2/t_2$, etc. Then $\bar{v} = (1/n) \sum\limits_{i=1}^{n} v_i = (1/n) \sum\limits_{i=1}^{n} (x_i/t_i)$. Show that $\bar{x}/\bar{t}$ is a good approximation for $\bar{v}$ if the "errors" in x and t are small, that is, if $|\Delta x_i| = |x_i - \bar{x}| \ll |\bar{x}|$ and $|\Delta t_i| \ll |\bar{t}|$ for all the measurements x_i and t_i. *Hint:* Write $\sum\limits_{i=1}^{n} (x_i/t_i)$ as

$$\sum_{i=1}^{n} \frac{\bar{x} + \Delta x_i}{\bar{t} + \Delta t_i} = \frac{\bar{x}}{\bar{t}} \sum_{i=1}^{n} \left(1 + \frac{\Delta x_i}{\bar{x}}\right)\left(1 + \frac{\Delta t_i}{\bar{t}}\right)^{-1}.$$

91. In Section 10 we discussed how to compute the sample variance for a quotient of two measured quantities. Similarly:

(a) Show that the variance of a sum or difference is the sum of the variances (see Problem 70b). Thus show that if A is measured with "error" ΔA and B with "error" ΔB, the "error" in $A + B$ or $A - B$ is $\sqrt{(\Delta A)^2 + (\Delta B)^2}$. The "error" here means standard deviation, but since probable error is by definition proportional to the standard deviation (see Problem 92), the proofs hold also if ΔA and ΔB are probable errors.

(b) Show that the variance of a product $C = AB$ is given by the same formula we obtained for a quotient, namely

$$\left(\frac{\Delta C}{C}\right)^2 = \left(\frac{\Delta A}{A}\right)^2 + \left(\frac{\Delta B}{B}\right)^2,$$

so the relative error $\dfrac{\Delta C}{C}$ in a product is

$$\sqrt{\left(\frac{\Delta A}{A}\right)^2 + \left(\frac{\Delta B}{B}\right)^2}.$$

Hint: Follow the method of Section 10.

(c) Obtain a general formula for the "error" in any computed function $f(x, y)$ of two measured quantities x and y. *Hint:* Approximate Δf_i by $df_i = (\partial f / \partial x) \, dx_i + (\partial f / \partial y) \, dy_i$ (where the partial derivatives are evaluated at $\bar{x}, \bar{y}$) and evaluate

$$\text{Var} f \cong \frac{1}{n} \sum_{i=1}^{n} (df_i)^2.$$

92. For a normal distribution, find from tables the value h such that half the area under the error curve is between $\mu - h$ and $\mu + h$ and half the area is outside this interval. (See Section 8 and Problems 78, 79, and 80.) You should find $h = 0.67\sigma$, where σ is the standard deviation. The quantity $r = 0.67\sigma_m$, obtained from the standard deviation in the mean, is called the probable error.

93. The following measurements of x and y have been made.
$\quad x$: 5.1, 4.9, 5.0, 5.2, 5.0, 4.9, 5.0, 4.8, 5.0, 5.1;
$\quad y$: 1.03, 1.05, 0.96, 1.00, 1.02, 0.95, 0.99, 1.01, 1.00, 0.99.
Find $\bar{x}, \bar{y}, s_x, s_y$ [see (10.1)], approximate values for σ_x and σ_y [see (10.2)], σ_m for x and for y [see (10.4)], and the probable error for x and for y (see Problem 92). Compute the average values of $x + y$, $x - y$, xy, x/y, $x^2 y^3$, $\ln x$, and the probable error for each of these functions of x and y (see Problems 91 and 92).

Some Suggested References

The following list includes books referred to in the text and some other suggested references. To find reference material on any given chapter of this text, look for books followed by that chapter number; for example, books containing material on Fourier Series (Chapter 6) have a [6] after the listing. Books of formulas or tables which may be useful at any time are not so labeled; neither are references for one specific theorem. Books marked S are included for various special reasons. Many of them are graduate level books; others are included for their more detailed or sophisticated treatment either of a mathematical topic or of its physical applications.

Abramowitz, Milton, and Irene A. Stegun, editors, *Handbook of Mathematical Functions With Formulas, Graphs, and Mathematical Tables*, National Bureau of Standards, Applied Mathematics Series, 55, U.S. Government Printing Office, Washington, D.C., 1964.

Agnew, Ralph Palmer, *Differential Equations*, McGraw-Hill, New York, 1942. [7]

Apostol, Tom M., *Mathematical Analysis*, Addison-Wesley, Reading, Mass., 1957. [1, 2, 4, 5, 6, 11, 13] S

Band, William, *Introduction to Mathematical Physics*, Van Nostrand, Princeton, 1959. [10, 14] S .

Beaumont, Ross A., and Richard W. Ball, *Introduction to Modern Algebra and Matrix Theory*, Rinehart, New York, 1954. [3, 10]

Bliss, Gilbert Ames, *Calculus of Variations*, Open Court, Chicago, 1925. [8]

Bôcher, Maxime, *Introduction to Higher Algebra*, Macmillan, New York, 1929. [3]

Brand, Louis, *Advanced Calculus*, Wiley, New York, 1955. [1, 4, 5, 6, 11]

Bronwell, Arthur, *Advanced Mathematics in Physics and Engineering*, McGraw-Hill, New York, 1953. [1, 2, 4, 5, 6, 7, 11, 12, 13, 14]

Buck, R. Creighton, *Advanced Calculus*, 2nd ed., McGraw-Hill, New York, 1965.

Byrd, P. F., and Morris D. Friedman, *Handbook of Elliptic Integrals for Engineers and Physicists*, Springer, Berlin-Göttingen-Heidelberg, 1954. [9]

Churchill, Ruel V., *Fourier Series and Boundary Value Problems*, McGraw-Hill, New York, 1941. [6, 12, 13, 14]

Churchill, Ruel V., *Introduction to Complex Variables and Applications*, McGraw-Hill, New York, 1948; 2nd ed., 1960. [11]

Churchill, Ruel V., *Modern Operational Methods in Engineering*, McGraw-Hill, New York, 1944. [13, 14]

Crowder, Harold K., and S. W. McCuskey, *Topics in Higher Analysis*, Macmillan, New York, 1964. [1, 5, 6, 8, 9, 11, 12, 13, 14]

C.R.C. Standard Mathematical Tables, Chemical Rubber Publishing Company, Cleveland. (Any recent edition.)

Dettman, John W., *Mathematical Methods in Physics and Engineering*, McGraw-Hill, New York, 1962. [8, 10, 13, 14] S

Dwight, Herbert Bristol, *Tables of Integrals and Other Mathematical Data*, Macmillan, New York. (Any edition.)

Emde, Fritz, *Jahnke-Emde, Tafeln höherer Funktionen, Tables of Higher Functions*, 4th ed., Teubner, Leipzig, 1948. [9, 12, 13, 14]

Erdélyi, A., *Asymptotic Expansions*, Dover, New York, 1956. [9] S

Erdélyi, Arthur, *Operational Calculus and Generalized Functions*, Holt, Rinehart and Winston, New York, 1962. [13] S

Erdélyi, A., editor, *Higher Transcendental Functions*, McGraw-Hill, New York, 1953, 3 vols. [9, 12]

Erdélyi, A., editor, *Tables of Integral Transforms*, McGraw-Hill, New York, 1954, 2 vols. [13]

Evans, Robley D., *The Atomic Nucleus*, McGraw-Hill, New York, 1955. [15]

Fagg, S. V., *Differential Equations*, Row, Peterson, Evanston, Ill., 1961. [7, 13]

Feller, William, *An Introduction to Probability Theory and Its Applications*, Vol. 1, 2nd ed., Wiley, New York, 1957. [15]

Finkbeiner, Daniel T., II, *Introduction to Matrices and Linear Transformations*, Freeman, San Francisco, 1960. [3, 10] S

Forsyth, A. R., *Calculus of Variations*, Dover, New York, 1960. [8] S

Franklin, Philip, *Methods of Advanced Calculus*, McGraw-Hill, New York, 1944. [1, 2, 4, 5, 6, 7, 8, 9, 11, 12, 14]

Frazer, R. A., W. J. Duncan, and A. R. Collar, *Elementary Matrices and Some Applications to Dynamics and Differential Equations*, Cambridge University Press, 1946. [3, 10]

Fuller, Leonard E., *Basic Matrix Theory*, Prentice-Hall, Englewood Cliffs, N.J., 1962. [3, 10]

Gaskell, Robert E., *Engineering Mathematics*, Dryden, New York, 1958. [3, 5, 6, 7, 9, 11, 13, 14]

Goldberg, Samuel, *Probability: An Introduction*, Prentice-Hall, Englewood Cliffs, N.J., 1960. [15]

Gray, A., G. B. Mathews, and T. M. MacRobert, *A Treatise on Bessel Functions and Their Applications to Physics*, Macmillan, London, 1922. [12] S

Hildebrand, F. B., *Advanced Calculus for Engineers*, Prentice-Hall, New York, 1949. [5, 7, 11, 12, 13, 14]

Hildebrand, F. B., *Methods of Applied Mathematics*, Prentice-Hall, New York, 1952. [3, 8, 10]

Hille, Einar, *Analytic Function Theory*, Vol. 1, Ginn, Boston, 1959.

Hochstadt, Harry, *Special Functions of Mathematical Physics*, Holt, Rinehart and Winston, New York, 1961. [12]

Holl, Dio L., Clair G. Maple, and Bernard Vinograde, *Introduction to the Laplace Transform*, Appleton-Century-Crofts, New York, 1959. [13]

Irving, J., and N. Mullineux, *Mathematics in Physics and Engineering*, Academic Press, New York, 1959. [3, 7, 8, 11, 12, 13, 14]

Jackson, Dunham, *Fourier Series and Orthogonal Polynomials*, Mathematical Association of America, 1941. [6, 12]

Jahnke, E., F. Emde, and F. Lösch, *Tables of Higher Functions*, 6th ed., McGraw-Hill, New York, 1960. See also Emde or other earlier editions of Jahnke-Emde. [9, 12, 13, 14]

Jeffreys, Harold, *Cartesian Tensors*, Cambridge University Press, 1957. [10]

Johnson, David E., and Johnny R. Johnson, *Mathematical Methods in Engineering and Physics, Special Functions and Boundary Value Problems*. Ronald, New York, 1965. [6, 12, 13, 14] S

Jones, D. S., *Generalized Functions*, McGraw-Hill, New York, 1966.

Kamke, E., *Differentialgleichungen, Lösungsmethoden und Lösungen, Band 1, Gewöhnliche Differentialgleichungen*, 3rd ed., Akademische Verlagsgesellschaft, Leipzig, 1944. [7, 12]

Kaplan, Wilfred, *Advanced Calculus*, Addison-Wesley, Reading, Mass., 1952. [1, 2, 4, 5, 6, 7, 11, 14]

Kaplan, Wilfred, *A First Course in Functions of a Complex Variable*, Addison-Wesley, Reading, Mass., 1953. [11]

Kaplan, Wilfred, *Operational Methods for Linear Systems*, Addison-Wesley, Reading, Mass., 1962. [6, 11, 13]

Kaplan, Wilfred, *Ordinary Differential Equations*, Addison-Wesley, Reading, Mass., 1958. [7, 13]

Kemeny, John G., Hazleton Mirkil, J. Laurie Snell, and Gerald L. Thompson, *Finite Mathematical Structures*, Prentice-Hall, Englewood Cliffs, N.J., 1959. [3, 10, 15]

Knopp, Konrad, *Theory and Application of Infinite Series*, Blackie, London, 1928. [1] S

Kreyszig, Erwin, *Advanced Engineering Mathematics*, Wiley, New York, 1962. [1, 2, 3, 5, 6, 7, 9, 10, 11, 12, 13, 14]

Lambe, C. G., and C. J. Tranter, *Differential Equations for Engineers and Scientists*, Row, Peterson, Evanston, Ill., 1961. [7, 12, 13]

Lass, Harry, *Vector and Tensor Analysis*, McGraw-Hill, New York, 1950. [5, 10]

LePage, Wilbur R., *Complex Variables and the Laplace Transform for Engineers*, McGraw-Hill, New York, 1961. [11, 13] S

Lighthill, M. J., *Introduction to Fourier Analysis and Generalised Functions*, Cambridge University Press, 1958. [13] S

Magnus, Wilhelm, and Fritz Oberhettinger, *Formulas and Theorems for the Special Functions of Mathematical Physics*, Chelsea, New York, 1949. [9, 12, 13]

Margenau, Henry, and George Moseley Murphy, *The Mathematics of Physics and Chemistry*, 2nd ed., Van Nostrand, Princeton, 1956. [3, 4, 5, 7, 8, 10, 12, 14]

Mathews, Jon, and R. L. Walker, *Mathematical Methods of Physics*, Benjamin, New York, 1964. [8, 10, 11, 12, 13, 14, 15] S

May, Kenneth O., *Elements of Modern Mathematics*, Addison-Wesley, Reading, Mass., 1959. [15]

Menzel, Donald H., editor, *Fundamental Formulas of Physics*, Dover, New York, 1960, 2 vols.

Morse, Philip M., and Herman Feshbach, *Methods of Theoretical Physics*, McGraw-Hill, New York, 1953. [5, 8, 9, 10, 11, 12, 13, 14] S

NBS Tables. See Abramowitz.

Nehari, Zeev, *Introduction to Complex Analysis*, Allyn and Bacon, Boston, 1961. [11] S

Oberhettinger, Fritz, *Tabellen zur Fourier Transformation*, Springer-Verlag, Berlin-Göttingen-Heidelberg, 1957. [13]

Oberhettinger, Fritz, and Wilhelm Magnus, *Anwendung der elliptischen Funktionen in Physik und Technik*, Springer-Verlag, Berlin-Göttingen-Heidelberg, 1949. [9] S

Osgood, William F., *Advanced Calculus*, Macmillan, New York, 1929. [2, 4, 5, 6, 7, 8, 9, 11, 14]

Parratt, Lyman G., *Probability and Experimental Errors in Science*, Wiley, New York, 1961. [15]

Parzen, Emanuel, *Modern Probability Theory and Its Applications*, Wiley, New York, 1960. [15]

Peirce, B. O., *A Short Table of Integrals*, 4th ed., revised by Ronald M. Foster, Ginn, Boston, 1956.

Perlis, Sam, *Theory of Matrices*, Addison-Wesley, Cambridge, Mass., 1952. [3, 10]

Phillips, E. G., *Functions of a Complex Variable With Applications*, Oliver and Boyd, Edinburgh, 1947. [11]

Pipes, Louis A., *Applied Mathematics for Engineers and Physicists*, McGraw-Hill, New York, 1958. [1, 2, 3, 4, 5, 6, 7, 9, 11, 12, 14]

Rainville, Earl D., *Special Functions*, Macmillan, New York, 1960. [9, 12] S

Reddick, H. W., and F. H. Miller, *Advanced Mathematics for Engineers*, 2nd ed., Wiley, New York, 1947. [1, 4, 5, 6, 7, 9, 11, 12, 14]

Relton, F. E., *Applied Bessel Functions*, Blackie, London, 1946. [12]

Rogosinski, Werner, *Fourier Series*, Chelsea, New York, 1950. [6]

Schelkunoff, S. A., *Applied Mathematics for Engineers and Scientists*, Van Nostrand, New York, 1948. [1, 2, 4, 5, 7, 10, 11, 12, 13]

Smith, Lloyd P., *Mathematical Methods for Scientists and Engineers*, Prentice-Hall, New York, 1953. [4, 5, 8, 10, 11, 12, 15] S

Sneddon, Ian N., *Fourier Transforms*, McGraw-Hill, New York, 1951. [13] S

Sokolnikoff, I. S., *Tensor Analysis, Theory and Applications*, Wiley, New York, 1951. [10] S

Sokolnikoff, I. S., and R. M. Redheffer, *Mathematics of Physics and Modern Engineering*, McGraw-Hill, New York, 1958. [1, 4, 5, 6, 7, 10, 11, 14, 15]

Spiegel, Murray R., *Schaum's Outline of Theory and Problems of Advanced Calculus*, Schaum, New York, 1963. [1, 4, 5, 6, 9, 11, 13]

Spiegel, Murray R., *Schaum's Outline of Theory and Problems of Complex Variables*, Schaum, New York, 1964. [2, 11]

Spiegel, Murray R., *Schaum's Outline of Theory and Problems of Laplace Transforms*, Schaum, New York, 1965. [13]

Spiegel, Murray R., *Schaum's Outline of Theory and Problems of Vector Analysis With an Introduction to Tensor Analysis*, Schaum, New York, 1959. [5, 10]

Taylor, Angus E., *Advanced Calculus*, Ginn, Boston, 1955. [1, 2, 4, 5, 6, 9]

Tenenbaum, Morris, and Harry Pollard, *Ordinary Differential Equations*, Harper and Row, New York, 1963. [7, 12]

Thomas, George B., Jr., *Calculus and Analytic Geometry*, 3rd ed., Addison-Wesley, Reading, Mass., 1960. [1, 2, 3, 4, 5, 7]

Thomson, William Tyrrell, *Laplace Transformation, Theory and Engineering Applications*, Prentice-Hall, New York, 1950. [13]

Tolstov, Georgi P., *Fourier Series*, Prentice-Hall, Englewood Cliffs, N.J., 1962. [6, 12, 13, 14] S

Wade, Thomas L., *The Algebra of Vectors and Matrices*, Addison-Wesley, Cambridge, Mass., 1951. [3, 10]

Watson, G. N., *A Treatise on the Theory of Bessel Functions*, 2nd ed., Cambridge University Press, 1944. [12] S

Weinberger, H. F., *A First Course in Partial Differential Equations With Complex Variables and Transform Methods*, Blaisdell, New York, 1965. [11, 13, 14]

Weinstock, Robert, *Calculus of Variations With Applications to Physics and Engineering*, McGraw-Hill, New York, 1952. [8]

Wilf, Herbert S., *Mathematics for the Physical Sciences*, Wiley, New York, 1962. [8, 9, 10, 11, 12] S

Wilson, Edwin Bidwell, *Advanced Calculus*, Dover, New York, 1958. [1, 2, 4, 5, 7, 8, 9, 11, 14]

Wolf, Frank L., *Elements of Probability and Statistics*, McGraw-Hill, New York, 1962. [15]

Wylie, C. R., Jr., *Advanced Engineering Mathematics*, 2nd ed., McGraw-Hill, New York, 1960. [3, 6, 7, 11, 12, 13, 14]

Answers to Selected Problems

Chapter 1

1. 0.0173 yd; 0.104 yd (compared to a total of 5 yd)

3. (b) 2/99 (d) 137/1100 (f) 1/132

10. (a) D (c) C

13. (a) D (c) C (e) C

14. (a) D (c) C (e) C (g) D (i) D (k) C (m) C (o) D (q) C
(s) C (u) C (w) C

16. Distance from right-hand end of book n to right-hand end of book $(n + 1)$
is $x_n = l/2n$, where l = length of a book.

20. (a) D (c) C

22. (a) C (c) D

29. (a) $|x| < 1$ (c) $|x| \leq 1$ (e) All x (g) No finite x (i) $-1 < x < 1$
(k) $0 \leq x \leq 1$

31. (a) $1 + 2x + 2x^2 + 2x^3 + \cdots$
(c) $x^2 - x^6/3! + x^{10}/5! - \cdots$
(e) $1 + 2x + 5x^2/2 + 8x^3/3 + \cdots$
(g) $1 - x/3! + x^2/5! - \cdots$
(j) $x - x^3/3 + x^5/(5 \cdot 2!) - x^7/(7 \cdot 3!) + \cdots$
(k) $-(x^3 + x^4/2 + x^5/3 + x^6/4 + \cdots)$
(m) $1 + x^2/2 + 3x^4/8 + 5x^6/16 + \cdots$
(o) $1 + x^2/2! + 5x^4/4! + 61x^6/6! + \cdots$

32. (a) $-(x^2/2 + x^4/12 + x^6/45 + \cdots)$

33. (a) $(x - 1) - \frac{1}{2}(x - 1)^2 + \frac{1}{3}(x - 1)^3 - \frac{1}{4}(x - 1)^4 + \cdots$
(c) $1 + (x - \frac{1}{2}\pi)^2/2! + 5(x - \frac{1}{2}\pi)^4/4! + 61(x - \frac{1}{2}\pi)^6/6! + \cdots$
(e) $1 + 2(x - \frac{1}{4}\pi) + 2(x - \frac{1}{4}\pi)^2 + 8(x - \frac{1}{4}\pi)^3/3 + \cdots$

34. (a) 0.479 (c) $\sqrt{26} = 5(1 + \frac{1}{25})^{1/2} = 5.099$
(e) 0.291 (g) 1.051 (i) -0.010

35. (a) 0.182 (c) 1.000 (to three decimal places) (e) 0.966

43. (a) $\frac{1}{2}$ (c) -1 (e) ∞

46. (a) ∞ (c) 0

47. (a) 0 (c) 0 (e) $\frac{1}{2}$

50. (b) $v/c \cong 1 - (5 \times 10^{-7})$ or $v \cong 0.9999995c$

51. For $\theta = 1°$: $F/W \cong 0.017453$ (1 term); $F/W \cong 0.017455$ (2 terms)

52. (a) 6000 lb, 1001 lb, 502.5 lb, 111.7 lb

Chapter 2

1. (g) $x = -\frac{1}{2}, y = -\frac{1}{2}, r = 1/\sqrt{2}, \theta = 5\pi/4$
(q) $x = -1, y = 0, r = 1, \theta = \pi$

2. (g) $1/(-i - 1) = -\frac{1}{2} + \frac{1}{2}i$ (q) $[(1 - i)/(1 + i)]^2 = -1$

4. (a) $x = -4, y = 3$ (c) $x = y = 0$ (e) $x = -1/7, y = -10/7$

5. (c) Circle (Find center and radius.)
(e) Straight line (What is its equation?)
(g) Hyperbola (What is its equation?)
(j) Circle (Find center and radius.)
(l) Ellipse (Find its equation; where are the foci?)
(m) Two straight lines (What lines?)

7. (a) $x = y = 1$ or $x = y = -1$
(c) $x = 0$, any y; or $y = 0$, any x
(d) $y = -x$

8. (a) $r = 1, x = \frac{4}{5}, y = -\frac{3}{5}$ (c) $r = 5\sqrt{5}, x = -11, y = -2$
(f) $r = 5, x = 3, y = -4$

9. (a) $(2 + 3i)/13; (x - yi)/(x^2 + y^2)$
(c) $(1 + i)/6; (x + 1 - iy)/[(x + 1)^2 + y^2]$
(e) $(-6 - 3i)/5; (1 - x^2 - y^2 + 2yi)/[(1 - x)^2 + y^2]$

10. (c) $v = (4t^2 + 1)^{-1}, a = 4(4t^2 + 1)^{-3/2}$

12. (c) D (e) D (f) Conditionally convergent (g) C

14. (b) $|z| < 1$ (c) All z (f) $|z| < 1$ (h) All z

(i) $|z - (3 - i)| < 1/\sqrt{2}$ (k) $|z| < \frac{1}{3}$ (l) $|z| > 1$

18. (a) $-4 + 4i$ (c) $-4 + 2i$ (e) $-(1 + i)/4$ (g) 16

20. (b) $3(1 - i)/\sqrt{2}$ (d) $-e(\frac{1}{2} + \frac{1}{2}i\sqrt{3})$ (f) 1 (h) $-\sqrt{3} + i$

21. (a) $\pm\frac{1}{2}\sqrt{3} \pm \frac{1}{2}i, \pm i$ (c) $[(1 + i)/4^{\frac{1}{6}}]e^{2n\pi i/5}, n = 0, 1, 2, 3, 4$
    (d) $\pm\frac{1}{2}(\sqrt{6} + i\sqrt{2})$ (g) $\pm\sqrt{2}(1 \pm i)$

31. (a) $i \sinh x,$ $|\sinh x|$
    (c) $\cos y \sinh x + i \sin y \cosh x,$ $(\sinh^2 x + \sin^2 y)^{\frac{1}{2}}$
    (e) $\cosh 2 \cos 3 - i \sinh 2 \sin 3,$ $(\cos^2 3 + \sinh^2 2)^{\frac{1}{2}}$
    (g) $\cos x,$ $|\cos x|$

35. (b) 1 (d) $\frac{1}{2}\pi + 2n\pi - i \ln(2 \pm \sqrt{3})$
    (f) $-ie^{-\pi/2+2n\pi}$ (h) $i(\frac{1}{2}\pi + 2n\pi)$ (j) $\cosh \pi$
    (l) $\sqrt{2}\,e^{-3\pi/4+2n\pi}[\cos(3\pi/4 + \ln\sqrt{2}) + i \sin(3\pi/4 + \ln\sqrt{2})]$

40. (a) Series: $3 - 2i$; parallel: $5 + i$
    (c) Series: 5; parallel: $(13 + 9i)/5$

41. $[R - i(\omega CR^2 + \omega^3 L^2 C - \omega L)]/[(\omega CR)^2 + (\omega^2 LC - 1)^2]$; this simplifies to
    $(L/RC) - i\omega L$ if $\omega L = 1/\omega C$.

Chapter 3

1. (a) $x = 1, y = 2$ (c) $x = 3, y = -1, z = 1$
    (e) $x = 2, y = -1, z = 1, w = 3$

2. (a) -11 (c) -721 (e) 2140

3. (a) $x = 100, y = 20$ (d) Bonus $= \$7000$, tax $= \$12,000$
    (f) $A = 1024, B = 640$

4. (a) $I_1 = \frac{8}{11}, I_2 = -\frac{23}{11}, I_3 = \frac{31}{11}$ (c) $I_1 = -\frac{32}{7}, I_2 = -\frac{12}{7}, I_3 = \frac{20}{7}$

16. (a) Independent (c) Independent (e) Dependent (h) Dependent
    (j) Dependent

17. (a) $r = 2$ (c) $r = 2$ (e) $r = 3$

18. (a) $r = 2; x = 1, y = z$ (c) $r = 2; x = -4, y = 3$
    (e) $r(A) = 3, r(M) = 2$, equations inconsistent
    (g) $r = 2; z = \frac{5}{7}, y = 2x + \frac{8}{7}$

19. (h) $\cot x - \cot 2x - \csc 2x = 0$ (k) See Chapter 2, Problem 30b.

22. For $\lambda = 2$: $x = 0, y = -3z$; for $\lambda = -3$: $x = -5y, z = 3y$; for $\lambda = 4$:
    $z = 3y, x = 2y$.

26. $A + B = \begin{pmatrix} 2 & 1 & 2 \\ 3 & 1 & 1 \\ 3 & 4 & 1 \end{pmatrix}$ $AB = \begin{pmatrix} 7 & -1 & 0 \\ 3 & 1 & -1 \\ 3 & 9 & 5 \end{pmatrix}$ $BA = \begin{pmatrix} 4 & -1 & 2 \\ 6 & 3 & 1 \\ 0 & 1 & 6 \end{pmatrix}$

27. You should have found BA, C^2, CB, C^3, C^2B, and CBA; all others are meaningless.

$$C^2B = \begin{pmatrix} 32 & 12 \\ 53 & 7 \\ -13 & -9 \end{pmatrix} \qquad CBA = \begin{pmatrix} 36 & 46 & 14 & -36 \\ 40 & 22 & 1 & 91 \\ -8 & -2 & 1 & -29 \end{pmatrix}$$

30. $x'' = -3x - 8y$, $y'' = 5x - 5y$

32. $x'' = y$, $y'' = -x$, $z'' = z$, that is, a $90°$ rotation about the z-axis

40. You should have found all except $A'B'$, BA', ABC, $AB'C$, $B^{-1}C$, and CB' which are meaningless.

$$B'AC = \begin{pmatrix} 2 & 2 \\ 1 - 3i & 1 \\ -1 - 5i & -1 \end{pmatrix} \qquad C^{-1}A = \begin{pmatrix} 0 & -i \\ 1 & -1 \end{pmatrix}$$

46. (a) $x = 5$, $y = 0$ (c) $x = -2$, $y = 1$, $z = 5$

Chapter 4

1. $\partial u/\partial x = 2xy^2/(x^2 + y^2)^2$, $\partial u/\partial y = -2x^2y/(x^2 + y^2)^2$

3. $\partial z/\partial u = u/(u^2 + v^2 + w^2)$

6. (a) $2x$ (c) $2x(1 + 2\tan^2\theta)$ (e) $2y$ (g) $4r^2\tan\theta$ (i) $r^2\sin 2\theta$
(k) $4r$ (m) 0 (o) $-4x\csc^2\theta$ (q) $2r\sin 2\theta$

8. (a) $1 + x + (x^2 - y^2)/2! + (x^3 - 3xy^2)/3! +$ terms of order ≥ 4

11. Decrease of $7\pi/2$ ft^2

13. 122 gal

15. 5%

17. 4.28 nt

19. Error $<0.3\%$ or about 1 in the third significant figure.

21. $e^{-y}\sinh t + z\sin t$

23. $2r(q^2 - p^2)$

25. $(1 - 2b - e^{2a})\cos(a - b)$

28. $dx/dy = z - y + \tan(y + z)$
$d^2x/dy^2 = \frac{1}{2}\sec^3(y + z) + \frac{1}{2}\sec(y + z) - 2$

30. $2x + 11y - 24 = 0$

31. $1800/11^3$

34. $y' = 4(\ln 2 - 1)/(2\ln 2 - 1)$

36. $\partial w/\partial u = -2(rv + s)w$, $\partial w/\partial v = -2(ru + 2s)w$

42. $\partial x/\partial s = -\frac{19}{13}$, $\partial x/\partial t = -\frac{21}{13}$, $\partial y/\partial s = \frac{24}{13}$, $\partial y/\partial t = \frac{6}{13}$

45. $(\partial p/\partial q)_m = -p/q$, $(\partial p/\partial q)_a = 1/(a\cos p - 1)$,
$(\partial p/\partial q)_b = 1 - b\sin q$, $(\partial b/\partial a)_p = (\sin p)(b\sin q - 1)/\cos q$
$(\partial a/\partial q)_m = [q + p(a\cos p - 1)]/(q\sin p)$

47. $(\partial x/\partial u)_v = (2yv^2 - x^2)/(2yv + 2xu)$,
$(\partial x/\partial u)_y = (x^2u + y^2v)/(y^2 - 2xu^2)$

49. $\left(\dfrac{\partial p}{\partial s}\right)_t = \dfrac{3q^3 + s}{st - 9p^2q^2}$, $\left(\dfrac{\partial p}{\partial s}\right)_q = \dfrac{1 - pq}{3p^3 + t}$

51. $\left(\dfrac{\partial x}{\partial z}\right)_s = \dfrac{3r^2x + 2r}{x - y}$, $\left(\dfrac{\partial x}{\partial z}\right)_r = \dfrac{3xs - 2}{2(x - y)}$, $\left(\dfrac{\partial x}{\partial z}\right)_y = \dfrac{6r(r + s)}{2 + 4r - 3sy + 6r^2y}$

52. $\left(\dfrac{\partial u}{\partial x}\right)_y = \dfrac{x(3x + 2y^2)}{4u} = \dfrac{1}{(\partial x/\partial u)_y}$, $\left(\dfrac{\partial u}{\partial x}\right)_v = \dfrac{3x(x^3 + y^3)}{u(2x^2 + 3y)} = \dfrac{1}{(\partial x/\partial u)_y}$

61. $l = w = 2h$

63. $\theta = 30°$, $x = z = y\sqrt{3}$

65. $(\frac{4}{3}, \frac{5}{3})$

69. $r:l:s = \sqrt{5}:(1 + \sqrt{5}):3$

73. $V = \frac{1}{3}$

75. $(\frac{8}{13}, \frac{12}{13})$

78. $d = \sqrt{2(\sqrt{5} - 1)}$

79. $\frac{1}{2}\sqrt{11}$

83. $m = \frac{5}{2}$, $b = \frac{1}{3}$

85. Let legs of right triangle be a and b, height of prism $= h$; then $a = b$, $h = (2 - \sqrt{2})a$.

87. (a) Maximum $T = \frac{1}{2}$, minimum $T = -\frac{1}{2}$.
(b) Maximum $T = 1$, minimum $T = -\frac{1}{2}$.
(c) Maximum $T = 1$, minimum $T = -\frac{1}{2}$.

89. (a) Largest sum $= 180°$; smallest sum $= 3\arccos(1/\sqrt{3})$ or about $165°$.
(b) Largest sum $= 3\arcsin(1/\sqrt{3})$ or about $105°$; smallest sum $= 90°$.

93. $(\partial w/\partial x)_y = (\partial f/\partial x)_{s,t} + 2(\partial f/\partial s)_{x,t} + 2(\partial f/\partial t)_{x,s} = f_1 + 2f_2 + 2f_3$

104. $(\sin x)/(2\sqrt{x})$

106. $dy/dx = (e^x - 1)/x$

108. (a) $dz/dx = -\sin(\cos x)\tan x - \sin(\sin x)\cot x$
(b) $(\sin 2)/2$

111. $\left(\dfrac{\partial u}{\partial x}\right)_y = \dfrac{-u\ln u}{ue^{-u^2}\ln u + ve^{-v^2}}$, $\left(\dfrac{\partial u}{\partial y}\right)_x = \dfrac{1}{vu^{v-1} + u^ve^{v^2-u^2}\ln u}$

115. $(2x + 1)/\ln(x + x^2) - 2/\ln 2x$

124. (a) $(-1, 2)$ is a minimum point.
(b) $(-1, -2)$ is a saddle point.

127. (b) $\bar{x} = \bar{y} = 4a/3\pi$
(c) $I = Ma^2/4$
(e) $\bar{x} = \bar{y} = 2a/\pi$

129. (c) $\bar{y} = 4a/3\pi$
(d) $I_x = Ma^2/4,\ I_y = 5Ma^2/4,\ I_z = 3Ma^2/2$
(e) $\bar{y} = 2a/\pi$
(f) $\bar{x} = 6a/5,\ I_x = 48Ma^2/175,\ I_y = 288Ma^2/175,\ I_z = 48Ma^2/25$
(g) $A = (\frac{2}{3}\pi - \frac{1}{2}\sqrt{3})a^2$

131. (a) $\frac{4}{3}\sqrt{2}$ (b) $s = \frac{3}{2}\sqrt{2} + \frac{1}{4}\ln(2\sqrt{2} + 3)$ (c) 2π (d) $13\pi/3$
(e) $s\bar{x} = \frac{51}{32}\sqrt{2} - \frac{1}{64}\ln(2\sqrt{2} + 3),\ s\bar{y} = \frac{13}{6}$, where s = arc length in (b).
(f) $(\frac{4}{3}, 0, 0)$ (g) $(\frac{149}{130}, 0, 0)$ (h) $2M/5$ (i) I/M has the same numerical value as $\bar{x}$ in part (e). (j) $\frac{2}{3}$ (k) $149M/130$ (l) $\frac{13}{6}$ (m) $\frac{64}{21}\sqrt{2}$
(n) $I/M = \frac{1414}{495}$

133. (c) $(0, 0, 3a/8)$ (d) $(0, 0, a/2)$ (e) $2Ma^2/3$

135. 12π

137. (c) $M = (16\rho/9)(3\pi - 4),\ I = (128\rho/15^2)(15\pi - 26)$
(e) $(M/25)[195\pi - 548)/(3\pi - 4)$

139. $2\pi ah$ (where h = distance between parallel planes)

141. $\pi(1 - e^{-1})/4$

143. (a) $u^2 + v^2$

145. $\pi/4$

148. $12(1 + 36\pi^2)^{\frac{1}{2}}$

150. $\rho G\pi a/2$

Chapter 5

7. $\arccos(-1/\sqrt{2}) = 3\pi/4$

9. (a) $\arccos\frac{1}{3}$ (c) $\arccos(2/\sqrt{6})$

10. (b) $8\mathbf{i} - 4\mathbf{j} + 8\mathbf{k}$

16. $(\mathbf{A} \cdot \mathbf{B})\mathbf{C} = 6\mathbf{C},\quad (\mathbf{A} \times \mathbf{B}) \cdot \mathbf{C} = \mathbf{A} \cdot (\mathbf{B} \times \mathbf{C}) = -8,$
$\mathbf{A} \times (\mathbf{B} \times \mathbf{C}) = -4(\mathbf{i} + 2\mathbf{k})$

21. (b) $(\mathbf{A} + \mathbf{B}) \cdot \mathbf{C} = -5$
(d) $\boldsymbol{\omega} = 2\mathbf{A}/\sqrt{6},\quad \mathbf{v} = \boldsymbol{\omega} \times \mathbf{C} = (2/\sqrt{6})(-3\mathbf{i} + 5\mathbf{j} + \mathbf{k})$

23. (b) $-9\mathbf{i} - 23\mathbf{j} + \mathbf{k},\ 1/\sqrt{21}$

27. (a) $\mathbf{r} = (2\mathbf{i} - 3\mathbf{j}) + (4\mathbf{i} + 3\mathbf{j})t$ [Note that $2\mathbf{i} - 3\mathbf{j}$ may be replaced by *any* point on the line; $4\mathbf{i} + 3\mathbf{j}$ may be replaced by *any* vector along the line. Thus, for example, $\mathbf{r} = 6\mathbf{i} - (8\mathbf{i} + 6\mathbf{j})t$ is just as good an answer, and similarly for all such problems.]
(d) $\mathbf{r} = \mathbf{i} + (2\mathbf{i} + \mathbf{j})t$

28. (a) $\mathbf{r} = 3\mathbf{j} - \mathbf{k} + (2\mathbf{i} - 2\mathbf{j} + 3\mathbf{k})t$ [See comment, answer to 27(a).]
(d) $\mathbf{r} = 2\mathbf{i} - \mathbf{k} + (3\mathbf{i} - 3\mathbf{j} + \mathbf{k})t$

30. $x - 4y - z + 5 = 0$

32. $\mathbf{r} = 8\mathbf{i} + \mathbf{j} + 7\mathbf{k} + (14\mathbf{i} + 2\mathbf{j} + 15\mathbf{k})t$

34. $\arccos \left(\frac{21}{22}\right)^{\frac{1}{2}}$

36. $d = 4/\sqrt{13}$

37. (a) 2

38. (a) $5^{\frac{1}{2}}$

39. (a) $\frac{3}{2}\sqrt{2}$

43. (a) $t = 2$
(b) $\mathbf{v} = 4\mathbf{i} - 2\mathbf{j} + 6\mathbf{k}$, $\quad |\mathbf{v}| = 2\sqrt{14}$
(c) $(x - 4)/4 = (y + 4)/(-2) = (z - 8)/6$, $\quad 2x - y + 3z = 36$

45. $d = \left(\frac{40}{7}\right)^{\frac{1}{2}}$

47. $-\mathbf{i}$

50. $5x - 3y + 2z + 3 = 0$; $\quad \mathbf{r} = \mathbf{i} + 2\mathbf{j} - \mathbf{k} + (5\mathbf{i} - 3\mathbf{j} + 2\mathbf{k})t$

51. (e) $(53)^{\frac{1}{2}}$

52. $\mathbf{j}$, $\quad 1$, $\quad -\frac{4}{5}$

55. (d) $\nabla \cdot \mathbf{V} = 5xy$, $\quad \nabla \times \mathbf{V} = \mathbf{i}xz - \mathbf{j}yz + \mathbf{k}(y^2 - x^2)$

56. (b) 0 (d) $2/R$

59. (a) $\pi + \pi^2/2$

61. (a) -4π (b) -16 (c) -8

62. (b) 0 (d) 2π

64. 3

66. (b) $3xy - x^3yz - z^2$ (d) $-y\sin^2 x$

67. Let $R_1 < R_2$ be the radii of the cylinders. Then $\phi = 0, r \le R_1$;
$\phi = (k/2\pi\epsilon) \ln (R_1/r)$, $R_1 \le r \le R_2$; $\phi = (k/2\pi\epsilon) \ln (R_1/R_2)$, $r \ge R_2$.

70. 16π

72. (b) -20 (d) -12 (f) 45π (h) 2

81. 4

83. $\frac{3}{16}\sqrt{6} + \frac{9}{16} \ln (\sqrt{2} + \sqrt{3})$

85. $2\pi a^2(\sqrt{2} - 1)$

Chapter 6

1. (a) Amplitude $= 4$, period $= 2\pi/3$, frequency $= 3/(2\pi)$,
velocity amplitude $= 12$.
(g) to (j) Consider the formulas of part (f).

7. (a) $2/\pi$ (c) $\frac{1}{2} + 1/\pi$ (e) 0

25. (c) $\frac{1}{2}\ln|1 - x^2| + \frac{1}{2}\ln|(1 - x)/(1 + x)|$

29. (b) $I(t) = (5/\pi)\left[1 + \sum_{\text{even } n} 2(1 - n^2)^{-1}\cos 120n\pi t\right] + (\frac{5}{2})\sin 120\pi t$

30. (c) $q(t) = CV\left[1 - 2(1 - e^{-\frac{1}{2}})\sum_{-\infty}^{\infty}(1 + 4in\pi)^{-1}e^{4in\pi t/RC}\right]$

31. Relative intensities $= 1:0:0:0:1/25:0:1/49:0:0:0 \ldots$

34. (a) $\pi^2/8$

Chapter 7

1. (a) $y = mx$, $m = \frac{3}{2}$

   (c) $\ln y = A(\csc x - \cot x)$, $A = \sqrt{3}$

   (e) $y = axe^x$, $y = xe^{x-1}$

   (g) $\tan\frac{1}{2}(x + y) = x + C$, $C = 1$

4. $I/J_0 = e^{-0.5} = 0.6$ for $s = 50$ ft.

   Half value thickness $= 100\ln 2 = 69.3$ ft.

   Half life $T = (\ln 2)/\lambda$.

5. Time constant $\tau = RC$ in (a). Corresponding quantities are a, $\lambda = (\ln 2)/T$, μ, $1/\tau$.

6. (b) $N = {}^*N_0 e^{Kt} - (R/K)(e^{Kt} - 1)$ where N_0 = number of bacteria at $t = 0$, KN = rate of increase, R = removal rate.

7. (a) $T = 100[1 - (\ln r)/(\ln 2)]$

9. (a) k = person's weight divided by his terminal speed.

   (b) $t = g^{-1} \cdot$ (terminal velocity) $\cdot$ (ln 100); typical terminal velocities are 0.02 to 0.1 cm/sec, so t is of the order of 10^{-4} sec.

11. $t = 100\ln\frac{9}{4} = 81.1$ min

14. $x = (c/F)[(m_0^2 c^2 + F^2 t^2)^{\frac{1}{2}} - m_0 c]$

15. (b) Orthogonal trajectories of $y = kx^n$ are $x^2 + ny^2 = C$.

16. (a) $y = \frac{1}{2}e^x + Ce^{-x}$

   (c) $y = (\frac{1}{2}x^2 + C)e^{-x^2}$

   (e) $y = (x + C)\cos x$

   (g) $\ln(y - 1) = C - (x^2 + 1)^{\frac{1}{2}}$, or $y = 1$

   (i) $y = \frac{1}{2}\ln x + C/\ln x$

   (k) $x = y^{\frac{2}{3}} + Cy^{-\frac{1}{3}}$

17. $S = 10^7[\frac{1}{2}(1 + 3t/10^4) + \frac{1}{2}(1 + 3t/10^4)^{-\frac{1}{3}}]$, where S = number of pounds of salt, and t is in hours.

19. (c) $N_n = c_1 e^{-\lambda_1 t} + c_2 e^{-\lambda_2 t} + \cdots$

   where

$$c_1 = \frac{\lambda_1\lambda_2\cdots\lambda_{n-1}N_0}{(\lambda_2 - \lambda_1)(\lambda_3 - \lambda_1)\cdots(\lambda_n - \lambda_1)}, \quad c_2 = \frac{\lambda_1\lambda_2\cdots\lambda_{n-1}N_0}{(\lambda_1 - \lambda_2)(\lambda_3 - \lambda_2)\cdots(\lambda_n - \lambda_2)},$$

   etc. (all λ's different).

20. (a) $y = x + 1 + Ke^x$

21. (a) $y^{\frac{1}{3}} = x - 3 + Ce^{-x/3}$

    (c) $y^3 = \frac{1}{3} + Cx^{-3}$

    (e) $x^2 - y^2 + 2x(y + 1) = C$

    (g) $y^{-1} = x^{-1} \ln x + Cx^{-1}$

    (i) $y^2 = Ce^{-x^2/y^2}$

24. Parabola; differential equation is $yy'^2 + 2xy' - y = 0$.

25. (b) $r = Ae^{-\theta}, r = Be^{\theta}$

28. (b) $y = (Ax + B)e^{2x}$

    (d) $y = e^{-x}(Ae^{ix} + Be^{-ix})$ or equivalent forms (5.17), (5.18).

    (f) $y = Ae^{4ix} + Be^{-4ix}$ or other forms as in (5.24).

    (h) $y = A + Be^{-5x}$

29. (b) $y = Ae^{-x} + Be^{ix}$

31. (a) $y = Ae^x + Be^{-3x} + Ce^{-5x}$

    (c) $y = Ae^{-x} + e^{x/2}(Be^{\frac{1}{2}ix\sqrt{3}} + Ce^{-\frac{1}{2}ix\sqrt{3}})$

    (e) $y = A + Be^{2x} + Ce^{-3x}$

35. $T = 2\pi\sqrt{R/g}$

39. For (5.30): $A = \mu/(\mu - \lambda), B = \lambda/(\lambda - \mu)$.

    For (5.31): $A = 1, B = b$.

    For (5.32): $c = \omega/\beta, \sin\gamma = \beta/\omega$.

43. (a) $y = Ae^{-\frac{1}{2}(1+\sqrt{21})x} + Be^{-\frac{1}{2}(1-\sqrt{21})x} + e^{2x}$

    (c) $y = (x^2 + Ax + B)e^{-x}$

    (e) $y = Ae^{ix} + Be^{-ix} + e^x$

    (g) $y = (Ax + B)e^x - \sin x$

    (i) $y = Ae^{ix} + Be^{-ix} - x\cos x$

    (k) $y = Ae^{\frac{1}{2}(1+\sqrt{5})x} + Be^{\frac{1}{2}(1-\sqrt{5})x} - e^{-x}\sin x$

    (m) $y = Ae^{\frac{1}{2}(1+i\sqrt{7})x} + Be^{\frac{1}{2}(1-i\sqrt{7})x} + (x - \frac{3}{4})e^{2x}$

    (o) $y = A\sin x + B\cos x - \frac{1}{4}x^2\cos x + \frac{1}{4}x\sin x$

48. (b) $y = Ae^{3x} + Be^{2x} + e^x + x$

51. (a) $y = e^{-x}(A\cos x + B\sin x) + \frac{1}{4}\pi + \sum_{\text{odd } n} \dfrac{4(n^2 - 2)\cos nx - 16n\sin nx}{\pi n^2(n^4 + 4)}$

55. Escape velocity $= \sqrt{2gR}$

58. (a) $y = Ax + Bx^{-3}$

    (c) $y = x[A\cos(\sqrt{5}\ln x) + B\sin(\sqrt{5}\ln x)] + \frac{1}{6}$

Chapter 8

2. (a) Circle

    (c) $y = a^{-1}\sin(ax + b)$

16. $\begin{cases} m(\ddot{r} - r\dot{\theta}^2) = -\partial V/\partial r \\ m(r\ddot{\theta} + 2\dot{r}\dot{\theta}) = -(1/r)(\partial V/\partial \theta) \\ m\ddot{z} = -\partial V/\partial z \end{cases}$

Comment: These equations are in the form $ma = F$; recall from Chapter 5, Sections 9 and 11, the polar coordinate form for $\mathbf{F} = -\nabla V$.

18. $l\ddot{\theta} + g \sin \theta = 0$

20. $\begin{cases} a\ddot{\theta} - a \sin \theta \cos \theta \, \dot{\phi}^2 - g \sin \theta = 0 \\ (d/dt)(\sin^2 \theta \, \dot{\phi}) = 0 \end{cases}$

25. Catenary

27. Circular cylinder

Chapter 9

2. (a) 0.909   (c) -4.33 (e) 1.54   (g) 3.33

4. (a) $\Gamma(\frac{5}{3}) = 0.903$ (c) $\Gamma(\frac{1}{2}) = \pi^{\frac{1}{2}}$ (e) $\frac{1}{3}\Gamma(\frac{2}{3}) = 0.451$
   (g) $-\Gamma(\frac{4}{3}) = -0.893$

11. (a) $\frac{1}{2}B(\frac{1}{2}, \frac{5}{2}) = 3\pi/16 = 0.59$ (c) $\frac{1}{3}B(\frac{1}{3}, \frac{1}{2}) = 1.4$
    (e) $\frac{1}{4}$ (g) $\frac{1}{2}B(\frac{1}{2}, \frac{1}{4}) = 2.62$

13. $2^{\frac{1}{2}}B(\frac{1}{2}, \frac{1}{4})\sqrt{l/g} = 7.4\sqrt{l/g}$ (Compare $2\pi\sqrt{l/g}$)

14. (b) $2B(\frac{2}{3}, \frac{4}{3})/B(\frac{1}{3}, \frac{4}{3}) = 0.913$
    (c) $(8\pi/3)B(\frac{5}{3}, \frac{1}{3}) = 32\pi^2/3^{\frac{3}{2}} = 20.3$

19. From (9.6): 2 term error $>$ value of function; 10 term error $= 0.03$. From (10.4): 2 term error $= 0.005$ (this is the best accuracy obtainable from the asymptotic series); 10 term error is in the second decimal place.

20. (a) 0.882   (c) $49e^{-25}/(250\pi^{\frac{1}{2}}) = 1.5 \times 10^{-12}$ (f) 5.6×10^{-4346} (i) 0.3174

21. $x^{n-1}e^{-x}[1 + (n - 1)x^{-1} + (n - 1)(n - 2)x^{-2} + \cdots]$

29. (a) $K = F(k, \pi/2) = (\pi/2)\{1 + (\frac{1}{2})^2 k^2 + [(1 \cdot 3)/(2 \cdot 4)]^2 k^4 + \cdots\}$
    (b) $E = E(k, \pi/2)$
    $= (\pi/2)\{1 - (\frac{1}{2})^2 k^2 - [1/(2 \cdot 4)]^2 \cdot 3k^4 - [(1 \cdot 3)/(2 \cdot 4 \cdot 6)]^2 \cdot 5k^6 \cdots\}$

30. (a) 1.58   (d) 7.30   (e) 3.96   (h) 0.945   (i) 3.95   (j) 9.09

32. 0.585

33. 3.82

Chapter 10

2. (a) $d_1 = 5, d_2 = 8; l_1 = 2\sqrt{10}, l_2 = 8; \cos \theta = 23/16\sqrt{10}$

11. For each eigenvalue, the components of a corresponding eigenvector are listed in parentheses; for example, $(1, 1)$ means $\mathbf{i} + \mathbf{j}$.

(a)   4 $(1, 1)$ (c)   5 $(18, 19, 15)$
       -1 $(3, -2)$ $\frac{1}{2}(1 + \sqrt{5})$ $(1 + \sqrt{5}, 0, 2)$
                                            $\frac{1}{2}(1 - \sqrt{5})$ $(1 - \sqrt{5}, 0, 2)$

(e)   5 $(1, 1, 1)$ (g)   4 $(2, 1, 3)$

     $3 + \sqrt{7}$ $(1, -3 - \sqrt{7}, 2 + \sqrt{7})$ 2 $(0, -3, 1)$

     $3 - \sqrt{7}$ $(1, -3 + \sqrt{7}, 2 - \sqrt{7})$ -3 $(5, -1, -3)$

(i)   3 $(0, -1, 2)$ (k) -4 $(-4, 1, 1)$

     4     $(1, 2, 1)$ 5 $(1, 2, 2)$

    -2 $(-5, 2, 1)$ -2 $(0, -1, 1)$

(l)   18 $(2, 2, -1)$

     9     $(1, -1, 0)$

     9     $(1, 1, 4)$

In (1), the two eigenvectors corresponding to the eigenvalue 9 may be any two vectors orthogonal to $(2, 2, -1)$ and orthogonal to each other.

12. (a) $D = \begin{pmatrix} 3 & 0 \\ 0 & 1 \end{pmatrix}$, $C = \dfrac{1}{\sqrt{2}} \begin{pmatrix} 1 & 1 \\ -1 & 1 \end{pmatrix}$

(c) $D = \begin{pmatrix} 11 & 0 \\ 0 & 1 \end{pmatrix}$, $C = \dfrac{1}{\sqrt{5}} \begin{pmatrix} 1 & -2 \\ 2 & 1 \end{pmatrix}$

(e) $D = \begin{pmatrix} 5 & 0 \\ 0 & 1 \end{pmatrix}$, $C = \dfrac{1}{\sqrt{2}} \begin{pmatrix} 1 & -1 \\ 1 & 1 \end{pmatrix}$

14. (a) $3X^2 - 2Y^2 = 24$

(b) $10X^2 = 35$

(e) $3X^2 + \sqrt{3}\,Y^2 - \sqrt{3}Z^2 = 12$

18. $x = y$ with $\omega = \sqrt{g/l}$; $x = -y$ with $\omega = \sqrt{3g/l}$

19. $h_r = 1$, $h_\theta = r$, $h_\phi = r \sin\theta$

$ds = \mathbf{e}_r\, dr + \mathbf{e}_\theta r\, d\theta + \mathbf{e}_\phi r \sin\theta\, d\phi$

$dV = r^2 \sin\theta\, dr\, d\theta\, d\phi$

$\mathbf{a}_r = \mathbf{i} \sin\theta \cos\phi + \mathbf{j} \sin\theta \sin\phi + \mathbf{k} \cos\theta = \mathbf{e}_r$

$\mathbf{a}_\theta = \mathbf{i}r \cos\theta \cos\phi + \mathbf{j}r \cos\theta \sin\phi - \mathbf{k}r \sin\theta = r\mathbf{e}_\theta$

$\mathbf{a}_\phi = -\mathbf{i}r \sin\theta \sin\phi + \mathbf{j}r \sin\theta \cos\phi = r \sin\theta\, \mathbf{e}_\phi$

20. (a) $h_u = h_v = (u^2 + v^2)^{1/2}$, $h_z = 1$

$ds = (u^2 + v^2)^{1/2}(\mathbf{e}_u du + \mathbf{e}_v dv) + \mathbf{e}_z\, dz$

$dV = (u^2 + v^2)\, du\, dv\, dz$

$\mathbf{a}_u = \mathbf{i}u + \mathbf{j}v = (u^2 + v^2)^{1/2}\mathbf{e}_u$

$\mathbf{a}_v = -\mathbf{i}v + \mathbf{j}u = (u^2 + v^2)^{1/2}\mathbf{e}_v$

$\mathbf{a}_z = \mathbf{k} = \mathbf{e}_z$

(d) $h_u = h_v = a(\cosh u + \cos v)^{-1}$

$ds = a(\cosh u + \cos v)^{-1}(\mathbf{e}_u\, du + \mathbf{e}_v\, dv)$

$dV = a^2(\cosh u + \cos v)^{-2}\, du\, dv$

$\mathbf{a}_u = (h_u^2/a)[\mathbf{i}(1 + \cos v \cosh u) - \mathbf{j} \sin v \sinh u] = h_u\mathbf{e}_u$

$\mathbf{a}_v = (h_v^2/a)[\mathbf{i} \sinh u \sin v + \mathbf{j}(1 + \cos v \cosh u)] = h_v\mathbf{e}_v$

21. See answer to Problem 16 of Chapter 8.

23. (a) $ds/dt = (u^2 + v^2)^{1/2}(e_u\dot{u} + e_v\dot{v}) + e_z\dot{z}$

$d^2s/dt^2 = e_u(u^2 + v^2)^{-1/2}[(u^2 + v^2)\ddot{u} + u(\dot{u}^2 - \dot{v}^2) + 2v\dot{u}\dot{v}]$
$\qquad + e_v(u^2 + v^2)^{-1/2}[(u^2 + v^2)\ddot{v} + v(\dot{v}^2 - \dot{u}^2) + 2u\dot{u}\dot{v}] + e_z\ddot{z}$

(d) $ds/dt = a(\cosh u + \cos v)^{-1}(e_u\dot{u} + e_v\dot{v})$

$d^2s/dt^2 = e_u a(\cosh u + \cos v)^{-2}$
$\qquad \times [(\cosh u + \cos v)\ddot{u} + (\dot{v}^2 - \dot{u}^2)\sinh u + 2\dot{u}\dot{v}\sin v]$
$\qquad + e_v a(\cosh u + \cos v)^{-2}$
$\qquad \times [(\cosh u + \cos v)\ddot{v} + (\dot{v}^2 - \dot{u}^2)\sin v - 2\dot{u}\dot{v}\sinh u]$

24. $\mathbf{V} = r\sin\theta\cos\theta\, e_r - r(1 + \sin^2\theta)e_\theta + \mathbf{k}$

31. (a) Let $h = h_u = h_v$ represent the u and v scale factors.

$$\nabla U = h^{-1}\left(e_u \frac{\partial U}{\partial u} + e_v \frac{\partial U}{\partial v}\right) + \mathbf{k}\frac{\partial U}{\partial z}$$

$$\nabla \cdot \mathbf{V} = h^{-2}\left[\frac{\partial}{\partial u}(hV_u) + \frac{\partial}{\partial v}(hV_v)\right] + \frac{\partial V_z}{\partial z}$$

$$\nabla^2 U = h^{-2}\left(\frac{\partial^2 U}{\partial u^2} + \frac{\partial^2 U}{\partial v^2}\right) + \frac{\partial^2 U}{\partial z^2}$$

$$\nabla \times \mathbf{V} = \left((h^{-1}\frac{\partial V_z}{\partial v} - \frac{\partial V_v}{\partial z}\right)e_u + \left(\frac{\partial V_u}{\partial z} - h^{-1}\frac{\partial V_z}{\partial u}\right)e_v$$

$$+ h^{-2}\left[\frac{\partial}{\partial u}(hV_v) - \frac{\partial}{\partial v}(hV_u)\right]e_z$$

(d) Same as (a) if $h = a(\cosh u + \cos v)^{-1}$ and terms involving either z derivatives or V_z are omitted. Note, however, that $\nabla \times \mathbf{V}$ has *only* a z component if $\mathbf{V} = e_u V_u + e_v V_v$ where V_u and V_v are functions of u and v.

40. (c) Ellipsoid

41. (d) Principal axes: $\qquad\qquad y = x \qquad y = -x \qquad z$
Corresponding moments of inertia: $I = 2m \quad I = 6m \quad I = 4m$

Chapter 11

1. (a) $u = x^3 - 3xy^2,\ v = 3x^2y - y^3$

(d) $u = (x^2 + y^2)^{1/2},\ v = 0$

(g) $u = \cos y \cosh x,\ v = \sin y \sinh x$

(i) $u = x/(x^2 + y^2),\ v = -y/(x^2 + y^2)$

(k) $u = 3x/[x^2 + (y - 2)^2],\ v = (-2x^2 - 2y^2 + 5y - 2)/[x^2 + (y - 2)^2]$

(m) $u = \ln(x^2 + y^2)^{1/2},\ v = \arctan(y/x)$ [angle in the quadrant of the point (x, y)]

(o) $u = \pm\{[x + (x^2 + y^2)^{1/2}]/2\}^{1/2},\ v = \pm\{[-x + (x^2 + y^2)^{1/2}]/2\}^{1/2}$, where the $\pm$ signs are chosen so that uv has the sign of y.

2. A = analytic, N = not analytic
   (a) A (c) N (e) N (g) A except at $z = 0$ (i) A (l) N

5. (d) $\tanh z = z - \frac{1}{3}z^3 + \frac{2}{15}z^5 \cdots$, $|z| < \pi/2$
   (e) $(2i + z)^{-1} = -\frac{1}{2}i + \frac{1}{4}z + \frac{1}{8}iz^2 - \frac{1}{16}z^3 \cdots$, $|z| < 2$

7. (a) Yes, $z \neq 0$ (b) No   (c) Yes, $z \neq 0$ (d) Yes   (e) No   (f) Yes, $z \neq 0$

8. (a) $-iz$ (c) $-iz^2/2$ (e) $\cos z$ (g) $\ln z^2$

9. (a) $\frac{1}{2} + i$ (c) 0   (e) -1

16. (a) $1/[z(z-1)] = -z^{-1} - 1 - z - z^2 - \cdots$, convergent if $0 < |z| < 1$;
   $R(0) = -1$.
   $1/[z(z-1)] = z^{-2} + z^{-3} + z^{-4} + \cdots$, convergent if $|z| > 1$.
   (c) $-\frac{1}{4}z^3 - \frac{1}{2}z^4 - \frac{11}{16}z^5 - \frac{13}{16}z^6 - \cdots$, convergent if $|z| < 1$; $R(0) = 0$.
   $1 + z + z^2 + \frac{3}{4}z^3 + \frac{1}{2}z^4 + \frac{5}{16}z^5 + \frac{3}{16}z^6 + \cdots + z^{-1} + z^{-2} +$
   $z^{-3} + \cdots$, convergent if $1 < |z| < 2$.
   $1 + 5z^{-1} + 49z^{-3} + 129z^{-4} + \cdots$, convergent if $|z| > 2$.

17. (a) $z^{-1} - 1 + z - z^2 \cdots$, $R = 1$
   (c) $z^{-3} - \frac{1}{6}z^{-1} + z/5! - \cdots$, $R = -\frac{1}{6}$
   (e) $\frac{1}{2}e[(z-1)^{-1} + \frac{1}{2} + (z-1)/4 \cdots]$, $R = \frac{1}{2}e$

19. (a) Simple pole
   (b) Regular point (if $f(z)$ is defined to be 1 at $z = 0$)
   (d) Simple pole
   (g) Pole, order 2

22. (b) $R(0) = -3$, $R(1) = 3$ (d) 2   (f) $-\frac{1}{16} + \frac{1}{24}i$ (h) $2^{1/2}(1 - i)/16$
   (j) $-ie^{-2}/4$ (l) $\frac{1}{2}$ (n) $1/6!$

23. (a) $2\pi i$ (c) 0   (e) 0   (g) $9\pi i$ (i) 0   (k) 0   (m) 0

24. (a) $\pi/6$ (c) $\pi/(1 - r^2)$ (e) $\pi/6$ (g) $2\pi/|\sin \alpha|$ (i) $\pi/10$ (k) $\pi/(4e^4)$
   (m) $(\pi/e)(2\sin 2 + \cos 2)$ (o) $7\pi/(108e^6)$

26. (a) π (c) $(\pi/2)\cos ab$ (e) $\pi/4$

27. (a, b, c) $\pi/2\sqrt{2}$ (e) $\frac{3}{16}\pi\sqrt{2}$

28. (b) $-\pi^2\sqrt{2}$

31. 2

33. $(2\pi)^{1/2}/4$

37. (a) One in each quadrant.
   (c) One negative real, one in quadrant I, one in quadrant IV.

38. (b) $i\pi$

41. (a) Regular, $R = -1$ (c) Regular, $R = -1$ (e) Simple pole, $R = -2$
   (g) Regular, $R = 0$ (i) Regular, $R = -1$

43. (a) $-2\pi i$

44. $x^2 = \frac{1}{2}[u + (u^2 + v^2)^{1/2}]$, $y^2 = \frac{1}{2}[-u + (u^2 + v^2)^{1/2}]$

45. (a) $u = y/2$, $v = -(x + 1)/2$
   (c) $u = e^x \cos y$, $v = e^x \sin y$
   (f) $(x^2/\sin^2 u) - (y^2/\cos^2 u) = 1$,
      $(x^2/\cosh^2 v) + (y^2/\sinh^2 v) = 1$

53. $T = 100y/(x^2 + y^2)$; isothermals $y/(x^2 + y^2) = \text{const}$; flow lines $x/(x^2 + y^2) = \text{const}$.

55. Streamlines $y - y/(x^2 + y^2) = \text{const}$.

57. (b) $T = (20/\pi)\text{arc tan}[2y/(1 - x^2 - y^2)]$, arc tan between $\pi/2$ and $3\pi/2$.

(d) $\Phi = \frac{1}{2}V_0 \ln \dfrac{(x + 1)^2 + y^2}{(x - 1)^2 + y^2}$;

$$\Psi = V_0 \text{arc tan} \frac{2y}{1 - x^2 - y^2}, \text{ arc tan between } \pi/2 \text{ and } 3\pi/2.$$

$$V_x = \frac{2V_0(1 - x^2 - y^2)}{(x^2 + y^2 + 1)^2 - 4x^2}, \quad V_y = \frac{-4V_0 xy}{(x^2 + y^2 + 1)^2 - 4x^2}.$$

Chapter 12

1. (a) $y = A \sin 2x + B \cos 2x$
(c) $y = A \sin x + B \cos x + x \sin x - x^2 \cos x$
(e) $y = Ce^{x^3}$

2. (a) $y = a_0 \left(1 + \dfrac{x^3}{3!} + \dfrac{4^2}{6!}x^6 + \dfrac{(7 \cdot 4)^2}{9!}x^9 + \cdots\right)$

$+ a_1 \left(x + \dfrac{2^2}{4!}x^4 + \dfrac{(5 \cdot 2)^2}{7!}x^7 + \dfrac{(8 \cdot 5 \cdot 2)^2}{10!}x^{10} + \cdots\right)$

(c) $y = a_0(1 - x^3/6 + x^6/180 - \cdots) + a_1(x - x^4/12 + x^7/504 - \cdots)$
(e) $y = a_0 \cosh(x\sqrt{2}) + a_1 \sinh(x\sqrt{2}) + e^{x^2}$

3. See answer to Problem 13.

5. (b) $(d^6/dx^6)(x^2 \sin x) = (30 - x^2)\sin x + 12x \cos x$

13. $P_3(x) = (5x^3 - 3x)/2$
$P_4(x) = (35x^4 - 30x^2 + 3)/8$
$P_5(x) = (63x^5 - 70x^3 + 15x)/8$
$P_6(x) = (231x^6 - 315x^4 + 105x^2 - 5)/16$

22. (a) $5P_0 - 2P_1$ (c) $8P_4/35 + 4P_2/7 + P_0/5$

24. (a) $3P_1/2 - 7P_3/8 + 11P_5/16 + \cdots$
(c) $P_n' = \sum(2l + 1)P_l$, where the sum is over odd l from 1 to $n - 1$ when n is even, and over even l from 0 to $n - 1$, when n is odd.

25. $\frac{4}{7}P_2 + \frac{1}{5}P_0 = \frac{6}{7}x^2 - \frac{3}{35}$

30. (a) $y = a_0 x^{-2} + b_0 x^3$
(c) $y = a_0 e^{-x} + b_0 x^{2/3}[1 - 3x/5 + (3x)^2/(5 \cdot 8) - (3x)^3/(5 \cdot 8 \cdot 11) + \cdots]$
(e) $y = a_0(x^{-1} - 1) + b_0 x^2(1 - x + 3x^2/5 - 8x^3/21 + \cdots)$
(g) $y = a_0[1 + 2x - (2x)^2/2! + (2x)^3/(3 \cdot 3!) - (2x)^4/(3 \cdot 5 \cdot 4!) + \cdots]$
$+ b_0 x^{2/3}[1 - 2x/5 + (2x)^2/(5 \cdot 7 \cdot 2!) - (2x)^3/(5 \cdot 7 \cdot 9 \cdot 3!) + \cdots]$

(i) $y = a_0 x^{\frac{1}{6}}[1 + 3x^2/2^5 + 3^2 x^4/(5 \cdot 2^{10}) + \cdots]$
$\qquad + b_0 x^{-\frac{1}{6}}[x + 3x^3/2^6 + 3^2 x^5/(7 \cdot 2^{11}) + \cdots]$

34. $R(0) = -\frac{1}{4}$

38. (a) $y = x^{-\frac{3}{2}} Z_{\frac{1}{2}}(x)$ (c) $y = x^{-\frac{1}{2}} Z_1(4x^{\frac{1}{2}})$ (e) $y = x Z_0(2x)$
$\qquad$ (g) $y = x^{-1} Z_{\frac{1}{2}}(\frac{1}{2}x^2)$

49. $y = x^{\frac{1}{2}} I_1(2x^{\frac{1}{2}})$. Note that the factor i does not need to be included, since *any* multiple of y is a solution.

59. 1.7 m for steel

60. $j_n(x) \sim x^{-1} \sin (x - n\pi/2)$

61. (a) $y = e^{x^2/2}(A + B \int e^{-x^2} dx)$
$\qquad$ (c) $y = Z_p(e^{x^2/2})$
$\qquad$ (e) $y = Ax \cos 3x + Bx \sin 3x$ or $y = x^{\frac{3}{2}} Z_{\frac{1}{2}}(3x)$
$\qquad$ (g) $y = Ax/(1 - x) + B[x + 1 + x(1 - x)^{-1} \ln x^2]$
$\qquad$ (i) $y = xe^{1/x}(A + B \int x^{-3} e^{-1/x} dx)$

62. (c) $y = (A + B \ln x)x$
$\qquad$ (d) $y = Ax/(1 - x) + B[2x(1 - x)^{-1} \ln x + 1 + x]$
$\qquad$ (e) $y = A(x^2 + 2x) + B[(x^2 + 2x) \ln x + 1 + 5x - x^3/6 + x^4/72 \cdots]$

63. (b) $y = x^2 \ln x$
$\qquad$ (d) $y = x \ln [x + (x^2 + 1)^{\frac{1}{2}}] - (x^2 + 1)^{\frac{1}{2}}$

Chapter 13

6. (b) $y = e^{-2t} - te^{-2t}$
$\qquad y = e^t - 3e^{-2t}$
$\qquad y = \frac{1}{3}e^t \sin 3t + 2e^t \cos 3t$

7. (e) $y = te^{-2t}(\cos t - \sin t)$

8. (b) $-v(p^2 + v^2)^{-1}e^{-px/v}$

11. (a) $y = te^{2t}$
$\qquad$ (c) $y = \frac{1}{2}(t^2 e^{-t} + 3e^t - e^{-t})$
$\qquad$ (d) $y = \sinh 2t$
$\qquad$ (e) $y = \cos t + \frac{1}{2} \sin t - \frac{1}{2}t \cos t$
$\qquad$ (h) $y = 2$
$\qquad$ (k) $y = (t + 2) \sin 4t$
$\qquad$ (l) $y = \sin t + 2 \cos t - 2e^{-t} \cos 2t$

12. (a) $y = t + \frac{1}{4} - \frac{1}{4}e^{4t}$
$\qquad z = \frac{1}{3} + e^{4t}$
$\qquad$ (b) $y = t \cos t - 1$
$\qquad z = \cos t + t \sin t$

13. (c) arc tan $\frac{2}{3}$
$\qquad$ (e) $5^{-\frac{3}{2}}$
$\qquad$ (g) $\frac{1}{2}(e^{-t} + \sin t - \cos t)$

17. $f(x) = \dfrac{2}{\pi} \displaystyle\int_0^\infty \dfrac{\sin \alpha - \alpha \cos \alpha}{\alpha^2} \sin \alpha x \, d\alpha$

19. $f(x) = \dfrac{1}{2\pi} \displaystyle\int_{-\infty}^{\infty} \dfrac{1 + e^{-i\alpha\pi}}{1 - \alpha^2} e^{i\alpha x} \, d\alpha$

21. $f(x) = \dfrac{2}{\pi} \displaystyle\int_{0}^{\infty} \dfrac{\cos(\alpha\pi/2)}{1 - \alpha^2} \cos \alpha x \, d\alpha$

25. $y = \begin{cases} \dfrac{1}{a^2}(\cosh at - 1), & t > 0, \\[2mm] 0, & t < 0. \end{cases}$

26. (a) $\frac{1}{2} t \sinh t$

(c) $\dfrac{1}{b^2 - a^2} \left(\dfrac{\cos bt}{b^2} - \dfrac{\cos at}{a^2} \right) + \dfrac{1}{a^2 b^2}$

31. (a) $\cosh t \cos t$

(c) $\frac{1}{2}(\cosh t - \cos t)$

(e) $\frac{1}{5}(\cos 2t + 2 \sin 2t - e^{-t})$

35. (a) $y = te^{-t}$

(c) $y = \frac{1}{3} e^{-t} \sin 3t$

Chapter 14

5. $T = \dfrac{20}{\pi} \displaystyle\sum_{n=1}^{\infty} \dfrac{(-1)^{n+1}}{n} e^{-n\pi y/10} \sin(n\pi x/10)$

9. $T = \displaystyle\sum_{\text{odd } n} \dfrac{400}{n\pi \sinh 3n\pi} \sinh \dfrac{n\pi}{10} (30 - y) \sin \dfrac{n\pi x}{10}$

$\qquad + \displaystyle\sum_{\text{odd } n} \dfrac{400}{n\pi \sinh (n\pi/3)} \sinh \dfrac{n\pi}{30} (10 - x) \sin \dfrac{n\pi y}{30}$

10. For $f(x) = x - 5$, $T = -\dfrac{40}{\pi^2} \displaystyle\sum_{\text{odd } n} \dfrac{1}{n^2} \cos \dfrac{n\pi x}{10} e^{-n\pi y/10}$

For $f(x) = x$, add 5 to the answer just given.

For finite plate, bottom edge at $f(x) = x$,

$$T = \frac{1}{6}(30 - y) - \frac{40}{\pi^2} \sum_{\text{odd } n} \frac{1}{n^2 \sinh 3n\pi} \sinh \frac{n\pi}{10}(30 - y) \cos \frac{n\pi x}{10}$$

13. $u = 100 - \dfrac{100x}{l} - \dfrac{400}{\pi} \displaystyle\sum_{\text{even } n} \dfrac{1}{n} e^{-(n\pi a/l)^2 t} \sin \dfrac{n\pi x}{l}$

17. $y = \dfrac{8h}{\pi^2} \displaystyle\sum_{n=1}^{\infty} B_n \sin \dfrac{n\pi x}{l} \cos \dfrac{n\pi vt}{l}$, where $B_1 = \sqrt{2} - 1$,

$B_2 = \frac{1}{2}$, $B_3 = \frac{1}{9}(\sqrt{2} + 1)$, $B_4 = 0, \ldots, B_n = (2 \sin n\pi/4 - \sin n\pi/2)/n^2$

19. $u \cong 9.76°$

21. $R = r^n, r^{-n}, n \neq 0; \ R = \ln r, \text{const.}, n = 0.$

$\qquad R = r^l, r^{-l-1}.$

23. $T = \dfrac{400}{\pi} \displaystyle\sum_{\text{odd } n} \dfrac{1}{n} \left(\dfrac{r}{10}\right)^{4n} \sin 4n\theta$

25. $T = \dfrac{50 \ln r}{\ln 2} + \dfrac{200}{\pi} \displaystyle\sum_{\substack{n=1 \\ \text{odd } n}}^{\infty} \dfrac{r^n - r^{-n}}{n(2^n - 2^{-n})} \sin n\theta$

29. $z = \dfrac{64 l^4}{\pi^6} \displaystyle\sum_{\text{odd } m,\, \text{odd } n} \dfrac{1}{n^3 m^3} \sin \dfrac{n\pi x}{l} \sin \dfrac{m\pi y}{l} \cos \dfrac{\pi v (m^2 + n^2)^{\frac{1}{2}} t}{l}$

31. $u = E_0(r - a^3/r^2) P_1(\cos \theta)$

33. $u = \dfrac{6400}{\pi^3} \displaystyle\sum_{\text{odd } n,\, m,\, p} \dfrac{1}{nmp} \sin \dfrac{n\pi x}{l} \sin \dfrac{m\pi y}{l} \sin \dfrac{p\pi z}{l} e^{-(a\pi/l)^2(n^2+m^2+p^2)t}$

34. $T = 100 + \dfrac{200a}{\pi r} \displaystyle\sum_{1}^{\infty} \dfrac{(-1)^n}{n} \sin \dfrac{n\pi r}{a} e^{-(a n\pi/a)^2 t}$

$\qquad = 100 + 200 \displaystyle\sum_{n=1}^{\infty} (-1)^n j_0(n\pi r/a) e^{-(a n\pi/a)^2 t}$

40. Let K = line charge per unit length. Then

$$V = -K \ln (r^2 + a^2 - 2ra \cos \theta) + K \ln a^2 - K \ln r^2$$
$$+ K \ln \left[r^2 + \left(\dfrac{R^2}{a}\right)^2 - 2\dfrac{R^2}{a} r \cos \theta \right]$$

Image method: K at $(a, 0)$, K at $(0, 0)$, $-K$ at R^2/a.

42. $u = \dfrac{200}{\pi} \displaystyle\int_{0}^{\infty} k^{-2}(1 - \cos 2k)e^{-ky} \cos kx \, dk$

47. $u(x, t) = 100 \operatorname{erf} \left(\dfrac{x}{2\alpha \sqrt{t}}\right) - 50 \operatorname{erf} \left(\dfrac{x-1}{2\alpha \sqrt{t}}\right) - 50 \operatorname{erf} \left(\dfrac{x+1}{2\alpha \sqrt{t}}\right)$

Chapter 15

2. $\frac{3}{8}, \frac{1}{8}$

5. $\frac{1}{4}, \frac{3}{4}, \frac{1}{3}, \frac{1}{2}$

12. (a) $\frac{3}{4}$ (b) $\frac{1}{5}$ (c) $\frac{2}{3}$ (d) $\frac{3}{4}$

14. (a) $\frac{3}{4}$ (b) $\frac{25}{36}$ (c) 37, 38, 39, 40

17. (a) 3 to 9 with $p(5) = p(7) = \frac{2}{9}$; others, $p = \frac{1}{9}$. (c) $\frac{1}{3}$

21. (a) $\frac{8}{9}, \frac{1}{2}$ (b) $\frac{3}{5}, \frac{1}{11}, \frac{2}{3}, \frac{2}{3}$

24. $\frac{48}{73}, \frac{13}{63}$

27. $\frac{1}{33}, \frac{2}{9}$

29. $\frac{39}{80}, \frac{5}{16}, \frac{1}{5}, \frac{11}{16}, \frac{374}{819}$

33. $\frac{5}{7}, \frac{2}{7}, \frac{11}{14}$

35. $\frac{2}{3}, \frac{1}{3}$

38. (a) $P(10, 8)$ (b) $C(10, 8)$ (c) $\frac{1}{45}$

41. $\frac{33}{16660}, \frac{33}{66640}, \frac{33}{108290}, \frac{3}{216580}$

42. $\frac{5}{16}, \frac{1}{32}$

44. $\frac{1}{26}$

45. $\frac{1}{221}, \frac{1}{33}, \frac{1}{17}$

54. (a) $\mu = 0, \sigma = \sqrt{3}$

    (c) $\mu = 2, \sigma = \sqrt{2}$

    (e) $\mu = 3(2p - 1), \sigma = 2[3p(1 - p)]^{\frac{1}{2}}$

55. $E(x) = \$12.25$

	$n = 4$	$n = 5$	$n = 6$	$n = 10$
65. Probability of exactly 3 heads	$\frac{1}{4}$	$\frac{5}{16}$	$\frac{5}{16}$	$\frac{15}{128}$
Probability of at most 3 heads	$\frac{15}{16}$	$\frac{13}{16}$	$\frac{21}{32}$	$\frac{11}{64}$
Probability of at least 3 heads	$\frac{5}{16}$	$\frac{1}{2}$	$\frac{21}{32}$	$\frac{121}{128}$
Most probable number of heads	2	2, 3	3	5
Expected number of heads	2	2.5	3	5

78. (a) 0.08   (b) 0.04   (c) 0.96   (d) 0.95

79. 0.32, 0.05, 0.003, 0.00006

83. Number of particles: 0   1   2   3   4   5

    Number of intervals: 405   810   810   540   270   108

85. $P_0 = 0.37, P_1 = 0.37, P_2 = 0.18, P_3 = 0.06$

93. $\bar{x} = 5, \bar{y} = 1, s_x = 0.11, s_y = 0.0286,$

    $\sigma_x = 0.12, \sigma_y = 0.030, \sigma_{mx} = 0.037, \sigma_{my} = 0.0095,$

    $r_x = 0.025, r_y = 0.0064,$

    $\overline{x + y} = 6$ with $r = 0.025, \overline{xy} = 5$ with $r = 0.040,$

    $\overline{x^2 y^3} = 25$ with $r = 0.54$

Index